PERIODIC TABLE OF THE El

MW00845782

1A 1																		8A 18

1A / 1

1 **H** Hydrogen 1.01

2A / 2

3 **Li** Lithium 6.94 — 4 **Be** Beryllium 9.01

11 **Na** Sodium 22.99 — 12 **Mg** Magnesium 24.31

3B / 3 — **4B / 4** — **5B / 5** — **6B / 6** — **7B / 7** — **8B (8 9 10)** — **1B / 11** — **2B / 12**

19 **K** Potassium 39.10 — 20 **Ca** Calcium 40.08 — 21 **Sc** Scandium 44.96 — 22 **Ti** Titanium 47.88 — 23 **V** Vanadium 50.94 — 24 **Cr** Chromium 52.00 — 25 **Mn** Manganese 54.94 — 26 **Fe** Iron 55.85 — 27 **Co** Cobalt 58.93 — 28 **Ni** Nickel 58.69 — 29 **Cu** Copper 63.55 — 30 **Zn** Zinc 65.38

37 **Rb** Rubidium 85.47 — 38 **Sr** Strontium 87.62 — 39 **Y** Yttrium 88.91 — 40 **Zr** Zirconium 91.22 — 41 **Nb** Niobium 92.91 — 42 **Mo** Molybdenum 95.94 — 43 **Tc** Technetium [98] — 44 **Ru** Ruthenium 101.07 — 45 **Rh** Rhodium 102.91 — 46 **Pd** Palladium 106.42 — 47 **Ag** Silver 107.87 — 48 **Cd** Cadmium 112.41

55 **Cs** Cesium 132.91 — 56 **Ba** Barium 137.33 — 57 **La** Lanthanum 138.91 — 72 **Hf** Hafnium 178.49 — 73 **Ta** Tantalum 180.95 — 74 **W** Tungsten 183.84 — 75 **Re** Rhenium 186.21 — 76 **Os** Osmium 190.23 — 77 **Ir** Iridium 192.22 — 78 **Pt** Platinum 195.08 — 79 **Au** Gold 196.97 — 80 **Hg** Mercury 200.59

87 **Fr** Francium [223] — 88 **Ra** Radium [226] — 89 **Ac** Actinium [227] — 104 **Rf** Rutherfordium 261.11 — 105 **Db** Dubnium [268] — 106 **Sg** Seaborgium [271] — 107 **Bh** Bohrium [270] — 108 **Hs** Hassium [269] — 109 **Mt** Meitnerium [276] — 110 **Ds** Darmstadtium [281] — 111 **Rg** Roentgenium [280] — 112 **Cn** Copernicium [285]

3A / 13 — **4A / 14** — **5A / 15** — **6A / 16** — **7A / 17**

2 **He** Helium 4.00

5 **B** Boron 10.81 — 6 **C** Carbon 12.01 — 7 **N** Nitrogen 14.01 — 8 **O** Oxygen 16.00 — 9 **F** Fluorine 19.00 — 10 **Ne** Neon 20.18

13 **Al** Aluminum 26.98 — 14 **Si** Silicon 28.09 — 15 **P** Phosphorus 30.97 — 16 **S** Sulfur 32.07 — 17 **Cl** Chlorine 35.45 — 18 **Ar** Argon 39.95

31 **Ga** Gallium 69.72 — 32 **Ge** Germanium 72.63 — 33 **As** Arsenic 74.92 — 34 **Se** Selenium 78.96 — 35 **Br** Bromine 79.90 — 36 **Kr** Krypton 83.80

49 **In** Indium 114.82 — 50 **Sn** Tin 118.71 — 51 **Sb** Antimony 121.76 — 52 **Te** Tellurium 127.60 — 53 **I** Iodine 126.90 — 54 **Xe** Xenon 131.29

81 **Tl** Thallium 204.38 — 82 **Pb** Lead 207.2 — 83 **Bi** Bismuth 208.98 — 84 **Po** Polonium [209] — 85 **At** Astatine [210] — 86 **Rn** Radon [222]

113 **Nh** Nihonium [284] — 114 **Fl** Flerovium [289] — 115 **Mc** Moscovium [288] — 116 **Lv** Livermorium [293] — 117 **Ts** Tennessine [294] — 118 **Og** Oganesson [294]

Legend:
- Alkali Metals
- Alkaline Earth Metals
- Transition Elements
- Halogens
- Noble Gases
- Lanthanides
- Actinides

6 — 58 **Ce** Cerium 140.12 — 59 **Pr** Praseodymium 140.91 — 60 **Nd** Neodymium 144.24 — 61 **Pm** Promethium [145] — 62 **Sm** Samarium 150.36 — 63 **Eu** Europium 151.96 — 64 **Gd** Gadolinium 157.25 — 65 **Tb** Terbium 158.93 — 66 **Dy** Dysprosium 162.50 — 67 **Ho** Holmium 164.93 — 68 **Er** Erbium 167.26 — 69 **Tm** Thulium 168.93 — 70 **Yb** Ytterbium 173.05 — 71 **Lu** Lutetium 174.97

7 — 90 **Th** Thorium 232.04 — 91 **Pa** Protactinium 231.04 — 92 **U** Uranium 238.03 — 93 **Np** Neptunium [237] — 94 **Pu** Plutonium [244] — 95 **Am** Americium [243] — 96 **Cm** Curium [247] — 97 **Bk** Berkelium [247] — 98 **Cf** Californium [251] — 99 **Es** Einsteinium [252] — 100 **Fm** Fermium [257] — 101 **Md** Mendelevium [258] — 102 **No** Nobelium [259] — 103 **Lr** Lawrencium [262]

List of Elements, Symbols, Atomic Number and Atomic Masses

Element	Symbol	Atomic Number	Atomic Mass
Actinium	Ac	89	[227]
Aluminum	Al	13	26.98
Americium	Am	95	[243]
Antimony	Sb	51	121.76
Argon	Ar	18	39.95
Arsenic	As	33	74.92
Astatine	At	85	[210]
Barium	Ba	56	137.33
Berkelium	Bk	97	[247]
Beryllium	Be	4	9.012
Bismuth	Bi	83	208.98
Bohrium	Bh	107	[270]
Boron	B	5	10.81
Bromine	Br	35	79.90
Cadmium	Cd	48	112.41
Calcium	Ca	20	40.08
Californium	Cf	98	[251]
Carbon	C	6	12.01
Cerium	Ce	58	140.12
Cesium	Cs	55	132.91
Chlorine	Cl	17	35.45
Chromium	Cr	24	52.00
Cobalt	Co	27	58.93
Copernicium	Cn	112	[285]
Copper	Cu	29	63.55
Curium	Cm	96	[247]
Darmstadtium	Ds	110	[281]
Dubnium	Db	105	[268]
Dysprosium	Dy	66	162.50
Einsteinium	Es	99	[252]
Erbium	Er	68	167.26
Europium	Eu	63	151.96
Fermium	Fm	100	[257]
Flerovium	Fl	114	[289]
Fluorine	F	9	19.00
Francium	Fr	87	223
Gadolinium	Gd	64	157.25
Gallium	Ga	31	69.72
Germanium	Ge	32	72.63
Gold	Au	79	196.97
Hafnium	Hf	72	178.49
Hassium	Hs	108	[269]
Helium	He	2	4.00
Holmium	Ho	67	164.93
Hydrogen	H	1	1.01
Indium	In	49	114.82
Iodine	I	53	126.90
Iridium	Ir	77	192.22
Iron	Fe	26	55.85
Krypton	Kr	36	83.80
Lanthanum	La	57	138.91
Lawrencium	Lr	103	[262]
Lead	Pb	82	207.2
Lithium	Li	3	6.94
Livermorium	Lv	116	[293]
Lutetium	Lu	71	174.97
Magnesium	Mg	12	24.31
Manganese	Mn	25	54.94
Meitnerium	Mt	109	[276]
Mendelevium	Md	101	[258]
Mercury	Hg	80	200.59
Molybdenum	Mo	42	95.96
Moscovium	Ms	115	[288]
Neodymium	Nd	60	144.24
Neon	Ne	10	20.18
Neptunium	Np	93	[237]
Nickel	Ni	28	58.69
Nihonium	Nh	113	[284]
Niobium	Nb	41	92.91
Nitrogen	N	7	14.01
Nobelium	No	102	[259]
Oganesson	Og	118	[294]
Osmium	Os	76	190.23
Oxygen	O	8	16.00
Palladium	Pd	46	106.42
Phosphorus	P	15	30.97
Platinum	Pt	78	195.08
Plutonium	Pu	94	[244]
Polonium	Po	84	[209]
Potassium	K	19	39.10
Praseodymium	Pr	59	140.91
Promethium	Pm	61	[145]
Protactinium	Pa	91	231.04
Radium	Ra	88	[226]
Radon	Rn	86	[222]
Rhenium	Re	75	186.21
Rhodium	Rh	45	102.91
Roentgnium	Rg	111	[280]
Rubidium	Rb	37	85.47
Ruthenium	Ru	44	101.07
Rutherfordium	Rf	104	261.11
Samarium	Sm	62	150.36
Scandium	Sc	21	44.96
Seaborgium	Sg	106	[271]
Selenium	Se	34	78.96
Silicon	Si	14	28.09
Silver	Ag	47	107.87
Sodium	Na	11	22.99
Strontium	Sr	38	87.62
Sulfur	S	16	32.06
Tantalum	Ta	73	180.95
Technetium	Tc	43	[98]
Tellurium	Te	52	127.60
Tennessine	Ts	117	[294]
Terbium	Tb	65	158.93
Thallium	Tl	81	204.38
Thorium	Th	90	232.04
Thulium	Tm	69	168.93
Tin	Sn	50	118.71
Titanium	Ti	22	47.87
Tungsten	W	74	183.84
Uranium	U	92	238.03
Vanadium	V	23	50.94
Xenon	Xe	54	131.293
Ytterbium	Yb	70	173.05
Yttrium	Y	39	88.91
Zinc	Zn	30	65.38
Zirconium	Zr	40	91.22

Chemistry

A FUNDAMENTAL OVERVIEW OF ESSENTIAL PRINCIPLES

FIRST EDITION

David R. Khan and Jason C. Yarbrough

 cognella® | ACADEMIC PUBLISHING

Bassim Hamadeh, CEO and Publisher
Bob Farrell, Acquisitions Editor
Gem Rabanera, Project Editor
Berenice Quirino, Associate Production Editor
Jess Estrella, Senior Graphic Designer
Stephanie Kohl, Licensing Associate
Don Kesner, Interior Designer
Natalie Piccotti, Senior Marketing Manager
Kassie Graves, Director of Acquisitions and Sales
Jamie Giganti, Senior Managing Editor

Cover image copyright© 2017 iStockphoto LP/Artem_Egorov.
        copyright © 2013 iStockphoto LP/BlackJack3D.
        PoorLeno, "Hydrogen Density Plots," https://commons.wikimedia.org/wiki/File:Hydrogen_Density_Plots.png.
        Copyright © Depositphotos/annyart.
        Copyright © Depositphotos/JMcreation.
Design image copyright: Museumsinsulaner, "Carl Georg Anton Braeb Schloss Sanssouci with Frame," https://commons.wikimedia.org/wiki/File:Carl_Georg_Anton_Graeb_Schloss_Sanssouci_c1843-45_with_frame.jpg.

Printed in the United States of America.

ISBN: 978-1-5165-3610-8 (pbk) / 978-1-5165-3611-5 (br) / 978-1-5165-4707-4 (al)

cognella® | ACADEMIC PUBLISHING

Chemistry

ACKNOWLEDGMENTS

I would like to thank all of the scientists who were involved in mentoring me throughout my professional career, to include Drs. Gregg Fields, Evonne Rezler, and Edna Cukierman. I also want to thank Shelby Phelps, Samantha McLeod, Rusty Hartman and Alexandra Muniz who were all an invaluable part of our team during the preparation of this textbook. Most importantly, I would like to thank my family for their support to include my wife Elexa Khan, and two daughters Kylee and Kyrstyana Khan. I am eternally grateful for all of your love and ongoing support.

–David R. Khan

As always I wish to acknowledge the love and support of my wife, Jillian Yarbrough, and my children, Jason, Julia and Jamie. They are balance, support, motivation and inspiration to me every day. I would also like to express my sincerest gratitude to all those who mentored and aided me throughout my education and career, especially Leo Bowman, Timothy Sherwood, Martin Perry, Joseph M. DeSimone and Donald J. Darensbourg. Additionally, I must extend tremendous thanks to the team of folks that can only be described as absolutely indispensable in completing this project. Specifically, these include Shelby Phelps, Samantha McLeod, Rusty Hartman and Alexandra Muniz, as well as graphic designer Brandon Steinle, of the West Texas A&M University IT group. To all of these, I say Thank You.

–Jason C. Yarbrough

TABLE OF CONTENTS

CHAPTER 4. THE MOLE, CHEMICAL EQUATIONS, AND STOICHIOMETRY 121

CHAPTER 5. DISSOLUTION AND REACTIONS IN AQUEOUS SOLUTION..169

CHAPTER 11. ACIDS, BASES, AND BUFFERS 433

CHAPTER 12. THERMODYNAMICS AND THERMOCHEMISTRY 479

CHAPTER 13. OXIDATION-REDUCTION AND ELECTROCHEMISTRY 559

CHAPTER 14. CHEMICAL KINETICS 605

CHAPTER 15. INTRODUCTION TO ORGANIC CHEMISTRY 633

The Basics of Chemistry

LEARNING OBJECTIVES AND OUTCOMES

After reading this chapter, you should be able to do the following:

- Define the study of chemistry.

- Define matter.

- Distinguish between a theory, law, observation, and hypothesis.

- Describe and apply the scientific method.

- Interpret and write numeric values in standard and scientific notation.

- Explain what a unit of measurement is.

- Distinguish between various systems of measurement.

- Re-express measurements given in one unit in a variety of other units using conversion factors.

- Convert between units raised to a power.

- Convert between different scales of temperature.

- Define and calculate density and use density as a conversion factor.

- Distinguish between exact and measured (or uncertain) numbers.

- Interpret and count significant figures as well as express measured values using significant figures.

- Use significant figures properly in calculations utilizing the correct order of operations.

- Solve complex problems utilizing the dimensional analysis method.

- Define each of the Key Terms listed at the end of this chapter dealing with these concepts.

Section 1.1 Introduction

Have you ever pondered things in the world around you, even those things often taken for granted? Ever wonder why the sky appears blue, why wood burns and water doesn't, or how you are able to experience the taste of foods and beverages? Well, chemists are also concerned with such questions. Chemists are concerned with understanding and explaining

Chemists are interested in understanding our physical universe, and therefore are interested in such things as why the sky appears blue, why wood burns and water doesn't, and what exactly is going on when we taste food and beverages.

The thought of chemistry can invoke images such as beakers, test tubes, lab coats, and eye goggles.

the physical universe by understanding the nature of the materials that compose our world at the atomic and molecular level. Understanding how atoms and molecules behave is at the heart of *chemistry*. Chances are that if you think about chemistry, a number of images come to mind, such as beakers, test tubes, lab coats, and eye goggles, but chemical processes are occurring everywhere, all of the time. They are at the foundation of many of our experiences, especially those involving our everyday environment.

What is Chemistry?

Chemistry, simply put, is the study of matter, its structure, properties, and the processes it undergoes. **Matter** (from the Latin word, materia, meaning material) is defined as anything that has mass and occupies space. This means that chemistry is the study of everything and anything in the universe. Therefore, it is fundamental to technological and scientific advances in any arena, whether it's medical technology, pharmaceuticals, materials, agriculture, computer or communications technologies, biology, or something else. The list is endless, and chemists are often engaged in a wide variety of professional endeavors both in and out of the laboratory. Chemists are CEOs, CTOs, attorneys, judges, inventors, engineers, political activists, and leaders as well as scientists. The reason is that there is literally no type of endeavor that is not underpinned in some way by chemistry. Because this is so, societies and civilizations have, for many centuries, been engaged in practices and technologies that would ultimately become part of the foundations of the various branches of modern chemistry. Some of these include

Chemists are CEO's, CTO's, attorneys, judges, inventors, engineers, political activists, and leaders.

fermentation processes in the production of beer and wine (organic and biochemistry), the mining of various ores and the extraction of metals therefrom (physical and inorganic chemistry) as well as extraction of medicinal compounds from plants and herbs (biochemistry and pharmaceuticals). If you find something in the physical world interesting or exciting, no matter what it is, chances are that chemical processes are at the root of it. Therefore, understanding our world means understanding the principles of chemistry.

Chemistry is fundamental to technological and scientific advancements in any area, including medical technology, pharmaceuticals, materials, agriculture, computer or communication technologies, and biology.

Section 1.2 The Scientific Method

Having said all of this, chemistry is an empirical science that is subject to the application of the Scientific Method. **The Scientific Method** is the *systematic* acquisition of knowledge through observation and experiment (Figure 1.1). Specific characteristics (steps in a process) define the scientific method. These include:

1. **Observation**—Understanding our physical world begins with making observations and asking questions about those observations. An observation may be *qualitative* and as simple as noting some phenomenon observed by the naked eye. An observation may also be *quantitative* in nature, requiring tools or instruments in order to be quantified, recorded, and understood.

   Sometimes specific observations are made consistently and are always the same. Such a set of observations can result in the formulation of a Scientific Law. A **Scientific Law** is

Some of the foundations of many branches of modern chemistry include the process of fermentation to make beer and wine, mining of various ores and the extraction of various metals, as well as the extraction of medicinal compounds from plants.

a summary statement (or mathematical equation) which describes a set of observations and can be used to make predictions about the outcome of future events or experiments. Scientific Laws do not, however, provide any explanation for themselves. For example, the Law of Conservation of Mass (discussed in further detail in Chapter 2) simply states that matter is neither created nor destroyed due to physical or chemical processes. It makes no attempt to explain why this should be. Rather, it simply states what has been consistently observed and is the basis for predictions about what may be observed in the future.

2. **Formulation of a Hypothesis**—Following observation, scientists can now prepare a hypothesis. A **hypothesis** is a tentative or speculative explanation for observations. This becomes the basis for future experiments.

3. **Experiment**—Having formulated a hypothesis, it can now be used to make predictions about experimental outcomes. Experiments are now designed and executed in order to test these hypothetical predictions. Assuming such predictions are validated by experiment, the hypothesis is verified. On the other hand, if the predictions are refuted through experimentation, the hypothesis must be rejected or, in some fashion, refined. Therefore, a solid scientific *hypothesis*, in addition to providing explanation for observed phenomena, must also be *testable* and *falsifiable*. Untestable hypotheses, because they are beyond the application of scientific method, are limited in their use because they cannot be validated through experimentation.

4. **Conclusions**—After reviewing the experimental data, if they support or fail to support the hypothesis, it can be concluded that the hypothesis is either valid or invalid. If it is validated, it becomes the basis for further experimental testing and refinement.

If a large body of experimentation, executed by a diverse community of scientists, consistently reinforces a given hypothesis, this may become the basis for the formulation of a Scientific Theory. A **Scientific Theory** is a model which describes the underlying explanations of observations. Theories are the height of scientific knowledge. They are models of how the world works, which are supported by large bodies of experimental

Figure 1.1 The Scientific Method

data and can be used to predict entirely new observations across a wide range of phenomena.

Section 1.3 Scientific Notation

In the course of executing experiments and making observations, chemists must often deal with quantitative data. In such instances, we are faced frequently with extremely large or extremely small numbers. In common usage, large numbers often carry commas every three spaces in order to make their interpretation easier. For example, the number one hundred fifty million, two hundred forty-seven thousand, one hundred sixty-two is usually written as 150,247,162 rather than 150247162. The commas allow us to quickly visualize the magnitude of each digit and, therefore, read and comprehend the number more effectively. As chemists however, we will often encounter numbers that are so much larger (or smaller) than 150 million that even this convention is ineffective. It is in these instances that we will need a different method for quickly and easily reading and writing such numbers. That method is *scientific notation*.

There are two parts to writing numbers in scientific notation, the first being a coefficient, while the second is the number 10 raised to a power (an exponent). Additionally, the coefficient must be ≥ 1 and < 10. Let's consider an example of a vastly large number. Consider a 1-carat diamond. Diamond is a form of elemental carbon, and in a 1-carat diamond there are 10,027,000,000,000,000,000,000 atoms of carbon (we will learn more about atoms later). Scientific notation offers us a much more convenient way to handle numbers of this size. To express this number in scientific notation, we must first determine the correct coefficient. To do this we need to move the decimal such that the resulting number is ≥ 1 and < 10 as follows:

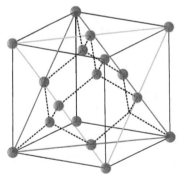

Diamond is a form of elemental carbon.

Standard Notation	Scientific Notation
10,027,000,000,000,000,000,000.	1.0027×10^{22}

22 ← 987 654 321

Because it was necessary to move the decimal 22 places to the left, the coefficient must be multiplied by 10 raised to the power of 22. If you multiply 1.0027 by 10^{22} in your calculator, you will see the result is 10,027,000,000,000,000,000,000. This means that even though we have re-written this number in a different form, we are still expressing precisely the same numerical value.

Let's tackle something a little different. Consider the value 0.000002346. Unlike the previous example, the value of this number is very small, far less than 1. However, just as before we will arrive at the appropriate coefficient if we move the decimal such that the number is ≥ 1 and < 10. This requires moving the decimal six spaces to the right, resulting in 2.346. Since we moved the decimal to the right (instead of the left) we will have to multiply the coefficient by 10 raised to the *negative* 6th power in order to maintain the same numerical value as shown here:

Standard Notation   Scientific Notation

0.000002346 2.346×10^{-6}

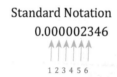

1 2 3 4 5 6

This means that when writing numbers in scientific notation, if the decimal is moved to the left, the resulting exponent will be positive, and if the decimal must be moved to the right, the exponent will be negative. Looked at another way, if the numerical value is less than 1, the exponent should be a negative number, and the exponent is positive if the numerical value is greater than 1. Tables 1.1 and 1.2 provide some illustrative examples of how to interpret the exponential part of scientific notation, as well as some examples of different numbers written in standard and scientific notation.

Table 1.1 Exponential Notation

Standard Notation	As a Power of Ten	Exponential or Scientific Notation
1,000,000	$1 \times (10)(10)(10)(10)(10)(10) =$	1×10^6
100,000	$1 \times (10)(10)(10)(10)(10) =$	1×10^5
10,000	$1 \times (10)(10)(10)(10) =$	1×10^4
1,000	$1 \times (10)(10)(10) =$	1×10^3
100	$1 \times (10)(10) =$	1×10^2
10	$1 \times (10) =$	1×10^1
1	$1 =$	1×10^0
0.1	$1 \times \left(\dfrac{1}{10}\right) =$	1×10^{-1}
0.01	$1 \times \left(\dfrac{1}{10}\right)\left(\dfrac{1}{10}\right) =$	1×10^{-2}
0.001	$1 \times \left(\dfrac{1}{10}\right)\left(\dfrac{1}{10}\right)\left(\dfrac{1}{10}\right) =$	1×10^{-3}

Standard Notation	As a Power of Ten	Exponential or Scientific Notation
0.0001	$1 \times \left(\frac{1}{10}\right)\left(\frac{1}{10}\right)\left(\frac{1}{10}\right)\left(\frac{1}{10}\right) =$	1×10^{-4}
0.00001	$1 \times \left(\frac{1}{10}\right)\left(\frac{1}{10}\right)\left(\frac{1}{10}\right)\left(\frac{1}{10}\right)\left(\frac{1}{10}\right) =$	1×10^{-5}
0.000001	$1 \times \left(\frac{1}{10}\right)\left(\frac{1}{10}\right)\left(\frac{1}{10}\right)\left(\frac{1}{10}\right)\left(\frac{1}{10}\right)\left(\frac{1}{10}\right) =$	1×10^{-6}

Table 1.2 Measured or Calculated Quantities Expressed in Scientific Notation

Quantity	Standard Notation	Scientific Notation
Volume of the Earth's Oceans	1,332,000,000,000,000,000 m^3	1.332×10^{18} m^3
Distance Light Travels in 1 Second	299,800,000 m	2.998×10^8 m
Distance to the Moon	384,400 km	3.844×10^5 km
Diameter of the Human Hair	0.00018 m	1.8×10^{-4} m
Diameter of a Copper Atom	0.000000000256 m	2.56×10^{-10} m

Example Problem 1.1

Convert the following to Scientific Notation:
  a.) 2700   b.) 0.002700

Solution:	
a.) **Step 1.** Move the decimal to realize a coefficient which is ≥ 1 and < 10. In this case this will require moving the decimal 3 spaces to the left.	$2700 \rightarrow 2.700$
Step 2. Account for moving the decimal 3 spaces to the left by multiplying by 10 raised to the 3rd power.	$\mathbf{2.700 \times 10^3}$
b.) **Step 1.** Again, move the decimal place to realize a coefficient which is ≥ 1 and < 10. In this case it will require moving the decimal 3 spaces to the right.	$0.002700 \rightarrow 2.700$
Step 2. Account for moving the decimal 3 spaces to the right by multiplying by 10 raised the negative 3rd power.	$\mathbf{2.700 \times 10^{-3}}$

Example Problem 1.2

Convert the following to standard notation:
  a.) 4.93×10^5 b.) 7.421×10^{-8}

Solution	
a.) Since the exponential part is 10 raised to the 5th power, move the decimal 5 spaces to the right and drop the exponential term.	$4.93 \times 10^5 \rightarrow \mathbf{493,000}$
b.) Since the exponential part is 10 raised to the negative 8th power, move the decimal 8 spaces to the left and drop the exponential term.	$7.421 \times 10^{-8} \rightarrow \mathbf{0.00000007421}$

Section 1.4 Units of Measurement and Density

Making measurements is something everyone does in some fashion every day. When you check the time on your phone, you are making a measurement. When you check the temperature in your home, you are making a measurement. When you cook from a recipe, you make multiple measurements. Indeed, making measurements is an indispensable part of everyday life. No less so for chemists. Scientists make measurements constantly. In doing so, what we are actually doing is comparing an observable (such as length, weight, temperature, etc.) to some accepted standard. That standard is the unit of measure in question. For example, if I measure the length of an object and find it to be 12 inches long, what does that really mean? Well, nothing, unless we all understand and agree to what the quantity of 1 inch is. The "inch" is that standard used to indicate a specified length. This is an example of a *unit of measurement*. A **Unit** is a generally accepted <u>quantity</u> which is used to accurately and reproducibly report experimental measurements.

It should be obvious then, that in order to take useful measurements, we need to agree upon certain generally accepted units for the measurement of all types of observables. In fact, this is vitally important for society in general. That is why most cultures throughout history have instituted entire systems of measurement for the purpose of facilitating a variety of important functions. Consider the importance of this in regard to things like navigation, commerce, and civil engineering to name a few. The most common system of measurement in the United States is known as the English or *Imperial System*. This system includes familiar units such as the pound (*lb*), the mile (*mi*), yards (*yds*), feet (*ft*), inches (*in*), quarts (*qt*), and gallons (*gal.*). However, as chemists we tend to prefer the use of the **International System of Units (SI),** which is the official system of measurement for most of the world. The SI system is based on the *metric system*, and Table 1.3 lists the base unit of measure for a variety of observables in the SI system along with the

Multiple measurements are also taken when you cook from a recipe

Measurements are taken when you check the time on your phone as well as the temperature in your home.

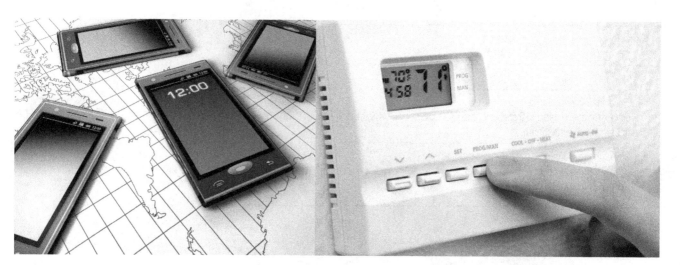

equivalent for each unit as expressed in the *metric* and *imperial systems*. For example, note the entry in Table 1.3 for length. The base unit in SI is the meter and is equal to 3.28 feet.

Table 1.3 SI, Metric, and Imperial Base Units.

Unit of Measure	SI Unit	Metric Unit	Imperial Unit
Length	1 Meter (*m*)	1 meter (*m*)	3.28 Feet (*ft*)
Mass	1 Kilogram (*kg*)	1000 Gram (*g*)	2.205 Pounds (*lb*)
Volume	1 Cubic Meter (*m*³)	1000 Liter (*L*)	264.2 Gallons (*gal*)
Time	1 Second (*s*)	1 Second (*s*)	1 Second (*s*)

Length or Distance

As stated in the previous section, the SI unit for length is the meter (*m*). The meter is most analogous to the yard in English units (a meter is equal to 1.09 yards). Just as a yard is further subdivided into smaller units of feet and inches, so the meter is subdivided into decimeters (10 *dm* = 1 *m*), centimeters (100 *cm* = 1 *m*), and millimeters (1,000 *mm* = 1 *m*). What makes the use of the meter (and really all metric units) useful is that the system is a "base 10" system. This means all of the base units and their sub-units are related to each other as powers of 10. We will discuss this further in the section dealing with *prefix multipliers*.

1 *m* = 100 *cm* = 1,000 *mm*
1 *cm* = 2.54 *in*
1 *m* = 1.094 *yds*

Figure 1.2 The definition of a meter is the distance that light travels in vacuum in the interval of 1/299,792,458 seconds. The official standard of 1 meter is a Platinum-Iridium bar located at the National Institute of Standards and Technology (NIST; www.nist.gov) in Gaithersburg, MD, USA.

An astronaut weighs less on the moon than on the Earth. However, the amount of matter that makes up the astronaut (Mass) is not changed regardless of location.

Mass on the Moon = 83.9 Kg

Mass on Earth = 83.9 Kg

Figure 1.3 A copy of the international standard kilogram is a Platnium-Iridium mass kept at the National Institute of Standards and Technology, (NIST; www.nist.gov) in Gaithersburg, MD, USA.

Mass

Mass is a measurement that is often confused with weight, but strictly speaking, it isn't the same as weight. Mass is the measure of how much "stuff" an object contains. More accurately, it is the quantitative measure of how much matter makes up a sample and is therefore not the same as weight. An object may weigh less on the moon than it does on Earth, but its mass (the amount of matter that makes it up) is not changed due to relocation to the moon. The SI base unit for mass is the kilogram (*kg*) (1 *kg* is equal to 2.2 *lbs*). Additionally, the kilogram is subdivided into smaller units such as the gram (1,000 *g* = 1 *kg*) and the milligram (1,000 *mg* = 1 *g*).

1 *kg* = 1,000 *g* = 1,000,000 *mg*
1 *kg* = 2.205 *lbs*
453.6 *g* = 1 *lb*

Volume

The volume of a sample is the measure of how much space it occupies. Therefore, volume can be thought of as the product of a sample's three dimensions (length × width × height) (Figure 1.4). Such an operation would give volume units of length raised to the 3rd power, such as cubic feet (ft^3) or cubic meters (m^3). The m^3 is the SI base unit of volume. However, the metric system has a unit specific to volume known as the liter (*L*). To provide some perspective, there are 3.785 *L* in 1 US gallon. In the laboratory, chemists often work with volumes far smaller than the liter, such as the milliliter (*ml*). There are 1000 *ml* in 1 *L* and further, 1 *ml* is exactly 1 cubic centimeter (cm^3).

1 *L* = 1000 *ml* = 1 dm^3 = 0.2200 *gal*
1 *ml* = 1 cm^3 = 1 *cc*

Figure 1.4 Units of Volume: 1 cubic meter (m^3) contains 1000 cubic decimeters (dm^3), which is the definition of 1 Liter.

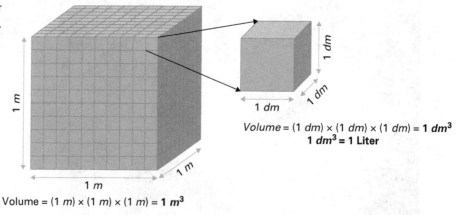

Prefix Multipliers

The great utility of the metric system is that all of the units can be amplified or subdivided into larger or smaller units as powers of 10. This is accomplished by using something called a *prefix multiplier*. A prefix multiplier is applied to a unit and either multiplies or divides it by some power of 10. As an example, when dealing with meters, it may be advantageous to deal with a unit of length larger than the meter. For instance, geographical distances are usually measured in *kilo*meters rather than meters. The prefix "kilo" multiplies the base unit by 1000, or 10^3. The distance from Dallas, Texas, to New York City is 2,570,122 meters, which is more practically expressed as 2,570 kilometers (*km*) (Figure 1.5). This prefix can be applied to any base unit with the same effect.

1 kilometer (*km*) = 1,000 meters (*m*)
1 kiloliter (*kL*) = 1,000 Liters (*L*)
1 kilogram (*kg*) = 1,000 grams (*g*)

Table 1.4 lists the prefix multipliers used in the metric system.

Figure 1.5 The distance from Dallas to New York City is 2,570 *km* or 2,570,122 meters.

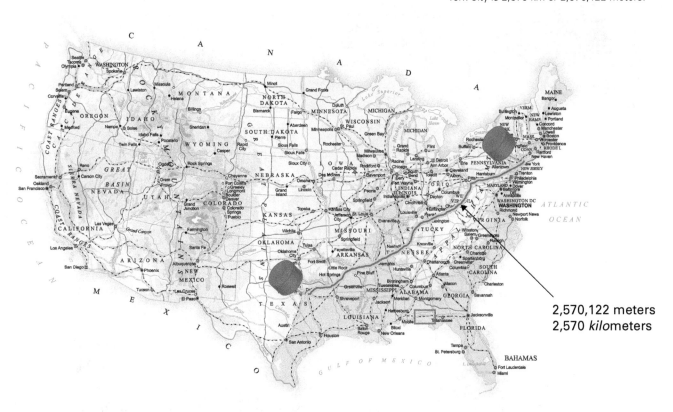

2,570,122 meters
2,570 *kilo*meters

Table 1.4 A Summary of the Prefix Multipliers used in the SI and Metric systems.

Prefix	Symbol	Meaning	Multiplier	Exponential Notation
Tera-	T	trillion	1,000,000,000,000	10^{12}
Giga-	G	billion	1,000,000,000	10^{9}
Mega-	M	million	1,000,000	10^{6}
Kilo-	k	Thousand	1,000	10^{3}
Hecto-	h	hundred	100	10^{2}
Deca-	da	ten	10	10^{1}
Deci-	d	tenth	0.1	10^{-1}
Centi-	c	hundredth	0.01	10^{-2}
Milli-	m	thousandth	0.001	10^{-3}
Micro-	μ	millionth	0.000001	10^{-6}
Nano-	n	billionth	0.000000001	10^{-9}
Pico-	p	trillionth	0.000000000001	10^{-12}
Femto-	f	quadrillionth	0.000000000000001	10^{-15}

Example Problem 1.3

Complete the following:
- a.) 1 km = _____ dm
- b.) 1 μm = _____ m
- c.) 1 Gg = _____ g
- d.) 14,000,000 m = _____ Mm
- e.) 2 kg = _____ ng

	Solution:	
a.)	Since 1 km is equal to 1,000 m and 1 meter is equal to 10 dm, there are 10 times 1,000 dm in 1 km.	$1\ km = 1{,}000\ m$ & $1\ m = 10\ dm$ Therefore, $1\ km = 1{,}000\ m = \mathbf{10{,}000\ dm}$
b.)	Since there are 10^{6} μm in 1 m, there is 10^{-6} m in 1 μm.	$10^{6}\ \mu m = 1\ m$ $\dfrac{10^{6}\ \mu m}{10^{6}} = \dfrac{1\ m}{10^{6}}$ Therefore, $\mathbf{1\ \mu m = 10^{-6}\ m}$
c.)	There are 1 billion (10^{9}) g in a Gg.	$\mathbf{1\ Gg = 10^{9}\ g}$

d.)	Since 1 Mm is 1 million (10^6) meters, 14,000,000 (14 million) meters is therefore equal to 14 Mm.	$1,000,000 \, m = 1 \, Mm$ Therefore, **$14,000,000 \, m = 14 \, Mm$**
e.)	Since 1 kg is equal to 1,000 g and 1 g is equal to 10^9 ng, therefore there are 10^9 times 1,000 ng in 1 kg.	$1 \, kg = 1,000 \, g \; \& \; 1 \, g = 10^9 \, ng$ Therefore, **$2 \, kg = 2,000 \, g = 2,000 \times 10^9 \, ng = 2 \times 10^{12} \, ng$**

Derived Units and Density

One of the things that we have mentioned is that *units* are quantities. As such, they can be multiplied and divided like any other algebraic quantity. Often, the results of applying mathematical operations to *units* is the formation of new units. These are sometimes referred to as **derived units**. We have already seen an example of these with volume. Units of volume are created by the multiplication of units of length, resulting in the derived units of cm^3, dm^3, or m^3 (see Figure 1.4). There are still others of which you are familiar and utilize every day. For example, imagine driving a car 60 miles and upon reaching the destination, noting that the trip took exactly two hours. From this we know that the average speed on this trip was 30 miles per hour (*mph* or *mi/hr*). *Mi/hr* is a measure of speed and is derived by dividing units of length (or distance) by units of time (the word "per" means "divided by").

60 miles traversed over a 2 hour period has an average speed of 30 miles/hour.

$$60 \text{ miles traversed over a 2 hour time period} \quad \rightarrow \quad \frac{60 \text{ mi.}}{2 \text{ hr.}} = 30 \frac{\text{mi.}}{\text{hr.}}$$

Another derived unit, which is also fundamentally important in the study of chemistry, is that of *density*. If you take the mass of a sample and divide it by the volume it occupies, you have something called *density*. **Density** is the quantitative relation between the mass of a substance and its volume. It is a measure of how much matter is contained in a given unit of volume for a particular substance.

$$d = \frac{sample \; mass}{sample \; volume}$$

Therefore, some examples of the units of density are grams per milliliter (*g/ml*), grams per *cc* (*g/cm³*) or even grams per liter (*g/L*). Because each substance has a unique density, it is often used to identify unknowns or at least to verify the purity of a sample material. Consider the example shown in Figure 1.6. Here we see that gold has a density of 19.32 *g/ml* whereas

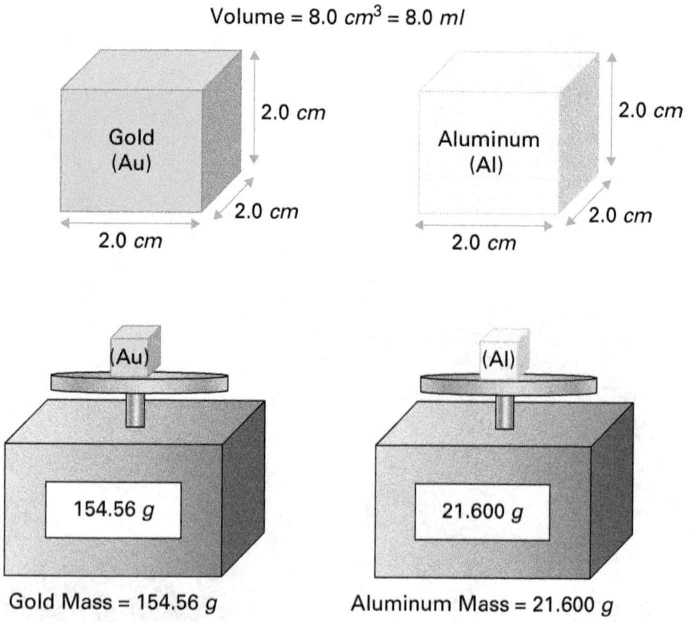

Volume = 8.0 cm^3 = 8.0 ml

Density of Gold $\quad d_{Au} = \dfrac{mass}{volume} = \dfrac{154.56\,g}{8.0\,ml} = \textbf{19.32}\,^g/_{ml}$

Density of Aluminum $\quad d_{Al} = \dfrac{mass}{volume} = \dfrac{21.600\,g}{8.0\,ml} = \textbf{2.70}\,^g/_{ml}$

Gold Mass = 154.56 g

Aluminum Mass = 21.600 g

Figure 1.6 From a known volume and mass, the density of any substance can be calculated. Two identical, cubic blocks are fabricated from two metals (Gold and Aluminum). Each will occupy the same volume but their masses are very different. The density is calculated as the ratio of Mass-over-Volume.

aluminum has a density of 2.70 g/ml. This means that within a given unit of volume, gold will have nearly ten times as much matter (mass) as aluminum. We will see in the following chapters that this is a direct consequence of the atomic structure of these two elements. Table 1.5 gives the densities of some common substances.

Table 1.5 Densities of Common Substances.

Substance	Density (g/ml)	Substance	Density (g/ml)
Aluminum	2.70	Air	0.00123
Magnesium	1.74	Charcoal	0.570
Titanium	4.50	Oak	0.570
Zinc	7.13	Ethanol	0.789
Nickel	8.91	Methanol	0.792
Copper	8.96	Ice	0.917
Silver	10.5	Water	1.00
Lead	11.3	Graphite	2.23
Mercury	13.5	Glass	2.56
Gold	19.3	Steel (Carbon Steel)	7.84
Platinum	21.5	The Earth	5.57

Calculating Density

Since it has been demonstrated that different substances have unique densities (Table 1.5), measuring density is often employed as a method of identifying a material. For example, assume we have three samples of copper (Cu). The sample masses are determined to be 11.29 g, 21.77 g, and 32.81 g. Additionally, their volumes are determined to be 1.26 ml, 2.43 ml, and 3.66 ml, respectively. If the samples are of the same substance (copper), we should expect that they should each have the same density and, further, that density should correspond to the known density of copper. This is indeed what we find in the following calculations:

Sample 1:

$$density = \frac{11.29\ g}{1.26\ ml} = 8.96\ g/ml$$

Sample 2:

$$density = \frac{21.77\ g}{2.43\ ml} = 8.96\ g/ml$$

Sample 3:

$$density = \frac{32.81}{3.66\ ml} = 8.96\ g/ml$$

No matter what the mass or volume of a sample may be, the ratio of mass to volume (the density of a substance) is always the same. If we know the mass and volume of a sample, we can calculate the density of that material as shown here in Example Problem 1.4.

Example Problem 1.4

If an unknown metal sample was found to have a mass of 87.3 g and a volume of 4.06 ml, calculate the density of the sample. Compare your answer to known densities of common materials in Table 1.5 and identify the metal.	
Solution	
Step 1. Write the expression for the calculation of density.	$d = \dfrac{m}{v}$
Step 2. Substitute the given mass and volume measurements into the expression and solve for density.	$d = \dfrac{87.3\ g}{4.06\ ml} = 21.5\ g/ml$
Step 3. Compare the calculated density to known density and find that the identity of the metal is therefore Platinum (Pt).	$d_{Pt} = 21.5\ g/ml$ **Platinum** (See Table 1.5)

When determining density, the manner in which we measure the mass of a sample is straightforward enough. We simply use a balance. To determine volume, however, a commonly used method is that of displacement based on Archimedes Principle. If we were to fill a graduated cylinder (Figure 1.7) to a certain volume, which we record in a notebook, we could then completely submerge our sample within the water contained in the cylinder causing the water level to rise. This results in a new reading which is recorded as well. The difference in these two readings is the volume of water displaced by the sample and is equal to our sample volume. This volume used in conjunction with the mass of the sample can be used to calculate density as in Example Problem 1.5.

Archimedes was a Greek mathematician born in approximately 287 B.C. and died in 212 B.C.. Archimedes developed a principle for which the volume of objects can be measured.

Demonstration of Archimedes
Principle.

ARCHIMEDES PRINCIPLE

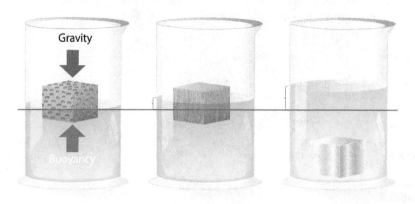

Figure 1.7 Submerged samples will displace a volume of water which must be equal to their own volumes.

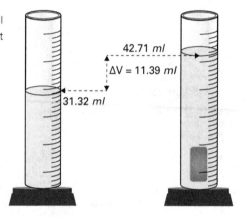

42.71 *ml*

$\Delta V = 11.39$ *ml*

31.32 *ml*

37.894 *g*

$$d_{Al} = \frac{\text{mass}}{\text{volume}} = \frac{21.600\ g}{8.0\ ml} = 2.70\ ^g/_{ml}$$

$$d = \frac{37.894\ g}{11.39\ ml} = 3.327\ ^g/_{ml}$$

Sample Mass = 37.894 *g*   Sample Volume = 11.39 *ml*   Sample Density = 3.327 *g/ml*

Example Problem 1.5

An unknown metal sample was weighed and found to have a mass of 2.75 *g*. The sample was then placed in a graduated cylinder containing water with a volume reading of 32.98 *ml*. Upon submersion of the sample, the water level rose to a new volume of 34.56 *ml*. Based on this, calculate the density of the sample and use Table 1.5 to identify the metal.
Solution:

Step 1. Determine the volume of the sample. This is accomplished by finding the difference between the initial volume and the final volume in the graduated before and after submersion of the metal sample.	$v = v_{final} - v_{initial}$ $v = 34.56\ ml - 32.98\ ml$ $v = 1.58\ ml$
Step 2. Write the expression for density and appropriately substitute the mass and volume of the sample into the equation. Complete the calculation to determine the density.	$d = \dfrac{m}{v}$ $d = \dfrac{2.75\ g}{1.58\ ml} = 1.74\ ^g/_{ml}$
Step 3. Find the known density of 1.74 *g/ml* on Table 1.5 to identify the sample.	$d_{Mg} = 1.74\ ^g/_{ml}$ **Magnesium** (See Table 1.5)

Units Raised to a Power

When dealing with derived units, it is common to encounter units raised to a power. An example of such an instance is area or volume. Consider a room with dimensions length, width, and height of 5 m, 6 m, and 3 m, respectively. We calculate volume by taking the product of the three dimensions which results in a unit of cubic meters as follows:

$$L \times W \times H = (5\ m)(6\ m)(3\ m) = 90\ m^3$$

The cubic meter (m^3) is a derived unit of volume. This seems straightforward enough and indeed, it is. However, what if we needed to express this quantity in cubic centimeters (cm^3) instead of cubic meters? How could we convert between units raised to a power? We cannot simply use the equivalence of 100 cm = 1 m. These are units of length not volume. However, if we "cube" both sides of this equality, we get a new relation, as follows:

$$100\ cm = 1\ m$$
$$(100\ cm)^3 = (1\ m)^3$$
$$100^3\ cm^3 = 1^3\ m^3$$
$$1,000,000\ cm^3 = 1\ m^3$$
$$10^6\ cm^3 = 1\ m^3$$

Remember, the units themselves are algebraic quantities, so if you cube the numbers, you must also cube the units. Thus, there are $10^6\ cm^3$ in 1 m^3, and, therefore, if we wish to convert the volume of our hypothetical room from 90 m^3 to an equivalent value in cm^3, we use this new equality to construct something called a conversion factor as follows.

Begin with the equality:

$$10^6\ cm^3 = 1\ m^3$$

Now, if we divide both sides by 1 m^3:

$$\frac{10^6\ cm^3}{1\ m^3} = \frac{1\ m^3}{1\ m^3}$$

Therefore:

$$\frac{10^6\ cm^3}{1\ m^3} = 1$$

And since any number can be multiplied by 1 without changing its value, we can use this ratio to effectively re-express a quantity, initially given in units of m^3, in units of cm^3 as follows:

$$90 m^3 \times \frac{10^6\ cm^3}{1\ m^3} = 90 \times 10^6\ cm^3 = 9 \times 10^7\ cm^3$$

Elevation signs on the highway tell you the elevation in "feet above sea level".

The units of cubic meters divide out (or cancel) as shown, and we are left with 9×10^7 cubic centimeters. Simply stated, conversion factors are ratios constructed from any mathematic equality which can be used to interconvert between different units. In this fashion, all conversions between units, including those raised to a power, can be carried out. A more detailed discussion on conversion factors will be explored in Section 1.6 – Dimensional Analysis.

Example Problem 1.6

Convert 2,300.014 mm^3 to m^3.	
Solutions:	
a.) **Step 1.** Identify the equality relating mm to meters.	$10^3 mm = 1 m$
Step 2. Since we are converting between cubic mm and cubic meters, we will need to likewise cube this equality.	$(10^3 mm)^3 = (1 m)^3$ $10^9 mm^3 = 1 m^3$
Step 3. We will now use this equality as a conversion factor (ratio) to convert mm^3 to m^3.	$2{,}300.014 \ mm^3 \times \dfrac{1 m^3}{10^9 mm^3} =$ $= 2.300014 \times 10^{-6} m^3$

Temperature

William Thomson (1824–1907) was born in Belfast, Ireland, United Kingdom. He is also known as "Lord Kelvin", and his work was influential in the development of the first and second laws of thermodynamics. His studies on heat and work ultimately lead to the concept of the absolute temperature scale.

Temperature is the measure of the average kinetic energy of the molecules or particles that make up a sample. Measuring temperature is a little more complex than that which we have discussed so far. This is because it isn't just about the unit with which we choose to measure the temperature, but also the point we define as zero. In other words, measuring temperature is more like measuring elevation than simply measuring distance. Let's consider the example of elevation. You may have heard that certain places are so many feet above sea level. In fact, that's what it means anytime you may have seen a sign on the highway that gives the elevation in feet. The assumption is that you understand that measurement as "feet above sea level." Why do we choose "sea level" as the point of reference versus something else, such as "the center of the Earth" or "Denver, CO"? The answer is "convenience." For example, we could accurately say that the summit of Mount Everest is 29,029 feet above sea level or 2.093×10^7 feet above the center of the Earth (Figure 1.8). As long as we all agree, it really doesn't matter what we choose, and in the previous example it is obviously more convenient to use a measurement above sea level rather than the center of the Earth. Nevertheless, elevation is a good example of when we need more than just the unit of measure itself; we also need a point of reference. In defining a particular unit and a particular reference point, we have constructed a "scale" of measurement. This is exactly how we measure temperature.

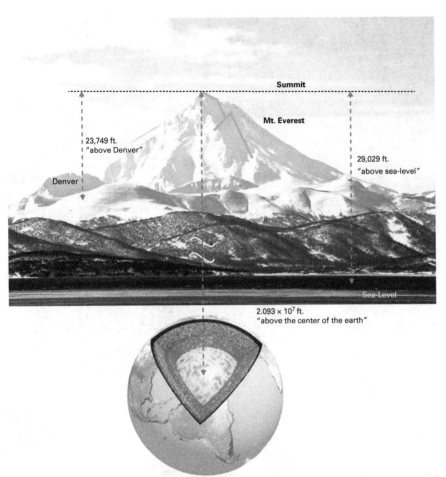

Three common temperature scales will be used in this course. These are the **Fahrenheit**, **Celsius**, and **Kelvin** (named after William Thomson, also known as "Lord Kelvin") scales (Figure 1.9). Each of these will have a different reference point (point defined as zero on the scale) and they may also have different units. The Fahrenheit scale is measured in units of "degrees Fahrenheit" (°F) and has a zero point at the freezing point of saturated salt water. Pure water freezes at 32°F and boils at 212°F on the Fahrenheit scale. In contrast, pure water freezes at 0°C and boils at 100°C on the Celsius scale. The Celsius scale is of particular practical convenience because its units and reference point are all based on the freezing and boiling points of pure water. The temperature scale used in the SI system is the Kelvin scale. The Kelvin scale is unique in that its zero point is the coldest possible temperature, **absolute zero**. Absolute zero is that temperature at which there is no thermal energy at all. As such, the point 0 Kelvin (0 K) is the lowest possible temperature. Water freezes at 273.15 K and boils at 373.15 K. Note, there is a 100 K difference between the freezing and boiling points of water on the Kelvin scale just as is the case on the Celsius scale. This is because the 1 Kelvin and 1 degree Celsius are identical units. The only difference between these scales is the zero points (see Figure 1.9). This makes it very easy to convert between these two scales:

$$K = {}^{\circ}C + 273.15$$

Figure 1.9 The three common temperature scales, Kelvin, Fahrenheit, and Celsius.

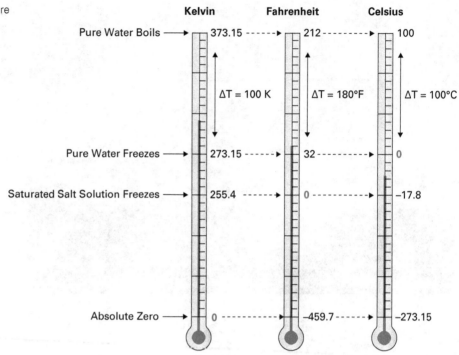

Conversion between Celsius and Fahrenheit is as follows:

$$°C = \frac{5}{9}(°F - 32)$$

Example Problem 1.7

The human body temperature is 98.6°F. a.) What is this temperature in °C? b.) What is it in K?	
Solution:	
a.) **Step 1.** Write the expression that relates temperatures on the Celsius and Fahrenheit scales.	$°C = \frac{5}{9}(°F - 32)$
Step 2. Substitute the given temperature in °F into the expression and solve for °C.	$°C = \frac{5}{9}(98.6°F - 32) = \frac{5}{9}(66.6) = \mathbf{37.0°C}$
b.) **Step 1.** Write the expression that relates temperatures on the Celsius and Kelvin scales.	$K = °C + 273.15$
Step 2. Substitute the temperature in °C from° the previous calculation into the expression and calculate the temperature in Kelvin.	$K = 37.0°C + 273.15$ $= \mathbf{310.2\ K}$

Section 1.5 Uncertainty in Measurements and Significant Figures

If you were to count the apples in a barrel, you may find that there are 130 apples. This is a number you can verify with absolute certainty. If you were to count the eggs in a carton and find that there are twelve, there is no uncertainty about the number twelve. However, when making a measurement, this isn't the case. There is always some uncertainty about any "measured" quantity. Conveniently, most of the time when we communicate measurements to each other, we do so with an implicit understanding of the relative certainty to which a particular measurement has been taken. For example, if you are riding in the back of a car and you ask the driver, "How fast are we going?" it is likely the driver will respond with a number rounded to the nearest 5 *mph*, such as 60 or 65 *mph*. It is unlikely that she might say, 65.32467 *mph*. This would be absurd for two reasons. First, knowing the speed to the nearest 100,000th of a *mph* is unnecessary. Second, it simply isn't possible to make a measurement to that level of certainty with a standard speedometer. So it goes in science as well. When we make a measurement, we have to understand all of the potential errors that can come into play, and we have to understand the limits of precision that are innate to the instrument or tool that we are using to record the measurement. This will dictate what we can know for certain and how we can properly communicate our work to other chemists and scientists.

Significant Figures

As indicated by the example in the previous paragraph, it is impossible to obtain an exact number for the measurements we make. Indeed, every measurement we attempt to take brings with it some level of uncertainty. Because of this, it is necessary to report measurements in such a way as

130 apples in a barrel and 12 eggs in a carton are numbers you can verify with absolute certainty.

Figure 1.10 Digital balances display the correct number of significant figures.

to indicate the margin of error associated with each of them. This is accomplished by reporting numbers to the correct number of **Significant Digits or Figures**. *Significant figures* are those digits in a measured or calculated number which are meaningful. This may seem a little vague right now, but it is not as complicated as it might sound. Let's consider an example. Examine Figure 1.10. If you were reading this balance, what number would you report for the mass of the sample? It is a digital balance, so the answer may seem obvious. You would report what you see, 1.379 *g*.

But what if I reported 1.37900 *g*? Is that correct? Even though the numeric values of those two numbers are the same, it is technically incorrect because by adding those additional zeros, I am saying that I have measured that mass to the 100,000th of a gram and that "zero" is not simply a placeholder but is the true value for those last two digits. The reality, however, is that we are not at all certain what those last two digits in the second number should be. This is because our balance simply is not capable of measuring to that level of precision. Therefore, it is appropriate to report only the digits that carry significance, 1.379 *g*, for the mass of our sample. Any other scientist reading our reported data will implicitly know the certainty to which we measured this number. In this case we would say that this measurement was made to four significant figures.

Reading and writing in significant figures is not always this straightforward, however. There are rules for counting significant figures. These are as follows:

COUNTING SIGNIFICANT FIGURES

1. All non-zero digits are significant. Therefore, 1.379 *g* has four significant figures. 65 *mph* has 2 significant figures, and so on.

2. There are three rules regarding the counting of zeros as significant or insignificant:

   a. Leading zeros are NEVER significant. Leading zeros are those that precede the first "non-zero" digit. For example, 0.003456 has four significant figures. 0.013 has 2 significant figures, and so on.

   b. Zeros between "non-zero" digits are always significant. Therefore, 607 has 3 significant figures. 11,001 has 5 significant figures, and so on.

   c. Trailing zeros may or may not be significant. If a reported number is written with a decimal, then we assume the use of trailing zeros is intended to convey significance. If, however, no decimal is written in the number, we interpret trailing zeros as insignificant. For example, 1,200. has four significant figures. The same number written without the decimal, 1,200, has two significant figures.

Understanding this last rule is usually the most complicated part of the process. However, if we remember this is just a convention used to indicate numerical precision of measured quantities, it becomes a little easier to understand.

Consider another example. Look at the three measurements indicated in Figure 1.11. In each of these three cases, the ruler used to measure the object is designed to measure to a different level of precision. In the first case (a), we can clearly see that the stick is longer than 40 inches. We also know with certainty that the stick is shorter than 50 inches. However, since the ruler only measures to the nearest 10 inches, we are forced to estimate the last digit of the measurement. As such, we would report a length of 44 inches. This means that this particular measurement can be made to only two significant digits. In the case of (b), the same approach is used; we estimate the last digit. In this case a measurement of 4.3 inches is appropriate (again, two significant figures). In the last case (c), the ruler can measure to the nearest 10th of an inch. So, again, we estimate to the nearest 100th (one digit beyond the graduations on the ruler). Here a reading of 2.29 inches is appropriate (three significant figures). When dealing with digital instruments this is less of an issue since there is no need to estimate the last digit. Regardless, **_significant figures should be understood to indicate each digit with certainty, except the last digit, which is estimated (to within ±1)_**. Consider the mass of a penny.

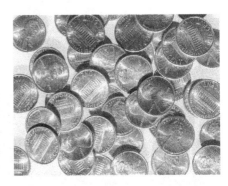

The mass of a penny can be measured.

The mass of a penny was measured to be 2.5013 g ⟶ 5 Significant Figures

Certain

Estimate

In this case, the mass of the penny is measured and reported to five significant figures. When reading this number, we can assume an uncertainty of plus or minus 1/10,000 (one ten thousandth) of a gram. This is because the last significant digit is in the ten thousandths place. This means the actual value of the penny's mass may be as large a 2.5014 g or as little as 2.5012 g (2.5013 ± 0.0001 g).

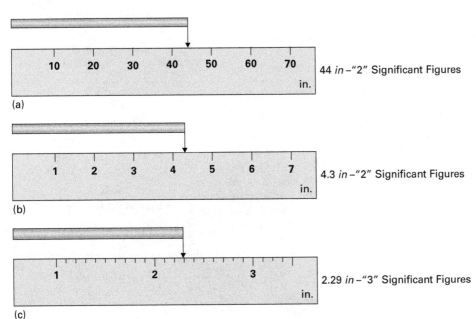

44 *in* –"2" Significant Figures

(a)

4.3 *in* –"2" Significant Figures

(b)

2.29 *in* –"3" Significant Figures

(c)

Figure 1.11 When reading graduations, the last significant figure must be estimated.

Exact Numbers

Unlike measured numbers, some numbers are known with absolute certainty. These are numbers obtained by counting or contained within a definition. For example, if I count and find that I have 10 apples in my refrigerator, that is an exact number. It is known with complete certainty. There is no ambiguity about the number 10 in this case. Another type of exact number is found in definitions. For example, there are 100 *cm* in 1 meter. In this case 100 *cm* is exact by definition. Or consider the equation for the kinetic energy of an object in motion:

$$KE = \frac{mv^2}{2}$$

In this case the number "2" would be considered exact (it is not a measured number), and because exact numbers are known with certainty, they are considered to have **infinite** significant figures. (This consideration will be important in the next section concerning calculations.)

Example Problem 1.8

Determine the number of significant figures in the following:
a.)   1.3 *in*   b.)   203 *m*   c.)   203 pennies   d.)   2,030 *m*   e.)   2.030 × 10³ *m*   f.)   1 *cm* = 0.01 *m*

	Solutions:	
a.)	Since there are only non-zero digits in 1.3 *in*, all digits are significant.	1.3 *in* **2 Significant Figures.**
b.)	Non-zero digits are significant and "interior" zeros are significant.	203 *m* **3 Significant Figures.**
c.)	Since this is an exact number there are infinite significant digits. Recall the definition of exact numbers.	203 pennies **Exact number = ∞ Significant Figures.**
d.)	Non-zero digits and interior zeros are significant. Trailing zeros are only significant if a decimal is present.	2,030 *m* **3 Significant Figures.**
e.)	In counting significant figures, we ignore the exponential part of scientific notation and only concern ourselves with the coefficient. Here the interior zero and non-zero digits are always significant and the trailing zero is significant because a decimal is present.	2.030 × 10³ *m* **4 Significant Figures.**
f.)	Since definitions (such as in this case – the definition of a centimeter) are exact, there are infinite significant figures.	1 cm = 0.01 *m* **Exact number = ∞ Significant Figures.**

Example Problem 1.9

Read the following measurements to the correct number of significant figures:

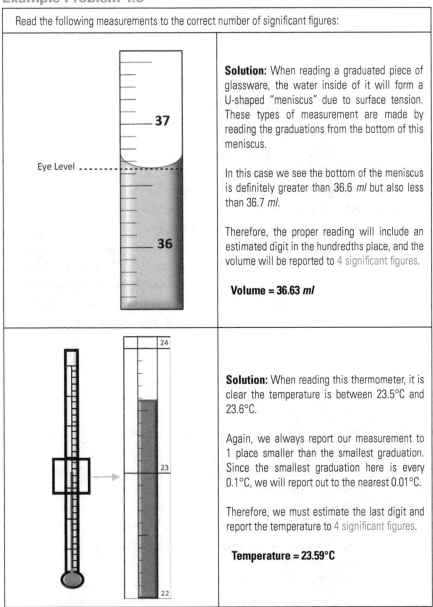

Solution: When reading a graduated piece of glassware, the water inside of it will form a U-shaped "meniscus" due to surface tension. These types of measurement are made by reading the graduations from the bottom of this meniscus.

In this case we see the bottom of the meniscus is definitely greater than 36.6 *ml* but also less than 36.7 *ml*.

Therefore, the proper reading will include an estimated digit in the hundredths place, and the volume will be reported to 4 significant figures.

Volume = 36.63 *ml*

Solution: When reading this thermometer, it is clear the temperature is between 23.5°C and 23.6°C.

Again, we always report our measurement to 1 place smaller than the smallest graduation. Since the smallest graduation here is every 0.1°C, we will report out to the nearest 0.01°C.

Therefore, we must estimate the last digit and report the temperature to 4 significant figures.

Temperature = 23.59°C

Calculating with Significant Figures

When it is necessary to perform calculations utilizing measured numbers as inputs (as we did in the density calculations previously), it is important that the numeric values generated in such calculations reflect the appropriate number of significant figures. That is to say, the result of a calculation cannot carry greater certainty than the inputs that were utilized to generate it. To this end, we have some rules to help us determine the appropriate number of significant figures for the results of calculations. The rules for doing so are different depending on which type of calculation is being performed. Let us begin with the simplest, multiplication and division.

1. **Multiplication and Division**—*In multiplication and division, the final result must have the same number of significant figures as that of the measured value with the fewest significant figures that was utilized in the calculation.*

For example, consider the following:

$$\frac{3.40 \times 2.8073}{4.551} = 2.097301692$$

If you use your calculator to determine the result in this case, it is likely giving you an answer similar to that given here (10 digits). Since none of the inputs has anything close to 10 significant digits, this result is reported incorrectly. In other words, it is not possible for the result to carry with it greater precision and certainty than the inputs which were used to calculate it. In order to determine the correct number of significant figures, we must identify the input which has the fewest significant figures. In this case that would be 3.40 (which has three significant digits). This means our result should also be reported to only three significant figures as well.

$$\frac{3.40 \times 2.8073}{4.551} = 2.097301692 = 2.10$$

In order to do this, we start at the first non-zero digit (2.097301692) and count over 3 places from left to right. This determines the position of the "last" significant digit in resulting number (2.097301692). At this point we must round off the last digit. When rounding, simply look at the digit immediately to the right of the last significant digit. If it is ≥ 5, round the last digit up by 1. If the digit to the right is ≤ 4, simply leave the last significant digit as it is and drop the rest of the digits. Therefore, our result is properly reported as 2.10.

You will not always have to drop digits. Sometimes you will need to add significant zeros. Let's look at another situation. Say the inputs for a calculation are as follows:

$$\frac{12.0}{2.00} = 6$$

If you perform the calculation above using your calculator, you will get "6" as the result. However, since both inputs have 3 significant figures, the result should also be reported to 3 significant figures. In this case you will need to add additional "significant" zeros.

$$\frac{12.0}{2.00} = 6 = 6.00$$

Note: Recall that the presence of a decimal indicates that trailing zeros (those following the last non-zero digit) are understood to be significant.

2. ***Addition and Subtraction*** – *In addition and subtraction the result will have the same number of decimal places as the measured input with the fewest decimal places.* There is a very simple method for ensuring this, illustrated as follows:

   Suppose you needed to add the numbers described in the following sum.

$$12.43 + 1.2357 + 421.220$$

   In order to ensure you report the result to the correct number of significant figures, the best method is:

   1. First write the numbers as a stack with each place (hundreds, tens, ones, tenths, hundredths, thousandths, etc.) aligned properly in columns as follows:

$$
\begin{array}{r}
12.43 \\
1.2357 \\
+ \quad 421.220 \\
\hline
\end{array}
$$

   2. Then, identify the last significant digit in each measured value in the stack (highlighted in red as shown).

$$
\begin{array}{r}
12.43 \\
1.2357 \\
+ \quad 421.220 \\
\hline
\end{array}
$$

   3. Of these last significant digits, draw a line immediately to the right of whichever one rests farthest to the left. In the case of our example, this is the digit "3" as shown.

$$
\begin{array}{r}
12.43 \\
1.2357 \\
+ \quad 421.220 \\
\hline
\end{array}
$$

   4. Perform the addition as you would normally, making sure that each digit in the result is properly aligned with the entire stack. When reading our result, each digit to the left of the vertical line is significant. Those to the right are not.

$$
\begin{array}{r}
12.43 \\
1.2357 \\
+ \quad 421.220 \\
\hline
434.8857 = 434.89
\end{array}
$$

5 Sig. Figures

5. Round the result to the last significant figure. In this case the last significant figure is the "8" occupying the hundredths place. Recall our rounding rules. Since the number immediately to the right is ≥ 5, we round the 8 to a 9 and drop the remaining digits. Therefore, our result is properly written to five significant figures as 434.89.

This same procedure can be applied to subtraction as well (See Example Problem 1.10).

Example Problem 1.10

Carry out the following to the correct number of significant figures.

a.) $\dfrac{3.10002}{3.78} =$

b.) $12.907 \times 2.341 =$

c.) $37.2 + 12.887 + 8.71043 =$

d.) $4.37 - 1.201 =$

Solutions:	
a.) In division the result of the calculation should be reported to the same number of significant figures as the input with the fewest significant figures. In this case that is 3.78 with three significant figures.	$\dfrac{3.10002}{3.78} = 0.8201111 = \mathbf{0.820}$
b.) The same rule applies in multiplication as in division. Since 2.341 has the fewest significant figures (4 Sig. Fig.), the result should be rounded to four significant figures.	$12.907 \times 2.341 = 30.215287 = \mathbf{30.22}$
c.) In addition, the result will have the same number of decimal places as the measured input with the fewest "significant" decimal places. In this case that is 37.2, which means the last significant digit in the result will be in the 10ths place (58.8, three significant figures).	$37.2 + 12.887 + 8.71043 =$ $$\begin{array}{r} 37.2 \\ 12.887 \\ + \quad 8.71043 \\ \hline 58.79743 \end{array}$$ $37.2 + 12.887 + 8.71043 = \mathbf{58.8}$

d.) The same rule applies in subtraction as in addition.	$4.37 - 1.201 =$ $\begin{array}{r} 4.37 \\ -\ \ 1.201 \\ \hline 3.169 \end{array}$ $4.37 - 1.201 = \mathbf{3.17}$

Order of Operations

When conducting more complex calculations which require a combination of mathematical operations, it isn't as easy to simply apply the rules for handling significant figures as described in the previous section. For this reason, we have a defined order of operations that allows us to always arrive at the correct number of significant figures.

ORDER OF OPERATION:

1. Parentheses – Any operations in parentheses should be carried out first and the correct number of significant figures determined.

2. Exponents

3. Multiplication/Division

4. Addition/Subtraction

By performing each operation in this order and determining the number of significant figures resulting in each operation, you should arrive at the result with correct significant figures. However, *no rounding of any numbers should be carried out until the entire calculation is completed.* An example is illustrative here. Let us perform the following calculation:

$$(4.321 + 12.7) \times 1.2 - 0.332 \div 0.166 = ?$$

Step 1 – Parentheses: The first step in the order of operations is "parentheses," so step 1 here is to perform the addition in parentheses $(4.321 + 12.7)$:

Since the last significant figure is the one-thousandths place (highlighted in red) for 4.321 and the tenths place for 12.7, the result will have its last significant digit in the tenths place as follows:

$$\begin{array}{r} 4.321 \\ +\ \ 12.7\ \ \\ \hline 17.021 \end{array}$$

$$(17.021) \times 1.2 - 0.332 \div 0.166 = ?$$

Note: Do not round until the entire calculation is completed.

Step 2 – Multiplication is the next operation in this example. Recall the rule for multiplication in the previous section:

2 Significant
Figures

$(17.021) \times 1.2 - 0.332 \div 0.166$

3 Significant
Figures

The result will have 2 significant figures. $\longrightarrow$ 20.4252
Therefore:

$$20.4252 - 0.332 \div 0.166 = ?$$

Step 3 – Division is next. Apply the multiplication/division rule just as in the previous step. However, in this case you will need to add "significant zeros" to the result your calculator gives ($0.332 \div 0.166 = 2$).

3 Significant
Figures

$$20.4252 - 0.332 \div 0.166 = ?$$

3 Significant
Figures

Therefore, the result is:

$$20.4252 - 2.00 = ?$$

Step 4 – Subtraction: We now apply the addition/subtraction rule to the final operation just as we did in Step 1.

Last Significant Figure
farthest to the left.

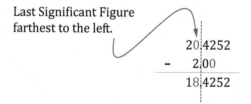

$$
\begin{array}{r}
20.4252 \\
- \quad 2.00 \\
\hline
18.4252
\end{array}
$$

Therefore, our calculation becomes:

$$20.4252 - 2.00 = 18.4252 = \mathbf{18} \text{ (2 significant figures)}$$

Example Problem 1.11

Perform the following calculations to the correct number of significant figures.

a.) $(0.0231)(42.00000)\left(\dfrac{6.980}{72.111}\right) =$

b.) $(3.124) \times \dfrac{(16.054 - 12.3)}{1.33 \times 10^4} =$

	Solutions:
a.) **Step 1.** Perform all operations in parentheses first. Note the position of the "last" significant figure (highlighted in red), but do not round until the end of the calculation.	$(0.0231)(42.00000)\left(\dfrac{6.980}{72.111}\right) =$ $(0.0231)(42.00000)(0.09679522) =$
Step 2. Next perform all multiplication. Recall that the result will have no more significant figures than the input with the fewest significant figures. In this case that is (0.0231), which has three significant figures. This means the result will have only three significant figures. This means that the last significant digit is "9" in the ten-thousandths place.	$(0.0231)(42.00000)(0.09679522) =$ $= 0.09391072$
Step 3. Since there are no more mathematical operations to perform, we will now round to the last significant digit.	$(0.0231)(42.00000)\left(\dfrac{6.980}{72.111}\right) = \mathbf{0.0939}$
b.) **Step 1.** Perform all operations in parentheses. This requires us to perform a subtraction. Again, note the last significant digit but refrain from rounding until the end of the calculation.	$(3.124) \times \dfrac{(16.054 - 12.3)}{1.33 \times 10^4} =$ $\begin{array}{r} 16.054 \\ -\ \ 12.3 \\ \hline 3.754 \end{array}$ $(3.124) \times \dfrac{(3.754)}{1.33 \times 10^4} =$
Step 2. Perform all multiplication and division. Since the value in parentheses (3.754) has the fewest significant figures (two significant figures), our result should be reported to two significant figures.	$(3.124) \times \dfrac{(3.754)}{1.33 \times 10^4} = 0.00088177$
Step 3. Since there are no more mathematical operations to perform, we will now round to the last significant digit.	$0.00088177 = \mathbf{0.00088}$

Section 1.6 Dimensional Analysis – Creating and Using Conversion Factors

Recall from the previous section that we defined *units* as generally accepted *quantities* which are used to accurately and reproducibly report experimental measurements. Further, the term "quantity" was stressed in the definition. This is because that is precisely what a unit is, a quantity, and like any quantity, units can be multiplied and divided. To make this point a little more obvious, let's consider a measured length of 8 *cm*. Now, what does this mean, to say that the length of something is 8 *cm*? Well, in a mathematical sense it means that we have measured and found the length of a particular object to be equal to 8 times the quantity of length known as a centimeter, L = 8 × (1 centimeter). This is what is meant by 8 *cm*. For this reason, units are very important algebraic terms that are indispensable when performing calculations. That is why they should never be forgotten or left out of any calculations in this course. Not only should you include them, you should multiply and divide them like any other quantity when performing your calculations. Doing so is the basis for a method of problem solving known as **dimensional analysis**.

Dimensional analysis is a method which relies on the construction and use of *conversion factors* to convert from one set of units to another in the expression of a given quantity. A **conversion factor** is a ratio, or quotient, that is prepared from an equivalence. For example, consider the meter. There are 100 *cm* in 1 *m*. We can express this mathematically as follows:

$$1\ m = 100\ cm$$

From this equality, we can construct two possible conversion factors (each simply being the inverse of the other).

$$\frac{1\ m}{100\ cm}\ and\ \frac{100\ cm}{1\ m}$$

Let's consider a problem. Suppose that I want to express the quantity 2.37 *m* in terms of centimeters. This can be accomplished by selecting the appropriate conversion factor and applying it as shown:

$$(2.37\ m) \times \left(\frac{100\ cm}{1\ m}\right) = 237\ cm$$

Note: If we are moving from units of meters to units of centimeters, we need to construct our conversion factor such that meters will cancel each other. This means that whichever unit you are trying to move "to" (in this case centimeters) needs to be in the numerator of the conversion factor. Let's see the result if we had approached this problem with the other possible conversion factor:

$$(2.37 \ m) \times \left(\frac{1 \ m}{100 \ cm} \right) = 0.0237 \frac{m^2}{cm}$$

In this case we end up with a very different number, but also notice how the units multiply and divide with each other to form new units. We are not looking for units of "meters-squared per centimeter." When we arrive at nonsensical units like this, it is a good indication that we have *not* constructed the conversion factor correctly, and we need to re-examine the calculation.

A great many problems in chemistry are nothing more than re-expressing a given quantity in terms of different units. These problems are generally solved by dimensional analysis in the following manner:

$$unit \ a \ \times \ \frac{x \ (unit \ b)}{y \ (unit \ a)} \ = \ unit \ b$$

Example Problem 1.12

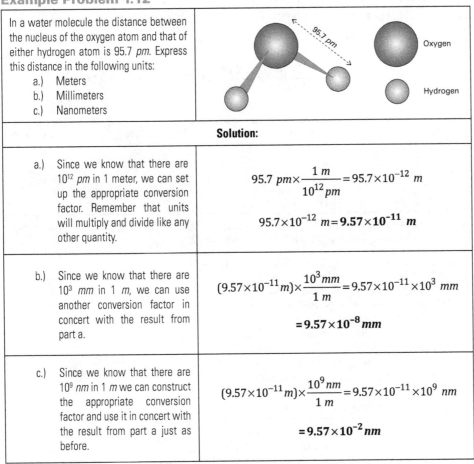

| In a water molecule the distance between the nucleus of the oxygen atom and that of either hydrogen atom is 95.7 pm. Express this distance in the following units:
 a.) Meters
 b.) Millimeters
 c.) Nanometers | |

	Solution:
a.) Since we know that there are 10^{12} pm in 1 meter, we can set up the appropriate conversion factor. Remember that units will multiply and divide like any other quantity.	$$95.7 \ pm \times \frac{1 \ m}{10^{12} \ pm} = 95.7 \times 10^{-12} \ m$$ $$95.7 \times 10^{-12} \ m = \mathbf{9.57 \times 10^{-11} \ m}$$
b.) Since we know that there are 10^3 mm in 1 m, we can use another conversion factor in concert with the result from part a.	$$(9.57 \times 10^{-11} m) \times \frac{10^3 \ mm}{1 \ m} = 9.57 \times 10^{-11} \times 10^3 \ mm$$ $$= \mathbf{9.57 \times 10^{-8} \ mm}$$
c.) Since we know that there are 10^9 nm in 1 m we can construct the appropriate conversion factor and use it in concert with the result from part a just as before.	$$(9.57 \times 10^{-11} m) \times \frac{10^9 \ nm}{1 \ m} = 9.57 \times 10^{-11} \times 10^9 \ nm$$ $$= \mathbf{9.57 \times 10^{-2} \ nm}$$

Solving Problems with Conversion Factors

In chemistry, it is often the case that we need to use more than one conversion factor in order to calculate a desired quantity. In such problems a given quantity and a desired quantity are specified. Then a review of needed relationships (equalities) for the desired conversion is conducted. This is often aided by the construction of a solution diagram. Let's consider a relatable example. If the distance between two towns is 24 miles, what is this distance in inches? The most common way to solve this problem is to first convert from miles to feet and then from feet to inches as described in the solution diagram shown here:

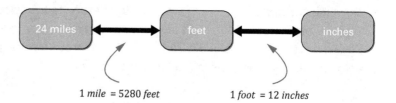

For each transition (arrow) in our diagram, we need an equality from which a conversion factor can be constructed. In this case, we have the relationships of 5280 feet per mile and 12 inches per foot. We can now translate our diagram into a calculation:

$$24 \ mi \ \times \ \frac{5280 \ ft}{1 \ mi} \ \times \ \frac{12 \ in}{1 \ ft} = 1{,}520{,}640 \ in = 1.5 \times 10^6 \ in$$

Note: We can check ourselves by ensuring that all units properly divide out (or cancel). One unit of interest (inches) should be the only unit remaining.

Example Problem 1.13

A biker is planning a 15-mile ride. He knows this route well and is aware that his average speed over the whole trip will be 20.2 *km/hr.* How many minutes will this trip take?
Solution:

Step 1. There are often many paths to the correct answer using dimensional analysis. Therefore, it is helpful to draw a solution diagram to plot the calculation prior to beginning. This helps define the information needed to construct the appropriate conversion factors. Since the distance is given in miles and the speed in *km/hr*, a good first step is to convert the distance to *km*.	15 miles ⟷ kilometers
Step 2. Since we need to find the time it takes to complete the trip, we can use the speed as a conversion factor relating distance to time. This will move from units of distance to units of time - hours.	15 miles ⟷ km ⟷ hours
Step 3. The problem requires us to report the projected time in units of minutes rather than hours. Therefore, we will use the equality 1 *hr* = 60 *min* to construct a conversion factor for converting hours to minutes.	15 mi ⟷ km ⟷ hr ⟷ min

Step 4. Now that we have completed our diagram, we can identify the equalities necessary to construct the conversion factors needed to carry out the calculation. Each arrow in the diagram represents a conversion factor, each of which is constructed from the identified equalities.	1. Miles to kilometers:
	    $1\ mi = 1.6093\ km$
	
	2. Kilometers to hours:
	    $20.2\ km = 1\ hr$
	
	3. Hours to minutes:
	    $60\ min = 1\ hr$

Step 5. We can now express these equalities as conversion factors in our calculation. In each one we need to place the unit we are "converting to" in the numerator as shown here. In this way all units are divided (or cancelled) out, and we are left with only the final desired unit, in this case, minutes.	$$15\ mi \times \underbrace{\frac{1.6093\ km}{1\ mi}}_{1.} \times \underbrace{\frac{1\ hr}{20.2\ km}}_{2.} \times \underbrace{\frac{60\ min}{1\ hr}}_{3.} =$$ $$= 72\ min$$

Example Problem 1.14

The density of lead is 11.3 g/ml If $1\ ml = 1\ cm^3$, re-express this density in units of kg/m^3.
Solution:

Step 1. Define the equality required to convert units of grams to kilograms. Using this, write the appropriate conversion factor.	$1000\ g = 10^3\ g = 1\ kg$
Step 2. Define the equality that relates centimeters to meters. Since we need to convert between cm^3 and m^3, we will need to "cube" this as shown.	$10^2\ cm = 1\ m$ $(10^2\ cm)^3 = (1\ m)^3$ $10^6\ cm^3 = 1\ m^3$
Step 3. Using this, apply the appropriate conversions to the given density in order to convert the units to kg and m^3.	$$11.3\ g/ml = \frac{11.3\ g}{1\ ml}$$ $$\frac{11.3\ g}{1\ ml} \times \frac{1\ kg}{10^3\ g} \times \frac{1\ ml}{1\ cm^3} \times \frac{10^6\ cm^3}{1\ m^3} =$$ $$= 1.13 \times 10^4\ kg/m^3$$

Density as a Conversion Factor

In the previous section we constructed conversion factors from the relation of 100 cm = 1 m. However, there are many different types of conversion factors that can be constructed and utilized. One of particular importance is *density*. Recall that we defined density as mass divided by volume for a sample material ($d = m / V$) and further that densities were different and unique to each substance. Therefore, density is a ratio that relates mass to volume for a given material. As such, it can be used to convert between units of mass and volume. Again, let's consider an example. Gold has a known density of 19.32 *g/ml*. What volume would be occupied by a gold sample with a mass of 2.37 *g*?

1. Since the density is given as 19.32 *g/ml*, this is just a shorter way of writing:

$$\frac{19.32 \; g}{1 \; ml}$$

2. This ratio can therefore be used as a conversion factor just as before. Since I wish to calculate a volume, I need to ensure it is written in a fashion that will result only in units of volume at the end of the calculation as shown here:

$$(2.37 g) \times \left(\frac{1 \; ml}{19.32 \; g} \right) = 0.123 \; ml$$

Example Problem 1.15

Mercury has a density of 13.5 *g/ml*. Determine the following:
  a.) The mass (in grams) of a 3.78-*ml* sample of Mercury.
  b.) The volume (in *ml*) of a 39.442-*g* sample of Mercury.	

Solutions:	
a.) Since we would like to determine (convert to) units of mass (grams), we need to express the density with mass in the numerator. In this way, when multiplied by the given volume, units of volume will cancel out.	$3.78 \; ml \times \dfrac{13.5 \; g}{1 \; ml} = \textbf{51.0 } \boldsymbol{g}$
b.) Since we would like to determine (convert to) units of volume (*ml*), we need to express the density with volume in the numerator. In this way, when multiplied by the given mass, units of mass will cancel out.	$39.442 \; g \times \dfrac{1 \; ml}{13.5 \; g} = \textbf{2.92 } \boldsymbol{ml}$

Key Terms

1. Absolute Zero

2. Celsius

3. Chemistry

4. Conversion Factor

5. Density

6. Derived Units

7. Dimensional Analysis

8. Experiment

9. Fahrenheit

10. Gram

11. Hypothesis

12. Imperial System

13. International System (SI)

14. Kelvin

15. Liter

16. Mass

17. Matter

18. Meter

19. Metric System

20. Observation

21. Prefix Multipliers

22. Scientific Law

23. Scientific Method

24. Scientific Notation

25. Significant Figures

26. Temperature

27. Theory

28. Unit of Measurement

29. Volume

Problems

INTRODUCTION AND SCIENTIFIC METHOD

1. What is chemistry?

2. What is the scientific method?

3. What is a hypothesis?

4. What is an observation?

5. What is a scientific law?

6. How are observations related to scientific laws?

7. What is a theory?

8. What is the difference between a law and a theory? Which one is more powerful?

9. Classify each of the following as an observation, hypothesis, scientific law, or theory:

   a. A sample of dry ice sublimes at room temperature.

   b. Two samples of water were acquired from two different sources within North America and found to contain the same ratio of oxygen to hydrogen according to mass.

   c. All samples of a given compound will exhibit the same ratio of constituent elements according to mass.

   d. Matter is composed of tiny indestructible particles called atoms. They combine in simple integer ratios to form compounds.

10. Classify each of the following as an observation, hypothesis, scientific law, or theory:

   a. Wood is burned inside a closed system. Following this reaction, the total mass of the system was measured and found to be the same as before the reaction.

   b. During chemical processes, all matter is conserved; it is neither created nor destroyed.

   c. The temperature of a sample of nitrogen gas is increased by a factor of two and the pressure of the gas is measured and found to be twice the original pressure.

   d. The pressure of gases is directly proportional to their absolute temperature, holding all other variables constant.

SCIENTIFIC NOTATION

11. Convert each of the following to scientific notation:

   a. 1101

   b. 0.031

   c. 456

   d. 0.0000033456

   e. 23,901,000

12. Convert each of the following to scientific notation:

   a. 2,398,800,000,000,000,000

   b. 0.00000000002319

   c. 1320

   d. 12,110,000,000,000

   e. 0.0000061901

13. Convert each of the following to scientific notation:

    a. 1,198,000

    b. 19,630,000,000

    c. 0.0000058897

    d. 0.0008536

    e. 0.078991

14. Convert each of the following to scientific notation:

    a. 999

    b. 832210

    c. 0.004572

    d. 0.00000055598

    e. 0.00034299

15. Convert each of the following to standard notation:

    a. 2.31×10^4

    b. 2.31×10^{-4}

    c. 3.0317×10^{10}

    d. 3.0317×10^{-10}

    e. 9.13×10^{-7}

16. Convert each of the following to standard notation:

    a. 4.21×10^6

    b. 7.343×10^{-2}

    c. 3.339×10^{-16}

    d. 9.9×10^{-20}

    e. 9.9×10^{20}

17. Convert each of the following to standard notation:

    a. 6.98×10^{-5}

    b. 6.98×10^{-10}

    c. 6.98×10^5

    d. 7.11×10^2

    e. 7.11×10^{-2}

18. Convert each of the following to standard notation:

    a. 1.49×10^2

    b. 5.26×10^{-8}

    c. 6.022×10^{23}

    d. 1.602×10^{-19}

    e. 2.18×10^{-18}

19. Determine the greatest of each of the following pairs:

    a. 6.626×10^{-34} and 6.626×10^{-43}

    b. 2.18×10^{-18} and 6.626×10^{18}

    c. 6.626×10^{-2} and 6.626×10^{-4}

    d. 4.132×10^{10} and 4.133×10^{10}

    e. 1.21×10^{3} and 1.45×10^{2}

20. Determine the greatest of each of the following pairs:

    a. 5.64×10^{-13} and 5.64×10^{-31}

    b. 7.12×10^{-14} and 7.12×10^{14}

    c. 3.91×10^{-7} and 3.91×10^{-4}

    d. 2.172×10^{3} and 2.173×10^{3}

    e. 2.27×10^{3} and 9.65×10^{2}

21. Complete the following table:

	Standard Notation	Scientific Notation
a.	12,001	
b.		4.52×10^{-7}
c.	0.000231	
d.		9.33×10^{-12}
e.	100	

22. Complete the following table:

	Standard Notation	Scientific Notation
a.	0.0001299	
b.		4.52×10^{-7}
c.	45,120,000,000	
d.		8.571×10^{6}
e.	0.00001	

UNITS OF MEASUREMENT AND DENSITY

23. What is a unit of measurement?

24. Name the base units of measurement for length, mass, volume, and time in the SI system.

25. What is meant by the term "derived unit"? Give two examples.

26. What are prefix multipliers and how are they used?

27. How many nm are in 1 meter? How many meters are in 1 *nm*?

28. How many meters are in 1 *km*? How many kilometers are in 1 *m*?

29. How many deciliters are in 1 *L*? How many liters are in 1 *dL*?

30. How many picoseconds are in 1 s? How many seconds are in 1 ps?

31. Complete the following:

    a. $1.20 \times 10^{12}\ m = $ _____ Tm

    b. $1.20 \times 10^{-12}\ g = $ _____ pg

    c. $3.2\ L = $ _____ ml

    d. $8.0\ mg = $ _____ cg

32. Complete the following:

    a. $4.61 \times 10^4\ m = $ _____ cm

    b. $7.56 \times 10^{-7}\ g = $ _____ mg

    c. $9.3\ L = $ _____ pl

    d. $31.56\ mg = $ _____ kg

33. Convert 2.135 L into the following units:

    a. ml

    b. ML

    c. kL

    d. nL

    e. pL

34. What is the volume, in m^3, of an object with the following dimensions? What is this same volume in dm^3? What is this volume in L?

        Length = 1.0 m

        Width = 3.0 m

        Height = 7.0 m

35. What is the volume, in cm^3, of an object with the following dimensions? What is this same volume in m^3? What is this volume in L?

        Length = 29 cm

        Width = 312 cm

        Height = 78 cm

36. If a room measures 3.0 m by 5.0 m by 6.0 m, what is the volume of the room in m^3, dm^3, cm^3, L, and ml?

37. Area: Complete the following conversions:

    a. $1\ s^2 = $ _____ ms^2

    b. $5.6\ cm^2 = $ _____ mm^2

    c. $4.8\ mm^2 = $ _____ m^2

    d. $78.2\ pm^2 = $ _____ nm^2

    e. $21.78\ km^2 = $ _____ Tm^2

38. Area: Complete the following conversions:

    a. 4.91×10^4 ft^2 = _____ yd^2

    b. 2.89×10^{-2} m^2 = _____ cm^2

    c. 1.99 dm^2 = _____ mm^2

    d. 7.32 Mm^2 = _____ m^2

    e. 8.112 nm^2 = _____ μm^2

39. Volume: Complete the following conversions:

    a. 4.91×10^4 dm^3 = _____ L

    b. 4.53×10^{-6} m^3 = _____ mm^3

    c. 1.99 cm^3 = _____ mL

    d. 7.39 Mm^3 = _____ m^3

    e. 4.333 nm^3 = _____ μm^3

40. Volume: Complete the following conversions:

    a. 6.22 km^3 = _____ Mm^3

    b. 9.1×10^3 mm^3 = _____ cm^3

    c. 9.1×10^3 cm^3 = _____ mm^3

    d. 6.42 m^3 = _____ cm^3

    e. 6.112 pm^3 = _____ mm^3

41. If a sample has a mass of 1.356 g and occupies a volume of 1.775 ml, what is its density in g/ml?

42. If a sample of lithium is cut into a cube with each side being 2.00 cm in length, what is the density of Lithium if the sample weighs 4.32 g?

43. If a sample has a mass of 4.13 g and occupies a volume of 3.780 ml, what is its density in g/ml?

44. A sample of magnesium has a volume of 4.94 ml. If the sample weighs 8.596 g, what is its density?

45. A metal ball has a radius of 0.751 cm. If the ball weighs 15.897 g, what is the density of the ball? Based on the data in Table 1.5, what is the identity of the metal?

46. An unknown solid compound has a mass of 54.84 g. When submerged under water in a graduated cylinder, the volume was displaced from 28.77 ml to 34.89 ml. What is the density of the sample?

47. An unknown solid compound has a mass of 13.2 g. When submerged under water in a graduated cylinder, the volume was displaced from 10.00 ml to 22.34 ml. What is the density of the sample?

48. An unknown solid compound has a mass of 7.82 *g*. If the sample displaces 3.11 *ml* of water in a graduated cylinder, what is the sample's density?

49. An unknown sample was submerged in a quantity of water contained in a graduated cylinder. Upon submersion, the water level rose from an initial volume of 12.50 *ml* to a final volume of 17.37 *ml*. If the sample's mass was measured to be 22.3 *g*, what is its density?

50. An unknown sample was submerged in a quantity of water contained in a graduated cylinder. Upon submersion, the water level rose from an initial volume of 14.30 *ml* to a final volume of 17.57 *ml*. If the sample's mass was measured to be 12.50 *g*, what is its density?

51. An unknown sample was submerged in a quantity of water contained in a graduated cylinder. Upon submersion, the water level rose from an initial volume of 42.71 *ml* to a final volume of 44.49 *ml*. If the sample's mass was measured to be 20.114 *g*, what is its density?

52. An unknown metal sample was weighed and found to have a mass of 22.587 *g*. The sample was then placed in a graduated cylinder containing water with a volume of 18.91 *ml*. Upon submersion of the sample, the water level rose to 21.43 *ml*. Based on this, calculate the density of the sample and use Table 1.5 to identify the metal.

53. An unknown sample was weighed and found to have a mass of 74.76 *g*. The sample was then placed in a graduated cylinder containing water with a volume of 39.66 *ml*. Upon submersion of the sample, the water level rose to 46.78 *ml*. Based on this, calculate the density of the sample and use Table 1.5 to identify the metal.

54. An unknown sample was weighed and found to have a mass of 3.402 *g*. The sample was then placed in a graduated cylinder containing water with a volume of 32.10 *ml*. Upon submersion of the sample, the water level rose to 33.36 *ml*. Based on this, calculate the density of the sample and use Table 1.5 to identify the metal.

55. Convert the following temperatures to the Kelvin Scale.

    a. 0°F

    b. 0°C

    c. 45.0°C

    d. 212°F

    e. 250°C

56. Convert the following temperatures into the Celsius Scale.

    a. 32°F

    b. 500.K

    c. 250.K

    d. 120°F

    e. 95°F

UNCERTAINTY IN MEASUREMENTS AND SIGNIFICANT FIGURES

57. Determine the number of significant figures in the following:

    a. 1.000 *nm*

    b. 100 *nm*

    c. 403,100 *L*

    d. 91,303 *ml*

    e. 9.1303 *ml*

58. Determine the number of significant figures in the following:

    a. 0.500 *ml*

    b. 9.1300 *L*

    c. 1,001 balloons

    d. 403°C

    e. 403.0°C

    f. 4.1×10^4 *mm*

59. Determine the number of significant figures in the following:

    a. 4.012×10^{-6} *m*

    b. 7.0123 *m*

    c. 0.0002341 *L*

    d. 0.004200 *ml*

    e. 100,100 *mi*

60. Determine the number of significant figures in the following:

    a. 2.100 *L*

    b. 2.100 *mL*

    c. 2,100 *L*

    d. 2,100.00 *L*

    e. 0.0021000 *mL*

61. Which of the following are exact numbers?

    a. The ball was dropped 23.2 feet.

    b. There are 7 students in class.

    c. The radius of a circle is the diameter divided by 2.

    d. There are 12 inches in 1 foot.

    e. The table is 12.5 feet long.

62. Which of the following are exact numbers?

    a. During a trip an automobile travels at an average speed of 23 *mph*.

    b. 12 = 1 dozen

    c. The mass of a coin is 4.31 *g*.

    d. There are 7 pencils in my briefcase.

    e. It is 32.25 *km* to the next town.

63. Write 1,278,342 to 3 significant figures.

64. Write 0.087217005 to 4 significant figures.

65. Write 2000 to 2 significant figures. (Hint: You may have to use scientific notation.)

66. Write each of the following to 4 significant figures:

    a. 1

    b. 10

    c. 123

    d. 1230001

    e. 2101.799

    f. 0.0221945

    g. 2,222,999

    h. 7.901296430

67. Perform the following calculation to the correct number of significant figures.

    $4.5 + 3.19 + 0.000321 =$

68. Perform the following calculation to the correct number of significant figures.

    $4.5 - 3.19 =$

69. Perform the following calculation to the correct number of significant figures.

    $$(3.98)(9.2134) =$$

70. Perform the following calculation to the correct number of significant figures.

    $$4.32 \div 67.009 =$$

71. Perform the following calculations to the correct number of significant figures.

    a. $53.23 - 1.0 =$

    b. $21.2241 + 7.23 + (4.321 \times 10^{-8}) =$

    c. $1.93001 + 2.403 + 6.0000 =$

    d. $77.88 + 88.1 - 10.0000 =$

72. Perform the following calculations to the correct number of significant figures.

    a. $9.0000 + 10.0000 - 1.00 =$

    b. $(2.0 \times 10^5) + 111 + 222 =$

    c. $23.321 + 1,000 - 10.25 =$

    d. $32.78 - 16.11124 - 6.234 =$

73. Perform the following calculations to the correct number of significant figures.

    a. $5 \times 1000 =$

    b. $5.32 \div 21.311 \times 120 =$

    c. $66.21 \times 2.3 \times 9.5 =$

    d. $12345 \div 1 =$

74. Perform the following calculations to the correct number of significant figures.

    a. $(4.7 \times 10^4) \times 2.398 =$

    b. $8.129 \div 4.07 \times 6.231 =$

    c. $3.4037 \div (1.82 \times 10^{-3}) \div 5.001 =$

    d. $100.0 \div 2.10 \times 1,000,000 =$

75. Explain the correct order of mathematical operations when carrying out calculations involving measured numbers.

76. Perform the following calculations to the correct number of significant figures.

    a. $4.57 \times \dfrac{4.113}{(12.89 + 1.9975)} + 12.095 =$

    b. $(12.43 + 2.10001) + (3.776 - 1.2015) =$

    c. $6.109 \times \dfrac{(9.531 - 4.23)}{(894.2 - 892.109)} + 10.2387 =$

    d. $4.1 \div 1.064 \times (4.21 - 6.321) =$

77. Perform the following calculations to the correct number of significant figures.

    a. $7.019 + 42.1 \div 3.9000 =$

    b. $9.927 \times \dfrac{4.0000}{2.0} + 11.1 =$

    c. $1.1 \times 5.890 \div (10.1 + 9.013) =$

    d. $\dfrac{(7.01 - 2.5)}{(8.09991 \times 1.0)} \times (11.0021 + 4.1) =$

DIMENSIONAL ANALYSIS – CREATING AND USING CONVERSION FACTORS

78. If the density of a sample is 0.8901 *g/ml*, what is the mass of the sample if it displaces 4.12 *ml* of water in a graduated cylinder?

79. The density of acetone (nail polish remover) is 0.7845 *g/ml*. What is the mass in *kg* of a sample with a volume of 2.73 *L*?

80. The density of isopropyl alcohol is 0.7860 *g/ml*. What is the mass of a sample (in grams) if its volume is 1.12 *ml*?

81. The density of water is 1.00 *g/ml*. If a 3.0 *L* container is full of water, what is the mass of the water in the container?

82. If a certain area is defined by a rectangle with a length of 7.31 miles and a width of 3.48 miles, what is this area in square meters?

83. If a backyard pool is 8.0 *m* long, 4.0 *m* wide, and has an average depth of 2.0 *m* (from the water level to the bottom), how many gallons of water are required to fill the pool?

84. How many inches are in 1 *Tm*? (Hint: 2.54 *cm* =1 *in*)

85. How many cm are in 1 foot? (Hint: 2.54 *cm* =1 *in*)

86. If a container weighs 111.34 *g* empty and is then filled with water, weighed again, and found to weigh 611.76 *g* when full, what volume can the container hold?

Image Credits

The Structure of Matter

LEARNING OBJECTIVES AND OUTCOMES

After reading this chapter, you should be able to do the following:

- Explain what matter is and be able to differentiate between a pure substance and a mixture.

- For pure substances, you should also be able to distinguish between an element and a compound, while for mixtures, you should be able to tell the difference between a homogenous and a heterogeneous mixture.

- Determine the difference between physical and chemical properties and changes.

- Explain John Dalton's atomic theory and discuss some of the key scientists involved in our current understanding of the structure of the atom.

- Define isotopes and explain how the atomic weight on the periodic table is determined using fractional isotopic abundance.

- Be able to work calculations involving isotopes.

- Demonstrate a basic understanding of the periodic table of the elements.

- Explain the basics of chemical bonding (introduction to ionic and covalent bonding).

- Define each of the Key Terms listed at the end of the chapter dealing with these concepts.

Section 2.1 Introduction

In Chapter 1, we explored some basic principles including the scientific method, significant figures, mass, volume, density, and temperature. Here, we further discuss the structure of matter and its properties. For example, notice that in Chapter 1, properties such as mass and volume are very much dependent upon the amount of the substance present. These types of properties are known as **extensive properties**, while density and temperature are independent of the amount of substance present and are therefore referred to as **intensive properties**. In this chapter, we dive further into the various properties of substances as we expand our understanding of matter in an attempt to appreciate the complexity of the

Matter is defined as anything that has mass and occupies space, which includes the planets and stars that we gaze upon on a beautiful clear night.

Your laptop computer that you are probably using right now has mass and takes up space on your desk, so it is also made up of matter.

The cell phone that you were just talking on is also made up of matter.

Cars are also made up of matter (including the gas and oil that they contain).

material world around us. For example, have you ever wondered what exactly is happening when water boils or freezes? How about why certain substances burn while others do not, and what type of changes are taking place at the molecular level? Why does iron rust? Well, the answers to these and many more questions are explored in this chapter.

Section 2.2 Matter, Physical and Chemical Properties and Changes

Everything in the universe is composed of **matter**, which is defined as anything that has mass and occupies space. This includes the planets and the stars that we gaze upon on a beautiful clear night. Your laptop computer, cell phone, car, gasoline, and the oil that you put in your car are all composed of matter. The air that you are breathing and taking into your lungs right now is composed of matter, and so are the tissues that make up your body. If you notice, all of these examples of matter have an associated physical state, which we classify as **the three states of matter, being solid, liquid, or gas.** While you might not be used to thinking about these three states of matter in this way, what essentially determines which state a substance is in depends on how far the particles (atoms and molecules) that make up a substance are spread apart from one another. In other words, how easily can these particles separate themselves from neighboring ones? This, in part, is determined by how strong the forces are which tend to hold them together. These are called intermolecular forces, which are discussed in further detail in Chapter 9. Each of these three phases can be delineated according to properties of shape, volume, fluidity, and compressibility. For instance, solids are characterized by having a definite shape and volume while exhibiting no fluidity and being incompressible. This is because in a solid, the particles that make up a sample are held very tightly together forming a very rigid structure. In such cases, the molecules or atoms of a solid are not able to move past each other or "flow" in any appreciable sense. Liquids, on the other hand, tend to also be incompressible with a definite volume; however, the shape of a liquid sample is indefinite due to its fluidity. The particles making up liquids are still held close together, but not so tightly or rigidly that they cannot flow past each other. Gases, by contrast, are characterized by indefinite shape, indefinite volume, fluidity, and compressibility. Gas molecules are hardly held together at all and typically are separated from one another by a great deal. Owing to this, they are certainly fluid and also can be compressed by application of a pressure. Because they are compressible, their volumes are indefinite.

The three states of matter are examples of **physical properties.** Other examples of physical properties can include color, density, boiling and melting points, as well as the odor of a particular substance. In contrast, a **chemical property** refers to the ability of a substance to form new substances. Chemical properties are manifested by changes that result in the formation of new substances. For example, the burning of a hydrocarbon (discussed further in Chapter 4) or the formation of rust are both examples of chemical changes in which new substances are produced.

Example Problem 2.1

Classify each of the following as being either a physical or a chemical property.
  1.) The color of a particular solution is blue.
  2.) Propane can produce carbon dioxide and water during a combustion reaction.
  3.) The density of water is 1.0 g/ml
  4.) The boiling point of water is 100°C.

Solution:	
1.) Color is an example of a physical property.	**Physical Property.**
2.) The ability of propane to produce carbon dioxide and water during a combustion reaction is an example of a chemical property.	**Chemical Property.**
3.) Density is an example of a physical property.	**Physical Property.**
4.) Boiling point is an example of a physical property.	**Physical Property.**

It is very important to note here that when a substance goes from one state to the next, it undergoes what we call a **physical change**, in which the only thing that is changing is the state or appearance of the substance, and not the chemical composition. In other words, if we examine water going from solid to liquid and then to a gas (Figure 2.1), notice that while the physical state is changing, its chemical composition is still H_2O, regardless of the change in physical state, and that all of the H_2O molecules are still intact. One obvious way that we can accomplish this is by increasing the temperature, which provides the energy necessary to overcome the forces that hold the particles together, thus allowing us to ultimately separate them from one another as they approach and enter the gas phase. Again, it is important to note that while we are providing a greater distance between the particles (i.e. in going from the liquid to the gas phase), the identity of the particles themselves remains the same. In contrast, a **chemical change** involves altering the composition of matter, which is rearranging atoms in such a way as to make different substances. If you were to separate the hydrogen from the oxygen in water through the application of an electric current (a process known as electrolysis – see Figure 2.2), this would be an example of a chemical change because two new products would be formed from the original H_2O molecule, gaseous hydrogen and oxygen.

Figure 2.1 Water undergoing a physical change.

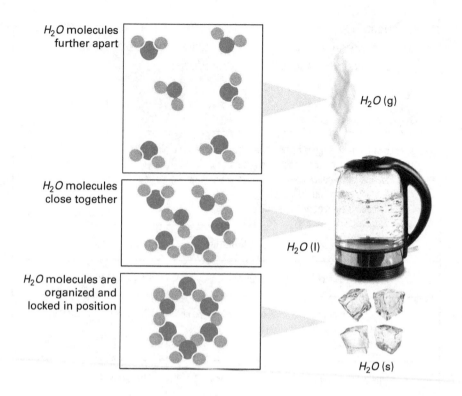

Figure 2.2 Water undergoing a chemical change during electrolysis.

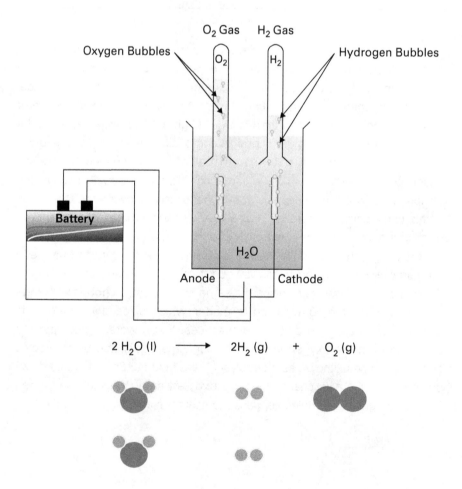

Section 2.3 Classification of Matter Based on Composition

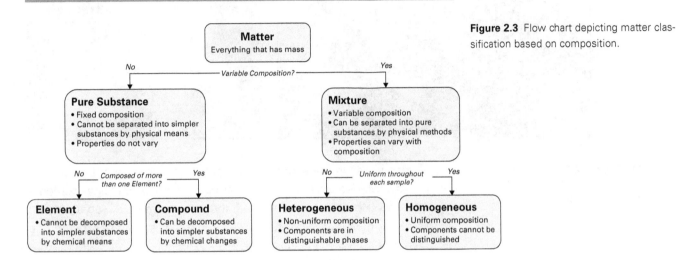

Figure 2.3 Flow chart depicting matter classification based on composition.

Having just examined the classification of matter according to physical state (liquid, solid, or gas), another method to classify matter is according to its composition (Figure 2.3). Any sample of matter can first be subdivided into two main categories, *pure substances* and *mixtures*. A **pure substance** is a sample of matter which cannot be separated or divided into simpler components by physical means. Put another way, a pure substance is composed of only one component (either an element or a compound). As such, pure substances exhibit a uniform or invariable composition from one sample to the next. For example, neon, pure water, and sugar (sucrose) are all examples of pure substances. Pure substances can be further divided into two additional categories; it is either an individual **element** or a compound. A **compound** is a substance composed of two or more elements that are joined together in fixed, definite proportions.

Unlike pure substances, **mixtures** are composed of two or more components such that they can have variable composition from one sample to the next. For example, the gasoline that you put in your car is actually a mixture of multiple compounds. If you sweeten your tea by adding sugar, you have just created a mixture. The air that you breathe is also a mixture. Mixtures can also be further categorized as being either *homogenous* or *heterogeneous*. A **homogeneous mixture** is characterized by having a

Gasoline and sweetened tea are both uniform throughout and are therefore examples of a homogenous mixtures.

Beef stew and wet sand are both not uniform throughout and are therefore examples of heterogeneous mixtures.

composition which is the same or uniform throughout a given sample. For example, sweetened tea and the air all around us are examples of homogenous mixtures. However, with mixtures, the composition may vary from one sample to the next. For instance, you may find that sweetened tea at one restaurant is sweeter than sweetened tea at another. It's the same mixture of components but with different relative compositions. On the other hand, a **heterogeneous mixture** is not uniform throughout a given sample; it varies in its composition when comparing one region of the sample to the next. For instance, beef stew or the wet sand that you encounter on the beach are both examples of heterogeneous mixtures. In both cases, you can easily differentiate either between the beef and the broth in the case of the beef stew, or pieces of coral, sand, and the water in wet sand.

As you think more about mixtures, you will quickly realize that most matter found in nature tends to be mixtures of various substances. Thus, our ability to separate mixtures into their individual components is important for a number of reasons. Many techniques can be used in order to accomplish this. For example, distillation (Figure 2.4), centrifugation (Figure 2.5), and filtration (Figure 2.6) are all techniques that can be used for separating mixtures. **Distillation** can involve the separation of two or more liquids that

Figure 2.4 Distillation involving the separation of two or more liquids that vary in boiling points.

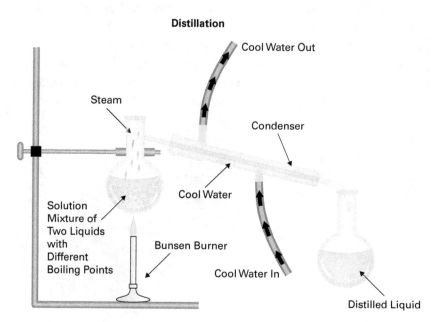

Distillation

have different boiling points. In this technique, the liquid with the lowest boiling point can be boiled off from the mixture of liquids to the gas phase, and then travel through a cooled condenser which will return the substance back to the liquid phase in a separate container from the original mixture. Incidentally, this technique can also be used to separate a liquid from a solid. For example, pure water can be separated from seawater using this technique in which the sample is heated, and only the pure water is boiled to steam leaving behind the solid salt. The steam or water vapor then travels through the cooled condenser and returns to the liquid phase as pure water in a separate container.

Centrifugation (sometimes referred to as "spinning down samples") involves the application of centripetal force, for example using a centrifuge, to allow for heavier substances to settle as sediment at the bottom of a mixture while lighter substances remain on the top. This is a common technique used for separating the various components that make up human blood. Blood samples can be placed in a centrifuge and spun at rapid speeds, which allow for heavier components (i.e. erythrocytes) to sediment at the bottom, while lighter components (i.e. plasma) remain at the top.

Figure 2.5 Centrifugation involves the application of centripetal force to allow for heavier substances to settle or sediment at the bottom of a mixture while lighter substances remain on the top.

Centrifugation

Heterogeneous mixture of blood components to include erythrocytes, leukocytes, platelets, and plasma.

As the rotor spins at rapid speeds, the mixture begins to separate. The heavier erythrocytes and leukocytes are pulled toward the bottom of the tube, while the lighter plasma and platelet components remain closer to the top.

The distinct layers of the blood components can be readily observed in the sample after centrifugation.

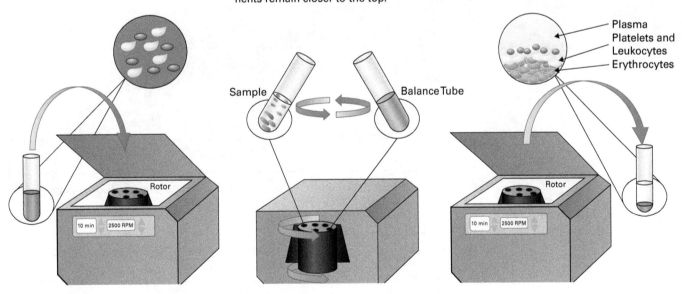

Filtration is yet another separation technique in which a solid can be separated from a liquid by simply pouring a solid/liquid mixture through filter paper, which captures the solid while the liquid flows through the paper into a new container. In some instances, the filter paper can then be heated in order to dry out the solid sample and remove all traces of the liquid prior to being weighed. In any event, the important thing to note is that there are many ways in which mixtures can be separated, some of which were outlined here.

Figure 2.6 Filtration apparatus that can be used to separate a solid from a liquid.

Filtration

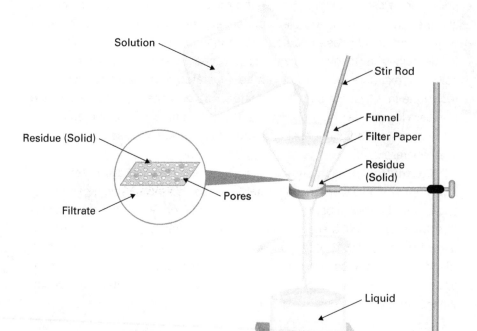

Example Problem 2.2

Classify each of the following as a mixture or a pure substance.
1.) Carbon monoxide
2.) Human Blood
3.) Tea with sugar
4.) Aluminum

Solution:	
1.) Carbon monoxide is composed of carbon and oxygen (two elements), and is therefore a pure substance and is a compound.	**Pure substance; compound.**
2.) Human blood is a complex heterogeneous mixture of erythrocytes, plasma, platelets, leukocytes, etc.	**Heterogeneous mixture.**
3.) Tea with sugar is a homogenous mixture of tea and sugar.	**Homogenous mixture.**
4.) Aluminum is an element on the periodic table and is a pure substance.	**Pure substance; element.**

Section 2.4 Foundational Chemical Laws and the Atomic Theory

The Law of Mass Conservation

John Dalton was born in Cumberland, England, in 1766 and later died of a stroke in Manchester, England, in 1844. He was a chemist/physicist most famous for his work developing the atomic theory of matter, which is the basis of our modern understanding of the structure of matter and will be discussed later in this section. However, before we can explore and understand Dalton's atomic theory, we must first discuss three major laws that contributed to the development and acceptance of this theory. These laws are the Law of Mass Conservation, the Law of Definitive Proportions, and the Law of Multiple Proportions. First, the **Law of Mass Conservation** states that the total mass of substances involved in a chemical reaction does not change, and thus matter is not created nor destroyed during the reaction. For example, in Figure 2.7, if we look at the formation of the yellow solid precipitate lead(II) iodide that forms (on the right of the equation) upon the addition of two clear colorless liquids, aqueous potassium iodide and aqueous lead(II) nitrate (both on the left of the equation), we see that the total mass at the beginning of the chemical reaction is the same after the reaction. This is a good example of the law of mass conservation.

John Dalton (1766–1844) was an English chemist and physicist who is most famously known for his work on the development of the atomic theory.

IS EQUAL TO THE...

Total mass **before** the reaction → Total mass **after** the reaction

Combine the two solutions

$2KI \, (aq) \; + \; Pb(NO_3)_2 \, (aq) \longrightarrow 2KNO_3 \, (aq) \; + \; PbI_2 \, (s)$

(Potassium iodide)   (Lead (II) nitrate)   (Potassium nitrate)   (Lead (II) iodide)

Figure 2.7 The Law of Mass Conservation states that the total mass of substances involved in a chemical reaction does not change, and thus matter is not created nor destroyed during the chemical reaction.

The Law of Definite Composition and Multiple Proportions

Second, we have the **Law of Definite Composition**, which states that all samples of a particular compound are composed of the same elements in the same proportions according to mass, no matter what their source or how they were prepared. For example, the molecular formula for water is always H_2O. Therefore, the mass ratio of hydrogen to oxygen will always be the same in any sample of pure water no matter the source. We will revisit this concept later in this chapter following our introduction to the periodic table and discussion on atomic mass of the elements found on the periodic table. Finally, the **Law of Multiple Proportions** states that if two elements (we will call them element 1 and element 2 for the purposes of this definition) react to form two different compounds, then the two masses of element 2 that combine with a fixed mass of element 1 *in* each of the two compounds can be expressed as a ratio of small whole numbers. While the definition of this law may sound complicated, if we look at an example of the application of this law, it makes things a lot easier and more understandable. For example, let's say that a certain mass of carbon reacts with 27.2 grams of oxygen in order to form carbon monoxide (CO). Then according to the law of multiple proportions, how many grams of oxygen would react with the same mass of carbon in the formation of carbon dioxide (CO_2)? Because we see that there are twice as many oxygen atoms in CO_2 as in CO, the answer is double the mass of oxygen that we had in the CO sample, given the same amount of carbon in both cases. Thus, the answer would be 54.4 grams of oxygen in CO_2.

In any event, we can now see how these laws can be explained by an atomic model. In 1808, John Dalton explained these laws, as well as many other contemporary observations by developing his atomic theory which states the following four postulates:

1.) Each element is composed of extremely small indestructible particles called atoms.

2.) All atoms of a given element have the same mass, size, and other properties that distinguish them from the atoms of the other elements.

3.) When atoms combine, they do so in simple, whole-number ratios to form chemical compounds.

4.) Atoms of one element cannot change into atoms of another element. However, in a chemical reaction they can change the way in which they are bound together with other atoms.

While in subsequent years our understanding of the elements has evolved somewhat, Dalton had created a theory of tremendous importance, and its basic principles have survived to this very day. In this next section, we dive even deeper into our understanding of the atom, which we now know is composed of even smaller particles referred to as subatomic particles.

Section 2.5 **Atomic Structure**

Radiation

Marie Curie was a physicist and chemist born in Poland in 1867, who later moved to France and is commonly referred to as "Madame" Curie today. In the very late 1800s, Marie Curie and coworkers, using isolated polonium and radium, suggested that atoms emitted some kind of very unique rays when they disintegrate. She termed this **radioactivity**, which we now define as the phenomenon exhibited by certain elements in which they spontaneously emit radiation (in the form of both particles and electromagnetic waves) resulting from changes in the nuclei of atoms. Substances that exhibit this phenomenon are termed radioactive, and early experiments had identified three different types of radiation (alpha particles as well as beta and gamma rays). While the discussion involving these different types of radiation is very interesting, it requires a more detailed explanation than is offered here. For now, we should be aware of the fact that alpha particles are positively charged and are much larger than the other two. In any event, this was a very significant scientific finding, and Marie Curie later went on to be the first woman to win a Nobel Prize for this discovery (shared with her husband) before she died in 1934 at the age of 66. In part, the reason for its significance is that it suggests that atoms can, in fact, break apart, which is at least partly contradictory to that which John Dalton put forth in his atomic theory, stating that atoms are indivisible. Therefore, atoms themselves must be composed of even smaller *subatomic* particles, which we will explore next following a brief discussion on electric charge.

Marie "Madame" Curie (1867–1934) coined the term "radioactivity" following her work with isolated polonium and radium. In 1903, she become the first woman to be awarded a Nobel Prize. Some believe that her death was in part attributed to her long-term exposure to radiation. At the time, the significant damaging effects of radiation were essentially unknown.

Did you know how chemistry might relate to your job as a non-chemist? In the medical profession involving oncology, it is sometimes necessary to use radiation therapy in order to treat patients with cancer. During this type of therapy, patients with cancerous tumors receive relatively high doses of radiation to the tumor area. Cancer cells die during the treatment due to the damaging effects of the radiation to DNA (deoxyribonucleic acids). DNA is our "genetic code," which contains the encoded genetic material necessary for living cells (including cancerous cells) to generate essential proteins required for life. Beams of radiation can pass through skin and other tissues that make up the human body to effectively reach cancerous cells, thereby exerting their destructive effects on DNA. While oncology physicians can help to determine the type and the extent of radiation that patients receive, oncology nurses also play a critical role in this process. For example, they constantly review patients' health history and safely administer medications while also monitoring both the emotional and physical status of the patient. While radiation therapy is reportedly a relatively painless process, the side effects of such treatments can vary, and oncology nurses help to comfort patients as they manage their symptoms and side effects throughout this type of therapy. As we can see, you do not have to be a chemist in order for chemistry to affect your everyday life, even if you are technically working in a "non-chemistry type" profession.

J.J. Thomson (1856–1940) was an English physicist who demonstrated that cathode rays were composed of previously unknown negatively charged particles, which we now know are electrons. Thomson was awarded the first Hughes Medal in 1902 for his work in the Physical Sciences, and later the Nobel Prize in Physics in 1906.

Electric Charge

Before delving into subatomic particles, it is instructive at this point to briefly discuss the concept of electric charge. Electric charge is simply a property of matter. Irrespective of magnitude, an electric charge can have one of two possible orientations (or signs). We often term these as positive or negative charges. You may have seen this in your own experience when dealing with batteries. Batteries often have their positive and negative poles labeled. The intricacies of charge are beyond the scope of this text; however, it is sufficient to simply say that a charged particle is one that will experience a force when exposed to an electric field. Further, when two charged particles are in proximity, like charges (positive/positive or negative/negative) will repel each other while unlike charges (positive/negative or negative/positive) will attract. Additionally, if two charges of equal magnitude but opposite sign come together, the result is a "net" zero or neutral charge. All of this is summarized in Figure 2.8.

Subatomic Particles

ELECTRONS

While working at Cambridge University in the late 1890s, an English physicist named Sir Joseph John Thomson (more commonly referred to as J.J. Thomson) discovered the electron. He demonstrated that **electrons** are low-mass particles present in all atoms and are the negatively charged constituents of cathode rays. **Cathode rays** are streams of electrons that can be observed in a partially evacuated glass vacuum tube called a **cathode ray tube** (Figure 2.9). A high electrical voltage can be applied to cathode ray

Robert A. Millikan (1868–1953) was an American experimental physicist who is primarily known for his measurement of the elementary electronic charge. In 1923, Millikan was honored with the Nobel Prize in Physics.

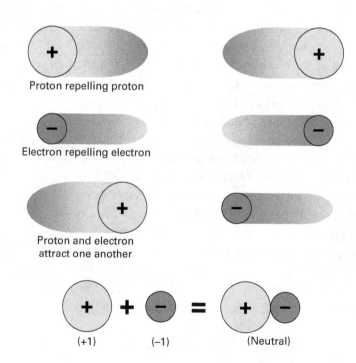

Proton repelling proton

Electron repelling electron

Proton and electron attract one another

(+1)   (−1)   (Neutral)

Figure 2.8 Figure depicting electrostatic forces (electrostatic repulsion and attraction).

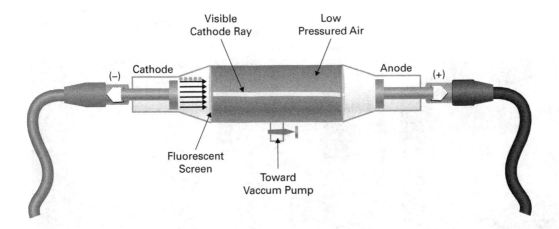

tubes, which are equipped with a negatively charged electrode, called a **cathode**, and a positively charged electrode called an **anode**. Thomson found that electrons traveled from the cathode to the anode; thus, he concluded that these negatively charged particles must have emerged from gas molecules that were close to the cathode. In any event, this proved that these subatomic particles carried a negative electrical charge. In fact, another scientist, Robert Millikan, would later measure the electric charge of an electron to be -1.602×10^{-19} Coulombs (C). A coulomb is a unit of measure for electric charge. Electrical charges give rise to **electrostatic forces**, which can be either repulsive or attractive forces (recall Figure 2.8). Thus, two positive charges would repel each other, and the same would be true for two negative charges. While Thomson's overall model of the atom, which he called the plum-pudding model (see below), was later proven to be inaccurate, he was given the 1906 Nobel Prize in physics for this work before he died in 1940 at the age of 83.

Ernest Rutherford was a physicist born in New Zealand in 1871 who would later come to be known as the father of nuclear physics. He studied under Thomson and set out to prove that Thomson's proposed plum-pudding model was, in fact, correct. To do this, Rutherford famously performed what is known as the gold foil experiment, which involved measuring the deflection of alpha particles as they passed through a sheet of gold foil. The results of these experiments performed by Rutherford and his colleagues had the unintentional results of disproving Thomson's proposed plum-pudding model of the atom. While much of the beam of alpha particles passed through the foil unimpeded (as the plum-pudding model would have predicted) many of the alpha particles were deflected, some at very extreme angles. This could only be caused if some of the particles were hitting other particles of equal or greater mass in much the same way that pool balls collide on a billiards table. Rutherford realized that matter was not distributed uniformly throughout the atom as the plum-pudding model had predicted, and further, most of the volume of an atom is empty space containing very small, dispersed, negatively charged electrons. Furthermore, most of the atom's mass is concentrated in a "nucleus." This nuclear model of the atom is the basis of our current understanding of atomic structure (Figure 2.10). Rutherford died in 1937 at the age of 66.

Figure 2.9 Cathode Ray Tube. Cathode rays are streams of electrons.

Ernest Rutherford (1871–1937) is known as the father of nuclear physics, and he famously performed what is known as the gold foil experiment, which had the unintentional effect of disproving Thomson's proposed plum-pudding model of the atom.

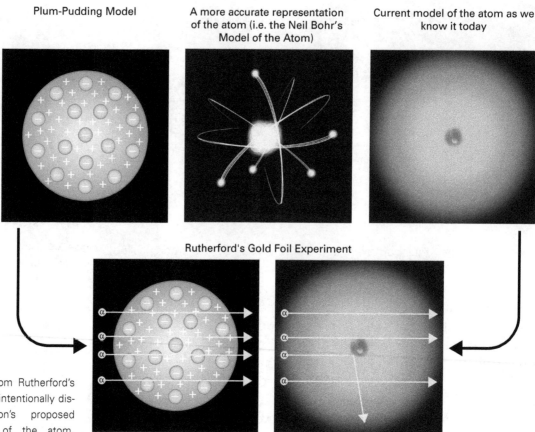

Plum-Pudding Model

A more accurate representation of the atom (i.e. the Neil Bohr's Model of the Atom)

Current model of the atom as we know it today

Rutherford's Gold Foil Experiment

Figure 2.10 Results from Rutherford's gold foil experiment unintentionally disproved J.J. Thomson's proposed plum-pudding model of the atom. Rutherford demonstrated that the atom is made up of mostly empty space with a dense mass at the center (nucleus).

Pool balls collide on a billiards table in a similar fashion to alpha-particle deflection in Rutherford's gold foil experiment.

PROTONS

Eugene Goldstein was a physicist born in Poland in 1850 and is generally credited with the discovery of the proton. In 1886, he discovered canal rays, which are also known as anode rays. Goldstein showed that canal rays were positively charged particles that are produced from gases upon collisions with electrons. We now know that these positively charged particles are called **protons**, which is derived from a Greek word meaning "the primary one". The number of protons that are contained in an atom defines it as being a particular element, and this number is referred to as the **atomic number**, which is one of two major numbers reported on the periodic table as we shall see later. Eugene Goldstein died in in 1930, but not before being awarded the Hughes Medal in 1908, which recognizes original discoveries in the physical sciences. The first Hughes Medal was awarded to J.J. Thomson in 1902. The fact that atoms contain positively charged particles makes sense as they can act as the counterpart to the negatively charged electrons, thus allowing the atom to remain neutral. This is so because the proton has been found to have an electric charge of $1.602 \times 10^{-19}\,C$, which is equal in magnitude but opposite in sign to that of an electron. Therefore, because atoms have equal numbers of protons and electrons, they are electrically neutral. Furthermore, because the electron and proton have charges of equal magnitude, we often refer to their charges in relative terms. We can see from Table 2.1 that the relative charge of an electron is −1 while that of a proton is +1, which is to say that their charges are equal in magnitude but opposite in sign.

Table 2.1 Properties of the proton, neutron, and electron subatomic particles.

Subatomic Particle	Relative Charge	Mass (*amu*)	Mass (grams)	Atomic Location
Proton	+1	1.00727	1.67262×10^{-24}	Nucleus
Neutron	0	1.00866	1.67493×10^{-24}	Nucleus
Electron	−1	0.00055	0.00091×10^{-24}	Outside Nucleus (Orbitals)

NEUTRONS

James Chadwick was an English physicist born in 1891, who eventually came to work under Ernest Rutherford as his student. While it made sense that atoms would contain both negatively and positively charged subatomic particles needed for neutrality, one pressing issue at the time for scientists was the fact that the model of the atom seemed incomplete, and that something just did not add up. For example, while they realized that protons contributed to the overall mass of the atom (and electrons did not significantly contribute), why is it that hydrogen has one proton and helium has two, yet helium has four times the mass of hydrogen? In 1932, results from experiments performed by Chadwick found evidence for the presence of a heavy, non-charged subatomic particle present in the nucleus of atoms, which we now know are called neutrons. While electrons do not significantly contribute to the overall mass of an atom, the mass of neutrons is similar to that of protons (Table 2.1), and therefore, like protons, neutrons also contribute to the mass of an element. As we can see from the table, protons have a mass of 1.67262×10^{-24} grams, while neutrons are slightly heavier with a mass of 1.67493×10^{-24} grams. A more common unit to express these masses is **atomic mass units** (*amu*). One amu is defined as being 1/12 the mass of a carbon atom, which contains six protons and six neutrons (also called a carbon-12 atom). Using this more convenient unit, we can define another number prominent on the periodic table, the **atomic mass**. The atomic mass of an element is the mass of one atom of the element expressed in units of *amu*. The atomic mass is also often referred to as the atomic weight. Additionally, it is sometimes advantageous to refer to the mass of an atom in relative terms. In these instances, we use something called the mass number. The **mass number** is the number of protons and neutrons associated with a given atom of an element. If we take an atom of oxygen, for example, with a mass number of 16 and atomic number of 8, then we know that it has eight protons and eight neutrons. That is:

James Chadwick (1891–1974) was a English physicist who is known for his discovery of the neutron.

Mass Number = # of protons + # of neutrons

If we know the atomic number and the mass number, we can then determine the number of electrons that are present in a neutral element given the following:

# of electrons = # of protons (in a neutral element)

Example Problem 2.3

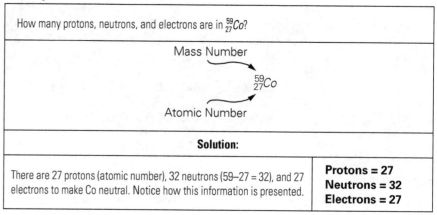

How many protons, neutrons, and electrons are in $^{59}_{27}Co$?

Mass Number

$^{59}_{27}Co$

Atomic Number

Solution:

There are 27 protons (atomic number), 32 neutrons (59–27 = 32), and 27 electrons to make Co neutral. Notice how this information is presented.	**Protons = 27** **Neutrons = 32** **Electrons = 27**

In the common notation illustrated in Example Problem 2.3, the smaller number is the number of protons (or atomic number), the larger number is the mass number, and the atomic symbol of the element cobalt is designated *Co*. Symbols are either presented as one capital letter, or in this case we see that it has a two-letter designation (the first one is capital followed by a second lower-case letter). Now, when we look at a periodic table, we must ask ourselves why are the atomic masses reported on the table not very close to whole numbers in many cases? In other words, if the mass number of a chlorine atom is 35, then how is its atomic mass listed as 35.45 *amu*? Why are fractions reported on the periodic table for atomic masses, when it is not technically possible to have a fraction of a proton or a neutron? To understand this, we next explore isotopes and natural abundance.

Section 2.6 Isotopes

Most elements in nature consist of atoms that have several different masses. If we know that all atoms of a given element have the same number of protons (remember the number of protons defines the element), then it must be the number of neutrons that can vary between atoms of the same element, and this provides for different observed masses. **Isotopes** are atoms that have the same atomic number but different mass numbers. For example, there are two kinds of naturally occurring isotopes of carbon, one with a mass of 12 *amu* ($^{12}_{6}C$) and another with a mass of approximately 13 *amu* ($^{13}_{6}C$) (Table 2.2). The nucleus of the $^{12}_{6}C$ isotope has six protons and six neutrons, while the nucleus of $^{13}_{6}C$ isotope has six protons and seven

Table 2.2 The two possible naturally occurring isotopes of carbon ^{12}C and ^{13}C.

Name	Symbol	Amount of Protons	Amount of Neutrons	Mass Number	Isotope Abundance (%)
Carbon – 12	^{12}C	6	6	12	98.93
Carbon – 13	^{13}C	6	7	13	1.07

Mass Spectrometry

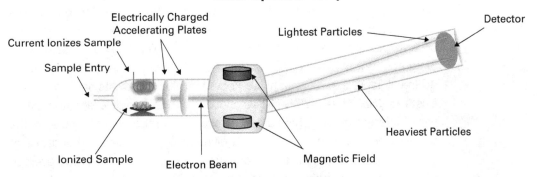

Isotopes of Carbon

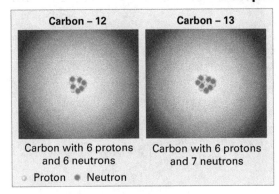

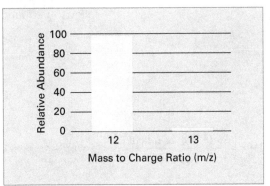

neutrons (Figure 2.11). Again, it is very important to note that while the number of neutrons varies between isotopes of a given element, the number of protons remains the same. If we look at neon, we now have three naturally occurring isotopes, $^{20}_{10}Ne$, $^{21}_{10}Ne$, and $^{22}_{10}Ne$. Thus, $^{20}_{10}Ne$ has 10 protons and 10 neutrons, $^{21}_{10}Ne$ has 10 protons and 11 neutrons, and $^{22}_{10}Ne$ has 10 protons and 12 neutrons.

Figure 2.11 Mass spectrometry and its data for carbon. Particles are separated based on their mass/charge (m/z) ratios.

Section 2.7 Atomic Mass and Isotope Abundance

The atomic mass of an element can be determined experimentally using an instrument called a mass spectrometer (Figure 2.11). Generally, mass spectrometry involves injecting a sample into an ionization chamber where the sample is electrically charged. The resulting charged atoms are accelerated by a series of charged accelerating plates into an analyzing chamber located within a magnetic field. The magnetic field then causes the beam of charged atoms to curve, and the mass of each atom can be determined by the extent of that curvature. Lighter objects will tend to have a greater curvature, while the path of heavier objects will tend to bend to a lesser extent. In this way, an accurate mass measurement can be determined. For example, we know that an accurate measured mass of $^{13}_{6}C$ is 13.003355 *amu*, $^{79}_{35}Br$ is 78.918336 *amu*, while $^{238}_{92}U$ is 238.050784 *amu*. Mass spectrometry can also give us valuable information with respect to isotope abundance. **Isotope abundance** is defined as the fraction (often reported as a percentage) of naturally occurring isotopes of a given element. For example, we know that 98.93% of carbon atoms are the $^{12}_{6}C$ ("carbon-12") isotope, while 1.07% exists as $^{13}_{6}C$ (recall Table 2.2). For neon, we know that 90.48% exists as $^{20}_{10}Ne$, 0.27% exists as $^{21}_{10}Ne$, while 9.25% is $^{22}_{10}Ne$. Since each of these different atom types has a different mass, what value is presented on the periodic table for the atomic mass? The answer to this involves using the isotopic abundance of each isotope of the element in question to calculate a weighted average of the individual isotopic masses that is representative of a given element. Thus, we calculate the atomic weight of each element on the periodic table using the following equation:

$$Atomic\ Mass = \sum_i \left(\frac{\%\ Isotope\ Abundance}{100\ \%} \right)(Isotope\ Mass)$$

or

$$AM = \left(\frac{\%\ IA\ for\ Isotope\ \#1}{100\%} \right)(Mass\ of\ Isotope\ \#1) + \left(\frac{\%\ IA\ for\ Isotope\ \#2}{100\%} \right)(Mass\ of\ Isotope\ \#2) + \dots$$

Repeat terms as necessary until all naturally occurring isotopes of a given element are included in the calculation.

Example Problem 2.4

Calculate the atomic mass that should be reported for silver knowing that only two isotopes for silver occur naturally ($^{107}_{47}Ag$ with a mass of 106.90509 *amu* and $^{109}_{47}Ag$ with a mass of 108.90476 *amu*). The percent abundance for $^{107}_{47}Ag$ and $^{109}_{47}Ag$ is 51.84% and 48.16%, respectively.

Solution:

$$AM_{Ag} = \sum_i \left(\frac{IA\%}{100\ \%} \right)(Mass_i)$$

$$AM_{Ag} = \left(\frac{51.84\%}{100\%} \right)(106.90509\ amu) + \left(\frac{48.16\%}{100\%} \right)(108.90476\ amu) = 107.87\ amu$$

For $^{107}_{47}Ag$ we get 55.42 *amu* (0.5184 × 106.90509) and 52.45 *amu* for $^{109}_{47}Ag$ (0.4816 × 108.90476). If we then just add the two numbers (55.42 + 52.45) we get 107.87 *amu*, which is the number reported on the periodic table.

$$AM_{Ag} = 107.87\ amu$$

Section 2.8 Introduction to the Periodic Table

Dmitri Mendeleev was a Russian chemist and inventor born in 1834 who was instrumental in development of what we now call the periodic table of elements based on the **Periodic Law**, which states that if the chemical elements are presented in order of increasing relative mass, their chemical and physical properties recur at various intervals in a cyclical manner. Therefore, he arranged the elements based on this principle, which at the time in 1863 contained less than 70 known elements. Since then, the periodic table has been considerably expanded and refined with the discovery or synthesis of new elements, and we now have the current-day periodic table (Figure 2.12). The modern periodic table is arranged according to increasing atomic number rather than relative mass. All elements from hydrogen (atomic number 1) to oganesson (atomic number 118) have been either discovered or synthesized in laboratories, and some common elements found on the periodic table are depicted in Figure 2.13. The most recent additions (i.e. elements 117 and 118) have, in fact, been confirmed by the International Union of Pure and Applied Chemistry (IUPAC). In any event, if we look at the periodic table, we notice that it is arranged such that it has various columns (from top to bottom) known as **groups or families**, as well as rows (left to right) known as **periods**. The ordering of the elements in this fashion based on principles put forth by Mendeleev demonstrates periodic trends by placing or aligning elements with similar chemical and physical properties in the same column. In fact, arranging the elements in this way allowed Mendeleev at the time to predict the existence of then-unknown elements, which were later proven to be accurate. For example, he predicted the existence of germanium before it was discovered in 1886 by German chemist Clemens Winkler. From this law we now know that lithium and sodium have similar chemical and physical properties because they appear in the same column on the current periodic table. The same can be said for sodium and potassium, or magnesium and calcium and so forth.

Dmitri Mendeleev (1834–1907) was a Russian chemist and inventor who published the first widely recognized periodic table and was instrumental in organizing the elements on the table based on Periodic Law. Mendelevium, or element 101, is included in the actinide series on the periodic table, and was named in honor of Dmitri Mendeleev.

Example Problem 2.5

Based on periodic law, which of the following elements would be expected to have similar chemical and physical properties as potassium? a.) Magnesium b.) Calcium c.) Rubidium d.) Strontium e.) Barium	
Solution:	
Potassium and rubidium are both in the same column (1A), and you would therefore expect them to have similar chemical and physical properties. You would also expect magnesium, calcium, strontium, and barium to also have similar chemical and physical properties to each other as they are also in the same column (2A).	**c.) Rubidium**

Clemens Winkler (1838–1904) was a German chemist who discovered the element germanium in 1886.

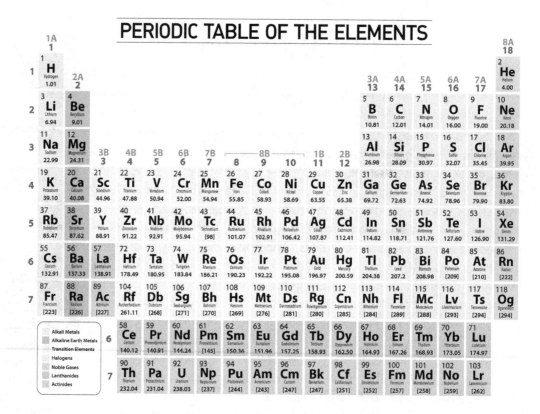

Figure 2.12 The Periodic Table of the Elements.

Upon further inspection of the period table, we notice that we have the **main group elements** (the "A" group elements) and the **transition elements** (the "B" group elements that appear in the middle of the table). The "A" elements are in the groups (columns) numbered from 1A-8A (also labeled 1, 2, 13, 14, 15, 16, 17, and 18), while the "B" group occupy columns 1B through 8B (also labeled 3 through 12). We also note that most elements found on the periodic table are **metals** and are located to the lower left of the periodic table, while **nonmetals** occupy the upper right side. Metals tend to be good conductors of heat and electricity, while nonmetals tend to be poor conductors of heat and electricity. In going from the left to the right on the periodic table we also note that the elements become less metallic in character. The **metalloids** separate these two categories on the table (i.e. boron, silicon, germanium, arsenic, antimony, and tellurium) and have mixed properties of both metals and nonmetals. There some important groups that should be noted. For instance, the elements that appear in group 1A are known as the **alkali metals** and are very reactive. Elements that appear in 2A are known as the **alkaline earth metals** and are also very reactive, although to a lesser extent than elements in 1A. As elements in both 1A and 2A are very reactive, they are only found in nature as compounds, which is to say combined with other elements. A common example of a compound containing an alkali metal is table salt, *NaCl*. This compound also introduces an example of an element in group 7A. These are known as **halogens** and are among the most reactive elements on the periodic table. Notice that chlorine is a halogen and combined with sodium in our *NaCl* example of a compound. The term "halogens" comes from the Greek meaning "salt-producing" as they tend to combine with metals to form salts. The **noble gases** are located in group 8A and are practically inert or unreactive. We shall examine why this

Table salt (NaCl) is an example of a compound. It is formed by combining sodium with chloride ions.

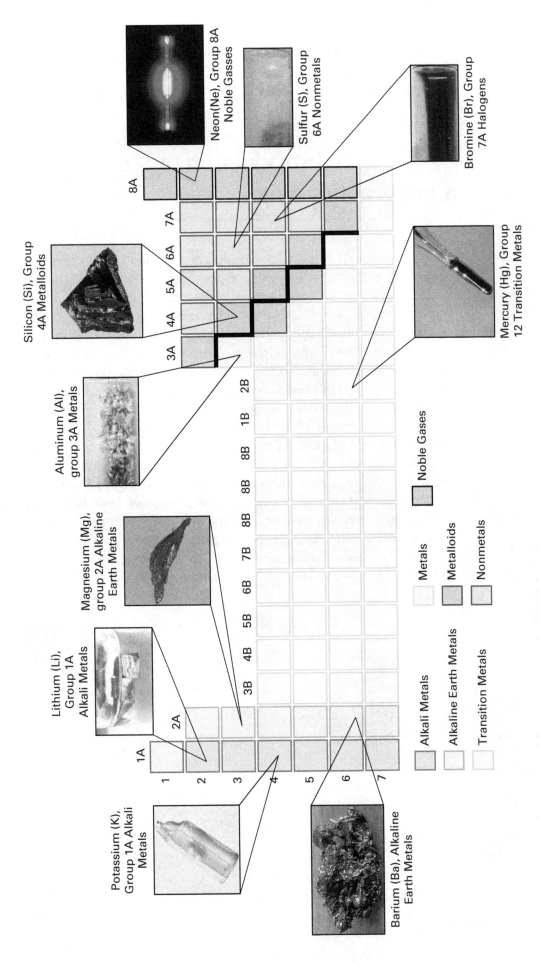

Figure 2.13 Some common elements on the Periodic Table.

Mendelevium is element 101 on the periodic table, and is included in the actinide series. It was named in honor of Dmitri Mendeleev.

is in subsequent chapters. Notice that at the bottom of the periodic table we also have the **lanthanide** and **actinide series**. Here we find element 101 (Mendelevium), which appears in the actinide series and was named in honor of Dmitri Mendeleev, who died in 1907.

Section 2.9 Introduction to Chemical Bonding

As we have seen in the last section with the formation of the compound *NaCl* from the constituent elements sodium (group 1A element) and chlorine (group 7A element), some elements on the periodic tend to be very reactive, such that they are only found in nature as compounds. In order to form a compound, **chemical bonds** must be formed, which are the forces that hold atoms together. There are two major types of chemical bonds, ionic bonds and covalent bonds. The compound sodium chloride is an example of the formation of an **ionic bond**. Ionic bonds are formed when electrons are transferred from one element to another (in this case, an electron is transferred from sodium giving it a net positive charge to chlorine, which would then be negatively charged). When elements either gain or lose one or more electrons, they become charged **ions**. *Metals* tend to lose electrons to form positively charged ions called **cations**, while *nonmetals* tend to gain electrons to form negatively charged ions called **anions**. ***As such, ionic bonds are nearly always between a metal and a nonmetal.*** In some cases, it can be relatively easy to determine the exact charge that an element will have when ionized because some elements always form ions with the same charge and are referred to as having an invariant charge (Figure 2.14; Table 2.3).

Figure 2.14 Ion charge of certain elements can be determined in some cases based on their placement on the periodic table.

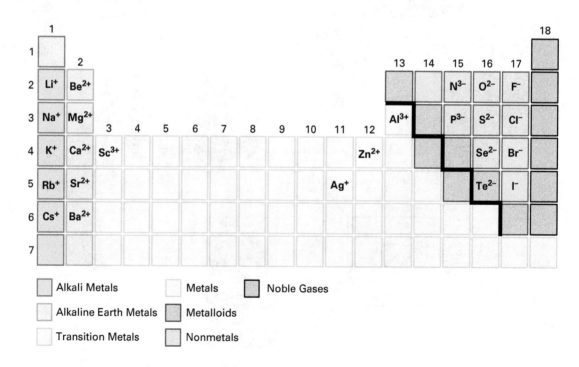

Table 2.3 List of common metals and nonmetals with invariant charges.

Metal Name	Cation	Group Number	Nonmetal Name	Anion	Group Number
Lithium	Li^+	1A	Nitrogen	N^{3-}	5A
Sodium	Na^+	1A	Phosphorus	P^{3-}	5A
Potassium	K^+	1A	Oxygen	O^{2-}	6A
Rubidium	Rb^+	1A	Sulfur	S^{2-}	6A
Cesium	Cs^+	1A	Selenium	Se^{2-}	6A
Beryllium	Be^{2+}	2A	Tellurium	Te^{2-}	6A
Magnesium	Mg^{2+}	2A	Fluorine	F^-	7A
Calcium	Ca^{2+}	2A	Chlorine	Cl^-	7A
Strontium	Sr^{2+}	2A	Bromine	Br^-	7A
Barium	Ba^{2+}	2A	Iodine	I^-	7A
Scandium	Sc^{3+}	3B			
Silver	Ag^+	1B			
Zinc	Zn^{2+}	2B			
Aluminum	Al^{3+}	3A			

*The charge of these elements cannot be determined based on their group number

For example, elements in 1A and 2A have a +1 charge and a +2 charge, respectively, and elements in group 7A have a -1 charge when involved in an ionic bond. Some elements, however, have what we call a variable charge; in other words, they can have more than one possible charge. For example, copper can have a +1 or +2 charge; iron can have either a +2 or a +3 charge; cobalt can also have either a +2 or a +3 charge. In any event, it is not really necessary to memorize all of the possible charges that elements with variable charge can have, as it is usually easily determined from the formula with a little bit of practice. We will go into more detail on this subject in the next chapter. Another type of chemical bond that is discussed in further detail in the next chapter is **covalent bonds**, in which elements share electrons (Figure 2.15). ***Covalent bonds are nearly always between two nonmetals.***

Figure 2.15 Pure substances can be elements or compounds, which can then be either ionic or covalent compounds.

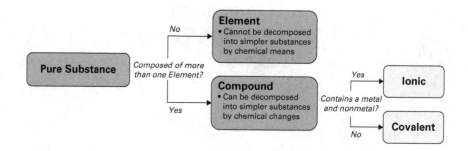

Example Problem 2.6

For each of the following compounds, determine whether they are involved in an ionic or covalent bond. If ionic, what are their charges and which element is the cation and anion?

a.) H_2O
b.) $NaCl$
c.) $CaCl_2$
d.) $CuCl$
e.) CO_2

Solution:

a.) Covalent (two nonmetals).
b.) Ionic (**Na^+ is the cation and Cl^- is the anion**). Na is in group 1A (metal), so it is +1, and Cl is in group 7A (nonmetal), so it has a −1 charge.
c.) Ionic (**Ca^{2+} is the cation and Cl^- is the anion**). Ca is in group 2A (metal), so it has a +2 charge, while Cl is in group 7A (nonmetal), so it has a −1 charge.
d.) Ionic (**Cu^+ is the cation and Cl^- is the anion**). Even though we know that Cu (metal) has a variable charge (could be either +1 or +2), we can determine that in this case it is +1 because of the −1 charge on the nonmetal Cl (this is an overall neutral compound).
e.) Covalent (two nonmetals).

Key Terms

1. Actinide Series

2. Alkali Metals

3. Alkaline Earth Metals

4. Anions

5. Anode

6. Atomic Mass

7. Atomic Mass Units

8. Atomic Number

9. Cathode

10. Cathode Ray Tube

11. Cathode Rays

12. Cations

13. Centrifugation

14. Chemical Bonds
15. Chemical Change
16. Chemical Property
17. Compounds
18. Covalent Bonds
19. Distillation
20. Electrons
21. Electrostatic Forces
22. Element
23. Extensive Properties
24. Filtration
25. Groups or Families
26. Halogens
27. Heterogeneous Mixture
28. Homogenous Mixture
29. Intensive Properties
30. Ion
31. Ionic Bond
32. Isotope Abundance
33. Isotopes
34. Lanthanide
35. Law of Definite Composition
36. Law of Mass Conservation
37. Law of Multiple Proportions
38. Main Group Elements
39. Mass Number
40. Matter
41. Metalloids
42. Metals
43. Mixture
44. Neutrons
45. Noble Gases
46. Nonmetals
47. Periodic Law
48. Periods
49. Physical Change
50. Physical Properties

51. Protons

52. Pure Substance

53. Radioactivity

54. Transition Elements

Problems

EXTENSIVE AND INTENSIVE PROPERTIES

1. What are extensive properties?

2. What are intensive properties?

3. Which of the following is an example of an extensive property?

   a. Volume

   b. Boiling Point

   c. Density

   d. Freezing Point

4. Which of the following is an example of an extensive property?

   a. Solubility

   b. Weight

   c. Density

   d. Freezing Point

5. Which of the following is an example of an intensive property?

   a. Mass

   b. Weight

   c. Melting Point

   d. Volume

6. Which of the following is an example of an intensive property?

   a. Length

   b. Density

   c. Weight

   d. Mass

7. Mass is an (extensive/intensive) property.

8. Density is an (extensive/intensive) property.

9. Color is an (extensive/intensive) property.

10. Volume is an (extensive/intensive) property.

11. Flammability is an (extensive/intensive) property.

12. The charge of an ion is an (extensive/intensive) property.

13. Classify each of the following as an extensive or intensive property.

    a. Length

    b. Mass

    c. Malleability

    d. Solubility

14. Classify each of the following as an extensive or intensive property.

    a. Freezing Point

    b. Temperature

    c. Conductivity

    d. Weight

15. Categorize the items below as having either extensive/intensive properties.

    a. Mass of a tea cup

    b. Volume of coffee in a mug

    c. Color of a balloon

    d. Circumference of a baseball

16. Categorize the items below as having either extensive/intensive properties.

    a. Temperature of liquid mercury

    b. Height of a person

    c. Boiling point of a substance

    d. The melting point of a substance

MATTER, PHYSICAL AND CHEMICAL PROPERTIES AND CHANGES

17. What is the definition of matter?

18. What are the three states of matter discussed in this chapter?

19. What are the characteristics that are exhibited by solids?

20. What are the characteristics that are exhibited by liquids?

21. What are the characteristics that are exhibited by gases?

22. What is a physical property?

23. What is a chemical property?

24. Which of the following is an example of a physical property?

    a. Corrosiveness

    b. Toxicity

    c. Flammability

    d. Boiling Point

25. Which of the following is an example of a physical property?

    a. Density

    b. pH

    c. Flammability

    d. Toxicity

26. Which of the following is an example of a chemical property?

    a. Color

    b. Melting Point

    c. Density

    d. pH

27. Which of the following is an example of a chemical property?

    a. Corrosiveness

    b. Boiling point

    c. Texture

    d. Color

28. What is a physical change?

29. What is a chemical change?

30. Classify the following as either a chemical or a physical change:

    a. The melting of ice into liquid water

    b. The rusting of iron

    c. Sugar dissolving in water

    d. The burning of propane for heat

31. Classify the following as either a chemical or a physical change:

    a. The evaporation of rubbing alcohol

    b. The brewing of tea

    c. A match igniting a firework

    d. The burning of coal

32. Which of the following is an example of a chemical change?

    a. Boiling of water

    b. Rusting of iron

    c. Evaporation of alcohol

    d. Dissolving of sugar in water

33. Which of the following is an example of a chemical change?

    a. A metal surface becomes dull due to continued abrasion

    b. Copper metal turns green with prolonged exposure to air

    c. Boiling water

    d. Breaking a block of aluminum into smaller pieces

34. Which of the following is an example of a physical change?

    a. The melting of ice into liquid water

    b. Burning wood

    c. Tarnishing of jewelry

    d. Baking a cake

35. Which of the following is an example of a physical change?

    a. Shaping clay into a ball

    b. The souring of milk

    c. Combustion of butane

    d. Rusting of iron

36. A match igniting a firework is an example of a (physical/chemical) change.

37. Breaking a glass bottle is an example of a (physical/chemical) change.

38. Shredding paper is an example of a (physical/chemical) change.

39. Cooking an egg is an example of a (physical/chemical) change.

40. Bubbles forming when hydrogen peroxide is applied to a cut is an example of a (chemical/physical) change.

41. Combining vinegar and baking soda to produce carbon dioxide gas is an example of a (chemical/physical) change.

CLASSIFICATION OF MATTER BASED ON COMPOSITION

42. What is a pure substance? Give an example.

43. What is a compound? Give an example.

44. What is a mixture? Give an example.

45. What is a homogenous mixture? What is a heterogeneous mixture?

46. Soil is an example of a (homogeneous/heterogeneous) mixture.

47. A dilute solution of hydrochloric acid is an example of a (homogeneous/heterogeneous) mixture.

48. Wet sand from the beach is a (homogeneous/heterogeneous) mixture.

49. Italian vinaigrette salad dressing is a (homogeneous/heterogeneous) mixture.

50. Sweetened tea is a (homogeneous/heterogeneous) mixture.

51. Mouthwash is a (homogeneous/heterogeneous) mixture.

52. Beef stew is a (homogeneous/heterogeneous) mixture.

53. What is distillation?

54. What is centrifugation?

55. What is filtration?

56. Label each of the following as either a pure substance or a mixture:

    a. Dilute solution of hydrochloric acid_____

    b. Distilled water _____

    c. Carbon monoxide_____

57. Label each of the following as either a pure substance or a mixture:

    a. Vinegar_____

    b. Coffee_____

    c. Gold_____

FOUNDATIONAL CHEMICAL LAWS AND ATOMIC THEORY

58. Define the law of conservation of mass.

59. If a 6.32-g sample composed of copper and chlorine were decomposed back to its constituent elements and 2.99 g of copper was recovered, what was the mass of the chlorine gas generated during this chemical reaction?

$$CuCl_2 \rightarrow Cu + Cl_2$$

60. 1.234 g of butane was burned (reacted with 4.416 g of oxygen) to form carbon dioxide and water. If 3.737 g of CO_2 is generated from this chemical reaction, what mass of water must have been formed?

$$C_4H_{10} + O_2 \rightarrow CO_2 + H_2O$$

Butane   Oxygen   Carbon Dioxide   Water

61. Define the law of definite composition.

62. If two samples of a compound composed of barium and chlorine are analyzed in the lab. Sample 1 contains 0.341 g of chlorine and 0.659 g of barium. If Sample 2 has 0.511 g of chlorine, then what is the mass of barium in Sample 2? (Hint: Use the Law of Definite Composition to solve the problem.)

63. There are two samples of a compound which is composed of only copper and chlorine. Sample 1 has a mass of 2.00 g and sample 2 has a mass of 1.55 g. It is found that 1.055 g of sample 1 is due to chlorine and therefore the copper composes

the remaining 0.945 g of the sample. According to the Law of Definite Composition, what are the masses of the copper and chlorine in Sample 2?

64. There are two samples of a compound which is composed of only iron and oxygen. Sample 1 has a mass of 2.74 g and sample 2 has a mass of 1.00 g. It is found that 2.130 g of sample 1 is due to iron and therefore the oxygen composes the remaining 0.610 g of the sample. According to the Law of Definite Composition, what are the masses of the iron and oxygen in Sample 2?

65. Define the law of multiple proportions.

66. A certain mass of carbon reacts with 6.80 grams of oxygen to form carbon monoxide. According to the law of multiple proportions, how many grams of oxygen would react with the same mass of carbon to form carbon dioxide?

ATOMIC STRUCTURE

67 Marie Curie and coworkers suggested that atoms emitted some kind of very unique rays when they disintegrate, which she termed _____.

68. What are cathode rays?

69. When referring to electrons and protons in an atom, explain why is it appropriate to deal in unit-less, relative charges of +1 and −1 for protons and electrons, respectively?

70. For each of the following elements, determine the number of protons, neutrons, and electrons

   a. $^{20}_{10}Ne$

   b. $^{12}_{6}C$

   c. $^{190}_{76}Os$

   d. $^{40}_{20}Ca$

71. For each of the following elements, determine the number of protons, neutrons, and electrons.

   a. $^{207}_{82}Pb$

   b. $^{16}_{8}O$

   c. $^{9}_{4}Be$

   d. $^{80}_{35}Br$

72. Complete the following table:

Symbol	Number of Protons	Number of Neutrons	Number of Electrons	Atomic Number	Mass Number
		7		6	
$^{14}_{7}N$					
	17	18			
		74		53	
$^{24}_{12}Mg$					

73. What is the number of protons, neutrons, and electrons for an isotope of tantalum (*Ta*) with a mass number of 181?

74. What is the number of protons, neutrons, and electrons for an isotope of zinc (*Zn*) with a mass number of 65?

75. What is the number of protons, neutrons, and electrons for an isotope of nickel (*Ni*) with a mass number of 58?

76. What is the number of protons, neutrons, and electrons for an isotope of rubidium (*Rb*) with a mass number of 85?

77. What is the number of protons, neutrons, and electrons for an isotope of gallium (*Ga*) with a mass number of 71?

78. What is the number of protons, neutrons, and electrons for an isotope of tin (*Sn*) with a mass number of 122?

79. What is the number of protons, neutrons, and electrons for an isotope of indium (*In*) with a mass number of 115?

80. What is the number of protons, neutrons, and electrons for an isotope of krypton (*Kr*) with a mass number of 83?

81. How many protons and neutrons are present in $^{45}_{21}Sc$?

82. How many protons and neutrons are present in $^{19}_{9}F$?

83. How many protons and neutrons are present in $^{11}_{5}B$?

84. What is the atomic number, mass number, and electron count for an isotope of barium (*Ba*) with 76 neutrons?

85. What is the atomic number, mass number, and electron count for an isotope of copper (*Cu*) with 36 neutrons?

86. What is the atomic number, mass number, and electron count for an isotope of selenium (*Se*) with 48 neutrons?

87. Below is a list of scientists (left column) and their major contributions to science (right column). Match the scientist with the scientific contribution for which they are famously known.

John Dalton	discovered the electron
Marie Curie	discovered the neutron
J. J. Thomson	gold foil experiment

Ernest Rutherford	discovered the proton
Eugene Goldstein	developed atomic theory
James Chadwick	coined the term "radioactivity"

88. _____ are atoms that have the same atomic number but different mass numbers.

89. Which of the following is an isotope of $^{20}_{11}X$?

   a. $^{24}_{12}X$

   b. $^{22}_{11}X$

   c. $^{27}_{13}X$

   d. $^{20}_{10}X$

90. Which of the following is an isotope of $^{20}_{10}X$?

   a. $^{24}_{12}X$

   b. $^{22}_{11}X$

   c. $^{27}_{13}X$

   d. $^{22}_{10}X$

91. There are two naturally occurring isotopes for potassium, $^{39}_{19}K$ with a mass of 38.96 *amu* and a percent abundance of 93.26%, and $^{41}_{19}K$ with a mass of 40.96 *amu* and a percent abundance of 6.73%. Calculate the atomic mass of potassium.

92. There are three naturally occurring isotopes for magnesium, $^{24}_{12}Mg$ with a mass of 23.99 *amu* and a percent abundance of 78.99%, $^{25}_{12}Mg$ with a mass of 24.99 *amu* and a percent abundance of 10.00%, and $^{26}_{12}Mg$ with a mass of 25.98 *amu* and a percent abundance of 11.01%. Calculate the atomic mass of magnesium.

93. Bromine has two naturally occurring isotopes, $^{79}_{35}Br$ and $^{81}_{35}Br$. $^{79}_{35}Br$ has an isotope abundance of 50.69% and $^{81}_{35}Br$ has a mass of 80.916 *amu* and an isotope abundance of 49.31%. What is the mass (in *amu*) of $^{79}_{35}Br$?

94. Chlorine has two naturally occurring isotopes, $^{35}_{17}Cl$ and $^{37}_{17}Cl$. $^{35}_{17}Cl$ has a mass of 34.969 *amu*, and $^{37}_{17}Cl$ has a mass of 36.966 *amu*. What is the isotope abundance (%) of each of these two isotopes?

95. Silicon has three naturally occurring isotopes. $^{28}_{14}Si$ has a mass of 27.98 *amu* and an isotope abundance of 92.23%. $^{29}_{14}Si$ has a mass of 28.98 *amu* and an isotope abundance of 4.68%. $^{30}_{14}Si$ has an isotope abundance of 3.09%. What is the mass of the $^{30}_{14}Si$ isotope?

96. Silver has two naturally occurring isotopes with isotopic masses of 106.905 *amu* and 108.905 *amu*. What is the percentage abundance of each isotope?

97. Copper has two naturally occurring isotopes, $^{63}_{29}Cu$ with a mass of 62.9296 *amu* and $^{65}_{29}Cu$ with a mass of 64.9278 *amu*. Which of these isotopes is present in the greatest natural isotope abundance?

98. Oxygen has an atomic mass of 15.9994 *amu*. Additionally, there are three naturally occurring isotopes of oxygen $^{16}_{8}O$, with a mass of 15.995 *amu*, $^{17}_{8}O$ with a mass of 16.999 *amu*, and $^{18}_{8}O$ with a mass of 17.999 *amu*. If $^{17}_{8}O$ has an isotope abundance of 0.037%, what are the natural isotope abundances of the other two isotopes of oxygen?

INTRODUCTION TO THE PERIODIC TABLE

99. Based on Periodic Law, you would expect _____ to have similar chemical and physical properties as sodium.

   a.) beryllium

   b.) magnesium

   c.) potassium

   d.) strontium

100. Based on Periodic Law, you would expect _____ to have similar chemical and physical properties as magnesium.

   a.) lithium

   b.) calcium

   c.) rubidium

   d.) cesium

101. Based on Periodic Law, you would expect _____ to have similar chemical and physical properties as fluorine.

   a.) sulfur

   b.) oxygen

   c.) selenium

   d.) chlorine

102. Based on Periodic Law, you would expect _____ to have similar chemical and physical properties as bromine.

   a.) sodium

   b.) beryllium

   c.) fluorine

   d.) argon

103. _____ is an example of a metal.

   a.) Sulfur

   b.) Arsenic

   c.) Aluminum

   d.) Silicon

104. _____ is an example of a nonmetal.

    a.) Boron

    b.) Carbon

    c.) Silver

    d.) Beryllium

105. _____ is an example of a metalloid.

    a.) Phosphorus

    b.) Zinc

    c.) Iodine

    d.) Arsenic

106. _____is an example of a transition metal.

    a.) Iron

    b.) Lithium

    c.) Neon

    d.) Calcium

107. _____ is an example of an element present in the lanthanide series.

    a.) Carbon

    b.) Lithium

    c.) Europium

    d.) Sulfur

108. _____ is an example of an element present in the actinide series.

    a.) Mendelevium

    b.) Lithium

    c.) Oxygen

    d.) Chlorine

109. The halogens appear in group _____.

    a.) 1A

    b.) 2A

    c.) 7A

    d.) 8A

110. The alkali metals appear in group _____.

    a.) 1A

    b.) 2A

    c.) 7A

    d.) 8A

111. The noble gases appear in group _____.

    a.) 1A

    b.) 2A

    c.) 7A

    d.) 8A

112. The alkaline earth metals appear in group _____.

    a.) 1A

    b.) 2A

    c.) 7A

    d.) 8A

113. Below is a list of elements (left column) and groups (right column) of various elements present on the periodic table. Match the elements to its group as it would appear on the periodic table.

Potassium	Alkaline Earth Metals
Strontium	Halogens
Tungsten	Transition Metals
Arsenic	Noble Gases
Bromine	Alkali Metals
Argon	Metalloid

114. Below is a list of elements (left column) and groups (right column) of various elements present on the periodic table. Match the elements to its group as it would appear on the periodic table.

Fluorine	Alkaline Earth Metals
Xenon	Halogens
Calcium	Transition Metals
Cesium	Noble Gases
Chromium	Alkali Metals
Boron	Metalloid

115. Below is a list of the names (left column) and the symbols (right column) of various elements present on the periodic table. Match each name to its symbol.

Aluminum	Au
Argon	Cl
Arsenic	Ar
Beryllium	H
Calcium	Be

Chlorine	Cu
Copper	Al
Chromium	Ca
Gold	As
Hydrogen	Cr

116. Below is a list of the names (left column) and the symbols (right column) of various elements present on the periodic table. Match each name to its symbol.

Lead	Zn
Lithium	Ne
Magnesium	O
Mercury	Pb
Neon	Ag
Oxygen	Si
Potassium	Mg
Silicon	Hg
Silver	K
Zinc	Li

INTRODUCTION TO CHEMICAL BONDING

117. What is a chemical bond?

118. What is an ionic bond?

119. What is a covalent bond?

120 In an ionic bond, metals tend to _____ electrons and have a _____ charge and are called _____, while nonmetals tend to _____ electrons and have a _____ charge and are called _____.

121. _____ is an example of an ionic compound.

    a. SO_2

    b. CO

    c. $BaCl_2$

    d. CO_2

122. _____ is an example of an ionic compound.

    a. CCl_2

    b. $FeBr_2$

    c. CS_2

    d. PCl_3

123. _____ is an example of a covalent compound.

    a. KCl

    b. $FeBr_2$

    c. $MgCl_2$

    d. PCl_3

124. Is the bond formed in the compound $NaCl$ ionic or covalent? If the bond is ionic, then identify the cation and anion as well as the charges of the elements involved in the compound.

125. Is the bond formed in the compound H_2O ionic or covalent? If the bond is ionic, then identify the cation and anion as well as the charges of the elements involved in the compound.

126. Is the bond formed in the compound $CaCl_2$ ionic or covalent? If the bond is ionic, then identify the cation and anion as well as the charges of the elements involved in the compound?

127. The following ionic compounds contain transition metals that have variable charges. Based on what you know about ionic bonding, label the correct charges for the following ions in the compound.

    a. $PbCl_2$

    b. Cu_2O

    c. FeO

    d. Fe_2O_3

128. The following ionic compounds contain transition metals that have variable charges. Based on what you know about ionic bonding, label the correct charges for the following ions in the compound.

    a. $CoBr_2$

    b. SnO

    c. Co_2O_3

    d. HgO

Image Credits

- Fig. 2.A: Copyright © Depositphotos/Lonely11.
- Fig. 2.B: Copyright © Depositphotos/cobalt88.
- Fig. 2.C: Copyright © Depositphotos/maxkabakov.
- Fig. 2.D: Copyright © 2006 by Fairv8, (CC BY-SA 3.0) at https://commons.wikimedia.org/wiki/File:1_Bryce_Washington_(SA),_Porsche_GT3_Cup.JPG.
- Fig. 2.1a: Copyright © Depositphotos/tanuha2001.
- Fig. 2.1b: Copyright © Depositphotos/31moonlight31.
- Fig. 2.1c: Copyright © Depositphotos/dvargg.
- Fig. 2.2: Copyright © 2005 Nécropotame, FAL 1.3 at: https://commons.wikimedia.org/wiki/File:Schemas_electrolyse_h2o.jpg. A copy of the license can be found here: http://artlibre.org/licence/lal/en/.
- Fig. 2.Ea: Copyright © Depositphotos/iodrakon.
- Fig. 2.Eb: Copyright © Depositphotos/karandaev.
- Fig. 2.Fa: Copyright © Depositphotos/duskbabe.
- Fig. 2.Fb: Copyright © Depositphotos/Alexis84.
- Fig. 2.G: Source: https://commons.wikimedia.org/wiki/File:Dalton_John_desk.jpg.
- Fig. 2.7: Copyright © Depositphotos/Morphart.
- Fig. 2.H: Source: https://commons.wikimedia.org/wiki/File:Madame_curie_3334194920_e4014f35a4_o.jpg.
- Fig. 2.I: Copyright © Depositphotos/michaeljung.
- Fig. 2.J: Source: https://commons.wikimedia.org/wiki/File:J.J_Thomson.jpg.
- Fig. 2.K: Source: https://commons.wikimedia.org/wiki/File:Millikan.jpg.
- Fig. 2.L: Source: https://commons.wikimedia.org/wiki/File:Ernest_Rutherford_(Nobel).jpg.
- Fig. 2.M: Copyright © Depositphotos/AlexeyKrotkov.
- Fig. 2.N: Source: https://commons.wikimedia.org/wiki/File:James_Chadwick.jpg.
- Fig. 2.O: Source: https://commons.wikimedia.org/wiki/File:Dmitri_Mendeleev.jpg.
- Fig. 2.P: Source: https://commons.wikimedia.org/wiki/File:PSM_V66_D490_Clemens_Alexander_Winkler.png.
- Fig. 2.12: Copyright © Depositphotos/Juliedeshaies.
- Fig. 2.13a: Copyright © 2009 by Jurii, (CC BY 3.0) at https://commons.wikimedia.org/wiki/File:Potassium.jpg.
- Fig. 2.13b: Source: https://commons.wikimedia.org/wiki/File:Barium_unter_Argon_Schutzgas_Atmosph%C3%A4re.jpg.
- Fig. 2.13c: Source: https://commons.wikimedia.org/wiki/File:Lithium_paraffin.jpg.
- Fig. 2.13d: Copyright © 2009 by Jurii, (CC BY 3.0) at https://commons.wikimedia.org/wiki/File:Magnesium-2.jpg.
- Fig. 2.13e: Copyright © 2009 by Jurii, (CC BY 3.0) at https://commons.wikimedia.org/wiki/File:Mercury-thermometer.jpg.

Compounds, Formulas, and Nomenclature

CHAPTER 3

LEARNING OBJECTIVES AND OUTCOMES

After reading this Chapter, you should be able to do the following:

- Understand and explain the nature of atoms, ions, and compounds.

- Predict the relative electric charge of *monatomic ions*.

- Understand and explain the nature of ionic and covalent bonds.

- Distinguish between ionic and molecular compounds.

- Write the formulas for *binary ionic compounds* containing metals with *invariant charge*.

- Write the systematic chemical names of *binary ionic compounds* containing metals with *invariant charge*.

- Write the formulas for *binary ionic compounds* containing metals with *variable charge*.

- Write the systematic chemical names of *binary ionic compounds* containing metals with *variable charge*.

- Write the formulas for *ionic compounds* containing polyatomic ions.

- Write the systematic chemical names of *ionic compounds* containing *polyatomic ions*.

- Write the formulas for *binary molecular (covalent) compounds*.

- Write the systematic chemical names of *binary molecular (covalent) compounds*.

- Define each of the key terms listed at the end of this chapter dealing with these concepts.

Section 3.1 Introduction

In the previous chapter we finished with a brief description of ions and bonding. In the current chapter we will expand on these concepts in an attempt to understand the nature of bonding and how chemical compounds are formed, named, and categorized. There are relatively few elements which exist naturally in their "uncombined," elemental, atomic states. Most exist in *chemical compounds*. What does this say about the relative stability of the elements? Why are they reactive? What is the driving force behind the formation of compounds? These are important questions, and chemists are extremely interested in understanding the mechanisms by which elements combine with each other. In other words, we are very interested in the nature of **chemical bonds**, which are the forces that hold atoms (elements) together, allowing for the formation of chemical *compounds*. Understanding how and why chemical bonds form tells us about the properties and behaviors of matter that we observe. It should not be surprising, therefore, that how we represent and name chemical compounds is based, to a large degree, on a classification according to different types of chemical bonds. We will explore chemical bonding in much greater detail in Chapters 7 and 8, but for now we will simply discuss some very basic ideas about chemical bonding which will be important to the discussion of formulas and nomenclature. To do this, it is illustrative to begin with a discussion of atoms and ions in a little more detail.

Section 3.2 Ions, Ionic Bonds, and the Formation of Ionic Compounds

Ionic compounds are composed of ions. Ions are charged particles which form when either an atom or molecule loses or gains electrons. *In chemical reactions this happens when metals react with nonmetals.* In such a circumstance, metals tend to lose or "give up" one or more electrons. This results in the formation of a positively charged ion, referred to as a **cation** (*kăt ī ŏn*). Likewise, the nonmetal will tend to gain the electrons lost by the metal to form an **anion** (*ăn ī ŏn*). An *anion* is a negatively charged ion. Another way to describe this is to say that **ionic bonds** *form through the complete transfer of one or more electrons from a metal to a nonmetal*. When this occurs, the resulting ions are then bonded together by virtue of the *electrostatic attraction* which exists between particles of opposite charge. Recall from the previous chapter that particles possessing charges of opposite sign (+ or −) experience an attractive force for each other. Further, when single atoms undergo reactions in which they lose or gain electrons, we refer to the resulting ions as **monatomic ions**. Monatomic ions are those composed of only a single atom. This suggests that some ions are composed of more than one atom. Such ions are referred to as **polyatomic ions**. *Polyatomic ions* will be discussed in greater detail in following sections of this chapter.

To better understand the formation of ions and ionic bonds, recall that atoms are composed of three fundamental particles: protons and neutrons, which comprise the nucleus of the atom, as well as electrons, which reside in the "electron cloud" in the region of space around the nucleus. With this in mind, let's consider for a moment what happens if an electron is gained or lost by an atom. If there are equal numbers of electrons and protons in a neutral atom, to gain or lose an electron would cause a charge imbalance. Consider Figure 3.1, which graphically depicts the formation of the *binary ionic compound* sodium chloride. It is referred to as a **binary compound** because it is composed of only two elements, sodium and chlorine. When these two elements move into proximity, the innate tendency of the metal (sodium) to lose a single electron and that of the nonmetal (chlorine) to gain an electron is realized. That is to say, a single electron is exchanged between the two elements. This results in the formation of the ionic compound sodium chloride. Because electrostatic forces are acting between all of the ions that make up the compound, ionic solids, such as sodium chloride, exist as arrays of many ions. All such *binary ionic compounds* form three-dimensional, crystalline, solid arrays of ions, as depicted in Figure 3.1.

Notice that in our example, the resulting compound has the same number of sodium ions as chloride ions. *The reason for this is that ionic compounds must exhibit a "net" charge of zero (neutral).* This means that all positive and negative charges in the compound must be equally balanced. Because sodium and chloride ions are both "singly" charged, the formation of a neutral compound requires equal numbers of both ions. This is not always the case, however. For example, consider calcium chloride. Calcium, unlike sodium, tends to lose two electrons instead of just one. Since we already know from the previous example that chlorine tends to gain just one electron, this means that the resulting compound will need to have twice as many chloride anions (charge = −1) as calcium cations (charge = +2).

Figure 3.1 The formation of ionic bonds occurs through the transfer of 1 or more electrons from a *Metal* to a *Nonmetal*. Here we see sodium metal give up an electron and chlorine readily accepts it, as nonmetals tend to do during chemical processes. Oppositely charged ions bond together due to electrostatic attraction forming 3-dimensional, crystalline arrays (rather than discrete, individual molecules).

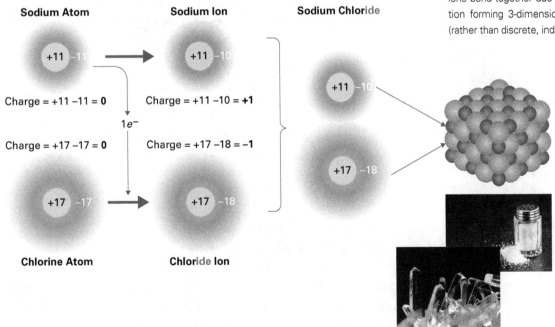

Sodium Atom

+11 −11

Charge = +11 −11 = **0**

Sodium Ion

+11 −10

Charge = +11 −10 = **+1**

1e⁻

Charge = +17 −17 = **0**

Charge = +17 −18 = **−1**

Chlorine Atom

+17 −17

Chloride Ion

+17 −18

Sodium Chloride

+11 −10

+17 −18

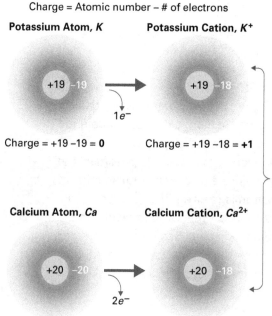

Charge = Atomic number – # of electrons

Figure 3.2 The charge on ions can be determined by subtracting the number of electrons on an atom with the number of protons in the nucleus. The formation of cations occurs through the loss of 1 or more electrons.

Note: Both of these ions adopt an electron count of **18**. This is the electron count on **Argon**, which is the nearest noble gas to each of these elements according to atomic number.

$$1\ Ca^{2+} + 2Cl^- \rightarrow CaCl_2$$

$$[1 \times (+2)] + [2 \times (-1)] = 0$$

In order to demonstrate this a little more clearly, let's explore how chemists represent ions and compounds. Consider Figure 3.2. Here we see a representation of the formation of two cations, that of potassium and calcium. In the case of potassium (K), we see there is a loss of one electron. This leaves the atom with 19 protons (atomic number 19) and only 18 electrons. As such, the potassium atom no longer enjoys a precise balance of positive and negative charges, leaving it with a net positive charge of +1. This is represented mathematically by the following expression:

Ionic Charge = Atomic Number – # of electrons

In this case of the potassium ion:

Charge = 19 – 18 = **+1**

Therefore, we would represent the potassium ion as the elemental symbol for potassium, K, with a superscript of 1+ or + as follows:

K^{1+} *or* K^+ (ones are often implied in symbols and formulas)

Likewise, when calcium loses two electrons (Figure 3.2), it adopts an ionic charge of 20 – 18 = +2 and is represented as Ca^{2+}.

In an entirely analogous fashion, when nonmetals gain electrons, the same kind of charge imbalance results, only here we have more negative charge than positive, resulting in the formation of anions. Consider Figure 3.3, which depicts a chlorine atom gaining one electron and a selenium atom

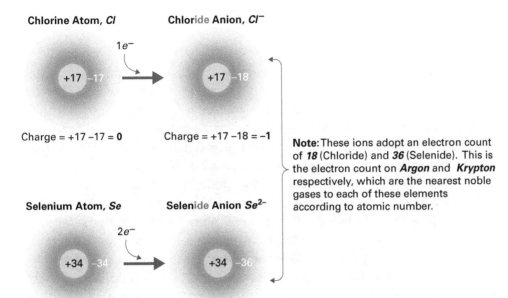

Note: These ions adopt an electron count of **18** (Chloride) and **36** (Selenide). This is the electron count on **Argon** and **Krypton** respectively, which are the nearest noble gases to each of these elements according to atomic number.

Figure 3.3 The formation of anions occurs through the gain of 1 or more electrons.

gaining two, resulting in the formation of chloride, Cl^-, and selenide, Se^{2-}, respectively. Note that unlike cations, when anions are formed, we change the name to include the suffix **-ide**. Hence, selenium becomes selenide, chlorine becomes chloride, and so on. Additionally, since we know that the atomic numbers of chlorine and selenium are 17 and 34, respectively, we can apply the same mathematical expression as before:

$$Charge = 17 - 18 = -1 \quad Therefore: Cl^-$$

$$Charge = 34 - 36 = -2 \quad Therefore: Se^{2-}$$

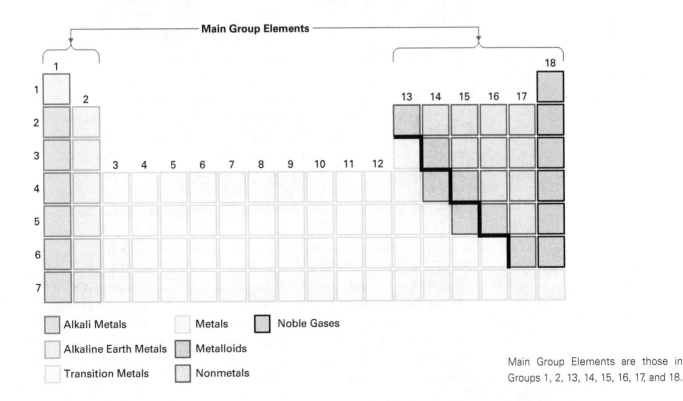

Main Group Elements are those in Groups 1, 2, 13, 14, 15, 16, 17, and 18.

Predicting Ionic Charges

To understand the relative numbers of cations and anions that compose specific compounds, as in the case of calcium chloride, we must be able to predict the number of electrons each element will gain or lose in forming ions. That is, we need to have a way to know or predict the charge on specific ions. Can this be done? The answer is "sometimes." As it turns out, for many *main group elements* this is readily possible. **Main group elements** are those elements which are located in groups 1A, 2A, 3A, 4A, 5A, 6A, 7A, and 8A of the periodic table (a.k.a. groups 1, 2, 13, 14, 15, 16, 17, and 18). To explore this, let's take a closer look at Figures 3.2 and 3.3. Notice for three of the four ions depicted in these figures, the electron count is 18 electrons. Additionally, the other ion, selenide, has an electron count of 36 electrons. Keeping these two numbers in mind, examine the periodic table and look for elements that have atomic number 18 and 36. These are argon (*Ar*) and krypton (*Kr*), respectively, and both are noble gases. It turns out that the reason noble gases are particularly unreactive is in large part because they have particularly stable electronic structures. As such, many of the other elements gain or lose specific numbers of electrons in order to acquire this same "stable" electronic structure of the noble gases.

Noble gases have a particularly stable electron configuration.

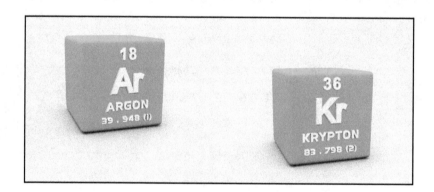

Understanding this, we can predict the charge on many of the main group ions by assuming the atoms of these various elements will adopt an electron count which is the same as that of the noble gas nearest to it according to atomic number. For example, consider aluminum. Aluminum has an atomic number of 13. The closest noble gas to 13 by atomic number is neon (*Ne*, atomic number = 10). If we assume an aluminum atom adopts an electron count of 10 (the same as the noble gas neon), we can predict its charge as follows:

$$Charge = Atomic\ Number - \#of\ elections = 13 - 10 = \textbf{+3}$$

Therefore, we would predict that aluminum ions are *cations* and that they have a charge of +3. What this really amounts to was summarized in Figure 2.14 in the previous chapter. Ions of Group 1A have a charge of +1 while groups 2A, 3A, 5A, 6A, and 7A have charges of +2, +3, −3, −2, and −1, respectively. Note that when applying this approach, we find, as stated previously, that metals lose electrons while nonmetals gain electrons. This axiom falls out naturally as a consequence of the proximity of metals and nonmetals to noble gas electronic structures. We will explore this concept further in Chapters 7 and 8.

Example Problem 3.1

Name and predict the charge on the following ions: a.) S b.) N c.) P d.) F e.) Rb f.) Ba g.) Li	
Solution:	
a.) Since sulfur is a Group 6A element we know that it will adopt a charge of 2–.	S^{2-}; **Sulfide**
b.) Since nitrogen is a Group 5A element, we know that it will adopt a charge of 3–.	N^{3-}; **Nitride**
c.) Since phosphorus is a Group 5A element, we know that it will adopt a charge of 3–.	P^{3-}; **Phosphide**
d.) Since fluorine is a Group 7A element, we know that it will adopt a charge of 1–.	F^{-}; **Fluoride**
e.) Since rubidium is a Group 1A element, we know that it will adopt a charge of 1+.	Rb^{+}; **Rubidium**
f.) Since barium is a Group 2A element, we know that it will adopt a charge of 2+.	Ba^{2+}; **Barium**
g.) Since Lithium is a Group 1A element, we know that it will adopt a charge of 1+.	Li^{+}; **Lithium**

Section 3.3 Formulas and Names of Binary Ionic Compounds

Now that we understand how ions and ionic compounds are formed when metals react with nonmetals, let's consider how they are represented. This is accomplished using *formulas*. A **formula** makes use of elemental symbols to indicate the various elements which compose a given compound along with corresponding numeric subscripts which indicate the relative number of each type of element or ion. For example, recall that in sodium chloride there are equal numbers of sodium ions and chloride ions. Therefore, the formula is given as:

$$NaCl = Na_1Cl_1$$

When no subscript appears to the right of an elemental symbol, an implied subscript of 1 is interpreted.

In other words, the numeric subscripts contained in the formulas of ionic compounds are understood to be the lowest whole-number ratio of the elements (or ions) that comprise the compound. For this reason, ionic formulas are often referred to as "formula units." A **formula unit** expresses the relative numbers (smallest whole-number ratio) of the types of elements or ions contained in an *ionic* compound. Another method of representing compounds is simply through names. When using names, it is important that we choose a system of naming that leaves no ambiguity respecting the nature of the compound. In the following sections we will discuss the conventions for naming and writing the formulas of the various common types of ionic compounds.

Writing Names of Binary Ionic Compounds Containing Monatomic Ions

When naming simple binary ionic compounds (or any ionic compound for that matter), the names are composed of two parts, the cation name followed by the anion name. This is relatively straightforward for monatomic ions since we have already seen that the name of cations is simply the same as the name of the element, and for anions we need only add a suffix of *-ide*. For example, if we wished to name the compound that forms from the elements potassium and bromine, we would first identify which element will form the cation (the metal), which is simply potassium. Then we would follow with the anion name, in this case bromide. This is depicted as follows:

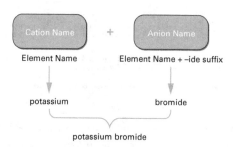

This is the basic process for naming ionic compounds. We will see later that for different types of ions, there are minor modifications to the naming convention. However, all ionic compound names will follow this basic form. Let's consider another example, Al_2O_3. Again, to name this compound we simply identify the name of the cation followed by the anion. Since the metal (cation) in this case is aluminum, and the nonmetal (anion) is oxygen, the name becomes aluminum oxide. Practice writing names of ionic compounds in the following set of example problems.

Example Problem 3.2

Write the names of the compounds which form from the following pairs of elements:
a.) potassium and sulfur
b.) calcium and nitrogen
c.) aluminum and chlorine

Solutions:	
a.) Potassium is a Group 1A metal and therefore forms a cation (K^+) and sulfur forms an anion (S^{2-}). The compound name will consist of the name of the metal followed by the nonmetal with an -ide suffix.	(Metal Name) + (Nonmetal Name -ide.) **Potassium Sulfide**
b.) Calcium is a Group 2A metal and therefore forms a cation (Ca^{2+}) and nitrogen forms an anion (N^{3-}). The compound name will consist of the name of the metal followed by the nonmetal with an -ide suffix.	(Metal Name) + (Nonmetal Name -ide.) **Calcium Nitride**
c.) Aluminum is a Group 3A metal and therefore forms a cation (Al^{3+}) and chlorine forms an anion (Cl^-). The compound name will consist of the name of the metal followed by the nonmetal with an -ide suffix.	(Metal Name) + (Nonmetal Name -ide.) **Aluminum Chloride**

Writing Formulas of Binary Ionic Compounds

We have just seen an example of how to write the names of binary ionic compounds. We will now address the method by which formulas can be discerned from names. This procedure is a little more complex because, in addition to the identities of the elements involved in the compound, we also need to know the charges of each ion. Put another way, because the charges of the ions in an ionic compound must be balanced, we first need to know the charges exhibited by both ions in order to choose the appropriate subscripts that will produce a neutral compound. There are a few steps involved in doing this. To illustrate these, consider the example of potassium nitride.

1. First, write the symbol for the cation (in this example, potassium ion). Recall that potassium is a Group 1A metal and therefore will adopt a charge of +1.

    $$K^+$$

2. Next, write the symbol for the anion (in this case, nitride ion). Nitrogen is a Group 5A element, so it will adopt a charge of –3.

    $$K^+ \quad N^{3-}$$

3. The charge on each ion now becomes the subscript on the neighboring element (excluding the positive or negative sign). In performing this operation, you are essentially balancing the charges.

$$K^+ \quad N^{3-} \quad \rightarrow \quad K_3N_1 \quad \rightarrow \quad K_3N$$

4. If necessary, reduce the subscripts to their lowest whole-number ratio. (Since 3:1 is already in its lowest ratio, our formula remains as is.)

$$K_3N$$

5. Finally, check to ensure that all positive and negative charges are balanced. To do this, simply multiply the charge on each ion by its subscript, then add the two terms together. If the charges are appropriately balanced, this sum should equal zero (neutral).

(Cation Subscript)(Cation Charge) + *(Anion Subscript) (Anion Charge)* = 0
$$(3)(+1) + (1)(-3) = (+3) + (-3) = 0$$

Therefore, since the charges are balanced, we would write the formula of potassium nitride as K_3N. The following example problems illustrate the application of these rules for some other ionic compounds.

Example Problem 3.3

Write the formulas for the following compounds: a.) cesium sulfide b.) magnesium iodide c.) aluminum oxide	
Solutions:	
a.) **Step 1 and 2:** Write the symbols for the cation and anion including charges.	$Cs^+ \; S^{2-}$
Step 3: Write the charge on each ion as the subscript for the other element.	$Cs^+ \; S^{2-}$ Cs_2S_1
Step 4: Reduce the subscripts to the lowest whole-number ratio.	Cs_2S
Step 5: Ensure all charges are balanced. The sum of all negative and positive charges equals zero.	$(2)(+1) + (1)(-2) = 0$
Since all charges balance, we can write our formula as:	Cs_2S
b.) **Step 1 and 2:** Write the symbols for the cation and anion including charges.	$Mg^{2+} \; I^-$
Step 3: Write the charge on each ion as the subscript for the other element.	$Mg^{2+} \; I^-$ Mg_1I_2

Step 4: Reduce the subscripts to the lowest whole-number ratio.	MgI_2
Step 5: Ensure all charges are balanced. The sum of all negative and positive charges equals zero.	$(1)(+2) + (2)(-1) = 0$
Since all charges balance, we can write our formula as:	$\boldsymbol{MgI_2}$
c.) **Step 1 and 2**: Write the symbols for the cation and anion including charges.	$Al^{3+}O^{2-}$
Step 3: Write the charge on each ion as the subscript for the other element.	$Al^{3+} \; O^{2-}$ Al_2O_3
Step 4: Reduce the subscripts to the lowest whole-number ratio.	Al_2O_3
Step 5: Ensure all charges are balanced. The sum of all negative and positive charges equals zero.	$(2)(+3) + (3)(-2) = 0$
Since all charges balance, we can write our formula as:	$\boldsymbol{Al_2O_3}$

Writing Names of Binary Ionic Compounds Containing Metals With Variable Charge

For nonmetal monatomic ions (anions), we can always assume the electron-count will be the same as the nearest noble gas, as described previously. This means that anions always have the same charge. However, this is only true for some of the main group metals. For metals, there is the possibility that their ions may adopt different charges under different circumstances, even in compounds which otherwise contain the same anion(s). This is particularly true of the transition metals and makes predicting charge or writing names and formulas a little more complex than for the previous examples. Metals which adopt multiple charges when forming ions are referred to as **metals of variable charge**, and those that do not are referred to as **metals of invariable charge**. Figure 3.4 illustrates the charges of common ions. Note that metals with variable charge are highlighted in red.

Because metals with variable charge can form more than one ion, the identity of the element alone is not sufficient to unambiguously identify the ion and, consequently, any compound which may contain that metal. For example, iron can adopt one of two charges when forming an ion. It can adopt either a +2 or a +3 charge. Therefore, the name iron oxide, for instance, is not sufficient to identify a particular compound unambiguously. Iron oxide may refer to either FeO or Fe_2O_3 with equal probability. Therefore, when naming ions of metals with variable charge, we include a roman numeral in parentheses immediately following the metal name to indicate the charge. The question then becomes, when dealing with these types of ions and compounds, how do we know what the charge on the cation is? The answer is through deduction. Because *anion* charges are invariant, we can use the subscripts in formulas along with the charge of the anion to

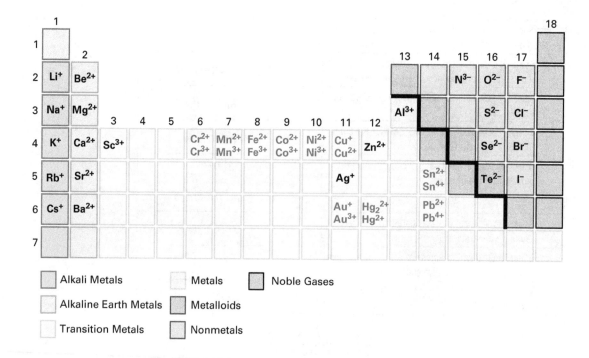

Figure 3.4 Some common monatomic ions. Most main group elements form just 1 monatomic ion. However, most transition and heavy metals form multiple monatomic ions (some of these are highlighted in red here).

deduce the charge on the metal. This can be accomplished for our iron oxide example, Fe_2O_3, by applying the following steps.

1. **Identify the anion and its charge.** (In this case the anion is the nonmetal oxygen, and its charge is -2 because it is a Group 6A element.)

$$Fe_2O_3 = (Fe^{+x})_2(O^{2-})_3$$

2. **Set the sum of the total negative and positive charges to zero.** Since the charges must be balanced, we can write the following expression just as before. However, this time we will represent the unknown charge of the metal cation as x.

$$Fe_2O_3 = (Fe^{+x})_2(O^{2-})_3$$

$$(2)(+x) + (3)(-2) = 0$$

3. **Rearrange the equation to solve for x (cation charge).**

$$(2)(+x) + (3)(-2) = 0$$
$$2x - 6 = 0$$
$$2x = +6$$
$$x = \frac{+6}{2} = +3$$

Therefore, in our example, we would identify the iron ion as iron(III) (iron three). Having done so, we can now apply our naming rules. The naming convention is the same as before. The only difference is that the name of the cation now includes the charge as a roman numeral in parentheses.

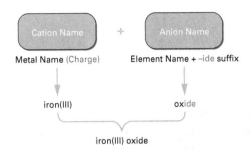

It is worth noting that this method of naming is appropriate only for metals with variable charge. It would be incorrect to include the charge as a roman numeral when naming compounds containing metals with invariable charge. Therefore, it is important to be able to make this distinction. Metals of *invariable* charge include Groups 1A and 2A metals as well as *Al, Ag, Zn,* and *Sc*. All other metals can be considered to form more than one ion.

Table 3.1 Names and Symbols of some common variable charge metals.

Formula	Name	Latin-Root Name
Cr^{2+}	Chromium (II)	Chromous
Cr^{3+}	Chromium (III)	Chromic
Co^{2+}	Cobalt (II)	Cobaltous
Co^{3+}	Cobalt (III)	Cobaltic
Cu^{+}	Copper (I)	Cuprous
Cu^{2+}	Copper (II)	Cupric
Au^{+}	Gold (I)	Aurous
Au^{3+}	Gold (III)	Auric
Fe^{2+}	Iron (II)	Ferrous
Fe^{3+}	Iron (III)	Ferric
Pb^{2+}	Lead (II)	Plumbous
Pb^{4+}	Lead (IV)	Plumbic
Mn^{2+}	Manganese (II)	Manganous
Mn^{3+}	Manganese (III)	Manganic
Ni^{2+}	Nickel (II)	Nickelous
Ni^{3+}	Nickel (III)	Nickelic
Hg_2^{2+}	Mercury (I)	Mercurous
Hg^{2+}	Mercury (II)	Mercuric
Sn^{2+}	Tin (II)	Stannous
Sn^{4+}	Tin (IV)	Stannic

The Common, Latin-Root System of Naming of Metal Cations

An older system of common nomenclature concerning metals of variable charge still finds use in some situations. This method assigns a suffix of -ous to the older Latin name of the cation with less positive charge and -ic to that of the cation with more positive charge. These names are summarized in Table 3.1. Let's consider the iron(II) and iron(III) ions. Their names under this method are as follows:

Fe^{2+} ferrous ion

Fe^{3+} ferric ion

The names of compounds using this older convention are formulated in the same fashion as we have previously discussed. For example, the compounds that these two ions would make with oxygen are

FeO ferrous oxide

Fe_2O_3 ferric oxide

Using this method of naming has some obvious drawbacks. First, it does not indicate the precise charge on the cations in question. For example, stannic ion refers to tin(IV) (Sn^{4+}) while ferric and cupric ions refer to iron(III) (Fe^{3+}) and copper(II) (Cu^{2+}), respectively. This presents a certain degree of ambiguity respecting the charge on various ions under this naming system. Additionally, there are some metals which form more than two ions. In these circumstances, the older naming system is not adequate to the task. For these reasons, this method is no longer commonly used.

Ferrous oxide (left) and ferric oxide (right).

Example Problem 3.4

Name the following ionic compounds:
a.) $CuCl_2$
b.) CrO
c.) Cr_2O_3

Solutions:	
a.) **Step 1 and 2:** Determine the charge on the anion and set the sum of all charges equal to zero. The charge on metal (Cu) we will represent as x.	$(Cu^{x+})_1(Cl^-)_2$ $(1)(x) + (2)(-1) = 0$
Step 3: Rearrange and solve for the cation charge x.	$(1)(x) + (2)(-1) = 0$ $x - 2 = 0$ $x = +2$
Name the compound:	**copper(II) chloride**
b.) **Step 1 and 2:** Determine the charge on the anion and set the sum of all charges equal to zero. The charge on metal (Cr) we will represent as x.	$(Cr^{x+})_1(O^{2-})_1$ $(1)(x) + (1)(-2) = 0$
Step 3: Rearrange and solve for the cation charge x.	$(1)(x) + (1)(-2) = 0$ $x - 2 = 0$ $x = +2$
Name the compound:	**chromium(II) oxide**
c.) **Step 1 and 2:** Determine the charge on the anion and set the sum of all charges equal to zero. The charge on metal (Cr) we will represent as x.	$(Cr^{x+})_2(O^{2-})_3$ $(2)(x) + (3)(-2) = 0$
Step 3: Rearrange and solve for the cation charge x.	$(2)(x) + (3)(-2) = 0$ $2x - 6 = 0$ $2x = +6$ $x = \dfrac{+6}{2} = +3$
Name the compound.	**chromium(III) oxide**

Did you know that compounds containing polyatomic ions are present in many common household products? For example, baking soda is a common name for sodium hydrogen carbonate, $NaHCO_3$ (also known as sodium bicarbonate). Calcium iodate, $Ca(IO_3)_2$, is a common ingredient in disinfectants and deodorants. Common bleach is an aqueous solution of sodium hypochlorite, $NaClO$. These are just a few. Next time you are using a cleaning product or open a package of food, check out the ingredients and see if you recognize the compounds that are listed and the ions which compose them.

Many household products contain polyatomic ions.

Section 3.4 Formulas and Names of Polyatomic Ions and Their Compounds

So far we have considered ionic compounds composed of *monatomic* ions. However, many compounds contain polyatomic ions. **Polyatomic ions** are composed of two or more atoms covalently bonded together. One way to think about this is to consider these as charged "molecules." As an example, one common polyatomic ion is phosphate, PO_4^{3-}, consisting of one phosphorus atom and four oxygen atoms. Phosphate carries a charge of -3. In other words, it contains three more electrons (50 electrons) than protons in the nuclei of the atoms which make it up (47 protons). Table 3.2 lists the names and formulas of common polyatomic ions. Note that the formulas of ions must include their relative electric charge as a superscript. Additionally, polyatomic ions can participate in the formation of ionic compounds through ionic bonding with other monatomic or poly-atomic ions. As such, we can represent these compounds through the same conventions in writing formulas and names as previously discussed with only minor modification.

Table 3.2 Names and Formulas of some common Polyatomic Ions.

Name	Formula	Name	Formula
Ammonium	NH_4^+	Dihydrogen phosphate	$H_2PO_4^-$
Acetate	$C_2H_3O_2^-$	Hypochlorite	ClO^-
Carbonate	CO_3^{2-}	Chlorite	ClO_2^-
Hydrogen carbonate (bicarbonate)	HCO_3^-	Chlorate	ClO_3^-
Hydroxide	OH^-	Perchlorate	ClO_4^-
Nitrite	NO_2^-	Permanganate	MnO_4^-
Nitrate	NO_3^-	Peroxide	O_2^{2-}
Chromate	CrO_4^{2-}	Sulfite	SO_3^{2-}
Dichromate	$Cr_2O_7^{2-}$	Sulfate	SO_4^{2-}
Cyanide	CN^-	Hydrogen sulfite (bisulfite)	HSO_3^-
Phosphate	PO_4^{3-}	Hydrogen sulfate (bisulfate)	HSO_4^-
Hydrogen phosphate	HPO_4^{2-}	Oxalate	$C_2O_4^{2-}$

Naming Polyatomic Ions

In order to begin a discussion on naming compounds containing polyatomic ions, it is appropriate to make a few comments regarding the names of the ions themselves. For many polyatomic ions, their names are simply to be learned. Some trends, however, can help in doing this. For example, consider the pair of ions NO_3^- and NO_2^-. In such pairs the ion with more oxygen atoms will have a name which ends in **-ate** while that with fewer oxygen atoms ends with **-ite**. Therefore, these two ions are named nitrate and nitrite respectively. Another example of such a pair is sulfate and sulfite, SO_4^{2-} and SO_3^{2-}. Additionally, there are series which have more than just two ions. In these cases, the ion with the most oxygen atoms will have a name which contains the prefix **per-** and the suffix **-ate**. The ion with the second highest number of oxygen atoms will simply end in **-ate**. The next one ends in **–ite**, and the ion with the fewest oxygen atoms will have a name with the prefix **hypo-** and the suffix **-ite**. For example, consider the "chlorate" series of ions listed in Table 3.2.

Many of these ions will often contain additional hydrogen atoms. When this occurs the name of the ion will include the word "hydrogen" and the charge will be increased by +1. For example, the polyatomic ion SO_4^{2-} is referred to as sulfate. The ion "hydrogen sulfate" has the formula, HSO_4^-. Note the addition of one hydrogen atom increases the charge on the ion by +1, from –2 to –1.

Naming Ionic Compounds Containing Polyatomic Ions

Just like compounds composed of monatomic ions, those containing polyatomic ions take their names from the names of the ions which compose them. In this sense, we simply apply the naming convention we have already learned to polyatomic ions. For example, suppose I have a compound composed of sodium and sulfate ions. Here, we would name the compound sodium sulfate as follows:

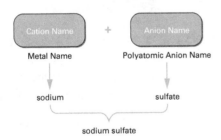

Since the sulfate ion is an anion, it is placed in the second part of the compound name. However, when dealing with a positively charged polyatomic ion such as ammonium, we simply apply the polyatomic name in the first part. In either case, no modification of the name of polyatomic ion is required. Sulfate remains simply sulfate, and ammonium remains ammonium. Additionally, all rules concerning the naming of metals of invariable or variable charge remain in place.

Writing Formulas of Ionic Compounds Containing Polyatomic Ions

Since we have learned how to recognize and name polyatomic ions and their compounds, we now turn our attention to writing formulas of such compounds. Again, the key to writing formulas of any class of ionic compound rests principally in balancing all positive and negative charges. Suppose we are dealing with the compound iron(II) phosphate. In order to write the correct formula, we will need to apply the same guidelines as previously described.

1. First write the symbol for the cation (in this example, iron(II) ion).

$$Fe^{2+}$$

2. Next write the symbol for the anion (in this case, phosphate ion). Phosphate is a polyatomic ion which carries a charge of –3.

$$Fe^{2+} \qquad PO_4^{3-}$$

3. The charge on each ion now becomes the subscript on the neighboring ion (excluding the positive or negative sign). In performing this operation, you should remember to treat the polyatomic ion as a single entity. This is accomplished through the use of parentheses as follows:

$$Fe^{2+} \diagup\!\!\!\!\diagdown PO_4^{3-} \quad \rightarrow \quad Fe_3(PO_4)_2$$

4. If necessary, reduce the subscripts to their lowest whole-number ratio. (Since 3:2 is already in its lowest ratio, our formula remains as is.)

$$Fe_3(PO_4)_2$$

5. Finally, check to ensure that all positive and negative charges are balanced. To do this, simply multiply the charge on each ion by its subscript, then add the two terms together. If the charges are appropriately balanced, this sum should equal zero (neutral).

$$(3)(+2)+(2)(-3) = (+6) + (-6) = 0$$

In this example, we find that the formula for iron(II) phosphate is $Fe_3(PO_4)_2$. Notice that we treat the phosphate ion as a single entity by placing it in parentheses and applying an additional independent subscript. This is done only when the subscript for the polyatomic ion is greater than one. When it is simply one, it is left out (implied), and no parentheses are used. It would not be correct to include parentheses in case of a subscript of 1. For example, the formula of iron(III) phosphate is simply $FePO_4$.

Example Problem 3.5

Write the names from the following formulas and the formulas from the names:
a.) iron(III) sulfate
b.) $Cr_3(PO_4)_2$
c.) magnesium nitrate
d.) $Zn(OH)_2$

Solutions:	
a.) Iron(III) is Fe^{3+} and sulfate is SO_4^{2-}. It requires two iron(III) ions and three sulfate ions to balance all charges.	$Fe^{3+}\ \ SO_4^{2-}\ =\ \textbf{Fe}_2\textbf{(SO}_4\textbf{)}_3$
b.) Phosphate is PO_4^{3-}. It requires three chromium(II) ions to balance two phosphate ions.	$(3)(x) + (2)(-3) = 0$ $x = 2$ **Chromium(II) Phosphate**
c.) Magnesium is Mg^{2+} and nitrate is NO_3^-. It requires one magnesium ion and two nitrate ions to balance all charges.	$Mg^{2+}\ \ NO_3^-\ =\ \textbf{Mg(NO}_3\textbf{)}_2$
d.) Zinc is a metal of invariable charge and therefore the name is simply zinc hydroxide.	**Zinc Hydroxide**

Section 3.5 Formulas and Names of Hydrates

Another type of ionic compound are those known as **hydrates**. Just as the name indicates, *hydrates* are ionic compounds which contain a specific number of water molecules within each formula unit. When ionic compounds are formed, they "crystallize" into arrays of ions as we have already discussed. When this occurs in the presence of water, the water molecules can "co-crystallize" into the crystalline lattice along with the ions. Because crystalline lattices are arranged in specific geometric patterns, the incorporation of water molecules is precise and regular throughout the crystal. For this reason, the water molecules in a hydrate are often referred to as "waters of crystallization" in addition to "waters of hydration."

Because the presence of water will affect many of the properties of the substance, it is important to take this into account when naming and writing formulas. Formulas of hydrates use a "dot" notation to indicate the number of water molecules in a given formula unit. To do this, the formula of the ionic compound in question is written and immediately following it is a dot after which a number of waters are indicated. For example, a common hydrate of nickel(II) sulfate is $NiSO_4 \cdot 6H_2O$. In this case, the formula indicates a hydrate with six water molecules associated with the formula unit. This is interpreted as a compound for which there is one nickel(II) ion for every sulfate ion and every six water molecules.

Naming hydrates is equally straightforward. It is simply the name of the ionic compound followed by the word "hydrate" modified by a prefix indicating the number of water molecules in the formula unit. For example, the name of the hydrate $CoCl_2 \cdot 6H_2O$ is cobalt(II) chloride *hexa*hydrate. The prefix *hexa-* indicates the number six. Other prefixes include *hemi-, mono-, di-, tri-, tetra-, penta-, hepta-, octa-, nona-* and *deca-* indicating one half, one, two, three, four, five, seven, eight, nine, and ten, respectively. Additionally, waters of hydration can be removed by heating a hydrate, forming a new substance. These are referred to as "anhydrous" compounds. **Anhydrous** simply means "without water" and is applied to compounds in order to indicate the compound is "dry." For example, if we were to vigorously heat the compound nickel(II) sulfate hexahydrate ($NiSO_4 \cdot 6H_2O$), this would drive off all of the waters of hydration, leaving us with what would be termed *anhydrous* nickel(II) sulfate ($NiSO_4$). Practice naming and writing formulas of the hydrates given in Example Problem 3.6.

Heating Nickel(II) Sulfate Hexahydrate drives off the waters of hydration leaving a new material, *anhydrous* Nickel(II) Sulfate.

Heat

$NiSO_4 \cdot 6H_2O$ Anhydrous $NiSO_4$

Example Problem 3.6

Write the name from the following formula and the formula from the name:
a.) iron(II) sulfate heptahydrate
b.) $CoCl_2 \cdot 6H_2O$

Solutions:	
a.) Iron(II) is Fe^{2+}, and sulfate is SO_4^{2-}. It requires one iron(III) ion and one sulfate ion to balance all charges. The prefix *hepta-* indicates seven water molecules.	$FeSO_4 \cdot 7H_2O$
b.) It requires one cobalt(II) ion to balance two chloride ions. Six water molecules require the prefix *hexa-*.	**cobalt(II) chloride hexahydrate**

Section 3.6 Formulas and Names of Molecular (Covalent) Compounds

As was stated earlier, there are two basic types of chemical bonds. They are referred to as *ionic* and *covalent* bonds and both involve the electrons of the bonding atoms. While ionic bonding results from the complete transfer of electrons from one atom to another, covalent bonds are characterized by the sharing of electrons between two atoms. This occurs when *nonmetals* react with other *nonmetals* and results in the formation of **molecules**. A *molecule* is a discrete collection of two or more atoms held together by covalent chemical bonds. In addition to resulting from electron sharing, *covalent bonds* are often thought of as being local or localized (existing only between the two elements involved in sharing of the bonding electrons) as well as directional (occurring at very specific angles to other bonds). Because of these characteristics, molecules can be represented in a number of different ways, some of which are described in Chapter 4. The most common method of depiction is with chemical or **molecular formulas**. A *molecular formula* makes use of the symbols of the elements comprising a molecule along with numeric subscripts to indicate the *exact number of atoms of each element contained within a molecule of a given compound*. This is in contrast to ionic *formula units* which use subscripts to indicate the *lowest whole-number ratio* of atoms of each element in the compound. This means that it is not possible to determine the formula of a molecular compound simply from the identity of the elements which comprise it. Let's consider a familiar example. A molecule of water consists of one oxygen atom bonded to two atoms of hydrogen and therefore is represented by the formula H_2O. In this case we can see immediately that this is a molecular or covalent compound because no metals are involved. As such, we interpret the formula as indicating not a ratio of ions but precise numbers of atoms of each element which make up a single molecule of this compound.

To make this just a little clearer, let's consider a different example. Suppose we have a molecule that has a covalent bonding arrangement as follows:

$$
\begin{array}{c}
\quad\;\; O \;\; H \;\; H \;\; O \\
\quad\;\; \| \;\;\; | \;\;\; | \;\;\; \| \\
H-O-C-C-C-C-O-H \\
\quad\quad\quad | \;\; | \\
\quad\quad\quad H \; H
\end{array}
$$

succinic acid

In this instance we would write a formula to represent this compound as $C_4H_6O_4$ to indicate there are four carbon atoms, six hydrogen atoms, and four oxygen atoms. In the case of molecular compounds, it is not proper to reduce the subscripts when writing molecular formulas. Further, in arriving at such a formula, it may not always be obvious which element should be represented first. However, it is correct by convention to always place the element which is most "metallic" or "metal-like" first. This is a nod to the naming conventions for ionic compounds and provides some consistency. The most metal-like element is simply the one which is farther to the left and/or farther down the periodic table. The only exception to this rule is the placement of hydrogen which may come first or second depending on the circumstances, as in the case of acids for example.

Additionally, because covalent bonding is not dependent on any requirements respecting charge or electrostatic attractions between ions, it is possible for elements to engage in covalent bonding with themselves. In fact, there are several elements which exist as molecules in their elemental states, including hydrogen (H_2), nitrogen (N_2), oxygen (O_2), fluorine (F_2), chlorine (Cl_2), bromine (Br_2), and astatine (At_2). These are the **diatomic molecular**

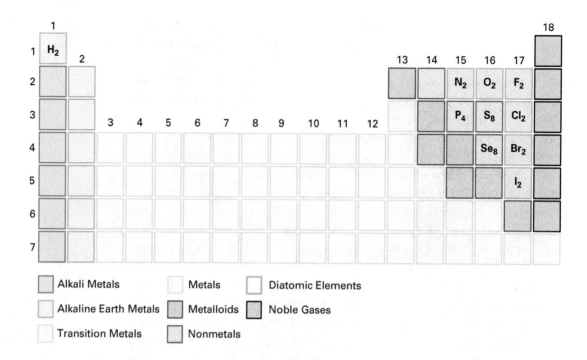

Figure 3.5 Diatomic and Polyatomic Molecular Elements.

elements. Additionally, phosphorus (P_4), sulfur (S_8), and selenium (Se_6 & Se_8) exist as **polyatomic molecular elements**. (Note: These are not compounds, but rather they are molecular elements. Compounds are comprised of two or more different elements.)

Naming Binary Molecular Compounds

Given the differences in the nature of covalent and ionic compounds and how they are represented formulaically, it should not be surprising that the naming convention for these compounds is somewhat different as well. When naming molecular compounds from formulas, there is no need to consider charges or anything of the sort. In this case we need only concern ourselves with the number of each type of atom in the molecule in question. We then use a prefix which indicates a particular number to modify the name of the element associated with that number (Table 3.3). For example, consider PCl_5. A molecule of this substance contains one atom of phosphorus and five atoms of chlorine. Just as with ionic compounds, the name of this (or any molecular compound) consists of two parts as follows:

Table 3.3 In naming simple binary molecular compounds, prefixes are used to indicate the number of atoms of each element in a given compound.

Number	Prefix
1	Mono
2	Di
3	Tri
4	Tetra
5	Penta
6	Hexa
7	Hepta
8	Octa
9	Nona
10	Deca

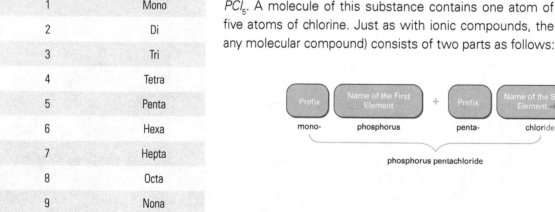

There a couple of things to note in this example. First, notice that even though we are not dealing with ions, we still add an *-ide* suffix to the end of the second element. Also, it is a rule that we never apply *mono-*, the prefix indicating one, to the first element. As such, the prefix *mono-* is dropped from the name phosphorus pentachloride. Additionally, we drop the "a" or "o" from any prefix ending in these vowels when the element name being modified begins with a vowel. For example, N_2O_4 is properly named dinitrogen tetroxide, wherein the "a" is dropped from the prefix *tetra-* when modifying the element "oxygen." Try naming the following compounds in Example Problem 3.7.

Example Problem 3.7

Write the names from the following formulas and the formulas from the names:

a.) N_2O_4

b.) carbon tetrafluoride

c.) I_2F_7

d.) sulfur trioxide

Solutions:		
a.)	Two nitrogen atoms and four oxygen atoms require the prefixes di- and tetra- respectively.	**dinitrogen tetroxide**
b.)	No prefix on the first element of a name indicates one atom of carbon. The prefix tetra- indicates four atoms of fluorine.	CF_4
c.)	Two iodine atoms and seven fluorine atoms requires the prefixes *di-* and *hepta-* respectively.	**diiodine heptafluoride**
c.)	No prefix on the first element of a name indicates one atom of sulfur. The prefix tri- indicates three atoms of oxygen.	SO_3

Key Terms

1. Anhydrous

2. Anion

3. Binary compound

4. Cation

5. Chemical bonds

6. Covalent bond

7. Covalent compound

8. Diatomic molecular element

9. Formula

10. Formula unit

11. Hydrate

12. Ion

13. Ionic bond

14. Ionic compound

15. Main group element

16. Metal of invariable charge

17. Metal of variable charge

18. Molecular compound

19. Molecular element

20. Molecular formula

21. Molecules

22. Monatomic ion

23. Polyatomic ion

24. Polyatomic molecular element

Problems

INTRODUCTION AND IONS, IONIC BONDS, AND IONIC COMPOUNDS

1. What is an ion?

2. What is a cation?

3. What is an anion?

4. What is meant by the term monatomic ion?

5. What is meant by the term polyatomic ion?

6. What is meant by the term binary compound?

7. Explain how ionic bonds form.

8. Why are ionic compounds neutral even though they are composed of charged ions?

9. What is the charge on a monatomic ion with 55 protons and 54 electrons?

10. What is the charge on a monatomic ion with 15 protons and 18 electrons?

11. What is the charge on a monatomic ion with 8 protons and 10 electrons?

12. What is the charge on a monatomic ion with 20 protons and 18 electrons?

13. Give the number of protons and electrons for the following:

    a. Al^{3+}

    b. Br^-

    c. S^{2-}

    d. Fe^{3+}

14. Give the number of protons and electrons for the following:

    a. Fe^{2+}

    b. F^-

    c. N^{3-}

    d. Ba^{2+}

15. Give the number of protons and electrons for the following:

    a. Na^+

    b. Se^{2-}

    c. Sr^{2+}

    d. Pb^{4+}

16. Give the number of protons and electrons for the following:

    a. Mg^{2+}

    b. Ca^{2+}

    c. P^{3-}

    d. Pb^{2+}

17. Name and predict the charge on the following ions:

    a. H

    b. Li

    c. O

    d. F

18. Name and predict the charge on the following ions:

    a. N

    b. Be

    c. Ba

    d. Cs

19. Name and predict the charge on the following ions:

    a. Cl

    b. S

    c. P

    d. Br

20. Name and predict the charge on the following ions:

    a. *Se*

    b. *I*

    c. *Rb*

    d. *Sr*

21. Name and predict the charge on the following ions:

    a. *Mg*

    b. *Na*

    c. *Ca*

    d. *Al*

FORMULAS AND NAMES OF BINARY IONIC COMPOUNDS

22. Explain what is meant by the term "formula unit."

23. Name the binary ionic compounds composed of the following pairs of elements:

    a. aluminum and sulfur

    b. magnesium and selenium

    c. aluminum and oxygen

    d. sodium and nitrogen

24. Name the binary ionic compounds composed of the following pairs of elements:

    a. potassium and chlorine

    b. strontium and phosphorus

    c. cesium and fluorine

    d. potassium and iodine

25. Name the binary ionic compounds composed of the following pairs of elements:

    a. rubidium and oxygen

    b. calcium and bromine

    c. aluminum and nitrogen

    d. sodium and iodine

26. Name the binary ionic compounds composed of the following pairs of elements:

    a. sodium and selenium

    b. potassium and sulfur

    c. barium and fluorine

    d. lithium and oxygen

27. Write the formulas of binary ionic compounds composed of the following pairs of elements:

    a. aluminum and chlorine

    b. calcium and selenium

    c. aluminum and bromine

    d. silver and nitrogen

28. Write the formulas of binary ionic compounds composed of the following pairs of elements:

    a. zinc and chlorine

    b. scandium and phosphorus

    c. silver and fluorine

    d. barium and iodine

29. Write the formulas of binary ionic compounds composed of the following pairs of elements:

    a. silver and oxygen

    b. calcium and sulfur

    c. zinc and sulfur

    d. scandium and oxygen

30. Write the formulas of binary ionic compounds composed of the following pairs of elements:

    a. sodium and iodine

    b. silver and sulfur

    c. barium and fluorine

    d. zinc and oxygen

31. Write the names of the following binary ionic compounds:

    a. Cr_2S_3

    b. $CuCl_2$

    c. Cr_3N_2

    d. NiF_2

32. Write the names of the following binary ionic compounds:

    a. FeS

    b. $FeCl_3$

    c. Co_3N_2

    d. CoI_3

33. Write the names of the following binary ionic compounds:
    a. Fe_3P_2
    b. PbS_2
    c. $PbCl_2$
    d. CoI_2

34. Write the names of the following binary ionic compounds:
    a. Hg_2Cl_2
    b. SnO_2
    c. CrS
    d. Cu_3P

35. Write the formulas of the following compounds:
    a. sodium sulfide
    b. barium nitride
    c. cesium oxide
    d. aluminum fluoride

36. Write the formulas of the following compounds:
    a. tin(II) oxide
    b. lead(IV) phosphide
    c. nickel (II) chloride
    d. manganese(IV) oxide

37. Write the formulas of the following compounds:
    a. aluminum iodide
    b. cobalt(III) selenide
    c. zinc oxide
    d. scandium chloride

38. Write the formulas of the following compounds:
    a. lithium oxide
    b. iron(II) phosphide
    c. potassium nitride
    d. copper(II) sulfide

FORMULAS AND NAMES OF POLYATOMIC IONS AND THEIR COMPOUNDS

39. Name the following compounds:

    a. $Cr_2(SO_4)_3$

    b. $Al(NO_3)_3$

    c. $Ba(OH)_2$

    d. Na_2O_2

40. Name the following compounds:

    a. $CsMnO_4$

    b. $FePO_4$

    c. Cu_2SO_4

    d. NH_4Cl

41. Name the following compounds:

    a. $Sc_2(SO_4)_3$

    b. $NaOH$

    c. K_3PO_4

    d. Cu_2SO_3

42. Name the following compounds:

    a. $NiCO_3$

    b. K_2HPO_4

    c. $Na_2Cr_2O_7$

    d. NH_4NO_2

43. Name the following compounds:

    a. $Al_2(CrO_4)_3$

    b. $Fe_3(PO_4)_2$

    c. $Fe(NO_3)_2$

    d. $Cr(C_2H_3O_2)_2$

44. Write the formulas for the following compounds:

    a. strontium iodide

    b. aluminum hydroxide

    c. potassium hypochlorite

    d. silver carbonate

45. Write the formulas for the following compounds:

a. copper(I) permanganate

b. cesium chlorate

c. rubidium nitrate

d. sodium hydrogen sulfite

46. Write the formulas for the following compounds:

a. magnesium phosphate

b. iron(III) chromate

c. ammonium sulfate

d. calcium hydrogen phosphate

47. Write the formulas for the following compounds:

a. copper(I) cyanide

b. strontium chlorite

c. lead(II) carbonate

d. tin(II) fluoride

48. Write the formulas for the following compounds:

a. calcium carbonate

b. ammonium bromide

c. cobalt(II) acetate

d. lithium chromate

49. Write the formula for the compounds that form from calcium and the following anions:

a. phosphate

b. cyanide

c. peroxide

d. dichromate

50. Write the formulas for the compounds that form from aluminum and the following anions:

a. dihydrogen phosphate

b. hydrogen phosphate

c. phosphate

d. nitrate

51. Write the formulas for the compounds that form from potassium and the following anions:

a. permanganate

b. acetate

c. dichromate

d. carbonate

52. Write the formulas for the compounds that form from iron(III) and the following anions:

    a. nitrite

    b. sulfate

    c. perchlorate

    d. hydrogen sulfite

FORMULAS AND NAMES OF INORGANIC HYDRATES

53. Write the formula of copper(II) sulfate pentahydrate.

54. Write the formula of iron(III) phosphate dihydrate.

55. Write the name of $MgSO_4 \cdot 7H_2O$.

56. Write the name of $NaC_2H_3O_2 \cdot 3H_2O$.

FORMULAS AND NAMES OF BINARY MOLECULAR (COVALENT) COMPOUND

57. Name the following compounds:

    a. CO_2

    b. NF_3

    c. PCl_3

    d. N_2O_4

58. Name the following compounds:

    a. N_2O

    b. S_2F_4

    c. PF_5

    d. SO_3

59. Write the names of the following compounds:

    a. XeF_4

    b. BBr_3

    c. CBr_4

    d. P_2S_5

60. Write the formulas of the following compounds:

    a. diboron dichloride

    b. diiodine pentoxide

    c. carbon tetrachloride

    d. nitrogen trifluoride

61. Write the formulas of the following compounds:
    a. tetraphosphorus decasulfide
    b. dinitrogen trioxide
    c. dinitrogen pentoxide
    d. sulfur dioxide
62. SO_2 is called sulfur dioxide but MgO_2 is simply called magnesium oxide. Why?
63. Are molecules present in a sample of CaF_2? Why or why not?
64. Are ions present in PCl_3? Why or why not?

Image Credits

- Fig. 3.1a: Copyright © Depositphotos/HandmadePicture.
- Fig. 3.1b: Copyright © Depositphotos/cj3333.
- Fig. 3.Ca: Copyright © Depositphotos/sciencepics.
- Fig. 3.Cb: Copyright © Depositphotos/sciencepics.
- Fig. 3.Da: Source: https://commons.wikimedia.org/wiki/File:Iron(II)_oxide.jpg.
- Fig. 3.Db: Source: https://commons.wikimedia.org/wiki/File:Iron(III)-oxide-sample.jpg.
- Fig. 3.Ea: Copyright © 2015 by Adina Firestone, (CC BY-SA 2.0) at https://commons.wikimedia.org/wiki/File:Clorox_Bleach_products.jpg.
- Fig. 3.Eb: Copyright © Depositphotos/Thamkc.
- Fig. 3.Fa: Copyright © 2006 by W. Oelen, (CC BY-SA 3.0) at https://commons.wikimedia.org/wiki/File:Nickel_sulfate_anh.jpg.
- Fig. 3.Fb: Copyright © 2005 by W. Oelen, (CC BY-SA 3.0) at https://commons.wikimedia.org/wiki/File:Nickel_sulfate_hydrate.jpg.

The Mole, Chemical Equations, and Stoichiometry

LEARNING OBJECTIVES AND OUTCOMES

After reading this chapter, you should be able to do the following:

- Explain what Avogadro's number is.

- Explain what a "mole" is.

- Determine molar mass and percent composition.

- Determine both empirical and molecular formulas.

- Understand and describe the different types of formulas (condensed structural, structural, carbon-skeleton formulas, as well as space-filling models).

- Balance chemical equations.

- Calculate theoretical yields from balanced chemical equations and a given amount of reactants.

- Identify limiting and excess reactants and calculate percent yield, as well as how much excess reactant remains following the chemical reaction.

- Define each of the Key Terms listed at the end of the chapter dealing with these concepts.

Section 4.1 Introduction

In Chapter 3, we learned how to name and write formulas for different types of chemical compounds. In this chapter, we explore using some of these formulas in chemical equations to understand what exactly is happening in a chemical reaction. We focus on answering various questions, such as whether or not there is a convenient way to describe the amounts of reactants as well as products in a given chemical equation. Can we determine percent composition, which is to say the amount of each element present in a compound, based on mass percent of the whole? Are there different types of chemical formulas that convey varying information about molecules, such as how molecules actually exist in three-dimensional

Chemical formulas and balanced chemical equations gives us a wealth of information about chemical reactions.

space? In keeping with what we already know from Chapter 2 regarding the Law of Mass Conservation, what does a balanced chemical equation tell us, and can we predict how much product will be produced for a given chemical reaction? Will some reactants be completely depleted before other reactants in a chemical equation? Does this then ultimately limit how much product can be produced? The answers to all of these questions and much more are provided in this chapter.

Section 4.2   The Mole

Amedeo Avogadro (1776–1856) was an Italian physicist. "Avogadro's number" was named in his honor.

Amedeo Avogadro was an Italian physicist who was born in Italy in 1776. In his honor, we have what chemists refer to as **Avogadro's number**, which is 6.022×10^{23}. This number represents the amount of entities (or things) in one **mole** (or *mol*), which is the SI unit for the amount of a substance. It is defined as the amount of a substance that contains the same number of entities as 12 grams of carbon-12 ($^{12}_{6}C$). As it turns out, there are 6.022×10^{23} carbon-12 atoms in exactly 12 grams. Therefore:

One Mole contains 6.022×10^{23} entities

Recall from Chapter 2, the definition of an atomic mass unit, amu, is 1/12 the mass of a carbon-12 isotope. While some of this may sound confusing, why don't we backup and look at the brief history of the mole so that we can get a better understanding of what this number means and how it was developed.

Brief History of the Mole

Jean Baptiste Perrin was a French chemist and physicist who was born in 1870 and is most famous for his work involving the Brownian motion of minute particles. Brownian motion is the random motion of particles suspended in a liquid or a gas and results from their collision with rapidly moving atoms or molecules. While Avogadro was the first to realize in the early 1800s that the volume of an ideal gas (discussed in more detail in Chapter 6 dealing with gases) is directly proportional to the number of atoms or molecules in a given sample of gas, it is through Perrin's work using a variety of methods that Avogadro's number was determined. In the early 1900s, Perrin proposed naming the constant in honor of Avogadro, and owing to this, we now have Avogadro's constant, 6.022×10^{23} entities (usually atoms or molecules) per mole. Nonetheless, Perrin was honored with the Nobel Prize for Physics in 1926 and later died in 1942. The term "moles" was first introduced by Friedrich Wilhelm Ostwald, who was a Russian-German chemist born in 1853. He originally defined this unit in terms of grams, and we therefore commonly express the atomic masses of elements on the periodic table today in terms of grams/mol. Recall, the term "moles" is Latin meaning a "heap" or "pile" (notice how big this number is!). As mentioned in Chapter 2, many early experiments in chemistry involved gold, and a fun exercise is the determination of Avogadro's number from actual data involving gold. For example, we know from x-ray diffraction studies that gold consists of repeating cubic units, which contain an atomic arrangement of four gold atoms. The length of one side of the cube is known to be approximately 4.077×10^{-8} cm (just a friendly reminder from math class that the volume of a cube is the length cubed, or L^3). With this data, along with the known density of gold ($19.3 \ g/cm^3$) and its molar mass from the periodic table ($196.97 \ g/mol$), we can determine Avogadro's number as follows:

Jean Baptiste Perrin (1870–1942) was a French chemist and physicist most famous for his work involving Brownian motion.

1.) First, we calculate the volume of the cube given a length of 4.077×10^{-8} cm.

$$Volume \ of \ the \ cube = (4.077 \times 10^{-8} \ cm)^3 = 6.77676 \times 10^{-23} \ cm^3$$

2.) Next, we simply use dimensional analysis as discussed in Chapter 1 to solve for $\dfrac{atoms}{mol}$ with this volume and the other given information (density and atomic mass of gold).

$$\frac{196.97 \ grams \ Au}{1 \ mol \ Au} \times \frac{1 \ cm^3 \ Au}{19.3 \ grams \ Au} \times \frac{4 \ atoms \ Au}{6.7767 \times 10^{-23} \ cm^3 \ Au} = 6.02 \times 10^{23} \ \frac{atoms}{mol}$$

Friedrich Wilhelm Ostwald (1853–1932) was a Russian-German chemist who received the Nobel Prize in Chemistry in 1909 for his work in catalysis, chemical equilibria, and reaction velocities.

In any event, Ostwald was the recipient of the Nobel Prize in Chemistry in 1909 before he died in 1932. Next we further explore molar mass.

Molar Mass

The **molar mass** is the mass of one mole of a given species expressed in grams, which can either be an element (either monoatomic or molecular) or a compound. In either case, we can get the numbers needed for these types of calculations from the periodic table, and the units are $\frac{grams}{mol}$. Thus, we can say that 1 mole of C contains 6.022 x 10^{23} C atoms and also has a mass of 12.01 grams. Also, recall from Chapter 2 (and on the periodic table) that carbon has an atomic mass of 12.01 atomic mass units (*amu*). Thus while one carbon atom weighs 12.01 *amu*, 6.022 x 10^{23} carbon atoms weigh 12.01 grams. Similarly, one diatomic molecule of O_2 has a mass of 32.00 *amu* (16.00 *amu* x 2), while one mole (or 6.022 x 10^{23} molecules) of O_2 has a mass of 32.00 grams. This can likewise be applied to a compound such as carbon monoxide. While one molecule of CO is 28.01 *amu* (12.01 *amu* + 16.00 *amu*), one mole (or 6.022 x 10^{23} molecules) of CO is 28.01 grams. It is very important not to let the concept of the mole confuse you. In fact, you can think about the mole in the same fashion as you would "a dozen" things, like donuts. In other words, one mole of anything (for the purposes of chemistry, this is usually atoms or molecules) is 6.022 x 10^{23} things, just like a dozen is 12 things. A major difference is, of course, that a mole is an enormous number that is essentially impossible to imagine or visualize. Another important point here is that while one mole of anything is 6.022 x 10^{23} things or "entities," the masses of different substances will vary. For example, consider boron, carbon, and nitrogen (Table 4.1). Notice that one mole of each of these elements is the same number of atoms (6.022 x 10^{23} atoms of boron, carbon, or nitrogen). However, the masses of one mole of each of these elements vary from 10.81 g to 12.01 g to 14.01 g, respectively.

A dozen donuts is 12 donuts, just as 1 mol of anything is 6.022 x 1023 things.

Table 4.1 Various elements along with their mass values either in amu, or grams/mole.

Element and Symbol	Mass of 1 atom (*amu*)	Number of atoms in 1 mole	Mass of 1 mole (grams)
Boron (B)	10.81 *amu*	6.022 x 10^{23}	10.81 g
Carbon (C)	12.01 *amu*	6.022 x 10^{23}	12.01 g
Nitrogen (N)	14.01 *amu*	6.022 x 10^{23}	14.01 g
Oxygen (O)	16.00 *amu*	6.022 x 10^{23}	16.00 g
Fluorine (F)	19.00 *amu*	6.022 x 10^{23}	19.00 g
Potassium (K)	39.10 *amu*	6.022 x 10^{23}	39.10 g
Sodium (Na)	22.99 *amu*	6.022 x 10^{23}	22.99 g
Calcium (Ca)	40.08 *amu*	6.022 x 10^{23}	40.08 g
Silver (Ag)	107.87 *amu*	6.022 x 10^{23}	107.87 g
Copper (Cu)	63.55 *amu*	6.022 x 10^{23}	63.55 g

Example Problem 4.1

Determine the molar mass of the following:
  a. gold (Au)
  b. silver (Ag)
  c. diatomic oxygen (O_2)
  d. water (H_2O)
  e. carbon dioxide (CO_2)

Solution:	
a. Au is monoatomic, so we look at the atomic mass on the periodic table and find 196.97 *amu*.	Molar Mass of $Au = \mathbf{196.97}\dfrac{\textit{grams}}{\textit{mol}}$
b. Ag is monoatomic, so we look at the atomic mass on the periodic table and find 107.87 *amu*.	Molar Mass of $Ag = \mathbf{107.87}\dfrac{\textit{grams}}{\textit{mol}}$
c. Diatomic oxygen (O_2) is a molecular element, so we need to account for both oxygens. Thus, $2 \times 16.00 = 32.00$ *amu*.	Molar Mass of $O_2 = \mathbf{32.00}\dfrac{\textit{grams}}{\textit{mol}}$
d. Water (H_2O) is a compound, so we need to account for both hydrogens and an oxygen. Thus, $(2 \times 1.01) + 16.00 = 18.02$ *amu*.	Molar Mass of $H_2O = \mathbf{18.02}\dfrac{\textit{grams}}{\textit{mol}}$
e. Carbon dioxide (CO_2) is a compound, so we need to account for carbon and both oxygens. Thus, $12.01 + (2 \times 16.00) = 44.01$ *amu*.	Molar Mass of $CO_2 = \mathbf{44.01}\dfrac{\textit{grams}}{\textit{mol}}$

Molar Mass and Avogadro's Number as Conversion Factors

As you can probably already see, molar mass (g / mol) can be used as a conversion factor between the amount of a substance (moles) and the mass (grams) of a substance, while Avogadro's number can be used as a conversion factor between the number of chemical entities (atoms or molecules) and the amount of a substance (moles) (Figure 4.1). Thus,

To find the number of moles for a given mass, we would use the molar mass as a conversion factor as follows:

$$\# \textit{ of mols} = \textit{mass (grams)} \times \frac{1 \textit{ mol}}{\# \textit{ of grams}}$$

To find the mass (grams) for a given number of moles, we would use the molar mass as a conversion as follows:

$$mass\ (grams) = \#\ of\ mols \times \frac{\#\ of\ grams}{1\ mol}$$

To find the number of entities for a given number of moles, we would use the following:

$$\#\ of\ entities = \#\ of\ mols \times \frac{6.022 \times 10^{23}\ entities}{1\ mol}$$

To find the number of moles for a given number of entities, we would use the following:

$$\#\ of\ mols = \#\ of\ entities \times \frac{1\ mol}{6.022 \times 10^{23}\ entities}$$

Figure 4.1 Molar mass (g/mol) can be used as a conversion factor between the amount of a substance (mols) and the mass (grams) of a substance. Similarly, Avogadro's number (6.022 x 10²³ atoms or molecules/mol) can be used as a conversion factor between the number of chemical entities (# of atoms or molecules) and the amount of a substance (mols).

Notice that in all of the above equations, we handle molar mass and Avogadro's number just like any other conversion factor using dimensional analysis.

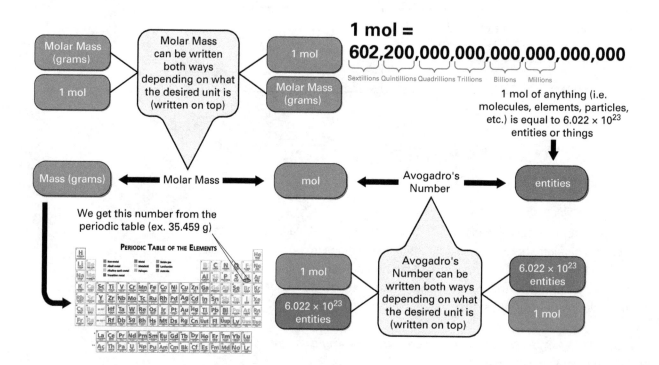

Example Problem 4.2

How many moles are in 11.12 grams of B_2O_3?	
Solution:	
1. First, let's find the molar mass of B_2O_3 because we know that we will need this information in order to convert between mass and moles.	$Molar\ Mass\ of\ B_2O_3 = (2 \times 10.81) + (3 \times 16.00) = 69.62\ g/mol$
2. Second, now that we have the molar mass of B_2O_3, we can use the following equation: $\# of\ mols = mass\ (grams) \times \dfrac{1\ mol}{\#\ of\ grams}$ 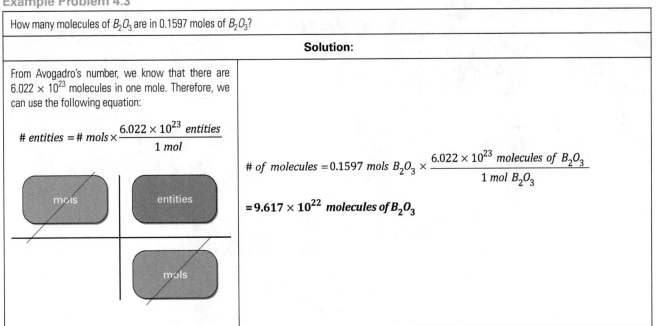	$\# mols = 11.12\,g\,B_2O_3 \times \dfrac{1\ mol\ B_2O_3}{69.62\,g\,B_2O_3} = \mathbf{0.1597\,mols\ B_2O_3}$

Example Problem 4.3

How many molecules of B_2O_3 are in 0.1597 moles of B_2O_3?	
Solution:	
From Avogadro's number, we know that there are 6.022×10^{23} molecules in one mole. Therefore, we can use the following equation: $\# entities = \# mols \times \dfrac{6.022 \times 10^{23}\ entities}{1\ mol}$	$\# of\ molecules = 0.1597\ mols\ B_2O_3 \times \dfrac{6.022 \times 10^{23}\ molecules\ of\ B_2O_3}{1\ mol\ B_2O_3}$ $= \mathbf{9.617 \times 10^{22}\ molecules\ of\ B_2O_3}$

Example Problem 4.4

What is the mass in grams of 9.617×10^{22} molecules of B_2O_3?

Solution:

1. First, we need to find moles of B_2O_3 from the number of molecules using Avogadro's number; then from there we can find the mass in grams using the molar mass of B_2O_3. We first use Avogadro's number (6.022×10^{23} molec./mol) as follows:

$$\text{\# of mols} = \text{\# of entities} \times \frac{1 \ mol}{6.022 \times 10^{23} \ entities}$$

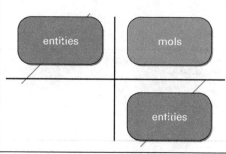

$$\text{\# of mols} = 9.617 \times 10^{22} \ molec. \ of \ B_2O_3 \times \frac{1 \ mol \ B_2O_3}{6.022 \times 10^{23} \ molecules \ of \ B_2O_3}$$

$$= 0.1597 \ mols \ B_2O_3$$

2. Now that we have moles of B_2O_3, we can determine the mass (g) using the molar mass of B_2O_3.

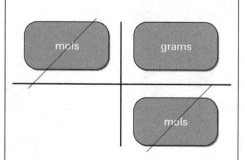

$$\text{Molar Mass of } B_2O_3 = (2 \times 10.81) + (3 \times 16.00) = 69.62$$

$$\text{Mass of } B_2O_3 (g) = 0.1597 \ mols \ of \ B_2O_3 \times \frac{69.62 \ g \ B_2O_3}{1 \ mol \ B_2O_3}$$

$$= 11.12 \ grams \ of \ B_2O_3$$

Note that if you feel comfortable at this point, you can use dimensional analysis as discussed in Chapter 1 and string all of this together in one step rather than two individual steps. That is,

$$\text{\# of entities} \times \frac{1 \ mol}{6.022 \times 10^{23} \ entities} \times \frac{Molar \ Mass \ (grams)}{1 \ mol} = Mass \ (grams)$$

$$9.617 \times 10^{22} \ molec. \ of \ B_2O_3 \times \frac{1 \ mol \ B_2O_3}{6.022 \times 10^{23} \ molecules \ of \ B_2O_3} \times \frac{69.62 \ g \ B_2O_3}{1 \ mol \ B_2O_3}$$

$$= 11.12 \ grams \ of \ B_2O_3$$

Hopefully, you can see the relationships between examples 4.2 and 4.4. We started with grams, moved through to the mole, then on to molecules, and finally all the way back to grams. This is also a very good way to check your work. Notice how we began and ended with 11.12 grams of B_2O_3.

Example Problem 4.5

How many molecules of NO_2 are in 18.62 grams of NO_2?	
Solution:	
In order to get the number of molecules here, we are first going to need to calculate moles from grams. Thus, let's find the molar mass of NO_2 because we know that we will need this information in order to convert between mass and moles.	Molar Mass of $NO_2 = (1 \times 14.01) + (2 \times 16.00) = 46.01 \frac{grams}{mol}$
Next, we use the following equation to get moles : $$\# \ of \ mols = mass \ (grams) \times \frac{1 \ mol}{\# \ of \ grams}$$ 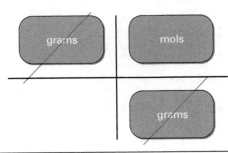	$\# \ of \ mols \ of \ NO_2 = 18.62 \ g \times \dfrac{1 \ mol \ NO_2}{46.01 \ g \ NO_2} = 0.4047 \ mols \ NO_2$
Finally, we use Avogadro's number to get molecules of NO_2. Thus, $$\# \ of \ entities = \# \ of \ mols \times \frac{6.022 \times 10^{23} \ entities}{1 \ mol}$$ 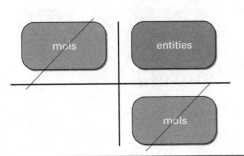	$\# \ of \ molecules \ of \ NO_2 = 0.4047 \ mols \ NO_2 \times \dfrac{6.022 \times 10^{23} \ molecules \ NO_2}{1 \ mol \ NO_2}$ $= 2.437 \times 10^{23}$ molecules of NO_2
Again, this can also be done in 1 step by stringing everything together: $$mass \ (grams) \times \frac{1 \ mol}{\# \ of \ grams} \times \frac{6.022 \times 10^{23} \ entities}{1 \ mol} = \# \ of \ entities$$ 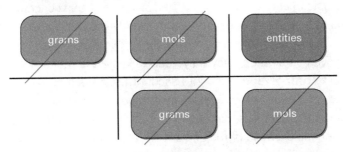 $$18.62 \ g \ NO_2 \times \frac{1 \ mol \ NO_2}{46.01 \ g \ NO_2} \times \frac{6.022 \times 10^{23} \ molecules \ NO_2}{1 \ mol \ NO_2}$$ $$= 2.437 \times 10^{23} \ \textbf{molecules } NO_2$$	

Example Problem 4.6

How many molecules of N_2O_4 are in 32.41 grams of N_2O_4?	
Solution:	
First, let's find the molar mass because we know that we will need that.	Molar Mass of $N_2O_4 = (2 \times 14.01) + (4 \times 16.00) = 92.02\ \dfrac{grams}{mol}$

Next, let's try to do this all in one step now.

$$mass\ (grams) \times \frac{1\ mol}{\#\ of\ grams} \times \frac{6.022 \times 10^{23}\ entities}{1\ mol} = \#\ of\ entities$$

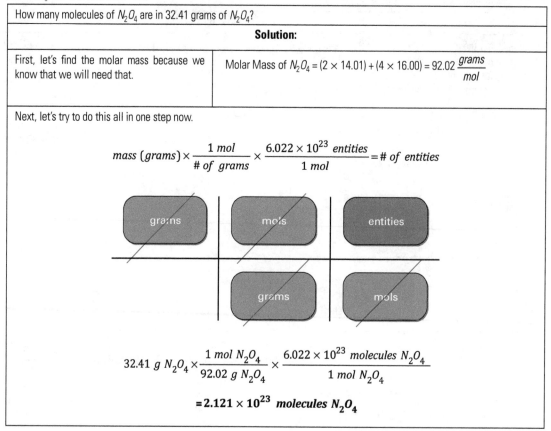

$$32.41\ g\ N_2O_4 \times \frac{1\ mol\ N_2O_4}{92.02\ g\ N_2O_4} \times \frac{6.022 \times 10^{23}\ molecules\ N_2O_4}{1\ mol\ N_2O_4}$$

$$= 2.121 \times 10^{23}\ molecules\ N_2O_4$$

Section 4.3 Percent Composition and Determining Compound Formulas

Percent Composition

In this next section, we explore percent composition. Here, we can use your grade in this class as an example in order to highlight the importance of this concept. In evaluating grades, we are interested in how many questions you correctly answer on an exam out of the total possible questions. Similarly, chemists are interested in things such as, "how much carbon is present in a particular hydrocarbon?", or they may need to know the metalloid composition of a semiconductor. **Percent composition** takes into account how much of each element is present in a given compound as a percentage. These percentages are calculated based on **mass**, such that the mass of a given element is expressed as a percentage of the molecular mass as a whole. Let's take the generic example of molecule X_2Y_3. If we wanted the mass percent of X, we would do so as follows:

$$Mass\ \%_X = \frac{Mass\ of\ Element\ X}{Mass\ of\ the\ Whole\ Molecule} \times 100\%$$

We can arrive at the appropriate inputs by making use of the subscripts in the chemical formula and the atomic masses of the elements that comprise the compound.

$$Mass\ \%_x = \frac{(2 \times AM_x)}{(2 \times AM_x) + (3 \times AM_y)} \times 100\%$$

Where, AM_x = atomic mass of X, and AM_y = atomic mass of Y.
If, however, we wanted the mass percent of Y using the generic molecule X_2Y_3, we would then use the following:

$$Mass\ \%_y = \frac{(3 \times AM_y)}{(2 \times AM_x) + (3 \times AM_y)} \times 100\%$$

As always with these types of problems, it is always a good idea to make sure that the mass percent values add up to 100 (considering rounding).

We can think of mass percent like an exam we take in Chemistry class. Our score is based on how many questions we correctly answer out of the total possible questions. Similarly, mass percent takes into account how much (based on mass) of one element is present in a given molecule compared to the total molecular mass.

Example Problem 4.7

What is the mass percent of hydrogen in water (H_2O)? What about oxygen? Do these values add up to 100?	
Solution:	
First, let's find the mass percent of hydrogen in H_2O. $$Mass\ \%_{Hydrogen} = \frac{(2 \times AM_H)}{(2 \times AM_H) + (1 \times AM_O)} \times 100\%$$	$$Mass\ \%_{hydrogen} = \frac{(2 \times 1.01\ amu)}{(2 \times 1.01\ amu) + (1 \times 16.00\ amu)} \times 100\% = \mathbf{11.2\%\ H}$$
Next, let's find the mass percent of oxygen in H_2O. $$Mass\ \%_{Oxygen} = \frac{(1 \times AM_O)}{(2 \times AM_H) + (1 \times AM_O)} \times 100\%$$	$$Mass\ \%_{oxygen} = \frac{(1 \times 16.00\ amu)}{(2 \times 1.01\ amu) + (1 \times 16.00\ amu)} \times 100\% = \mathbf{88.8\%\ O}$$
Percentages add up to 100 (considering rounding)?	Yes, $\mathbf{11.2 + 88.8 = 100}$

Example Problem 4.8

What is the mass percent of carbon, hydrogen, and oxygen in glucose ($C_6H_{12}O_6$)?	
Solution:	
First, let's find the mass percent of carbon in $C_6H_{12}O_6$. $$Mass\ \%_{Carbon} = \frac{(6 \times AM_C)}{(6 \times AM_C) + (12 \times AM_H) + (6 \times AM_O)} \times 100\%$$	$$Mass\ \%_{carbon} = \frac{(6 \times 12.01\ amu)}{(6 \times 12.01\ amu) + (12 \times 1.01\ amu) + (6 \times 16.00\ amu)} \times 100\%$$ $$= \mathbf{39.99\%\ C}$$
Next, let's find the mass percent of hydrogen in $C_6H_{12}O_6$. $$Mass\ \%_{Hydrogen} = \frac{(12 \times AM_H)}{(6 \times AM_C) + (12 \times AM_H) + (6 \times AM_O)} \times 100\%$$	$$Mass\ \%_{Hydrogen} = \frac{(12 \times 1.01\ amu)}{(6 \times 12.01\ amu) + (12 \times 1.01\ amu) + (6 \times 16.00\ amu)} \times 100\%$$ $$= \mathbf{6.73\%\ H}$$
Finally, let's find the mass percent of oxygen in $C_6H_{12}O_6$. $$Mass\ \%_{Oxygen} = \frac{(6 \times AM_O)}{(6 \times AM_C) + (12 \times AM_H) + (6 \times AM_O)} \times 100\%$$	$$Mass\ \%_{Oxygen} = \frac{(6 \times 16.00\ amu)}{(6 \times 12.01\ amu) + (12 \times 1.01\ amu) + (6 \times 16.00\ amu)} \times 100\%$$ $$= \mathbf{53.28\%\ O}$$
Percentages add up to 100 (considering rounding)?	Yes.

Percent Composition as a Conversion Factor

We have now demonstrated it is possible to calculate a percent composition for any element in any compound if the formula of the compound is known. This will prove useful in a number of ways. For instance, it is possible to determine the mass of constituent elements within a specific sample of a given compound, assuming the formula is known. This is accomplished by determining the percent composition for the element of interest and using it as a conversion factor between the mass of the compound and that of the element. To illustrate this, let's walk through an example. Consider the compound $SeOF_2$. If we were to calculate the percent composition of Se in $SeOF_2$ we would arrive there as follows:

$$Mass\ \%_{Se} = \frac{(1 \times AM_{Se})}{(1 \times AM_{Se}) + (1 \times AM_O) + (2 \times AM_F)} \times 100\%$$

$$Mass\ \%_{Se} = \frac{(1 \times 78.96\ amu)}{(1 \times 78.96\ amu) + (1 \times 16.00\ amu) + (2 \times 19.00\ amu)} \times 100\%$$

$$Mass\ \%_{Se} = \frac{78.96\ amu}{132.96\ amu} \times 100\% = \mathbf{59.39\%}$$

In this way we determine the percent composition of selenium in our compound is 59.39%. In order to construct a conversion factor which relates mass of a constituent element (selenium) to mass of the parent compound, we need to think of the percent composition in the following way: In every 100 g of our sample compound, $SeOF_2$, there are 59.39 g of Se. This can be expressed as a ratio in one of two ways:

$$\frac{59.39\ g\ Se}{100\ g\ SeOF_2} \quad or \quad \frac{100\ g\ SeOF_2}{59.39\ g\ Se}$$

Returning to our example, assume we have a sample of $SeOF_2$ and we have weighed it and found its mass to be 43.21 g. If we wanted to know what portion of this total mass is just selenium, we would use the following conversion:

$$43.21\ g\ SeOF_2 \times \frac{59.39\ g\ Se}{100\ g\ SeOF_2} = 25.66\ g\ Se$$

In this way, we have determined our sample contains 25.66 g of selenium. Additionally, we could perform the same procedure concerning the elements oxygen and fluorine in our sample. Indeed, this is another example of how much information is implicitly contained in simple chemical formulas.

Calculation of Empirical Formulas

Now that we have explored determining percent composition from a given molecular formula and its use as a conversion factor, let us now consider the reverse. That is to say, if we have the percent composition of a given molecule, can we then determine the formula? In this section, we look at how having the percent composition data can allow us to ascertain the ratio of the different atoms in a given compound. In so doing, we determine the **empirical formula**. In an *empirical formula*, the subscripts represent the lowest whole number ratio of the different atoms that make up the compound in question. For instance, the empirical formula for benzene (C_6H_6) is CH and for ethylene (C_2H_4) it is CH_2, and so on. Empirical formulas are used because sometimes we do not know more about the compound than the ratio of elements which constitute it. Recall that in Chapter 3 we learned that it isn't possible to determine the molecular formulas of covalent compounds simply by knowing the identity of the elements in the compound. In such instances, the empirical formula can be calculated from experimentally determined percent composition data. (Percent composition data can be determined from experimental procedures such as atomic emission or absorption spectroscopies, for instance.) This can be accomplished by applying the following rules:

1. First, if you are given percent composition data, assume a 100-gram sample. Thus, we can convert all of the percentages to grams. For example, 35% becomes 35 grams, 5% becomes 5 grams, and so on. If simply given mass data (grams), just use the given masses and skip this step. (Let's continue to use our example, $SeOF_2$.)

$$Se \rightarrow 59.39\% \rightarrow 59.39 \; g$$
$$O \rightarrow 12.03\% \rightarrow 12.03 \; g$$
$$F \rightarrow 28.58\% \rightarrow 28.58 \; g$$

2. Calculate the number of moles of each element from grams using the molar masses of each atom present in the molecule.

$$(59.39 \; g \; Se) \times \frac{1 \; mol \; Se}{78.96 \; g \; Se} = 0.75215 \; mol \; Se$$

$$(12.03 \; g \; O) \times \frac{1 \; mol \; O}{16.00 \; g \; O} = 0.75188 \; mol \; O$$

$$(28.58 \; g \; F) \times \frac{1 \; mol \; F}{19.00 \; g \; F} = 1.5042 \; mol \; F$$

3. Next, we write a pseudoformula (it is called a "pseudo" or "not genuine" formula because we are not done yet, and you may have fractional numbers as subscripts which we will need to ultimately convert to whole numbers).

$$Se_{0.75215}O_{0.75188}F_{1.5042}$$

4. Divide all of the subscripts by the smallest number. This is done essentially so that we can make one of the numbers whole, which will make things a little easier to deal with in the following steps.

$$Se_{\frac{0.75215}{0.75188}}O_{\frac{0.75188}{0.75188}}F_{\frac{1.5042}{0.75188}} \rightarrow Se_1O_1F_2$$

5. If you now have all whole numbers, skip this step and move onto step 6. If not, multiply everything in the formula (all subscripts) by some multiplier (see Table 4.2) such that you get all whole numbers.

    In this case we already have all whole numbers: $Se_1O_1F_2$

6. Write your empirical formula and make sure that you have the simplest possible ratio of atoms.

    1:1:2 is the lowest whole number ratio: $SeOF_2$

This may still seem complicated, so it may help to look at another example.

 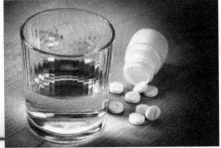

Many of us will take an aspirin when we experience pain such as a headache. We can use the percent composition data from laboratory analysis of aspirin to determine its empirical formula, which, in this case, is also its molecular formula.

Example Problem 4.9

Many of us will take an aspirin when we experience pain such as a headache. Laboratory results from the chemical analysis of aspirin reveal the following information:

Aspirin contains 60.0% carbon, 4.48% hydrogen, and 35.5% oxygen. Determine the empirical formula of aspirin.

Solution:	
1. First, assume a 100-gram sample.	Therefore, 60.0% carbon = 60.0 g carbon 4.48% hydrogen = 4.48 g hydrogen 35.5% oxygen = 35.5 g oxygen
2. Second, calculate the number of moles of each element from grams using the atomic weights of each atom present in the molecule.	$60.0 \ g \ carbon \times \dfrac{1 \ mol \ carbon}{12.01g \ carbon} = 5.00 \ mols \ carbon$ $4.48 \ g \ hydrogen \times \dfrac{1 \ mol \ hydrogen}{1.01g \ hydrogen} = 4.44 \ mols \ hydrogen$ $35.5 \ g \ oxygen \times \dfrac{1 \ mol \ oxygen}{16.00g \ oxygen} = 2.22 \ mols \ oxygen$
3. Next, we write a pseudoformula.	$C_{5.00}H_{4.44}O_{2.22}$
4. Now, we then divide by the smallest number (2.22 moles in this case for oxygen).	$Carbon = \dfrac{5.00 \ mols \ carbon}{2.22} = 2.25 \ mol \ carbon$ $Hydrogen = \dfrac{4.44 \ mols \ hydrogen}{2.22} = 2.00 \ mol \ hydrogen$ $Oxygen = \dfrac{2.22 \ mols \ oxygen}{2.22} = 1.00 \ mol \ oxygen$
5. Notice that in this case we did not get all whole numbers (i.e. 2.25 moles for carbon), so we must multiply everything by a factor of 4 (Table 4.2 can help you with common multipliers needed for whole numbers). This is done because we cannot have fractions as subscripts in our final empirical formula.	Thus, Carbon = 4 x 2.25 = 9 Hydrogen = 4 x 2.00 = 8 Oxygen = 4 x 1.00 = 4
6. Finally, we write our empirical formula.	$C_9H_8O_4$

Table 4.2 Multipliers

Decimal	Multiplier Needed for Whole Number
0.5	Multiply by 2
0.33 or 0.67	Multiply by 3
0.25 or 0.75	Multiply by 4

Calculating Molecular Formulas

Now that we know how to determine an empirical formula of a molecule from experimental data, how useful is this information? For example, consider the empirical formula, CH_2O. This simply tells us that the ratio of carbon to hydrogen to oxygen is 1:2:1, respectively. However, we do not necessarily know exactly how many atoms of carbon, hydrogen, and oxygen are present in the molecule simply by knowing this ratio. This empirical formula could, and does, represent multiple molecular formulas. These include $C_2H_4O_2$, $C_4H_8O_4$, $C_6H_{12}O_6$, and so on, as long as the ratio is maintained. Notice the ratio is the same in all cases. In other words, because an empirical formula gives us only the ratios of atoms and not necessarily the exact numbers of each atom present in a given molecule, we cannot (have not) identified our compound. We need more information in order to unambiguously identify our compound, and in doing so determine the **molecular formula**, which tells us the exact number of atoms present in the molecule. The molecular formula, as we will see, is incredibly useful to us. For example, we can use molecular formulas to depict molecules in various structures, all of which depict important information about the molecule. Molecules can be depicted in **condensed structural formulas**, **structural formulas**, **carbon skeleton formulas** (line formulas), as well as the **space-filling models** (Table 4.3). However, in order to calculate the molecular formula from the empirical formula, we need one more piece of information regarding the molecule in question, the molar mass of the compound. It turns out that it is possible to determine the molar mass of a compound even if we do not yet know its molecular formula. For example, if we had not only the empirical formula but also mass spectrometry data (discussed in Chapter 2), we could then determine the molecular formula from the empirical formula. This is because the mass of the molecule as determined by mass spectrometry is simply a whole-number multiple factor of the empirical formula mass, which we already have. Thus, in Example Problem 4.9, if we knew that the molecular weight of aspirin is 180.2 *g/mol* as determined by mass spectrometry, we would have been able to determine that the empirical formula is, in fact, also the molecular formula. In other words, if you were to calculate the empirical formula mass of aspirin ($C_9H_8O_4$), you would get 180.2 *g/mol* as follows:

$$(9 \times 12.01) + (8 \times 1.01) + (4 \times 16.00) = 180.2 \ g/mol$$

However, while the empirical and molecular formulas are the same in this particular example, this is not always the case. For example, if we were to determine that the molecular mass is twice the empirical-formula mass, we would then multiply the subscripts in the empirical formula by two to get the molecular formula. This is, again, because the molecular mass and the molecular formula of a compound are both whole-number multiples of the empirical formula mass and the empirical formula, respectively. Let's consider the generic example A_xB_y. If this was the empirical formula, and we were to determine that the molecular mass was twice the empirical formula mass, this would indicate that molecular formula must be a multiple of two times the empirical formula, $A_{2x}B_{2y}$. If we were to determine that the molecular mass was three times the empirical formula mass, then the molecular formula would be a multiple of three times the empirical formula, $A_{3x}B_{3y}$, and so forth. The key, therefore, is determining what this multiplier is by using the molar mass of the compound in conjunction with the empirical formula. This can be accomplished as follows:

1. If we have the molar mass and the empirical formula, the first thing to do is calculate the Empirical Formula Mass (EM). If we consider our generic empirical formula, A_xB_y, this is entirely analogous to calculating the molar mass from the molecular formula.

$$EM = (x)(AM_A) + (y)(AM_B)$$

2. Next, to determine our multiplier (n), we simply divide the molar mass by the empirical formula mass.

$$n = \frac{Molar\ Mass}{EM}$$

3. Now simply multiply the empirical formula subscripts by this whole number multiple, n, to arrive at a molecular formula.

$$\left\{A_xB_y\right\} \times n = A_{nx}B_{ny}$$

Remember, n is always a whole number, never a fraction. Again, while this may sound a little confusing, it may help to look at a specific example of this.

Example Problem 4.10

Laboratory results from the chemical analysis of an unknown molecule reveal the following information regarding the molecule:	
The molecule contains 40.0% carbon, 6.73% hydrogen, and 53.3% oxygen by mass. Mass spectrometry data have determined that the molecule has a mass of 180.18 g/mol. Determine the empirical and molecular formulas for this molecule (this can then be used to identify the molecule).	
Solution:	
1. Assume a 100-gram sample.	Therefore, 40.0% carbon = 40.0 g carbon 6.73% hydrogen = 6.73 g hydrogen 53.3% oxygen = 53.3 g oxygen
2. Calculate the number of moles of carbon, hydrogen and oxygen.	$40.0\ g\ carbon \times \dfrac{1\ mol\ carbon}{12.01g\ carbon} = 3.33\ mols\ carbon$ $6.73\ g\ hydrogen \times \dfrac{1\ mol\ hydrogen}{1.01g\ hydrogen} = 6.66\ mols\ hydrogen$ $53.3\ g\ oxygen \times \dfrac{1\ mol\ oxygen}{16.00g\ oxygen} = 3.33\ mols\ oxygen$
3. Write a pseudoformula, where the moles of each element are written as subscripts	$C_{3.33}H_{6.66}O_{3.33}$

4. Divide by the smallest number (3.33 moles in this case for carbon and oxygen).	$\text{Carbon} = \dfrac{3.33 \text{ mols carbon}}{3.33} = 1.00 \text{ mol carbon}$ $\text{Hydrogen} = \dfrac{6.66 \text{ mols hydrogen}}{3.33} = 2.00 \text{ mol hydrogen}$ $\text{Oxygen} = \dfrac{3.33 \text{ mols oxygen}}{3.33} = 1.00 \text{ mol oxygen}$
5. Convert subscripts to whole numbers. Notice that in this case we have already arrived at all whole numbers. Therefore, a common multiplier (from Table 4.2) is *not* needed in this example.	Thus, our empirical formula becomes: CH_2O
6. Calculate the empirical formula mass of CH_2O.	$EM = \left(1 \times 12.01 \dfrac{g}{mol}\right) + \left(2 \times 1.01 \dfrac{g}{mol}\right) + \left(1 \times 16.00 \dfrac{g}{mol}\right)$ $EM = 30.03 \dfrac{g}{mol}$
7. Determine the whole number multiplier, n. This is accomplished by dividing our molar mass (determined via mass spec. experiments), 180.18 g/mol, by our empirical formula mass, 30.03 g/mol.	$\dfrac{\left(180.18 \dfrac{g}{mol}\right)}{\left(30.03 \dfrac{g}{mol}\right)} = 6$
8. Since we now know that the molecule weighs six times our empirical formula mass, we multiply all of the subscripts in our empirical formula by six to get our molecular formula.	$\{CH_2O\} \times 6 = C_6H_{12}O_6$ $C_6H_{12}O_6$
This molecule is in fact glucose. Here we see what is known as the "Ball and Stick" model of the molecule, which is yet another type of formula that you might run across in your studies. Notice that in this depiction, carbon is gray, hydrogen is white, and oxygen is red. If you, in fact, count all of the atoms up in this molecule and then multiply by their respective atomic masses, you will arrive at 180.2 g/mol. Note that other types of formulas/structures for glucose are also summarized in Table 4.4.	

In this section, we have examined percent composition and have used this information to determine both empirical and molecular formulas. Furthermore, we have seen how knowing the molecular formula allows us to depict molecules in various ways. Next, we further examine how useful molecular formulas can be when used in balanced chemical equations to describe chemical reactions.

Table 4.3 List of various hydrocarbons (compounds containing only carbon and hydrogen) along with their empirical formula, molecular formula, as well as their molecular weights. Also, hydrocarbons depicted as condensed structural formulas, structural formulas, carbon skeleton formulas (line formulas), as well as the space filling models.

Chemical Name	Empirical Formula	Molecular Formula	Molecular Weight (g/mol)	Condensed Structural Formula	Structural Formula	Carbon Skeleton Formula/Line Formula	Space-Filling Model
Ethane	CH_3	C_2H_6	30.08	CH_3-CH_3			
Propane	C_3H_8	C_3H_8	44.11	$CH_3-CH_2-CH_3$			
Butane	C_2H_5	C_4H_{10}	58.14	$CH_3-CH_2-CH_2-CH_3$			
Pentane	C_5H_{12}	C_5H_{12}	72.17	$CH_3-CH_2-CH_2-CH_2-CH_3$			
Hexane	C_3H_7	C_6H_{14}	86.20	$CH_3-CH_2-CH_2-CH_2-CH_2-CH_3$			
Heptane	C_7H_{16}	C_7H_{16}	100.23	$CH_3-CH_2-CH_2-CH_2-CH_2-CH_2-CH_3$			
Octane	C_4H_9	C_8H_{18}	114.26	$CH_3-CH_2-CH_2-CH_2-CH_2-CH_2-CH_2-CH_3$			

Table 4.4 Glucose

D-Glucose	Molecular Weight = 180.18 *g/mol*
Empirical Formula	CH_2O
Molecular Formula	$C_6H_{12}O_6$
Condensed Structural Formula	$OHC–CHOH–CHOH–CHOH–CHOH–CH_2OH$
Structural Formula	
Carbon Skeleton Formula/Line Formula	
Space-Filling Model	

Section 4.4 Chemical Equations

Chemical reactions are happening all the time, all around us. Chemists depict these chemical reactions in **chemical equations** which provide information regarding the compounds involved in a reaction as well as the physical state of each compound. Additionally, chemical equations allow for quantitative studies of chemical reactions. For example, let's consider iron reacting with oxygen to yield iron(III) oxide.

$$4Fe\ (s) + 3O_2\ (g) \rightarrow 2Fe_2O_3\ (s)$$

First, we notice that we have the physical state of each compound. We commonly come across solids (s), liquids (l), gases (g), and (aq) (meaning aqueous or dissolved in water) physical states in chemical reactions. Additionally, the arrow indicates the direction of the reaction and therefore the initial compounds (**reactants** – to the left of the arrow) and the final compounds which are formed from the reactants. These are referred to as the **products** and are written to the right of the reaction arrow. Further, from this *balanced* chemical equation, we can now attempt to answer the following questions:

1. How much O_2 is required to completely react with a given amount of *Fe*?

2. How much *Fe* would be required to completely react with a given amount of O_2?

3. How much Fe_2O_3 will be produced with a given amount of starting materials (either Fe or O_2)?

4. Will one of the starting materials run out before the other if given limited amounts of both?

Thus, we can see how important balanced chemical equations can be in order to answer these questions. For example, consider the complete combustion of methane (Figure 4.2). Notice that all of the atoms are accounted for in both the reactants and the products, which can now provide us with a wealth of information. Thus, we now explore balancing chemical equations.

Figure 4.2 Balancing equations (complete combustion reaction of methane).

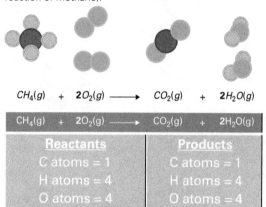

$$CH_4(g) \;+\; 2O_2(g) \longrightarrow CO_2(g) \;+\; 2H_2O(g)$$

$CH_4(g)$ + $2O_2(g)$ $\longrightarrow$ $CO_2(g)$ + $2H_2O(g)$	
Reactants	**Products**
C atoms = 1	C atoms = 1
H atoms = 4	H atoms = 4
O atoms = 4	O atoms = 4

Balancing Chemical Equations

Before we can really tackle any of the above questions, we must first learn to balance chemical equations. For some, this will come easily, while for others this may take some more practice. This is done in order to ensure that the same number of atoms that appear on the left of the arrow (*reactants*) also appear on the right (*products*). For example, let us again consider iron reacting with oxygen to yield iron(III) oxide in the unbalanced equation:

$$Fe\,(s) + O_2\,(g) \rightarrow Fe_2O_3\,(s)(unbalanced)$$

We might first notice a total of three oxygens on the right and only two on the left. This is a violation of the *law mass conservation* and must be reconciled. This is accomplished using coefficients to balance out the numbers of each type of atom on the right and left sides of the equation. In this example, the lowest common whole number multiple between the three and two (oxygens) is six. Therefore, in order to get six oxygens on the right, we put a two coefficient in front of Fe_2O. Now that we have a total of six oxygens on the right, we must then put a three coefficient in front of O_2 in order to also have six oxygens on the left. Let's look at what we have so far.

$$Fe\,(s) + \mathbf{3}O_2\,(g) \rightarrow \mathbf{2}Fe_2O_3\,(s)(unbalanced)$$

Never balance chemical equations by adding subscripts! The reason for this is that by changing the coefficients, you are just simply changing the number of molecules, which is what you want to do here. However, changing the subscripts changes the substance itself (i.e. water is H_2O, and hydrogen peroxide is H_2O_2, which is a very different compound!). In any event, notice that by adding a coefficient of two in front of Fe_2O_3 in order to balance the oxygen, we have also created a situation where we now have a total of four iron atoms on the right, therefore we add a four coefficient in front of Fe on the left to balance iron. We now have our balanced equation.

$$4Fe(s) + 3O_2(g) \rightarrow 2Fe_2O_3(s)\ (balanced)$$

As mentioned earlier, this just takes practice, so let's look at some example problems. Notice that sometimes it helps to balance the compounds in the chemical equation first and free elements last. This is because by changing the coefficient of a free element you are not also altering the amounts of other elements, which have already been adjusted in the initial steps. The other thing to keep in mind when attempting to balance chemical equations is that if things are not working out, you might just start over from scratch and try by beginning with another atom first.

Table 4.5 Table depicting the atom count in the balanced chemical equation involving iron reacting with oxygen to yield iron(III) oxide.

$4\ Fe(s) + 3\ O_2(g) \rightarrow 2\ Fe_2O_3(s)$	
Reactants	Products
Fe atoms = 4	Fe atoms = 4
O atoms = 6	O atoms = 6

Photosynthesis is a process used by plants and other organisms to generate chemical energy.

Example Problem 4.11

Photosynthesis is a process used by plants and other organisms to generate chemical energy, which can support the organism's activities. This process involves the production of aqueous glucose ($C_6H_{12}O_6$) and gaseous oxygen from gaseous carbon dioxide and liquid water. Write the balanced equation for the photosynthesis reaction.	
Solution:	
1. Write out all the formulas for the reactants and products along with their respective physical states in an unbalanced equation.	$CO_2\ (g) + H_2O\ (l) \rightarrow C_6H_{12}O_6\ (aq) + O_2\ (g)(unbalanced)$
2. Begin by balancing the atoms in the most complex compound. In this case, that is glucose, $C_6H_{12}O_6$. Notice that there are a total of six carbon atoms on the right in glucose ($C_6H_{12}O_6$) and only one on the left in CO_2. Put a six coefficient in front of CO_2 in order to balance carbon.	$6CO_2\ (g) + H_2O\ (l) \rightarrow C_6H_{12}O_6\ (aq) + O_2\ (g)(unbalanced)$
3. Having balanced carbon, notice that we now have 13 oxygen atoms on the left (12 from $6CO_2$ and one from H_2O) and eight on the right (six from $C_6H_{12}O_6$ and two from O_2). Let's leave oxygen alone for now, as we can balance this free element last with relative ease. Let's focus on hydrogen instead. Notice that we have two hydrogen atoms on the left from H_2O and 12 on the right from $C_6H_{12}O_6$. Put a six coefficient on the left in front of H_2O so that we have 12 hydrogen atoms on both sides of the chemical equation.	$6CO_2\ (g) + 6H_2O\ (l) \rightarrow C_6H_{12}O_6\ (aq) + O_2\ (g)(unbalanced)$
4. Now focus on oxygen. (Always save the free elements for last.) We now have 18 oxygen atoms on the left (12 from $6CO_2$ and six from $6H_2O$) and eight oxygen atoms on the right (six from $C_6H_{12}O_6$ and two from O_2). If we now put a six coefficient on the right in front of O_2, we will have a total of 18 oxygen atoms on both sides of the chemical equation.	$6CO_2\ (g) + 6H_2O\ (l) \rightarrow C_6H_{12}O_6\ (aq) + 6O_2\ (g)$
5. Make sure the equation is now balanced.	**Table 4.6** Table depicting the atom count in the balanced chemical equation for the photosynthesis reaction.

$6\ CO_2(g) + 6\ H_2O(l) \rightarrow C_6H_{12}O_6(aq) + 6\ O_2(g)$	
Reactants	Products
C atoms = 6	C atoms = 6
O atoms = 18	O atoms = 18
H atoms = 12	H atoms = 12

Notice that in this last example, we balanced the oxygen last. That is because we had the free element oxygen (O_2) in the product that can be adjusted at the end without disturbing the amounts of any other atoms in the equation. Let's consider another example.

Example Problem 4.12

Write the balanced chemical equation involving the production of gaseous nitrogen monoxide and gaseous water from gaseous ammonia and gaseous oxygen.	
Solution:	
1. First, let's write out all the formulas for the reactants and products along with their respective physical states in an unbalanced equation.	$NH_3\ (g) + O_2\ (g) \rightarrow NO\ (g) + H_2O\ (g)(unbalanced)$

2. Second, begin balancing atoms in the most complex compound (in this case NH_3). You should immediately notice that nitrogen is already balanced with one on each side. If we leave oxygen last (O_2 is a free element in the reactant), then we focus on hydrogen. There are three hydrogen atoms on the left (from NH_3) and two on the right (from H_2O). The lowest common whole number multiple of two and three is six. Therefore, we can put a two coefficient on the left in front of NH_3, and a three coefficient on the right in front of H_2O.	$2NH_3\ (g) + O_2\ (g) \rightarrow NO\ (g) + 3H_2O\ (g)(unbalanced)$
3. Now we notice that the nitrogen is no longer balanced (two on the left from $2\ NH_3$ and one on the right from NO). Put a two coefficient on the right in front of NO.	$2NH_3\ (g) + O_2\ (g) \rightarrow 2NO\ (g) + 3H_2O\ (g)(unbalanced)$
4. We now move on to the oxygen and notice that we have somewhat of a dilemma. There are two oxygens on the left (from O_2) and five on the right (two from $2\ NO$ and three from $3\ H_2O$). We can balance the oxygen for now by putting a coefficient of $2\frac{1}{2}$ on the left in front of O_2, which would give us five oxygen atoms on both sides of the chemical equation.	$2NH_3\ (g) + 2\frac{1}{2}O_2\ (g) \rightarrow 2NO\ (g) + 3H_2O\ (g)(unbalanced)$
5. While the equation is in theory balanced, we cannot have a fraction in the final chemical equation. To alleviate this issue, we can simply multiply everything by two to give us whole numbers.	$2 \times (2NH_3\ (g) + 2\frac{1}{2}O_2\ (g) \rightarrow 2NO\ (g) + 3H_2O\ (g)(unbalanced))$ $4NH_3\ (g) + 5O_2\ (g) \rightarrow 4NO\ (g) + 6H_2O\ (g)$
Let's make sure the equation is now balanced.	**Table 4.7** Table depicting the atom count in the balanced chemical equation involving the production of gaseous nitrogen monoxide and gaseous water from gaseous ammonia and gaseous oxygen.

$4\ NH_3(g) + 5\ O_2(g) \rightarrow 4\ NO(g) + 6\ H_2O(g)$	
Reactants	Products
N atoms = 4	N atoms = 4
H atoms = 12	H atoms = 12
O atoms = 10	O atoms = 10

Using Balanced Chemical Equations to Calculate Quantities of Reactants and Products

Having learned to balance chemical equations, let's look at how we can get useful quantitative information from them. To do this, we must first understand **Stoichiometry** (from the Greek "Stoicheon" meaning element and "-metry" meaning to count or measure.). Stoichiometry is the calculation of the relative quantities of reactants and products in chemical reactions. For example, let's again consider iron reacting with oxygen to yield iron(III) oxide.

$$4Fe\ (s) + 3O_2\ (g) \rightarrow 2Fe_2O_3\ (s)$$

In looking at this balanced equation, we can see that four moles of *Fe* is stoichiometrically equivalent to three moles of O_2 and two moles of Fe_2O_3. Thus, their respective **stoichiometric ratios** would be 4:3:2. (Note: We could just as easily express this ratio in terms of molecules, rather than moles; however, in practice, we almost exclusively deal in moles when performing stoichiometric calculations.) What exactly does this mean and how does this help us to quantify reactants and products? Well, this means that four moles of *Fe* will react with three moles of O_2 to produce two moles of Fe_2O_3. Therefore, this allows us to relate different chemical entities in a chemical reaction to one another, and thus we can get valuable quantitative information such as masses of different chemical entities in the reaction. Notice, however, that the ratio between two chemical entities in a reaction is a molar one, *not based on mass*. Therefore, this is always done through the mole. Let's assume, for example, that we have 15.12 grams of iron. According to the reaction equation, how would we determine the mass in grams of Fe_2O_3 which can be produced if we use (consume) all 15.12 grams of iron (assuming O_2 is in excess). The first step in addressing this question is to convert our known quantity (mass of iron) to moles. This is accomplished by using the molar mass of iron as a conversion factor. Once we know how many moles of iron we have, we can convert this to moles of any other reactant or product in our reaction using the molar ratios given in the balanced reaction equation. In this case we are interested in the equivalent quantity of Fe_2O_3 for which we know there is a 2:4 molar ratio with *Fe*. We then convert moles of iron(III) oxide to mass in grams using its molar mass. Let's take a look:

$$4Fe\ (s) + 3O_2\ (g) \rightarrow 2Fe_2O_3\ (s)$$

$$15.12\ g\ Fe \times \frac{1\ mol\ Fe}{55.85\ g\ Fe} \times \frac{2\ mol\ Fe_2O_3}{4\ mol\ Fe} \times \frac{159.7\ g\ Fe_2O_3}{1\ mol\ Fe_2O_3} = 21.61740\ g\ Fe_2O_3 = 21.62\ g\ Fe_2O_3$$

Thus, we could theoretically produce 21.62 g of Fe_2O_3 if we were to use all 15.12 grams of iron (assuming O_2 is present in excess). In a similar fashion, we can also ascertain how much oxygen would be consumed to produce this quantity of Fe_2O_3. This can be calculated in two different ways. We can start with 15.12 g of the other reactant (*Fe*), or we can calculate how much oxygen is consumed based on the production of 21.62 g of Fe_2O_3. Let's take a look at both ways to make sure we get the same answer:

$$15.12\ g\ Fe \times \frac{1\ mol\ Fe}{55.85\ g\ Fe} \times \frac{3\ mol\ O_2}{4\ mol\ Fe} \times \frac{32.00\ g\ O_2}{1\ mol\ O_2} = 6.497\ g\ O_2$$

$$21.61740\ g\ Fe_2O_3 \times \frac{1\ mol\ Fe_2O_3}{159.7\ g\ Fe_2O_3} \times \frac{3\ mol\ O_2}{2\ mol\ Fe_2O_3} \times \frac{32.00\ g\ O_2}{1\ mol\ O_2} = 6.497\ g\ O_2$$

As we can see, we get 6.497 g O_2 regardless of the method used. Note that in both calculations the stoichiometric ratios are highlighted in red. In any event, as with most things in chemistry, the best way to learn this is to practice. Therefore, we will work some practice examples using the combustion of various hydrocarbons (compounds containing only carbon and hydrogen—recall Table 4.3). **Combustion reactions** can be thought of as "burning" reactions (such as the fuel in your car), and the complete combustion of hydrocarbons involving oxygen always produces CO_2 and H_2O.

Propane gas is commonly used to fuel our barbeque grills.

Example Problem 4.13

Propane gas is commonly used to fuel our barbeque grills. How much carbon dioxide is produced (grams) in the complete combustion reaction of 13.42 g of propane gas (C_3H_8)?

Solution:	
1.	First, let's write out all the formulas for the reactants and products along with their respective physical states in an unbalanced equation.	$C_3H_8\ (g) + O_2\ (g) \rightarrow CO_2(g) + H_2O\ (g)(unbalanced)$
2.	Second, we balance the equation using the steps previously discussed. You might first notice that a three coefficient is needed on the right in front of CO_2 to balance the three carbon atoms in the propane molecule (C_3H_8) on the left. Also, a four coefficient is needed on the right in front of H_2O so that there are eight hydrogen atoms on each side of the equation. Finally, a five coefficient is needed on the left in front of oxygen to balance the ten oxygen atoms present on the right of the equation in the products.	$C_3H_8\ (g) + 5O_2\ (g) \rightarrow 3CO_2(g) + 4H_2O\ (g)$

3. Now, we use dimensional analysis to solve for grams of product (CO_2):

Molar Mass of $C_3H_8 = 44.10 \dfrac{g}{mol}$

Molar Mass of $CO_2 = 44.01 \dfrac{g}{mol}$

Molar Mass of $H_2O = 18.02 \dfrac{g}{mol}$

> Stoichiometric ratio taken from the coefficients in the balanced chemical equation

grams	mols	Mols Stoichiometric Ratio	grams
	grams	Mols Stoichiometric Ratio	mols

$$13.42\ g\ C_3H_8 \times \frac{1\ mol\ C_3H_8}{44.10\ g\ C_3H_8} \times \frac{3\ mol\ CO_2}{1\ mol\ C_3H_8} \times \frac{44.01\ g\ CO_2}{1\ mol\ CO_2} = \textbf{40.18}\ \boldsymbol{g\ CO_2}$$

Example Problem 4.14

How much water is produced (grams) in the complete combustion reaction of 13.42 g of propane gas (C_3H_8)?

Solution:	
1. First, let's write out all the formulas for the reactants and products along with their respective physical states in an unbalanced equation.	$C_3H_8\ (g) + O_2\ (g) \rightarrow CO_2\ (g) + H_2O\ (g)\ (unbalanced)$
2. Second, we balance the equation using the steps previously discussed. You might first notice that a three coefficient is needed on the right in front of CO_2 to balance the three carbon atoms in the propane molecule (C_3H_8) on the left. Also, a four coefficient is needed on the right in front of H_2O so that there are eight hydrogen atoms on each side of the equation. Finally, a five coefficient is needed on the left in front of oxygen to balance the ten oxygen atoms present on the right of the equation in the products.	$C_3H_8\ (g) + 5O_2\ (g) \rightarrow 3CO_2\ (g) + 4H_2O\ (g)$

3. Now, we use dimensional analysis to solve for grams of product (H_2O):

Molar Mass of $C_3H_8 = 44.10\dfrac{g}{mol}$

Molar Mass of $CO_2 = 44.01\dfrac{g}{mol}$

Molar Mass of $H_2O = 18.02\dfrac{g}{mol}$

> Stoichiometric ratio taken from the coefficients in the balanced chemical equation

grams	mols	Mols Stoichiometric Ratio	grams
	grams	Mols Stoichiometric Ratio	mols

$$13.42\ g\ C_3H_8 \times \frac{1\ mol\ C_3H_8}{44.10\ g\ C_3H_8} \times \frac{4\ mol\ H_2O}{1\ mol\ C_3H_8} \times \frac{18.02\ g\ H_2O}{1\ mol\ H_2O} = \textbf{21.93}\ \textbf{\textit{g}}\ \textbf{\textit{H}}_2\textbf{\textit{O}}$$

Butane gas is commonly used in lighters.

Notice how we arrived at very different numbers for the two products—CO_2 and H_2O—in the last two examples (Example Problem 4.13 and 4.14). This is due to the fact that the stoichiometric ratio between propane and CO_2 is different from that of propane and H_2O (1:3 versus 1:4 respectively). Also, CO_2 and H_2O have very different molecular weights, which really highlight the importance of using molar ratios (not mass) in these types of problems. Work the following example problem to make sure that you have a good grasp of this concept.

Example Problem 4.15

Butane gas is commonly used in lighters. How much carbon dioxide and water are produced (grams) in the complete combustion reaction of 11.16 g of butane gas (C_4H_{10})?	
Solution:	
1. First, let's write out all the formulas for the reactants and products along with their respective physical states in an unbalanced equation.	$C_4H_{10}\,(g) + O_2\,(g) \rightarrow CO_2\,(g) + H_2O\,(g)\,(unbalanced)$
2. Second, we balance the equation using the steps previously discussed. Notice that a four coefficient is needed on the right in front of CO_2 to balance the four carbon atoms in the butane molecule (C_4H_{10}) on the left. Also, a five coefficient is needed on the right in front of H_2O so that there are ten hydrogen atoms on each side of the equation. We then temporarily put a $6\frac{1}{2}$ coefficient in front of O_2 on the left of the equation so that we have 13 oxygen atoms on each side. Finally, we multiply everything by two so that we have all whole numbers.	$C_4H_{10}\,(g) + 6\frac{1}{2}O_2\,(g) \rightarrow 4CO_2\,(g) + 5H_2O\,(g)\,(unbalanced)$ $2 \times \left(C_4H_{10}\,(g) + 6\frac{1}{2}O_2\,(g) \rightarrow 4CO_2\,(g) + 5H_2O\,(g)\,(unbalanced) \right)$ **Balanced Equation** $2C_4H_{10}\,(g) + 13O_2\,(g) \rightarrow 8CO_2\,(g) + 10H_2O\,(g)$

3. Now, we use dimensional analysis to solve for grams of products (CO_2 and H_2O):

Molar Mass of $C_4H_{10} = 58.14\dfrac{g}{mol}$

Molar Mass of $CO_2 = 44.01\dfrac{g}{mol}$

Molar Mass of $H_2O = 18.02\dfrac{g}{mol}$

Stoichiometric ratio taken from the coefficients in the balanced chemical equation

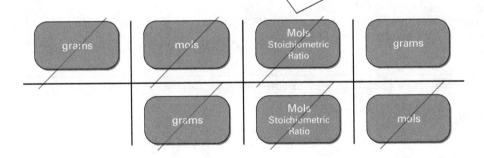

Carbon dioxide:

$$11.16\ g\ C_4H_{10} \times \frac{1\ mol\ C_4H_{10}}{58.14\ g\ C_4H_{10}} \times \frac{8\ mol\ CO_2}{2\ mol\ C_4H_{10}} \times \frac{44.01\ g\ CO_2}{1\ mol\ CO_2} = \mathbf{33.79\ g\ CO_2}$$

Water:

$$11.16\ g\ C_4H_{10} \times \frac{1\ mol\ C_4H_{10}}{58.14\ g\ C_4H_{10}} \times \frac{10\ mol\ H_2O}{2\ mol\ C_4H_{10}} \times \frac{18.02\ g\ H_2O}{1\ mol\ H_2O} = \mathbf{17.29\ g\ H_2O}$$

Octane is the principal component of the gasoline that you put in your car.

Example Problem 4.16

Octane is the major component of the gasoline that you regularly put in your car. How much carbon dioxide and water are produced (grams and molecules) in the complete combustion reaction of 542.1 g of octane (C_8H_{18})?

Solution:

1. First, let's write out all the formulas for the reactants and products along with their respective physical states in an unbalanced equation.	$C_8H_{18}\ (l) + O_2\ (g) \rightarrow CO_2(g) + H_2O\ (g)(unbalanced)$
2. Second, we balance the equation using the steps previously discussed. Notice that an eight coefficient is needed on the right in front of CO_2 to balance the eight carbon atoms in the octane molecule (C_8H_{18}) on the left. Also, a nine coefficient is needed on the right in front of H_2O so that there are 18 hydrogen atoms on each side of the equation. We then temporarily put a $12\frac{1}{2}$ coefficient in front of O_2 on the left of the equation so that we have 25 oxygen atoms on each side. Finally, we multiply everything by two so that we have all whole numbers.	$C_8H_{18}\ (l) + 12\frac{1}{2}O_2\ (g) \rightarrow 8CO_2(g) + 9H_2O\ (g)\ (unbalanced)$ $2 \times \left(C_8H_{18}\ (l) + 12\frac{1}{2}O_2\ (g) \rightarrow 8CO_2(g) + 9H_2O\ (g)\ (unbalanced) \right)$ Balanced Equation $2C_8H_{18}\ (l) + 25O_2\ (g) \rightarrow 16CO_2\ (g) + 18H_2O\ (g)$

3. Now, we use dimensional analysis to solve for grams and the number of molecules of products (CO_2 and H_2O):

Molar Mass of $C_8H_{18} = 114.26 \dfrac{g}{mol}$

Molar Mass of $CO_2 = 44.01 \dfrac{g}{mol}$

Molar Mass of $H_2O = 18.02 \dfrac{g}{mol}$

Stoichiometric ratio taken from the coefficients in the balanced chemical equation

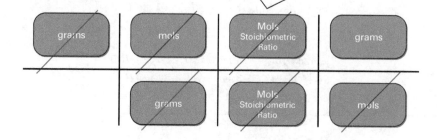

Carbon dioxide (grams):

$$542.1 \; g \; C_8H_{18} \times \frac{1 \; mol \; C_8H_{18}}{114.26 \; g \; C_8H_{18}} \times \frac{16 \; mol \; CO_2}{2 \; mol \; C_8H_{18}} \times \frac{44.01 \; g \; CO_2}{1 \; mol \; CO_2} = \mathbf{1.670 \times 10^3 \; g \; CO_2}$$

Water (grams):

$$542.1 \; g \; C_8H_{18} \times \frac{1 \; mol \; C_8H_{18}}{114.26 \; g \; C_8H_{18}} \times \frac{18 \; mol \; H_2O}{2 \; mol \; C_8H_{18}} \times \frac{18.02 \; g \; H_2O}{1 \; mol H_2O} = \mathbf{7.695 \times 10^2 \; g \; H_2O}$$

Stoichiometric ratio taken from the coefficients in the balanced chemical equation

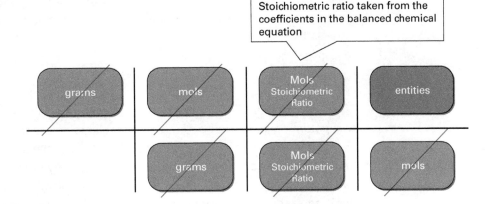

Carbon dioxide (molecules):

$$542.1 \; g \; C_8H_{18} \times \frac{1 \; mol \; C_8H_{18}}{114.26 \; g \; C_8H_{18}} \times \frac{16 \; mol \; CO_2}{2 \; mol \; C_8H_{18}} \times \frac{6.022 \times 10^{23} \; molecules \; of \; CO_2}{1 \; mol \; CO_2}$$

$$= \mathbf{2.286 \times 10^{25} \; molecules \; of \; CO_2}$$

Water (molecules):

$$542.1 \; g \; C_8H_{18} \times \frac{1 \; mol \; C_8H_{18}}{114.26 \; g \; C_8H_{18}} \times \frac{18 \; mol \; H_2O}{2 \; mol \; C_8H_{18}} \times \frac{6.022 \times 10^{23} \; molecules \; of \; H_2O}{1 \; mol H_2O}$$

$$= \mathbf{2.571 \times 10^{25} \; molecules \; of \; H_2O}$$

Notice that we have used complete combustion reactions in this section, but this can be done with any balanced chemical equation, which we will see in the next section. It is also probably a good idea to point out how cumulative the subject of chemistry is. Notice that in the last example, we have incorporated many topics in one question. Example Problems 4.15 and 4.16 dealt with balancing a chemical equation, calculating moles from mass using molar mass, stoichiometric ratios based on the balanced chemical equation, and then converting back to grams from moles again using molar mass, or, to number of molecules using Avogadro's number (Example Problem 4.16). Next, we explore how to predict the theoretical yield of products when faced with limited reactants, as well as calculating percent yield.

Limiting Reactant and Percent Yield

We used balanced chemical equations in order to predict how much product can be produced based on a certain amount of reactant. However, many times in chemistry we come across problems in which we are "limited" by a reactant, while having more than enough of another. In the previous example problems, notice that only a certain amount of one reactant (the hydrocarbon in the last section) is given, while we are to assume that we have more than enough of the other (O_2 in our combustion reactions). But what if that were not the case? In other words, what happens if you are given a certain amount of each reactant? For example, let us consider the following generic equation:

$$A + B \rightarrow C$$

If we are given a certain amount of "A" *and* a certain amount of "B," we will potentially run out of one of these reactants before the other. In other words, the reaction can only produce "C" until one of the reactants runs out, regardless of whether or not there is a large quantity of the other reactant left over. In such cases, the reactant that is depleted first is referred to as the **limiting reactant** (or **limiting reagent**), while those reactants left over are said to be in **excess** (or the **excess reactants**). In order to fully understand this concept, think about making salami sandwiches (Figure 4.3). If you were told that you have six slices of salami and 13 pieces of bread, and, knowing that, in order to prepare a sandwich, one slice of salami is required for every two pieces of bread, how many whole sandwiches can be made?

The answer is obviously six. Notice that it does not matter that I now have an extra slice of bread; it would just be left over and unused. The concept of limiting reactant is similar. Thus, in order to make accurate stoichiometric calculations, we must first determine which reactant "limits" us in how much product we can make. We can do this using balanced chemical equations as long as we know which reactant will be depleted first. Therefore, we calculate the number of moles of product that, in theory, could be produced from the given amount of each reactant in the balanced chemical equation. The *smallest* amount (moles) of product produced would then determine the limiting reactant. Additionally, this is the theoretical maximum obtainable yield of product, given the specific initial quantities of the reactants. This is referred to the **theoretical yield**. While this may sound confusing, think about our sandwich analogy. Six sandwiches can be made (smaller number) from six slices of salami, even though we have an extra piece of bread (you can think of this as $6\frac{1}{2}$ sandwiches from 13 slices of bread, assuming excess salami, but since six slices of salami will only produce six sandwiches we would never realize the extra $\frac{1}{2}$ sandwich). Because six sandwiches is smaller than $6\frac{1}{2}$, the salami "limits" us on

Figure 4.3 Using salami sandwiches as an analogy to help us understand the concept of limiting reactant. Only 6 whole salami sandwiches can be made from 6 slices of salami and 13 pieces of bread if 1 slice of salami is required for every 2 pieces of bread. Notice that we have 1 slice of bread in excess.

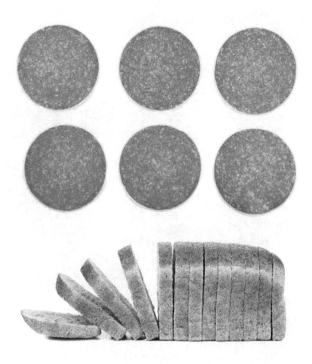

how many sandwiches we can make. Once we have identified the limiting reactant in these types of problems, we have at the same time determined the **theoretical yield** of the product using the calculations previously described. This brings us to another concept, *percent yield*. Following any reaction, we will often compare the theoretical yield to the amount of product actually isolated or **actual yield** (experimentally derived number). This allows us to calculate the **percent yield**, which is the actual yield divided by the theoretical yield and multiplied by 100 to give a percentage, as follows:

$$Percent\ Yield = \frac{Actual\ Yield}{Theoretical\ Yield} \times 100\%$$

The actual yield is always smaller than the theoretical yield as things generally do not go perfectly in chemistry. For example, there is always some loss of product along the way (i.e. human or experimental design error). Thus, the percent yield is essentially a measure of how well our experiments were performed. Let's say that we have completed our experiment(s) and hypothetically find that our product weighs 48 grams. If we had calculated a theoretical yield of 61 grams, we have the following:

$$Percent\ Yield = \frac{48\ grams}{61\ grams} \times 100\% = 79\%$$

Therefore, we can say, in this case, that our percent yield is 79%, which is really pretty good in chemistry.

Another calculation that we can make now involves determining how much excess reactant would be left over following the chemical reaction. Now that we know how many moles of product can theoretically be produced by using all of the limiting reactant, we then can use that number to calculate how many moles of the excess reactant are used up in the chemical reaction using the stoichiometric ratio between the two. We then simply subtract the number of moles (or grams) of excess reactant used from the number of moles (or grams) of excess reactant that we started with before the chemical reaction took place. Thus, we have:

mols of product theoretically produced
→ *mols of excess reactant used (using the stoichiometric ratio)*
→ *mols of excess reactant remaining (subtract mols of excess reactant used from initial mols of excess reactant)* →
grams of excess reactant remaining following the chemical reaction
(using the molar mass of the excess reactant).

This may seem complicated, so it may help to see exactly how this is done by reading through the following examples involving these types of calculations.

Neutralization reaction involving Phosphoric Acid and Sodium Hydroxide.

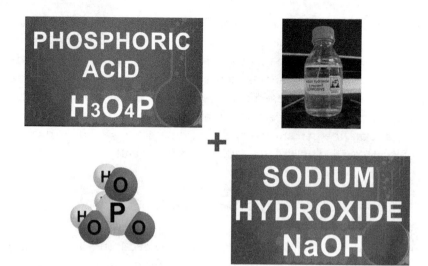

Example Problem 4.17

Phosphoric acid and sodium hydroxide react in an acid/base neutralization reaction according to the following unbalanced equation:

$$H_3PO_4 \ (aq) + NaOH \ (aq) \rightarrow Na_3PO_4 (aq) + H_2O \ (l) \ (unbalanced)$$

If we have 15.40 grams of phosphoric acid (H_3PO_4) and 17.80 grams of sodium hydroxide ($NaOH$), how much sodium phosphate (Na_3PO_4) can be produced? What is the limiting and excess reactant? What is the percent yield if we have an experimentally determined mass of 19.12 grams of Na_3PO_4 produced? How much of the excess reactant remains following the chemical reaction?

Solution:

1. First, we balance the chemical equation as previously described. Notice that a three coefficient is required in front of *NaOH* on the left (reactants) to balance the three sodium atoms on the right (products). Also, a three coefficient is required in front of H_2O on the right (products) in order to balance a total of six hydrogen atoms in the reactant.

$$H_3PO_4 (aq) + 3NaOH \ (aq) \rightarrow Na_3PO_4 \ (aq) + 3H_2O \ (l)$$

2. Next, calculate the number of moles of Na_3PO_4 that would be produced if we were to hypothetically use up all of our phosphoric acid (H_3PO_4).

$$H_3PO_4 \ (aq) + 3NaOH \ (aq) \rightarrow Na_3PO_4 \ (aq) + 3H_2O \ (l)$$

Stoichiometric ratio taken from the coefficients in the balanced chemical equation

| grams | mols | Mols Stoichiometric Ratio |
| grams | Mols Stoichiometric Ratio |

$$15.40 \ g \ H_3PO_4 \times \frac{1 \ mol \ H_3PO_4}{98.00 \ g \ H_3PO_4} \times \frac{1 \ mol \ Na_3PO_4}{1 \ mol \ H_3PO_4} = 0.15714286 \ mols \ Na_3PO_4$$

3. Now calculate the number of moles of Na_3PO_4 that would be produced if we were to hypothetically use up all of our sodium hydroxide ($NaOH$).

$$H_3PO_4 \ (aq) + 3NaOH \ (aq) \rightarrow Na_3PO_4 \ (aq) + 3H_2O \ (l)$$

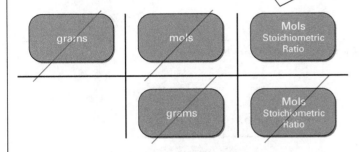

Stoichiometric ratio taken from the coefficients in the balanced chemical equation

$$17.80 \ g \ NaOH \times \frac{1 \ mol \ NaOH}{40.00 \ g \ NaOH} \times \frac{1 \ mol \ Na_3PO_4}{3 \ mol \ NaOH} = 0.14833333 \ mols \ Na_3PO_4$$

4. Since 0.1483 moles is a smaller number than 0.1571 moles, sodium hydroxide is our limiting reactant as we will run out of this reactant first, making phosphoric acid our excess reactant. Therefore, we use the smaller number (0.1483) to determine the theoretical yield of our product of interest (Na_3PO_4).

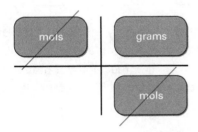

$$0.14833333 \ mols \ Na_3PO_4 \times \frac{163.94 \ g \ Na_3PO_4}{1 \ mol \ Na_3PO_4} = \textbf{24.32} \ \textbf{\textit{g}} \ \textbf{\textit{Na}}_\textbf{3}\textbf{\textit{PO}}_\textbf{4} \ \textbf{\textit{produced}}$$

5. If 24.32 g of Na_3PO_4 is our theoretical yield, and 19.12 g of Na_3PO_4 is our actual yield (given information in the question), we can now figure out our percent yield.	$\dfrac{19.12 \ g \ Na_3PO_4}{24.32 \ g \ Na_3PO_4} \times 100\% =$ $= \textbf{78.62\% \textit{yield}}$
6. ***Determining how much of the excess reactant remains following the chemical reaction.*** We have used all of our limiting reactant ($NaOH$) to produce 0.1483 moles of product (Na_3PO_4). Thus, we can now use this number to determine how many moles of the excess reactant (H_3PO_4) was consumed in the reaction for the formation of 0.1483 moles of Na_3PO_4.	$0.1483 \ mols \ Na_3PO_4 \times \dfrac{1 \ mol \ H_3PO_4}{1 \ mol \ Na_3PO_4}$ $= \textbf{0.1483} \ \textbf{\textit{mols}} \ \textbf{\textit{H}}_\textbf{3}\textbf{\textit{PO}}_\textbf{4} \ \textbf{\textit{consumed}}$

7.	Now, calculate the number of moles of H_3PO_4 that we started with.	$15.40 \ g \ H_3PO_4 \times \dfrac{1 \ mol \ H_3PO_4}{98.00 \ g \ H_3PO_4}$ $= \textbf{0.1571} \ \textbf{\textit{mols}} \ \textbf{\textit{H}}_3\textbf{\textit{PO}}_4$
8.	We can now subtract the number of moles consumed (0.1483 moles H_3PO_4) from the number of moles that we started with (0.1571 moles H_3PO_4).	$0.1571 \ mols \ H_3PO_4 \ (before \ reaction) -$ $0.1483 \ mols \ H_3PO_4 \ (consumed) =$ $\textbf{0.0088} \ mols \ H_3PO_4 \ remaining$

Or, if we wish to express this as a mass in grams:

$$0.0088 \ mols \ H_3PO_4 \times \dfrac{98.00 \ g \ H_3PO_4}{1 \ mol \ H_3PO_4} = \textbf{0.86} \ \textbf{\textit{g}} \ \textbf{\textit{H}}_3\textbf{\textit{PO}}_4 \ \textbf{\textit{remaining}}$$

following the chemical reaction.

As mentioned earlier, chemistry is a very cumulative subject. In this next example, let's practice balancing another chemical equation followed by determination of the limiting reactant and theoretical yield, except this time we will also practice writing chemical formulas from their respective chemical names as discussed in Chapter 3.

Silver Sulfide (Ag_2S).

Example Problem 4.18

Aqueous silver nitrate reacts with aqueous sodium sulfide to produce solid silver sulfide and aqueous sodium nitrate. What is the balanced equation for this chemical reaction? Also, if we have 47.28 grams of silver nitrate and 12.37 grams of sodium sulfide, how much silver sulfide can be produced? What are the limiting and excess reactants? What is the percent yield if we have an experimentally derived value of 29.21 grams of silver sulfide produced? How much of the excess reactant remains following the chemical reaction?
Solution:
1.   First, we must write out the unbalanced chemical equation based on the given information in the question (it might be necessary to review Chapter 3 if you are unsure about deriving the formulas from the given chemical names). $AgNO_3 \ (aq) + Na_2S \ (aq) \rightarrow Ag_2S \ (s) + NaNO_3 \ (aq) \ (unbalanced)$

2. Next, we balance the chemical equation just as previously described. Notice that we have two silver atoms on the right (products) and only one on the left (reactants). Therefore, we put a two coefficient in front of $AgNO_3$ on the left (reactants). We also notice that we have two sodium atoms on the left (reactants) and only one on the right (products). Thus, we put a two coefficient in front of $NaNO_3$ on the right (products).

$$2AgNO_3 \ (aq) + Na_2S \ (aq) \rightarrow Ag_2S \ (s) + 2NaNO_3 \ (aq)$$

3. Next, calculate the number of moles of Ag_2S that would be produced if we were to hypothetically use up all of our silver nitrate ($AgNO_3$).

$$2AgNO_3 \ (aq) + Na_2S \ (aq) \rightarrow Ag_2S \ (s) + 2NaNO_3 \ (aq)$$

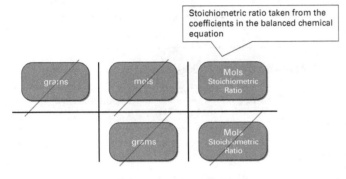

Stoichiometric ratio taken from the coefficients in the balanced chemical equation

$$47.28 \ g \ AgNO_3 \times \frac{1 \ mol \ AgNO_3}{169.88 \ g \ AgNO_3} \times \frac{1 \ mol \ Ag_2S}{2 \ mols \ AgNO_3} = 0.13915705 \ mols \ Ag_2S$$

4. We now calculate the number of moles of Ag_2S that would be produced if we were to hypothetically use up all of our sodium sulfide (Na_2S).

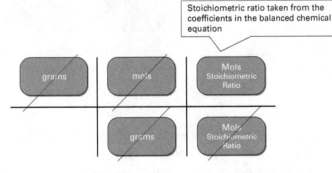

Stoichiometric ratio taken from the coefficients in the balanced chemical equation

$$2AgNO_3 \ (aq) + Na_2S \ (aq) \rightarrow Ag_2S \ (s) + 2NaNO_3 \ (aq)$$

$$12.37 \ g \ Na_2S \times \frac{1 \ mol \ Na_2S}{78.05 \ g \ Na_2S} \times \frac{1 \ mol \ Ag_2S}{1 \ mol \ Na_2S} = 0.15848815 \ mols \ Ag_2S$$

5. Since 0.1392 moles is a smaller number than 0.1585 moles, silver nitrate is our limiting reactant (this reactant will be depleted first), making sodium sulfide our excess reactant. Thus, we use the smaller number (0.1392 moles) to determine the theoretical yield of our product of interest (Ag_2S).

$$0.13915705 \ mols \ Ag_2S \times \frac{247.81 \ g \ Ag_2S}{1 \ mol \ Ag_2S} = \mathbf{34.48 \ g \ Ag_2S}$$

6. Since 34.48 g of Ag_2S is our theoretical yield and 29.21 g of Ag_2S is our actual yield (given information in the question), we can now calculate the percent yield.

$$\frac{29.21\ g\ Ag_2S}{34.48\ g\ Ag_2S} \times 100 = \textbf{84.72\% yield}$$

7. ***Determining how much of the excess reactant remains following the chemical reaction.***

   We now know that we have used all of our limiting reactant ($AgNO_3$) to produce 0.1392 moles of product (Ag_2S). Thus, we can now use this number to determine how many moles of the excess reactant (Na_2S) was consumed in the reaction for the formation of 0.1392 moles of Ag_2S.

   $$0.1392\ mols\ Ag_2S \times \frac{1\ mol\ Na_2S}{1\ mol\ Ag_2S} = \textbf{0.1392 mols Na}_2\textbf{S consumed}$$

8. Calculate the number of moles of Na_2S that we started with.

   $$12.37\ g\ Na_2S \times \frac{1\ mol\ Na_2S}{78.05\ g\ Na_2S} = \textbf{0.1585 mols Na}_2\textbf{S}$$

9. We can now subtract the number of moles consumed (0.1392 moles Na_2S) from the number of moles that we started with (0.1585 moles Na_2S).

   0.1585 *mols Na_2S (before reaction)* − 0.1392 *mols Na_2S (consumed)* = **0.0193** *mols Na_2S remaining*

   Or, if we want to express this in grams:

   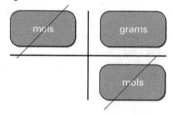

   $$0.0193\ mols\ Na_2S \times \frac{78.05\ g\ Na_2S}{1\ mol\ Na_2S} = \textbf{1.506 g Na}_2\textbf{S remaining following}$$

Notice that using a balanced equation and the appropriate molar stoichiometric ratio, we can relate chemical quantities between a reactant to another reactant, a reactant to any of the products, products to each other, and products back to reactants (Figure 4.4).

Figure 4.4 Using a balanced equation and the appropriate molar stoichiometric ratios, we can relate chemical quantities between a reactant to another reactant, a reactant to any of the products, products to each other and products back to reactants.

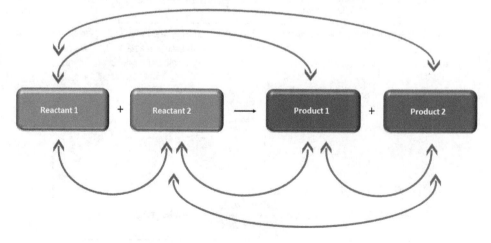

Did you know how chemistry might relate to your job as a non-chemist? We can now see how useful, quantitative data can be obtained from balanced chemical equations using stoichiometric ratios. This is very important in industry for companies producing a valuable product. It is not too difficult to imagine that companies want to know how much product they can produce, given certain investments of capital and other resources, as well as how they can improve efficiency if faced with relatively low percent yields in order to maximize their profits. For example, silver sulfide was the product in the last example problem. This compound is known to be useful as a photosensitizer in photography. This is just one example of useful commercial compounds that are produced every day through chemical processes. We will soon see that these stoichiometric ratios derived from balanced chemical equations are extremely useful to us in subsequent chapters throughout our studies in chemistry, including the next chapter on Solutions and Solution Stoichiometry.

Companies producing a valuable product are very much interested in knowing how much product they can produce, as well as how they can improve efficiency in order to maximize their profits.

Silver sulfide is known to be useful as a photosensitizer in photography.

Key Terms

1. Actual yield
2. Avogadro's Number
3. Carbon skeleton formulas
4. Chemical equations
5. Combustion reactions
6. Condensed structural formulas
7. Empirical formulas
8. Excess reactant (Reagent)
9. Limiting reactant (Reagent)
10. Mass percent
11. Molar mass
12. Mole (mol)
13. Molecular formula

14. Percent yield

15. Space-filling models

16. Stoichiometric ratios

17. Stoichiometry

18. Structural formulas

19. Theoretical yield

Problems

MOLAR MASS

1. What is molar mass?

2. Determine the molar mass of each of the following elements:

    a. sulfur

    b. zinc

    c. oxygen

    d. strontium

3. Determine the molar mass of each of the following elements:

    a. bromine

    b. fluorine

    c. iron

    d. barium

4. How many carbon, hydrogen, and oxygen atoms are in C_4H_9OH?

5. How many aluminum, oxygen, and hydrogen atoms are in $Al(OH)_3$?

6. Determine the molar mass of each of the following:

    a. Cu_2S

    b. CO

    c. Fe_2O_3

    d. C_6H_6

7. Determine the molar mass of each of the following:

    a. H_2O

    b. CO_2

    c. Na_2SO_4

    d. $Al(OH)_3$

MOLAR MASS AND AVOGADRO'S NUMBER AS
CONVERSION FACTORS

8. What is Avogadro's number?

9. How do we calculate the number of moles of particular substance if given the number of grams?

10. How do we calculate the number of grams of particular substance if given the number of moles?

11. How do we calculate the number of entities of particular substance if given the number of moles?

12. How do we calculate the number of moles of particular substance if given the number of entities?

13. How many moles are in 11.89 g of $NaNO_3$?

14. How many moles are in 23.38 g of Na_2SO_4?

15. How many moles are in 5.48 g of C_6H_6?

16. What is the mass of 1.743 moles of Fe_3O_4?

17. What is the mass of 0.9368 moles of Cu_2S?

18. What is the mass of 0.1639 moles of $CuSO_4$?

19. How many SF_6 molecules are in 1.35 moles of SF_6?

20. How many C_3H_8 molecules are in 0.9832 moles of C_3H_8?

21. How many C_5H_{12} molecules are in 4.295 moles of C_5H_{12}?

22. How many moles of boron trifluoride is equivalent to 3.285×10^{24} molecules of boron trifluoride?

23. How many moles of nitrogen monoxide is equivalent to 7.93×10^{25} molecules of nitrogen monoxide?

24. How many moles of C_6H_{14} is equivalent to 9.84×10^{17} molecules of C_6H_{14}?

25. How many octane (C_8H_{18}) molecules are in 12.72 kg of octane?

26. Ethylene glycol is commonly used in antifreeze mixtures. What is the mass (kg) of 4.28×10^{25} molecules of ethylene glycol $(C_2H_6O_2)$?

PERCENT COMPOSITION

27. What is percent composition and how is it calculated?

28. What is the mass percent of carbon in each of the following hydrocarbons?

    a. CH_4

    b. C_2H_6

    c. C_3H_8

    d. C_4H_{10}

29. What is the mass percent of Cl in $C_2Cl_4F_2$?

30. What is the mass percent of Br in $SnBr_2Cl_2$?

31. What is the mass percent of O in $Al_2(SO_4)_3$?

32. Calculate the mass percent of each element in HNO_3.

33. Caffeine ($C_8H_{10}N_4O_2$) is a central nervous system stimulant and is currently one of the world's most widely consumed drugs. Calculate the mass percent of each element in caffeine.

34. What is the mass of lead in 20.0 grams of PbS?

35. What is the mass of copper in 10.0 grams of CuS?

36. If you want to obtain 15.0 grams of iron from iron(III) oxide, what mass of iron(III) oxide must you use?

DETERMINING EMPIRICAL AND MOLECULAR FORMULAS

37. What does an empirical formula tell us?

38. What does a molecular formula tell us?

39. Based on what you know about empirical and molecular formulas, fill in the missing spaces in the chart below.

Empirical Formula	Molecular Formula	Molar Mass (g/mol)
	C_8H_{18}	
	C_3H_8	44.11
	C_2H_6	
C_5H_{11}		142.32

40. Based on what you know about empirical and molecular formulas, fill in the missing spaces in the chart below.

Empirical Formula	Molecular Formula	Molar Mass (g/mol)
	C_5H_{12}	72.17
C_3H_7		86.20
	C_4H_{10}	
C_7H_{16}		100.23

41. The empirical formula for succinic acid is $C_2H_3O_2$. Knowing that succinic acid has a molar mass of 118.10 g/mol, what is its molecular formula?

42. The empirical formula for glucose is CH_2O. Knowing that glucose has a molar mass of 180.18 g/mol, what is its molecular formula?

43. The pseudoformula for malic acid is $CH_{1.5}O_{1.25}$. What is the empirical formula for malic acid? Knowing that malic acid has a molar mass of 134.10 g/mol, what is its molecular formula?

44. Nicotine is a highly addictive stimulant drug that can be found in the tobacco plant *Nicotiana tabacum* and is commonly used in cigarettes. It is 74.1% carbon, 8.60% hydrogen, and 17.3% nitrogen, and has a molar mass of 162.26 *g/mol*. What are the empirical and molecular formulas of nicotine?

45. Warfarin is an anticoagulant drug that can be given to patients in order to prevent blood clots in veins or arteries. This can have the effect of reducing the risk of stroke, heart attack, or other serious medical conditions. Warfarin is known to be 74.0% carbon, 5.24% hydrogen, and 20.7% oxygen, and has a molar mass of 308.35 *g/mol*. What are the empirical and molecular formulas of Warfarin?

46. Most of us have visited the dentist to get work done on our teeth and have been treated with the local anesthetic Novocain. Novocain is 66.1% carbon, 8.55% hydrogen, 11.9% nitrogen, and 13.5% oxygen, and has a molar mass of 236.35 *g/mol*. What are the empirical and molecular formulas of Novocain?

BALANCING CHEMICAL EQUATIONS

47. Why is a balanced chemical equation important?

48. In a chemical equation, the notation "(l)" means that the substance is a _____.

49. In a chemical equation, the notation "(aq)" means that the substance is _____.

50. In a chemical equation, the notation "(s)" means that the substance is a _____.

51. In a chemical equation, the notation "(g)" means that the substance is a _____.

52. When $N_2(g)$ reacts with $H_2(g)$, it produces ammonia, $NH_3(g)$. Write a balanced equation for this reaction.

53. When solid aluminum chloride reacts with liquid water, it produces solid aluminum hydroxide and aqueous hydrochloric acid (HCl). Write a balanced chemical equation for this reaction.

54. The complete combustion of gaseous methane (CH_4) in the presence of oxygen produces carbon dioxide gas and water vapor. Write a balanced chemical equation for this reaction.

55. When solid nickel(II) carbonate reacts with aqueous nitric acid (HNO_3), it produces aqueous nickel(II) nitrate, carbon dioxide gas, and liquid water. Write a balanced chemical equation for this reaction.

56. During alcohol production, aqueous ethyl alcohol (C_2H_5OH) is formed along with gaseous carbon dioxide when solid sucrose ($C_{12}H_{22}O_{11}$) undergoes fermentation by yeasts in the presence of liquid water. Write a balanced chemical equation for this reaction.

USING BALANCED CHEMICAL EQUATIONS TO CALCULATE QUANTITIES OF REACTANTS AND PRODUCTS

57. From the balanced chemical equation in question #52, what is the stoichiometric ratio between N_2 and H_2?

58. From the balanced chemical equation in question #52, what is the stoichiometric ratio between N_2 and NH_3?

59. From the balanced chemical equation in question #52, what is the stoichiometric ratio between H_2 and NH_3?

60. Consider the following balanced chemical equation:

$$H_2\ (g) + Cl_2\ (g) \rightarrow 2HCl\ (g)$$

   a. How much *HCl* (moles) can be produced from 0.136 moles of H_2 (assume excess of Cl_2)?

   b. How much Cl_2 (moles) is required to completely react with 0.827 moles of H_2?

   c. How much *HCl* (grams) can be produced from 5.85 grams of H_2 (assume excess of Cl_2)?

   d. How much Cl_2 (grams) is required to completely react with 2.42 grams of H_2?

61. Aqueous cobalt(III) nitrate reacts with aqueous ammonium sulfide to produce solid cobalt(III) sulfide and aqueous ammonium nitrate.

   a. How much cobalt(III) sulfide (moles) can be produced from 2.94 moles of cobalt(III) nitrate (assume excess of ammonium sulfide)?

   b. How much ammonium sulfide (moles) is required to completely react with 0.941 moles of cobalt(III) nitrate?

   c. How much cobalt(III) sulfide (grams) can be produced from 3.76 grams of cobalt(III) nitrate (assume excess of ammonium sulfide)?

   d. How much ammonium sulfide (grams) is required to completely react with 7.92 grams of cobalt(III) nitrate?

LIMITING REACTANT AND PERCENT YIELD

62. What is the limiting reactant and why does the reaction stop once this particular reactant has been consumed?

63. What is the excess reactant?

64. How do we calculate percent yield?

65. Given that you have 8.00 grams of each reactant in the balanced chemical equations below, which one is the limiting reactant and how much product of interest (in **BOLD**) is

produced (moles) assuming the limiting reactant is completely consumed?

a. Fe_2O_3 (s) $+ 3CO$ (g) $\rightarrow$ **2Fe (s)** $+ 3CO_2$ (g)

b. $4HCl$ (aq) $+ O_2$ (g) $\rightarrow 2H_2O$ (l) $+$ **2Cl$_2$ (g)**

c. $2NaOH$ (aq) $+ CO_2$ (g) $\rightarrow$ **Na$_2$CO$_3$ (aq)** $+ H_2O$ (l)

d. C_3H_8 (g) $+ 5O_2$ (g) $\rightarrow$ **3CO$_2$ (g)** $+ 4H_2O$ (g)

66. Given that you have 8.00 grams of each reactant in the balanced chemical equations below, which one is the limiting reactant and how much product of interest (in **BOLD**) is produced (moles) assuming the limiting reactant is completely consumed?

a. $Ca(OH)_2$ (aq) $+ 2HBr$ (aq) $\rightarrow$ **CaBr$_2$(aq)** $+ 2H_2O$ (l)

b. SiO_2 (s) $+ 2C$ (s) $\rightarrow$ **Si (s)** $+ 2CO$ (g)

c. Na_2S (aq) $+ Cu(NO_3)_2$ (aq) $\rightarrow 2NaNO_3$(aq) $+$ **CuS (s)**

d. CH_4 (g) $+ H_2O$ (g) $\rightarrow CO$ (g) $+$ **3H$_2$ (g)**

67. Based on your answers from question #65, predict how much product of interest (in **BOLD**) is produced in grams (assuming that all of the limiting reactant is consumed).

a. What is the mass of **Fe** produced (grams) in this chemical reaction?

b. What is the mass of **Cl$_2$** produced (grams) in this chemical reaction?

c. What is the mass of **Na$_2$CO$_3$** produced (grams) in this chemical reaction?

d. What is the mass of **CO$_2$** produced (grams) in this chemical reaction?

68 Based on your answers from question #66, predict how much product of interest (in **BOLD**) is produced in grams (assuming that all of the limiting reactant is consumed).

a. What is the mass of **CaBr$_2$** produced (grams) in this chemical reaction?

b. What is the mass of **Si** produced (grams) in this chemical reaction?

c. What is the mass of **CuS** produced (grams) in this chemical reaction?

d. What is the mass of **H$_2$** produced (grams) in this chemical reaction?

69. Sodium fluoride is a common additive to toothpaste and is known to help improve dental health by strengthening the enamel on the surface of teeth, as well as preventing the formation of cavities. The chemical synthesis of sodium fluoride is illustrated below in the following balanced chemical equation:

$$2Na \ (s) + F_2 \ (g) \rightarrow 2NaF \ (s)$$

If 15.5 grams of both sodium and fluorine are used, how much sodium fluoride can be produced? What is the limiting and excess reactant? What is the percent yield if we have an experimentally derived actual yield of 23.4 grams of sodium fluoride produced?

70. Scrap aluminum can be treated with chlorine gas to yield aluminum chloride according to the following balanced chemical equation:

$$2Al\ (s) + 3Cl_2\ (g) \rightarrow 2AlCl_3\ (s)$$

If 13.2 grams of scrap aluminum and 16.3 grams of chlorine gas are combined in the reaction, how much aluminum chloride can be produced (grams)? What is the limiting and excess reactant? What is the percent yield if we have an experimentally derived actual yield of 16.2 grams of iron metal produced?

71. Consider the reaction between iron(III) oxide and carbon monoxide according to the following balanced chemical equation:

$$Fe_2O_3\ (s) + 3CO\ (g) \rightarrow 2Fe\ (s) + 3CO_2\ (g)$$

If 45.1 grams of iron(III) oxide and 19.3 grams of carbon monoxide are combined in the reaction, how much iron metal can be produced (grams)? What is the limiting and excess reactant? What is the percent yield if we have an experimentally derived actual yield of 19.8 grams of iron metal produced?

72. Aspirin ($C_9H_8O_4$) is a medication that can be taken in order to manage pain, fever, and inflammation. It can be produced by the reaction of salicylic acid and acetic anhydride as depicted in the following balanced chemical equation:

$$C_7H_6O_3\ (s) + C_4H_6O_3\ (l) \rightarrow C_9H_8O_4\ (s) + CH_3CO_2H\ (l)$$

If 20.0 grams of both salicylic acid and acetic anhydride are used to produce aspirin, how much aspirin can be produced (grams)? What is the limiting and excess reactant? What is the percent yield if we have an experimentally derived actual yield of 19.4 grams of aspirin produced?

73. From the given information in question #69, how much (grams) of the excess reactant remains following the chemical reaction (assume complete consumption of the limiting reactant)?

74. From the given information in question #70, how much (grams) of the excess reactant remains following the chemical reaction (assume complete consumption of the limiting reactant)?

75. From the given information in question #71, how much (grams) of the excess reactant remains following the chemical reaction (assume complete consumption of the limiting reactant)?

76. From the given information in question #72, how much (grams) of the excess reactant remains following the chemical reaction (assume complete consumption of the limiting reactant)?

Image Credits

- Fig. 4.Aa: Copyright © Depositphotos/urfingus.
- Fig. 4.Ab: Copyright © Depositphotos/agsandrew.
- Fig. 4.B: Source: https://commons.wikimedia.org/wiki/File:Amadeo_Avogadro.png.
- Fig. 4.C: Source: https://commons.wikimedia.org/wiki/File:Jean_Perrin_1908.jpg.
- Fig. 4.D: Source: https://commons.wikimedia.org/wiki/File:Wilhelm_Ostwald.jpg.
- Fig. 4.E: Copyright © Depositphotos/merc67.
- Fig. 4.1: Copyright © Depositphotos/Juliedeshaies.
- Fig. 4.F: Copyright © Depositphotos/IconicBestiary.
- Fig. 4.Ga: Copyright © by Depositphotos/tonodiaz.
- Fig. 4.Gb: Copyright © by Depositphotos/tolokonov.
- Table 4.3a: Source: https://commons.wikimedia.org/wiki/File:Ethane-3D-space-filling.png.
- Table 4.3b: Source: https://commons.wikimedia.org/wiki/File:Propane-3D-space-filling.png.
- "Table 4.3c: Source: https://commons.wikimedia.org/wiki/File:Butane-3D-space-filling.png."
- Table 4.3d: Source: https://commons.wikimedia.org/wiki/File:Pentane_3D_spacefill.png.
- Table 4.3e: Source: https://commons.wikimedia.org/wiki/File:Hexane_3D_spacefill.png.
- "Table 4.3f: Source: https://commons.wikimedia.org/wiki/File:Heptane_3D_spacefill.png."
- "Table 4.3g: Source: https://commons.wikimedia.org/wiki/File:Octane_3D_spacefill.png."
- Fig. 4.H: Source: https://commons.wikimedia.org/wiki/File:D-glucose-chain-3D-balls.png.
- Table 4.4: Source: https://commons.wikimedia.org/wiki/File:D-glucose-chain-3D-vdW.png.
- Fig. 4.Ia: Copyright © Depositphotos/Alan.
- Fig. 4.Ib: Copyright © Depositphotos/vladvitek.
- Fig. 4.Ic: Copyright © Depositphotos/vencav.
- Fig. 4.Ja: Copyright © Depositphotos/bellafotosolo.
- Fig. 4.Jb: Copyright © Depositphotos/urfingus.
- Fig. 4.K: Copyright © Depositphotos/OlesyaKuzina.
- Fig. 4.La: Copyright © Depositphotos/marrakeshh.
- Fig. 4.Lb: Copyright © Depositphotos/Syda_Productions.
- Fig. 4.3a: Copyright © Depositphotos/belchonock.
- Fig. 4.3b: Copyright © Depositphotos/indigolotos.
- Fig. 4.Ma: Copyright © Depositphotos/designer491.
- Fig. 4.Mb: Copyright © Depositphotos/olla.davies.
- Fig. 4.Mc: Copyright © Depositphotos/designer491.

Dissolution and Reactions in Aqueous Solution

LEARNING OBJECTIVES AND OUTCOMES

After reading this Chapter, you should be able to do the following:

- Explain the polarity of water.

- Define the components of a solution.

- Identify strong and weak electrolytes.

- Predict the solubility of ionic compounds in water.

- Write balanced molecular, complete ionic, and net ionic equations.

- Explain and predict precipitation reactions.

- Explain and predict gas evolving reactions.

- Define solution concentration.

- Calculate solution concentrations in units of molarity, molality, mole fraction, and mass percent.

- Explain colligative properties.

- Calculate vapor pressures, freezing points, and boiling points of solutions.

- Explain the concept of osmosis and calculate the osmotic pressure of a solution.

- Define each of the Key Terms listed at the end of this chapter dealing with these concepts.

Section 5.1 Introduction

Approximately 70% of the Earth's surface is covered by water. This water comprises all of the rivers, streams, ponds, lakes, and oceans with which you are familiar. In fact, oceans account for approximately 95% of all the water on the planet. Further, sea water contains large amounts of dissolved compounds, including ions of nearly every naturally occurring element. The most abundant of these are sodium and chloride, which is the reason for

Water comprises over 70% of the Earth's surface and is essential to the ecology and every living organism.

Composition of the Human Body

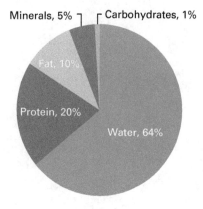

The human body is 64% water by mass.

the "saltiness" of sea water. Moreover, biological organisms are comprised principally of water. Indeed, the human body is 2/3 water by mass. As such, biological processes can generally be considered as the result of multiple series of chemical reactions, all of which occur entirely dissolved in **aqueous solution**. To understand this term more clearly, let's define what is meant by the term *solution*. A **solution** is a *homogeneous* mixture of two or more substances. The substance which is present in greater quantity is referred to as the **solvent,** while the lesser component is the **solute**. The term **aqueous solution,** therefore, refers to a mixture in which water acts as the *solvent*. Given the ubiquity of water and its importance to the various ecological and biological processes that make life on our planet possible, it should not be surprising to learn that many of the reactions we study in the laboratory occur in aqueous solution. To adequately understand and describe such reactions, it is important for us to understand something about how compounds behave when dissolved in solution. The current chapter, therefore, will focus on solutions (particularly aqueous solutions), properties of solutions, and the chemical processes which take place in solution.

Section 5.2 Water—A Polar Molecule

To appropriately understand the power of water as a solvent, we should first consider the nature of the water molecule. At the molecular level, water's ability to act as a solvent arises from the uneven distribution of the electrons over the atoms which make up the water molecule (Figure 5.1). Recall from Chapter 3, we learned that covalent ("molecular") compounds arise from the sharing of electrons between two atoms. When this occurs between two identical atoms, such as the two chlorine atoms in the elemental chlorine molecule Cl_2, the "bonding" electrons are shared evenly between the two bonding atoms. However, when two bonding atoms are of different elements, each will exert a different pull, or attraction, on the bonding electrons. In such instances, the electrons spend more time around one atom over the other. This will be covered in much greater detail in Chapters 8 and 9. In the case of each of the $O-H$ bonds in a water molecule (see Figure 5.1), the O atom exerts a greater pull on the bonding electrons than does the H atom. This results in a partial negative charge located around the oxygen atom and a partial positive charge centered on the hydrogen atom (Figure 5.1(a.)). Notice this is represented using the symbols δ^+ and δ^-, which indicate partial positive and negative charges, respectively. When a bond exhibits this kind of uneven charge distribution, it is referred to as a **polar bond**. The term "polar" arises from two opposite charges separated by a distance, a circumstance which is referred to as an **electric dipole**.

The combination of this electric dipole which results from each of the $O-H$ bonds, in addition to the bent shape of the water molecule, results in a **polar molecule**. A polar molecule is a compound which contains one or more polar bonds such that the net result is a molecular electric dipole

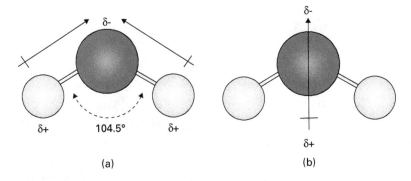

(a)   (b)

Figure 5.1 (a) Anytime two different elements engage in covalent bonding, the bonding electrons will be polarized to which ever atom has the greatest attraction for electrons. This results in a partial charge separation as shown here for the two $O-H$ bonds in a water molecule (b). If there are more than one polar bond in a molecule, these can sum together to form a net molecular dipole.

as shown in Figure 5.1(b). Here we see the additive result of the two polar bonds is a dipole oriented such that the partially negative pole is near the oxygen atom, and the partially positive pole is between the two hydrogen atoms. It is this "polar" nature of water that will be the basis for its behavior as a solvent.

Section 5.3 Aqueous Solutions of Ionic Compounds

In Chapter 3 we also learned that ionic compounds are composed of metals and nonmetals. Additionally, we know that ionic bonds are formed due to the electrostatic attractions between oppositely charged ions. When ionic compounds are dissolved in water, the electric dipole of the water molecule can interact *electrostatically* with the ions in the compound. For instance, the positive pole of the water molecules will be attracted to the negatively charged chloride ions when sodium chloride (table salt) is dissolved in water. Likewise, the negative poles of water molecules will have a similarly favorable attraction to the positively charged sodium ions. When the collective attraction between an ion in a solid compound and multiple water molecules is more favorable than the electrostatic attraction between the cations and anions that compose the compound, the ions will **dissociate**—break away from the solid compound and move into the aqueous phase as "freely *solvated* ions" (see Figure 5.2). The term **solvated** refers to the fact that the newly "freed" ions are surrounded by multiple water molecules, collectively referred to as a "**solvation sphere.**" Water molecules engaged in the solvation of such ions are oriented such that their positive poles are directed toward anions and vice versa (see Figure 5.2).

Figure 5.2 Ionic compounds dissolve in water by dissociation into the individual constituent ions which make up the compound. These ions enter the solution phase as a consequence of favorable interactions with polar water molecules. These water molecules form a solvation sphere around each dissociated ion through favorable electrostatic interactions.

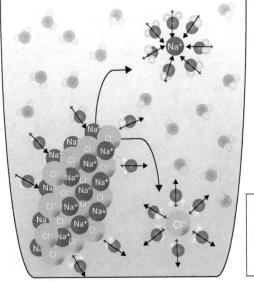

Electric Conductivity and Electrolytes

Ions which are surrounded by a solvation sphere of water molecules are now free to move about, and as such, they randomly disperse into solution. However, when two electrodes are introduced into the solution and an electric current is applied, cations migrate to the negative electrode, and anions migrate to the positive electrode. It is in this way that the ions are able to conduct charge (electric current) through the solution. In other words, the ions are mobile charge carriers and are able to conduct electricity through a solution in the same way that electrons conduct current through a metal wire. Compounds which, when dissolved in water, form solutions that will conduct electricity are referred to as **electrolytes**. Because of the mechanism by which ionic compounds dissociate into mobile, solvated ions in solution, all ionic compounds which are soluble in water are strong *electrolytes*.

Solvated ions will conduct electricity through aqueous media.

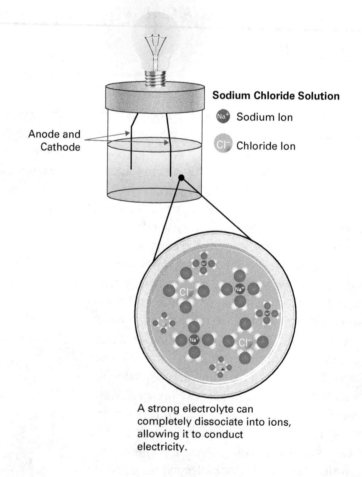

Sodium Chloride Solution

Na⁺ Sodium Ion

Cl⁻ Chloride Ion

Anode and Cathode

A strong electrolyte can completely dissociate into ions, allowing it to conduct electricity.

Calculating Moles of Ions in Solution

As we have already learned, chemical formulas can be used as conversion factors relating moles of constituent ions (or atoms) to moles of the parent compound. In the same fashion, we can use the formula of the "undissolved compound" to determine the amount of each type of ion which is, or will be, present in solution once the compound has been dissolved. Let's consider the dissolution of magnesium chloride in water for example. We can represent this with the following equation:

$$MgCl_2\,(s) \rightarrow Mg^{2+}(aq) + 2\,Cl^-(aq)$$

Notice that the subscripts in the formula of the "undissolved" solid magnesium chloride become coefficients for the individual "solvated" ions in solution. In this way, we understand that the dissolution of one mole of $MgCl_2$ yields one mole of Mg^{2+} ions and two moles Cl^- ions in the resulting solution. Understanding these numeric relationships, it is possible to calculate the number of moles of various solvated ions in solution through stoichiometric conversions. Let's consider another example to illustrate how this can be done. Suppose we dissolve 12.00 g of potassium sulfate in a quantity of water. How many moles of potassium ion will be present in solution (assuming this compound is completely soluble)? We can answer this question first by writing the balanced equation for the dissolution of K_2SO_4 in water, as shown:

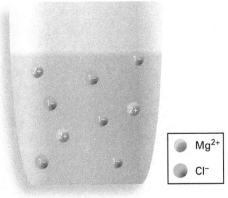

When $MgCl_2$ is dissolved the resulting solution contains 2 solvated chloride ions for every 1 magnesium ion.

$$K_2SO_4(s) \rightarrow 2\,K^+(aq) + SO_4^{2-}(aq)$$

Now we can easily convert our given data, 12.00 g K_2SO_4, into the equivalent quantity expressed as moles of $K^+(aq)$ using the stoichiometric relationships expressed in our equation, just as we have already learned in Chapter 4.

$$12.00\;g\,K_2SO_4 \times \frac{1\,mol\,K_2SO_4}{174.27\;g\,K_2SO_4} \times \frac{2\,mol\,K^+}{1\,mol\,K_2SO_4} = 0.1377\,mol\,K^+(aq)$$

Note: We begin by converting the mass of potassium sulfate to moles using molar mass as a conversion factor. We further multiply this quantity by the stoichiometric ratio 2 moles K^+ to 1 mol K_2SO_4, which is taken directly from the coefficients in our balanced equation, indicating there will be 0.1377 moles K^+ in our solution. Also, we can further calculate the number of potassium ions in solution by simply multiplying our result by Avogadro's number as follows:

$$12.00\;g\,K_2SO_4 \times \frac{1\,mol\,K_2SO_4}{174.27\;g\,K_2SO_4} \times \frac{2\,mol\,K^+}{1\,mol\,K_2SO_4} \times \frac{6.022 \times 10^{23}\,K^+ions}{1\,mol\,K^+} = 8.293 \times 10^{22}\,K^+ions$$

The following example problems provide some further practice in calculating moles of ions in solution.

The dissolution of potassium sulfate in water.

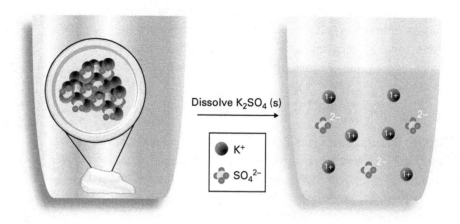

Example Problem 5.1—Ionic Compounds in Aqueous Solution

How many moles of anions are in the following solutions?

a.) 1.00 g $NaCl$ dissolved in water.

b.) 12.50 g Na_3PO_4 dissolved in water.

c.) 8.25 g $Al(NO_3)_3$ dissolved in water.

d.) 1.75 g $Fe_2(SO_4)_3$ dissolved in water.

Solutions:	
a.) Write the equation which depicts the dissolution of the ionic compound into solvated ions. Convert 1.00 g $NaCl$ to moles of $NaCl$ and use the equation to convert to moles of Cl^-.	$$NaCl(s) \xrightarrow{H_2O} Na^+(aq) + Cl^-(aq)$$ $$1.00\ g\ NaCl \times \frac{1\ mol\ NaCl}{58.44\ g\ NaCl} \times \frac{1\ mol\ Cl^-}{1\ mol\ NaCl} =$$ $$= 0.017111567\ mol\ Cl^- = \mathbf{0.0171\ mol\ Cl^-}$$
b.) Write the equation which depicts the dissolution of the ionic compound into solvated ions. Convert 12.50 g Na_3PO_4 to moles of Na_3PO_4 and use the equation to convert to moles of PO_4^{3-}.	$$Na_3PO_4(s) \xrightarrow{H_2O} 3Na^+(aq) + PO_4^{3-}(aq)$$ $$12.50\ g\ Na_3PO_4 \times \frac{1\ mol\ Na_3PO_4}{163.94\ g\ Na_3PO_4} \times \frac{1\ mol\ PO_4^{3-}}{1\ mol\ Na_3PO_4} =$$ $$= 0.076247408\ mol\ PO_4^{3-} = \mathbf{0.07625\ mol\ PO_4^{3-}}$$
c.) Write the equation which depicts the dissolution of the ionic compound into solvated ions. Convert 8.25 g $Al(NO_3)_3$ to moles of $Al(NO_3)_3$ and use the equation to convert to moles of NO_3^-.	$$Al(NO_3)_3(s) \xrightarrow{H_2O} Al^{3+}(aq) + 3NO_3^-(aq)$$ $$8.25\ g\ Al(NO_3)_3 \times \frac{1\ mol\ Al(NO_3)_3}{213.01\ g\ Al(NO_3)_3} \times \frac{3\ mol\ NO_3^-}{1\ mol\ Al(NO_3)_3} =$$ $$= 0.116191728\ mol\ NO_3^- = \mathbf{0.116\ mol\ NO_3^-}$$
d.) Write the equation which depicts the dissolution of the ionic compound into solvated ions. Convert 1.75 g $Fe_2(SO_4)_3$ to moles of $Fe_2(SO_4)_3$ and use the equation to convert to moles of SO_4^{2-}.	$$Fe_2(SO_4)_3(s) \xrightarrow{H_2O} 2Fe^{3+}(aq) + 3SO_4^{2-}(aq)$$ $$1.75\ g\ Fe_2(SO_4)_3 \times \frac{1\ mol\ Fe_2(SO_4)_3}{399.82\ g\ Fe_2(SO_4)_3} \times \frac{3\ mol\ SO_4^{2-}}{1\ mol\ Fe_2(SO_4)_3} =$$ $$= 0.013127954\ mol\ SO_4^{2-} = \mathbf{0.0131\ mol\ SO_4^{2-}}$$

Section 5.4 Predicting Solubility of Ionic Compounds

Not all ionic compounds are soluble in water. Compounds that dissolve in water are referred to as **soluble**, and those that do not are called **insoluble**. Even though many compounds will readily dissolve, some ionic compounds exhibit little to no solubility in water under ambient conditions. Whether a compound is soluble or not is dependent on multiple variables, and clear prediction of solubility is difficult. Nevertheless, over the years, chemists have developed a set of general rules or guidelines about what types of ionic compounds will be "water-soluble." These guidelines are summarized in Table 5.1.

The solubility rules are divided into two general categories: compounds which are typically soluble in water and those that are not. To understand how best to apply these rules, it is helpful to consider an example. Suppose we wished to predict whether the compounds sodium phosphate and zinc sulfide are soluble. In the first case, we examine the rules and find that compounds containing sodium ion (Na^+) are always soluble with no exceptions. On this basis, we would then predict the compound sodium phosphate Na_3PO_4 to be soluble in water. This may appear, at first, to conflict with the rule regarding phosphate compounds, which states that phosphates are typically insoluble. However, Na_3PO_4 is explicitly listed as an exception to the rule of the insolubility of phosphates. As such, both rules are consistent. Respecting zinc sulfide, on the other hand, the rules indicate that sulfides are typically insoluble, and further, Zn^{2+} is not listed as an exception to the insolubility of sulfides. Therefore, we would predict zinc sulfide to be insoluble in water.

Table 5.1 Solubility Rules for Ionic Compounds in Water.

Soluble Compounds	
Compounds containing:	**Exceptions:**
Li^+, Na^+, K^+, and NH_4^+	None
NO_3^-, ClO_3^-, ClO_4^- and $C_2H_3O_2^-$	None
Cl^-, Br^-, and I^-	Halides of Ag^+, Hg_2^{2+} and Pb^{2+}
SO_4^{2-}	Sulfates of Ag^+, Ca^{2+}, Sr^+, Ba^{2+} and Pb^{2+}
Insoluble Compounds	
Compounds containing:	**Exceptions:**
CO_3^{2-}, and PO_4^{3-}	Carbonates and phosphates of Li^+, Na^+, K^+ and NH_4^+
OH^- and S^{2-}	Hydroxides and sulfides of Li^+, Na^+, K^+, NH_4^+, Mg^{2+} (sulfides only), Ca^{2+}, Sr^{2+} and Ba^{2+}

It is important to note that even though these guidelines seem to place an "either-or" determination on the question of solubility, this really is not the case. All ionic compounds exhibit "some" solubility in water. However, in some cases it is so slight as to be virtually nonexistent. This is evident when one considers the fact that the solubility of many compounds can be dramatically increased with higher temperature. In fact, many compounds that are listed as insoluble according to the solubility rules in Table 5.1 are readily soluble at elevated temperatures. As such, solubility should be understood as a continuum, and, further, when we state that a compound is insoluble, this simply means that it is "effectively" insoluble under normal conditions.

Example Problem 5.2—Predicting Solubility of Ionic Compounds

Use the solubility rules summarized in Table 5.1 to predict whether the following ionic compounds are soluble or insoluble.

a.) K_2SO_4

b.) Hg_2Cl_2

c.) CaS

d.) $NaC_2H_3O_2$

Solutions:		
a.)	The solubility rules state that compounds containing K^+ are generally soluble with no exceptions.	**Soluble**
b.)	The solubility rules state that compounds containing Cl^- are generally soluble. However, mercury(I) chloride is listed as an exception to the general solubility of chlorides.	**Insoluble**
c.)	The solubility rules state that compounds containing S^{2-} are generally insoluble. However, calcium sulfide is listed as an exception to the general insolubility of sulfides.	**Soluble**
d.)	The solubility rules state that compounds containing $C_2H_3O_2^-$ (acetate) and/or sodium are generally soluble with no exceptions.	**Soluble**

Section 5.5   Dissolution of Molecular (Covalent) Compounds in Water

In addition to ionic compounds, water dissolves many molecular compounds as well. Some familiar examples include rubbing alcohol (C_3H_8O), acetic acid (vinegar, $HC_2H_3O_2$) as well as sugar (sucrose, $C_{12}H_{22}O_{11}$). All such compounds also contain polar bonds and, as such, are also characterized as polar compounds. Unlike ionic compounds, however, most molecular compounds do not dissociate into ions but rather remain intact as solvated molecules. Owing to this, no mobile, charged particles are present in solutions of most molecular compounds, and, therefore, such solutions do not conduct electricity. For this reason, these compounds are referred to as **nonelectrolytes**.

The only exception to the "nonelectrolyte" behavior of molecular compounds exists within a family of compounds known as *acids*. **Acids** are unique in that they are covalent compounds; however, when they dissolve in water, they dissociate into ions. To be more precise, acids dissociate in such a fashion that they produce H^+(aq) ions when dissolved in water. We will cover acids in more detail in Chapter 11.

Section 5.6 Writing Chemical Equations for Reactions in Aqueous Solution

Because of the unique circumstances which arise from the mechanisms of the dissolution of chemical compounds, especially ionic compounds, chemists have devised three basic types of equations to describe chemical processes which occur in aqueous solutions. These are *molecular, ionic* (or *complete ionic*), and *net ionic* equations. To understand the features and meaning of each of these types of chemical equations, it is illustrative to consider a specific example. Let's assume we are describing the reaction of aqueous lead(II) nitrate with aqueous potassium iodide.

1. **Molecular Equation**—Molecular equations represent all reactants and products in a reaction as if they are ***not*** dissociated, freely solvated ions in solution. Rather, in a molecular equation each reactant and product is represented as a compound rather than ions. Let's consider the molecular equation representing our example reaction of lead(II) nitrate with potassium iodide:

$$Pb(NO_3)_2(aq) + 2\,KI(aq) \rightarrow PbI_2(s) + 2\,KNO_3(aq)$$

    It should be obvious that the molecular equation is identical to the equations we are already accustomed to writing. However, when describing reactions in aqueous solution, this type of equation provides the least amount of information regarding the circumstances of the reaction in question. This is because ionic compounds, generally speaking, do not exist in solution. Rather, ionic compounds dissociate into free (solvated) ions when they dissolve and enter solution.

2. **Ionic Equation**—Ionic equations (also known as *"Complete Ionic Equations"*) present a more accurate (or complete) picture because they represent all "soluble" ionic compounds as dissolved, dissociated ions. To be precise, all strong electrolytes in aqueous solution should be represented as ions in the ionic equation. Such a representation will have some obvious advantages, as it more closely depicts the circumstances of the reacting species in solution. In order to re-write our molecular equation in the form of a complete ionic equation, we simply separate all ionic species in aqueous solution (aq) into their constituent ions as follows:

$$Pb(NO_3)_2(aq) + 2\,KI(aq) \rightarrow PbI_2(s) + 2\,KNO_3(aq)$$

$$Pb^{2+}(aq) + 2\,NO_3^-(aq) + 2\,K^+(aq) + 2\,I^-(aq) \rightarrow PbI_2(s) + 2\,K^+(aq) + 2\,NO_3^-(aq)$$

Notice first, that only the ionic compounds which are soluble are represented as free ions in the ionic equation. However, lead(II) iodide, which is insoluble and therefore indicated in the solid state (s), is represented as an intact compound. In ionic equations, all compounds in the solid (s), liquid (l), or gaseous (g) state are represented as intact compounds. Only species which completely dissociate into ions when dissolved in water and are in aqueous solution (aq) are represented as free ions.

3. **Net Ionic Equation** – Net ionic equations are written such that all species which undergo no change during the reaction are omitted from the equation. Such species are referred to as **spectator ions** and are identified in the complete ionic equation as ions which are the same on the left and right side of the reaction arrow. These are understood to be undergoing *no chemical change* and, as a consequence, are incidental to the reaction in question and need not always be represented in the reaction equation. To better understand this concept, let's consider our complete ionic equation:

$$Pb^{2+}(aq) + 2\,NO_3^-(aq) + 2\,K^+(aq) + 2\,I^-(aq) \rightarrow PbI_2(s) + 2\,K^+(aq) + 2\,NO_3^-(aq)$$

Notice that the nitrate and potassium ions (highlighted in red font) are depicted in the complete ionic equation as undergoing no change as a result of our reaction. Therefore, the net ionic equation will simply omit these ions altogether as follows:

$$Pb^{2+}(aq) + 2\,I^-(aq) \rightarrow PbI_2(s)$$

Thus, we understand the net ionic equation to indicate that the only species undergoing reaction are the lead(II) and iodide ions to form lead(II) iodide. This is indeed the case, and the spectator ions, potassium and nitrate, are merely incidental to this process and could easily have been any number of other ions.

Example Problem 5.3 — Writing Complete and Net Ionic Equations

Write the balanced complete and net ionic equations for the following reaction.

$$CaCl_2(aq) + Na_3PO_4(aq) \rightarrow Ca_3(PO_4)_2(s) + NaCl(aq) \text{ (unbalanced)}$$

Solution:

Step 1. Balance the equation.

$$3CaCl_2(aq) + 2Na_3PO_4(aq) \rightarrow Ca_3(PO_4)_2(s) + 6NaCl(aq)$$

Step 2. Write the complete ionic equation with all strong electrolytes in solution (aq) as separate, solvated ions.

$$3CaCl_2(aq) + 2Na_3PO_4(aq) \rightarrow Ca_3(PO_4)_2(s) + 6NaCl(aq)$$

$$3Ca^{2+}(aq) + 6Cl^-(aq) + 6Na^+(aq) + 2PO_4^{3-}(aq) \rightarrow Ca_3(PO_4)_2(s) + 6Na^+(aq) + 6Cl^-(aq)$$

Complete Ionic Equation:

$$3Ca^{2+}(aq) + 6Cl^-(aq) + 6Na^+(aq) + 2PO_4^{3-}(aq) \rightarrow Ca_3(PO_4)_2(s) + 6Na^+(aq) + 6Cl^-(aq)$$

Step 3. Write the net ionic equation by omitting the spectator ions. Spectator ions are those that undergo no change (are the same on the left and right side of the reaction arrow). In this case the spectator ions are Na^+ and Cl^- (highlighted in red).

$$3Ca^{2+}(aq) + 6Cl^-(aq) + 6Na^+(aq) + 2PO_4^{3-}(aq) \rightarrow Ca_3(PO_4)_2(s) + 6Na^+(aq) + 6Cl^-(aq)$$

Net Ionic Equation: $3Ca^{2+}(aq) + 2PO_4^{3-}(aq) \rightarrow Ca_3(PO_4)_2(s)$

Example Problem 5.4 — Writing Complete and Net Ionic Equations

Write the balanced complete and net ionic equations for the following reaction.

$$CuCl_2(aq) + MgS(aq) \rightarrow CuS(s) + MgCl_2(aq)$$

Solution:

Step 1. Balance the equation. In this case the equation is already balanced.

$$CuCl_2(aq) + MgS(aq) \rightarrow CuS(s) + MgCl_2(aq)$$

Step 2. Write the complete ionic equation with all strong electrolytes in solution (aq) as separate, solvated ions.

$$CuCl_2(aq) + MgS(aq) \rightarrow CuS(s) + MgCl_2(aq)$$

$$Cu^{2+}(aq) + 2Cl^-(aq) + Mg^{2+}(aq) + S^{2-}(aq) \rightarrow CuS(s) + Mg^{2+}(aq) + 2Cl^-(aq)$$

Complete Ionic Equation:

$$Cu^{2+}(aq) + 2Cl^-(aq) + Mg^{2+}(aq) + S^{2-}(aq) \rightarrow CuS(s) + Mg^{2+}(aq) + 2Cl^-(aq)$$

Step 3. Write the net ionic equation by omitting the spectator ions. Spectator ions are those that undergo no change (are the same on the left and right side of the reaction arrow). In this case the spectator ions are Mg^{2+} and Cl^- (highlighted in red).

$$Cu^{2+}(aq) + 2Cl^-(aq) + Mg^{2+}(aq) + S^{2-}(aq) \rightarrow CuS(s) + Mg^{2+}(aq) + 2Cl^-(aq)$$

Net Ionic Equation: $Cu^{2+}(aq) + S^{2-}(aq) \rightarrow CuS(s)$

Section 5.7 Types of Aqueous Reactions

Precipitation Reactions

A **precipitation reaction** occurs when two aqueous solutions of ionic compounds are brought together and react to form an *insoluble, solid* product, a **precipitate**. Precipitates form for the same reason that some ionic compounds are insoluble. In other words, when the attractive force acting between two ions is more favorable than that between the ions and the solvent (water), then an insoluble, solid, ionic compound will form. The reaction discussed in the previous section between lead(II) nitrate and potassium iodide is an example of such a *precipitation* reaction (see Figure 5.3). When these two aqueous solutions are mixed together, the lead(II) and iodide ions come together and form a new, insoluble compound, PbI_2. This is, of course, precisely what the net ionic equation in the previous section clearly depicts.

Predicting Precipitation Reactions

Figure 5.3 Precipitation reaction between aqueous Lead(II) Nitrate and Sodium Iodide. When these two solutions are mixed the Lead(II) cations and the Iodide anions spontaneously form the insoluble compound Lead(II) Iodide.

To predict whether a precipitation reaction will occur when mixing two aqueous solutions, we can look to the solubility rules in Table 5.1. Specifically, given two reactants in aqueous solution, we identify potential products and determine whether any or all of these are insoluble. The formation of

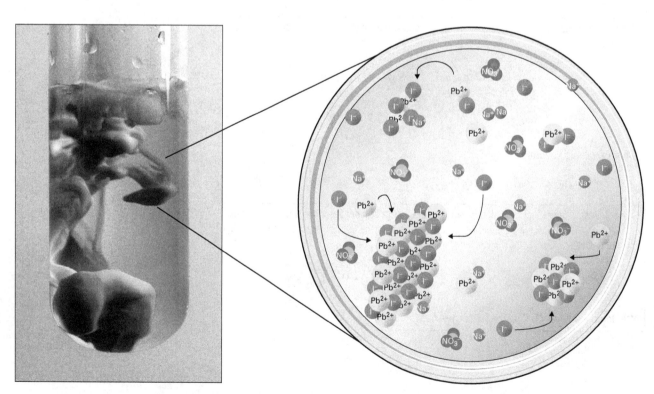

$$Pb(NO_3)_2 \text{ (aq)} + 2NaI \text{ (aq)} \rightarrow PbI_2 \text{ (s)} + 2NaNO_3 \text{ (aq)}$$

an insoluble product is essentially what a precipitation is. The reactants in such cases are always soluble in water, and, as such, they will completely dissociate into solvated cations and anions. However, if either of the cations in solution can form an insoluble compound with either of the anions, a precipitation reaction will occur. To illustrate this idea let's assume that we have an aqueous solution of $Pb(NO_3)_2$ which is mixed with a solution of potassium sulfate, K_2SO_4, and further, we wish to determine if there will be a precipitation reaction and, if so, write the balanced chemical equation representing it.

The first thing to consider in this example is the nature of the reacting species as they exist in the solutions we have described here. Each of these two solutions is characterized by a mixture of freely solvated ions as depicted in the following equations:

$$Pb(NO_3)_2(s) \xrightarrow{H_2O} Pb^{2+}(aq) + 2NO_3^-(aq)$$

$$K_2SO_4(s) \xrightarrow{H_2O} 2K^+(aq) + SO_4^{2-}(aq)$$

When these two solutions are mixed, if any combination of cation and anion present in the resulting mixture can form an insoluble compound, they will, and a precipitation reaction will occur. With this in mind, let's proceed through the following steps:

1. **Write the two compounds $Pb(NO_3)_2$ and K_2SO_4 as reactants on the left side of the reaction arrow.** Since we already know these compounds are soluble and are "in solution," their states should be denoted as (aq) as follows:

$$Pb(NO_3)_2(aq) + K_2SO_4(aq) \rightarrow$$

2. **Determine the possible products which can form from the reactants.** This is done by exchanging the cations and anions from the reactant compounds such as to form two new ionic compounds as follows:

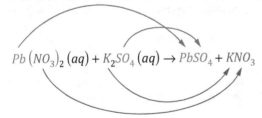

$$Pb(NO_3)_2(aq) + K_2SO_4(aq) \rightarrow PbSO_4 + KNO_3$$

Note: Reactions which are described as an exchange of ions are referred to as *double displacement* or **metathesis reactions**. Also, it is important to write formulas of our potential products according to the rules for writing formulas, which we learned in Chapter 3.

3. **Using the solubility rules (Table 5.1), determine the solubility of each product.**

   a. If either product (or both) is insoluble, it will precipitate from the solution, and a reaction will occur. In such a case, the product is labeled as being in the solid state, (s).

b. If a product is soluble, it is simply labeled as being in aqueous solution, (aq).

c. If both products are soluble, then no precipitate forms, and there will be no reaction. In such a case, we simply write "no reaction" after the arrow.

$$Pb(NO_3)_2 \, (aq) + K_2SO_4 \, (aq) \rightarrow PbSO_4 \, (s) + KNO_3 \, (aq) \, (unbalanced)$$

Note: In this case, the rules indicate that sulfate compounds are generally soluble. However, compounds containing Pb^{2+} are listed as exceptions to the solubility of sulfates. Therefore, $PbSO_4$ is insoluble, and we indicate this by placing an "s" in parentheses following its formula. Additionally, all compounds containing either nitrate or potassium ions are soluble with no exceptions, and, as such, KNO_3 is soluble.

4. **Balance the equation**. Since we have determined that a potential product is insoluble, we know that a precipitate will form, and therefore, we should proceed by balancing our equation. For the current example, this requires only that a coefficient of "2" be placed in front of potassium nitrate in our equation.

$$Pb(NO_3)_2 \, (aq) + K_2SO_4 \, (aq) \rightarrow PbSO_4 \, (s) + 2 \, KNO_3 \, (aq)$$

In this way, we have determined that a reaction between aqueous lead(II) nitrate and potassium sulfate will occur through precipitation of lead(II) sulfate from the reaction solution, and further, we have written a balanced molecular equation to describe precisely that reaction. The following practice problems will demonstrate other examples of this process.

Example Problem 5.5 – Predicting Precipitation Reactions

Does a precipitation reaction occur when the pair of solutions listed below is mixed? If so, write the balanced chemical equation representing the reaction. If not, write "no reaction."   Sodium Carbonate (aq) + Calcium Nitrate (aq)
Solution:
Step 1. Write the two compounds as reactants on the left side of the reaction arrow. In this case it is necessary to apply the rules regarding writing formulas we learned in Chapter 3. $$Na_2CO_3(aq) + Ca(NO_3)_2(aq) \rightarrow$$
Step 2. Determine the possible products. This is accomplished by exchanging the cations and anions which comprise the reactants.   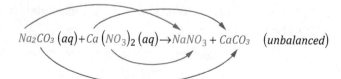 $$Na_2CO_3 \, (aq) + Ca\,(NO_3)_2 \, (aq) \rightarrow NaNO_3 + CaCO_3 \quad (unbalanced)$$

Step 3. Using the solubility rules (Table 5.1), determine the solubility of each product. If either product (or both) is insoluble, it will precipitate from the solution, and a reaction will occur. In such a case the product is labeled as being in the solid state (s). If a product is soluble, it is simply labeled as being in aqueous solution (aq). If both products are soluble, then no precipitate forms, and there will be no reaction. In such a case, we simply write "no reaction" after the arrow.

$$Na_2CO_3(aq) + Ca(NO_3)_2(aq) \rightarrow NaNO_3(aq) + CaCO_3(s) \, (unbalanced)$$

According to the solubility rules, all compounds containing either Na^+ or NO_3^- are soluble in water with no exceptions. As such, we place an "aq" in parenthenes after $NaNO_3$ in our equation. However, we also find that compounds containing CO_3^{2-} are generally insoluble and calcium carbonate is not offered as an exception to the insolubility of carbonates. Therefore, calcium carbonate is insoluble, and as such, we indicate this with an "s" in parentheses.

Step 4. Since we have established that calcium carbonate will precipitate from the reaction mixture, we can now balance our equation.

$$Na_2CO_3(aq) + Ca(NO_3)_2(aq) \rightarrow 2\,NaNO_3(aq) + CaCO_3(s)$$

The above equation therefore represents the precipitation reaction which will occur upon mixing of aqueous solutions of sodium carbonate and calcium nitrate.

Example Problem 5.6 – Predicting Precipitation Reactions

Does a precipitation reaction occur when the solutions listed below are mixed? If so, write the balanced chemical equation representing the reaction. If not write "no reaction."

Magnesium Chloride (aq) + Potassium Acetate (aq)

Solution:

Step 1. Write the two compounds as reactants on the left side of the reaction arrow. In this case, it is necessary to apply the rules regarding writing formulas we learned in Chapter 3.

$$MgCl_2(aq) + KC_2H_3O_2(aq) \rightarrow$$

Step 2. Determine the possible products. This is accomplished by exchanging the cations and anions which comprise the reactants.

$$MgCl_2(aq) + KC_2H_3O_2(aq) \rightarrow Mg(C_2H_3O_2)_2 + KCl \, (unbalanced)$$

Step 3. Determine the solubility of the potential products (Table 5.1) and indicate whether there is a precipitate or "no reaction."

$$MgCl_2(aq) + KC_2H_3O_2(aq) \rightarrow No\ Reaction$$

Since both potential products are soluble, there will be no precipitate formed and therefore no reaction.

Example Problem 5.7—Predicting Precipitation Reactions— Ionic Equations

Write the balanced molecular, complete ionic, and net ionic equations for the reaction (if any) when the following pair of aqueous solutions are mixed.

Iron(III) Chloride (aq) + Silver Nitrate (aq)

Solution:

Step 1. Write the two compounds as reactants on the left side of the reaction arrow. In this case it is necessary to apply the rules regarding writing formulas we learned in Chapter 3.

$$FeCl_3(aq) + AgNO_3(aq) \rightarrow$$

Step 2. Determine the possible products. This is accomplished by exchanging the cations and anions which comprise the reactants.

$$FeCl_3(aq) + AgNO_3(aq) \rightarrow Fe(NO_3)_3 + AgCl \text{ (unbalanced)}$$

Step 3. Determine the solubility of the potential products (Table 5.1) and indicate whether there is a precipitate or "no reaction."

$$FeCl_3(aq) + AgNO_3(aq) \rightarrow Fe(NO_3)_3(aq) + AgCl(s) \text{ (unbalanced)}$$

In this case, the silver chloride is insoluble according to the rules in Table 5.1. We indicate the formation of the precipitate with an "s" in parentheses.

Step 4. Since we have established that *AgCl* will precipitate from the reaction mixture, we can now balance our equation.

$$FeCl_3(aq) + 3\,AgNO_3(aq) \rightarrow Fe(NO_3)_3(aq) + 3\,AgCl(s)$$

Thus, we have written the balanced molecular equation for the precipitation reaction which occurs between aqueous iron(III) chloride and silver nitrate.

Step 5. To write the complete ionic equation we simply represent all strong electrolytes (in solution) as separate, freely solvated ions as follows:

$$FeCl_3(aq) + 3\,AgNO_3(aq) \rightarrow Fe(NO_3)_3(aq) + 3\,AgCl(s)$$

Complete Ionic Equation:

$$Fe^{3+}(aq) + 3Cl^-(aq) + 3Ag^+(aq) + 3NO_3^-(aq) \rightarrow Fe^{3+}(aq) + 3NO_3^-(aq) + 3AgCl(s)$$

Step 6. To write the net ionic equation we simply omit the spectator ions:

$$Fe^{3+}(aq) + 3Cl^-(aq) + 3Ag^+(aq) + 3NO_3^-(aq) \rightarrow Fe^{3+}(aq) + 3NO_3^-(aq) + 3AgCl(s)$$

Net Ionic Equation: $\quad 3Cl^-(aq) + 3Ag^+(aq) \rightarrow 3AgCl(s) \text{ or } Cl^-(aq) + Ag^+(aq) \rightarrow AgCl(s)$

Acid/Base Neutralizations

Another important class of aqueous metathesis reaction is **acid-base neutralizations**. As stated earlier, an **acid** is defined as a molecular compound which, when dissolved in water, undergoes ionization to form $H^+(aq)$ ions. We can write an equation to describe the ionization of acids in water just as we did for the dissolution of ionic compounds as follows:

$$HCl(g) \xrightarrow{H_2O} H^+(aq) + Cl^-(aq)$$

Acids are generally composed of hydrogen and a nonmetal (or polyatomic ion). Because of the prominent role of hydrogen in the unique behavior of acids, hydrogen is often written first in the formulas of acids. Also, hydrogen acts like a cation in the case of acids and, as we learned in Chapter 3 regarding writing formulas, cations are written first. Hence, this is the convention for acids in general, and the formula for our example here, hydrochloric acid, is written as *HCl (aq)*.

Acids are ubiquitous (all around us), and we encounter them every day in a variety of ways. For instance, acids are present in foods, particularly citric fruits such as oranges, lemons, and limes. It is here that the characteristic sour taste of acids is most familiar to us. Additionally, acids are used in batteries and household cleaners as well as medical and agricultural applications. Owing to this, acids are a clearly prevalent and important class of aqueous solution.

Acids are found in a variety of foods, household products, and other applications.

Because they ionize in solution, acids behave as *electrolytes* even though they are technically molecular compounds. However, unlike soluble ionic compounds, acids do not always "completely" ionize when dissolved in water. Some acids, referred to as **weak acids**, are only partially ionized when dissolved in water. For this reason, we can classify acids as being either *weak acids* or *strong acids*. Table 5.2 lists common acids and bases and categorizes them as strong and weak.

Strong acids completely dissociate into ions when dissolved in water, and, therefore, they behave as **strong electrolytes** in the same fashion as soluble ionic compounds. **Weak acids** only partially ionize when dissolved in water. As such, a significant portion of the acid molecules remain intact and consequently, weak acids will conduct a smaller electric current. For this reason weak acids are referred to as **weak electrolytes**. Figure 5.4 depicts the relative ability of strong and weak electrolytes to conduct electric current. Acetic acid is an example of a weak acid, and we represent its dissociation in water as follows:

Acetic Acid is the active component of vinegar.

$$HC_2H_3O_2(aq) \rightleftharpoons H^+(aq) + C_2H_3O_2^-(aq)$$

Table 5.2 Common Acids and Bases.

Acids		
Formula	Name	Strong/Weak
HCl	Hydrochloric Acid	Strong
HBr	Hydrobromic acid	Strong
HI	Hydroiodic Acid	Strong
HNO_3	Nitric acid	Strong
H_2SO_4	Sulfuric Acid	Strong
$HClO_4$	Perchloric Acid	Strong
HF	Hydrofluoric Acid	Weak
H_3PO_4	Phosphoric Acid	Weak
$HC_2H_3O_2$	Acetic Acid	Weak
Bases		
Formula	Name	Strong/Weak
$NaOH$	Sodium Hydroxide	Strong
$LiOH$	Lithium Hydroxide	Strong
KOH	Potassium Hydroxide	Strong
$RbOH$	Rubidium Hydroxide	Strong
$CsOH$	Cesium Hydroxide	Strong
$Ca(OH)_2$	Calcium Hydroxide	Strong
$Sr(OH)_2$	Strontium Hydroxide	Strong
$Ba(OH)_2$	Barium Hydroxide	Strong
NH_3	Ammonia	Weak

Here the double arrow indicates that the acid is moving back and forth between the intact molecule and dissociated ions. This means that at any given instant, there is a certain fraction of the acid molecules which have dissociated. This is characteristic for each acid at equilibrium (when the relative rate of dissociation and recombination are the same). We will explore the concept of reaction equilibrium in greater detail in Chapter 10.

Bases, in contrast to acids, are compounds that, when dissolved in water, produce hydroxide ions, OH^-. Calcium hydroxide is a common example of a base, and the following equation depicts the dissolution of calcium hydroxide in water:

$$Ca\left(OH\right)_2 (s) \xrightarrow{H_2O} Ca^{2+}(aq) + 2OH^-(aq)$$

When acids and bases are mixed, OH^- anions from the base combine with the H^+ cations from the acid to form water, H_2O. Hence, *the reaction of an acid with a base produces a salt (ionic compound) and water.* This is referred

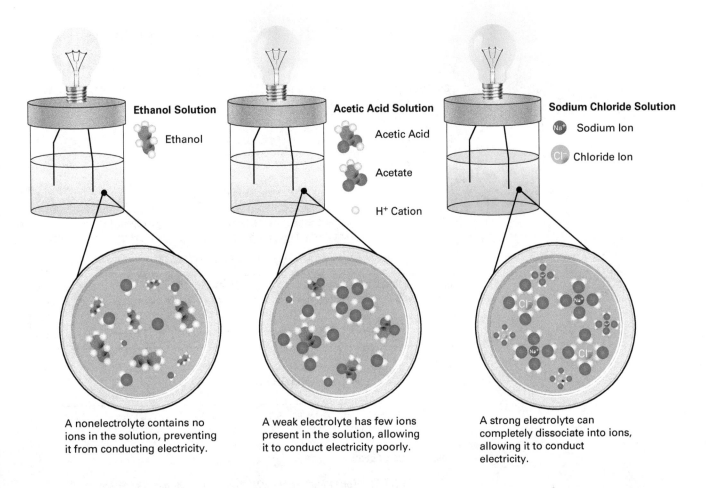

Ethanol Solution	**Acetic Acid Solution**	**Sodium Chloride Solution**
Ethanol	Acetic Acid	Na+ Sodium Ion
	Acetate	Cl⁻ Chloride Ion
	H⁺ Cation	
A nonelectrolyte contains no ions in the solution, preventing it from conducting electricity.	A weak electrolyte has few ions present in the solution, allowing it to conduct electricity poorly.	A strong electrolyte can completely dissociate into ions, allowing it to conduct electricity.

to as an **acid-base neutralization reaction**. The ionic compound (generically referred to as a salt) is formed from the anion of the acid and the cation of the base and is usually soluble (but not always). Let's consider the neutralization reaction of our two examples, HCl and $Ca(OH)_2$, as follows:

Figure 5.4 a.) Molecular compounds (excluding acids) are nonelectrolytes (left), weak acids and bases are weak electrolytes (middle), and soluble ionic compounds such as sodium chloride (as well as strong acids and bases) are strong electrolytes (right).

$$2\,HCl(aq) + Ca(OH)_2(aq) \rightarrow CaCl_2(aq) + 2\,H_2O(l)$$
$$\text{Acid} \qquad \text{base} \qquad \text{salt} \qquad \text{water}$$

The key outcome of a neutralization reaction is the combination of H^+ and OH^- ions to form water. In this way the acid and base are eliminated, leaving only a salt and water. This is easily illustrated by looking at the net ionic equation representing such a reaction. Again, let's consider our example:

Molecular Equation:

$$2HCl(aq) + Ca(OH)_2(aq) \rightarrow CaCl_2(aq) + 2H_2O(l)$$

Complete Ionic Equation:

$$2H^+(aq) + 2Cl^-(aq) + Ca^{2+}(aq) + 2OH^-(aq) \rightarrow Ca^{2+}(aq) + 2Cl^-(aq) + 2H_2O(l)$$

Net Ionic Equation:

$$2H^+(aq) + 2OH^-(aq) \rightarrow 2H_2O(l) \quad \text{or} \quad H^+(aq) + OH^-(aq) \rightarrow H_2O(l)$$

We will cover acids and bases more comprehensively in Chapter 11. For now, you should be able to recognize acid/base neutralization reactions and write balanced molecular, complete ionic, and net ionic equations for them.

Example Problem 5.8 — Acid/Base Neutralization Reactions

Write the complete and net ionic equation for the neutralization of the following acid and base:

$$H_2SO_4(aq) + Mg(OH)_2(aq)$$

Step 1. In the same fashion as precipitation reactions, we immediately recognize that the cation and anion from the base and acid, respectively, will be "exchanged" to form a salt and water as follows:

$$H_2SO_4(aq) + Mg(OH)_2(aq) \rightarrow MgSO_4 + H_2O(l) \, \textit{(unbalanced)}$$

Step 2. Determine the solubility of the "salt." In this case, we find that $MgSO_4$ is soluble according to the rules in Table 5.1. As such, this reaction will include an "aq" in parentheses following $MgSO_4$.

$$H_2SO_4(aq) + Mg(OH)_2(aq) \rightarrow MgSO_4(aq) + H_2O(l) \, \textit{(unbalanced)}$$

Step 3. Balance the equation.

$$H_2SO_4(aq) + Mg(OH)_2(aq) \rightarrow MgSO_4(aq) + 2H_2O(l)$$

Step 4. Write the complete ionic equation by representing all strong electrolytes as separate, freely solvated ions, as we have demonstrated in the previous sections.

Complete Ionic Equation:

$$2H^+(aq) + SO_4^{2-}(aq) + Mg^{2+}(aq) + 2OH^-(aq) \rightarrow Mg^{2+}(aq) + SO_4^{2-}(aq) + 2H_2O(l)$$

Step 5. If we now omit our spectator ions, Mg^{2+} and SO_4^{2-}, we have a balanced net ionic equation.

$$2H^+(aq) + SO_4^{2-}(aq) + Mg^{2+}(aq) + 2OH^-(aq) \rightarrow Mg^{2+}(aq) + SO_4^{2-}(aq) + 2H_2O(l)$$

Net Ionic Equation: $2H^+(aq) + 2OH^-(aq) \rightarrow 2H_2O(l) \quad \text{or} \quad H^+(aq) + OH^-(aq) \rightarrow H_2O(l)$

Gas Evolving Reactions

Gas evolving reactions occur when an insoluble gas is produced by the reaction of two ionic compounds in aqueous solution. Just as in the case of precipitation reactions, the evolution of the insoluble product provides the driving force for the reaction. There are few water-soluble gases. These are essentially limited to HCl and NH_3. The limited solubility of other gases forces reactions in solution to proceed to completion if gases are formed as a product. As it turns out, this is exactly what happens when *ionic carbonates, sulfides, or sulfites* react with an acid. For example, consider the following reaction:

$$Na_2CO_3(aq) + 2HCl(aq) \rightarrow 2NaCl(aq) + \left[H_2CO_3(aq)\right]$$

In such a case, the product H_2CO_3 (carbonic acid) in brackets is very unstable and will immediately decompose into water and CO_2.

$$H_2CO_3(aq) \rightarrow H_2O(l) + CO_2(g)$$

Thus:

$$Na_2CO_3(aq) + 2HCl(aq) \rightarrow 2NaCl(aq) + \left[H_2O(l) + CO_2(g) \right]$$

Since CO_2 is essentially insoluble in water, the gas will immediately evolve from the reaction mixture and do so until all of the reactants are consumed. Therefore, the molecular and net ionic equations for this reaction are as follows:

Molecular Equation:

$$Na_2CO_3(aq) + 2HCl(aq) \rightarrow 2NaCl(aq) + H_2O(l) + CO_2(g)$$

Net Ionic Equation:

$$2H^+(aq) + CO_3^{2-}(aq) \rightarrow H_2O(l) + CO_2(g)$$

Table 5.3 summarizes the rules for gas evolving reactions. Using these guidelines, the following example problem provides some further practice in identifying gas-evolving reactions.

Table 5.3 Gas-Evolving Reactions.

Reactant	Intermediate	Gas	Example
Metal Carbonates or Hydrogen Carbonates + Acid	H_2CO_3	CO_2	$2\ HCl(aq) + Na_2CO_3(aq) \rightarrow 2\ NaCl(aq) + CO_2(g) + H_2O(l)$
Metal Sulfides + Acid	N/A	H_2S	$2\ HCl(aq) + Na_2S(aq) \rightarrow 2\ NaCl(aq) + H_2S(g)$
Metal Sulfites and Hydrogen Sulfites + Acid	H_2SO_3	SO_2	$2\ HCl(aq) + Na_2SO_3(aq) \rightarrow 2\ NaCl(aq) + SO_2(g) + H_2O(l)$
Ammonium Salts + Base	NH_4OH	NH_3	$NaOH(aq) + NH_4Cl(aq) \rightarrow NaCl(aq) + NH_3(g) + H_2O(l)$

Example Problem 5.9 Predicting Gas Evolving Reactions

Write a balanced molecular, complete ionic, and net ionic equation for the reaction (if any) which occurs when the following aqueous solutions are mixed:

$$HCl(aq) + Na_2SO_3(aq)$$

Solution:

Step 1. Just as in the case of precipitation reactions and acid-base neutralizations we begin by performing a "double-displacement" exchange of ions and balancing the equation:

$$2HCl(aq) + Na_2SO_3(aq) \rightarrow 2NaCl + H_2SO_3$$

Step 2. Based on the rules in Table 5.3 we recognize immediately that the product H_2SO_3 is an unstable intermediate which will immediately decompose into water and $SO_2(g)$. Additionally, we understand from the solubility rules that $NaCl$ is soluble in water and so, remains in solution.

$$2HCl(aq) + Na_2SO_3(aq) \rightarrow 2NaCl(aq) + \left[H_2SO_3 \right]$$

Molecular Equation:

$$2HCl(aq) + Na_2SO_3(aq) \rightarrow 2NaCl(aq) + H_2O(l) + SO_2(g)$$

Step 3. Having written the balanced molecular equation, we can now write the complete ionic equation by representing all strong electrolytes in solution as separate, freely solvated ions:

Complete Ionic Equation:

$$2H^+(aq) + 2Cl^-(aq) + 2Na^+(aq) + SO_3^{2-}(aq) \rightarrow 2Na^+(aq) + 2Cl^-(aq) + H_2O(l) + SO_2(g)$$

Step 4. If we now omit our spectator ions, Na^+ and Cl^-, we have a balanced net ionic equation.

$$2H^+(aq) + 2Cl^-(aq) + 2Na^+(aq) + SO_3^{2-}(aq) \rightarrow 2Na^+(aq) + 2Cl^-(aq) + H_2O(l) + SO_2(g)$$

Net Ionic Equation: $\quad 2H^+(aq) + SO_3^{2-}(aq) \rightarrow H_2O(l) + SO_2(g)$

Section 5.8 Solution Concentration

It is common knowledge that solutions will hold different properties than either the pure solute or solvent. As a simple example of this, think about a cool glass of water on a hot day. If you have been out in the heat for a while, you would likely welcome a sip of that cold glass of water. But what if I dissolved just a little bit of salt in it. Now how does it sound? Not so good. The properties of the solution are different from the pure solvent (water) and, therefore, so are its effects on you if you drink it. Consider another example. What about salt spread on an icy road. As the salt mixes with the water (ice), the freezing and boiling points of the resulting mixture are much different from that of pure water. The same effect is seen in the use of antifreeze in cars and trucks. This is an example of how our understanding of solutions helps us in practical applications.

Antifreeze and Salt Trucks are a direct application of an understanding of the colligative property of Freezing Point Depression.

So far, we have dealt only with aqueous solutions. This is appropriate as aqueous solution chemistry is central to laboratory chemistry, and it is often easier to store and mix substances in aqueous solution than it is to store solids. Additionally, as we shall see in this section, it is possible to precisely measure the amounts of substances dissolved in solution. For these and many other reasons, a solid understanding of aqueous solution chemistry is necessary. However, it is important to recognize that solutions can be prepared with any number of solvents in addition to water. Recall that our definition of a *solution* was simply a homogeneous mixture wherein the substance present in greatest quantity is referred to as the *solvent* and the other as the *solute*. This definition clearly leaves room for any solvent or solute combination; the solvent need not be water. In fact, the solvent need not be liquid either. There are many examples of solutions in the gaseous or solid states. Metal alloys for instance are examples of solutions. Think of 18-karat gold or brass. Consider the air that you breathe. Air is a mixture of nitrogen, oxygen, water vapor, and other gases such as argon. While the subject of this chapter shall remain focused on solutions for which the solvent is liquid (principally water), it should not come as a surprise that quantitative descriptions of solutions come in a variety of forms depending on the nature of the solution and the circumstances under which it is being evaluated. In this section, we shall consider quantitative descriptions of solutions and the relationships between solution composition and its properties. The quantitative measure of the composition of a solution is referred to as *concentration*. **Concentration** can be generally defined as the amount of solute dissolved in a given amount of solvent or solution.

The concept of concentration is present in many situations. To use an analogy, imagine four football players inside a closet. Most of us would consider this an extremely uncomfortable situation. There would be too many people in the closet. Additionally, football players tend to take up more space than the average person. We can imagine nearly all of the space in the closet would be occupied by the players with very little extra space for anything else. Keeping this in mind, consider these same four football players on a football field. We have the same number of players, but we can agree that there really aren't that many football players on the field, and there is plenty of space. We could quantify this by applying some units of measure relating the number of players to the space within which they are contained. Let's assume the closet floor is four feet by four feet. Therefore our four players are contained in an area of 16 square feet. We can communicate this concentration in units of players per square foot as follows:

Players on a football field.

$$\frac{4\ players}{16\ ft^2} = 0.25\ \frac{players}{ft^2}$$

Let's apply the same logic to the football field. A standard football field is 120 yards long (360 feet) and 160 feet wide, so our players are now occupying an area of 57,600 square feet. This results in a player concentration of 6.944×10^{-5} players per square foot.

$$\frac{4\ players}{57,600\ ft^2} = 6.944 \times 10^{-5}\ \frac{players}{ft^2}$$

Obviously, the concentration in the second case is very much smaller than that calculated for the closet. The number of players involved in each case is exactly the same. Nevertheless, the two situations are completely different. The concept of solution concentration is very much the same as our example, except instead of players, we have amount of solute and instead of area (ft^2), we have volumes or masses of solvent or solution. The following sections will explore some common units of concentration and their applications.

Units of Concentration I—Molarity

Perhaps one of the most useful and common ways to express concentration is in units of *molarity*. **Molarity** is defined as the amount of solute (moles) divided by the volume of solution in liters:

$$Molarity\,(M) = \frac{amount\ of\ solute\,(mols)}{volume\ of\ solution\,(Liters)}$$

Note that it is the volume of "solution" in the denominator. Molarity refers to the volume of the entire solution, not the "solvent". As such, a solution is said to be 1.0 "molar" (1.0 *M*) when it has 1.0 mole of solute dissolved in enough solvent to produce one liter of total solution. In order to clearly understand this, it is helpful to consider how solutions of predetermined concentrations (molarity) are made. The following is a step-wise procedure for the preparation of solutions with desired molarities (see Figure 5.5).

Preparing a Solution. Generally, there are three basic steps in the preparation of solutions. To illustrate these, let's assume we wish to make 0.500 *L* of a solution that is 0.500 "molar" in potassium chloride, *KCl*. To do this the following steps apply:

1. **Weigh out the appropriate amount of the solute.** This requires that we convert our desired volume (0.500 *L*) to the

Figure 5.5 There are three basic steps to preparing solutions of known molarity. **Step 1:** Determine and weigh out the appropriate amount of the solute. **Step 2:** Transfer the solute to a volumetric flask of appropriate volume with enough water to completely dissolve the solute with stirring. **Step 3:** Following dissolution of the solute, dilute the solution to the graduated volume on the flask.

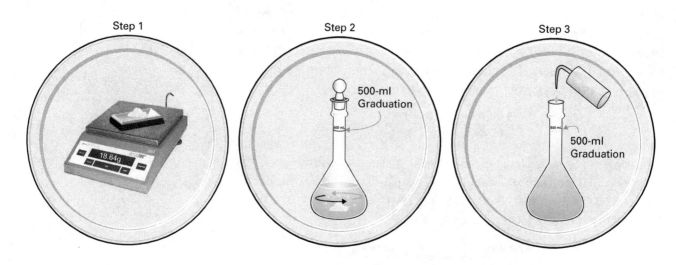

| Step 1 | Step 2 | Step 3 |

amount of solute in units of moles, which is then converted to the corresponding mass of *KCl* as follows:

$$0.500 \, L \, soln \times \frac{0.500 \, mols \, KCl}{1 \, L \, soln} \times \frac{74.55 \, g \, KCl}{1 \, mol \, KCl} = 18.64 \, g \, KCl$$

Note: Here we use our target concentration of 0.500 *M* as a conversion factor, relating 0.500 *L* of solution to moles of solute. Based on this calculation, we now weigh out 18.64 *g KCl* and transfer it to a 500-*ml* volumetric flask. A volumetric flask is graduated with a single mark to measure a specific volume (see Figure 5.5).

2. **Dissolve the solute.** Having transferred the solute to the 500-*ml* volumetric flask, enough water is added to the flask to completely dissolve the solute. The flask is swirled until all of the solid material is completely dissolved.

3. **Bring the solution up to the desired volume.** In this case, the desired volume is 500 *ml*. This is done by adding water up to the single graduation mark in the neck of the flask. The solution is then thoroughly mixed as shown in Figure 5.5.

To clearly see that we have prepared a 0.500 *M KCl* solution upon completion of these three steps, consider the following. We weighed out 18.64 *g KCl*:

$$18.64 \, g \, KCl \times \frac{1 \, mol \, KCl}{74.55 \, g \, KCl} = 0.250 \, mol \, KCl$$

This is 0.250 *mols KCl* which was then dissolved in enough water to produce 0.500 *L* of solution. The resulting concentration in molarity is therefore:

$$\frac{0.250 \, mol \, KCl}{0.500 \, L \, Solution} = 0.500 \, M \, KCl$$

Note that units of molarity are denoted with a capital *M* as shown above, and the solution described here would be referred to as a 0.500 "molar" (*M*) potassium chloride solution. Additionally, notice we do not mix 0.250 *mol* of potassium chloride with 0.500 *L* of water. Rather we dissolve the solute in enough water (solvent) to generate 0.500 *L* of solution. The distinction between solvent and solution is important. Adding 0.500 *L* of water would produce a volume of solution greater than 0.500 *L* due to the volume occupied by the solute. The resulting concentration would therefore be slightly less than 0.500 *M*. The following example problem provides some additional practice.

Example Problem 5.10—Preparing Solutions with Desired Concentrations

Describe how you would prepare 1.50 *L* of an aqueous 0.250 *M* NaCl solution.	
Solution:	
First, we need to determine the number of moles of *NaCl* which are required for 1.50 *L* at the given concentration.	$1.50 \, L \times \dfrac{0.250 \, mol \, NaCl}{1 \, L \, Sol'n} = \textbf{0.375 \textit{mol} NaCl}$

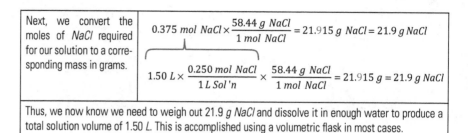

Next, we convert the moles of *NaCl* required for our solution to a corresponding mass in grams.

$$0.375 \; mol \; NaCl \times \frac{58.44 \; g \; NaCl}{1 \; mol \; NaCl} = 21.915 \; g \; NaCl = 21.9 \; g \; NaCl$$

$$1.50 \; L \times \frac{0.250 \; mol \; NaCl}{1 \; L \; Sol'n} \times \frac{58.44 \; g \; NaCl}{1 \; mol \; NaCl} = 21.915 \; g = 21.9 \; g \; NaCl$$

Thus, we now know we need to weigh out 21.9 *g NaCl* and dissolve it in enough water to produce a total solution volume of 1.50 *L*. This is accomplished using a volumetric flask in most cases.

Notice how in the previous problem we use the molarity of the solution as a conversion factor between solution volume and moles of solute. This is always possible for a given solution because concentration is an *intensive property*. As such, any sample taken from a given solution will have the same concentration whether it is 10 *ml* or 10 L. Just like density, concentration can be used as a conversion factor, which, in the case of units of molarity, relates moles of solute to liters of solution. For example, consider a solution with a known concentration, 0.500 *M KCl*. In this example, the following equality holds:

$$1.00 \; L \; Solution = 0.500 \; moles \; KCl$$

As we learned in Chapter 1, conversion factors can be constructed from such equalities as follows:

$$\frac{0.500 \; mols \; KCl}{1.00 \; Liters \; Sol'n} \quad or \quad \frac{1.00 \; Liters \; Sol'n}{0.500 \; mols \; KCl}$$

When we consider this in concert with Avogadro's Number as well as the molar mass and the formula of the solute, we are able to count moles, molecules, and ions in a given volume of solution with very good precision. It is here that the utility of the unit of molarity is most obvious. It readily allows the chemist to quickly convert between measured volumes of solution and moles of solute. Figure 5.6 graphically depicts a flow-chart summary of these relationships.

Figure 5.6 Overview of the relationships between mass, volume (solution), number, and amount (moles). Any two of these quantities can be interconverted using molar mass, concentration, and/or Avogadro's number as conversion factors.

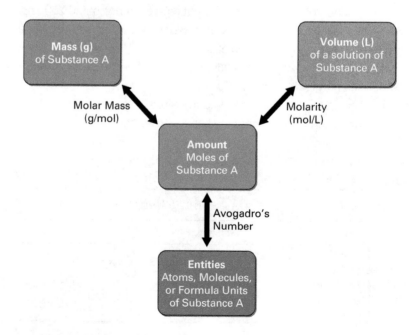

Example Problem 5.11—Using Concentration as a Conversion Factor

What mass of Na_2SO_4 is contained in 25.0 ml of a 0.125 M Na_2SO_4 solution?
Solution:

The central task here is to determine the number of moles of Na_2SO_4 in the given volume of solution. This requires that we use the given molarity as a conversion factor as shown.	$25.0\,ml\,Na_2SO_4 \times \dfrac{1\,L}{1000\,ml} \times \dfrac{0.125\,mol\,Na_2SO_4}{1\,L\,Sol'n} =$ $= 0.003125\,mol\,Na_2SO_4 = \mathbf{0.00313}\,\textbf{\textit{mol Na}}_\mathbf{2}\textbf{\textit{SO}}_\mathbf{4}$
We can now convert the moles of Na_2SO_4 to grams (Molar mass = 142.05 g/mol).	$0.003125\,mol\,Na_2SO_4 \times \dfrac{142.05\,g\,Na_2SO_4}{1\,mol\,Na_2SO_4} = \mathbf{0.444}\,\textbf{\textit{g Na}}_\mathbf{2}\textbf{\textit{SO}}_\mathbf{4}$
Therefore, 25 ml of a 0.125 M Na_2SO_4 solution contains 0.444 g Na_2SO_4.

Solution Dilution

Chemists frequently purchase concentrated solutions referred to as "stock solutions." This is because it is often convenient to store compounds in solution rather than in the solid or gaseous states. Stock solutions are often highly concentrated for reasons of economy. Owing to this, laboratory procedures typically require much lower concentrations than those found in the stockroom. As such, chemists must be able to selectively *dilute* stock solutions to any desired concentration. **Dilution** is the process of adding solvent such that the resulting solution has a specific concentration (which is necessarily lower than the initial concentration). The question is, for any given solution, how do we know how much solvent to add? This question is easily answered when we consider that when adding solvent, we are not changing the amount (moles) of solute dissolved in the solution. We are simply increasing the solution's overall volume. Since we learned in the previous section that the product of the volume of solution (in liters) and the concentration (in molarity) gives us the moles of solute, the following equation must hold:

$$M_iV_i = M_fV_f$$

Where M_i and V_i are the initial molarity and volume, and M_f and V_f are the final molarity and volume (following dilution). This equation simply states that the moles of solute remain constant through the dilution process. Let's consider an example. Suppose we have 20.0 ml of a 15.0 M $NaOH$ solution, and we need to prepare a 0.200 M $NaOH$ solution. To what volume should we dilute the 20.0 ml of 15.0 M $NaOH$ solution to arrive at a concentration of 0.200 M? In other words, what is the final volume, V_f, of our diluted solution? To answer this, we rearrange our equation to solve for V_f the final volume of the "diluted" solution:

$$M_iV_i = M_fV_f \quad \rightarrow \quad V_f = \frac{M_iV_i}{M_f}$$

Figure 5.7 Preparing a dilute solution from a more concentrated solution via dilution.

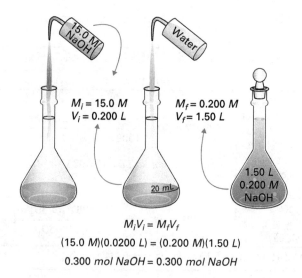

$$M_iV_i = M_fV_f$$

$$(15.0\ M)(0.0200\ L) = (0.200\ M)(1.50\ L)$$

$$0.300\ mol\ NaOH = 0.300\ mol\ NaOH$$

Now substitute the given values:

$$V_f = \frac{(15.0\ M)(0.0200\ L)}{0.200\ M}$$

$$V_f = 1.50\ L$$

Therefore, to prepare a 0.200 *M NaOH* solution, we would take the 20.0-*ml* 15.0 *M* stock solution of *NaOH* and add enough water to bring its volume up to 1.50 liters (See Figure 5.7).

Let's consider another example. Suppose we would like to know the volume of a 3.00 *M* solution of calcium nitrate required to prepare 750 *ml* of a 0.150 *M* solution of calcium nitrate. In this case, we know the initial concentration, the final concentration, and the final volume. Therefore, we are interested in determining the required initial volume of solution, prior to dilution. Again, we manipulate our equation to solve for the required variable, V_i as follows:

$$M_iV_i = M_fV_f$$

Divide both sides by M_i:

$$V_i = \frac{M_fV_f}{M_i}$$

Substitute the given values:

$$V_i = \frac{(0.150\ M)(0.750\ L)}{3.00\ M} = 0.0375\ L = 37.5\ ml$$

Therefore, we have determined that dilution of 37.5 *ml* of 3.00 *M Ca(NO₃)₂* to a volume of 750 *ml* will produce the desired concentration of 0.150 *M*. The following example problems provide some more practice in the application of the concept of dilution.

Example Problem 5.12—Solution Dilution

What volume of a 16.0 M H_2SO_4 stock solution is required to prepare 500.0 ml of a 0.500 M H_2SO_4 solution?	
Solution:	
In this case, we recognize that the question is simply asking what the initial volume of solution is, prior to dilution. First, rearrange the "dilution" equation to provide an expression for V_i.	$M_i V_i = M_f V_f$ $V_i = \dfrac{M_f V_f}{M_i}$
Next, identify the variables.	$M_i = 16.0\,M$ $M_f = 0.500\,M$ $V_f = 500.0\,ml$
Now, simply substitute the given values and calculate V_i.	$V_i = \dfrac{(0.500\,M)(500.0\,ml)}{(16.0\,M)} = 15.625\,ml$ $V_i = 15.6\,ml$

Therefore, in order to prepare 500.0 ml of a 0.500 M H_2SO_4 solution, we require 15.6 ml of the 16.0 M H_2SO_4 stock solution, which is then diluted up to a volume of 500.0 ml with addition of solvent (water).

Example Problem 5.13—Solution Dilution

What is the concentration of the resulting solution if 10.0 ml of a 4.30 M Na_2SO_4 solution is diluted to 75.0 ml?	
Solution:	
In this case, we recognize that the question is asking what the final concentration (molarity) of the solution is, following dilution. First, rearrange the "dilution" equation to provide an expression for M_f.	$M_i V_i = M_f V_f$ $M_f = \dfrac{M_i V_i}{V_f}$
Next, identify the variables.	$M_i = 4.30\,M$ $V_i = 10.0\,ml$ $V_f = 75.0\,ml$
Now, we simply substitute the given values and calculate M_f.	$M_f = \dfrac{(4.30\,M)(10.0\,ml)}{(75.0\,ml)} = 0.573333\,M$ $M_f = 0.573\,M\ Na_2SO_4$

Therefore, if 10.0 ml of a 4.30 M Na_2SO_4 solution is diluted to 75.0 ml with addition of water, the resulting solution will have a concentration of 0.573 M.

Units of Concentration II—Molality, Mole Fraction, and Mass Percent

Other units of concentration other than molarity provide quantification of the number of solute molecules or ions per solvent molecules, either directly or indirectly. Three units which fit this characterization are *molality*, *mole fraction*, and *mass percent*. Each of these units finds utility under different circumstances. These will be discussed in greater detail in the following sections of this chapter. For now, let's simply define each unit.

Molality

Molality is defined as the amount of solute (moles) per kg of solvent:

$$\text{Molality } (m) = \frac{moles\ solute}{mass\ of\ solvent\ (kg)}$$

Let's illustrate this by returning to our previous example of potassium chloride. Suppose we wish to prepare a solution that is 0.500 "molal" in this case. Here, we simply weigh out 0.500 *mols KCl* and 1.00 *kg* of water and mix these two quantities until the potassium chloride is completely dissolved:

$$\frac{0.500\ moles\ KCl}{1.00\ kg\ H_2O} = 0.500\ m\ KCl$$

A solution prepared in this fashion would be described as a 0.500 molal potassium chloride solution (0.500 *m KCl*). We use a lower-case, italicized *m* as the abbreviation for molality.

Example Problem 5.14—Molality

A solution is prepared by dissolving 4.50 g of $Ba(NO_3)_2$ in 150.0 g of water. What's the concentration in unit of molality of the resulting solution? (The molar mass of $Ba(NO_3)_2$ is 261.35 g/mol.)

Solution:	
First, we should determine how many moles of our solute we have dissolved in the solution.	$4.50\ g\ Ba(NO_3)_2 \times \dfrac{1\ mol\ Ba(NO_3)_2}{261.35\ g\ Ba(NO_3)_2} = 0.01722\ mol$ $= \mathbf{0.0172\ mol\ Ba(NO_3)_2}$
Next, we calculate molality as moles solute per *kg* of solvent (water).	$m = \dfrac{\left(4.50\ g\ Ba(NO_3)_2 \times \dfrac{1\ mol\ Ba(NO_3)_2}{261.35\ g\ Ba(NO_3)_2}\right)}{\left(150.0\ g \times \dfrac{1\ kg}{1000\ g}\right)} = 0.11480\ m\ Ba(NO_3)_2$ $\mathbf{m = 0.115\ m\ Ba(NO_3)_2}$

The dissolution of 4.50 g of $Ba(NO_3)_2$ in 150 g of water produces a solution concentration of 0.115 *m* (a 0.115 molal $Ba(NO_3)_2$ solution).

Mole Fraction

Another common unit of concentration is *mole fraction*. **Mole fraction** is defined as the amount (moles) of one component of a mixture divided by the total amount (moles) of all the components of a mixture. Mole fraction is often represented by the Greek letter chi, X, and is calculated as follows:

$$\text{Mole Fraction} = \chi_A = \frac{n_A}{n_{total}}$$

$$n_{total} = n_A + n_B + \dots$$

Where n_{total} is the sum of the moles of all components in the mixture, n_A is the number of moles of component A, n_B is the number of moles of component B and so on.

To more clearly illustrate mole fraction as a unit of concentration, it is helpful to consider an example. Suppose we have 50.00 g of isopropyl alcohol (C_3H_8O) which we mix with 200.00 g of water and form a homogenous mixture, a solution. To calculate the concentration of this solution in terms of mole fraction we first need to determine the moles of each component. We need, therefore, to calculate the molar mass of isopropyl alcohol (60.11 g/mol) and water (18.02 g/mol). Having done so, we are now able to convert the given masses to units of moles as follows:

1. $n_{C_3H_8O} = 50.00\ g\ C_3H_8O \times \dfrac{1\ mol\ C_3H_8O}{60.11\ g\ C_3H_8O} = 0.831808351\ mol\ C_3H_8O$

2. $n_{H_2O} = 200.00\ g\ H_2O \times \dfrac{1\ mol\ H_2O}{18.02\ g\ H_2O} = 11.098779\ mol\ H_2O$

Next, we simply divide the moles of solute (C_3H_8O) by the sum of the moles of all components of the mixture:

$$\chi_{C_3H_8O} = \frac{n_{C_3H_8O}}{n_{C_3H_8O} + n_{H_2O}} = \left(\frac{0.831808351\ mol\ C_3H_8O}{0.831808351\ mol\ C_3H_8O + 11.098779\ mol\ H_2O} \right) = 0.06972$$

Therefore, we would describe our isopropyl alcohol as having a mole fraction of $\chi_{C_3H_8O} = 0.06973$. (Note: Since our solution in this case is comprised of only two components, we know the mole fraction of the water is simply, $\chi_{H_2O} = 1 - \chi_{C_3H_8O} = 0.93027$.) Example Problem 5.15 provides some further practice in calculating mole fractions of components of solutions.

Mass Percent

Mass percent (or weight percent) is perhaps the simplest of the units of concentration to calculate. It is defined as the mass of solute divided by the mass of the solution (times 100%) as follows:

$$Mass\ Percent = \left(\frac{mass\ of\ solute}{mass\ of\ solution} \right) \times 100\%$$

Let's return to the isopropyl alcohol example. To describe the composition of our solution in terms of mass percent, we simply divide the 50.00 g C_3H_8O by the 200.0 g of solvent plus the 50.00 g of C_3H_8O and multiply by 100% as follows:

$$\left(\frac{50.00\ g\ C_3H_8O}{50.00g\ C_3H_8O + 200.0\ g\ H_2O} \right) \times 100\% = 20.00\%$$

Note that is important to ensure that the units of mass are the same; it would not be appropriate to perform this calculation with different units of mass for the solute and solvent.

Example Problem 5.15—Mass Percent and Mole Fraction

A solution is prepared by dissolving 4.50 g of $Ba(NO_3)_2$ in 150.0 g of water. What's the concentration in units of mass percent and mole fraction of the resulting solution? (The molar mass of $Ba(NO_3)_2$ is 261.35 g/mol.)

	Solutions:
Mass percent is a straight-forward calculation. Simply take the mass of the solute and divide by the mass of the solution (solute and solvent).	$$\left(\frac{4.50 \, g \, Ba(NO_3)_2}{4.50 \, g \, Ba(NO_3)_2 + 150.0 \, g \, H_2O} \right) \times 100\% = 2.9126\% \, Ba(NO_3)_2$$ $$\mathbf{2.91\% \, Ba(NO_3)_2}$$
Mole fraction requires us to find the number of moles of both the solvent and solute (all components of the mixture).	$$n_{Ba(NO_3)_2} = 4.50 \, g \, Ba(NO_3)_2 \times \frac{1 \, mol \, Ba(NO_3)_2}{261.35 \, g \, Ba(NO_3)_2}$$ $$= 0.017218 \, mol \, Ba(NO_3)_2$$ $$n_{H_2O} = 150.0 \, g \, H_2O \times \frac{1 \, mol \, H_2O}{18.02 \, g \, H_2O} = 8.3241 \, mol \, H_2O$$ $$\Downarrow$$ $$\chi_{Ba(NO_3)_2} = \frac{n_{Ba(NO_3)_2}}{n_{Ba(NO_3)_2} + n_{H_2O}} = \frac{0.017218 \, mol}{0.017218 \, mol + 8.3241 \, mol} =$$ $$\chi_{Ba(NO_3)_2} = 0.0020639 = \mathbf{0.00206}$$

Section 5.9 Stoichiometry of Reactions in Solution

Recall the principles of stoichiometry of chemical reactions which we learned in Chapter 4. To utilize the balanced chemical equation to help us in determining related quantities of reactants and products, we first convert given quantities to units of moles. Having done so, we learned that it is possible to use the coefficients in a balanced chemical equation to construct molar ratios which serve as conversion factors relating the moles of reactants and products. Additionally, we learned how to determine the limiting reagent, theoretical yield, and percent yield for a given reaction with given quantities of reactants. All of these principles can be applied to reactions in solution. However, when dealing with solutions, we will use solution volumes and molarities (rather than sample masses and molar masses) to determine the moles of compounds in solution.

To illustrate this, imagine we are observing the reaction which occurs when an aqueous solution of sodium hydroxide, *NaOH*, is combined with solid sodium dihydrogen phosphate, NaH_2PO_4, as described in the following reaction equation:

$$NaH_2PO_4(s) + 2\,NaOH(aq) \rightarrow Na_3PO_4(aq) + 2\,H_2O(l)$$

We can readily see from our balanced equation that 1 *mol* NaH_2PO_4 reacts with 2 *mols* *NaOH* to form 1 *mol* Na_3PO_4 and 2 *mols* H_2O. The use of these stoichiometric ratios is the same as we have learned previously. Just as in our previous examples, we must first convert all given quantities into units of moles in order to conduct stoichiometric calculations. For those species in solution, this is done through interconversion between volumes of solution (in liters) and moles of solute using concentration (molarity) as a conversion factor. With this understanding, we can now answer any problem concerning stoichiometry in solution (Figure 5.8).

For instance, assuming we have 250 *ml* of *NaOH* solution and its concentration is 0.472 *M*, what is the required mass of NaH_2PO_4 to react completely with this volume of *NaOH*? To answer this question, we should first recognize that only one reactant is in solution, and further, in order to convert from moles of NaH_2PO_4 to grams (mass), we will need the molar mass of NaH_2PO_4. We calculate the molar mass of NaH_2PO_4 as 119.98 *g/mol*. We are now ready to perform our calculation. We begin with our given volume and concentration of *NaOH* and proceed through the calculations sequentially as follows:

Figure 5.8 Flow-chart summary of the relevant stoichiometric relationships between, entities, mass, volume (solution), and amount (moles).

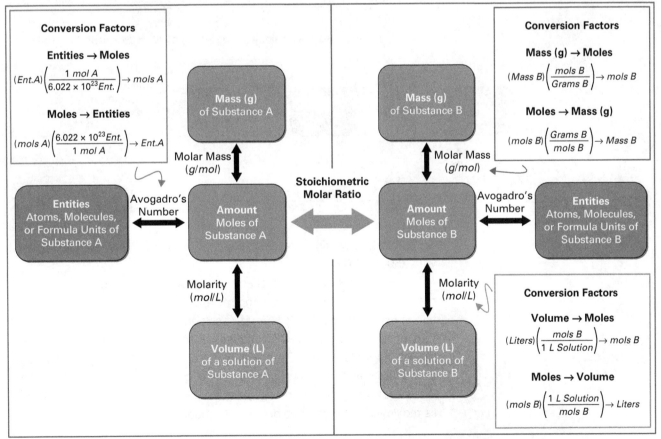

Compound A   Compound B

1. We first need to convert our volume from milliliters to liters:

$$250 \, ml \, NaOH \times \frac{1 \, L}{1000 \, ml} = 0.250 \, L$$

2. Now we can convert the liters of our solution into moles of our solute (*NaOH*) using concentration as a conversion factor as follows:

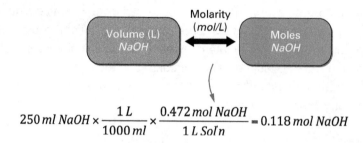

$$250 \, ml \, NaOH \times \frac{1 \, L}{1000 \, ml} \times \frac{0.472 \, mol \, NaOH}{1 \, L \, Sol'n} = 0.118 \, mol \, NaOH$$

3. It is now possible to apply the stoichiometric molar ratio to convert from mols *NaOH* to mols NaH_2PO_4.

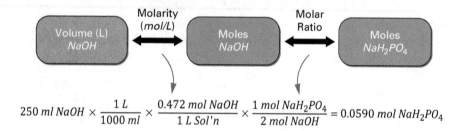

$$250 \, ml \, NaOH \times \frac{1 \, L}{1000 \, ml} \times \frac{0.472 \, mol \, NaOH}{1 \, L \, Sol'n} \times \frac{1 \, mol \, NaH_2PO_4}{2 \, mol \, NaOH} = 0.0590 \, mol \, NaH_2PO_4$$

4. We can now calculate the mass of NaH_2PO_4 from its molar mass:

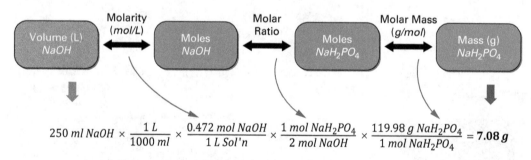

$$250 \, ml \, NaOH \times \frac{1 \, L}{1000 \, ml} \times \frac{0.472 \, mol \, NaOH}{1 \, L \, Sol'n} \times \frac{1 \, mol \, NaH_2PO_4}{2 \, mol \, NaOH} \times \frac{119.98 \, g \, NaH_2PO_4}{1 \, mol \, NaH_2PO_4} = 7.08 \, g$$

So, in this case we find that it will require 7.08 *g* NaH_2PO_4 to completely react with 250 *ml* of 0.472 *M NaOH*.

Let's assume another scenario. Suppose we need to determine the maximum amount of Na_3PO_4 (in grams) that can be produced from the reaction of 550 *ml* of the 0.472 *M NaOH* solution and 15.12 *g* NaH_2PO_4. This is a theoretical yield problem which requires us to determine the limiting reagent as well. As we learned in Chapter 4, in this case we will calculate the amount of product that can be produced from the given quantity of each reactant. Whichever one gives us the smallest amount of product limits the reaction (is the limiting reagent) and defines the theoretical yield.

1. Determine the amount of product formed from complete consumption of 550 *ml* of 0.472 *M NaOH*:

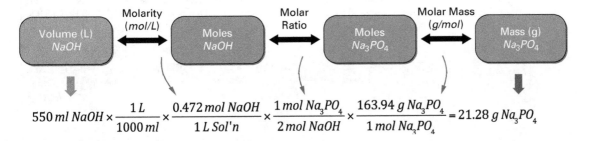

$$550\,ml\,NaOH \times \frac{1\,L}{1000\,ml} \times \frac{0.472\,mol\,NaOH}{1\,L\,Sol'n} \times \frac{1\,mol\,Na_3PO_4}{2\,mol\,NaOH} \times \frac{163.94\,g\,Na_3PO_4}{1\,mol\,Na_3PO_4} = 21.28\,g\,Na_3PO_4$$

2. Determine the amount of product formed from complete consumption of 15.12 *g NaH₂PO₄*:

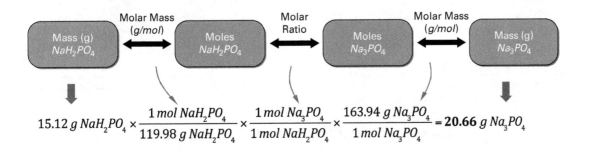

$$15.12\,g\,NaH_2PO_4 \times \frac{1\,mol\,NaH_2PO_4}{119.98\,g\,NaH_2PO_4} \times \frac{1\,mol\,Na_3PO_4}{1\,mol\,NaH_2PO_4} \times \frac{163.94\,g\,Na_3PO_4}{1\,mol\,Na_3PO_4} = \mathbf{20.66\,g\,Na_3PO_4}$$

Since we have determined that 15.12 *g NaH₂PO₄* produces a lower amount of product (20.66 *g*), we conclude that *NaH₂PO₄* is our limiting reagent, and the theoretical yield for this reaction is 20.66 *g Na₃PO₄*.

Note: These calculations are no different from any of the other stoichiometry calculations we have already done. The only difference here is that, because one of the reactants is in solution, we determine its amount (moles) using solution volume (in liters) and its concentration (in molarity). In a sense, we have added an additional tool for performing stoichiometric calculations. Figure 5.8 is a flow chart which details stoichiometric calculations, now including solution concentrations and volumes as potential inputs. If we follow this flow chart, we can determine all the necessary conversion factors for any desired calculation starting from any set of given information. The following example problems provide more practice concerning stoichiometry in solution.

Example Problem 5.16 – Solution Stoichiometry

What volume of 0.114 *M HCl* is required to completely react with 7.50 *g* of *Ca(OH)₂*?

$$2HCl(aq) + Ca(OH)_2(s) \rightarrow CaCl_2(aq) + 2H_2O(l)$$

Solution:

Here we are given a known mass of the compound $Ca(OH)_2$. First, we convert the mass to moles and use the stoichiometric molar ratio (reaction equation coefficients) to relate moles $Ca(OH)_2$ to moles HCl. This quantity is then converted to a volume using the concentration of HCl. (Use Figure 5.8 to visualize the steps in our solution, as follows.)

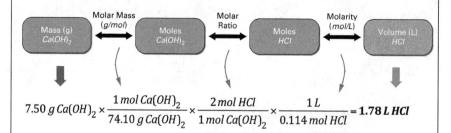

$$7.50 \ g \ Ca(OH)_2 \times \frac{1 \ mol \ Ca(OH)_2}{74.10 \ g \ Ca(OH)_2} \times \frac{2 \ mol \ HCl}{1 \ mol \ Ca(OH)_2} \times \frac{1 \ L}{0.114 \ mol \ HCl} = 1.78 \ L \ HCl$$

Therefore, we know that it will require 1.78 L of the 0.114 M HCl solution to completely consume the 7.50 g of $Ca(OH)_2$.

Example Problem 5.17 — Solution Stoichiometry

Consider the following precipitation reaction. Calculate the mass (g) of $Ba_3(PO_4)_2$ formed from the reaction of 1.50 L of a 0.0750 M $Ba(NO_3)_2$ and 1.35 L of a 0.0650 M Na_3PO_4 solution.

$$3 \ Ba(NO_3)_2 (aq) + 2 \ Na_3PO_4 (aq) \rightarrow Ba_3(PO_4)_2 (s) + 6 \ NaNO_3 (aq)$$

Solution:

This problem requires that we determine a theoretical yield. Additionally, since the quantities of both reactants are given, we will need to determine the limiting reagent. As such, we will need to calculate a yield for each of the two reactants:

1. Calculate the yield in grams that can be formed from 1.50 L of 0.0750 M $Ba(NO_3)_2$. Figure 5.8 provides a solution map for this calculation:

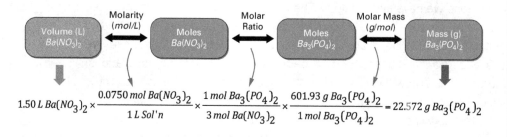

$$1.50 \ L \ Ba(NO_3)_2 \times \frac{0.0750 \ mol \ Ba(NO_3)_2}{1 \ L \ Sol'n} \times \frac{1 \ mol \ Ba_3(PO_4)_2}{3 \ mol \ Ba(NO_3)_2} \times \frac{601.93 \ g \ Ba_3(PO_4)_2}{1 \ mol \ Ba_3(PO_4)_2} = 22.572 \ g \ Ba_3(PO_4)_2$$

2. Calculate the yield in grams that can be formed from 1.35 L of 0.0650 M Na_3PO_4. Figure 5.8 provides a solution map for this calculation as well:

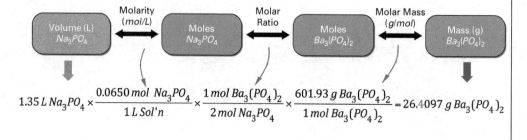

$$1.35 \ L \ Na_3PO_4 \times \frac{0.0650 \ mol \ Na_3PO_4}{1 \ L \ Sol'n} \times \frac{1 \ mol \ Ba_3(PO_4)_2}{2 \ mol \ Na_3PO_4} \times \frac{601.93 \ g \ Ba_3(PO_4)_2}{1 \ mol \ Ba_3(PO_4)_2} = 26.4097 \ g \ Ba_3(PO_4)_2$$

Since the 1.50 *L* of *Ba(NO₃)₂* solution provides the smallest yield, we recognize that it is the limiting reagent, and therefore, this reaction will form 22.6 *g* of *Ba₃(PO₄)₂* precipitate.

Limiting Reagent = *Ba(NO₃)₂*
Theoretical Yield = 22.6 *g Ba₃(PO₄)₂*

Section 5.10 Colligative Properties

Colligative Properties

As was stated earlier in this chapter, solutions tend to have markedly different properties than those of the pure solvent. Three such properties to which we now turn our attention are vapor pressure, boiling point, and freezing point. As it turns out, when water contains dissolved compounds within it, the vapor pressure of water over the aqueous solution (in a closed container) is predictably different than is observed for pure water, as are the freezing and boiling point of the solution. These properties are collectively referred to as *colligative properties*. **Colligative properties** are those which depend on the relative ratio of the number of solute particles (ions or molecules) to the number of solvent molecules in a given solution. Because of this dependence on the relative number of solute particles to solvent particles, it is convenient to employ units of concentration that relate this ratio more directly than does molarity. Recall that in the case of molarity, there is no way to know or quantify the amount (or number) of solvent molecules. As such, when dealing with colligative properties, other units of concentration, such as mole fraction and molality, are more useful. The following sections will explore the relationship between solution concentration and its impact on vapor pressure, boiling point, and freezing point.

Vapor Pressure Lowering: Raoult's Law

We will explore the concept of vapor pressure in more detail in Chapter 9, concerning intermolecular forces. For our current purposes, we will simply refer to vapor pressure in very rudimentary terms. Simply put, **vapor pressure** is the contribution to the overall pressure in a closed container which is due to the evaporation of a liquid contained therein. For example, imagine a sealed jar which contains some quantity of liquid water. Once sealed, some of the water will evaporate resulting in some water in the vapor phase. The amount of water in the vapor phase depends on several things, including temperature and the rates of evaporation and condensation. When the system has reached equilibrium, that is the rate of evaporation is the same as condensation, there is a constant amount of water in the vapor phase. The contribution of this water vapor to the overall pressure in the container is what is referred to as the *equilibrium vapor pressure* or simply **vapor**

pressure. Suffice to say that different liquids have different vapor pressures, and the vapor pressure of a given liquid is highly dependent on temperature.

How does the presence of a solute effect the vapor pressure of the solvent? *The simple answer to this question is that the vapor pressure of a solution is always lower than that of the pure solvent under identical circumstances.* Indeed, the vapor pressure over a solution is dependent on the mole fraction of the solvent, χ_{solv}, and the vapor pressure of the pure solvent, P^o_{solv}, at the same temperature. This is described for us in the following equation:

$$P_{soln} = \chi_{solv} P^o_{solv}$$

Where P_{soln} is the vapor pressure of the solution, χ_{solv} is the mole fraction of the solvent in the solution, and P^o_{solv} is the vapor pressure of the pure solvent at the same temperature. This is commonly referred to as Raoult's Law, named for the 19th-century scientist François M. Raoult. However, this relationship only holds for solutions in which the solute itself has little to no tendency to evaporate and contribute significantly to the pressure as well. Such solutions are referred to as ideal solutions.

Let's consider an example. The vapor pressure of water at 25°C is 23.8 *torr* (see Chapter 6 for more information on units of pressure). If we prepared a solution of sugar (sucrose, $C_{12}H_{22}O_{11}$; molar mass = 342.31 *g/mol*) by mixing 75.0 *g* sucrose with 450.0 *g* water, what would be the vapor pressure of our solution at 25°C in units of *torr*? Since Raoult's Law relates the vapor pressure of solution to the mole fraction of solvent, we first need to determine the amount of each component in moles and use this information to calculate a mole fraction for the solvent, water.

François-Marie Raoult (1830–1901) was a French chemist who conducted research concerning the properties of solutions and established Raoult's Law in 1887.

Moles of water:

$$\text{Moles } H_2O = n_{H_2O} = 450.0 \, g \, H_2O \times \frac{1 \, mol \, H_2O}{18.02 \, g \, H_2O} = 24.97225 \, mol \, H_2O = 24.97 \, mol \, H_2O$$

Moles of sucrose:

$$\text{Moles } C_{12}H_{22}O_{11} = n_{C_{12}H_{22}O_{11}} = 75.0 \, g \, C_{12}H_{22}O_{11} \times \frac{1 \, mol \, C_{12}H_{22}O_{11}}{342.34 \, g \, C_{12}H_{22}O_{11}} = 0.2191 \, mol \, H_2O = 0.219 \, mol \, H_2O$$

Mole Fraction of water:

$$\chi_{H_2O} = \frac{n_{H_2O}}{n_{H_2O} + n_{C_{12}H_{22}O_{11}}} = \frac{24.97225 \, mol}{25.19133 \, mol} = 0.991303 = 0.9913$$

Having determined the mole fraction of water in the solution, we simply apply Raoult's Law to calculate the vapor pressure as follows:

$$P_{soln} = \chi_{H_2O} P^o_{H_2O} = (0.9913)(23.8 \, torr) = 23.593 \, torr = \textbf{23.6 } \textit{\textbf{torr}}$$

Thus, we determined the vapor pressure over the sugar solution will be 23.6 *torr* at 25°C. Go over the following example problems for more practice. Figure 5.9 summarizes the relationships between mass, amount, mole fraction, and solution vapor pressure.

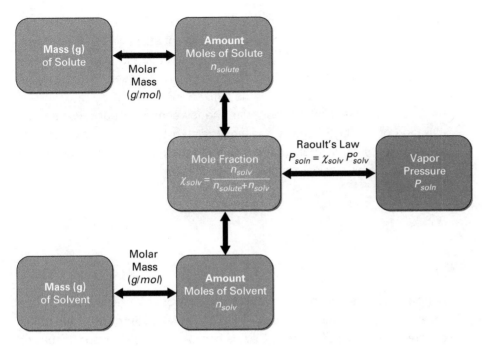

Example problem 5.18—Raoult's Law

Determine the vapor pressure of a solution consisting of 146 g glycerin ($C_3H_8O_3$) dissolved in 400.0 g of water at 25°C. (The vapor pressure of water at 25°C is 23.76 $torr$).	
Solution:	
1. Determine the moles of glycerin.	$146\ g\ C_3H_8O_3 \times \dfrac{1\ mol\ C_3H_8O_3}{92.11\ g\ C_3H_8O_3} = \mathbf{1.58506\ mol\ C_3H_8O_3}$
2. Determine the moles of water.	$400.0\ g\ H_2O \times \dfrac{1\ mol\ H_2O}{18.02\ g\ H_2O} = \mathbf{22.197558\ mol\ H_2O}$
3. Calculate the mole fraction of the solvent (water).	$\chi_{H_2O} = \dfrac{n_{H_2O}}{n_{total}} = \dfrac{n_{H_2O}}{n_{C_3H_2O_3}+n_{H_2O}} =$ $\dfrac{22.197558\ mol}{1.58506\ mol + 22.197558\ mol} = \mathbf{0.9333521}$
4. Calculate the vapor pressure of the solution according to Raoult's Law.	$P_{solution} = \chi_{H_2O}P^o_{H_2O}$ $P_{solution} = (0.9333521)(23.76\ torr) = \mathbf{22.18\ torr}$
Therefore, we would expect this solution to exhibit a vapor pressure of 22.18 $torr$.	

Boiling Point Elevation

Another example of a colligative property of solutions is **boiling point elevation**. The boiling point of a solution is higher than that for the pure solvent. The reason for this stems from the fact that the dissolution of a solute into a solvent lowers its vapor pressure. Recall that the vapor pressure of any liquid is highly dependent on temperature, and boiling of a liquid will occur at the temperature at which the vapor pressure is equal to the ambient or external pressure, P_{ext}. This is the reason why boiling points are lower at high elevation where the atmospheric pressure is lower. Since the vapor pressure of a solution is lower than that of the pure solvent at any given temperature, including the boiling point, T_b, it stands to reason that the vapor pressure of a solution will reach equivalence with the ambient pressure, P_{ext}, at a higher temperature than that needed for the pure solvent.

Therefore, just like the case with the lowering of vapor pressure, the elevation of the boiling point is directly related to the composition of the solution, to its concentration. The change in the boiling point for a solution relative to the pure solvent is given by the following expression:

$$\Delta T_b = K_b m$$

Where:

$$\Delta T_b = T_b(solution) - T_b(solvent)$$

Additionally, m is the concentration of the solution in molality, and K_b is the *molal boiling point elevation constant*. The **molal boiling point elevation constant** has units of degrees Celsius per molal unit (°C/m) and is specific to a given solvent (Table 5.4). Further, molality is used in dealing with boiling point elevation because it relates the amount of solute particles to particles of solvent. The important issue is the actual particles of solute present in solution. For example, suppose we dissolve 1.00 *mol* of sucrose in 1.00 *kg* of water at one atmosphere (an atmosphere is a unit of pressure equal to the atmospheric pressure at sea level at 25°C). In this case, we can calculate the boiling point elevation as:

$$\Delta T_b = K_b m$$

$$\Delta T_b = (0.512°C/m)(1.00\,m) = 0.512°C$$

Here we see that K_b = 0.512°C/m for water and the molality of the solution described here is 1.00 m. We now know that under these conditions the

Table 5.4 Boiling Point Elevation and Freezing Point Depression Constants for some Common Solvents.

Solvent	K_b(°C/m)	Normal Boiling Point (T_b)	K_f(°C/m)	Normal Freezing Point (T_f)
Acetic Acid	3.08	117.9	3.90	16.6
Benzene	2.53	80.1	5.12	5.5
Chloroform	3.63	61.8	4.68	−63.5
Carbon Tetrachloride	5.03	76.7	29.8	−22.9
Ethanol	1.22	78.2	1.99	−114.1
Diethyl Ether	2.02	34.6	1.79	−116.3
Water	0.512	100.0	1.86	0.0

solution will boil at 100.512°C instead of 100.000°C (which the boiling point of pure water). In other words:

$$\Delta T_b = 0.512°C = T_b(solution) - T_b(solvent)$$

Therefore:

$$T_b(solution) = T_b(solvent) + 0.512°C = 100.000°C + 0.512°C = \textbf{100.512°C}$$

However, what about ionic compounds which dissociate into multiple ionic species in solution? Because ionic compounds dissociate, we should observe a more pronounced effect on the elevation of the boiling of solutions. For instance, regarding our previous example of a sucrose solution, we should theoretically achieve the same elevation in boiling point by dissolving half as many moles of *NaCl* in the same mass of water, 1.00 *kg*. This is because the issue is the number of particles in solution, not the necessarily the moles of the compound dissolved. Because ionic compounds dissolve in water by dissociation into freely solvated ions, the dissolution of a given amount of an ionic compound will result in a larger number of moles of dissolved particles. To make this a little clearer, we can represent the dissolution of *NaCl* with the following equation:

$$NaCl(s) \xrightarrow{H_2O} Na^+(aq) + Cl^-(aq)$$

Here we can clearly see that if 0.500 *mol NaCl* is dissolved in water, this will result in 0.500 *mol Na*$^+$ and 0.500 *mol Cl*$^-$ in the solution. This is a total of 1.000 *mol* of solute particles. Hence, dissolution of 0.500 *mol NaCl* in 1.00 *kg* water at 1 *atm* will result in a solution that boils at 100.512°C. This is because one mole of the formula unit, *NaCl*, dissociates into two moles of dissolved particles as shown above. This ratio of dissolved particles to dissolved formula units (when dealing with strong electrolytes) is referred to as the **van't Hoff factor (*i*)**.

$$i = \frac{moles\ of\ particles\ in\ solution}{moles\ of\ formula\ units\ dissolved}$$

We use the van't Hoff factor to modify the equation for boiling point elevation as follows:

$$\Delta T_b = iK_b m$$

The *van't Hoff factor* will always be unity (*i* = 1) for nonelectrolytes. Table 5.5 summarizes the van't Hoff factor for some common solutes. Notice that there are "expected" values along with actual measured values for the van't Hoff factor. This is because most electrolytes deviate from ideal behavior, and the van't Hoff factor is usually lower than expected. For example, for an electrolyte such as *NaCl* we would expect a van't Hoff factor of 2. However, from experiments we know that *i* varies with concentration. In fact, it is observed that *i* decreases with increasing concentration. In other words, the observed van't Hoff factor approaches "ideal" behavior with increasing

Table 5.5 Expected and Observed van't Hoff Factors of Selected Compounds (for 0.05 m solutions).

Electrolyte	i (expected)	i (observed)
$NaCl$	2.0	1.9
KCl	2.0	1.85
$MgCl_2$	3.0	2.7
$MgSO_4$	2.0	1.3
$FeCl_3$	4.0	3.4
HCl	2.0	1.9
Sucrose	1.0	1.0

Jacobus H. van't Hoff was the first recipient of the Nobel Prize in chemistry. A physical chemist born in 1852, van't Hoff's work in the areas of chemical kinetics, equilibrium, and stereochemistry is foundational to modern physical chemistry.

dilution (very low concentration). We see from Table 5.5 that the value of i for a 0.05 m $NaCl$ solution is actually 1.9.

One way to understand the deviation from ideal behavior is to understand that positive ions will tend to aggregate near negative ions and vice versa. In other words, even though electrolytes dissociate into freely solvated ions, the ions are not "completely" independent. This is further demonstrated when we consider that multiple charged ions exhibit larger deviations from ideal behavior than do singly charged ions. For example, the expected van't Hoff factor for $FeCl_3$ is $i = 4$, and the empirically determined value is 3.4 (at 0.05 m concentration). Here the iron(III) ion is triply charged and exhibits a much greater deviation from ideal behavior than does $NaCl$ with its expected and actual van't Hoff factors of 2.0 and 1.9, respectively.

Example Problem 5.19

Assuming ideal behavior, what mass of potassium chloride must be added to 0.500 kg of water to produce a boiling point of 103.0°C assuming ideal behavior? ($K_b = 0.512$°C/m for water)

Solution:	
First, it is important to recognize that KCl is a strong electrolyte and therefore, exhibits an "ideal" van't Hoff factor of $i = 2$.	$$KCl(s) \xrightarrow{H_2O} K^+(aq) + Cl^-(aq)$$ $$\Delta T_b = iK_bm = (2)K_bm$$
Second, since $T_b(solution)=103.0$°C and $T_b(solvent) = 100.0$°C, we can solve for ΔT_b.	$$\Delta T_b = T_b(solution) - T_b(solvent)$$ $$\Delta T_b = 103.0°C - 100.0°C = \mathbf{3.0°C}$$
Next, we rearrange the boiling point elevation equations to yield an expression for the required concentration of KCl (molality).	$$\Delta T_b = iK_bm$$ $$m = \frac{\Delta T_b}{iK_b}$$ $$m = \frac{3.0°C}{(2)(0.512°C/m)} = \mathbf{2.92969\,m}$$

Because we know that the solution will contain 0.500 *kg* water, we can solve for moles of *KCl*	$m = \dfrac{moles\ solute}{mass\ solvent\ (kg)}$ $moles\ KCl = (m) \bullet (kg\ water)$ $\left(2.92968\ \dfrac{mol\ KCl}{kg\ H_2O}\right)(0.500\ kg\ H_2O) = \mathbf{1.464844\ mol\ KCl}$
Finally, we convert the moles of *KCl* to units of mass. (Molar mass = 74.55 g/mol)	$1.464844\ mol\ KCl \times \dfrac{74.55\ g\ KCl}{1\ mol\ KCl} = 109.20412\ g\ KCl$ $= \mathbf{110\ g\ KCl}$

Therefore, we know that it will require 110 *g KCl* to elevate the boiling point 0.500 *kg* of water to 103.0°C.

Freezing Point Depression

Just as the dissolution of a solute into a solvent alters the boiling point, so too does it alter the freezing point. *The freezing point of a solution will be lower than that of the pure solvent.* This phenomenon is referred to as **freezing point depression** and is given by the following expression:

$$\Delta T_f = iK_f m$$

Again, where ΔT_f represents the deviation of the freezing point of the solution from that of the pure solvent. K_f is the **molal freezing point depression constant**, i is the van't Hoff factor and m is the molality of the solution. K_f is given in units of °C/m just as before (Table 5.4). However, ΔT_f is defined a little differently than ΔT_b. Because the freezing point of the solution is lower than that of the pure solvent, ΔT_f is defined as follows:

$$\Delta T_f = T_f(solvent) - T_f(solution)$$

Just as before, if we calculate the freezing point of a 1.00 *m* sucrose, a 0.500 *m NaCl* and a 0.25 *m Na₃PO₄* solution, we will theoretically arrive at the same freezing point for all three, −1.86°C (*assuming ideal behavior*). This is because K_f = 1.86°C/m for water, and each of these solutions contains 1.00 mole of particles dissolved in 1 *kg* of water. Figure 5.10 summarizes the relationships between solution concentration, boiling point elevation, and freezing point depression.

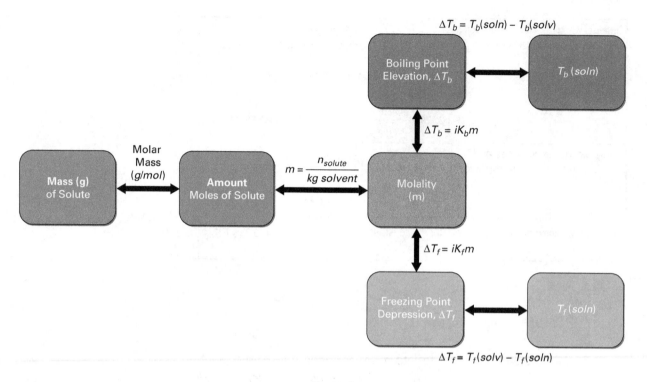

Figure 5.10 Flow-chart summary of the relationships involved in calculation of the boiling and freezing points of solutions.

Example Problem 5.20

Determine the freezing point of a solution consisting of 1.46 g glycerin ($C_3H_8O_3$) dissolved in 400.0 g of water.

Solution:	
First, we determine the moles of glycerin.	$1.46 \ g \ C_3H_8O_3 \times \dfrac{1 \ mol \ C_3H_8O_3}{92.11 \ g \ C_3H_8O_3} = 0.0158506 \ mol \ C_3H_8O_3$
Second, we can calculate the molality of our solution since we are given the mass of our solvent, water.	$m = \dfrac{0.0158506 \ mol \ C_3H_8O_3}{400.0 \ g \times \dfrac{1 \ kg}{1000 \ g}} = 0.03962653 \ m \ C_3H_8O_3$
Next, since we recognize that glycerin is a nonelectrolyte, we know that $i = 1$. We now have defined all variables needed to calculate ΔT_f.	$\Delta T_f = iK_f m$ $\Delta T_f = (1)(1.86°C/m)(0.03962653\ m) = 0.0737053°C$
Finally, we rearrange our equation to derive an expression for T_f(**solution**) and solve.	$\Delta T_f = T_f(solvent) - T_f(solution)$ $T_f(solution) = T_f(solvent) - \Delta T_f$ $T_f(solution) = 0.00°C - 0.0737053°C = -0.0737°C$
Therefore, we have determined that the solution composed of 1.46 g glycerin and 400.0 g water will exhibit a freezing point of -0.0737°C.	

Osmosis

Another property of solutions is their tendency to undergo *osmosis*. **Osmosis** is the net flow of solvent molecules from a solution of lower concentration to a solution of higher concentration. Osmosis will typically occur in circumstances where a semipermeable barrier or membrane separates two solutions. A **semipermeable membrane** is a thin barrier which allows only certain types of molecules to pass through the barrier while blocking others. A common example of this phenomenon is often illustrated by description of an osmotic cell. Figure 5.11 depicts a simple osmotic cell wherein a sample of pure water is separated from a sample of salt solution. The two liquids are separated by a semipermeable membrane which allows only water to pass through. Initially, the "water level" on each side of the cell is the same. However, with time, the water preferentially (by osmosis) flows from the pure water side of the cell through the membrane to the salt solution. The result is the "water level" on the right side of the cell rises while that on the left is reduced. As the solution side of the cell rises, it exerts increasingly higher pressure (due to its weight). Eventually, the pressure exerted by the column of solution counterbalances the pressure of the osmotic flow and an equilibrium of forces is achieved. The pressure where this equilibrium is achieved is called the osmotic pressure. Put more simply, **osmotic pressure** is the pressure required to just stop osmotic flow. While this pressure will always be achieved at some point (equilibrium) in any osmosis experiment, it can also be achieved artificially simply by applying the osmotic pressure externally. The osmotic pressure at any time is a function of the solution concentration (molarity) and can be calculated as follows:

$$\Pi = icRT$$

Figure 5.11 The rate of solvent flow across a semipermeable membrane is greater from pure solvent to solution than it is from solution to pure solvent (a), causing the "water level" on the solution side of the membrane to rise. As the water level rises it exerts an ever increasing pressure in opposition to the net flow of solvent until it is sufficient to stop osmotic flow (equilibrium). This pressure at equilibrium is referred to as the osmotic pressure (b). This can also be accomplished through an applied external pressure (c).

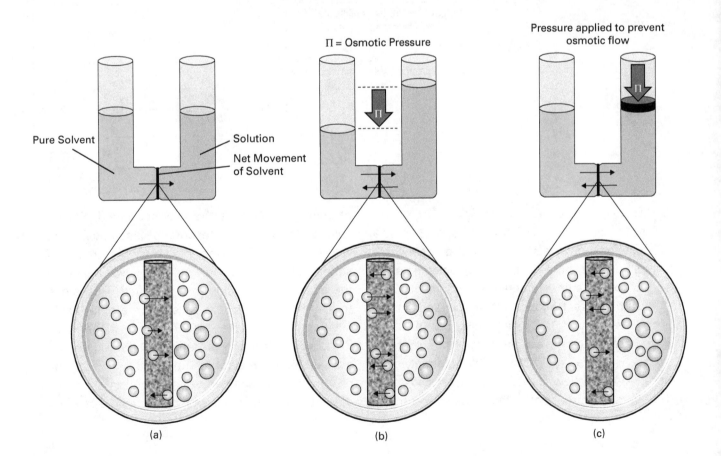

(a) (b) (c)

Figure 5.12 A semipermeable membrane may operate on the basis of size-exclusion, where large solvated ions or dissolved molecules cannot pass through pores/channels.

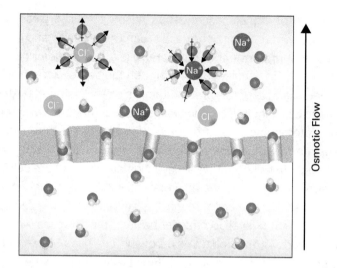

Where Π is the osmotic pressure (in atmospheres), i is the van't Hoff factor, c is the concentration of the solution (molarity), T is the temperature (in Kelvin) and R is the "ideal gas constant (0.08206 $atm \cdot L/mol \cdot K$). An *atmosphere* (*atm*) is a unit of pressure equivalent to the atmospheric pressure of the Earth at sea level. We cover units of pressure and the ideal gas constant in more detail in Chapter 6.

Example Problem 5.21

Calculate the osmotic pressure exerted by a solution that is 0.15 M in solute particles at a temperature of 25°C.	
Solution:	
First, convert the temperature of 25°C to the Kelvin temperature scale.	$K = °C + 273$ $= 25°C + 273 = \mathbf{298\ K}$
Next, simply apply the given information to the equation for osmotic pressure.	$\Pi = cRT$ $\Pi = \left(0.15\ \dfrac{mol}{L} \right)\left(0.08206\ \dfrac{atm \cdot L}{mol \cdot K} \right)\left(298\ K \right) = \mathbf{3.67\ atm}$

Did you know how chemistry might relate to your job as a non-chemist? Osmosis is of particular interest for individuals in the field of healthcare. This is because the cells in living organisms behave as semipermeable membranes, and the balance of solute concentrations both inside and outside living cells must be maintained. For example, dehydrated patients are often rehydrated intravenously. However, it is not possible to simply allow pure water to flow directly into a patient's vein. The IV solution must have the same concentration of solute particles as the patient's blood. Such a solution is said to be **isotonic** (or isosmotic). Pure water (or a solution with a lower concentration of solute) is **hypotonic** and would result in swelling of the blood cells, causing them to burst. This is due to osmotic flow into the cells. On the other hand, solutions with solute concentrations higher than the physiological concentrations in the blood cells are said to be **hypertonic**. Intravenous introduction of a hypertonic solution would result in shriveling of the blood cells (due to net osmotic flow of water out of the cells). It is for this reason that patients are hydrated using 0.9% saline solution (0.16 *M NaCl*) rather than pure water. This concentration is isotonic and results in no deleterious effects.

You may have also heard that ingestion of seawater or salt water produces an illness referred to as **hypernatremia.** Again, this is due to the effects of osmosis. Hypernatemia is essentially characterized as a severe disruption of *osmoregulation* of the tissues of the body due to ingestion of fluids with very high concentrations of sodium (hypertonic fluids).

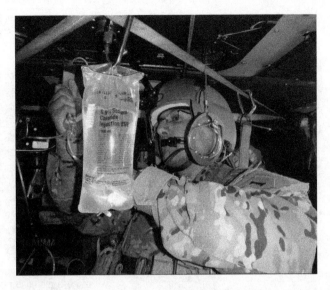

Patients are hydrated intravenously using a 0.9% sodium chloride solution. Here we see U.S. Army Spc. Israel Figueroa preparing an IV bag for use aboard a UH-60 Black Hawk helicopter during a medical evacuation mission in Zabul province, Afghanistan, Jan. 2, 2014.

Colligative Properties and Determination of Molar Mass

In Chapter 4 we learned how to calculate the molecular formula of a compound from the empirical formula if we also know the molar mass of the compound. However, how is it possible to know the molar mass of the compound in question if we do not know what its formula is? An understanding of colligative properties provides an answer to this question. By measuring the freezing point depression, boiling point elevation, or change in vapor pressure of a solution prepared from a known mass of solute (the identity of which is unknown), we can calculate the concentration and moles of solute. Taken together, the mass of the solute and the corresponding number of moles of solute allow for calculation of molar mass. The following example problem provides further illustration of how molar mass is calculated from colligative properties.

Example Problem 5.22

If 90.0 g of a nonelectrolyte solute is dissolved into 0.500 kg of water and the boiling point is measured and found to be 101.48°C, what is the molar mass of the unknown solute? ($K_b = 0.512$°C/m for water)

	Solution:
First, we determine the boiling point elevation for the solution.	$\Delta T_b = T_b(solution) - T_b(solvent)$ $\Delta T_b = 101.48$°C $- 100.0$°C $= \mathbf{1.48}$°**C**
Second, recognizing the $i = 1$ for nonelectrolytes, derive an expression for the molality of the solution.	$\Delta T_b = iK_b m$ $m = \dfrac{\Delta T_b}{iK_b}$ $m = \dfrac{1.48°C}{(1)(0.512°C/m)} = \mathbf{2.890625\,m}$
Understanding that the solution contains 0.500 kg of water, we can use the concentration as a conversion factor to calculate the moles of solute.	$0.500\,kg\,H_2O \times \dfrac{2.890625\,mol\,solute}{1\,kg\,H_2O} = \mathbf{1.445313\,mol\,solute.}$
Since we have determined the moles of unknown solute, we can use this data with the given mass to calculate the molar mass.	$Molar\,Mass = \dfrac{90.0\,g}{1.445313\,mol} = 62.27025\,\dfrac{g}{mol} = \mathbf{62.3\,\dfrac{g}{mol}}$

Therefore, we have empirically determined the unknown compound to have molar mass of 62.3 g/mol. The unknown compound was, in fact, ethylene glycol ($C_2H_6O_2$) with an actual molar mass of 62.1 g/mol. Our empirical determination provided a reasonable value. More careful measurement of $T_b(solution)$ will likely produce a value closer to the actual molar mass.

Key Terms

1. Acid
2. Acid/base neutralization reaction
3. Aqueous solution
4. Base
5. Boiling point elevation
6. Colligative properties
7. Complete ionic equation
8. Concentration
9. Dissociation
10. Double displacement reaction
11. Electric dipole
12. Electrolyte
13. Freezing point depression

14. Gas evolving reaction

15. Hypernatremia

16. Hypertonic

17. Hypotonic

18. Insoluble

19. Isotonic

20. Mass percent

21. Metathesis reaction

22. Molal boiling point elevation constant

23. Molal freezing point depression constant

24. Molality

25. Molarity

26. Mole fraction

27. Molecular equation

28. Net ionic equation

29. Nonelectrolyte

30. Osmosis

31. Polar

32. Polar bond

33. Polar molecule

34. Precipitate

35. Precipitation reaction

36. Raoult's law

37. Solubility

38. Soluble

39. Solute

40. Solution

41. Solvated

42. Solvation sphere

43. Solvent

44. Spectator ion

45. Strong acid

46. Strong electrolyte

47. van't Hoff Factor

48. Vapor pressure

49. Weak acid

50. Weak electrolyte

Problems

AQUEOUS SOLUTIONS OF IONIC COMPOUNDS AND PREDICTING SOLUBILITY

1. What is an electrolyte? What general class of compounds are electrolytes?

2. What is a weak electrolyte? What general class of compounds are weak electrolytes?

3. Describe the mechanism of the dissolution of ionic compounds in water. How does the polarity of water play a role?

4. What is meant by the term solvated?

5. Using the solubility rules, determine whether the following compounds are soluble or insoluble in water.

   a. $CaCl_2$

   b. Li_2SO_4

   c. CaS

   d. $Fe_3(PO_4)_2$

6. Using the solubility rules, determine whether the following compounds are soluble or insoluble in water.

   a. $PbSO_4$

   b. $NaNO_3$

   c. BaS

   d. $Pb(ClO_3)_2$

7. Using the solubility rules, determine whether the following compounds are soluble or insoluble in water.

   a. Hg_2Br_2

   b. K_2CO_3

   c. $Ca(NO_3)_2$

   d. $BaBr_2$

8. Using the solubility rules, determine whether the following compounds are soluble or insoluble in water.

   a. $MgCl_2$

   b. $Ba(C_2H_3O_2)_2$

   c. Rb_2S

   d. $CsOH$

9. Which of the following is an electrolyte? Explain your answers.

   a. $C_{12}H_{22}O_{11}$

   b. $NaCl$

    c. $MgBr_2$

    d. $Mg(C_2H_3O_2)_2$

10.   Which of the following is an electrolyte? Explain your answers.

    a. PCl_3

    b. $Fe(NO_3)_3$

    c. $SrSO_4$

    d. C_3H_7OH

11.   Write a balanced equation depicting the dissolution of the following compounds in water.

    a. K_2CO_3

    b. $Ca(NO_3)_2$

    c. $Ba(C_2H_3O_2)_2$

    d. Li_2SO_4

12.   Write a balanced equation depicting the dissolution of the following compounds in water.

    a. $NaCl$

    b. K_2SO_4

    c. $Mg(ClO_4)_2$

    d. HCl

13.   Write a balanced equation depicting the dissolution of the following compounds in water.

    a. KOH

    b. $(NH_4)_2CO_3$

    c. Na_2SO_4

    d. K_3PO_4

14.   Write a balanced equation depicting the dissolution of the following compounds in water.

    a. NH_4NO_3

    b. $NaOH$

    c. Li_2S

    d. CsI

15.   How many total moles of ions are present in solution when the following are dissolved in water?

    a.   8.00 g $NaCl$

    b.   8.00 g $NaOH$

    c.   10.00 g $NaCl$

    d.   10.00 g $NaOH$

16. How many total moles of ions are present in solution when the following are dissolved in water?

    a. 4.72 g $NaC_2H_3O_2$

    b. 1.33 g K_2SO_4

    c. 11.34 g $Fe_2(SO_4)_3$

    d. 5.66 g $Pb(NO_3)_2$

17. How many ions are present in solution when the following are dissolved in water?

    a. 47.12 g K_3PO_4

    b. 13.56 g $CuSO_4 \cdot 5H_2O$

    c. 4.22 g Na_3PO_4

    d. 6.22 g NH_4Cl

18. How many ions are present in solution when the following are dissolved in water?

    a. 5.55 g K_2SO_4

    b. 3.11 g $CoCl_2$

    c. 3.11 g $CoCl_2 \cdot 6H_2O$

    d. 2.67 g $Fe_2(SO_4)_3$

WRITING CHEMICAL EQUATIONS OF REACTIONS IN AQUEOUS SOLUTION—PRECIPITATION REACTIONS

19. Balance the following reaction equations and write the complete and net ionic equations for each one (complete with the physical state (*s, l, g, or aq*) of each ion or compound noted in the equation).

    a. $Pb(NO_3)_2 + KI \rightarrow PbI_2 + KNO_3$

    b. $NaOH + Mg(C_2H_3O_2)_2 \rightarrow NaC_2H_3O_2 + Mg(OH)_2$

20. Balance the following reaction equations and write the complete and net ionic equations for each one (complete with the physical state (*s, l, g, or aq*) of each ion or compound noted in the equation).

    a. $Li_2S + Ca(ClO_3)_2 \rightarrow LiClO_3 + CaS$

    b. $Mn(NO_3)_2 + Li_3PO_4 \rightarrow Mn_3(PO_4)_2 + LiNO_3$

21. Write the balanced complete and net ionic equations for the reaction, if any, that occurs when solutions of sodium sulfate and barium chloride are mixed.

22. Write the balanced complete and net ionic equations for the reaction, if any, that occurs when solutions of sodium chloride and silver nitrate are mixed.

23. Write the balanced complete and net ionic equations for the reaction, if any, that occurs when solutions of potassium phosphate and lithium chloride are mixed.

24. Write the balanced complete and net ionic equations for the reaction, if any, that occurs when solutions of nickel(II) bromide and ammonium sulfide are mixed.

WRITING CHEMICAL EQUATIONS OF REACTIONS IN AQUEOUS SOLUTION— ACID/BASE NEUTRALIZATIONS AND GAS EVOLVING REACTIONS

25. Explain the difference between a strong acid and a strong base.

26. Explain the difference between strong and weak acids.

27. Write the molecular, complete ionic, and net ionic equations for the following combinations of acids and bases.

   a. $HCl(aq) + NaOH(aq)$

   b. $H_2SO_4(aq) + Ba(OH)_2(aq)$

   c. $HCl(aq) + Ca(OH)_2(aq)$

28. Write the molecular, complete ionic, and net ionic equations for the following combinations of acids and bases.

   a. $HNO_3(aq) + NaOH(aq)$

   b. $H_2SO_4(aq) + KOH(aq)$

   c. $HI(aq) + Sr(OH)_2(aq)$

29. Write balanced molecular, complete ionic, and net ionic equations for the following gas evolving reactions.

   a. $HCl(aq) + Na_2S(aq) \rightarrow$

   b. $HClO_4(aq) + K_2CO_3(aq) \rightarrow$

   c. $H_2SO_4(aq) + K_2SO_3(aq) \rightarrow$

30. Write balanced molecular, complete ionic, and net ionic equations for the following gas evolving reactions.

   a. $HBr(aq) + NaHCO_3(aq) \rightarrow$

   b. $HNO_3(aq) + K_2S(aq) \rightarrow$

   c. $H_3PO_4(aq) + NiCO_3(aq) \rightarrow$

SOLUTION CONCENTRATION—MOLARITY AND DILUTION

31. Calculate the molarity of each of the following solutions.

   a. 16.31 g $NaCl$ in 167.0 ml of solution.

   b. 12.31 g $C_{12}H_{22}O_{11}$ in 556.0 ml of solution.

   c. 3.65 g Na_2CO_3 in 150.00 ml of solution.

32. Calculate the molarity of each of the following solutions.

    a. 2.33 g $Al_2(SO_4)_3$ in 75.00 ml of solution.

    b. 6.12 g KCl in 45.00 ml of solution.

    c. 23.11 g $CaCl_2$ in 500.0 ml solution.

33. What mass of Na_2SO_4 will be required to prepare 500 ml of a 1.50 M Na_2SO_4 solution?

34. What mass of $NaOH$ is required to prepare 250 ml of a 0.500 M $NaOH$ solution?

35. What volume of a 1.00 M KOH solution contains 5.61 g KOH?

36. What volume of a 0.453 M $MgSO_4$ solution contains 2.311 g $MgSO_4$?

37. What mass of K_2CO_3 is required to produce 500 ml of a solution that has a K^+ concentration of 0.150 M?

38. If a 1.75 M $MgCl_2$ is prepared, what is the concentration (molarity) of Cl^- ions?

39. What is the concentration (molarity) of acetate ions in the following solutions?

    a. 0.125 M $NaC_2H_3O_2$

    b. 0.125 M $Mg(C_2H_3O_2)_2$

    c. 0.125 M $Al(C_2H_3O_2)_3$

40. What is the concentration (molarity) of ammonium ions in the following solutions?

    a. 0.300 M $NH_4C_2H_3O_2$

    b. 0.300 M $(NH_4)_2SO_4$

    c. 0.300 M $(NH_4)_3PO_4$

41. How many moles of sulfate ions are present in the following solutions?

    a. 42.6 ml of 0.125 M $ZnSO_4$

    b. 77.22 ml 0.255 M $Al_2(SO_4)_3$

    c. 3.89 ml of 0.413 M $(NH_4)_2SO_4$

42. How many moles of nitrate ions are present in the following solutions?

    a. 1.33 ml of 0.478 M NH_4NO_3

    b. 0.550 ml of 1.67 M $Al(NO_3)_3$

    c. 26.75 ml of 0.250 M $Mg(NO_3)_2$

43. What volume of a 5.00 M $BaCl_2$ solution is required to prepare 500.0 ml of a 0.200 M $BaCl_2$ solution?

44. What volume of a 12.00 *M HCl* solution is required to prepare 225.0 *ml* of a 1.25 *M HCl* solution?

45. If 10.00 *ml* of a 0.156 *M SrCl$_2$* solution is diluted to 75.00 *ml*, what is the concentration (molarity) of the diluted solution?

46. If 150.00 *ml* of a 1.13 *M NaOH* solution is diluted to 765.0 *ml*, what is the concentration (molarity) of the diluted solution?

47. A sucrose solution is diluted from 100.0 *ml* to 565.0 *ml* and a new (diluted) concentration of 1.56 *M*. What is the initial concentration of the sucrose solution?

48. An *NH$_4$NO$_3$* solution is diluted from 50.00 *ml* to 325.0 *ml* and a new (diluted) concentration of 0.0750 *M*. What was the initial concentration of the *NH$_4$NO$_3$* solution?

49. To what volume must you dilute 10.00 *ml* of a 15.0 *M HNO$_3$* solution to achieve a concentration of 1.45 *M*?

50. To what volume must you dilute 75.00 *ml* of a 3.50 *M NaOH* solution to achieve a concentration of 0.850 *M*?

SOLUTION CONCENTRATION—MOLALITY, MOLE FRACTION, AND MASS PERCENT

51. Calculate the molality of the following solutions.

    a. 36.19 *g* of ethanol (C_2H_5OH) in 1.15 *kg* of water.

    b. 23.67 *g HClO$_4$* in 450.0 *g* of water.

    c. 86.45 *g K$_3$PO$_4$* in 546 *g* of water.

52. Calculate the molality of the following solutions.

    a. 42.49 *g* of isopropyl alcohol (C_3H_7OH) in 965 *g* of water.

    b. 25.72 *g* ethylene glycol ($C_2H_6O_2$) in 333.0 *g* of water.

    c. 86.45 *g Ba(NO$_3$)$_2$* in 678 *g* of water.

53. Calculate the mole fraction of the solute in the following solutions.

    a. 36.19 *g* of ethanol (C_2H_5OH) in 1.15 *kg* of water.

    b. 23.67 *g HClO$_4$* in 450.0 *g* of water.

    c. 86.45 *g K$_3$PO$_4$* in 546 *g* of water.

54. Calculate the mole fraction of the solute in the following solutions.

    a. 42.49 *g* of isopropyl alcohol (C_3H_7OH) in 965 *g* of water.

    b. 25.72 *g* ethylene glycol ($C_2H_6O_2$) in 333.0 *g* of water.

    c. 86.45 *g Ba(NO$_3$)$_2$* in 678 *g* of water.

55. Calculate the mass percent of the following solutions.

    a. 36.19 g of ethanol (C_2H_5OH) in 1.15 kg of water.

    b. 23.67 g $HClO_4$ in 450.0 g of water.

    c. 86.45 g K_3PO_4 in 546 g of water.

56. Calculate the mass percent of the following solutions.

    a. 42.49 g of isopropyl alcohol (C_3H_7OH) in 965 g of water.

    b. 25.72 g ethylene glycol ($C_2H_6O_2$) in 333.0 g of water.

    c. 86.45 g $Ba(NO_3)_2$ in 678 g of water.

57. An aqueous solution is 31.00 % H_2SO_4 by mass. Express this concentration in molality and mole fraction.

58. An aqueous solution is 17.00 % $NaHCO_3$ by mass. Express this concentration in molality and mole fraction.

59. Give the concentration of a 0.567 m $SrCl_2$ solution in units of mass percent and mole fraction.

60. Give the concentration of a 1.41 m K_2SO_4 solution in units of mass percent and mole fraction.

STOICHIOMETRY OF REACTIONS IN SOLUTION

61. What volume (in milliliters) of 0.133 M H_2SO_4 is required to completely react with 5.00 ml of a 0.100 M NaOH solution according to the following reaction equation?

$$H_2SO_4(aq) + 2\,NaOH(aq) \rightarrow Na_2SO_4(aq) + 2\,H_2O(l)$$

62. What volume (in milliliters) of 0.245 M $Pb(NO_3)_2$ is required to completely react with 12.00 ml of a 0.250 M KI solution according to the following reaction equation?

$$Pb(NO_3)_2(aq) + 2\,KI(aq) \rightarrow PbI_2(s) + 2\,KNO_3(aq)$$

63. When 15.67 ml of 0.250 M NaCl is mixed with 23.11 ml of 0.187 M $Ba(NO_3)_2$ a precipitation reaction occurs according to the reaction equation below. This reaction was carried out and 0.351 g of $BaCl_2$ was recovered.

$$2\,NaCl(aq) + Ba(NO_3)_2(aq) \rightarrow BaCl_2(s) + 2\,NaNO_3(aq)$$

Determine the following:

a. Limiting reagent

b. Theoretical yield ($BaCl_2$)

c. % Yield

64. When 308.3 *ml* of 4.78 *M* HNO_3 is allowed to react with 15.75 *g Al* a reaction occurs according to the reaction equation below. This reaction was carried out, and 1.12 *g* of H_2 gas was recovered.

$$2\,Al(s) + 6\,HNO_3(aq) \rightarrow 2\,Al(NO_3)_3(aq) + 3\,H_2(g)$$

Determine the following:

a. Limiting reagent

b. Theoretical yield (*g* H_2)

c. % Yield

d. The mass of excess reagent remaining after the reaction.

COLLIGATIVE PROPERTIES—RAOULT'S LAW

65. What is the vapor pressure of a solution containing 35.6 *g* glycerin ($C_3H_8O_3$) in 150 *g* water at 35°C? The vapor pressure of pure water at the same temperature is 42.2 *torr*.

66. What is the vapor pressure of a solution containing 25.34 *g* *NaCl* in 132 *g* water at 25°C? The vapor pressure of pure water at the same temperature is 23.76 *torr*.

67. If the vapor pressure of a solution containing an unknown mass of glycerin ($C_3H_8O_3$) and 123 *g* water is 22.86 *torr* at 25°C, what is the mole fraction of water? What is the mole fraction of glycerin?

68. If the vapor pressure of a solution containing sucrose ($C_{12}H_{22}O_{11}$) and 100.0 *g* water is 23.453 *torr* at 25°C, what is the mole fraction of sucrose? What is the mass (*g*) of sucrose in the solution?

69. If the vapor pressure of a solution containing 23.88 *g* of an unknown carbohydrate and 250 *g* water is 26.204 *torr* at 27°C, what is the mole fraction of water in the solution? What is the molar mass of the unknown? (The vapor pressure of pure water at 27°C is 26.74 *torr*.)

COLLIGATIVE PROPERTIES—BOILING POINT ELEVATION AND FREEZING POINT DEPRESSION

70. Which of the following solutions has a higher boiling point?

a. 27.00 *g* of ethanol (C_2H_5OH) in 350 *g* water.

b. 27.00 *g* of isopropanol (C_3H_7OH) in 350 *g* water.

71. Which of the following solutions has a higher boiling point?

a. 17.00 *g* of glucose ($C_6H_{12}O_6$) in 200 *g* water.

b. 17.00 *g* of sucrose ($C_{12}H_{22}O_{11}$) in 200 *g* water.

72. What is the boiling point of a solution comprised of 20.00 g of ethanol (C_2H_5OH) in 200.0 g water?

73. What is the boiling point of a solution comprised of 15.00 g of potassium chloride (KCl) in 200.0 g water? (Assume ideal behavior respecting the van't Hoff factor.)

74. What is the boiling point of a solution comprised of 15.00 g of isopropanol (C_3H_7OH) in 200 g water?

75. What is the boiling point of 0.198 m glucose in water?

76. What is the boiling point of 0.267 m ethylene glycol in water?

77. What is the boiling point of a solution prepared by dissolving 23.4 g spartiene ($C_{15}H_{26}N_2$) in 523 g of chloroform. The boiling point of pure chloroform is 61.7°C.

78. Which of the following solutions has a lower freezing point?

    a. 27.00 g of ethanol (C_2H_5OH) in 350 g water.

    b. 27.00 g of isopropanol (C_3H_7OH) in 350 g water.

79. Which of the following solutions has a lower freezing point?

    a. 15.00 g of t-butylphenol ($C_{10}H_{14}O$) in 200 g ethanol.

    b. 15.00 g of butyrolactone ($C_4H_6O_2$) in 200 g ethanol.

80. What is the freezing point of an aqueous 0.224 m sucrose solution?

81. What is the freezing point of an aqueous 0.885 m glycerin solution?

82. What is the freezing point of a solution consisting of 19.34 g of t-butylpehnol ($C_{10}H_{14}O$) and 340 g ethanol?

83. What is the freezing point of a solution consisting of 12.37 g of butyrolactone ($C_4H_6O_2$) in 200.0 g of benzene?

84. The boiling point of a solution which contains 32.65 g of an unknown organic compound dissolved in 334 g of diethyl ether is 35.517°C. If the boiling point of pure ethyl ether is 34.5°C, what is the molar mass of the unknown compound?

85. The boiling point is found to be 78.745°C for a solution that consists of 45.32 g of an unknown organic compound dissolved in 298 g of ethanol. If the empirical formula of the compound was determined to be $C_{11}H_{22}O$ by combustion analysis, what is its molecular formula?

86. The freezing point is found to be –64.221°C for a solution consisting of 10.50 g of an unknown organic compound and 342 g or chloroform. If the freezing point of pure chloroform is –63.5°C and the empirical formula of the unknown compound is found to be $C_5H_8O_2$ by combustion analysis, what is the molecular formula of the unknown?

COLLIGATIVE PROPERTIES—OSMOSIS

87. Explain what is meant by Isotonic.

88. Explain what is meant by hypertonic and hypotonic.

89. What is the osmotic pressure of a 500.0-ml solution containing 5.50 g of glycerin ($C_3H_8O_3$) at 25°C?

90. What mass of sucrose ($C_{12}H_{22}O_{11}$) is required to achieve an osmotic pressure of 4.34 atm when combined with enough water to generate 345 ml of solution at 25°C?

Image Credits

Gases

| LEARNING OBJECTIVES AND OUTCOMES |

After reading this chapter, you should be able to do the following:

- Perform conversions between various units of pressure when dealing with gases.

- Perform calculations involving simple gas laws (Boyle's law, Charles's law, and Avogadro's law).

- Demonstrate an understanding of Ideal Gas Law and perform calculations involving the same.

- Apply the Ideal Gas Law to calculations involving density and stoichiometric calculations involving gases.

- Explain Dalton's law of partial pressures and perform calculations involving mixtures of gases (including mole fraction and collection of gases over water).

- Explain and perform calculations involving deviations from ideal behavior ("real" gases).

- Briefly describe the Kinetic Molecular Theory of Gases (*Special Topics*).

- Define each of the Key Terms listed at the end of the chapter dealing with these concepts.

Section 6.1 Introduction

When one thinks of gases, many thoughts may come to mind. Perhaps you may think of the hot steam of gases erupting from the top of a volcano or the gas emissions that are expelled from the exhaust of your car following the combustion reaction that takes place. Or maybe you think of your gas stove at home, or perhaps it invokes thoughts of gas masks and gas cylinders. As we saw in Chapter 2, gases are one of the fundamental states of matter that we discussed (the other two being solids and liquids). What distinguishes a gas from a solid or a liquid really is the vast separation of the individual gas particles, which, unlike the other two states of matter, essentially makes colorless gases invisible to the human eye. In fact, because most gases are difficult to observe directly, we study gases essentially through the use of four physical properties: *pressure, volume, temperature, and number (or amount) of particles (moles)*, all of which will be discussed in this chapter as they relate to **gas laws**, which are statements (usually mathematical expressions) that describe the behavior of gases. Furthermore, we also know that gases can come in many forms. For example, we know that gases can be in the pure form and made up of individual atoms (i.e. the noble gases), they can be diatomic molecular elements (such as oxygen, O_2), or they can be compound molecules such as carbon monoxide, CO. Furthermore, many times we find ourselves dealing with a mixture of different types of gases, such as the air that you are breathing right now. For example, dry air contains approximately 78.09% nitrogen, 20.95% oxygen, 0.93% argon, and 0.039% carbon dioxide, as well as trace amounts of other gases (Table 6.1). A mixture of gases can mix in any proportion, and, as we saw in Chapter 5 with liquids, they are *miscible* with each other. Substances are said to be **miscible** if they can mix together in *any given proportion* to form a homogeneous mixture (a solution). In this chapter, we begin to explore how all of this influences gas laws and the underlying assumptions that we can make when dealing specifically with gases rather than liquids and solids. We also explore the limits of these assumptions and then further investigate how we handle these types of "non-ideal" situations.

Table 6.1 Composition of Dry Air.

Gas	Abundance (%)
Nitrogen	78.09
Oxygen	20.95
Argon	0.93
Carbon Dioxide	0.039
Trace Amounts of Other Gases	

Many thoughts may come to mind when thinking about gases to include gases erupting from the top of a volcano, gas emissions from a car, our gas stoves, gas masks, and gas cylinders.

Section 6.2 **Physical Properties Related to Gas Laws**

Pressure

Pressure (P) is defined as the force applied to the surface of an object (such as the inner surfaces of a container within which the gas is contained) per unit area over which that force is distributed. In other words, pressure is a force per unit area, and we can therefore simply define pressure mathematically as follows:

$$P = \frac{F}{A}$$

Where "*P*" is pressure, "*F*" is normal force, and "*A*" is the area of the contact surface. As we know from our everyday experience involving gases, the pressure or force built up in gases causes them to move from areas of high pressure to areas of lower pressure. For example, if you let air out of a balloon, you notice that the gas rapidly escapes from inside the balloon (area of higher pressure) to the outside environment (area of lower pressure). We have methods to measure the pressure of gases. For example, atmospheric pressure can be measured using a scientific instrument known as a **barometer**, which is commonly used in meteorology (Figure 6.1). The mercury barometer (*Hg* barometer) was invented in 1643 by Evangelista Torricelli, who is most famous for this accomplishment. He was born in 1608 in Italy and died in 1647 at the age of only 39. In fact, one of the many units of measurement for pressure, namely "*torr*", is named in his honor. The torr is defined as $\frac{1}{760}$ of one standard atmosphere (*atm*), with 1 *atm* being defined as atmospheric pressure at sea level (Table 6.2).

Evangelista Torricelli (1608–1647) is most famous as being the inventor of the first mercury barometer in 1643. The unit of pressure "torr", is named after him in his honor. The torr is defined as being of standard atmospheres (atm).

Figure 6.1 The mercury barometer can measure atmospheric pressure and was first invented in 1643 by Evangelista Torricelli.

What are the other units of measurement and how are they mathematically related to each other? Well, the mercury barometer measures the "rise" in the mercury column with the build up of external pressure (Figure 6.1); therefore, we can use this level of "rise" as yet another means for measuring pressure. That is, pressure can also be measured in terms of millimeters or inches of mercury (1 *atm* = 760 *mmHg* = 29.92 *in Hg*). The SI unit of pressure is the pascal (*Pa*). One pascal is defined as one newton (force) per square meter (area), and one mm Hg is equal to $\frac{101,325}{760}$ pascals, or approximately 133.3 *Pa*. We also have the pound per square inch (*psi*), which is yet another commonly used unit to measure pressure. One *atm* of pressure (or 760 *torr*) is equal to approximately 14.7 *psi*. In any event, Table 6.2 contains a summary of these and other commonly used units of pressure

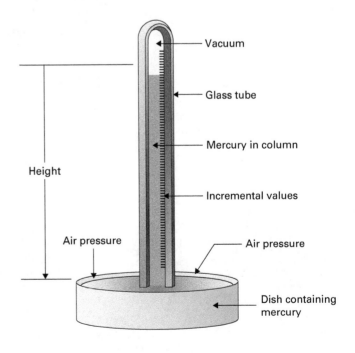

Table 6.2 Table of the various units of pressure.

Unit of Pressure	Numerical Values at Sea Level
atmosphere (*atm*)	1
millimeters of mercury (*mmHg*)	760 (exact)
inches of mercury (*in Hg*)	29.92
torr (*torr*)	760 (exact)
bar (*b*)	1.01325
millibar (*mb*)	1013.25
pounds per square inch (*psi*)	14.7
pascal (*Pa*)	101,325
kilopascal (*kPa*)	101.325

and their mathematical relationships to one another. As we will soon see, converting between these various units will be an important factor in this chapter, so let's do some examples.

Example Problem 6.1

Convert 3.56 atm of pressure to the following units:
a. *mmHg*
b. *in Hg*
c. *torr*
d. *psi*

Solution:

From Table 6.2, we find the conversion factors to all of these and solve using dimensional analysis.

a.) $3.56 \; atm \times \dfrac{760 \; mmHg}{1 \; atm} = 2.71 \times 10^3 \; mmHg$

b.) $3.56 \; atm \times \dfrac{29.92 \; inches \; of \; Hg}{1 \; atm} = 107 \; in \; Hg$

c.) $3.56 \; atm \times \dfrac{760 \; torr}{1 \; atm} = 2.71 \times 10^3 \; torr$

d.) $3.56 \; atm \times \dfrac{14.7 \; psi}{1 \; atm} = 52.3 \; psi$

Did you know how chemistry might relate to your job as a non-chemist? We have all gone to the doctor's office, and one of the very first things the nurse and/or doctor does is to take the patient's blood pressure. Blood pressure is generally taken using a **sphygmomanometer** (in addition to a stethoscope), which was invented by Austrian-Jewish physician Samuel Siegfried Karl Ritter von Basch in 1881 and then improved upon in subsequent years. It is composed of an inflatable cuff designed to collapse and then release arterial flow. The **systolic pressure** is the pressure when the heart is in contraction, while the **diastolic pressure** is the pressure placed on the arterial walls while the heart is at rest. Generally, a systolic pressure of 120–130 *mmHg* and diastolic pressure of 70–80 *mmHg* are considered normal. Notice that the units of pressure are in *mmHg*, one of several units of pressure discussed in this section. If you work in essentially any aspect of the medical profession taking care of patients, then the concept of pressure is very important to you, especially as it relates to blood pressure.

Blood pressure is generally taken using a sphygmomanometer in addition to a stethoscope.

Volume

As we have seen in Chapter 1, **volume (*V*)** is defined as the space occupied by a particular substance. Volume can be measured in various units to include the liter, which will be a very important unit to us later in this chapter. We will see in the following sections that the unit of liters is much more convenient for dealing with gases as opposed to the millimeter, which is a common unit used in dealing with liquids and solids. This is due to the much larger volumes occupied by gases. While we can still use milliliters in some gas law equations (i.e. Charles's law), the liter will be a necessary unit when dealing with certain gas laws (i.e. the ideal gas law). In any event, both of these gas laws will be discussed in this chapter, and we will soon see how the volume is mathematically related to other physical properties, such as the pressure and temperature of a gas.

The volume of gases is mostly occupied by empty space owing to the vast separation of gas particles.

Temperature

In Chapter 1, we also defined **temperature (T)** as a measurement of the average kinetic energy of the molecules or particles that make up a particular sample. As we know, the higher the temperature, the faster the molecules move, resulting in a gas with lower density when compared to cooler gases. This explains why a hot air balloon can rise high in the sky. The air that is heated and trapped in the balloon is warmer (and therefore less dense) than the surrounding cooler, more dense air. Also, recall that temperature can be measured in degrees Celsius (°C) or Fahrenheit (°F), as well as Kelvin (K). In this chapter, we will see that Kelvin is of particular importance to us as we further discuss various gas laws.

The hot air in a hot air balloon is less dense than the surrounding cooler air, therefore the balloon can rise high above the ground.

Moles

The fourth physical property that we must discuss before delving into the simple gas laws is the number of **moles (n)** within a particular gas sample. Recall from Chapter 4 that the mole is the SI unit for the amount of a substance, and that one mole of anything is 6.022×10^{23} entities (or things). This will have implications as it relates to volume in the third simple gas law (Avogadro's law) discussed later in this chapter.

Section 6.3 Simple Gas Laws

Boyle's Law

Robert William Boyle (1627–1691) was an Anglo-Irish chemist/physicist, inventor, and philosopher born in Ireland in 1627. He is most famously known for Boyle's law, which states that the pressure and volume of a gas are inversely related given a constant temperature in a closed system.

Robert William Boyle was an Anglo-Irish chemist/physicist, inventor, and philosopher born in Ireland in 1627. While he had relatively primitive views of the elements, Boyle is widely recognized as one of the founders of modern chemistry. He is most famously known for **Boyle's law**, which states that the pressure and volume of a gas are inversely related given a constant temperature in a closed system. Thus,

$$V \propto \frac{1}{P} \text{ when } n \text{ and } T \text{ are constant}$$

Therefore, when the pressure of a given amount of gas is increased at a fixed temperature, then the volume decreases by a related amount (Figure 6.2). Conversely, if the pressure of a given amount of gas is decreased at a fixed temperature, then the volume increases by a related amount.

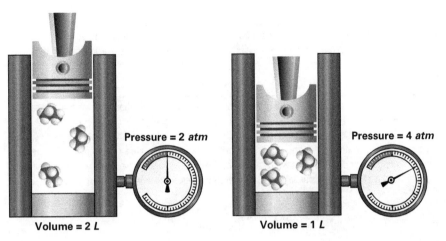

Figure 6.2 Demonstration of Boyle's law. The volume is reduced by half from 2 liters to 1 liter when the pressure doubles from 2 *atm* to 4 *atm*.

Thus, we see in Figure 6.2 that the volume is reduced by half from 2 liters to 1 liter when the pressure doubles from 2 *atm* to 4 *atm*. Notice that in this figure we have two sets of conditions, condition 1 (left) and condition 2 (right). Therefore, we can express this mathematically using Boyle's law:

$$P_1V_1 = P_2V_2$$

Using this law and applying it to the sets of conditions in Figure 6.2 we get:

$$P_1V_1 = P_2V_2$$

$$(2 \, atm) \times (2 \, L) = (4 \, atm) \times (1 \, L)$$

Notice that we get 4 on each side of the equation in this example; therefore, we can also say that *PV = constant* and that pressure and volume are inversely related (when one goes up the other goes down and vice versa). Robert Boyle died in 1691 at the age of 64, but not before publishing *The Sceptical Chymist*, which is seen as a cornerstone book in the field of chemistry. We will now work some examples using Boyle's law.

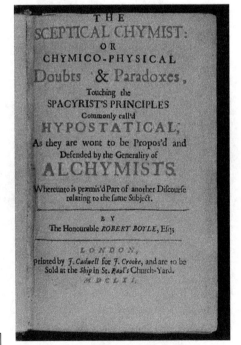

The *Sceptical Chymist* was a book published in London, England, in 1661 by Robert Boyle, who is widely recognized as one of the founders of modern chemistry. The book is presented in the form of a dialogue, in which Boyle presents his hypothesis of matter and atoms.

Example Problem 6.2

A sample of nitrogen gas has a pressure of 1.21 *atm* in a container that has a volume of 2.72 liters. What is the pressure (*atm*) of the gas when it is transferred to a container with a volume of 1.31 liters?
Solution:

| First, notice that there are two sets of conditions here. The first condition involves the gas having a pressure of 1.21 *atm* with a volume of 2.72 *L*. The second condition has a new volume of 1.31 *L*, and it is our job to find the new pressure. All of these types of questions have four variables, three of which are given to you, and you solve for the fourth. First, we recognize this as Boyle's law and set up the equation and solve. | $P_1V_1 = P_2V_2$

$(1.21 \, atm) \times (2.72 \, L) = (x \, atm) \times (1.31 \, L)$

We then simply solve for *x* and get **2.51 *atm*** as our answer.

$P_2 = \dfrac{P_1V_1}{V_2} = \dfrac{(1.21 \, atm)(2.72 \, L)}{1.31 \, L} = \mathbf{2.51 \, atm}$ |

Example Problem 6.3

A sample of carbon dioxide gas has a pressure of 3.71 *atm* in a container that has a volume of 331 *ml*. What is the pressure (*atm*) of the gas when it is transferred to a container with a volume of 2.18 liters?

Solution:

Again, notice that there are two sets of conditions here. The first condition involves the gas having a pressure of 3.71 *atm* with a volume of 331 *ml*. The second condition has a new volume of 2.18 *L*, and it is our job to find the new pressure. Again, notice that there are four variables, three of which are given, and we solve for the fourth. The only difference in this problem when compared to the last example is the units. Notice that we have ml and *L*, so we need to convert one of them so we are dealing with similar units in our solution of this example. Thus, we will first convert ml to *L*.

$$331\ ml \times \frac{1\ L}{1{,}000\ ml} = 0.331\ L$$

Now, we again recognize this as Boyle's law and set up the equation and solve.	$$P_1V_1 = P_2V_2$$ $$(3.71\ atm) \times (0.331\ L) = (x\ atm) \times (2.18\ L)$$ We then simply solve for *x* and get **0.563 *atm*** as our answer.
Notice that if you converted *L* to *ml* instead, you would get the same answer. For these types of problems, you just have to make sure that you have the same units.	$$P_1V_1 = P_2V_2$$ $$P_2 = \frac{P_1V_1}{V_2} = \frac{(3.71\ atm)(331\ ml)}{2180\ ml} = 0.563\ atm$$

Notice that when using Boyle's law, we can really use different units and still arrive at the correct answer. For example, if we take a pressure of 1.09 *atm* (828 *mmHg*) and volume of 2.01 *L* (2,010 *ml*), and solve for the new volume if the pressure is increased to 1.92 *atm* (1,459 *mmHg*), we get the following two possible ways to work this problem:

$$P_1V_1 = P_2V_2$$

$$V_2 = \frac{P_1V_1}{P_2}$$

1.) $V_2 = \dfrac{(1.09\ atm) \times (2.01\ L)}{(1.92\ atm)} = \textbf{1.14\ L}$

2.) $V_2 = \dfrac{(828\ mmHg) \times (2{,}010\ ml)}{(1{,}459\ mmHg)} = 1{,}140\ ml = \textbf{1.14\ L}$

Notice how we have correctly calculated the same answer either way, **1.14 *L***. However, later in this chapter when dealing with other gas laws (i.e. the ideal gas law), it will be very important that the units used are *atm* for pressure and liters for volume, which shall be explained in further detail later. For now, however, it may be a good idea for you to always work with these units, atmospheres for pressure and liters for volume, when dealing with any of the gas laws we will cover in this chapter, just to be safe. If conversions are required before and/or after you use any of the gas law equations based on given information or correct units needed for the answer, then so be it. We now look at the next simple gas law.

Charles's Law

Jacques Alexandre César Charles was an inventor, scientist, and mathematician born in 1746 in France. He is known for being the first to fly in a hydrogen-filled balloon in 1783 and for his work with gases in general before he died in 1823. **Charles's law** states that if a given quantity of gas is maintained at constant pressure, then the volume of the gas is directly proportional to the temperature expressed in Kelvin. Thus,

$$V \propto T \text{ when } n \text{ and } P \text{ are constant}$$

If the temperature increases, then so does the volume, and if the temperature decreases, the volume also decreases given a fixed quantity of gas at constant pressure (Figure 6.3). Notice that as the temperature decreases in Figure 6.3, so does the size of the balloon. Conversely, if the temperature is increased, then the size of the balloon gets bigger.

As with Boyle's law, notice that we again have two sets of conditions (the temperature is either decreased or increased). Therefore, we can express this mathematically using Charles's law:

$$\frac{V_1}{T_1} = \frac{V_2}{T_2}$$

As with Boyle's law, we can relate this to a constant value, or $\frac{V}{T} = constant$. Also, notice a very important point here, which is that the unit for temperature is in Kelvin, not Celsius or Fahrenheit. Therefore, if you are given a temperature in either Celsius or Fahrenheit, **you must first convert to Kelvin before attempting to solve these types of problems.** This way you avoid the possibility of having negative numbers (or a zero in the denominator) in your equation, which would not make sense. For example, it would not make sense to have a negative volume. In fact, if we look at various gases plotted on a graph of gas volume versus temperature, and extrapolate the

Jacques Alexandre César Charles (1746–1823) was an inventor, scientist, and mathematician born in 1746 in France. He is known for being the first to fly in a hydrogen-filled balloon. Charles's Law is named after him which states that if a given quantity of gas is maintained at constant pressure, then the volume of the gas is directly proportional to the Kelvin temperature.

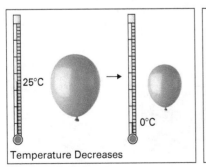

Temperature Decreases

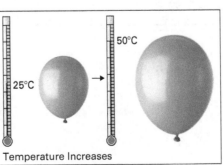

Temperature Increases

Figure 6.3 Demonstration of Charles's Law. As the temperature drops from 25°C to 0°C, the balloon gets smaller, and if the temperature is increased from 25°C to 50°C, it gets bigger. Thus, the volume of the gas is directly proportional to the Kelvin temperature given a fixed quantity of gas.

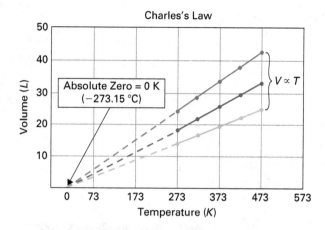

Figure 6.4 Several gases depicted with solid lines on a graph of volume (L) on the y-axis versus temperature (K) on the x-axis. The dotted lines represent the volumes of these gases if extended until they intersect the x-axis at absolute zero.

temperature all the way back to absolute zero, we would see that the gas would have a zero volume (Figure 6.4).

Notice on the graph that the dotted lines represent the volumes of these gases if extended all the way until they intersect the x-axis at absolute zero (0 K, or −273.15 °C). This is of course just in theory (hence the dotted, not solid lines) as gases will not reach a zero volume because they would actually liquefy well above that temperature. In any event, let's work some examples involving Charles's law.

Example Problem 6.4

A sample of hydrogen gas has a volume of 5.0 *ml* at 22.0°C in a gas-tight container, which is then submerged in an ice bath at 0.0°C. What is the new volume (*ml*) assuming constant pressure?

Solution:

We first recognize that this is Charles's law (the variables being volume and temperature, while pressure is constant). We also must recognize that if we are going to use this particular gas law, the temperature needs to be in Kelvin. Therefore, we first convert 22.0°C and 0.0°C to Kelvin.	$T_1 = 22.0°C + 273.15 = 295.2\ K$ $T_2 = 0.0°C + 273.15 = 273.2\ K$
Now, we set up the equation for Charles's law and substitute our values.	$\dfrac{V_1}{T_1} = \dfrac{V_2}{T_2}$ $V_2 = \dfrac{V_1 T_2}{T_1}$ $V_2 = \dfrac{(5.0\ ml) \times (273.2\ K)}{(295.2\ K)} = 4.6\ ml$
As mentioned earlier, sometimes it will be imperative that we use liters for volume, and sometimes it will not matter (as is the case here). If you wanted to be safe either way, and not have to remember when you can and cannot use *ml*, we can convert ml to *L*, then back to ml to report our answer. Either way in this case, you would get the same correct answer.	$V_2 = \dfrac{(5.0 \times 10^{-3}\ L) \times (273.2\ K)}{(295.2\ K)}$ $= 4.6 \times 10^{-3}\ L = 4.6\ ml$

Example Problem 6.5

A sample of oxygen gas has a volume of 12 *L* at 98°F in a gas-tight container, which is then cooled to 62°F. What is the new volume (*L*) assuming constant pressure?	
Solution:	
We again recognize that this is Charles's law (the variables being volume and temperature, while pressure is constant). We also must recognize that if we are going to use this particular gas law, the temperature needs to be in Kelvin. Therefore, we first convert 98°F and 62°F to Kelvin.	T_1 $$K = \frac{5}{9}(98°F - 32) + 273.15 = 310\ K$$ T_2 $$K = \frac{5}{9}(62°F - 32) + 273.15 = 290\ K$$
Now, we set up the equation for Charles's law and substitute in our values.	$$\frac{V_1}{T_1} = \frac{V_2}{T_2}$$ $$V_2 = \frac{V_1 T_2}{T_1}$$ $$V_2 = \frac{(12\ L) \times (290\ K)}{(310\ K)} = 11\ L$$

Combining Boyle's and Charles's Laws

Thus far, we have discussed Boyle's law, which states that the pressure and volume of a gas are inversely proportional, as well as Charles's law, which states that volume and temperature (Kelvin) of a gas are directly proportional. That is:

$$P_1 V_1 = P_2 V_2 \quad and \quad \frac{V_1}{T_1} = \frac{V_2}{T_2}$$

For both of these laws, notice that we have two sets of condition with four variables in each case. However, what if we are confronted with six variables? In other words, is it possible that we have a situation in which we are dealing with two sets of conditions containing six variables? For example, consider a situation in which you have a gas with a given pressure, volume, and temperature in condition one (P_1, V_1 and T_1), all of which change in condition two (P_2, V_2 and T_2). In such a situation, we can combine Boyle's and Charles's law and get the following equation:

$$\frac{P_1 V_1}{T_1} = \frac{P_2 V_2}{T_2}$$

Let's look at a couple of examples where this can be applied.

Example Problem 6.6

A particular sample of carbon dioxide gas has a pressure of 482 *mmHg* at 32.0°C in a 3.20 *L* flask. What is the new pressure (*atm*) if the temperature is decreased to 25.0°C?

Solution:

First, we will convert pressure from *mmHg* to *atm* for two reasons. One, the question asks us for *atm*. Second, as mentioned earlier, it is a good habit when working with gases to use *atm* for pressure to be safe. Some equations will require us to be in this unit, while some will not. However, if you also convert pressure to *atm* and then convert back to another unit if necessary after using these gas laws, you will get the correct answer and never have to worry about when it is needed or not. We also convert temperature to Kelvin as that is needed here.

$$P_1 = 482 \; mmHg \times \frac{1 \; atm}{760 \; mmHg} = 0.634 \; atm$$

$$T_1 = 32.0°C + 273.15 = 305.2 \; K$$

$$T_2 = 25.0°C + 273.15 = 298.2 \; K$$

Next, we recognize that we have two sets of conditions here (before and after) with six variables (albeit, one of these variables is not changing, namely volume). Thus, we can use our equation involving the combination of Boyle's and Charles's laws to solve for the new pressure (P_2).

$$\frac{P_1 V_1}{T_1} = \frac{P_2 V_2}{T_2}$$

$$P_2 = \frac{P_1 V_1 T_2}{V_2 T_1}$$

$$= \frac{(0.634 \; atm) \times (3.20 \; L) \times (298.2 \; K)}{(3.20 \; L) \times (305.2 \; K)}$$

$$= \mathbf{0.619 \; atm}$$

This answer makes sense because as the temperature drops a little, we expect the pressure to also be slightly less than the original pressure as these two variables are directly related. Also, notice in this particular case, that we could have eliminated volume from the equation and still found the correct answer. The reason for this is that the volume is not changing and therefore drops out of the equation. Thus, we get the following:

$$\frac{P_1}{T_1} = \frac{P_2}{T_2}$$

$$\frac{P_1}{T_1} = \frac{P_2}{T_2}$$

Rearrange to solve for P_2:

$$P_2 = \frac{P_1 T_2}{T_1}$$

$$= \frac{(0.634 \; atm) \times (298.2 \; K)}{(305.2 \; K)}$$

$$= \mathbf{0.619 \; atm}$$

Example Problem 6.7

A sample of hydrogen gas in a 1.21 L container has a pressure of 0.982 atm at 25.0°C. What is the new pressure (in atm, psi and $torr$) of the gas if it is then stored in a 1.68 L container at 0.0°C?
Solution:
We again recognize that we can use our equation involving the combination of Boyle's and Charles's laws to solve for the new pressure (P_2) as we again have two sets of conditions (before and after) with six variables. However, unlike the last example where volume dropped out of the equation because it was not changing, we cannot do that here as it is changing from 1.21 L to 1.68 L. Also, we notice that the original pressure is already in atm (we can convert to psi and $torr$ once we have our answer for P_2 in atm). So, we first convert both temperatures (T_1 and T_2) to Kelvin and then rearrange our equation to solve for P_2.

$$T_1 = 25.0°C + 273.15 = 298.2\ K$$

$$T_2 = 0.0°C + 273.15 = 273.2\ K$$

$$\frac{P_1 V_1}{T_1} = \frac{P_2 V_2}{T_2}$$

$$P_2 = \frac{P_1 V_1 T_2}{V_2 T_1} = \frac{(0.982\ atm) \times (1.21\ L) \times (273.2\ K)}{(1.68\ L) \times (298.2\ K)}$$

$$= \textbf{0.648 } \textbf{\textit{atm}}$$ |

| Now, we convert atm to psi and $torr$. | $$0.648\ atm \times \frac{14.7\ psi}{1\ atm} = \textbf{9.53 } \textbf{\textit{psi}}$$ $$0.648\ atm \times \frac{760\ torr}{1\ atm} = \textbf{492 } \textbf{\textit{torr}}$$ |

Avogadro's Law

As mentioned earlier in Chapter 4, Amedeo Avogadro was the first to recognize through his early work with gases that the volume of a gas is directly proportional to the number of atoms or molecules in the gas. In other words, **Avogadro's law** states that the volume of a gas is directly related to the amount of moles (n) of the gas sample at a given temperature and pressure. Thus,

$$V \propto n \ \text{ when } T \text{ and } P \text{ are constant}$$

$$\frac{V_1}{n_1} = \frac{V_2}{n_2}$$

This makes sense if we look at a simple example. If you were to fill a balloon with helium gas, then add more gas to the balloon, you would expect the balloon to become larger, which it does (Figure 6.5). Let's look at a couple of examples where we can apply Avogadro's law.

Figure 6.5 Avogadro's Law. The volume of a gas is directly related to the amount of mols (*n*) of the gas at a given temperature and pressure.

Example Problem 6.8

A balloon contains 0.316 moles of helium gas and has a volume of 4.92 L. What is the new volume (*L*) if an additional 0.226 moles of helium is added (constant pressure and temperature)?

Solution:

We recognize that this is Avogadro's law (the variables being volume and moles, while both pressure and temperature are constant). Also, we want to make sure that we read the question carefully. For example, notice that additional moles were added to the balloon. Therefore, we must add the additional 0.226 moles to the original 0.316 moles already in the balloon to get n_2, then solve for V_2.

$$\frac{V_1}{n_1} = \frac{V_2}{n_2}$$

$$V_2 = \frac{V_1 n_2}{n_1}$$

$$V_2 = \frac{(4.92\ L) \times (0.316 + 0.226)}{(0.316)} = 8.44\ L$$

Example Problem 6.9

If 0.321 moles of helium gas are released from a balloon that originally contained the equivalent of 3.26 grams of helium gas with a volume of 6.02 L, what is the new volume (*L*) if pressure and temperature remain constant?

Solution:

Again, we recognize that this is Avogadro's law (the variables being volume and moles, while both pressure and temperature are constant). However, we must first calculate the original amount of moles of helium in the balloon as this is given to us as the equivalent in grams.	$3.26\ g\ He \times \dfrac{1\ mol\ He}{4.00\ g\ He} = 0.815\ mols\ He$
Now that we have original moles of helium, we can substitute our values into our equation and solve for V_2. However, make sure that you subtract the 0.321 moles of released helium from the original moles of helium for n_2.	$\dfrac{V_1}{n_1} = \dfrac{V_2}{n_2}$ $V_2 = \dfrac{V_1 n_2}{n_1}$ $V_2 = \dfrac{(6.02\ L) \times (0.815 - 0.321)}{(0.815)} = 3.65\ L$

Section 6.4 **Ideal Gas Law**

So far, we have discussed three simple gas laws. Boyle's law states that the pressure and volume of a gas are inversely related, Charles's law relates volume of a gas directly to its Kelvin temperature, while Avogadro's law states that the volume of a gas is directly related to the amount of moles of gas. If we combine these three laws, we can state the following:

$$V \propto \frac{nT}{P}$$

This can then be made into a mathematical equation by introducing a proportionality constant, called the gas constant, which we can designate as "R". Thus,

$$V = \frac{RnT}{P}$$

Upon rearrangement we get,

$$PV = nRT$$

This is the **ideal gas law**, which we call "ideal" even though there really is no such thing as an "ideal" gas (we will see this later in the chapter). However, real gases at relatively moderate conditions (pressure of 1 *atm* and room temperature) tend to behave close enough to what we call an ideal gas such that $PV = nRT$ can be used to describe their behavior. Now that we have established the fact that we can use this equation to adequately describe the behavior of gases, what value do we use for R? Well, we can use the ideal gas law equation to solve for R if we have numerical values for all other variables in the equation (P, V, n, and T). To do this, we must first assume that 1 *mol* of an "ideal" gas occupies 22.414 *L* under standard conditions (called the **standard molar volume**). **Standard temperature and pressure (STP)** conditions of a gas involve a temperature of 273.15 K (or 0°C) and a pressure of 1 *atm*. Therefore, we rearrange the ideal gas law equation to solve for R:

$$PV = nRT$$

$$R = \frac{PV}{nT}$$

$$R = \frac{(1\ atm) \times (22.414\ L)}{(1\ mol) \times (273.15\ K)} = 0.082057\ \frac{atm \cdot L}{mol \cdot K}$$

Notice that if we are going to use this value for R in our equation, all of our other values for pressure, volume, amount, and temperature must be in atm, liters, moles, and Kelvin, respectively. Now that we have defined R, let's work some problems involving the ideal gas law.

Example Problem 6.10

What is the pressure (*atm*) of 0.896 moles of oxygen gas that is in a container with a volume of 15.0 *L* at a temperature of 325K?
Solution:
Notice how questions involving the ideal gas law equation are very different from the three simple gas laws that we discussed earlier. There, we always had two sets of conditions. Here, however, we have one condition involving pressure, volume, moles, and temperature, all of which are in the ideal gas law equation. Thus, we use this equation and substitute in our values as given in the question. $$PV = nRT$$ $$P = \frac{nRT}{V}$$ $$= \frac{(0.896 \; mols) \times \left(0.082057 \; \frac{L \cdot atm}{mol \cdot K} \right) \times (325 \; K)}{15.0 \; L}$$ $$= \mathbf{1.59 \; atm}$$

Example Problem 6.11

What is the temperature (°C) of 0.874 moles of helium gas at a pressure of 858 *mmHg* that is in a container with a volume of 22.0 *L*?
Solution:
Again, we first must recognize that this is in fact an ideal gas law question. However, unlike our last example, some conversions here will be necessary. First, we convert *mmHg* to atm. $$858 \; mmHg \times \frac{1 \; atm}{760 \; mmHg} = 1.13 \; atm$$
Next, we rearrange the ideal gas law equation and solve for *T*. $$PV = nRT$$ $$T = \frac{PV}{nR}$$ $$= \frac{(1.13 \; atm) \times (22.0 \; L)}{(0.874 \; mols) \times \left(0.082057 \; \frac{L \cdot atm}{mol \cdot K} \right)} = 347 \; K$$
Finally, we convert Kelvin to Celsius.	°C = 347 K − 273.15 = **74°C**

Section 6.5 Applications Involving the Ideal Gas Law

Density

Some very common calculations needed when dealing with gases involve density. Therefore, we will now rearrange the ideal gas law to solve for density of a gas. First, we note that moles (*n*) is simply mass (*m*) divided by molar mass (*MM*). Thus we can substitute this in for moles.

$$PV = nRT \quad \xrightarrow{n = \frac{m}{MM}} \quad PV = \frac{m}{MM}RT$$

We know that density is mass (m) divided by volume (V). Therefore, we rearrange the above equation so that we have m/V (density) on one side of the equation:

$$Density = \frac{m}{V} = \frac{P \cdot MM}{R \cdot T}$$

Just remember when using the above equation that the units for density are g/L. This is a typical unit of density for gases.

Example Problem 6.12

Chloroform is a colorless, sweet-smelling chemical commonly used in laboratories, which vaporizes readily. What is the density $\left(\frac{g}{L}\right)$ of chloroform ($MM = 119.37\frac{g}{mol}$) vapor in a flask at 25.00°C and a pressure of 295 *torr*?

Solution:

First, we recognize this as being an application involving the ideal gas law, specifically, rearrangement of the ideal gas law to solve for density $\left(\frac{g}{L}\right)$. This being the case, we also know that the units for pressure, molar mass, and temperature have to be *atm*, $\frac{g}{mol}$ and Kelvin. Therefore, we convert 295 *torr* to *atm* for pressure and 25.00°C to K for temperature.

$$295 \; torr \times \frac{1 \; atm}{760 \; torr} = 0.388 \; atm$$

$$25.00°C + 273.15 = 298.15 \; K$$

$$Density = \frac{P \cdot MM}{R \cdot T}$$

$$= \frac{(0.388 \; atm) \times \left(119.37 \; \frac{g}{mol}\right)}{\left(0.082057 \; \frac{L \cdot atm}{mol \cdot K}\right) \times (298.15 \; K)} = \mathbf{1.89} \; \frac{g}{L}$$

Example Problem 6.13

What is the molar mass $\left(\frac{g}{mol}\right)$ of a 1.15 *L* sample of gas that has a mass of 1.74 *g*, a pressure of 0.949 *atm* and a temperature of 32.00°C?

Solution:

First, we again recognize this as being an application involving the ideal gas law. Specifically, re-arrangement of the ideal gas law to solve for density $\left(\frac{g}{L}\right)$ because we have both the mass and the volume. This being the case, we also know that the units for pressure, molar mass, and temperature have to be *atm*, $\frac{g}{mol}$, and Kelvin. Therefore, we convert 32.00°C to K for temperature.

$$32.00°C + 273.15 = 305.15 \; K$$

$$Density = \frac{P \cdot MM}{R \cdot T}$$

$$\frac{1.74 \; g}{1.15 \; L} = \frac{(0.949 \; atm) \times (MM)}{\left(0.082057 \; \frac{L \cdot atm}{mol \cdot K}\right) \times (305.15 \; K)}$$

$$\mathbf{MM = 39.9} \; \frac{g}{mol}$$

Chloroform is a chemical liquid commonly used in laboratories, which vaporizes readily.

Figure 6.6 The Ideal Gas Law can be used along with stoichiometric ratios from balanced chemical equations to calculate quantities of reactants and products.

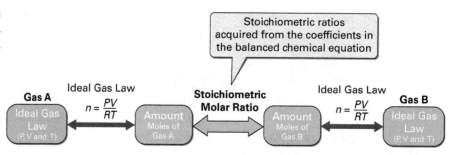

Stoichiometry and the Ideal Gas Law

Recall from Chapter 4 that we have used stoichiometric ratios from balanced chemical equations to calculate quantities of reactants and products. This same concept can also be applied using the ideal gas law. For example, as long as we have enough information regarding the conditions under which the gas reaction is taking place such as pressure, volume, and temperature, we can calculate moles and apply the stoichiometric ratio to convert between reactants and products. Let's look at a couple of examples. In the first example, we will use the ideal gas law twice as we go between two different gases (reactant to product) using the stoichiometric ratio from the balanced equation.

In the second example, we will use the ideal gas law once and then the stoichiometric ratio between reactants in the chemical balanced equation.

Example Problem 6.14

Nitrogen gas (N_2) reacts with hydrogen gas (H_2) to form ammonia gas (NH_3) according to the following balanced chemical equation:

$$N_2 \; (g) + 3H_2 \; (g) \rightarrow 2NH_3 \; (g)$$

If 25.0 L of H_2 gas at 25.00°C and 638 $mmHg$ is combined with excess N_2 gas according to the above chemical equation, how many moles of NH_3 gas is produced? If the NH_3 gas is then stored in a 15.0 L container at the same temperature, what is the pressure (atm) of the gas?

Solution:	
First, we recognize this as being an application involving the ideal gas law. Therefore, we also know that the units for temperature and pressure have to be Kelvin and *atm*. Thus, we convert 25.00°C to K for temperature and 638 *mmHg* to atm for pressure.	$25.00°C + 273.15 = 298.15 \; K$ $638 \; mmHg \times \dfrac{1 \; atm}{760 \; mmHg} = 0.839 \; atm$

Now that we have the correct units, we can use the ideal gas law to solve for moles, H_2 which we can then use to get moles NH_3 using the stoichiometric ratio between the two from the balanced equation. Finally, we can then get the pressure of the NH_3 gas using the ideal gas law again.

$$PV = nRT$$

$$n = \frac{PV}{RT} = \frac{(0.839\ atm) \times (25.0\ L)}{\left(0.082057\ \dfrac{L \cdot atm}{mol \cdot K}\right) \times (298.15\ K)} = 0.857\ mols\ H_2$$

$$0.857\ mols\ H_2 \times \frac{2\ mols\ NH_3}{3\ mols\ H_2} = \textbf{0.572 mols NH}_3\ \textbf{produced}$$

$$PV = nRT$$

$$P = \frac{nRT}{V} = \frac{(0.572\ mols\ NH_3) \times \left(0.082057\ \dfrac{L \cdot atm}{mol \cdot K}\right) \times (298.15\ K)}{15.0\ L} = \textbf{0.933 atm}$$

Example Problem 6.15

An Oxygen Breathing Apparatus (OBA) is a rebreather primarily used by firefighters. They contain potassium superoxide (KO_2), which is a yellow solid that decomposes in moist air. The superoxide consumes exhaled carbon dioxide by the firefighter and replaces it with oxygen according to the following balanced chemical equation:

$$4KO_2\ (s) + 2CO_2\ (g) \rightarrow 2K_2CO_3\ (s) + 3O_2\ (g)$$

What mass (g) of KO_2 is required to completely react with 9.12 L of CO_2 gas at 25.00°C and 752 $mmHg$?

Solution:

We again recognize this as being an application involving the ideal gas law. Therefore, we also know that the units for temperature and pressure have to be Kelvin and *atm*. Thus, we convert 25.00°C to K for temperature and 752 *mmHg* to *atm* for pressure.	$25.00°C + 273.15 = 298.15\ K$ $752\ mmHg \times \dfrac{1\ atm}{760\ mmHg} = 0.989\ atm$
Now that we have the correct units, we can use the ideal gas law to solve for moles CO_2, which we can then use to get moles KO_2 using the stoichiometric ratio between the two from the balanced equation. Finally, we can then simply calculate grams of KO_2 from its molar mass (71.10 g/mol).	$PV = nRT$ $n = \dfrac{PV}{RT} = \dfrac{(0.989\ atm) \times (9.12\ L)}{\left(0.082057\ \dfrac{L \cdot atm}{mol \cdot K}\right) \times (298.15\ K)} = 0.369\ mols\ CO_2$ $0.369\ mols\ CO_2 \times \dfrac{4\ mols\ KO_2}{2\ mols\ CO_2} = 0.738\ mols\ KO_2\ produced$ $0.738\ mols\ KO_2 \times \dfrac{71.10\ g\ KO_2}{1\ mol\ KO_2} = \textbf{52.5 g KO}_2$

An Oxygen Breathing Apparatus (OBA) is a rebreather primarily used by firefighters.

Section 6.6 Mixtures of Gases and Partial Pressures

As mentioned in the introduction of this chapter and listed in Table 6.1, we remember that the air that we are breathing right now is actually a mixture of gases. Dry air is composed of nitrogen, oxygen, argon, and carbon dioxide in addition to trace amounts of other gases. In fact, when dealing with gases, it is very common that we come across mixtures of gases. Therefore, we now turn our attention to calculations involving this concept.

Dalton's Law of Partial Pressures

Recall from Chapter 2 that John Dalton was an English chemist and physicist who is most famously known for his work on the development of the atomic theory. Well, he is also known for his work on gases and specifically for work involving partial pressure of gases. **Dalton's law of partial pressures** states that the total pressure exerted in a mixture of gases is equal to the sum of the individual partial pressures of the gases involved in the mixture. Therefore, if we take a generic gas mixture of individual gases "A," "B," and "C," we can say the following:

$$P_{total} = P_A + P_B + P_C$$

P_{total} is the total pressure of the gas mixture, P_A is the partial pressure of gas "A," P_B is the partial pressure of gas "B," and P_C is the partial pressure of gas "C." A **partial pressure** of a gas is simply the contribution to the total pressure of the system which is due to a single component of the mixture. Note that we can combine this information with the ideal gas law, which will allow us to determine the number of moles of individual gases in a mixture if we know its partial pressure. Thus, if we were to take our generic mixture of gases "A," "B," and "C" as listed above, we get the following:

$$P_A V = n_A RT; \quad P_B V = n_B RT; \quad P_C V = n_C RT$$

We just have to remember that whatever information is put into the ideal gas law, that is what is put out. In other words, if you were to put total pressure of the mixture of gases into the ideal gas law, you would get total moles of the mixture of gases (n_{total}). Conversely, if you were to put in partial pressure of an individual gas into the equation, you would get the number of moles of that individual gas (not n_{total}). Thus, we can say the following:

$$P_{total} V = n_{total} RT$$

As with most concepts in chemistry, a couple of examples here will help tremendously. However, let's discuss one more concept first that will also help us with these types of calculations. If you notice from the above equations, we can also calculate **mole fractions (X)** of each component gas, as we learned in Chapter 5. Thus:

$$X_A = \frac{n_A}{n_{total}} \; ; \; X_B = \frac{n_B}{n_{total}} \; ; \; X_C = \frac{n_C}{n_{total}}$$

Where X_A is the mole fraction of gas "A," X_B is the mole fraction of gas "B," and X_C is the mole fraction of gas "C." While it may seem somewhat unclear now how this can help us, we will soon see how this information can be extremely valuable. For example, if we know the total pressure of a mixture of gases, we can use the ideal gas law to solve for total moles, n_{total} (with V and T known). If we also know the mole fractions of each of the individual gases present in the mixture, we can then calculate the number of moles of each of the gases in the mixture by simply multiplying the mole fraction by total moles (n_{total}). Therefore, if we take the individual gas component "A," we can rearrange the above equation to get the following:

$$n_A = X_A \times n_{total}$$

Where n_A is the number of moles of gas "A," X_A is the mole fraction of gas "A," and n_{total} is the total number of moles of all gases present in the mixture. From there, it is possible to then calculate grams using the molar mass of the gases. Further, we can also calculate the partial pressure of each individual gas component in the mixture by simply multiplying the mole fraction by the total pressure. For example, if we again take the individual gas component "A," we can say the following:

$$P_A = X_A P_{total}$$

Let's look at a couple of specific examples in order to get a better idea of how this can be applied.

Example Problem 6.16

If a mixture of helium ($X_{He} = 0.62$) and oxygen ($X_{O_2} = 0.38$) gases are placed in an 8.9 L container at 25.00°C at a total pressure of 1.4 atm, how much helium (grams) and oxygen (grams) are in the container?

Solution:

We recognize that this is a mixture of two different gases (He and O_2). If we can calculate the total moles of the mixture, we can then use the mole fractions to calculate the number of moles of helium and then oxygen in the mixture. From there, we can use the molar masses of each gas to get grams. Since we plan to use the ideal gas law, however, we must first convert 25.00°C to Kelvin for temperature.

$$25.00°C + 273.15 = 298.15 \; K$$

Now we use the ideal gas law to get total moles.

$$PV = nRT$$

$$n = \frac{PV}{RT} = \frac{(1.4 \; atm) \times (8.9 \; L)}{\left(0.082057 \; \dfrac{L \cdot atm}{mol \cdot K}\right) \times (298.15 \; K)} = 0.51 \; mols \; total$$

Next, we can use the mole fractions to calculate the number of moles of helium and then oxygen.

$$X_A = \frac{n_A}{n_{total}}$$

$$n_A = X_A \times n_{total}$$

and

$$n_B = X_B \times n_{total}$$

Thus, we substitute He in for A and O_2 in for B,

$$n_{He} = (0.62) \times (0.51 \; mols) = 0.32 \; mols \; He$$

$$n_{O_2} = (0.38) \times (0.51 \; mols) = 0.19 \; mols \; O_2$$

Now we simply use the molar mass for He (4.00 g/mol) and for O_2 (32.00 g/mol) to get grams.

$$0.32 \; mols \; He \times \frac{4.00 \; g \; He}{1 \; mol \; He} = \textbf{1.3 g He}$$

$$0.19 \; mols \; O_2 \times \frac{32.00 \; g \; O_2}{1 \; mol \; O_2} = \textbf{6.1 g O_2}$$

Example Problem 6.17

If 1.04 g of hydrogen gas and 2.85 g of argon gas are placed in a 13.0 L container and maintained at 27.00°C, what is the total pressure (atm) of the mixture of gases? What are the partial pressures (atm) of the hydrogen and argon gases?

Solution:

We recognize that this is a mixture of two different gases (H_2 and Ar), so we have to be careful about what information we use in the ideal gas law equation (i.e. partial pressure vs. total pressure etc.). First, we know that we have to calculate moles from grams, and we are also going to need to convert 27.00°C to Kelvin for temperature.

$$1.04 \; g \; H_2 \times \frac{1 \; mol \; H_2}{2.02 \; g \; H_2} = 5.15 \times 10^{-1} \; mols \; H_2$$

$$2.85 \; g \; Ar \times \frac{1 \; mol \; Ar}{39.95 \; g \; Ar} = 7.13 \times 10^{-2} \; mols \; Ar$$

$$total \; mols = 5.15 \times 10^{-1} \; mols \; H_2 + 7.13 \times 10^{-2} \; mols \; Ar = 5.86 \times 10^{-1} \; mols \; total$$

$$27.00°C + 273.15 = 300.15 \; K$$

Now that we have the correct units, we can use the ideal gas law to solve for total pressure.

$$PV = nRT$$

$$P_{total} = \frac{n_{total}RT}{V}$$

$$= \frac{(5.86 \times 10^{-1} \ mols) \times \left(0.082057 \ \frac{L \cdot atm}{mol \cdot K}\right) \times (300.15 \ K)}{13.0 \ L}$$

$$= 1.11 \ atm \ (total \ pressure)$$

Method #1. Now, to find the partial pressures of both hydrogen and argon, we can do this two different ways. In the first method, we will plug moles of H_2 into the ideal gas law to get the partial pressure of H_2, and then repeat for Ar.

$$P_{H_2} = \frac{n_{H_2}RT}{V}$$

$$= \frac{(5.15 \times 10^{-1} \ mols \ H_2) \times \left(0.082057 \ \frac{L \cdot atm}{mol \cdot K}\right) \times (300.15 \ K)}{13.0 \ L}$$

$$= 9.76 \times 10^{-1} \ atm \ (P_{H_2})$$

$$P_{Ar} = \frac{n_{Ar}RT}{V}$$

$$= \frac{(7.13 \times 10^{-2} \ mols \ Ar) \times \left(0.082057 \ \frac{L \cdot atm}{mol \cdot K}\right) \times (300.15 \ K)}{13.0 \ L}$$

$$= 1.35 \times 10^{-1} \ atm \ (P_{Ar})$$

Method #2. In the second method, we determine the partial pressures of both H_2 and Ar by using the mole fractions $\left(\frac{n_{H_2}}{n_{total}} \ and \ \frac{n_{Ar}}{n_{total}}\right)$ of each of these components, and then multiply these numbers by the total pressure (1.11 atm).

$$P_{H_2} = \left(\frac{n_{H_2}}{n_{total}}\right) \times P_{total} = \left(\frac{5.15 \times 10^{-1} \ mols \ H_2}{5.86 \times 10^{-1} \ mols}\right) \times 1.11 \ atm$$

$$= 9.76 \times 10^{-1} \ atm \ (P_{H_2})$$

$$P_{Ar} = \left(\frac{n_{Ar}}{n_{total}}\right) \times P_{total} = \left(\frac{7.13 \times 10^{-2} \ mols \ Ar}{5.86 \times 10^{-1} \ mols}\right) \times 1.11 \ atm$$

$$= 1.35 \times 10^{-1} \ atm \ (P_{Ar})$$

Verify Answer. Now let's double check our answer by adding the partial pressures to make sure that we get the total pressure of the mixture of gases.

$$P_{H_2} + P_{Ar} = P_{total}$$

Or,

$$9.76 \times 10^{-1} \ atm + 1.35 \times 10^{-1} \ atm$$

$$= 1.11 \ atm \ (total \ pressure) ✔$$

Collecting Gases over Water

Very often, a particular gas is collected by the displacement of water. During this process, the desired gas mixes with the water and is therefore not pure, as some of the water vaporizes into the gas. The water can then exert a partial pressure, known as its **vapor pressure**, which contributes to the total pressure (similar to a mixture of two different gases, each exerting a partial pressure). The vapor pressure contributed by the water to the total pressure is dependent on temperature, with higher temperatures resulting in higher vapor pressures. In any event, when working with gases mixed with water, the vapor pressure that the water contributes to the total pressure has to be accounted for, which we can get from Table 6.3. For example, if we are collecting oxygen gas over water at 25°C, and we have a total pressure of 746 *torr*, what would the partial pressure of the oxygen be? Well, from Table 6.3, we see that at 25°C the vapor pressure of water is 23.8 *torr*; therefore, we subtract this amount from the total pressure (746 *torr*). Thus, we get the following:

$$P_{O_2} = 746 \; torr - 23.8 \; torr = 722 \; torr$$

Let's look at an example of this.

Example Problem 6.18

What is the partial pressure (*torr*) of hydrogen gas that is collected over water at 25.00°C and has a total pressure of 755 *torr*? Assuming that 654 *ml* of H_2 gas was collected, what mass (grams) was collected?	
Solution:	
First, we recognize that this gas was collected over water, and therefore the vapor pressure from the water has to be accounted for. From Table 6.3, we see that the vapor pressure of water is 23.8 *torr*. Thus, we subtract this amount form the total pressure (755 *torr*) to get the partial pressure of the hydrogen gas. We will then need to convert this to *atm* so that we can use the ideal gas law in the next step. We will also convert 25.00°C to Kelvin and 654 *ml* to liters in this step.	$P_{H_2} = 755 \; torr - 23.8 \; torr = \textbf{731 \; torr}$ $731 \; torr \times \dfrac{1 \; atm}{760 \; torr} = 0.962 \; atm$ $25.00°C + 273.15 = 298.15 \; K$ $654 \; ml \times \dfrac{1 \; L}{1,000 \; ml} = 0.654 \; L$
Now that we have the partial pressure for the H_2 gas and the correct units needed for the ideal gas law, we will rearrange the ideal gas law to solve for moles H_2.	$PV = nRT$ $n_{H_2} = \dfrac{P_{H_2} V}{RT}$ $= \dfrac{(0.962 \; atm) \times (0.654 \; L)}{\left(0.082057 \; \dfrac{L \cdot atm}{mol \cdot K} \right) \times (298.15 \; K)}$ $= 2.57 \times 10^{-2} \; mols \; H_2$
Now we simply use the molar mass of H_2 to solve for grams H_2.	$2.57 \times 10^{-2} \; mols \; H_2 \times \dfrac{2.02 \; grams \; H_2}{1 \; mol \; H_2}$ $= \textbf{5.19} \times \textbf{10}^{-2} \; \textbf{grams } \textbf{H}_2$

Table 6.3 Vapor pressure (*torr*) of water at various temperatures.

Temperature (°C)	Pressure (*torr*)	Temperature (°C)	Pressure (*torr*)
0	4.6	55	118.2
5	6.5	60	149.6
10	9.2	65	187.5
15	12.8	70	233.7
20	17.6	75	289.1
25	23.8	80	355.1
30	31.9	85	433.6
35	42.2	90	525.8
40	55.4	95	633.9
45	72.0	100	760.0
50	92.6		

Section 6.7 Real Gases: Deviations from Ideal Behavior

As we have seen so far in this chapter, the ideal gas law is extremely useful at relating the four physical properties (pressure, volume, temperature, and number of particles) when working with gases close to room temperature and approximately 1 *atm* of pressure. However, at higher pressures and lower temperatures, gases tend to deviate from ideal behavior. The reason for this is based on assumptions that are made when dealing with gases. For example, one assumption is that the individual sizes of the gas molecules are negligible as most of a gas is empty space. However, at higher pressures this assumption is no longer valid. You can think of this as "squeezing out" all of the empty space leaving behind the gas molecules in a much smaller space. In this scenario, you can now imagine how the individual sizes of the gas molecules are going to influence the overall volume as different gas molecules are going to have different sizes. For example, CO_2 has a molar mass of 44.01 *g/mol*, while H_2 has a molar mass of only 2.02 *g/mol*. Another assumption that we generally make with gases under standard conditions is that there is very little to no interaction between gas molecules. While this may be true for the most part at elevated temperatures when individual gas molecules have a lot of kinetic energy, this is no longer valid at lower temperatures. At these lower temperatures, gas molecules are moving much slower past one another and therefore have more time to interact with each other. This results in the gas molecules not hitting the sides of their container as hard as the ideal gas law would predict, which affects the overall pressure of the gas. In any event, to account for these effects that lead to

Table 6.4 Van der Waals Constants for some common gases.

Gases	a (L² atm/mol²)	b (L/mol)
He	0.0342	0.0237
Ne	0.211	0.0171
Ar	1.35	0.0322
Kr	2.32	0.0398
Xe	4.19	0.0511
H_2	0.244	0.0266
N_2	1.39	0.0391
O_2	1.36	0.0318
Cl_2	6.49	0.0562
CO	1.45	0.0395
CO_2	3.59	0.0427
H_2O	5.46	0.0305
CH_4	2.25	0.0428

non-ideal behavior of gases, Johannes van der Waals developed an equation that we can use. The equation is as follows:

$$\left(P + a\left[\frac{n}{V}\right]^2\right) \times (V - bn) = nRT$$

Here a and b are experimentally determined constants specific to the identity of the gas (Table 6.4), $a\left[\frac{n}{V}\right]^2$ is the pressure correction term which accounts for intermolecular forces, and bn is the volume correction term that accounts for individual sizes of the gas molecules. Johannes van der Waals was a Dutch theoretical physicist born in 1837 and is most famously known for his work with gases and liquids, particularly the development of this equation. He died in 1923 but not before being awarded the Nobel Prize for Physics in 1910. Let's now look at an example of how this can be applied.

Example Problem 6.19

Calculate the pressure (atm) of 5.00 $mols$ Helium gas in a 1.00 L container at 298.15 K using both the ideal gas law and van der Waals equation $\left(a = 0.0342 \dfrac{L^2 \times atm}{mol^2} \text{ and } b = 0.0237 \dfrac{L}{mol}\right)$.		
Solution:		
First, we will calculate pressure using the ideal gas law and the given information. $PV = nRT$	$PV = nRT$ $P = \dfrac{nRT}{V}$ $P = \dfrac{(5.00 \; mols \; He) \times \left(0.082057 \; \dfrac{L \cdot atm}{mol \cdot K}\right) \times (298.15 \; K)}{1.00 \; L}$ $P = \mathbf{122 \; atm}$	

Johannes van der Waals (1837–1923) was a Dutch theoretical physicist born in the Netherlands and is most famously known for his work with gases and liquids. He was awarded the Nobel Prize for Physics in 1910.

Now we will use van der Waals equation to solve for pressure. $$\left(P + a\left[\frac{n}{v}\right]^2\right) \times (v - bn) = nRT$$ For helium gas according to Table 6.4, we will use the following constants: $$a = 0.0342 \frac{L^2 \times atm}{mol^2} \ and$$ $$b = 0.0237 \frac{L}{mol}$$	$$\left(P + a\left[\frac{n}{v}\right]^2\right) \times (v - bn) = nRT$$ $$P = \frac{nRT}{(v - bn)} - \left(a\left[\frac{n}{v}\right]^2\right)$$ $$P = \frac{(5.00\ mols\ He) \times \left(0.082057 \frac{L \cdot atm}{mol \cdot K}\right) \times (298.15\ K)}{1.00\ L - (0.0237 \frac{L}{mol\ He} \times 5.00\ mols\ He)}$$ $$- \left(0.0342 \frac{L^2 \times atm}{mol^2}\left[\frac{5.00\ mols\ He}{1.00\ L}\right]^2\right)$$ $$P = \frac{122.3265\ L \cdot atm}{(1.00\ L - 0.1185\ L)} - 0.0342 \frac{L^2 \times atm}{mol^2} \times 25.0 \frac{mols^2}{L^2}$$ $$P = 138.77\ atm - 0.855\ atm$$ $$= \mathbf{138\ atm \sim 140\ atm\ (2\ sig.\ fig.)}$$
While at first glance this may not seem very significant, but a difference of 16 *atm* is very noteworthy considering the pressure at sea level is only 1 *atm*.	Difference between the two answers: $$138\ atm - 122\ atm = 16\ atm$$

SPECIAL TOPICS: Kinetic-Molecular Theory of Gases. The kinetic-molecular theory deals with gases on a microscopic level (i.e. individual gas molecules). This can then be used to explain the macroscopic properties that we have discussed in this chapter, such as pressure, volume, and temperature. For example, we know that gases have an associated pressure as a result of the constant random motion of gas molecules which collide with each other and the walls of their container. If the volume is decreased, then the frequency of gas molecules colliding with the sides of the container goes up and so does the pressure. If the temperature is increased, then the kinetic energy of the gas molecules is increased, resulting in more frequent collisions and once again the pressure increases. In fact, this is related mathematically in **Maxwell's equation**, named after James Clerk Maxwell, which can be found in the "Special Topics - Chapter 6: Gases" section of Appendix I. Here, you will also find a discussion on **diffusion** which is the process by which gas molecules spread out in response to a concentration gradient, as well as **effusion** which is defined as the process by which a gas escapes a container through a small hole. **Graham's Law of Effusion** is also discussed.

James Clerk Maxwell (1831-1879) was a Scottish physicists whose work led to the development of a statistical method for describing the kinetic behavior of gases. This method is known as the Maxwell-Boltzmann distribution.

Thomas Graham (1805-1869) was a Scottish chemist who formulated a series of laws, known as Graham's laws, regarding the diffusion and effusion of gases.

Key Terms

1. Avogadro's law
2. Bar (*bar*)
3. Barometer
4. Boyle's law
5. Dalton's law of partial pressures
6. Diastolic pressure
7. Diffusion
8. Effusion
9. Graham's law of effusion
10. Inches of mercury (*in Hg*)
11. Kilopascal (*kPa*)
12. Kinetic-molecular theory of gases
13. Maxwell's equation
14. Millibar (*mbar*)
15. Millimeters of mercury (*mmHg*)
16. Mole fraction (*X*)
17. Moles (*n*)
18. Pascal (*Pa*)
19. Pounds per square inch (*psi*)
20. Pressure (*P*)
21. Sphygmomanometer
22. Standard atmospheres (*atm*)
23. Standard molar volume
24. Standard temperature and pressure
25. Systolic pressure
26. Temperature (*T*)
27. Torr (*torr*)
28. Vapor pressure
29. Volume (*V*)

Problems

PHYSICAL PROPERTIES RELATED TO GAS LAWS

1. How do we define pressure?

2. Fill in the missing information in the following chart:

Unit of Pressure	Numerical Values at Sea Level
atmosphere (*atm*)	1
millimeters of mercury (*mmHg*)	
torr (*torr*)	
	14.7
	101,325

3. Convert 1.42 *atm* to the following units:

   a. *torr*

   b. *Pa*

   c. *mmHg*

   d. *psi*

4. Convert 546 *torr* to the following units:

   a. *atm*

   b. *in Hg*

   c. *psi*

   d. *bar*

5. How do we define volume?

6. How do we define temperature?

7. Covert the following temperatures to Kelvin.

   a.) 32.0°C

   b.) 112.0°F

   c.) 213.0°F

   d.) 58.0°C

8. Covert the following temperatures to Kelvin.

   a.) 25.0°C

   b.) 202.0°F

   c.) 98.6°F

   d.) 37.0°C

SIMPLE GAS LAWS (BOYLE'S, CHARLES'S, AND AVOGADRO'S LAWS)

9. What is Boyle's law?

10. A particular sample of gas has an initial volume of 4.1 *L* and a pressure of 1.3 *atm*. If the volume is increased to 5.8 *L*, what is the new pressure (*atm*)?

11. A sample of hydrogen gas has an initial volume of 2.8 *L* and a pressure of 16.2*psi*. What is the pressure (*atm*) if the volume is decreased to 1.6 *L*?

12. If a sample of oxygen gas in a cylinder originally occupies a volume of 6.72 *L* and has a pressure of 775 *mmHg*, and is then decompressed such that the gas has a new pressure of 0.832 *atm*, what is the new volume?

13. What is Charles's law?

14. If a 5.2 *L* sample of gas in a container is cooled from 36.0°C to 20.0°C, what is the final volume (*L*) of the gas?

15. If a 32.5 *ml* sample of gas in a container is heated from 78.8 °F to 93.2 °F, what is the final volume (*L*) of the gas?

16. A particular sample of carbon dioxide gas has a volume of 4.60 *L* at 25.0°C. This sample is then heated and now has a volume of 6.10 *L*. What is the new temperature (°C) of the gas?

17. What is the mathematical equation involving pressure, volume, and temperature that we get by combining Boyle's and Charles's law?

18. Hydrogen gas is placed in a 3.20 *L* container and has a pressure of 0.78 *atm* and temperature of 24.0°C. If the container is then heated to 36.0°C, what is the new pressure (*atm*) assuming the volume is maintained.

19. A balloon is inflated such that it has a volume 9.80 *L* and is maintained at 1.10 *atm* of pressure and a temperature of 28.0°C. If the temperature and pressure is then increased to 44.0°C and 1.98 *atm*, what is the new volume (*L*) assuming the balloon can readily shrink and expand?

20. If a gas-filled balloon that originally had a volume of 7.20 *L* and pressure of 465 *mmHg*, now has a volume of 3.50 *L*, temperature of 11.9°C and pressure of 828 *mmHg*, what was the original temperature (°C)?

21. What is Avogadro's law?

22. A balloon originally contains 4.33 *mols* of helium gas and has a volume of 3.21 *L*. If 2.11 *mols* of gas are then released from the balloon, what is the new volume (*L*)? Assume constant pressure and temperature.

23. If a particular gas is added to a balloon that already contains 0.712 *mols* of that gas with a volume of 2.85 *L*, how many additional *mols* were added knowing that the new volume is now 4.12 *L*? Assume constant pressure and temperature.

24. A balloon contains 1.43 *mols* of a particular gas and has a volume of 5.08 *L*. If 0.812 *mols* are then added to the balloon, what is the new volume (*L*)? Assume constant pressure and temperature.

THE IDEAL GAS LAW

25. What is the ideal gas law?

26. When using the ideal gas law, is the identity of the gas an important factor that is accounted for in the equation?

27. What volume would 0.286 *mols* of argon gas occupy at a pressure of 1.35 *atm* and a temperature of 265 K?

28. How many *mols* of an ideal gas are in a 2.10 *L* container maintained at 36.0°C and 1.87 *atm* of pressure?

29. What volume would 0.311 *mols* of hydrogen gas occupy at a pressure of 17.3 *psi* and a temperature of 252 K?

30. What is the temperature (°C) if 1.48 *mols* of an ideal gas are maintained at 921 *mmHg* of pressure in a 31.4 *L* container?

31. How many *mols* of an ideal gas are in a 13.5 *L* container maintained at 32.9°C and 1.79 *atm* of pressure?

32. What volume would 0.431 *mols* of an ideal gas occupy at a pressure of 28.0 *in Hg* and a temperature of 278 K?

33. What is the temperature (K) if 1.21 *mols* of an ideal gas are maintained at 23.7 *psi* of pressure in an 18.3 *L* container?

34. What is the pressure (*atm*) if 0.473 *mols* of oxygen gas are maintained at a temperature of 18°C in an 11.2 *L* container?

35. How many *mols* of hydrogen gas are in a 26.3 *L* container maintained at 42.9°C and 22.6 *psi* of pressure?

36. What volume would 2.01 *mols* of carbon dioxide gas occupy at a pressure of 711 *torr* and a temperature of 65°F?

37. What is the temperature (°C) if 1.26 *mols* of helium gas are maintained at 659 *mmHg* of pressure in a 33.7 *L* cylinder?

38. What is the pressure (*psi*) if 1.07 *mols* of an ideal gas are maintained at a temperature of 39°C in a 20.3 *L* container?

39. A balloon is inflated to a volume of 32.4 *L* at a pressure of 736 *torr* and a temperature of 29°C. How many *mols* of gas must the balloon contain?

40. If a 19.2 *g* block of dry ice (carbon dioxide) undergoes complete sublimation (conversion from solid to gas) in a 3.21 *L* container that is maintained at 24°C, what is the pressure of the container?

APPLICATIONS INVOLVING THE IDEAL GAS LAW

41. What is the equation that we get when we rearrange the ideal gas law to solve for density of a gas?

42. What is STP?

43. What is the standard molar volume?

44. What is the density of hydrogen gas at STP?

45. What is the density of nitrogen gas at STP?

46. What is the density of argon gas at STP?

47. What is the density of carbon dioxide gas at STP?

48. Rank the gases in questions #44–47 from the least dense gas to the gas with the highest density.

49. A particular sample of gas has a density of 1.78 *g/L* at a temperature and pressure of 39°C and 1.03 *atm*. What is the molar mass of the gas?

50. What is the density of a gas (molar mass = 44.2 *g/mol*) that is stored at a temperature and pressure of 39°C and 1.03 *atm*?

51. A particular sample of gas has a mass of 0.496 *g* and volume of 279 *ml* at a temperature and pressure of 22°C and 741 *torr*. What is the molar mass of the gas?

52. If a given sample of gas has a density of 2.64 *g/L* at a temperature and pressure of 34°C and 16.8 *psi*, what is the molar mass of the gas?

53 Aluminum powder reacts with oxygen gas to form aluminum oxide according to the following unbalanced equation:

$$Al\ (s) + O_2\ (g) \rightarrow Al_2O_3\ (unbalanced)$$

What is the balanced equation for this reaction?

54. According to the balanced chemical equation from question # 53, what volume (*L*) of oxygen gas is required to completely react with 38.6 *g* of aluminum powder at a temperature and pressure of 24°C and 927 *mmHg*?

55. Methanol gas can be formed by reacting carbon monoxide gas with hydrogen gas according to the following balanced chemical equation:

$$CO\ (g) + 2\ H_2\ (g) \rightarrow CH_3OH\ (g)$$

What volume (L) of hydrogen gas is needed to completely react with 2.73 *mols* of carbon monoxide at a temperature and pressure of 77°F and 1.28 *atm*?

56. Consider the following balanced chemical equation involving the burning of ethane (C_2H_6) in air:

$$2\,C_2H_6\,(g) + 7\,O_2\,(g) \rightarrow 4\,CO_2\,(g) + 6H_2O\,(g)$$

What volume (L) of carbon dioxide is produced if 1.86 *mols* of ethane are completely consumed at a temperature and pressure of 25°C and 17.5 *psi*?

MIXTURES OF GASES AND PARTIAL PRESSURE

57. What is Dalton's law of partial pressures?

58. What is the total pressure (*atm*) of a gas mixture containing 0.894 *g* hydrogen gas and 3.95 *g* neon gas in a 12-liter container at 28°C?

59. What are the partial pressures of the hydrogen and neon gases from question #58?

60. What are the *mol* fractions of the hydrogen and neon gases from question #58?

61. What is the total pressure (*atm*) of a mixture of the following gases given their individual partial pressures: *Ne* (255 *mmHg*), N_2 (112 *mmHg*) and CO_2 (156 *mmHg*)?

62. How many total *mols* are in the mixture of gases from question #61 in a 24.2 *L* container at 30°C? How many *mols* of each component (*Ne*, N_2 and CO_2) are there?

63. If a mixture of 3.5 *g* of oxygen gas and 7.2 *g* of helium gas are maintained in a container at 1.9 *atm*, what is the *mol* fraction and the partial pressure (*atm*) of oxygen?

64. From the information given in question #63, what is the *mol* fraction and the partial pressure (*atm*) of helium?

65. What are the *mol* fractions and partial pressures of a mixture of 0.687 *mols* of helium gas and 0.219 *mols* of carbon dioxide gas maintained in a container with a total pressure of 2.11 *atm*?

66. What are the *mol* fractions and partial pressures of a mixture of 2.22 *mols* of argon gas and 1.09 *mols* of oxygen gas maintained in a 38.4 *L* container at a temperature of 28°C?

REAL GASES: DEVIATIONS FROM IDEAL BEHAVIOR

67. Describe why the kinetic molecular theory breaks down at high pressures.

68. Describe why the kinetic molecular theory breaks down at low temperatures.

69. What is van der Waal's equation?

70. Using the ideal gas law, calculate the pressure of 1.00 *mol* of carbon dioxide gas at 273 K in a 5.00 *L* container. What is the pressure if we were to use van der Waals equation

(where $a = 3.59 \dfrac{L^2 \cdot atm}{mol^2}$ and $b = 0.0427 \dfrac{L}{mol}$?)

Image Credits

The Quantum Atom: Atomic Structure and Periodicity

LEARNING OBJECTIVES AND OUTCOMES

After reading this chapter, you should be able to do the following:

- Calculate the wavelength and frequency of light.

- Calculate the energy of photons of EM radiation.

- Describe the photoelectric effect.

- Describe the Bohr model of the atom.

- Predict the wavelength and frequency of the spectral lines of hydrogen and hydrogen-like atoms according to the Bohr model.

- Describe and calculate the de Broglie wavelength of a particle.

- Describe Heisenberg's uncertainty principle.

- Describe the quantum model of the atom according to Schrödinger's equation.

- Describe the three quantum numbers which define atomic orbitals.

- Write ground state electron configurations for main group and transition elements and their monatomic ions.

- Describe and apply periodic trends in properties such as atomic, ionic radii, and ionization energy.

- Define each of the Key Terms listed at the end of the chapter dealing with these concepts.

Section 7.1 Introduction

What is an atom? One definition from the Merriam-Webster dictionary is an atom is "one of the minute indivisible particles of which, according to ancient materialism, the universe is composed." Indeed, the first atomic doctrine of the natural world was proffered by Democritus and his contemporaries circa 400 BC. However, it wasn't until the atomic theory of Dalton that a concrete modern scientific basis for the "atom" emerged. Nevertheless, mere belief

Democritus was an ancient Greek philosopher who lived from 460–370 BC. He is primarily remembered for his formulation of the atomic theory of the universe.

in the atom is insufficient. What is the composition of the atom? How is it structured? Following these questions, as we learned in Chapter 2, scientists such as J.J. Thompson, R.A. Millikan, and Ernst Rutherford each contributed to the elucidation of the nuclear model of the atom composed of protons, neutrons, and electrons. While this seems satisfactory, there are still uncertainties. We know from Mendeleev's periodic law and the periodic table that the elements arranged in order of increasing atomic number will exhibit similar chemical properties in a periodic fashion. Indeed, this is a beautiful and most astounding property of the chemical elements, but why should this be so? Clearly the structure of the atoms (as described by the atomic number) gives rise to the observed chemical properties of the elements. To understand this relationship, chemists and physicists in the first half of the twentieth century would have to develop theories which presented major and fundamental challenges to the classical understanding of matter and energy. A radical new theory emerged, **Quantum Mechanics**. This new theory proved difficult and uncomfortable. Nevertheless, it provides marvelous predictive power in describing the behavior of matter at the atomic and subatomic scale. As we will see in this chapter, it is the quantum atom that provides the answer for the periodic properties of the elements.

Section 7.2 Energy and Mass

The universe is composed of two components, matter and energy. So far, we have defined matter as anything with mass and volume. Indeed, for many years this definition was at the heart of the distinction between matter and energy. Matter was traditionally considered distinct from energy by virtue of its mass, which, of course, energy did not possess. However, this "axiom" along with the "law of conservation of matter," as it was known, was drawn into question early in the twentieth century by Einstein and his famous Theory of Relativity. Einstein suggested that radiant energy (light) did indeed possess mass and, as such, was subject to the same effects in a gravitational field as matter. This has been proven many times over and was initially demonstrated by the bending of light due to gravity fields. Einstein's famous equation which relates mass and energy is given as:

$$E = mc^2$$

Where E is energy, m is mass (kg) and c is the speed of light (m/s). Therefore, by dimensional analysis, Einstein gives us energy in units of $\frac{kg \cdot m^2}{s^2}$. This is a common unit of energy and is referred to as a joule.

$$1\ joule = 1\frac{kg \cdot m^2}{s^2}$$

Albert Einstein (1879–1955) is best known for his famous Theory of Relativity. Nevertheless, he was awarded a Nobel Prize in Physics for his contribution to the understanding of the Photoelectric Effect and the wave-particle duality of EM radiation, a foundational contribution to the development of Quantum Mechanics.

Recall that a Newton (N) is a unit of force defined as $1\ \frac{kg \cdot m}{s^2}$. The joule is the SI standard unit of energy defined as work done by a force of 1 N acting over a distance of 1 *m*. As such, we will use the joule exclusively as the standard unit of energy in this text.

Section 7.3 The Wave Nature of Light— Electromagnetic Radiation

Scientists have understood that light propagates as a wave for centuries. Nevertheless, much of our fundamental understanding of light comes from the work of nineteenth-century scientists, most notably James Clerk Maxwell. Maxwell showed that light could be understood as oscillating electric and magnetic fields. Therefore, we refer to all forms (frequencies) of "light" as **electromagnetic (EM) radiation**.

James Clerk Maxwell (1831–1879) was a Scottish physicist credited with the formulation of the classical theory of EM radiation.

Characteristics of Waves

Waves are described according to three main characteristics: amplitude, wavelength, and frequency. If we consider a wave as depicted in Figure 7.1, we can define **amplitude** as simply the "height" of the wave. In other words, if we describe a wave as a mathematical function, the amplitude is the "value" of that function at any point along the *x*-coordinate. The **wavelength (λ)** is defined as the distance along the *x*-coordinate between adjacent peaks (maxima – highest points) or adjacent troughs (minima – lowest points). The wavelength defines one complete cycle or oscillation of the wave and is expressed in units of distance (meters, etc.). Notice that the value of the amplitude of the wave goes to zero in some places along each cycle. These points of "zero-amplitude" are referred to as **nodes**.

In addition to the *wavelength,* we also characterize waves by their *frequencies*. **Frequency (v)** is defined as the number of cycles (wavelengths) which pass an arbitrary point in space in one second. As such, the *frequency* is a function of both the velocity of the wave and its *wavelength* and is typically expressed in units of *cycles per second*, or simply, "*per second*" ($\frac{1}{s}$ or s^{-1}, also known as **Hertz (*Hz*)**. Since, we are primarily concerned with EM radiation,

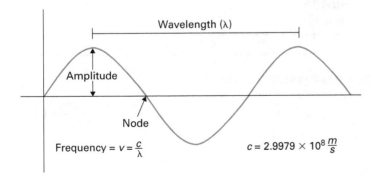

Frequency $= v = \frac{c}{\lambda}$

$c = 2.9979 \times 10^8 \frac{m}{s}$

Figure 7.1 Waves are characterized by amplitude, wavelength and frequency.

the velocity is invariant. The speed of light in a vacuum is 2.9979×10^8 *m/s*. Because the speed of light is a constant, it is possible to calculate the wavelength if the frequency is known and vice versa. For example, let's assume EM radiation with a wavelength, $\lambda = 492$ *nm*. What is the frequency? If we use the expression given in Figure 7.1, we will need to convert λ from units of nm to meters because we understand the speed of light in units of *m/s*:

$$v = \frac{c}{\lambda} = \frac{2.9979 \times 10^8 \; m \cdot s^{-1}}{\left(492 \, nm \times \dfrac{1\,m}{10^9 \, nm} \right)} = 6.09 \times 10^{14} \, s^{-1}$$

Example Problem 7.1 – Frequency and Wavelength

Calculate the frequencies of EM radiation with the following wavelengths (λ).

a.   100. *pm*

b.   434 *nm*

c.   327 *cm*

Solutions:	
a. Recall that the relationship between wavelength and frequency is as follows: $$v = \frac{c}{\lambda}$$ Further, we need to convert λ from pm to m so that our units work out properly.	$$v = \frac{c}{\lambda} = \frac{2.9979 \times 10^8 \; m \cdot s^{-1}}{\left(100. \, pm \times \dfrac{1\,m}{10^{12}\, pm} \right)} = 3.00 \times 10^{18} \, s^{-1}$$
b. Recall that the relationship between wavelength and frequency is as follows: $$v = \frac{c}{\lambda}$$ Further, we need to convert λ from nm to m so that our units work out properly.	$$v = \frac{c}{\lambda} = \frac{2.9979 \times 10^8 \; m \cdot s^{-1}}{\left(434 \, nm \times \dfrac{1\,m}{10^9\, nm} \right)} = 6.91 \times 10^{14} \, s^{-1}$$
c. Recall that the relationship between wavelength and frequency is as follows: $$v = \frac{c}{\lambda}$$ Further, we need to convert λ from cm to m so that our units work out properly.	$$v = \frac{c}{\lambda} = \frac{2.9979 \times 10^8 \; m \cdot s^{-1}}{\left(327 \, cm \times \dfrac{1\,m}{10^2\, cm} \right)} = 9.17 \times 10^7 \, s^{-1}$$

Example Problem 7.2 – Frequency and Wavelength

Calculate the wavelengths (*m*) of EM radiation with the following frequencies (v).

a. $1.78 \times 10^{17} \, s^{-1}$

b. $5.66 \times 10^{14} \, s^{-1}$

c. $3.92 \times 10^8 \, s^{-1}$

Solutions:	
a. Recall that the relationship between wavelength and frequency is as follows: $$v = \frac{c}{\lambda}$$	$$v(\lambda) = \frac{c}{\lambda}(\lambda) \;\rightarrow\; \lambda = \frac{c}{v}$$ $$\lambda = \frac{c}{v} = \frac{2.9979 \times 10^8 \; m \cdot s^{-1}}{\left(1.78 \times 10^{17} s^{-1} \right)} = 1.69 \times 10^{-9} \, m$$

b.	Recall that the relationship between wavelength and frequency is as follows: $v = \dfrac{c}{\lambda}$	$v(\lambda) = \dfrac{c}{\lambda}(\lambda) \;\rightarrow\; \lambda = \dfrac{c}{v}$ $\lambda = \dfrac{c}{v} = \dfrac{2.9979 \times 10^8 \; m \cdot s^{-1}}{(5.66 \times 10^{14} s^{-1})} = 5.29 \times 10^{-7} \; m$
c.	Recall that the relationship between wavelength and frequency is as follows: $v = \dfrac{c}{\lambda}$	$v(\lambda) = \dfrac{c}{\lambda}(\lambda) \;\rightarrow\; \lambda = \dfrac{c}{v}$ $\lambda = \dfrac{c}{v} = \dfrac{2.9979 \times 10^8 \; m \cdot s^{-1}}{(3.92 \times 10^8 s^{-1})} = 0.765 m$

Interference and Diffraction

Another characteristic of waves is the manner in which they interact with each other. When two waves come together and interact, they engage in what is referred to as interference. Waves can interfere *constructively*, wherein their amplitudes are in phase such as to add up resulting in a new wave of greater amplitude. Conversely, waves can interfere *destructively* when their amplitudes are out of phase, wherein a new wave of diminished or zero amplitude results.

Waves are also known to undergo diffraction. Diffraction is a word that describes the tendency of waves to bend around obstacles. For instance, consider light shining on a barrier. For our purposes, we can describe this as a wave-front propagating toward and striking a barrier. Imagine further that this barrier has in it a small hole or slit. As the light passes through that hole to the other side of the barrier, the wave-font will "bend" such that light will propagate in all directions as though the slit is a new "point-source" of light. If we have two slits in the barrier with an appropriate separation between them, it will result in the formation of two newly formed wave-fronts on the opposite side of the barrier. These will interfere with each other. Whether the interference is constructive or destructive at any point depends on the difference in the path length from that specific point to each of the two slits. If it is a whole number multiple of the wavelength of the light in question, the two wave-fronts will be in phase and the interference will be constructive. If not, the interference will be destructive to varying degrees resulting in a pattern of bright and dark regions. This is referred to as a diffraction or interference pattern. It is precisely because light behaves in this fashion that it has been understood as a wave for centuries.

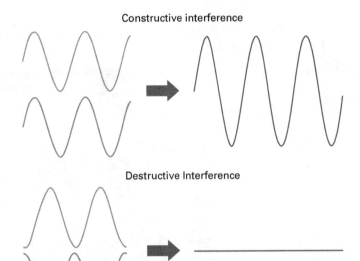

Constructive interference

Destructive Interference

Waves interact by either enhancing or diminishing their amplitudes. When two waves engage in constructive interference, their amplitudes combine in a resulting wave of greater amplitude. When two waves are out of phase, they will engage in destructive interference and their amplitudes will cancel with each other, resulting in a wave of diminished or zero amplitude.

Interference or Diffraction pattern from a double slit experiment, using monochromatic X-ray radiation ($\lambda = 250 \; pm$).

The Electromagnetic (EM) Spectrum

So far, we have used the terms EM radiation and light interchangeably. However, visible light represents only a small fraction of the entire EM spectrum. In fact, you may be familiar with many forms of radiation that are simply invisible forms of light (EM Radiation). These include gamma rays, x-rays, ultraviolet radiation, infrared radiation, microwaves, and radio waves. These different types of radiation are only distinguished as different frequency ranges across a large continuum of EM frequencies. For example, radio waves have a smaller frequency than microwaves, which are still smaller than infrared and visible light. Figure 7.2 depicts the entire EM spectrum and details the frequencies associated with the different types of EM radiation.

Figure 7.2 Visible light represents only a small portion of the electromagnetic (EM) spectrum.

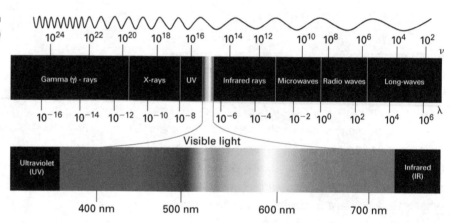

Section 7.4 The Particle Nature of Light

Planck's Quantum Theory

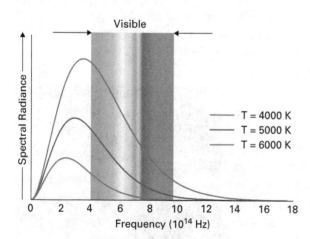

Figure 7.3 Blackbody Radiation emitted at temperatures of 4000, 5000 and 6000 K respectively.

Around 1900, physicists were interested in several observations concerning the behavior of light which were not easily explained by classical physics. This was particularly so regarding certain interactions between light and matter. One such circumstance was the observed emission spectra of heated bodies. For example, imagine a generic metal sample. If you heat this metal sufficiently, it will begin to glow, first red and then brighter yellow then white at sufficiently high temperature. In other words, if you heat (energize) a metal, it will emit EM radiation, the maximum frequency of which depends on the temperature. The light we see coming from the metal is again only part of the overall spectrum of frequencies emitted (Figure 7.3).

The problem presented by the spectra depicted in Figure 7.3 is that classical physics would predict the spectral radiance of the emitted light should increase continuously with frequency. However, we can clearly see that the observed spectra in all cases showed a steady increase in radiance until a maximum value is reached, after which it drops off. Physicists were at a loss to reconcile this phenomenon on the basis of classical kinetic theory of molecular motion. In 1900, however, Max Planck, a German physicist, hypothesized that the source of the emitted radiation was vibrating (oscillating) atoms and further that these molecular oscillators could <u>NOT</u> absorb EM energy in a continuous fashion. Rather, he postulated that the energy could only be emitted or absorbed in specific quantities of energy that he referred to as **quanta**. Further, he stated that the energy of these quanta is proportional to the frequency of the vibration as described in the now famous "Planck's Equation":

$$E = h\nu = \frac{hc}{\lambda} \qquad h = 6.626 \times 10^{-34} \, J \cdot s$$

Where E is energy (J), ν is frequency (s^{-1}) and h is a proportionality constant universally known as **Planck's Constant**. While this had the advantage of explaining the observed emission spectra, it introduced, for the first time, the notion of the quantization of energy in the interactions between light and matter. This is an uncomfortable idea to say the least, and to be fair, Planck never really warmed up to it. He felt such a constraint to be more of a mathematical trick, which happened to fit the data, than a real description of the phenomenon. Nevertheless, Planck is credited with devising the first *quantum theory*.

Max Planck (1858–1947) was a German physicist most famous for developing the first quantum theory from his studies of "blackbody" radiation.

The Photoelectric Effect

A few years after Planck's work another puzzling phenomenon remained unexplained by the classical theories of physics. The **photoelectric effect** is the term used to describe the phenomenon of electric current induced by light striking a metal. When monochromatic light of sufficient energy strikes a metal, electrons are ejected. The term **monochromatic** simply means that the light is of a single, uniform wavelength or frequency. When an electric potential is applied to a photoelectric cell as depicted in Figure 7.4, ejected *photoelectrons* can flow from the metal (cathode) to the anode resulting in a current which now flows through the evacuated cell. In this way, the cell acts as a light-activated switch, a technology that finds widespread use in things like automatic doors among other applications. The effect was thought to be due to the absorption, by the electron, of the radiant energy (light), freeing it from the metal surface. This is straightforward enough were it not for a couple of difficult observations. First, to observe freed photoelectrons, the light must be of a minimum "threshold" frequency or higher. Additionally, different metals exhibited different threshold frequencies. This was problematic as classical wave theory relates the energy to amplitude, not frequency. As such, electrons should have been ejected irrespective of frequency. This presented the second difficulty. Since the amplitude (intensity) was related to energy absorbed by the electrons, very dim light should have ejected electrons only after a lag time, the electrons requiring time to absorb enough

Figure 7.4 A Photoelectric cell has a positive electrode (the anode) and a metal electrode (the cathode). If light of sufficient frequency ($v \geq v_t$) strikes the metal surface, photoelectrons are ejected and a current flow is registered.

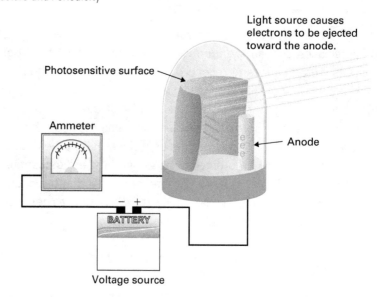

Light source causes electrons to be ejected toward the anode.

Photosensitive surface

Ammeter

Anode

e e e

− +

BATTERY

Voltage source

energy to be freed from the metal. However, what was observed was instant ejection of electrons regardless of whether the light was dim or bright, as long as the light was of a frequency at or above the threshold frequency of the metal in question.

Albert Einstein provided the explanation for these observations with a brilliant but unexpected proposal. Einstein postulated that rather than acting like a wave, light was particulate in nature. The idea was that light could only be absorbed in discrete particles or bundles of energy which he termed **photons**. In this way, Einstein gave further credibility to Planck's equation by stating that atoms can change their energy, ΔE_{atom}, through absorption or emission of one photon of light, the energy of which is related to frequency according to Planck:

$$E_{photon} = h v = \frac{hc}{\lambda}$$

The way to understand this, is to think of a beam of light as a stream of light particles. The intensity of the light is related to the number of photons, not the energy of the individual photons themselves. Since the atom can only absorb discrete photons, the photon must be of sufficient energy to eject an electron. Since the energy of a photon is directly proportional to its frequency, the threshold frequency, v_t, requirement for ejection of photo-electrons is satisfied as follows:

$$\phi = h v_t$$

Where ϕ represents the minimum energy (J) required to free an electron from a given metal. This is referred to as the **binding energy** (also referred to as the work function) of the metal. It is this binding energy that defines the threshold frequency, v_t, for the metal surface in question. Therefore, only photons for which $v \geq v_t$ will be able to provide sufficient energy to free an electron. Because the electron can only be freed by absorbing a photon of sufficient energy and CANNOT save up energy of successive photons, there is no lag time in the observation of photoelectrons.

Example Problem 7.3—The Energy of a Photon

What is the energy of a photon of EM radiation with a wavelength of 486 *nm*? What is the energy of 1 *mol* of such photons?	
Solution:	
We know from Planck's equation that energy of EM radiation is quantized into specific amounts. Einstein termed these photons of EM radiation. Their energies are given as: $$E = h\nu = \frac{hc}{\lambda}$$	$$E = \frac{hc}{\lambda} = \frac{(6.626 \times 10^{-34}\,J \cdot s)(2.9979 \times 10^{8}\,m \cdot s^{-1})}{\left(486\,nm \times \frac{1\,m}{10^{9}\,nm}\right)}$$ $$E = 4.09 \times 10^{-19}\,J$$
Since we just calculated the energy of a single photon, we simply multiply this number by Avogadro's number to obtain the energy of a mole of photons.	$$E = (4.09 \times 10^{-19}\,J)(6.022 \times 10^{23}\,mol^{-1})$$ $$E = 246\,kJ \bullet mol^{-1}$$

Example Problem 7.4—The Photoelectric Effect

The binding energy of Gallium is $6.92 \cdot 10^{-19}J$. What is the minimum frequency of EM radiation required to eject photoelectrons from Ga?	
Solution:	
Recall that the threshold frequency (ν_t) condition suggested by Einstein is as follows: $$\phi = h\nu_t$$	$$\phi = h\nu_t$$ $$\frac{\phi}{h} = \frac{h\nu_t}{h} \;\rightarrow\; \nu_t = \frac{\phi}{h}$$ $$\nu_t = \frac{\phi}{h} = \frac{(6.92 \times 10^{-19}\,J)}{(6.626 \times 10^{-34}\,J \cdot s)} = 1.04 \times 10^{15}\,s^{-1}$$

Section 7.5 Atomic Spectra

Another difficult observation was that of atomic line spectra. When atoms in the gaseous state are excited or energized by an electric potential, light is emitted. This is a well-known phenomenon which you can observe anytime you read a neon sign. The problem arises when this emitted light is passed through a prism. As you may know, when you pass white light through a prism, all the frequencies of visible light are separated into a "continuous" spectrum which exhibits all the colors (frequencies) of a rainbow. However, when the light emitted from an atom is passed through a prism, it is also separated into just a few discrete lines as shown in Figure 7.5. In other words, atomic emission spectra are not continuous but rather exhibit only a few specific frequencies. Furthermore, the frequencies observed are very different for different elements. These are referred to as **atomic line emission spectra** and are like fingerprints for specific elements.

The goal of many in the nineteenth century was to determine the relationship between these emitted frequencies and explain the reason for the line spectra. In this effort, two scientists were able to derive an equation which would predict the wavelengths of the emission spectrum of the

Figure 7.5 Examples of the atomic emission spectra for hydrogen, helium, and magnesium.

hydrogen atom. Their names were Johann Balmer and Johannes Rydberg, and their equation has become known simply as the **Rydberg Equation**:

$$\frac{1}{\lambda} = R\left(\frac{1}{2^2} - \frac{1}{n^2}\right)$$

where n is an integer greater than 2, and R is the **Rydberg Constant** $(1.0974 \times 10^7\ m^{-1})$. When $n = 3$, 4, 5, and 6, the equation correctly predicts the observed wavelengths of the hydrogen emission spectrum of 656 *nm*, 486 *nm*, 434 *nm*, and 410 *nm*, respectively. Transitions from excited states down to $n = 2$ are collectively referred to as the **Balmer Series**.

Section 7.6 **The Bohr Model of the Hydrogen Atom**

Niels Bohr (1885–1962) was a Danish physicist who is most noted for his contributions to the development of Quantum Mechanics, for which he received a Nobel Prize in 1922. He is most noted for the development of his quantum model of the hydrogen atom.

In 1913 in response to the experimental observations surrounding atomic line spectra, a Danish physicist named Niels Bohr proposed a *quantum* model for the hydrogen atom. *He postulated that the electron in the hydrogen atom could only move in certain "allowed"* **orbits** *at fixed distances from the nucleus.* This constraint effectively "quantizes" the energy of the electron. In other words, Bohr postulated that electrons could only have certain specific or "allowed" angular momenta and therefore only allowed energies at certain increments. Bohr referred to these allowed energy states as **stationary states**. While this postulate was inconsistent with classical physics, it had the advantage of fitting with the observable data and explaining the phenomenon of atomic line spectra. Of particular note, was Bohr's derivation of an equation for the energy of electrons in each stationary state, n:

$$E_n = -R_H Z^2\left(\frac{1}{n^2}\right)$$

Where E_n is the energy of the electron in the nth orbit or stationary state, R_H is the Rydberg constant for the hydrogen atom expressed in joules rather than reciprocal meters $(2.18 \times 10^{-18} J)$, and Z is the nuclear charge (simply +1

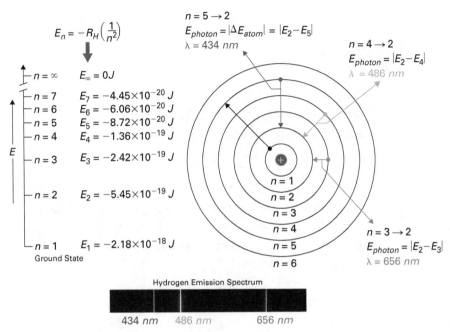

Figure 7.6 According to Bohr, the lines in emission spectra result from electrons falling from an excited state to a lower-energy state.

for the hydrogen atom). The variable n is simply an integer which can take any value of 1 or greater ($n = 1, 2, 3, 4, 5.....$). The negative sign indicates the energy of an electron in an atom is always less than that of a "free" electron (for which we will set the energy equal to zero, or $n = \infty$). As such, as n increases so does the energy. This means that the lowest allowed energy level is that for which $n = 1$, corresponding to the orbit closest to the nucleus and because it is the lowest energy stationary state, it is referred to as the **ground state**, the most stable state (see Figure 7.6).

With this model in mind, we can now explain and predict the observed frequencies in the emission spectrum of hydrogen if we consider a second major postulate of Bohr's theory of atomic structure, which is that *the hydrogen atom will naturally remain in its ground state unless perturbed by the absorption of a photon of EM radiation (energy).* If we begin here with the hydrogen atom in its ground state (the electron resides in the 1st orbit, $n = 1$), it is possible for the electron to absorb energy in the form of a photon of EM radiation moving the electron into a higher energy state. However, the energy of the incoming photon must be precisely equal to the difference in energy of the ground state and another allowed state. When this occurs, the electron is said to be excited to a higher energy state ($n > 1$), referred to as an **excited state**. Because Bohr's model allows us to calculate the energies of the stationary states, we can predict these energy differences and therefore the frequencies and wavelengths of photons which can be absorbed *or emitted* by the hydrogen atom. Figure 7.6 summarizes the calculated energies of the orbits of an electron in a hydrogen atom. Notice that due to the inverse-square dependence of the energy on n, the difference in the energies of the orbits is increasingly smaller as the value of n increases. Further, when the electron is completely freed from the atom ($n = \infty$), its energy is zero.

To better understand this, let's consider an example. Assume that an electron in a hydrogen atom has been excited to the 5th orbit or stationary state ($n = 5$). From this excited state the electron *relaxes* to a lower energy state, $n = 2$. The energy loss due to such a transition cannot simply be ignored. Rather it is manifested in the emission of a photon of EM radiation. Using this model, we can now predict the wavelength of the emitted photon as follows:

1. First, we must understand that the energy of the photon is equal to the energy difference between the final and initial energy states of the electron:

$$\Delta E_{atom} = E_{photon}$$

2. You should understand this expression as the atom losing energy and the energy loss is manifested as the emission of a photon. Further, we know from Planck and Einstein that the energy of a photon can be expressed as a function of wavelength as follows:

$$\Delta E_{atom} = \frac{hc}{\lambda}$$

3. Additionally, the energy change due to the electronic transition from $n = 5$ to $n = 2$ is simply expressed as $\Delta E_{atom} = |E_2 - E_5|$:

$$|E_2 - E_5| = \frac{hc}{\lambda}$$

4. We can now easily solve for wavelength, λ:

$$\lambda = \frac{hc}{|E_2 - E_5|}$$

Since Figure 7.6 summarizes these energies we simply determine the difference, $|E_2 - E_5| = |-5.45 \times 10^{-19} J + 8.72 \times 10^{-20} J| = 4.58 \times 10^{-19} J$:

$$\lambda = \frac{hc}{4.58 \times 10^{-19} J} = \frac{(6.626 \times 10^{-34} J \cdot s)\left(2.9979 \times 10^8 \frac{m}{s}\right)}{4.58 \times 10^{-19} J} = 4.34 \times 10^{-7} m = 434\, nm$$

Indeed, 434 *nm* is the wavelength of one of the visible lines observed in the emission spectrum of hydrogen. A more generic expression for the energy change of the atom due to an electronic transition is:

$$\Delta E_{atom} = -R_H \left(\frac{1}{n_f^2} - \frac{1}{n_i^2} \right)$$

where R_H is the Rydberg constant for the hydrogen atom ($2.18 \times 10^{-18} J$) and n_f and n_i are the final and initial states of the electron, respectively. Notice this equation is entirely analogous to the Rydberg Equation given in the previous section. Indeed, the Bohr Model of the Atom now allowed for an explanation of the various series of spectral lines which had been observed for hydrogen (Figure 7.7).

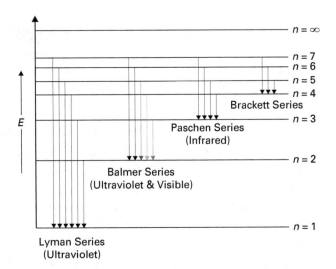

Example Problem 7.5 — Electronic Transitions and the Bohr Model of the Hydrogen Atom.

Determine the wavelength of a photon of EM radiation emitted when an electron in a hydrogen atom makes a transition from the $n = 4$ to the $n = 2$ stationary states.	

Solution:	
First, we can use the following equation to determine the energy difference between the fourth and second stationary states. $$\Delta E_{atom} = -R_H \left(\frac{1}{n_f^2} - \frac{1}{n_i^2} \right)$$	If $n_f = 2$ and $n_i = 4$: $$\Delta E_{atom} = -R_H \left(\frac{1}{2^2} - \frac{1}{4^2} \right)$$ $$E_{atom} = -R_H \left(\frac{1}{4} - \frac{1}{16} \right) = -R_H \left(\frac{3}{16} \right)$$ $$\Delta E_{atom} = -(2.18 \times 10^{-18}\,J)(0.1875)$$ $$\Delta E_{atom} = -4.088 \times 10^{-19}\,J$$
Next, recall that the energy of an emitted photon must equal this energy difference:	$$E_{photon} = \left| \Delta E_{atom} \right|$$ $$E_{photon} = 4.088 \times 10^{-19}\,J$$
We now use Planck's equation to calculate the wavelength of the photon: $$E_{photon} = \frac{hc}{\lambda}$$	$$E_{photon} = \frac{hc}{\lambda}$$ $$\lambda = \frac{hc}{E_{photon}} = \frac{(6.626 \times 10^{-34}\,J \cdot s)\left(2.9979 \times 10^8\,\frac{m}{s}\right)}{4.088 \times 10^{-19}\,J}$$ $$\lambda = 4.860 \times 10^{-7}\,m \times \frac{10^9\,nm}{1\,m} = \mathbf{486.0\,nm}$$

Section 7.7 The Wave Property of the Electron

Louis-Victor-Pierre-Raymond de Broglie (1892–1987) was a French physicist credited with development of the wave-particle duality of matter, a foundational precept of Quantum Mechanics.

While Bohr had taken a huge leap forward in making a connection between the structure of the atom and the observable spectral data, he was not able to offer a reason why his interpretation was the correct one. Indeed, he had not detailed a reason for why the electron's angular momentum should be quantized. That question would be addressed by another physicist, Louis Victor de Broglie. In 1925, de Broglie postulated that if Einstein's explanation of the photoelectric effect could attribute particulate properties to light, could electrons exhibit a wave property? If so, an electron wave, electrostatically bound to an atomic nucleus, would act like a standing wave. A standing wave would explain the quantized angular momenta. Therefore, de Broglie argued the following:

1. Photons have no resting mass and their energies are given as a function of wavelength (or frequency):

$$E = \frac{hc}{\lambda}$$

2. Recall that Einstein theorized that photons have a relativistic mass and their energies are given as follows:

$$E = mc^2$$

3. Therefore:

$$mc^2 = \frac{hc}{\lambda}$$

4. Thus:

$$\lambda = \frac{h}{mc}$$

Where h is Planck's constant, m is the relativistic mass of a photon and c is the speed of light. Thus, de Broglie argued from pure analogy that a particle would have a wave property with a wavelength given by the same expression:

$$\lambda = \frac{h}{mv}$$

where v is the velocity of the particle and m is its mass in kilograms. *Thus, it appears that the velocity of a particle defines its wavelength.* This was later corroborated by experiment when George Paget Thomson at the University of Aberdeen passed an electron beam through a metal film and observed a diffraction pattern, demonstrating its wave character. At the same time, Clinton Joseph Davisson and Lester Halbert Germer

Sir George Paget Thomson (1892–1975) was an English physicist credited with the first empirical demonstration of the wave properties of electrons via electron diffraction.

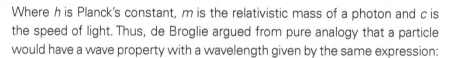

at Bell Labs also independently demonstrated the diffraction of a beam of electrons. This was a tremendous breakthrough because it brought the idea of wave-particle duality squarely into the mainstream. We now had good evidence that energy and matter exhibited a wave-like and a particle-like nature and, further, we have equations that seem to suggest that wavelength and mass are inversely related. The more pronounced one is, the less pronounced the other seems to be. We will have more to say on this topic in the coming sections.

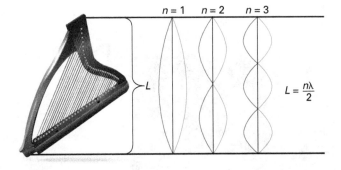

Nevertheless, it is apparent that if an electron has a significant wave-like nature, its existence in an atom would be that of a standing wave. A standing wave in physics is a wave which has a constant amplitude at each point along the axis of the wave. A vibrating harp string is an example of a standing wave. If an electron were a wave, bound to orbit the nucleus of an atom, it would exhibit only a set of specific, allowed motions under such a circumstance. In other words, it would quite naturally be quantized into orbits at specific distances from the nucleus where the orbital path length would be a whole number multiple of the wavelength of the electron-wave (see figure 7.8). Consider a harp string as shown in Figure 7.8. When a string is struck, it vibrates adopting a wave form. Note that at each end of the harp string the amplitude must be zero. This boundary condition requires that the vibrating string only adopt allowed vibrational modes for which the boundary condition is maintained. This is simply the nature of a standing wave, and this, argued de Broglie, is why the energy of the electron is quantized.

Figure 7.8 Vibrating harp strings are examples of standing waves. The amplitude of a standing wave in a harp string must be zero at both ends (where the string is fixed to the instrument). This means that only waves for which the relation $L = \frac{n\lambda}{2}$ is satisfied are allowed. In this case, n is a quantum number with integer values, $n = 1, 2, 3, \ldots$. Each different value of n defines a different standing wave-function.

Example Problem 7.6 — de Broglie Wavelength

Determine the wavelength of an electron travelling at a speed of $1.99 \times 10^7 \frac{m}{s}$ (The mass of an electron is $9.11 \times 10^{-28} g$).	
Solution:	
In this case, according to de Broglie we have all the information we need to make this determination. $$\lambda = \frac{h}{mv}$$ Where λ is the wavelength of the electron, m is its mass (in kg) and v is its velocity (in $\frac{m}{s}$). If a $1\,J = 1\,\frac{kg \cdot m^2}{s^2}$ and Planck's constant is in units of $J \cdot s$, then we can express Planck's constant as $\frac{kg \cdot m^2}{s}$. This will require that we convert our mass to kg.	$$\lambda = \frac{h}{mv}$$ $$\lambda = \frac{\left(6.626 \times 10^{-34} \dfrac{kg \cdot m^2}{s}\right)}{\left(9.11 \times 10^{-28} g \times \dfrac{1\,kg}{10^3\,g}\right)\left(1.99 \times 10^7 \dfrac{m}{s}\right)} =$$ $$\lambda = 3.65 \times 10^{-11}\,m$$

Section 7.8 Heisenberg's Uncertainty Principle

Werner Karl Heisenberg (1901–1976) was a German physicist noted for his contribution to the creation of Quantum Mechanics, for which he received a Nobel Prize in 1932. He is most famous for his development of the uncertainty principle.

According to classical physics, there is no limitation placed on the certainty to which any observable or set of observables can be measured. For example, it is possible to know both the position and the momentum of a classical particle simultaneously with a large degree of certainty. However, this is not so for quantum mechanical particles. This concept was formalized by Werner Heisenberg in 1927. Heisenberg stated that there were pairs of observables that could not be known simultaneously with high precision. Position and momentum or energy and time are two such sets of **complementary** observables. Additionally, building on de Broglie's and Einstein's contributions, Werner Heisenberg derived a mathematical expression for his famous **uncertainty principle**:

$$\Delta x \Delta p_x \geq \frac{h}{4\pi}$$

Where Δx is the uncertainty in the position of a particle (in one dimension, x), and Δp_x is the uncertainty in momentum (in the x-direction). As such, if we know the position of a particle with a great certainty (Δx is very small) then Δp_x would have to be correspondingly large for the relation to hold. This means we can either know a great deal about the position of the particle-wave or we can know a great deal about its momentum but not both. Since we know that momentum is simply the product of mass and velocity, we can express the uncertainty principle as follows:

$$\Delta x \Delta v_x \geq \frac{h}{4\pi m}$$

Max Born (1882–1970) was a German physicist noted for his contributions to a range of topics in chemistry and physics. In 1926, he introduced the interpretation of the wave-function ψ, in Schrödinger's equation as probability waves, a contribution to Quantum Mechanics for which he received a Nobel Prize in 1954.

where Δv_x is the associated uncertainty in the velocity of the particle in the x-direction and m is the mass of the particle. What does this mean for an electron-wave in an atom? Put simply, the uncertainty principle tells us that if we wish to know the energy of an electron with great precision, we cannot be certain of the position of that electron in the space around the nucleus of the atom. In other words, we can only ask about the probability of finding an electron (with a known energy) in a given region of space about the nucleus. This idea was first proposed by Max Born when he quite startlingly suggested that the electron-wave should be considered as a "probability wave" rather than a sort of delocalized or "spread out" electron. A probability wave is one in which the amplitude at any point is not "how much" of the electron is present there, but rather is the "probability" of finding the electron at that point. If this is true, the question remains, what does the electron-wave look like? This is the subject of the next section.

Section 7.9 Schrödinger's Equation and the Atomic Orbital

With the development of the wave-particle duality of matter and energy, quantum mechanics was born. In its infancy, it provided a new way of looking at many questions which had not yet been tackled by classical physics. The behavior of electrons in atoms was a question which remained wide open, and in 1926, Erwin Schrödinger derived an equation which described just that for electrons in the hydrogen atom. The simplest way to express the Schrödinger Equation is as follows:

$$H\psi = E\psi$$

where H is a set of mathematical instructions, collectively referred to as the **Hamiltonian** operator, which "operate" on a wave-function, ψ, to yield the total energy, E, of the wave-function times the wave-function back again. A **wave-function** is a three-dimensional mathematical description of the electron-wave. Hence, each solution to this equation provides the wave-function of the electron associated with one of the allowed energy states of the hydrogen atom. The mathematics involved in these complex calculations is well beyond the scope of this text; however, the important thing to note here is that this equation provided a method for deriving mathematical functions which give a description of the electron-wave in the hydrogen atom. Unlike in the Bohr model where the electrons were said to be in orbits with fixed distances to the nucleus, Schrödinger's equations resulted in wave-functions which provided a **probability density** of finding the electron within a given volume of space. This is accomplished by taking the square of the wave-function, ψ^2. Here it is instructive to discuss the characteristics of the wave functions in a little more detail:

1. Each wave function, ψ, is associated with an energy value, E_n, for the electron in the hydrogen atom.

2. The square of the wave function, ψ^2, is the probability density of an electron for a given region of space, also referred to the **electron density**. The region of space wherein the electron is most likely to be found according to ψ^2 is referred to as its **orbital.** As such, ψ^2 is the mathematical description of electronic orbitals.

3. Each allowed solution to Schrödinger's equation, ψ, includes a set of three integer values referred to as **quantum numbers**. These are the **principal quantum number (n),** the **angular momentum quantum number (l)** (also known as the azimuthal quantum number), and the **magnetic quantum number (m_l)**. These numbers define the features of the wave functions and occur only in certain allowed combinations, which will be covered in the following section.

Erwin Schrödinger (1887–1961) was an Austrian physicist and Nobel Laureate. He is credited with derivation of the wave equation which correctly predicts the energy states of a hydrogen atom. This equation, known as Schrödinger's equation, is one of the most important achievements of the twentieth century.

To summarize, the solutions to Schrödinger's equation for the hydrogen atom provide the wave-functions for the electron in each of the allowed energy states. The square of each wave-function, ψ^2, is the probability density of finding the electron in the space around the atomic nucleus associated with a given energy state. Combinations of integers, known as quantum numbers, define the energy states as well as the nature and characteristics of each of the associated wave-functions.

Quantum Numbers

It is important to understand first what quantum numbers are and are not. They are not preconceived adjustments or fudge-factors introduced into the wavefunctions to ensure a fit to experimental models. They are simply the natural consequence of the mathematics associated with wave behavior. As such, they provide us with valuable information and act as a system of coordinates which uniquely define each allowed energy level available to an electron in an atom. Let's now discuss each quantum number individually.

n, The Principal Quantum Number—The principal quantum number generally defines the size of the orbital (ψ^2) and the overall energy of the electron in that orbital. It can have any positive integer value from 1 to infinity. It is the principal quantum number which is analogous to the value of n in the Bohr description of the hydrogen atom. Further, for hydrogen-like atoms (atoms having only one electron) the energy of the electron is calculated in the same fashion as that described by Bohr. However, unlike the Bohr model, electrons in an atom with the same principal quantum number, n, are said to be in the same principal quantum shell or simply "shell." We have dispensed with the notion of well-defined, fixed orbits.

l, The Angular Momentum Quantum Number (also referred to as the Azimuthal Quantum Number)—Electrons can occupy a number of possible "subshells" for a given value of n. These are defined by the angular momentum quantum number, l (also sometimes referred to as the **azimuthal quantum number**). Within a given shell, each allowed value of l defines a characteristic orbital shape. Additionally, the range of allowed values for l is limited by the value of n for a given shell. The allowed values for l are any integer value starting from zero up to $n - 1$.

$$l = 0, 1, 2, \ldots (n-1)$$

Therefore, if $n = 1$, there is only one allowed value for l, which is simply 0. This means that there is only one possible orbital type in the first shell of any atom ($n = 1$, $l = 0$). However, in the second shell, $n = 2$, the possible values of l are 0 and 1, meaning there are two possible wave-functions (orbitals) which could be occupied in the second shell. Therefore, as n increases, there is an increasing number of possible subshells. Additionally, there is a convention for labeling each value of l with a lower-case letter as shown in Table 7.1.

m_l, The Magnetic Quantum Number—Within each subshell there can be multiple "suborbitals". The magnetic quantum number defines the allowed orientations of suborbitals within a subshell. For a given value of l, the allowed values for m_l are zero and all positive and negative integer values from $-l$ to $+l$.

$$m_l = -l, \ldots, -2, -1, 0, 1, 2, \ldots +l$$

Therefore, if $l = 3$ (the "f" subshell), there are seven allowed orientations of the f-suborbitals in that particular subshell, one for each allowed value of m_l. For all practical purposes, we can consider these seven wave-functions essentially the same, only differing in their spatial orientations. For this reason, you will often see the suborbitals in each subshell written or referred to with "spatial labels." For instance, the wave-functions which constitute the "p" subshell of the second principal shell ($n = 2$, $l = 1$) will often be distinguished as the $2p_x$, $2p_y$, and $2p_z$, where the subscripts x, y, and z refer to the three spatial coordinates (arbitrarily) defined by convention to coincide with the three mutually perpendicular "p" orbitals within the second principal shell. Each of these orientations along the x, y, and z coordinates corresponds to one of the three allowed values of m_l (–1, 0, +1). Additionally, the coefficient "2" preceding the "p" label in each case refers to the principal shell (i.e. $n = 2$ for each of the three wave-functions).

To summarize, the three quantum numbers define the structure of allowed wave-functions which are available to electrons in atoms. This is essentially the electronic structure of that atom. The energy levels, referred to as stationary states in Bohr's model, are given by each unique value of n, where $n = 1$ defines the lowest energy state and for which the orbital is smallest. We refer to these energy levels as shells. As the value of n increases, the shells are larger, farther from the nucleus, and higher in energy. The atom's shells are then further divided into one or more subshells, defined by the value of l, the angular momentum quantum number. Each unique value of l defines the shape of the orbital(s) which are given the labels of s, p, d, and f by convention. The magnetic quantum number, m_l, then specifies the spatial orientation of each orbital within a given subshell. Taken together, a unique set of three quantum numbers, n, l, and m_l, define the size and energy, shape, and spatial orientation of each specific orbital within an atom. Another way to think of them is that each set of three quantum numbers is like a set of coordinates which tells "where" within an atom's structure a particular electron resides, just like an address with a zip code. Table 7.1 summarizes the electronic structure of the atoms as described by quantum numbers.

Examination of Table 7.1 readily provides some insights. If you begin with a given value of n, which then defines the allowed values of l and m_l within that shell, there some useful relationships:

1. n = the number of allowed values of l. In other words, there are "n" possible subshells for a given value of n.

2. There are $2l + 1$ orbitals within each subshell. This is the same thing as saying there are $2l + 1$ allowed values of m_l for a given value of l.

3. There are n^2 orbitals, total, allowed or available within a given shell.

Table 7.1 Summary of Quantum Numbers.

Principal Quantum Number, n	Allowed Values of l (label)	Allowed Values of m_l	Number of Sub-orbitals (in the Sub-shell), $2l + 1$	Number of Sub-orbitals (in the Shell), n^2
1	0 (s)	0	1 (1s)	1
2	0 (s)	0	1 (2s)	4
	1 (p)	−1, 0, +1	3 (2p)	
3	0 (s)	0	1 (3s)	9
	1 (p)	−1, 0, +1	3 (3p)	
	2 (d)	−2, −1, 0, +1, +2	5 (3d)	
4	0 (s)	0	1 (4s)	16
	1 (p)	−1, 0, +1	3 (4p)	
	2 (d)	−2, −1, 0, +1, +2	5 (4d)	
	3 (f)	−3, −2, −1, 0, +1, +2, +3	7 (4f)	

For example:

1. In the third principal shell ($n = 3$), there are "3" subshells corresponding to the "3" allowed values of l, which are $l = 0, 1,$ and 2, corresponding to the s, p, and d subshells, respectively.

   a. For $l = 0$, there is only one allowed value of m_l ($m_l = 0$). This means there is one "3s" orbital ($2l + 1 = 1$).

   b. When $l = 1$, m_l can be −1, 0 and +1. This corresponds to the three "3p" orbitals ($2l + 1 = 3$).

   c. Additionally, $l = 2$ is also an allowed value of l in the third shell, giving rise to allowed values of m_l of −2, −1, 0, +1 & +2, corresponding to the five "3d" orbitals ($2l + 1 = 5$).

2. Therefore, in total the third shell ($n = 3$) contains a total of nine ($n^2 = 9$) sub-orbitals (one "3s" orbital, three "3p" orbitals and five "3d" orbitals).

Example Problem 7.7—Quantum Numbers

List the possible values of l for an electron in the following shells:
a. $n = 2$
b. $n = 3$
c. $n = 4$

Solutions:	
a. Possible values of l are all integer values from 0 up to $n − 1$. (There are "n" possible values of l.)	When $n = 2$, the highest value for l is $n − 1 = 2 − 1 = 1$. Therefore, there are two values possible for l. $$l = 0, 1$$ For this reason, there are two subshells in the 2nd shell, the s subshell ($l = 0$) and the p subshell ($l = 1$).

b.	Possible values of l are all integer values from 0 up to $n-1$. (There are "n" possible values of l.)	When $n=3$, the highest value for l is $n-1=3-1=2$. Therefore, there are three values possible for l. $l = 0, 1, 2$ For this reason, there are three subshells in the 3rd shell, the s subshell ($l=0$), the p subshell ($l=1$), and the d subshell ($l=2$).
c.	Possible values of l are all integer values from 0 up to $n-1$. (There are "n" possible values of l.)	When $n=4$, the highest value for l is $n-1=4-1=3$. Therefore, there are four values possible for l. $l = 0, 1, 2, 3$ For this reason, there are four subshells in the 4th shell, the s subshell ($l=0$), the p subshell ($l=1$), the d subshell ($l=2$), and the f subshell ($l=3$).

Example Problem 7.8—Quantum Numbers

How many orbitals are in the 4th shell ($n=4$)? List the unique combination of three quantum numbers for each orbital in the 4th shell and their labels (such as "$2s$" or "$3p$").

Solutions:		
l	**m_l**	**Label**
0	0	$4s$
1	$-1, 0, +1$	$4p$
2	$-2, -1, 0, +1, +2$	$4d$
3	$-3, -2, -1, 0, +1, +2, +3$	$4f$

There are $n^2 = 4^2 = 16$ orbitals in the 4th shell.

Example Problem 7.9—Quantum Numbers

Determine which of the following sets of quantum numbers is erroneous and which are allowed. If a set is allowed, give its label (such as "$2s$" or "$3p$").
a. $n=2, l=2, m_l=-1$
b. $n=2, l=1, m_l=+1$
c. $n=4, l=0, m_l=0$
d. $n=3, l=2, m_l=-3$

Solutions:
a. Recall that l only has allowed values from 0 to $n-1$. Since, in this case $l > (n-1)$, this set is not allowed.   <div align="center">Not allowed. $n=2, l=2, m_l=-1$</div>
b. These are an allowed set of quantum numbers, which describe a $2p$ orbital. (Recall the label "p" refers to an orbital for which $l=1$.)   <div align="center">Allowed – $2p$</div>
c. These are an allowed set of quantum numbers, which describe a $4s$ orbital. (Recall the label "s" refers to an orbital for which $l=0$.)   <div align="center">Allowed – $4s$</div>

d. This set is not allowed. Recall that m_l can only have allowed values from $-l$ to l.

Not allowed. $n = 3, l = 2, m_l = -3$

Section 7.10 Shapes of Orbitals

Recall from the previous section that the wave-function of an electron is a probability wave. This means that the "value" (amplitude) of the wave-function at a specific point in space relates the probability of finding the electron at that point. However, amplitudes are both positive and negative at different locations, and we know that a negative probability is impossible. Therefore, we take the wave-function squared, ψ^2, as the **probability density** (the probability per unit volume) of finding the electron in a given region of space. Figure 7.9 shows the probability distribution of the electron in the $1s$ and $2p$ orbitals of the hydrogen atom. Here, we interpret the darker regions to be points of higher probability and lighter regions are of lower probability. For example, for the s-orbital, if we take the origin of our coordinate system as the position of the atomic nucleus, we see that all points of a given distance, r, from the nucleus have the same probability in all directions. In a three-dimensional sense, we would refer to this as spherical symmetry, and therefore we say that the s orbitals have a spherical shape. This can be visualized by defining a surface which encloses the region of space around the nucleus which contains 90% of the probability of finding the electron. Doing so for the $1s$ orbital produces a sphere. This is what is meant when we refer to the orbital shapes.

The s Orbital, $l = 0$. For an electron that has a value of $l = 0$, the shape of its orbital is spherical. In other words, the electron density is spherically symmetric about the nucleus (See Figure 7.9). Since a sphere can adopt only one unique orientation, only one value is allowed for the magnetic quantum number, $m_l = 0$. Therefore, for any principal shell, there can be only a single s orbital within the s subshell. If the total probability of finding the electron within

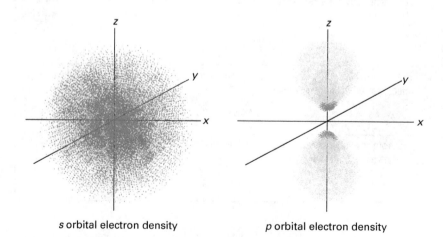

Figure 7.9 Dot density maps of the $1s$ and $2p$ orbitals. Regions with greater concentrations of dots represent a higher probability of finding an electron.

s orbital electron density

p orbital electron density

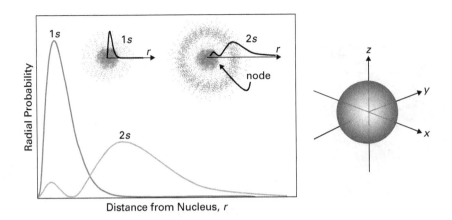

this sphere is plotted as a function of the distance from the nucleus, *r*, we have what is referred to as the **radial probability distribution**. Figure 7.10 shows the radial probability distributions for the 1*s* and 2*s* wave-functions. Notice that as the value of the principal quantum number increases from 1 to 2, a node is introduced into the radial probability distribution. Recall that a **node** is a point where the amplitude, or probability of finding an electron, goes to zero. For any *s* orbital, the number of nodes is given by $n - 1$, where *n* is the principal quantum number. Additionally, as n increases, the size of the *s* orbitals also increases. In other words, the electron(s) in a 3*s* orbital occupy a larger region of space and are farther from the nucleus than electrons in the 2*s* orbital.

The *p* Orbital, *l* = 1. There is no *p* subshell in the first principal shell. This is because 1 is not an allowed value of *l* when $n = 1$. Unlike the *s* orbitals, *p* orbitals are not spherical and have a "planar" *node* at the nucleus with two lobes extending outward from the nucleus on either side of the *nodal plane*. Figure 7.11 shows the shapes of the three 2*p* orbitals. Because $m_l = -1, 0, 1$, when $l = 1$, there are three distinct orientations which are allowed. This means that for each *p* subshell, there are three *p* orbitals oriented such that their nodal planes are coincident with the *xy*, *xz*, and *yz* planes defined by our coordinate system in Figure 7.11. In other words, the orbitals in any *p* subshell are perpendicular to one another. Additionally, it is customary to distinguish these by labeling the *p* orbital with lobes lying along the *x*-axis as the $2p_x$ orbital while the $2p_y$ and $2p_z$ labels refer to the orbitals with lobes lying along the *y*- and *z*-axes, respectively. Just as in the case of the *s* orbitals, the size of the *p* orbitals increase as *n* increases.

The *d* Orbital, *l* = 2. Again, we recognize that there are no *d* subshells in the principal shells $n = 1, 2$. The first *d* subshell to emerge in the structure

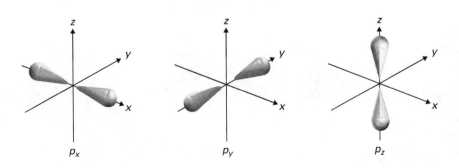

Figure 7.11 The *p* orbitals.

Figure 7.12 The *d* orbitals.

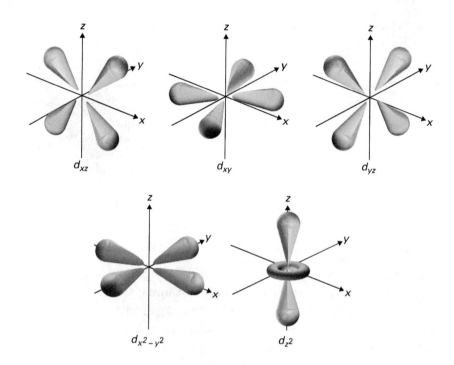

d_{xz}

d_{xy}

d_{yz}

$d_{x^2-y^2}$

d_{z^2}

of the atom is in the third shell, $n = 3$. Figure 7.12 shows a depiction of the five different 3*d* orbitals. There are always five *d* orbitals in any *d* subshell because when $l = 2$, there are five allowed orientations ($m_l = -2, -1, 0, 1, 2$). Notice from Figure 7.12, there are four 4-lobed *d* orbitals, which are commonly labeled as the d_{xz}, d_{xy}, d_{yz} and $d_{x^2-y^2}$ orbitals. Additionally, the d_{z^2} orbital has a different shape consisting of two lobes which lie along the *z*-axis and a "doughnut" or "belt" (mathematically referred to as toroid) which lies in the *xy* plane.

Figure 7.13 The *f* orbitals.

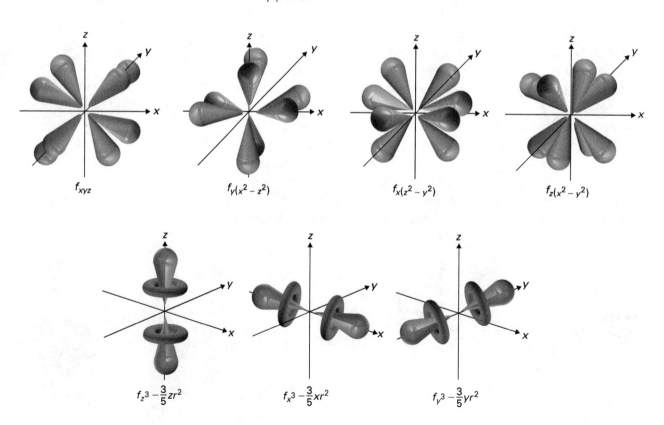

f_{xyz}

$f_{y(x^2-z^2)}$

$f_{x(z^2-y^2)}$

$f_{z(x^2-y^2)}$

$f_{z^3-\frac{3}{5}zr^2}$

$f_{x^3-\frac{3}{5}xr^2}$

$f_{y^3-\frac{3}{5}yr^2}$

The *f* Orbital, *l* = 3. The first appearance of *f* orbitals occurs in the fourth shell ($n = 4$). Figure 7.13 depicts the shapes of the 4*f* orbitals along with their conventional labels. Because these orbitals will not be involved in any of the bonding theory we will cover in this text, we include them here only to present a complete picture of the atomic structure.

Section 7.11 **Electron Spin**

We have so far learned that an electron can be described with a unique set of three quantum numbers, n, l, and m_l. However, this is not sufficient to completely describe an electron. Indeed, the atomic emission spectral data also indicate that electrons exhibit a magnetic moment. This requires a fourth quantum number referred to as the **electron spin quantum number, m_s**. This number takes its name from classical physics, which tells us that a charged particle will exhibit a magnetic moment when spinning on its axis. As such, a classical charged particle can spin in one of two directions producing one of two magnetic moments of opposite direction (see Figure 7.14). Thus, the spin quantum number can have only one of two values, $m_s = +\frac{1}{2}$ or $-\frac{1}{2}$. It is possible to interpret this as meaning the electron can spin in one of two directions, however, this is merely an analogy to classical physics and need not be considered as a description of the electron in concrete terms. It is also important to note that the spin quantum number does not describe properties of the orbital; it is not a solution to Schrödinger's equation.

Invoking this fourth quantum number may not seem to carry much weight when discussing atomic structure, especially since electron spin has no input in defining the properties of orbitals. However, it does gain significance when we consider the work of a physicist named Wolfgang Pauli. Pauli postulated: *No two electrons in an atom can have the same set of four quantum numbers.* This has since been termed the **Pauli Exclusion Principle**. It is in this context that the significance of the spin quantum number is apparent. Since two electrons with the same set of three quantum numbers n, l, and m_l are necessarily occupying the same orbital, they must therefore have different spin quantum numbers. Because there are only two possible values of m_s, an orbital can contain no more than two electrons and their spins must be opposing. This is significant to the arrangement of electrons in an atom, especially in atoms other than hydrogen which possess more than one electron. When two electrons occupy the same orbital with opposing spin quantum numbers, they are said to be **spin-paired**.

Wolfgang Pauli (1900–1958) is a Swiss-American physicist credited with the discover of the now famous Pauli Principle, which is of fundamental important to our understanding of the structure of matter. Pauli was awarded the Nobel Prize for his contributions in 1945.

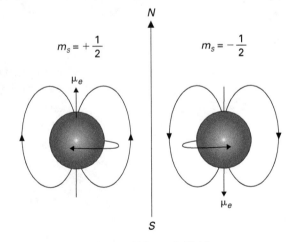

External Magnetic Field

Figure 7.14 A charged particle with spin can act as a magnet. In the presence of an external magnetic field, the spin can have one of two orientations, clockwise or counterclockwise. In other words, the magnetic moment of the electron, μ_e, can be either parallel or antiparallel (up or down) relative to the external field.

Paramagnetism

A magnetic field slightly repels most substances. Such substances are referred to as **diamagnetic**. However, many substances, such as certain metals for example, are attracted to a magnetic field. These materials are said to be **paramagnetic**. Paramagnetism is due to the spin of electrons in atoms and molecules. It arises when there are "unpaired" electrons in an atom. The magnetic moment of an unpaired electron will align itself with an external magnetic field and therefore realize an attractive force. However, when electrons are spin-paired, each electron cancels the magnetic field of the other. As such, *materials in which all electrons are spin-paired are diamagnetic, while those which possess unpaired electrons are paramagnetic.*

Section 7.12 Multi-electron Atoms and Energy Level Splitting

So far, we have discussed the shapes of orbitals and only partially started an exploration of the arrangement of electrons in these orbitals. However, we have not yet examined much on the topic of the orbital (electron) energies in an atom. Recall that in a previous section we stated the principal quantum number defined the size and relative energy of the orbital. This is true for a hydrogen atom. This means that, for hydrogen, all the subshells in a given principal shell are of the same energy—they are referred to as **degenerate**. In fact, the equation offered by Bohr in calculating the energy of his "orbits" still holds for the hydrogen atom, and, therefore, we can easily calculate these energies. Further, even though many orbitals are available to the single electron in hydrogen, it will always most naturally reside in the energy level which is most stable (lowest in energy)—the orbital closest to the nucleus, the 1s orbital. This lowest energy state is referred to as the **ground state** just as in the case of Bohr's model.

However, the agreement with Bohr's model ends with the hydrogen atom. To completely understand why this is so, it is first important to recognize that the electrostatic forces acting between charged particles play the principal role in determining the energy of atomic orbitals. In the case of hydrogen, the energy of an electron is determined from the electrostatic attraction between the negatively charged electron and the positively charged nucleus. **Coulomb's Law** summarizes this energy of the electrostatic interaction:

$$E \propto \frac{q_1 q_2}{r}$$

Where E is the potential energy of two charged particles, q_1 and q_2 are the charges of the two particles and r is the distance between the two particles. In this case, we can intuit that when the two charges, q_1 and q_2, are opposite (one positive and the other negative), the product of $q_1 q_2$ results in a negative (stabilizing) contribution to the energy. In other words, this has the effect of lowering the overall energy of the system. Lower energy states are more stable. The greater the magnitude of q_1 or q_2, the more stabilizing (attractive) the interaction. Likewise, the closer the two particles are to one another, the more stabilizing the interaction. On the other hand, if the two particles exhibit like charges (either both are positive or both are negative), the contribution to the energy of the system due to the electrostatic interaction will now be positive. This raises the energy, or destabilizes, the system. In this case, greater separation of the particles (larger values of r) is more stabilizing, and the particles naturally separate if possible.

Let's return to hydrogen. Since we understand the energy of the electron is based on electrostatic attraction to the nucleus, larger orbitals are higher in energy because the electron is farther from the nucleus. As such, for hydrogen the energy of the electron is only a function of the principal quantum number, n. However, with multi-electron atoms, the presence of more than one electron introduces an additional contribution to the energy of the whole system. These are electron-electron repulsions. In such cases, it is no longer just the distance between the electrons and nucleus (that is the orbital size) which dictates the energy of the electron, but now it is also the shape of the orbitals, as this effects how the electrons are arranged or distributed in space relative to each other. We will now explore this effect further in terms of two concepts, *shielding* and *penetration*.

Shielding

Shielding is the phenomenon whereby electron-electron repulsions counteract the electron-nuclear attraction "felt" by an electron. Generally speaking, an electron farther from the nucleus will "feel" a reduced "effective" nuclear charge due to repulsions with other electrons which are closer to the nucleus. Consider a sodium ion, Na^+. In this case, the nucleus has a charge, $Z = +11$. Now imagine we add another electron to the outer shell of the ion to produce a sodium atom, Na^0. That additional electron once associated with this atom, will experience the attractive force with the nuclear charge ($Z = +11$) but also the repulsive forces of the other ten electrons combined. These repulsive interactions will have the effect of counteracting or shielding the outer electron from the full effects of the nuclear charge such that the outer electron is said to experience an effective nuclear charge, Z^*:

$$Z^* = Z - S$$

where S is referred to as a screening constant. For now, we will assume electrons are only shielded by electrons which are in a lower shell (lower values of n) and not shielded by those other electrons in the same shell or higher. As such, we can say that for our example, the outer electron of the sodium atom will behave as though it is experiencing an effective nuclear charge of +1:

$$Z^* = Z - S = 11 - 10 = +1$$

This is simply because the other ten electrons are in lower energy shells and, as such, serve to shield the last electron from the nucleus.

Example Problem 7.10 – Determining Effective Nuclear Charge

Determine the effective nuclear charge felt by the valence electrons in a sulfur atom.	
Solution:	
Recall our approximation: $$Z^* = Z - S$$ Where Z is the atomic number of the atom and S is a shielding constant.	For sulfur: $Z = 16$ $Z^* = 16 - S$
S is equal to the number of electrons in lower or "inner shells. Since the valence electrons of sulfur are in the third shell, we only count electrons for which $n < 3$ in determining the shielding constant, S.	$S = 10$ $Z^* = 16 - 10$ $\mathbf{Z^* = +6}$
Therefore, we can approximate that the valence electrons will effectively "feel" an attraction to the nucleus as though its charge is +6.	

Penetration

Because this shielding effect exists between the electrons in a multi-electron atom, the degree to which an electron can *penetrate* through the electron cloud toward the nucleus will influence its energy. It is for this reason that within a given shell, the various subshells will now have different energies. For example, if we examine the total radial probability functions in Figure 7.15 for the $1s$, $2s$, and $2p$ orbitals, we see that the $2s$ and $2p$ orbitals occupy or share space with the $1s$ orbital. Because the $1s$ orbital, having a lower value of n, is obviously much closer to the nucleus than the $2s$ and $2p$, electrons in the $1s$ subshell will shield electrons in the $2s$ and $2p$ from the nucleus. However, the $2s$ electrons will be shielded to a somewhat lesser extent than the $2p$ electrons. This is because, as we can see, the $2s$ orbital penetrates through the $1s$ region of space more effectively than the $2p$ orbital. In other words, electrons in outer energy shells (higher values of n) will have lower energies the closer they can penetrate toward the nucleus. In our example (Figure 7.15) we can clearly see that the $2s$ orbital achieves greater proximity to the nucleus than does the $2p$. Owing to this, the $2s$ orbital is observed to be lower in energy than the $2p$ orbital, even though both orbitals belong to the second shell ($n = 2$).

Figure 7.15 The $2s$ orbital penetrates the $1s$ region of space more effectively than does the $2p$ and, as such, the $2s$ orbital is shielded from the nucleus to a lesser extent.

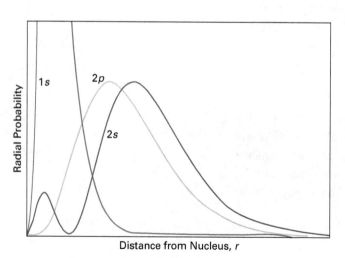

Radial Probability

1s

2p

2s

Distance from Nucleus, r

Energy-Level Splitting among Subshells

Keeping all of this in mind, we can say that the sub-orbitals in each shell exhibit a relative penetration in the order of $ns > np > nd > nf$ which corresponds inversely to their relative energies (within that shell). Figure 7.16 shows the relative energies of the sub-orbitals in a multi-electron atom. We see here that as we move from the first shell to the next and so on, the energies of the orbitals are closer and closer. When we get to the fourth, fifth, and sixth shell, the spacing is so close that the orbitals from different shells begin to overlap. We see the $4s$ orbital is lower in energy than the $3d$ orbitals and the $6s$ is lower than both the $4f$ and the $5d$. This is significant in determining how electrons are arranged in the ground state for different multi-electron atoms—the subject of the next section.

Section 7.13 Ground State Electron Configurations

At this point we should stop and quickly review some concepts.

1. For multi-electron atoms, we will define the ground state as that arrangement or configuration of electrons which collectively is lowest in energy.

2. The sub-orbitals in multi-electron atoms increase in energy in the following order:

Lowest 1s, 2s, 2p, 3s, 3p, 4s, 3d, 4p, 5s, 4d, 5p, 6s, 4f, 5d, 6p, ... → Highest

3. The Pauli Exclusion Principle says that no two electrons in an atom can have the same set of four quantum numbers (no more than two electrons can occupy the same orbital at the same time and their spins must be opposed).

4. Because each orbital can hold two electrons, there is a limit to the number of electrons which can occupy each type of sub-orbital:

    a. The s subshell (1 orbital) = 2 electrons

    b. The p subshell (3 orbitals) = 6 electrons

    c. The d subshell (5 orbitals) = 10 electrons

    d. The f subshell (7 orbitals) = 14 electrons

To know the ground state electron configuration of any given multi-electron atom, there are a couple of additional rules we need to learn. The first comes quite naturally, in that it is intuitive, that if, for a given number of electrons, we fill up our orbitals in order from lowest energy first to higher energy orbitals, the resulting arrangement will have the lowest total energy possible. This is referred to as the **Aufbau Principle**. Aufbau is a German word which, roughly

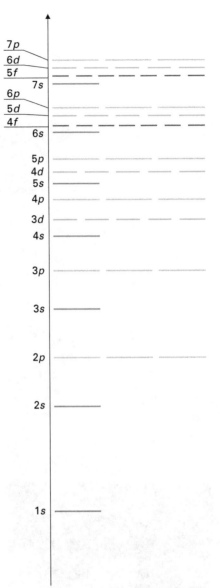

Figure 7.16 The energy levels for each shell in a multi-electron atom increase with increasing values of *n*. Additionally, within each shell the energy levels are split with energy increasing with increasing values of *l*. As the difference in energy between the shells diminishes as *n* increases, the subshells from adjacent principal shells begin to overlap for values of $n \geq 3$.

translated, means "to build up." For example, let's consider an oxygen atom, O. Since the atomic number of O is 8, we know that we must arrange eight electrons into the atomic orbitals. This is done beginning with the lowest energy orbital, the 1s, with each additional electron being placed pair-wise into the next lowest energy orbital, one after another, as follows:

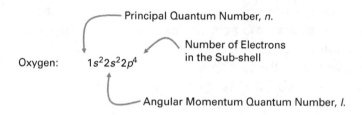

This is the common notation used to write **electron configurations**. Electron configuration is defined as a notation which details the orbitals which electrons occupy in an atom. Here the numeric coefficients "1" and "2" give the principal quantum number of each orbital, "s" and "p" indicate the value of l, and the number of electrons in each subshell is given by a superscript. Therefore, in the oxygen atom, we see that two electrons are placed in the 1s orbital. Additionally, since there is only one orbital in an s subshell, we know the subshell is full with two electrons at which point the next electron must go into the next lowest orbital (the 2s). Having filled the 2s sub-orbital, we now have four of eight electrons remaining, all of which can be placed in the 2p subshell. Because a p subshell contains three p orbitals, it can accommodate a maximum of six electrons, which is sufficient to accommodate the remaining four electrons. Therefore, the ground state electron configuration of oxygen is $1s^2 2s^2 2p^4$. Since fluorine is the next element on the periodic table, we know that it has one more electron, and so its electron configuration is as follows:

$$\text{Fluorine:} \qquad 1s^2 2s^2 2p^5$$

Following fluorine are neon and sodium:

$$\text{Neon:} \qquad 1s^2 2s^2 2p^6$$
$$\text{Sodium:} \qquad 1s^2 2s^2 2p^6 3s^1$$

If we continue to fill the orbitals successively, according to energy, we can write out the electron configurations of all the elements adding one electron at a time.

Another method that is used to describe electron configurations is the orbital diagram. The orbital diagram uses boxes to depict each orbital. Within an orbital (box), electrons are depicted with arrows pointed up or down to indicate their relative spin states. We can demonstrate this by returning to our oxygen example:

Friedrich Hund (1896–1997) was a German physicist credited with the development of the rule of maximum multiplicity, which is now a guiding principle in understanding electrons configurations. This rule is often simply referred to as Hund's rule.

Oxygen: ⇅ ⇅ ⇅ ↑ ↑

1s 2s   2p

Here we see two electrons occupying the 1s orbital. An arrow graphically represents the spin quantum number of each electron, oriented one up and one down, indicating these electrons have opposing spin states of and $m_s = +\frac{1}{2}$ and $-\frac{1}{2}$, respectively. Two such electrons are said to be **spin-paired**. The Pauli Principle precludes any additional electrons in the 1s orbital. As such, the next two electrons are attributed to the next lowest energy orbital, the 2s. We now have four electrons remaining. These are distributed into the three 2p orbitals. Notice, however, that because we have only four electrons in the 2p subshell, the electrons are distributed with one electron in each orbital first, with parallel spins. Only when the fourth electron is added do we pair the electrons into the same orbital, with the additional electron now having the opposite spin. This is an example of *Hund's Rule* (named for German physicist Friedrich Hund – 1896–1997). **Hund's Rule** states that electrons occupying degenerate orbitals must do so such that their total spin is maximized. In other words, when filling orbitals which have the same energy, we fill the orbitals singly first with parallel spins. To illustrate this, the following are the electron configurations and orbital diagrams for the "second row" elements of the periodic table. Note that all orbitals in a given subshell are degenerate (of equal energy).

Lithium:	$1s^2 2s^1$	[↑↓] [↑] 1s 2s
Beryllium:	$1s^2 2s^2$	[↑↓] [↑↓] 1s 2s
Boron:	$1s^2 2s^2 2p^1$	[↑↓] [↑↓] [↑][ ][ ] 1s 2s 2p
Carbon:	$1s^2 2s^2 2p^2$	[↑↓] [↑↓] [↑][↑][ ] 1s 2s 2p
Nitrogen:	$1s^2 2s^2 2p^3$	[↑↓] [↑↓] [↑][↑][↑] 1s 2s 2p
Oxygen:	$1s^2 2s^2 2p^4$	[↑↓] [↑↓] [↑↓][↑][↑] 1s 2s 2p
Fluorine:	$1s^2 2s^2 2p^5$	[↑↓] [↑↓] [↑↓][↑↓][↑] 1s 2s 2p
Neon:	$1s^2 2s^2 2p^6$	[↑↓] [↑↓] [↑↓][↑↓][↑↓] 1s 2s 2p

Notice that when we reach neon, we have enough electrons to completely fill the outer quantum shell ($n = 2$). As we will soon see, a completely filled outer shell represents a particularly stable configuration. Atoms which possess such a configuration are especially unreactive (Noble Gases).

Condensed Electron Configurations

Electron configurations can be simplified for the second-row elements and all those that follow on the periodic table. In the **condensed electron configuration**, all electrons in orbitals of "inner," full shells are represented by the elemental symbols of a group 8A element (a noble gas). This is because electron configurations of the noble gases are characterized by completely full outer shells. In this case, it is helpful to distinguish between the outer shell electrons and those in the orbitals of the "inner" shells. Electrons in the outermost shell of an atom are referred to as **valence electrons**. Electrons which are not in the valence shell are referred to as **core electrons**. Core electrons are those in the orbitals of the "inner" shell(s). Further, the Aufbau principle requires that core electron shells in the ground state are necessarily full shells and as such are equivalent to the ground state electron configurations of the noble gases. For instance, let's consider our previous example of the sodium electron configuration:

Sodium: $1s^2 2s^2 2p^6 3s^1$

If we locate the noble gas which immediately precedes sodium on the periodic table, neon, we see that its electron configuration is $1s^2 2s^2 2p^6$. Therefore, we can replace this notation simply with the elemental symbol of neon in brackets as follows:

	Standard Notation		*Condensed Notation*
Sodium:	$1s^2 2s^2 2p^6 3s^1$	$\rightarrow$	$[Ne]3s^1$

Example Problem 7.11—Electron Configurations and Orbital Diagrams

Write the electron configuration for each of the following elements. Write the orbital diagrams for their valence electrons only.

a. B

b. Br

c. Mg

d. P

Solution:

a. Boron has five electrons. According to Aufbau, we will place these into the $1s$, $2s$, and $2p$ orbitals.

$[He]2s^2 2p^1$

↑↓		↑			

$2s$ $2p$

b. Bromine has 35 electrons. According to Aufbau, we will place these into the $1s$, $2s$, $2p$, $3s$, $3p$, $4s$, $3d$, and $4p$ orbitals.

$[Ar]4s^2 3d^{10} 4p^5$

↑↓		↑↓	↑↓	↑

$4s$ $4p$

c. Magnesium has 12 electrons. According to Aufbau, we will place these into the 1*s*, 2*s*, 2*p* and 3*s* orbitals.	[*Ne*]$3s^2$ [↑↓] 3*s*
d. Phosphorus has 15 electrons. According to Aufbau, we will place these into the 1*s*, 2*s*, 2*p*, 3*s* and 3*p* orbitals.	[*Ne*]$3s^2 3p^3$ [↑↓] [↑][↑][↑] 3*s* 3*p*

Valence Electrons and the Periodic Table

Because the electron configurations represented by the "noble gas" notation in the previous section include only those electrons in lower energy shells, these are referred to as **core electrons.** However, it is the valence electrons which are responsible for the observed chemical properties of an element. Understanding the significance of valence electrons, let's take another look at the periodic table. If we consider the valence electron configuration of the elements, as shown in Figure 7.17, we see very quickly that elements in each group on the periodic table all have the same number of valence electrons, with entirely analogous configurations; the only difference

Figure 7.17 Valence electron configurations according to position on the periodic table.

PERIODIC TABLE OF THE ELEMENTS

	1A 1	2A 2	3B 3	4B 4	5B 5	6B 6	7B 7	8	8B 9	10	1B 11	2B 12	3A 13	4A 14	5A 15	6A 16	7A 17	8A 18
1	1 **H** $1s^1$																	2 **He** $1s^2$
2	3 **Li** $2s^1$	4 **Be** $2s^2$											5 **B** $2s^2 2p^1$	6 **C** $2s^2 2p^2$	7 **N** $2s^2 2p^3$	8 **O** $2s^2 2p^4$	9 **F** $2s^2 2p^5$	10 **Ne** $2s^2 2p^6$
3	11 **Na** $3s^1$	12 **Mg** $3s^2$											13 **Al** $3s^2 3p^1$	14 **Si** $3s^2 3p^2$	15 **P** $3s^2 3p^3$	16 **S** $3s^2 3p^4$	17 **Cl** $3s^2 3p^5$	18 **Ar** $3s^2 3p^6$
4	19 **K** $4s^1$	20 **Ca** $4s^2$	21 **Sc** $4s^2 3d^1$	22 **Ti** $4s^2 3d^2$	23 **V** $4s^2 3d^3$	24 **Cr** $4s^1 3d^5$	25 **Mn** $4s^2 3d^5$	26 **Fe** $4s^2 3d^6$	27 **Co** $4s^2 3d^7$	28 **Ni** $4s^2 3d^8$	29 **Cu** $4s^1 3d^{10}$	30 **Zn** $4s^2 3d^{10}$	31 **Ga** $4s^2 4p^1$	32 **Ge** $4s^2 4p^2$	33 **As** $4s^2 4p^3$	34 **Se** $4s^2 4p^4$	35 **Br** $4s^2 4p^5$	36 **Kr** $4s^2 4p^6$
5	37 **Rb** $5s^1$	38 **Sr** $5s^2$	39 **Y** $5s^2 4d^1$	40 **Zr** $5s^2 4d^2$	41 **Nb** $5s^1 4d^4$	42 **Mo** $5s^1 4d^5$	43 **Tc** $5s^2 4d^5$	44 **Ru** $5s^1 4d^7$	45 **Rh** $5s^1 4d^8$	46 **Pd** $4d^{10}$	47 **Ag** $5s^1 4d^{10}$	48 **Cd** $5s^2 4d^{10}$	49 **In** $5s^2 5p^1$	50 **Sn** $5s^2 5p^2$	51 **Sb** $5s^2 5p^3$	52 **Te** $5s^2 5p^4$	53 **I** $5s^2 5p^5$	54 **Xe** $5s^2 5p^6$
6	55 **Cs** $6s^1$	56 **Ba** $6s^2$	57 **La** $6s^2 5d^1$	72 **Hf** $6s^2 5d^2$	73 **Ta** $6s^2 5d^3$	74 **W** $6s^2 5d^4$	75 **Re** $6s^2 5d^5$	76 **Os** $6s^2 5d^6$	77 **Ir** $6s^2 5d^7$	78 **Pt** $6s^1 5d^9$	79 **Au** $6s^1 5d^{10}$	80 **Hg** $6s^2 5d^{10}$	81 **Tl** $6s^2 6p^1$	82 **Pb** $6s^2 6p^2$	83 **Bi** $6s^2 6p^3$	84 **Po** $6s^2 6p^4$	85 **At** $6s^2 6p^5$	86 **Rn** $6s^2 6p^6$
7	87 **Fr** $7s^1$	88 **Ra** $7s^2$	89 **Ac** $7s^2 6d^1$	104 **Rf** $7s^2 6d^2$	105 **Db** $7s^2 6d^3$	106 **Sg** $7s^2 6d^4$	107 **Bh** ---	108 **Hs** ---	109 **Mt** ---	110 **Ds** ---	111 **Rg** ---	112 **Cn** ---	113 **Nh** ---	114 **Fl** ---	115 **Mc** ---	116 **Lv** ---	117 **Ts** ---	118 **Og** ---
			6	58 **Ce** $6s^2 4f^1 5d^1$	59 **Pr** $6s^2 4f^3$	60 **Nd** $6s^2 4f^4$	61 **Pm** $6s^2 4f^5$	62 **Sm** $6s^2 4f^6$	63 **Eu** $6s^2 4f^7$	64 **Gd** $6s^2 4f^7 5d^1$	65 **Tb** $6s^2 4f^9$	66 **Dy** $6s^2 4f^{10}$	67 **Ho** $6s^2 4f^{11}$	68 **Er** $6s^2 4f^{12}$	69 **Tm** $6s^2 4f^{13}$	70 **Yb** $6s^2 4f^{14}$	71 **Lu** $6s^2 4f^{14} 5d^1$	
			7	90 **Th** $7s^2 6d^2$	91 **Pa** $7s^2 5f^2 6d^1$	92 **U** $7s^2 5f^3 6d^1$	93 **Np** $7s^2 5f^4 6d^1$	94 **Pu** $7s^2 5f^6$	95 **Am** $7s^2 5f^7$	96 **Cm** $7s^2 5f^7 6d^1$	97 **Bk** $7s^2 5f^9$	98 **Cf** $7s^2 5f^{10}$	99 **Es** $7s^2 5f^{11}$	100 **Fm** $7s^2 5f^{12}$	101 **Md** $7s^2 5f^{13}$	102 **No** $7s^2 5f^{14}$	103 **Lr** $7s^2 5f^{14} 6d^1$	

Figure 7.18 A diagram of the expanded periodic table wherein the color-coded blocks correspond to the valence shell sub-orbitals which are filled with increasing atomic number.

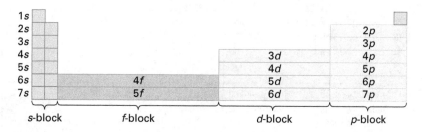

is the valence shell – which corresponds to the period in which each element is found.

For example, consider the halogens (Group 17 or 7A). The valence electron configuration for all the elements in this group is generally

$$ns^2np^5$$

where n is the principal quantum number and corresponds directly with the period in which a given element is found, $n = 2, 3, 4, 5$ & 6 for *F, Cl, Br, I,* & *At,* respectively. Indeed, the entire periodic table is laid out in order of valence electron orbitals in increasing energy. This is a natural consequence of arranging the elements in order of atomic number and clearly reveals the underlying explanation of the *Periodic Law* first proposed by Mendeleev.

Therefore, as we read the periodic table from left to right, electrons are added successively to orbitals in an atom (according to Aufbau, Pauli, and Hund). Owing to this we can begin to see certain regions or blocks of the table corresponding to specific valence electron configurations as described in the following (see Figure 7.18):

1. Groups 1A and 2A are collectively referred to as the "*s*-block." This is because as we proceed from left to right we successively populate the valence *s* subshell with electrons.

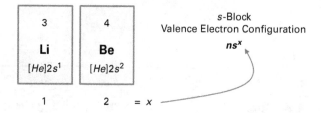

2. Groups 3A, 4A, 5A, 6A, 7A, and 8A are collectively referred to as the "*p*-block" wherein we are successively filling the valence *p* subshell from left to right.

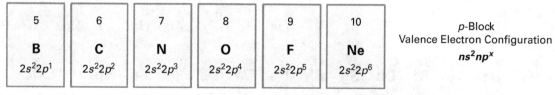

Note again that with each step to the right, we add an additional electron to the *p* orbitals in the valence shell of the elements in the *p*-block. *For this reason, we know simply by noting the position of an element on the periodic table its electron configuration in the ground state.*

3. Groups 3B through 8B, 1B, and 2B are collectively referred to as the "*d*-block."

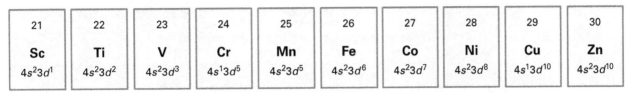

d-Block
Valence Electron Configuration
$ns^2(n-1)d^x$

Note in the case of the *d*-block elements that the electron configurations are not what we would expect for *Cr* and *Cu*. In other words, these configurations do not conform exactly to the Aufbau principle. This is because the energy required to promote an electron from the 4*s* orbital is less costly than the special stability associated with having a half-filled or full *d* subshell. For this reason, *Cr* has only one electron in the 4*s* orbital and five electrons in the 3*d* subshell. The same effect is observed for *Cu* ($[Ar]4s^1 3d^{10}$). These are examples of *irregular electron configurations*. **Irregular electron configurations** are those which do not completely correspond with the expected order of filling according to the Aufbau principle. A total of 19 elements exhibit irregular electrons configurations (highlighted in red in Figure 7.17).

4. The Lanthanides and Actinides are collectively referred to as the *f*-block.

Example 7.12 — Using the Position of an Element on the Periodic Table to Write Electron Configurations

Use each of the following elements' position on the periodic table to determine their electron configurations.

a. *Pb*

b. *Ba*

c. *As*

Solutions:	
a.	The element *Pb* is located in the *p*-block of the table in the sixth period. Additionally, it is in the second space from the left to right in the *p*-block. This means that the last term of its electron configuration is $6p^2$. The Aufbau principle requires further that every term which precedes the 6*p* subshell must be full.	$[Xe]6s^2 4f^{14} 5d^{10} 6p^2$
b.	The element *Ba* is located in the *s*-block of the table in the sixth period. Additionally, it is in the second space from the left to right in the *s*-block. This means that the last term of its electron configuration is $6s^2$. The Aufbau principle requires further that every term which precedes the 6*s* subshell must be full.	$[Xe]6s^2$

c.	The element *As* is located in the *p*-block of the table in the fourth period. Additionally, it is in the third space from the left to right in the *p*-block. This means that the last term of its electron configuration is $4p^3$. The Aufbau principle requires further that every term which precedes the $4p$ subshell must be full.	$[Ar]4s^2 3d^{10} 4p^3$

Section 7.14 Ionic Electron Configurations

Recall that we learned in Chapter 2 that the main group metals (the metals of the *s*-block) form monatomic ions by losing electrons to achieve a noble gas electron *count*. We can now restate this a little more precisely. The *s*-block metals form monatomic ions by losing all their valence electrons and, as such, adopting a new configuration which has a completely full valence *p* subshell. For example, we learned that Group 2 metals invariably lose two electrons when forming ions to adopt a charge of 2+. Let's consider *Mg*. We know the ground state electron configuration of *Mg* is $[Ne]3s^2$. To write the configuration of the cation Mg^{2+} *we simply remove the correct number of electrons from the orbitals with the highest value of* n *as follows*:

$$Mg(s) \rightarrow Mg^{2+} + 2e^-$$

$$[Ne]3s^2 \rightarrow [He]2s^2 2p^6$$

The point to understand concerning many of the main group elements like the *s*-block elements is that the driving force for losing or gaining a given number of electrons is to achieve a completely full valence shell (a noble gas electron configuration). A full valence shell represents a particularly stable configuration. Notice that for *Mg* the loss of two electrons empties its valence shell and re-establishes the second principal shell as the valence shell in the newly formed ion, a configuration which is identical to that of *Ne*. It is the full valence shells of the noble gases which affords them their special stability.

For anions, we simply add the correct number of electrons to one or more empty or partially filled orbitals of the valence shell. Table 7.2 summarizes the electron configurations of selected monatomic ions of the second period of the periodic table.

Table 7.2 Valence Electron Configurations of some of the Second Row Monatomic Ions.

Element	Electron Configuration	Ion	Ionic Electron Configuration
Li	$1s^2 2s^1$	Li^+	$1s^2 = [He]$
Be	$1s^2 2s^2$	Be^{2+}	$1s^2 = [He]$
N	$1s^2 2s^2 2p^3$	N^{3-}	$1s^2 2s^2 2p^6 = [Ne]$
O	$1s^2 2s^2 2p^4$	O^{2-}	$1s^2 2s^2 2p^6 = [Ne]$
F	$1s^2 2s^2 2p^5$	F^-	$1s^2 2s^2 2p^6 = [Ne]$

Example Problem 7.13—Ionic Electron Configurations (Main Group Elements)

Write the electron configurations for Pb, Pb^{2+}, and Pb^{4+}. Are these paramagnetic or diamagnetic?	
Solution:	
Lead is in the sixth period and in the second position of the *p*-block. As such we know the last term of the electron configuration is $6p^2$. Additionally, there are unpaired electrons, and as such, it is paramagnetic.	$[Xe] 6s^2 4f^{14} 5d^{10} 6p^2$ Paramagnetic
To write the electron configuration for Pb^{2+} we simply remove two electrons with the highest value of n. Since four electrons are in the sixth shell, we remove two from the highest energy orbitals. Since there are no unpaired electrons, this ion is diamagnetic.	$[Xe] 6s^2 4f^{14} 5d^{10}$ diamagnetic
To write the electron configuration for Pb^{4+} we simply remove the remaining two electrons in the sixth shell. Since there are no unpaired electrons, this ion is diamagnetic.	$[Xe] 4f^{14} 5d^{10}$ diamagnetic

Electron Configurations of the Transition Metal Cations

When writing electron configurations of cations, the electrons in orbitals with the highest value of *n* are removed first. This is so, even when dealing with transition metals where it may seem that electrons in the highest energy orbitals should ionize first (not necessarily those with the highest value of *n*). For example, if I am dealing with iron(II), and I wish to write the correct electron configuration, I begin with the configuration of the parent, neutral element:

Iron: $[Ar] 4s^2 3d^6$

Now, since we are concerned with iron(II), we need to remove two electrons. These two electrons will come from the 4*s* orbital. This is because the valence electrons will ionize first, even though the 3*d* orbitals are higher in energy. As such, the proper electron configuration for iron(II) is:

Iron(II): $[Ar] 3d^6$

Note that since there are now no electrons occupying the 4s orbital, we need not include it in the configuration at all. If we wish to write the electron configuration of iron(III), the removal of the third electron can now come from the 3d orbitals since there are no remaining electrons in the fourth shell.

Iron(III): $[Ar]3d^5$

Example Problem 7.14—Electron Configurations of Transition Metals and their Ions

Write the electron configurations of Cu, Cu^+ and Cu^{2+}. Indicate whether these are diamagnetic or paramagnetic.	
Solution:	
Normally, we begin by applying Hund, Pauli, and Aufbau to write the ground state electron configuration of the neutral Cu atom. In this case, however, we know from Figure 7.17 that Cu exhibits an irregular configuration.	$[Ar]4s^13d^{10}$ Paramagnetic
To write the configuration of Cu^+ we must remove one electron and further it must come from an orbital with the highest value of n. In this case that is the 4s orbital.	$[Ar]3d^{10}$ Diamagnetic
Since the 4s orbital is now empty, the next electron is removed from the 3d orbital to give us the configuration of the Cu^{2+} ion.	$[Ar]3d^9$ Paramagnetic
Thus, one way we can verify the electron configuration of ions is by measuring their magnetic properties. In this case, with the removal of each successive electron, we move from paramagnetic (Cu) to diamagnetic (Cu^+) and back to paramagnetic (Cu^{2+}), a trend we would not observe if the configuration of Cu included a full 4s subshell.	

The International Solvay Conference on Electrons and Photons of 1927 is perhaps the most famous scientific conference in the 20th Century. The worlds most noted physicists met here to discuss the newly developed quantum theory. Among those in attendance were Einstein, Marie Currie, Planck, Pauli, Bohr, Schrödinger, Born, and de Broglie to name a few. Of the 29 physicists in attendance, 17 would be awarded the Nobel Prize.

Section 7.15 **Periodic Trends**

Atomic Radius

Understanding the structure of the periodic table according to the quantum mechanical model of the atom provides a theory to explain Mendeleev's periodic law, which we learned in Chapter 2. In other words, quantum mechanics provides a theoretical basis for understanding the periodic trends observed in the elements. We understand these trends as corresponding to the valence electron structure in atoms. One such trend is the observed size of atoms. We characterize the size of an atom by its radius. There a few different ways to define the radius of an atom. For example, in diatomic, molecular elements such as O_2 or Cl_2, we can define the radius of the covalently bonded atoms as being one half of the distance between the two nuclear centers in the molecule. This definition is referred to as the **covalent radius**. Essentially, such a definition comes down to establishing a reasonably accurate **bond length**. Bond length is defined as the distance between nuclei in two atoms mutually engaged in a covalent bond. The distances between atoms can be empirically measured using methods of spectroscopy such as microwave or nuclear magnetic resonance spectroscopies as well as various diffraction methods (x-ray diffraction, electron diffraction, etc.). The details of such methods are, of course, beyond the scope of this text; however, suffice to say that such methods have been brought to bear on a large number of chemical species, and such data have been used to establish tables of average covalent radii of many elements.

Additionally, Dutch physicist J. D. van der Waals found that to explain the behavior of non-ideal gases (see Chapter 6), it was necessary to define a finite volume occupied by atoms in gaseous molecules. He defined this volume on the basis of a radius which represented the distance of closest approach which can be made to an atom by another atom to which it is not chemically bonded. Such a radius is referred to as the **van der Waals radius** (see Figure 7.19).

The more general term of "**atomic radius**" simply refers to an average radius as measured from a large number of elements or compounds. A reasonable set of such radii are illustrated in Figure 7.20. It is apparent from the data presented in the figure that there are clear trends in the atomic radii of main group elements. *The radii increase from top to bottom down each column of the periodic table and decrease from left to right across each row (or period) of the periodic table.* This trend can be explained (according to the quantum model of the atom) as follows:

1. First, we must understand that the size of an atom is determined by the distance from the nucleus of the outermost (valence) electrons in the atom. In other words, the highest occupied principal quantum shell contains the electrons which are

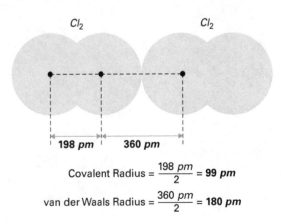

Figure 7.19 Comparison of covalent and van der Waals radii.

Cl_2 Cl_2

198 pm   **360 pm**

$$\text{Covalent Radius} = \frac{198\ pm}{2} = \mathbf{99\ pm}$$

$$\text{van der Waals Radius} = \frac{360\ pm}{2} = \mathbf{180\ pm}$$

Figure 7.20 Atomic Radii increase from top to bottom and decrease from left to right on the periodic table (the radii are given here in picometers).

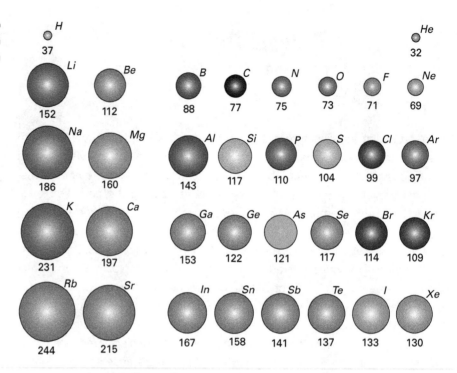

farthest from the atomic nucleus. These electrons define the outer edge or surface of the atom. Since we know that as the value of principal quantum number defines the distance from the nucleus for electrons in an atom, the higher the value of n (for the valence shell), the larger the radius of the atom. Since each additional row (down) the periodic table represents a successively higher value of n for the valence electrons, we expect the atomic radii to increase as we proceed down each column. In other words, each step down adds an additional shell to the atom, thereby increasing atomic radius.

2. With respect to decreasing atomic radius across a row from left to right, this is a consequence of the effective nuclear charge, Z^*, experienced by the valence electrons. As it turns out, as we move successively from one element to the next across a period, we add an additional proton and electron with each step to the right. This means that the nuclear charge increases by +1 each step of the way. However, the additional electrons occupy valence orbitals and, as such, provide little to no additional shielding of the valence shell from the increasing nuclear charge. Recall that only the inner "core" electrons contribute appreciably to the shielding effect. As the effective nuclear charge increases, the valence electrons experience an increasing electrostatic attraction to the nucleus. This has the effect of pulling them in closer to the nucleus, reducing the atomic radius from left to right across a given period in the table.

This effect is not evident among the transition metals. This is because as electrons are added from left to right in a transition series, they occupy the $(n - 1)d$ orbitals. These orbitals do not belong to the valence shell, and, therefore, each electron does contribute to the shielding of the valence shell.

Owing to this, Z^* remains essentially constant across the transition series, resulting in no net trend in atomic radii. The transition elements do, however, exhibit the general trend of increasing radii down each column.

Example Problem 7.15—Atomic Radii

Arrange the following atoms in order of increasing atomic size or radius. Cl, Al, Mg, O, Ca	
Solution:	
We know from the periodic trend that the smallest atom will be one farthest to the upper right of the periodic table. This means that we expect O to be the smallest.	$O < (Cl, Al, Mg) < Ca$
Starting from O, there are no ther elements on the list in the same row, so, we look to the next row down. Here we see that Cl, Al, and Mg are all in the third period. Here we know that atomic radius decreases from left to right, making Cl the smallest, then Al followed by Mg.	$O < Cl < Al < Mg < Ca$
Since we know radius increases down the periodic table we see that the next largest element is Ca.	$O < Cl < Al < Mg < Ca$

Ionic Radius

Cations are always smaller than their neutral parent elements. For example, consider Na and Na^+. The radius of Na is 186 pm, while the radius of Na^+ is 95 pm (See Figure 7.21). This is due to the fact that the loss of one or more electrons will increase the effective nuclear charge felt by the remaining valence electrons. This will again cause the valence electrons to be pulled in closer to the nucleus due to the increased electrostatic attraction. The result is that cations are smaller than neutral atoms of the same element. The opposite is true of anions. *Anions are always larger than their neutral parent*

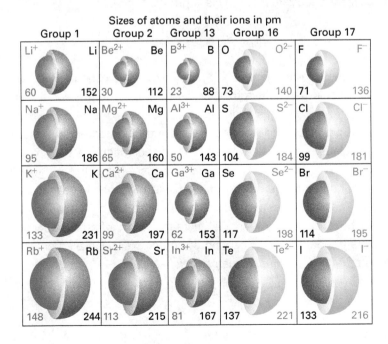

Figure 7.21 Relative atomic radii of selected 1st, 2nd, 3rd and 4th row monatomic cations and anions.

elements. Nevertheless, within the context of either cations or anions, the basic trends we have observed concerning atomic radii are also evident for ions as well. More generally, it can be said that for *isoelectronic* species, the more negative the charge, the larger the radius. Conversely, the more positive the charge, the smaller the radius. Species with the same electron configuration are said to be **isoelectronic**.

Example Problem 7.16—Ionic Radii

Arrange the following atoms in order of decreasing atomic size or radius. $Ca^{2+}, K^+, Cl^-, S^{2-}$	
Solution:	
First, we should recognize that these species are isoelectronic. As such, their radii decrease from most negative to most positive.	$S^{2-}, Cl^-, K^+, Ca^{2+}$

Ionization Energy

The **ionization energy** of an element is defined as the energy required to remove 1 mole of electrons from 1 mole of atoms of that element in the gaseous state. Because of the favorable electrostatic attraction between the negatively charged electron and the positively charged nucleus, the removal of an electron from an atom *always* requires the input of energy. Further, as electrons are removed, increasingly more energy is required to remove each successive electron. In other words, the ionization energy increases as electrons are removed. The energy required to remove the first electron from a neutral atom is referred to as the **first ionization energy**, IE_1. The energy required to remove the next electron from this newly formed, singly charged cation is called the second ionization energy, IE_2. Then the third, fourth and so on. These are referred to as **successive ionization energies**. Further, each successive ionization energy is larger than the last:

$$IE_1 < IE_2 < IE_3 < IE_4 < \ldots$$

As it turns out, the first ionization energy exhibits a periodic trend as well. By now it should be intuitive that the farther from the nucleus an electron resides the less energy is required to remove it. This is so because the strength or magnitude of the electrostatic attraction between the electron and the nucleus is inversely related to their separation. As such, we would expect the first ionization energy to be successively smaller as the value of the principal quantum number of the valence electrons increases. *In other words, IE_1 decreases as we move down a column on the periodic table.* Likewise, because we know that Z^* increases from left to right across each row of the periodic table (excepting of course transition elements), so IE_1 *increases from left to right on the periodic table.*

Example Problem 7.17—Trends in First Ionization Energy

Arrange the following in order of increasing first ionization energy. F, I, Sr, Ba	
Solution:	
Since the first ionization energy increases from the lower left to the upper right corner of the periodic table, we know that *F* will have the highest first ionization energy.	$(I, Sr, Ba) < F$
Since *I* and *Sr* are in the same row, we know that *I* will have the higher first ionization energy, then *Sr* followed by *Ba*.	$Ba < Sr < I < F$

Successive Ionization Energies

Another trend which we can discuss in the context of the quantum model of the atom is the trend in successive ionization energies for a given element. As an example, let's consider beryllium. Beryllium has the following electron configuration:

Be: $[He]2s^2$

It will require 900 *kJ/mol* to remove the first electron from Beryllium ($IE_1 = 900$ *kJ/mol*) to form Be^+:

Be^+: $[He]2s^1$

It requires nearly twice the energy to remove the second electron ($IE_2 = 1758$ *kJ/mol*) and we now have Be^{2+}:

Be^{2+}: $[He] \rightarrow 1s^2$

Because the valence shell has now been completely emptied, any additional electrons which may be removed must come from an "inner" shell. In other words, the next electron removed from Be^{2+} is a *core* electron. *The energy required to remove a core electron is always substantially higher than that required to remove valence electrons.* For beryllium, IE_3 is nearly 17 times IE_1 and approximately 8.5 times that of IE_2 ($IE_3 = 15,050$ *kJ/mol*). Successive ionization energies increase steadily until enough electrons are removed to empty the original valence shell. When the first inner shell electron is removed, the ionization energy is remarkably higher than any of the valence shell ionization energies. Table 7.3 summarizes the successive ionization energies for the third row elements of the periodic table.

Table 7.3 Successive Ionization Energies (*kJ/mol*) of the Third Row Elements.

Element	IE_1	IE_2	IE_3	IE_4	IE_5	IE_6	IE_7
Na	496	4,561	6,910	9,543	13,354	16,613	20,117
Mg	738	1,451	7,733	10,543	13,630	18,020	21,710
Al	578	1,817	2,745	11,576	14,842	18,379	23,326
Si	787	1,578	3,232	4,355	16,091	19,805	23,780
P	1,012	1,907	2,912	4,964	6,272	21,270	25,430
S	1,000	2,252	3,357	4,556	7,005	8,500	27,110
Cl	1,251	2,300	3,822	5,160	6,540	9,460	11,020
Ar	1,520	2,665	3,930	5,768	7,240	8,780	11,990

Example Problem 7.18—Successive Ionization Energies

An unknown element of the third period has the following successive ionization energies:

$$IE_1 = 1012 \ kJ/mol$$
$$IE_2 = 1907 \ kJ/mol$$
$$IE_3 = 2912 \ kJ/mol$$
$$IE_4 = 4964 \ kJ/mol$$
$$IE_5 = 6272 \ kJ/mol$$
$$IE_6 = 21{,}270 \ kJ/mol$$

How many valence electrons does this element have? What is the identity of this element?

Solution:

First, we note that there is a steady increase in the ionization energies until we reach the sixth ionization energy. Here we see that between the fifth and sixth ionization energy an unusually large increase occurs. This tells us that the sixth electron removed comes from a core or inner shell. Therefore, there are five valence electrons on the unknown atom. The element in the third period with five valence electrons is phosphorus.

5 valence electrons

Phosphorus
$[Ne]3s^2 3p^3$

Electron Affinity

Electron Affinity is defined as the energy released when a mole of atoms in the gaseous state gains an electron. For example, the electron affinity of chlorine is as follows:

$$Cl(g) + 1e^- \rightarrow Cl^-(g) \qquad EA_1 = -349 \ kJ/mol$$

Unlike the ionization energies, the trends in electron affinities are much looser and not as definite. Generally, electron affinities are increasingly negative from left to right in each row of the periodic table and decrease in magnitude (increasingly positive) moving down the periodic table for the alkali metals. This trend of decreasing *EA* down this column is not as clear for other groups of the periodic table.

SPECIAL TOPICS: Nuclear Chemistry. To cover the topic of atomic structure comprehensively, it is appropriate that we should also consider nuclear structure and the processes it undergoes. A brief treatment of nuclear chemistry can be found in the "Special Topics – Chapter 7: Nuclear Chemistry" section of Appendix I. Here, we cover such processes as **positron emission**, α **decay**, β **decay** as well as **nuclear fusion** and **nuclear fission**.

Key Terms

1. Actinides
2. Amplitude
3. Angular momentum quantum number
4. Atomic (line) emission spectra
5. Atomic radius
6. Aufbau principle
7. Balmer series
8. Binding energy
9. Bohr model
10. Bond length
11. Condensed electron configuration
12. Core electrons
13. Coulomb's law
14. Covalent radius
15. *d*-block
16. de Broglie wavelength
17. Degenerate
18. Destructive interference
19. Diamagnetic
20. Effective nuclear charge
21. Electromagnetic radiation
22. Electron affinity
23. Electron configuration
24. Electron density
25. Electron spin quantum number
26. Excited state
27. *f*-block
28. First ionization energy
29. Frequency
30. Ground state
31. Hamiltonian

32. Heisenberg's uncertainty principle
33. Hertz
34. Hund's rule
35. Interference
36. Ionic radius
37. Ionization energy
38. Irregular electron configuration
39. Joule
40. Lanthanides
41. Magnetic quantum number
42. Monochromatic radiation
43. Node
44. Orbital
45. Orbital box diagram
46. Paramagnetic
47. Pauli exclusion principle
48. *p*-block
49. Photoelectric effect
50. Photons
51. Planck's constant
52. Planck's equation
53. Principal quantum number
54. Probability density
55. Quanta
56. Quantum
57. Rydberg constant
58. Rydberg equation
59. *s*-block
60. Shielding
61. Stationary states
62. Successive ionization energies
63. Valence electrons
64. Van der Waal's radius
65. Wave-function
66. Wavelength

Problems

THE WAVE NATURE OF LIGHT – ELECTROMAGNETIC RADIATION

1. What is light?

2. What is the speed of light?

3. Define wavelength.

4. Define amplitude.

5. Define frequency.

6. Write the equation which describes the relationship between wavelength, frequency, and velocity of light waves.

7. For the following pairs, which has less energy:

   a. Microwaves or radio waves

   b. Gamma rays or infrared radiation

8. For the following pairs, which has less energy:

   a. Green light or red light

   b. Ultraviolet or infrared

9. Which of the following wavelengths of light is associated with the highest frequency?

   a. 10 *nm*

   b. 100 *nm*

   c. 100 *μm*

   d. 100 *mm*

10. Which of the following wavelengths of light is associated with the lowest frequency?

    a. 10 *nm*

    b. 100 *nm*

    c. 100 *μm*

    d. 100 *mm*

11. What is the frequency of EM radiation with a wavelength of 300 *nm*?

12. What is the frequency of EM radiation with a wavelength of 4.55×10^{-5} *m*?

13. What is the frequency of EM radiation with a wavelength of 7.34×10^{-14} *m*?

14. What is the frequency of EM radiation with a wavelength of 5.97×10^{-6} *m*?

15. What is the wavelength of EM radiation with a frequency of 3.21×10^{20} s^{-1}?

16. What is the wavelength of EM radiation with a frequency of 4.94×10^{14} s^{-1}?

17. What is the wavelength of EM radiation with a frequency of $6.33 \times 10^6 \, s^{-1}$?

18. What is the wavelength of EM radiation with a frequency of $8.22 \times 10^{10} \, s^{-1}$?

THE PARTICLE NATURE OF LIGHT

19. Which of the following forms of EM radiation has the highest energy photons?
    a. Gamma rays
    b. Ultraviolet radiation
    c. Visible light
    d. Microwaves
    e. Radio waves

20. Which of the following forms of EM radiation has the lowest energy photons?
    a. Gamma rays
    b. Ultraviolet radiation
    c. Visible light
    d. Microwaves
    e. Radio waves

21. If monochromatic visible light has a wavelength of 495 *nm*, what is the energy of one photon of this light? What is the energy of 1 *mol* of such photons?

22. If EM radiation has a frequency of $7.43 \times 10^{14} s^{-1}$, what is its wavelength and energy? What is the energy of 1 *mol* of such photons?

23. If a photon has an energy of $4.78 \times 10^{-19} J$, what is its wavelength? What is its frequency?

24. If violet light has a wavelength of 390 *nm*, what is the energy of one photon of this light? What is the energy of 1 *mol* of such photons?

25. If EM radiation has a frequency of $4.33 \times 10^{10} s^{-1}$, what is its wavelength and energy? What is the energy of 1 *mol* of such photons?

26. If a photon has an energy of $6.08 \times 10^{-19} J$, what is its wavelength? What is its frequency?

27. One of the "lines" in the emission spectrum of mercury is green light with a wavelength of 546 *nm*. What is the frequency of this line? What is the energy of a photon of this radiation? What is the energy of 1 *mol* of such photons?

28. The emission spectrum of mercury has lines at 436, 546, 577, and 579 *nm*. Which of these has the highest energy? What is the energy of a mole of photons of this radiation?

29. One of the lines in the emission spectrum of Lithium is at 671 *nm*. What is the frequency and energy of a photon of this radiation? What is the energy of 1 mole of such photons?

30. If the energy required to eject photoelectrons from copper (the binding energy, ϕ) is 437.1 *kJ/mol*, what is the threshold frequency of this metal?

31. If the threshold frequency of magnesium is $8.85 \times 10^{14} s^{-1}$, what is its binding energy, ϕ (*in kJ/mol*)?

32. If vanadium has a threshold frequency of $1.04 \times 10^{15} s^{-1}$ and is irradiated with light of wavelength, $\lambda = 334$ *nm*, should we expect to observe photoelectrons ejected from the metal? Why or why not?

33. Will visible light with a wavelength of 654 *nm* eject photoelectrons from gold if its binding energy is 527.8 *kJ/mol*?

ATOMIC SPECTRA AND THE BOHR MODEL OF THE HYDROGEN ATOM

34. What are two main postulates of the Bohr theory of the atom?

35. What is the equation for the energy of an electron in the nth orbit, or energy state, of a hydrogen atom (according to Bohr)?

36. Describe what is meant when the hydrogen atom is said to be in the ground state. How is this different from the hydrogen atom in an excited state?

37. What is the rationale for the emission of a photon from the hydrogen atom according to Bohr?

38. According to Bohr's model of the hydrogen atom, what is the energy of an electron in the fourth orbit or stationary state?

39. According to Bohr's model of the hydrogen atom, what is the energy of an electron in the seventh orbit or stationary state?

40. Assuming the Bohr model of the hydrogen atom can be applied to any "hydrogen-like" system (a single electron atom), what is the energy of an electron in the ground state of a He^+ cation?

41. Assuming the Bohr model of the hydrogen atom can be applied to any "hydrogen-like" system (a single electron atom), what is the energy of an electron in the ground state of a Li^{2+} cation?

42. Which of the following transitions results in emission of a photon of highest energy?

    a. $n = 4 \rightarrow n = 3$

    b. $n = 5 \rightarrow n = 4$

    c. $n = 2 \rightarrow n = 1$

43. Which of the following transitions results in emission of a photon of lowest energy?

    a. $n = 4 \rightarrow n = 3$

    b. $n = 5 \rightarrow n = 4$

    c. $n = 7 \rightarrow n = 6$

44. The following transitions are associated with the "Paschen Series" of lines in the emission spectrum of hydrogen. Calculate the wavelength and frequency of photons emitted due to these transitions:

    a. $n = 7 \rightarrow n = 3$

    b. $n = 6 \rightarrow n = 3$

    c. $n = 5 \rightarrow n = 3$

    d. $n = 4 \rightarrow n = 3$

45. The following transitions are associated with the "Lyman Series" of lines in the emission spectrum of hydrogen. Calculate the wavelength and frequency of photons emitted due to these transitions:

    a. $n = 5 \rightarrow n = 1$

    b. $n = 4 \rightarrow n = 1$

    c. $n = 3 \rightarrow n = 1$

    d. $n = 2 \rightarrow n = 1$

46. A photon with a wavelength of 12.36 μm is emitted from a hydrogen atom in an excited state. Determine the value of n_i and n_f for this transition.

47. A photon with a wavelength of 2624 nm is emitted from a hydrogen atom in an excited state. Determine the value of n_i and n_f for this transition.

48. One of the lines of the emission spectrum of hydrogen is at 410.2 nm. What states are involved in the transition which results in this emission (what are the values of n_i and n_f)?

49. One of the lines of the emission spectrum of hydrogen is at 486 nm and is due to the transition $n = 4 \rightarrow n = 2$. What is the wavelength of a photon emitted from a He^+ cation due to this same transition? Explain why these are different.

50. One of the lines of the emission spectrum of hydrogen is at 434 nm and is due to the transition $n = 5 \rightarrow n = 2$. What is the wavelength of a photon emitted from a Li^{2+} cation due to this same transition? Explain why these are different.

DE BROGLIE AND THE WAVE PROPERTY OF THE ELECTRON

51. What determines the de Broglie wavelength of a given particle?

52. What is the equation for the de Broglie wavelength?

53. If an electron has a wavelength of 6.13 nm, what is its velocity? (Recall the mass of an electron is $m_e = 9.11 \times 10^{-28}\,g$)

54. If an electron has a wavelength of 5.87 nm, what is its velocity?

55. What is the de Broglie wavelength of an electron traveling at a velocity of 2.13×10^5 m/s.

56. If a bullet leaves the barrel of a gun at a velocity of 690. m/s, what is the wavelength of the bullet if it weighs 30.0 *g*?

HEISENBERG'S UNCERTAINTY PRINCIPLE AND SCHRÖDINGER'S EQUATION

57. What was meant by Max Born when he postulated that the electron wave-function is a probability wave?

58. What is the physical meaning of the square of the wave-function, ψ^2?

59. What is an orbital?

60. What are the three quantum numbers which describe an orbital?

61. What properties do each quantum number define or specify?

62. Explain the rules for allowed combinations of quantum numbers in a given wave-function.

63. If $n = 3$, what are the allowed values of l?

64. If $n = 5$, what are the allowed values of l?

65. If $l = 2$, what are the possible values of m_l?

66. If $l = 3$, what are the possible values of m_l?

67. For a 2*p* orbital, what are the possible combinations of n, l, and m_l?

68. For a 3*d* orbital, what are the possible combinations of n, l, and m_l?

69. For a 5*f* orbital, what are the possible combinations of n, l, and m_l?

70. For a 1*s* orbital, what are the possible combinations of n, l, and m_l?

71. What values of l are associated with the labels *s*, *p*, *d*, and *f*.

72. Determine whether each of the following combinations of quantum numbers are allowed or erroneous. If allowed, identify which orbital is defined by each set. If erroneous, explain why each set is not allowed.

    a. $n = 3, l = 2, m_l = +3$

    b. $n = 4, l = 3, m_l = -3$

    c. $n = 2, l = 1, m_l = +1$

    d. $n = 3, l = 0, m_l = -1$

73. Determine whether each of the following combinations of quantum numbers are allowed or erroneous. If allowed, identify which orbital is defined by each set. If erroneous, explain why each set is not allowed.

    a. $n = 5, l = 0, m_l = 0$

    b. $n = 4, l = 1, m_l = 0$

    c. $n = 1, l = 1, m_l = 0$

    d. $n = 3, l = 2, m_l = -1$

74. List all possible sets of quantum numbers which describe a 5*f* orbital.

75. List all possible sets of quantum numbers which describe a 4*d* orbital.

76. Which of the following orbitals do not exist?

    a. 1*s*

    b. 2*d*

    c. 3*f*

    d. 4*f*

77. Which of the following orbitals do not exist?

    a. 1*p*

    b. 2*d*

    c. 3*d*

    d. 2*f*

78. How many orbitals are in the fourth shell?

79. How many orbitals are in the second shell?

ELECTRON SPIN AND GROUND STATE ELECTRON CONFIGURATIONS

80. What is the Pauli Exclusion Principle?

81. What is Hund's rule?

82. What is meant by the term valence shell? Valence electrons?

83. What is meant by the term core electrons?

84. Explain the concept of shielding and effective nuclear charge.

85. What is the effective nuclear charge "felt" by the valence electrons of a *Mg* atom?

86. What is the effective nuclear charge "felt" by the valence electrons of a *N* atom?

87. What is the *s*-block on the periodic table? Why is it called the *s*-block?

88. What is the *d*-block on the periodic table? Why is it called the *d*-block?

89. What is the electron configuration of *S*? Draw the orbital diagram of the valence shell of *S*.

90. What is the electron configuration of *Br*? Draw the orbital diagram of the valence shell of *Br*.

91. What is the electron configuration of *Sr*? Draw the orbital diagram of the valence shell of *Sr*.

92. What is the electron configuration of *Li*? Draw the orbital diagram of the valence shell of *Li*.

93. What is the electron configuration of *C*? Draw the orbital diagram of the valence shell of *C*.

94. What is the electron configuration of *F*? Draw the orbital diagram of the valence shell of *F*.

95. Using the condensed notation, write the electron configuration of the following elements:

    a. *Fe*

    b. *Sr*

    c. *Pb*

    d. *Ti*

96. Using the condensed notation, write the electron configuration of the following elements:

    a. *Co*

    b. *Mn*

    c. *Se*

    d. *I*

IONIC ELECTRON CONFIGURATIONS

97. Write the electron configuration for each ion and indicate whether the ion is paramagnetic or diamagnetic.

    a. Cu^{2+}

    b. Ag^{+}

    c. Br^{-}

    d. Se^{2-}

98. Write the electron configuration for each ion and indicate whether the ion is paramagnetic or diamagnetic.

    a. P^{3-}

    b. Fe^{2+}

    c. Cd^{2+}

    d. Rb^{+}

99. Write the electron configuration for each ion and indicate whether the ion is paramagnetic or diamagnetic.

    a. V^{5+}

    b. O^{2-}

    c. K^{+}

    d. Fe^{3+}

100. Write the electron configuration for each ion and indicate whether the ion is paramagnetic or diamagnetic.

    a. Al^{3+}

    b. Ge^{2+}

    c. Ti^{4+}

    d. F^-

PERIODIC TRENDS

101. Arrange the following elements according to increasing size: Li, Ca, Sr, Ba

102. Arrange the following elements according to increasing size: Te, F, Br, I

103. Arrange the following elements according to increasing size: Li, Fr, Cs, K

104. Arrange the following elements according to increasing size: C, Al, K, Na

105. Indicate which element or ion in each of the following pairs has the larger radius:

    a. F and F^-

    b. Mg and Mg^{2+}

    c. Al and Al^{3+}

    d. Al and O

106. Indicate which element or ion in each of the following pairs has the larger radius:

    a. O and O^{2-}

    b. Ne and Mg^{2+}

    c. Ar and S^{2-}

    d. S and S^{2-}

107. Arrange the following elements according to increasing first ionization energy: Li, Ca, Sr, Ba

108. Arrange the following elements according to increasing first ionization energy: F, Br, Te, I

109. Arrange the following elements according to increasing first ionization energy: Li, Fr, Cs, K

110. Arrange the following elements according to increasing first ionization energy: C, Al, K, Na

111. Identify the third row element with the following successive ionization energies:

    $IE_1 = 578 \ kJ/mol$

    $IE_2 = 1,817 \ kJ/mol$

    $IE_3 = 2,745 \ kJ/mol$

    $IE_4 = 11,576 \ kJ/mol$

112. Identify the third row element with the following successive ionization energies:

$IE_1 = 786 \, kJ \,/\, mol$

$IE_2 = 1{,}580 \, kJ \,/\, mol$

$IE_3 = 3{,}230 \, kJ \,/\, mol$

$IE_4 = 4{,}360 \, kJ \,/\, mol$

$IE_5 = 16{,}100 \, kJ \,/\, mol$

Image Credits

Bonding and Molecular Geometry

LEARNING OBJECTIVES AND OUTCOMES

After reading this chapter you should be able to do the following:

- Identify and describe ionic, covalent, and metallic bonding in compounds.

- Describe the basic suppositions on which Lewis's theory is based.

- Write Lewis symbols of elements and monatomic ions.

- Apply the octet rule to determine Lewis structures of ionic compounds and predict their formulas.

- Apply the octet rule to write Lewis structures of covalent compounds and polyatomic ions, including resonance structures when necessary.

- Use formal charge assignments to identify preferred resonance structures.

- Predict bond polarity on the basis of differences in electronegativity.

- Describe the basic suppositions and concepts of Valence Shell Electron Pair Repulsion Theory.

- Use VSEPR and the idea of electron groups to determine electronic and molecular geometries of molecules, including prediction of bond angles.

- Predict molecular polarity on the basis of molecular geometry and bond polarities.

- Describe the basic suppositions on which Valence Bond Theory is based.

- Use hybridization in VB theory to explain molecular shape and bond angles.

- Describe the basic suppositions on which Molecular Orbital Theory is based.

- Draw MO diagrams for diatomic molecules and use them to predict the existence, stability, and magnetic properties of such compounds.

- Define and apply the Key Terms listed at the end of this chapter.

Section 8.1 Introduction

In Chapter 7 we learned that quantum theory provides a model for the structure of matter at the atomic scale and for the interaction of matter with energy. In the current chapter we will build on that knowledge to move from an examination of the structure of atoms to the structure of compounds. At the center of this discussion is the propensity for most elements to engage in the formation of *chemical bonds*. Indeed, there are less than 100 naturally occurring elements. Without the chemical bond, the universe would be a very different place. What makes these relatively few elements so prolific in the formation of new substances through bonding? The answer to this question lies in the arena of chemical energy. Recall from Chapter 7 that we stated that an atom will remain in its "lowest energy" or *ground state* unless perturbed by the absorption of energy. Additionally, we defined the energy of such states based on the proximity of oppositely charged particles to one another (electron-nuclear attractions) according to *Coulomb's Law*:

$$E \propto \frac{q_1 q_2}{r}$$

In this way we have established that the lower the potential energy of a system, the more stable it is. Understanding this concept, we must conclude that bonding occurs between elements because it has the effect of lowering the energy of the elements involved in chemical bonding. This is indeed the case. As such, the simple answer to the question as to why two elements should form a bond is that such an arrangement is more stable (lower in energy) than that realized by the two free elements. The current chapter will explore the leading theories which provide a basis for understanding chemical bonding.

Section 8.2 Types of Chemical Bonds and Electronegativity

We will discuss three types of chemical bonds. Generally speaking, the nature of the bonding interaction is dependent on the nature of the atoms themselves. For our current purposes, it is helpful to think of the elements as being either *metals or nonmetals*. Further, there are three distinguishable permutations of bonding combinations of metals and nonmetals, if we confine ourselves to dealing with pairs of atoms only. These are metal-to-nonmetal, nonmetal-to-nonmetal, and metal-to-metal. The bonding type will be different for each of these combinations:

Ionic bonding—*Ionic bonding is characterized by the complete transfer of one or more electrons from a metal to a nonmetal. As such, we understand ionic bonding to occur between metals and nonmetals.* Further, the transfer of electron(s) from the metal to nonmetal results in the formation of a metal cation and a nonmetal anion. The electrostatic attraction between atoms of opposite charge is the basis for this bonding interaction and has the effect of directing these ions into large three-dimensional, solid arrays of ions (see Figure 8.1). As such, the formulas written for *ionic solids* provide only the simplest ratio of ion types in a compound and are therefore referred to as *formula units*.

Covalent Bonding—*Covalent bonding occurs between nonmetals and other nonmetals.* When two nonmetals come together to form a bond, they will do so by "sharing" electrons. Each nucleus in such a bond will exert an attractive force for the valence electrons of a neighboring atom. This has the effect of keeping the two atoms bound close together. Additionally, we say that the atoms in a covalent bond share a "pair" of valence electrons, each atom donating one electron to the bonding inter-action (see Figure 8.1).

Metallic Bonding—*Metallic bonding occurs when metals bond to metals and is characterized by pooling of valence electrons over a large number of atoms.* Metals are relatively large compared to nonmetals (recall trends in atomic radii from Chapter 7) and in addition their outer valence electrons are not held very strongly (metals tend to have lower ionization energies) and, as such, they tend to share their valence electrons with other metal atoms. Unlike covalent bonding, this arrangement is not localized to a pair of atoms but rather delocalized over an entire sample of metal. Therefore, it is appropriate to consider atoms which make up a metal sample as "cationic cores" (the nuclei plus the core electrons) surrounded by a "sea" of valence electrons which are delocalized over the entire sample (see Figure 8.1). This bonding arrangement gives rise to the high electrical conductivity of metals.

Electronegativity

It is instructive at this point to introduce an additional property of the elements, *electronegativity*. **Electronegativity** refers to the relative attraction that a bonded atom has for shared, "bonding" electrons. As we have already mentioned, the stability realized through chemical bonding arises from the favorable electrostatic interactions between nuclei and electrons. Further,

Ionic Bonds	Covalent Bonds	Metallic Bonds
Electrons Transferred from Metals to Nonmetals	Electrons Shared between Nonmetals (& Metalloids)	Electrons Delocalized over a large number of Metallic "Cores."

Figure 8.1 The three types of chemical bonds are ionic, covalent, and metallic.

Linus Pauling (1901–1994) was an American chemist and peace activist. He was awarded the Nobel Prize in Chemistry in 1954 and the Nobel Peace Prize in 1962. Among his many contributions to science, he is well known for his work in Bonding Theory and Molecular Biology. His famous textbook, *The Nature of the Chemical Bond* is considered one of the most important scientific works of the 20th Century.

it follows that the ability of an atom to attract shared electrons is a function of its nuclear charge (*Z*) and the distance of its valence shell to its nucleus. In other words, because different atoms have different nuclei and electronic structures, it should not be surprising that they do not necessarily "share" bonding electrons equally. Therefore, in many bonding situations, one atom will often have a greater attraction to the bonding electron pair. This means that the bonding electrons reside more closely toward one atom over the other. This concept will be of significance in the current chapter, especially in later sections concerning bond and molecular polarity. For now, suffice to say that atoms which are more electronegative exert a greater electrostatic pull on shared electrons in a covalent bond, resulting in an uneven distribution of those electrons.

In 1932, American chemist Linus Pauling was able to quantify this property and introduced the Pauling Electronegativity Scale (see Figure 8.2). This is a relative (unit-less) scale from 0 to 4 of electronegativities (*EN*). It is readily apparent, and not at all surprising, that *EN*'s increase from left to right and from bottom up on the periodic table, with fluorine as the most electronegative element and francium (and cesium) the least. We can ignore the Noble Gases.

1A																	8A
H 2.1	2A											3A	4A	5A	6A	7A	He ---
Li 1.1	Be 1.5											B 2.0	C 2.5	N 3.0	O 3.5	F 4.0	Ne ---
Na 0.9	Mg 1.2	3B	4B	5B	6B	7B		8B		1B	2B	Al 1.5	Si 1.8	P 2.1	S 2.5	Cl 3.0	Ar ---
K 0.8	Ca 1.0	Sc 1.3	Ti 1.5	V 1.6	Cr 1.6	Mn 1.5	Fe 1.8	Co 1.8	Ni 1.8	Cu 1.9	Zn 1.6	Ga 1.6	Ge 1.8	As 2.0	Se 2.4	Br 2.8	Kr ---
Rb 0.8	Sr 1.0	Y 1.2	Zr 1.4	Nb 1.6	Mo 1.8	Tc 1.9	Ru 2.2	Rh 2.2	Pd 2.2	Ag 1.9	Cd 1.7	In 1.7	Sn 1.8	Sb 1.9	Te 2.1	I 2.5	Xe ---
Cs 0.7	Ba 0.9	La 1.1	Hf 1.3	Ta 1.5	W 1.7	Re 1.9	Os 2.2	Ir 2.2	Pt 2.2	Au 2.4	Hg 1.9	Tl 1.8	Pb 1.9	Bi 1.9	Po 2.0	At 2.2	Rn ---
Fr 0.7	Ra 0.9	Ac 1.1															

Figure 8.2 The Pauling Electronegativity Scale. Electronegativities increase from left to right and from the bottom to the top of each group on the periodic table.

Section 8.3 Lewis Theory

We will explore three bonding theories. Of these, the first and simplest is Lewis theory, named for American chemist Gilbert N. Lewis. This theory makes use of an understanding of the number of valence electrons on each element and from this predicts the formation of ions, ionic bonds, or covalent bonds. To do this we will represent valence electrons as dots in what are termed **Lewis Dot Symbols** (for elements) or **Lewis Structures** (for compounds). In a Lewis dot symbol of an element, the elemental symbol represents the atomic core of the element in question, and the valence electrons are represented as the appropriate number of dots around the symbol. For example, let's consider fluorine. We know that fluorine is in Group 7A and has the following ground state electron configuration:

$$[He]2s^2 2p^5$$

From this we readily see that there are seven valence electrons on fluorine. Therefore, our Lewis dot symbol will be as follows:

$$\cdot \ddot{\underset{\cdot\cdot}{F}} :$$

$[He]2s^2 2p^5 \rightarrow$ 7 valence electrons

Here we interpret the symbol F to represent a fluorine nucleus plus a core electron configuration, [He]. For main group elements the group number tells us immediately the number of valence electrons for a given element (see Figure 8.3).

Rules for writing the Lewis dot symbol for main group elements:

1. Note the group number (1A through 8A) which tells us the number of valence electrons.

2. Write the elemental symbol and place a dot on each of its four sides singly first, only pairing them when necessary (similar to Hund's rule from Chapter 7).

3. Continue until all valence electrons are represented.

1A								8A
H 1e⁻	2A		3A	4A	5A	6A	7A	He 8e⁻
Li 1e⁻	Be 2e⁻		B 3e⁻	C 4e⁻	N 5e⁻	O 6e⁻	F 7e⁻	Ne 8e⁻
Na 1e⁻	Mg 2e⁻		Al 3e⁻	Si 4e⁻	P 5e⁻	S 6e⁻	Cl 7e⁻	Ar 8e⁻
K 1e⁻	Ca 2e⁻		Ga 3e⁻	Ge 4e⁻	As 5e⁻	Se 6e⁻	Br 7e⁻	Kr 8e⁻
Rb 1e⁻	Sr 2e⁻		In 3e⁻	Sn 4e⁻	Sb 5e⁻	Te 6e⁻	I 7e⁻	Xe 8e⁻
Cs 1e⁻	Ba 2e⁻		Tl 3e⁻	Pb 4e⁻	Bi 5e⁻	Po 6e⁻	At 7e⁻	Rn 8e⁻
Fr 1e⁻	Ra 2e⁻							

Figure 8.3 Elements in the same group have similar valence electron configurations and, therefore, the same number of dots in their Lewis symbols.

Example Problem 8.1 – Lewis Dot Symbols

Write the Lewis dot symbol for the main group elements of the third period of the periodic table.	
Solution:	
Sodium, *Na*, is the first element in the third row and because it is in group 1A, we know it has one valence electron.	Na •
Magnesium, *Mg*, is the next element in the third row. Because it is in group 2A, it has two valence electrons.	• Mg •
Aluminum is in group 3A and therefore we know it will have three valence electrons.	• Al •
Silicon is in group 4A and therefore will have four valence electrons.	• Si •
Phosphorus (group 5A) has five valence electrons.	• P •
Sulfur (group 6A) has 6 valence electrons.	• S :

Chlorine (group 7A) has seven valence electrons.	$: \overset{..}{\underset{.}{Cl}} :$
Argon (group 8A) has eight valence electrons.	$: \overset{..}{\underset{..}{Ar}} :$

The Octet Rule

Lewis dot symbols provide a simple visual account of the paired and unpaired valence electrons in an element or monatomic ion. Lewis theory uses this valence electron count for each element as a basis for how it predicts bonding between different elements. As such, the Lewis symbol provides insight into why bonds form. First, unpaired electrons are less stable than paired electrons. In other words, there is a special stability to paired electrons, and the only elements for which all electrons are paired (according to their Lewis dot symbol) are the noble gases. This is another way of saying that a full valence shell consisting of eight electrons (or two electrons in the case of He) is the most stable configuration. This basic idea is the central theme of bonding in Lewis theory and is referred to as the *octet rule*. The **octet rule** states that *atoms will gain, lose, or share electrons such as to attain a full valence shell of eight electrons referred to as an* **octet** *(or two in the case of Li, Be, and H, referred to as a* **duet***)*. With the octet rule in mind, there are two additional caveats:

1. First, main group metal atoms will lose all of their valence electrons to form cations which possess an octet. Essentially, they adopt the valence configuration of the previous Noble Gas on the periodic table (just as we learned in Chapter 3 when predicting the charge of monatomic cations).

2. Second, the number of unpaired electrons in the Lewis dot symbol of nonmetals is the number of electrons they will gain or share in forming anions or covalent bonds.

Lewis Theory and Ionic Bonding

Recall from a previous section, we learned that in ionic bonding, electrons are transferred from metal to nonmetals to form cations and anions. We can now predict precisely how many of such electrons are lost and gained according to the octet rule. For example, let's consider *Mg* and *Cl*. We see that if a bond forms in this case, it will be an ionic bond as we have both a metal and nonmetal. Let's begin by writing the Lewis dot symbol for each of these:

First, we see that *Mg* is in Group 2A and therefore has two valence electrons. Its electron configuration is as follows along with its corresponding Lewis symbol:

Mg: $[Ne]3s^2$ $\cdot Mg \cdot$

Likewise, *Cl* is a Group 7A element and therefore has seven valence electrons:

Cl: $[Ne]3s^2\,3p^5$

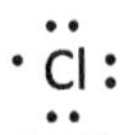

$\cdot\ddot{\underset{\cdot\cdot}{Cl}}:$

Applying our rules, we see that the magnesium must lose two electrons to gain an octet, and chlorine (having seven valence electrons) must gain one electron to obtain an octet. As such, the magnesium will need two chlorines to satisfy this requirement.

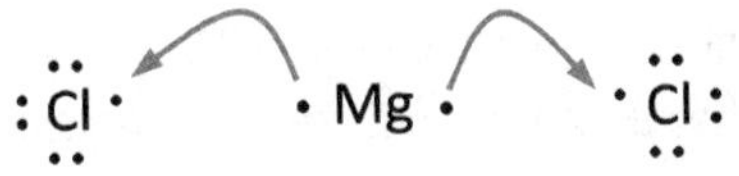

$:\ddot{Cl}\cdot \qquad \cdot Mg\cdot \qquad \cdot\ddot{Cl}:$

If we literally represent such a transfer by removing dots from *Mg* and adding them to *Cl*, the result is as follows:

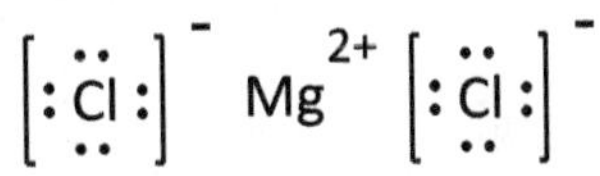

$$\left[:\ddot{\underset{\cdot\cdot}{Cl}}:\right]^{-}\ Mg^{2+}\ \left[:\ddot{\underset{\cdot\cdot}{Cl}}:\right]^{-}$$

Note: We represent monatomic cations with no dots in the Lewis dot symbol. This is a nod to the fact that metals lose all of their valence electrons in obtaining an octet through ion formation. Additionally, we bracket the dots on an anion to indicate "possession" of its eight valence electrons. Also, note that by merely counting valence electrons and applying the octet rule, Lewis theory has correctly predicted the ionic charges of the magnesium and chloride ions, as well as the formula of the ionic compound, magnesium chloride, *MgCl₂*. Collectively, we would refer to this depiction of magnesium chloride as the Lewis dot structure or **Lewis Structure** of this compound. The following example problem provides some additional practice at predicting and drawing Lewis structures for ionic compounds.

Example Problem 8.2 – Lewis Structures: Ionic Compounds

Use the Lewis symbols of calcium and bromine to predict the formula of calcium bromide.	
Solution:	
We know from the periodic table that calcium is a group 2A metal with two valence electrons to donate in the formation of an octet. Likewise, bromine is a group 7A nonmetal which requires one additional electron to form an octet. As such, we will require two bromine atoms to accommodate the two electrons transferred from calcium. This is apparent upon writing the Lewis dot symbols for each element as shown here.	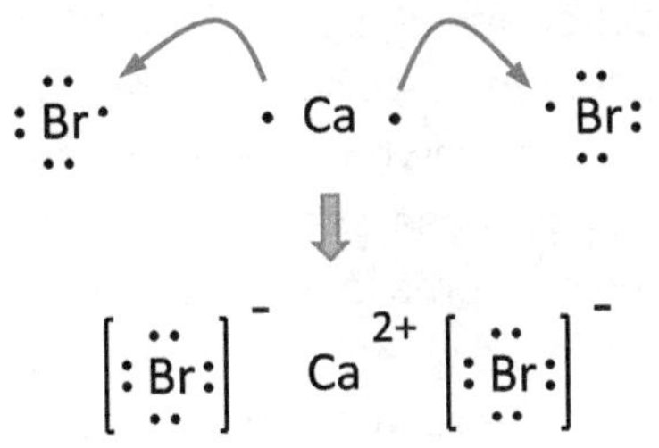 $:\ddot{Br}\cdot \quad \cdot Ca\cdot \quad \cdot\ddot{Br}:$ $\left[:\ddot{Br}:\right]^{-} Ca^{2+} \left[:\ddot{Br}:\right]^{-}$
Given the Lewis structure we have constructed, we predict the formula of calcium bromide to be *CaBr₂*.	*CaBr₂*

Section 8.4 Lewis Theory – Covalent Compounds

Why does hydrogen form diatomic molecules, H_2? Why is water H_2O rather than HO or H_3O? Lewis theory, through application of the octet rule to covalent bonding, provides a basis for understanding and predicting such observations. To understand how Lewis theory predicts covalent bonding, consider again the familiar example of water. Water consists of hydrogen and oxygen. Let's begin by writing the Lewis dot symbols of these two elements:

H·   ·Ö:

$1s^1$ $[He]2s^22p^4$

First, we know that hydrogen is a Group 1A element and therefore has one valence electron while oxygen is a Group 6A element with six valence electrons. This leaves hydrogen with one unpaired electron, meaning it will "share" this electron in a covalent bonding arrangement. However, we see that oxygen has two such unpaired electrons. For this reason, two hydrogen atoms will be required to satisfy the octet for oxygen.

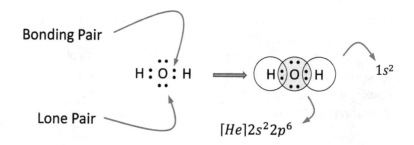

In this case oxygen will share each electron in two covalent bonds with two hydrogen atoms. Likewise, each hydrogen atom will share its single valence electron. In this way each atom realizes an electron pair, where an unpaired electron resided prior to bonding. Additionally, because the electrons are shared, the Lewis structure is drawn such that the "shared" electrons, or dots, are drawn in the region between the two bonding elements. This is because these shared electrons count toward the octet (or duet) of both bonding atoms in each bond as shown above. Therefore, Lewis theory predicts that oxygen will share two ("unpaired") electrons while two hydrogen atoms will each share one electron to form two covalent bonds. We refer to shared electrons as bonding electron pairs or **bonding pairs**. Electron pairs which are not shared are referred to as **nonbonding pairs**, also called **lone pairs**.

Lewis theory also explains why oxygen forms diatomic molecules in its elemental state. Consider two oxygen atoms as follows:

$$\cdot \ddot{\underset{\displaystyle \cdot}{O}}: \qquad \cdot \ddot{\underset{\displaystyle \cdot}{O}}:$$

$$[He]2s^2 2p^4 \qquad [He]2s^2 2p^4$$

It is clear that since each atom can share two unpaired electrons, the result will be two bonding pairs of electrons as follows:

$$:\ddot{O}::\ddot{O}:$$

When two pairs of bonding electrons are shared between the same two atoms, this is referred to as a **double bond.** Double bonds are generally stronger than single bonds, and they are also shorter. Let's consider another diatomic element, N_2. If we examine the Lewis dot symbol of the N, we see we need to form three bonding pairs to complete an octet for each atom:

$$\cdot \ddot{\underset{\displaystyle \cdot}{N}} \cdot \quad \cdot \ddot{\underset{\displaystyle \cdot}{N}} \cdot \quad \longrightarrow \quad :N:::N:$$

When three bonding pairs are shared between the same two atoms, this is referred to as a **triple bond**. Again, triple bonds generally have shorter bond lengths and are stronger than double bonds (which are shorter and stronger than single bonds).

Also, bonding electron pairs can also be represented with solid lines as follows:

$$H\!-\!\ddot{\underset{\displaystyle \cdot\cdot}{O}}\!-\!H \qquad :\ddot{O}\!=\!\ddot{O}: \qquad :N\!\equiv\!N:$$

Here we interpret each individual line as representing a shared or bonding pair of electrons. As such, two lines represent a double bond (two shared pairs) and three lines represent a triple bond (three shared pairs).

So far, we have considered some fairly simple examples of covalent molecules to demonstrate the application of Lewis theory to covalent bonds. To address the need to handle more complex combinations of atoms, the following section will explore a set of systematic steps in writing Lewis Structures.

Section 8.5 Lewis Structures of Covalent Compounds

To illustrate the basic steps involved in writing Lewis structures, let's consider another example. We will apply the following steps to derive the Lewis structure of formaldehyde, CH_2O.

1. **Write the correct skeletal structure.** To properly write a Lewis structure, all the atoms should be in the proper relative locations. Unfortunately, there is no obvious way to know exactly what the arrangement of atoms looks like without experimental data. Nevertheless, we can apply some basic guidelines to help us begin with a probable arrangement. First, we should always place the least electronegative (most metal-like) atom as the central atom. Having done this, we should also remember that **hydrogen is never the central atom.** This is because hydrogen forms a duet and therefore can only form a single bond. In the case of formaldehyde, carbon is the central atom as it is the least electronegative candidate (see Figure 8.2).

$$
\begin{array}{c}
O \\
C \\
H \quad\;\; H
\end{array}
$$

2. **Sum the valence electrons of all the atoms in the molecule.** The main task in writing Lewis structures is to distribute the valence electrons over the molecule once a skeletal structure has been established. Also, it is important to remember, if writing the structure of a polyatomic ion, you must add one electron to the total count for every negative charge and subtract one electron for every positive charge on the ion in question. In the case of formaldehyde, we find that we have 12 valence electrons available to us.

$$
\begin{array}{c}
O \\
C \\
H \quad\;\; H
\end{array}
$$

$$
\begin{array}{ccc}
H & C & O
\end{array}
$$
$2(1) + 4 + 6 = 12 \textbf{ valence electrons}$

3. **Place a single shared electron pair between the central atom and each terminal atom.** This is necessary because there must be at least one single bond between each of the terminal atoms and the central atom. We must also subtract the number of electrons used to perform this task from our total, leaving us with six electrons.

$12 - 6 = 6e^-$

4. **Use the remaining electrons to complete the octet of as many terminal atoms as possible.** Any electrons remaining can be applied to the central atom (there are none in our example). (Recall, hydrogen does not form an octet but rather a duet.)

$6-6 = 0e^-$

5. **If the central atom does not have an octet at this point, move nonbonding electron pairs from the terminal atoms into bonding regions, forming double or triple bonds with the central atom.** This is done on an "as-needed" basis to complete the octet of the central atom. In this case we can move one of the nonbonding pairs from the oxygen atom into a bonding arrangement with carbon, forming a double bond.

In this manner we arrive at the correct Lewis structure of formaldehyde. The following example problems provide some additional practice in writing Lewis structures of covalent compounds.

Example Problem 8.3 – Writing Lewis Structures

Construct the Lewis Structure of nitrogen trifluoride, NF_3.

Solution:

Step 1. Write the skeletal structure of the molecule. This is accomplished by placing the atom with the lowest electronegativity in the center and symmetrically distributing the terminal atoms around it.	
Step 2. Determine the total number of valence electrons for the compound. In this case, we would add five valence electrons for the nitrogen to 21 electrons ($3 \times 7e^-$) from the three fluorine atoms.	$5\,e^- + 3(7\,e^-) = 26\,e^-$
Step 3. Draw a single bond from the central atom (nitrogen) to each of the terminal atoms (the three fluorines). To do so in this case, we will need to use six of the 26 electrons we have available to us.	$26 - 6 = 20\,e^-$

Step 4. From the remaining 20 electrons, complete the octet for each of the (three) terminal atoms. In the case of nitrogen trifluoride, that will require 18 electrons of the remaining 20, leaving us with only two electrons.	:F: | :F—N—F: 20 − 18 = **2 e⁻**
Step 5. Place the remaining electrons with the central atom.	:F: | :F—N—F: No remaining electrons. All octets are satisfied.

Example Problem 8.4 – Writing Lewis Structures

Construct the Lewis Structure of carbon dioxide, CO_2.	
Solution:	
Step 1. Write the skeletal structure of the molecule. This is accomplished by placing the atom with the lowest electronegativity in the center and symmetrically distributing the terminal atoms around it.	O C O
Step 2. Determine the total number of valence electrons for the compound. In this case, we would add four valence electrons for the carbon to 12 electrons ($2 \times 6\,e^-$) from the two oxygen atoms.	$4\,e^- + 2(6\,e^-) = \mathbf{16}\,\boldsymbol{e^-}$
Step 3. Draw a single bond from the central atom (carbon) to each of the terminal atoms (the two oxygens). To do so in this case, we will need to use four of the 16 electrons we have available to us.	O—C—O $16 - 4 = \mathbf{12}\,\boldsymbol{e^-}$
Step 4. From the remaining 12 electrons, complete the octet for each of the (two) terminal atoms. In the case of carbon dioxide, that will require all the remaining 12 electrons.	:Ö—C—Ö: No remaining electrons.
Step 5. At this point we have exhausted our total of 16 electrons. Nevertheless, carbon still is four electrons shy of an octet. To complete the octet, we now move a nonbonding electron pair from each of the two oxygens into a bonding region between the oxygens and the carbon. This is the formation of two double bonds.	:Ö—C—Ö: ⬇ :Ö=C=Ö:

Example Problem 8.5 – Writing Lewis Structures of Oxyacids

Construct the Lewis Structure for phosphoric acid, H_3PO_4.

Solution:	
Step1: Draw the skeletal structure with the least electronegative atom in the center. For oxyacids, always place the hydrogens such that they will be bonded to the terminal oxygens of the polyatomic ion, which is phosphate in this case.	H O O P O H O H
Step 2: Tabulate the total number of valence electrons available in this structure.	$3(1)+4(6)+5=\mathbf{32}\ \boldsymbol{e^-}$
Step 3: Create three single bonds between the central phosphorus atom and the terminal atoms. This requires we use 14 of our 32 available electrons leaving us with 18 remaining.	H | O | O—P—O—H | O | H $32-14=\mathbf{18}\ \boldsymbol{e^-}$ remaining
Step 4: Complete the octets of the terminal atoms, requiring the remaining 18 electrons. Since all atoms involved are now enjoying an octet or a duet, there is no need to proceed further. (Nevertheless this structure will be further developed when we deal with expanded octets and formal charge in the following sections.)	H | :Ö: | :Ö—P—Ö—H | :Ö: | H No remaining electrons. This structure remains to be fully developed. The preferred Lewis structure is completed in Example Problem 8.9.

Section 8.6 Resonance Structures

Sometimes it is possible to predict more than one acceptable Lewis structure for a particular compound. For example, let's consider SO_2. If we apply the procedure from the previous section, we arrive at the following Lewis structure:

$$:\overset{\cdot\cdot}{\underset{\cdot\cdot}{O}}-\overset{\cdot\cdot}{S}=\overset{\cdot\cdot}{O}:$$

However, there was no compelling reason why only the right-most oxygen atom should engage in a double bond, while the left one doesn't. As such, an equally good Lewis structure representation of SO_2 is:

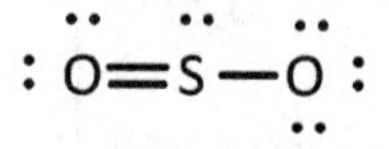

$$\ddot{:}\overset{..}{O}=\overset{..}{S}-\overset{..}{\underset{..}{O}}\,\ddot{:}$$

This presents a dilemma. Which is correct? Are they both correct? To help address this, consider that if we accept either or both of these structures as accurate, it suggests that the SO_2 molecule has one longer (single) $S\text{–}O$ bond and one shorter (double) $S=O$ bond. However, when we examine SO_2 empirically, we find that it has two $S\text{–}O$ bonds of equal length. Further, the bond lengths of these bonds are intermediate in length, between what would be expected for single and double $S\text{–}O$ bonds. Therefore, the only possible conclusion is that neither of these Lewis structures is correct. Again, Linus Pauling provides a solution that expands the utility of our theory. Pauling suggested the theory of **resonance** to explain this discrepancy. In this theory, the structures we have developed for SO_2 are referred to as **resonance structures** of this compound. We represent resonance structures as shown below:

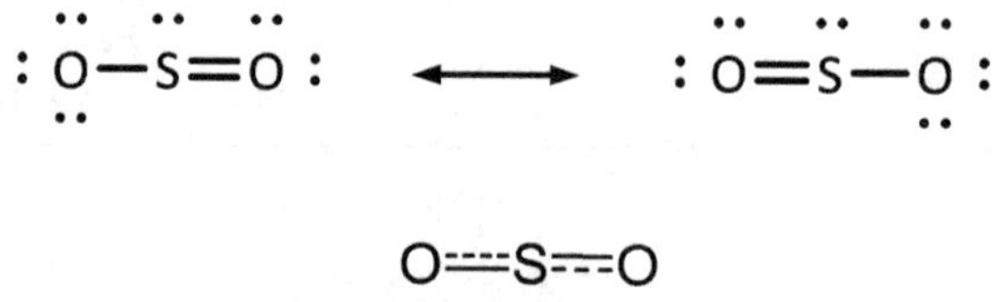

$$\ddot{:}\overset{..}{\underset{..}{O}}-\overset{..}{S}=\overset{..}{O}\,\ddot{:} \quad\longleftrightarrow\quad \ddot{:}\overset{..}{O}=\overset{..}{S}-\overset{..}{\underset{..}{O}}\,\ddot{:}$$

$$O\text{=\!=\!=}S\text{=\!=\!=}O$$

Resonance Hybrid

These two structures are energetically equivalent, as they have the same bonding arrangement. The actual structure of the molecule is a sort of average or blend of the two resonance structures, often referred to as a **resonance hybrid**. In general, we can predict resonance structures by writing the Lewis structure in the normal way. If at the end of the process, there is a multiple bond, resonance structures exist if the octet of the central atom can be completed by using an electron pair from more than one terminal atom in forming a multiple bond. A good example of this is the carbonate ion. The following example details the how we arrive at the proper resonance structures for this ion.

Example Problem 8.6 – Resonance Structures

Draw the three resonance structures for carbonate, CO_3^{2-}.	
Solution:	
Step1: Draw the skeletal structure with the least electronegative atom in the center.	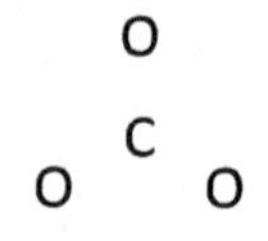 O C O O

Step 2: Tabulate the total number of valence electrons available in this structure. Recall that because carbonate is a polyatomic ion, we will need to add two additional electrons to accommodate its relative charge of −2.	$4+3(6)+2=\mathbf{24}\ e^{-}$
Step 3: Create three single bonds between the central carbon atom and the three terminal oxygens atoms. This requires we use six of our 24 available electrons leaving us with 18 remaining.	$24-6=\mathbf{18}\ e^{-}$ remaining
Step 4: Complete the octets of the terminal atoms, requiring the remaining 18 electrons.	No remaining electrons.
Step 5: With no remaining electrons available to us, we will need to complete the octet of the carbon atom by sharing an additional electron pair from one of the oxygen atoms. There are three equally valid candidates for the formation of this double bond. As such, we know that this structure has three equivalent resonance structures.	
A common representation of such structures is the depiction of the **resonance hybrid** which delocalizes the additional bonding pair of electrons over all three bonds.	

Formal Charge

Another discrepancy that Lewis theory presents arises from the fact that in actual covalent molecules, the electrons are not distributed over the molecule as evenly as Lewis structures seem to suggest. Additionally, understanding the concept of resonance structures, it should not be surprising to learn that we can also find multiple resonance structures for a given compound which are NOT equivalent. Taken together, these two points bring us to the concept of formal charge. **Formal charge** is a "fictional" charge assigned to each atom in a Lewis structure. Formal charge is calculated by assuming absolutely equal sharing of bonding electrons in a molecule according to the following equation:

$$Formal\ Charge = Valence\ Electrons - Nonbonding\ Electrons - \frac{1}{2}(bonding\ electrons)$$

In other words, formal charge arises from the difference between the number of valence electrons an element has in its atomic state and the number of electrons assigned by a particular Lewis structure. Let's consider an example. If we write the Lewis structure of SO_2 again, we arrive at one of its resonance structures:

$$:\ddot{O}\!-\!S\!=\!\ddot{O}:$$

We see here that sulfur has two nonbonding electrons and has six bonding electrons assigned to it. Since we know that sulfur is a Group 6A element, it therefore has six valence electrons, and we calculate its formal charge in this structure as:

$$FC_S = 6 - 2 - \frac{1}{2}(6) = 6 - 2 - 3 = +1$$

We can do the same procedure for the left and right oxygen atoms:

$$FC_O^{Left} = 6 - 6 - \frac{1}{2}(2) = 6 - 6 - 1 = -1$$

$$FC_O^{Right} = 6 - 4 - \frac{1}{2}(4) = 6 - 4 - 2 = 0$$

Formal charges are labeled as follows:

$$\overset{-1}{:\ddot{O}}\!-\!\overset{+1}{S}\!=\!\overset{0}{\ddot{O}}:$$

The utility of formal charge comes into play when we must determine how to prioritize non-equivalent Lewis structures. It is not always obvious how the skeletal structure should be arranged, even when the central atom is readily apparent. Additionally, not all possible resonance structures for a compound are equivalent; some are more appropriate in describing the bonding character of a molecule than others. Formal charge can be used to help us distinguish between such competing structures. This is done through application of three guidelines:

1. The sum of all formal charges in a molecule must equal zero, and the sum of all formal charges in a polyatomic ion must equal the charge on that ion.

2. Smaller formal charges on individual atoms are preferred to larger ones (zero is most preferred). In other words, we should attempt to minimize or avoid formal charges altogether if possible.

3. When formal charges are present, negative formal charge should preferentially reside on the most electronegative atom possible.

With this in mind, let's consider another example. If we set out to predict the Lewis structure of the polyatomic ion cyanate, OCN^-, because carbon is the least electronegative of these three, it is the central atom. However, the terminal atoms are different elements, and therefore, it is unclear exactly which of the three possible resonance structures below will contribute most to the structure:

$$\left[:O\equiv C - \ddot{N}:\right]^{-} \longleftrightarrow \left[:\ddot{O}=C=\ddot{N}:\right]^{-} \longleftrightarrow \left[:\ddot{O}-C\equiv N:\right]^{-}$$

If we calculate the formal charge for each atom in the left most structure we have:

$$FC_O = 6 - 2 - \frac{1}{2}(6) = +1$$

$$FC_C = 4 - 0 - \frac{1}{2}(8) = 0$$

$$FC_N = 5 - 6 - \frac{1}{2}(2) = -2$$

The sum of these formal charges equals −1, which is the charge on the cyanate ion. If we do this for the remaining structures, we arrive at the following:

$$\left[:O\equiv C - \ddot{N}:\right]^{-} \longleftrightarrow \left[:\ddot{O}=C=\ddot{N}:\right]^{-} \longleftrightarrow \left[:\ddot{O}-C\equiv N:\right]^{-}$$
$$+1 \quad 0 \quad -2 \qquad\quad 0 \quad 0 \quad -1 \qquad\quad -1 \quad 0 \quad 0$$

Since the first structure has two atoms with nonzero formal charges, while the remaining two have only one, we can dispense with it immediately. Of the remaining two structures, the right one places the negative formal charge on the more electronegative "O" atom while the left one places it on the less electronegative "N" atom. As such, we expect the right-most structure to make the greatest contribution to the resonance hybrid structure of the cyanate ion.

Example Problem 8.7 – Resonance and Formal Charge

Use formal charge to determine why the first of the three structures below is the best description of the bonding in nitrous oxide, N_2O.

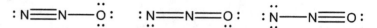

Solution:	

If we calculate the formal charges for the first structure, we arrive at −1 for oxygen, +1 for the nitrogen atom to the right, and 0 for the nitrogen at the left. This is because we know that oxygen and nitrogen are in groups 6A and 5A, respectively, and, as such, we know nitrogen to have five and oxygen to have six valence electrons. If we subtract the nonbonding electrons and one half of the bonding electrons from these, we arrive at the formal charges shown here.

$$FC = Valence - Nonbonding - \frac{1}{2}bonding$$

$$FC_O = 6 - 6 - \frac{1}{2}(2) = -1$$

$$FC_N^{Right} = 5 - 0 - \frac{1}{2}(8) = +1$$

$$FC_N^{Left} = 5 - 2 - \frac{1}{2}(6) = 0$$

If we do likewise for the second structure, we find there is a positive and negative 1 formal charge on the right and left nitrogen atom, respectively, and zero for oxygen.

$$FC_O = 6 - 4 - \frac{1}{2}(4) = 0$$

$$FC_N^{Right} = 5 - 0 - \frac{1}{2}(8) = +1$$

$$FC_N^{Left} = 5 - 4 - \frac{1}{2}(4) = -1$$

The same analysis for the third structure gives −2 formal charge to the leftmost nitrogen atom and +1 to both remaining atoms.

$$FC_O = 6 - 2 - \frac{1}{2}(6) = +1$$

$$FC_N^{Right} = 5 - 0 - \frac{1}{2}(8) = +1$$

$$FC_N^{Left} = 5 - 6 - \frac{1}{2}(2) = -2$$

We can tabularize these results to make this result more visible.

	Structure 1			Structure 2			Structure 3		
	N	N	O	N	N	O	N	N	O
Valence Electrons	5	5	6	5	5	6	5	5	6
Lone Pair Electrons	2	0	6	4	0	4	6	0	2
Bonding Electrons	6	8	2	4	8	4	2	8	6
$FC = valence - Lone - \frac{1}{2}bonding$	0	+1	−1	−1	+1	0	−2	+1	+1

Therefore, of these three structures, the third one is least preferred as it has the most nonzero formal charges. Additionally, it places a large negative formal charge on the least electronegative element. Between the first and second structures, the first is preferred. This is because, even though each has the same number and magnitude of nonzero formal charges assigned, the second structure places the negative formal charge on the least electronegative element. As such, we would expect the first structure to be the best representation of the bonding arrangement in this compound.

$$
\begin{array}{ccc}
0 & +1 & -1 \\
: N \equiv N - \ddot{\underset{..}{O}} :
\end{array}
$$

Section 8.7 Exceptions to the Octet Rule

Some elements and compounds do not lend themselves to the octet rule. These are categorized into three types of exceptions, which include species with an odd number of electrons, electron-deficient species (also referred to as incomplete octets), and expanded octet species.

Free Radicals – Odd-Electron Species

When a Lewis structure has an odd number of valence electrons, it is called a **free radical**. Free radicals are characterized by "unpaired" electrons and are highly reactive. For example, consider nitrogen monoxide, *NO*. There are a total of 11 valence electrons to be distributed over this molecule (six from oxygen and five from nitrogen). As such, its Lewis structure is as follows:

$$: \dot{N} = \ddot{O} :$$

Notice that we can only accommodate a valence electron count of seven for the nitrogen atom in this case. Nevertheless, nitrogen monoxide is a known compound, so we must conclude that Lewis theory (the octet rule) does not provide a good description of these odd-electron species. However, it is true that such species are rare, and those that do exist are quite reactive.

Incomplete Octets

Some elements tend to form incomplete octets. The most prominent among these are boron and aluminum. Rather than adopting an eight-electron valence configuration, these species will adopt a six-electron configuration.

As an example, BF_3 provides for only six valence electrons on the central atom, boron.

$$
\begin{array}{c}
: \ddot{F} : \\
| \\
: \ddot{F} \diagdown B \diagup \ddot{F} : \\
\end{array}
$$

Example Problem 8.8 – Incomplete Octets

Write the correct Lewis structure for BCl_3.	
Solution:	
Step 1: Draw the skeletal structure with the least electro-negative atom in the center.	Cl Cl B Cl
Step 2: Tabulate the total available valence electrons for this structure. For main group elements this is simply the sum of their group numbers.	$3+3(7)=\mathbf{24}\ e^-$
Step 3: Create single bonds between the central atom and the terminal atoms. This requires six of the 24 available electrons.	Cl⟍ ⟋Cl B Cl
Step 4: Complete the octet of all terminal atoms. This requires all of the remaining 18 electrons. Further, since boron forms an incomplete octet, it requires six valence electrons, and we are finished.	:C̈l⟍ ⟋C̈l: B :C̈l:

Expanded Octets

Some elements adopt **expanded octets**, meaning that they take on more than eight valence electrons. This is due to the fact that many elements have additional (empty) *d* orbitals which can contribute to their bonding structure. *As such, elements in the third row (or later rows) on the periodic table can accommodate up to 12 or more electrons in their Lewis structures.* For example, consider SF_6. Here we identify sulfur as the central atom, and there are 48 valence electrons in this compound. In order to accommodate a single bond from the central atom to all terminal atoms, we require the sulfur to accept 12 valence electrons. This is possible only because sulfur, being a third row element, can make use of empty $3d$ orbitals in its valence shell to accept more than four electron pairs. The remaining 36 electrons are used to complete the octets of the six fluorine atoms:

$$
\begin{array}{c}
: \ddot{F} : \\
: \ddot{F} \diagdown | \diagup \ddot{F} : \\
S \\
: \ddot{F} \diagup | \diagdown \ddot{F} : \\
: \ddot{F} : \\
\end{array}
$$

With this concept in mind, we can reconsider the guidelines we learned about formal charge. For example, consider the sulfate anion, SO_4^{2-}. If we apply the standard procedure for determining the Lewis structure and assigning formal charges, we arrive at the following (where formal charges are denoted in red font):

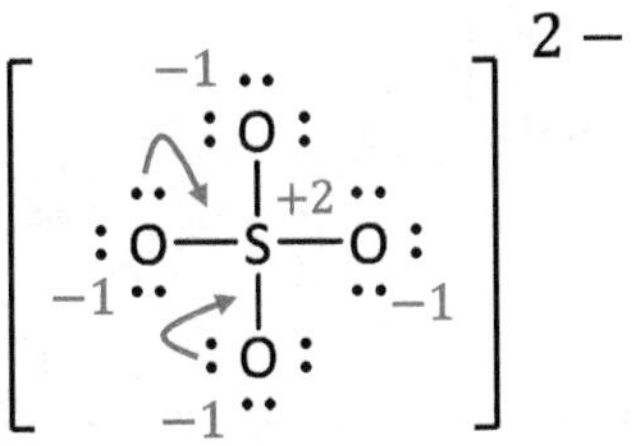

At first glance, this seems a reasonable structure according to the rules we have learned so far. Indeed, we find that the sum of the formal charges equals the total charge on the ion $(4(-1) + (+2) = -2)$. However, we should immediately see that there is a nonzero formal charge assigned to every atom in this structure. Recall that structures with minimal number formal charges are preferred. Additionally, we also know that sulfur is a third row element and, as such, can accommodate an expanded octet. By rearranging the electron distribution such that nonbonding electrons are moved from atoms with negative formal charge toward the atoms with positive formal charge (sulfur), we can effectively minimize the formal charges on our structure:

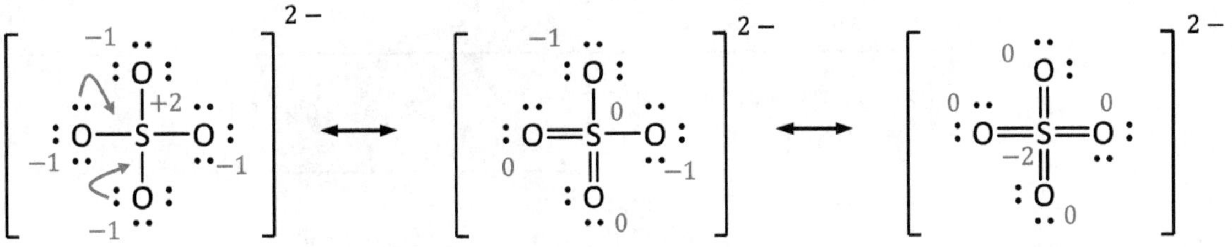

Preferred Structure

In this case, we maintain the octets for all four oxygen atoms, while expanding the octet of sulfur to 12 electrons. Additionally, we have eliminated formal charges for the sulfur as well as two of the oxygen atoms. There is a good reason why we perform this adjustment for only two of the four oxygen atoms. If we moved lone pairs on the remaining oxygens into a bonding arrangement with sulfur, we would maintain the correct sum of formal charges, but we would then be placing negative formal charge on the least electronegative atom (sulfur). This would also concentrate a formal charge of greater magnitude (-2) on the sulfur atom as well, which is also not preferred. As such, the best Lewis structure for the sulfate ion is the one with only two double bonds (middle structure).

Example Problem 8.9 – Expanded Octets

Assign formal charge to the atoms in the Lewis structure of phosphoric acid from example problem 8.5. Are there any preferred structures for phosphoric acid other than that which was determined in example 8.5?

	Solution:
We begin with the structure determined in example 8.5.	
Each of the three hydrogen atoms is identical; therefore we can determine their formal charges in one calculation. Each has one bonding pair of electrons and no lone pairs. Since hydrogen has one valence electron, we calculate its formal charge as:	$$FC_H = Valence - Nonbonding - \frac{1}{2} bonding$$ $$FC_H = 1 - 0 - \frac{1}{2}(2) = 0$$
Formal charge of oxygen is more complex. There are two different situations for oxygen in this case. Three oxygens have two lone pairs while one of them has three lone pairs. Let's calculate the formal charge for those with only two lone pairs first. Oxygen has six valence electrons.	$$FC_O' = Valence - Nonbonding - \frac{1}{2} bonding$$ $$FC_O' = 6 - 4 - \frac{1}{2}(4) = 0$$
Now let's calculate formal charge for the remaining oxygen.	$$FC_O'' = 6 - 6 - \frac{1}{2}(2) = -1$$
Phosphorus has four bonding pairs and no lone pairs. Therefore its formal charge is calculated as shown:	$$FC_P = 5 - 0 - \frac{1}{2}(8) = +1$$
Therefore we can label our structure with the appropriate formal charges (zeros are left out for clarity). If we move a nonbonding pair from an atom of negative formal charge toward the central atom, the magnitude of each will be reduced by one.	
This leaves all formal charges at zero, which is preferred. Additionally, because phosphorus is a third-row element, it can accommodate an expanded octet. As such, the preferred Lewis structure of phosphoric acid contains a double bond between phosphorus and one of the oxygens.	

Section 8.8 Valence Shell Electron Pair Repulsion Theory (VSEPR)

In addition to providing a model for the bonding arrangements between atoms in a molecule, bonding theories (like Lewis theory) also provide a basis for explaining and predicting molecular geometry or shape. Molecular shape, as it turns out, is very important in many chemical and biological processes. In fact, many biological processes are highly tuned and sensitive to even the slightest variations in the shape of molecules as we learn later in Chapter 16, "Introduction to Biochemistry." As such, understanding molecular geometry and the underlying reasons for it are of importance to chemists. In order to expand our exploration of Lewis theory to include predictions about the shapes of molecules, we must employ a corollary theory. This theory is referred to as **Valence Shell Electron Pair Repulsion Theory (VSEPR)**.

As the name implies, this theory assumes that electron pairs in the valence shell of the central atom of a molecule will exert an electrostatic repulsive force on each other. Owing to this, these electron pairs will naturally arrange themselves as far from each other as possible, minimizing this repulsive interaction. However, because not all of the electron pairs about the central atom are bonding pairs, we must recognize that the VSEPR model will predict molecular shape insofar as it is a derivative of the arrangement of all electron pairs (bonding and nonbonding) about the central atom. As such, we will define two terms to describe this distinction, the *electronic geometry* and the *molecular geometry*.

1. **Electronic Geometry** refers to the three-dimensional arrangement of all of the electrons on the central atom. This is the direct result of the application of the VSEPR model.

2. **Molecular Geometry** refers to the three-dimensional arrangement of the terminal atoms around the central atom. This is a derivative of the electronic geometry.

As it turns out, if all of the electron pairs on the central atom are bonding pairs (no lone pairs), then the molecular geometry and the electronic geometry are one and the same. However, it is the presence of a combination of bonding and lone pairs which causes these two geometries to be differentiated. For simplicity, we will begin by confining ourselves to molecules for which all valence shell electron pairs on the central atom are bonding pairs.

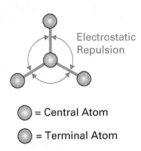

= Central Atom

= Terminal Atom

VSEPR Theory predicts the arrangement of atoms in a molecule on the basis of electrostatic repulsions acting between pairs of valence electrons on a central atom.

It will be necessary in the remaining sections of Chapter 8 to depict 3-dimensional arrangements of atoms in various bonding arrangements. To accommodate this, chemists use a convention whereby wedges (solid and hashed) are used to depict bonds. A solid wedge indicates a bond is projected out of the plane defined by the page toward the reader. Likewise a hashed wedge indicates a bond projected out of plane and away from the reader (behind the page). Solid lines are simply bonds which are coplanar with the page.

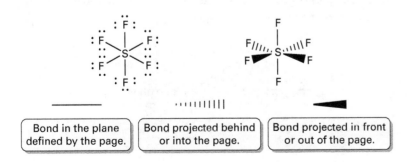

| Bond in the plane defined by the page. | Bond projected behind or into the page. | Bond projected in front or out of the page. |

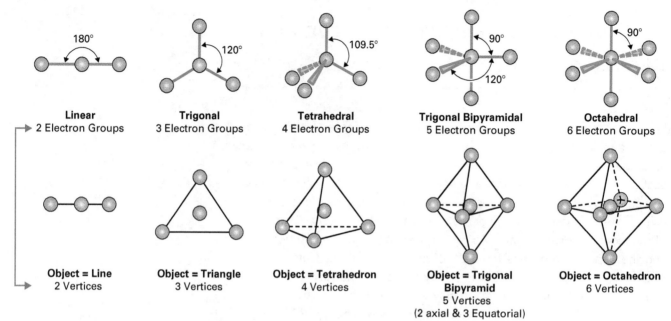

Figure 8.4 The electronic geometry can be described by geometric objects or shapes which have vertices (or endpoints) equal to the number of electron groups distributed about the central atom. Therefore each vertex on a given shape is occupied by a terminal atom (when the electron group at that location is a "bonding" group).

No Lone Pairs on the Central Atom

Sometimes two bonding electron pairs will occupy the same space or position on the central atom. For example when there is a double bond, two pairs are shared in the region of space directly between the central and terminal atom. For this reason we will make another distinction. We will define an **electron group** as one or more pairs of electrons which occupy the same space. In other words, a double or a triple bond will be defined as a single electron group. It is the number of electron groups (*EG*) that will determine the electronic geometry in the VSEPR model. If we imagine the central atom as a sphere with electron groups on its surface, and note that these groups repel one another such as to naturally arrange themselves as far apart as possible (while still remaining on the surface of the sphere), we can predict the position of those *EG*s quite readily. There are five basic geometries we will associate with specific numbers of *EG*s as shown in Figure 8.4. These are **linear** (*EG* = 2), **trigonal** (*EG* = 3), **tetrahedral** (*EG* = 4), **trigonal bipyramidal** (*EG* = 5), and **octahedral** (*EG* = 6). The names are taken from geometric objects or shapes which are defined by the positions of the terminal atoms (See Figure 8.4). For example, the terminal atoms on an octahedral molecule occupy positions that correspond to the six vertices of an eight-sided octahedron. Let's consider a series of examples:

Linear (*EG* = 2) – Carbon Dioxide: Recall from example problem 8.4 that the Lewis structure of carbon dioxide is as follows:

$$\ddot{\text{O}}=\text{C}=\ddot{\text{O}} \qquad \begin{array}{l}\text{2 Electron Groups}\\(EG = 2)\end{array}$$

In this case, since there are two bonds and no lone pairs on the central atom (carbon), we have only two electron groups. According to VSEPR, these two groups will arrange themselves as far apart (on the central atom) as possible. For two groups this would be on complete opposite sides of the central atom, resulting in an angle between the two double bonds (bond angle) of 180°. This is why VSEPR says that two *EG*s results in a *linear* geometry, depicted generically as:

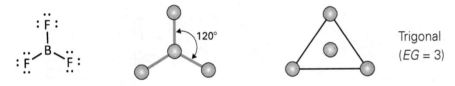

Trigonal (*EG* = 3), Boron Trifluoride: If we draw the Lewis structure of BF_3, we have the following:

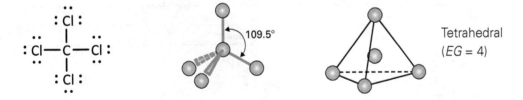

Trigonal
(*EG* = 3)

Here we have three bonds and no lone pairs on the central atom, so we have three electron groups (*EG* = 3). Therefore, the three fluorine atoms are coplanar with boron. In such an arrangement the fluorine atoms reside at the vertices of an imaginary triangle. As such, we would say the electronic and molecular geometries of BF_3 are **trigonal**, and the bond angle associated with the *trigonal* geometry is 120°.

   Tetrahedral (*EG* = 4), Carbon Tetrachloride: The Lewis structure of CCl_4 is:

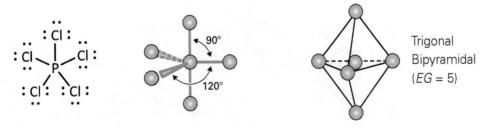

Tetrahedral
(*EG* = 4)

In this case, we can clearly see four bonds and no lone pairs on the central atom. This is the first point at which the electron groups will result in a nonplanar arrangement of the terminal atoms. The chlorine atoms reside at the vertices of a four-sided tetrahedron; hence, both the electronic and molecular geometries are referred to as **tetrahedral,** with bond angles of 109.5°.

   Trigonal Bipyramidal (*EG* = 5), Phosphorus Pentachloride: Again we construct the Lewis structure of PCl_5:

Trigonal
Bipyramidal
(*EG* = 5)

For this molecule, the Lewis structure shows us five bonds and no lone pairs on the central atom. Therefore, we have five electron groups. The VSEPR arrangement therefore requires the terminal chlorines to reside the vertices of two trigonal pyramids (one pointed up, the other down). As such, there are two characteristic bond angles; those between the bonds in the equatorial, "trigonal" plane are 120°, and the two axial bonds (pointed straight up and down) are at 90° to the equatorial plane. Therefore, the electronic and molecular geometries are one and the same, **trigonal bipyramidal**. Note, unlike the terminal atoms in other geometries, the positions of the terminal atoms in trigonal bipyramidal molecules are not symmetrically equivalent. This will be an important point in the next section.

Octahedral ($EG = 6$), Selenium Hexafluoride: The Lewis structure of selenium hexafluoride is as follows:

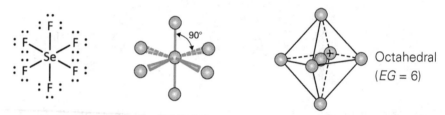

Octahedral ($EG = 6$)

Examination of the Lewis structure above reveals six bonds and no lone pairs on the central atom. Therefore we have six electron groups. Six valence electron groups distributed evenly about the selenium (central) atom results in a distribution of fluorine atoms such that they define the six vertices of an eight-sided octahedron, with bond angles of 90°. Therefore we say that the electronic and molecular geometry in this case are both **octahedral**.

Example Problem 8.10 – VSEPR

Determine the electronic and molecular geometry of SiH_4.	
Solution:	
We first must construct the correct Lewis structure of the compound in question as we have done previously in example problems 8.3 through 8.9.	H | H—Si—H | H
Because there are four bonds and no lone pairs, we conclude that the central atom must accommodate four electron groups.	
The electronic geometry which corresponds to four electron groups is tetrahedral. Therefore, the electronic geometry is tetrahedral.	4 Electron Groups; **$EG = 4$** Electronic Geometry = Tetrahedral
Because there are no lone pairs, the molecular geometry is the same as the electronic geometry. In other words, all of the electron groups in this case are bonding groups. As such, we expect the molecule to adopt a tetrahedral shape.	4 Electron Groups; $EG = 4$ **Electronic Geometry = Tetrahedral** No Lone Pairs ($EG = 4$): **Molecular Geometry = Tetrahedral** 109.5°

Example Problem 8.11 – VSEPR

Determine the electronic and molecular geometry of AsF_5.	
Solution:	
We first must construct the correct Lewis structure of the compound in question as we have done previously in example problems 8.3 through 8.10.	
Because there are five bonds and no lone pairs, we conclude that the central atom must accommodate five electron groups.	
The electronic geometry which corresponds to five electron groups is Trigonal Biyramidal. Therefore the electronic geometry is Trigonal Bipyramidal.	5 Electron Groups; **$EG = 5$** Electronic Geometry = Trigonal Bipyramidal
Because there are no lone pairs, the molecular geometry is the same as the electronic geometry. In other words, all of the electron groups are in this case are bonding groups. As such, we expect the molecule to adopt a trigonal bipyramidal shape.	5 Electron Groups; $EG = 5$ **Electronic Geometry = Trigonal Bipyramidal** No Lone Pairs ($EG = 5$): **Molecular Geometry = Trigonal Bipyramidal**

The Effect of Lone Pairs on Molecular Geometry

Now that we have explored the molecular and electronic geometries of molecules which have no lone pairs on the central atom, let's consider the effect of lone pairs. Since the presence of a lone pair of electrons on the central atom occupies a position that would otherwise contain a bonding pair, the molecular geometry will be different from the electronic geometry in these cases. In other words, lone pairs do not change the electronic geometry; only the molecular geometry is affected. However, as we will see, the molecular geometry is a derivative of the electronic geometry. Let's consider our previous example of SO_2.

Trigonal Bent – *A Derivative of the Trigonal Electronic Geometry* ($EG = 3$): If we account for the ability of sulfur to accommodate an expanded octet, the Lewis structure for SO_2 is as follows:

Formal Charges   Formal Charges   Formal Charges

Preferred

Here we find that there are two bonds and one lone pair on the central atom. Therefore, we have three electron groups, and, as such, we conclude the **electronic geometry** is *trigonal*. However, because there are only two terminal atoms, the **molecular geometry** is *not trigonal* but rather adopts a "bent" geometry as shown here.

The distribution of 3 electron groups around the central atom is always trigonal (electronic geometry). However, because the molecular geometry only refers to the relative arrangement of the atoms present in the molecule, it will now adopt a geometry referred to as **trigonal bent**.

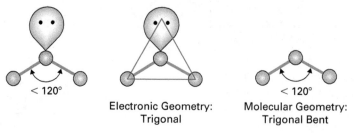

Electronic Geometry:
Trigonal

Molecular Geometry:
Trigonal Bent

Recall the **molecular geometry** *refers only to the arrangement of the terminal atoms relative to each other and the central atom and completely ignores lone pairs.* Additionally, because the three electron groups are not identical in nature, they do not exert an identical repulsive force on one another. As it turns out, *lone pairs occupy greater space on the central atom and exert a greater repulsive force on the neighboring electron pairs.* This has the effect of squeezing or reducing the bond angle. Therefore, the bond angle for SO_2 is < 120°, and its molecular geometry is referred to as **trigonal bent**. This term indicates that the observed "bent" geometry is a derivative of a trigonal electronic geometry, and the expected bond angle is therefore less than, but relatively close to, 120°.

Pyramidal and Tetrahedral Bent – *Derivatives of the Tetrahedral Electron Geometry (EG = 4):* Consider three examples, CH_4, NH_3, and H_2O. If we construct Lewis structures for each of these three molecules, we arrive at the following:

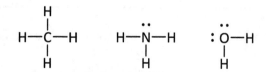

In the case of methane (CH_4) there are four electron groups (no lone pairs and four bonds), and therefore the electronic and molecular geometry are the same, *tetrahedral.* For ammonia (NH_3), we have four electron groups as well (three bonds and one lone pair). Therefore, ammonia has a tetrahedral electronic geometry. However, since there are only three terminal atoms, the molecular geometry adopts the shape of a triangular pyramid referred to as a **pyramidal** geometry (shown below). In the case of water, we again have four electron groups (two lone pairs and two bonds), and therefore the molecular geometry which results is referred to as **tetrahedral bent**.

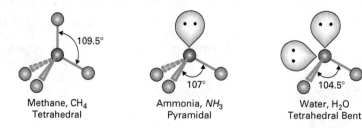

Methane, CH_4
Tetrahedral

Ammonia, NH_3
Pyramidal

Water, H_2O
Tetrahedral Bent

Once again, we see the effect of the lone pairs on the bond angles. The presence of one lone pair reduces the expected tetrahedral bond angle of 109.5° to 107° for ammonia and the presence of two lone pairs reduces it even further to 104.5° for water.

See-Saw, T-Shaped, and Linear – *Derivatives of the Trigonal Bipyramidal Electronic Geometry (EG = 5)*: If we apply the same logic to the trigonal bipyramidal geometry as was done for trigonal and tetrahedral, we can derive the three additional molecular geometries which result from the presence of one, two, and three lone pairs, respectively. However, because not all positions are symmetrically equivalent in the trigonal bipyramidal geometry, we cannot simply place the lone pairs at any of the five positions on the central atom. The lone pairs occupy greater space and exert a greater repulsive force than do bonding electron pairs, and therefore, they preferentially occupy the positions in the *equatorial*, trigonal plane rather than the two *axial* positions. This is because the equatorial positions afford more space and therefore minimal repulsion for the neighboring groups. For this reason, lone pairs never occupy the axial positions in a molecule with trigonal bipyramidal electronic geometry. Therefore, the molecular geometries which arise from the presence of lone pairs are generically depicted below.

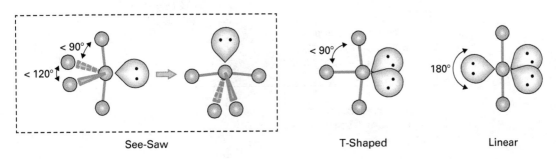

See-Saw   T-Shaped   Linear

We see from these three molecular geometries that the presence of one and two lone pairs reduces the bond angles from their characteristic values to < 120° and < 90° for the equatorial and axial terminal atoms, respectively. However, this is not the case for the linear geometry. Because the three lone pairs are evenly distributed over all three equatorial positions, the bond angle is the expected value of 180°.

Square Pyramidal and Square Planar – *Derivatives of the Octahedral Electronic Geometry (EG = 6)*: While there are theoretically four additional molecular geometries possible for the octahedral geometry, we will only encounter two of these, shown below:

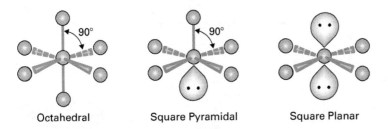

Octahedral   Square Pyramidal   Square Planar

Since the positions of the terminal atoms in a molecule with octahedral symmetry are indistinguishable, the placement of the first lone pair is arbitrary. This results in a **square pyramidal** molecular geometry (the terminal atoms occupy the positions of the vertices of an imaginary pyramid with a square-shaped base). Again, the lone pair causes a deviation from the characteristic bond angles to values < 90° for a square pyramidal molecule. However, the placement of the second lone pair is not arbitrary. Lone pairs will always naturally occupy positions directly opposite each other in order to realize minimal repulsion, resulting in a **square planar** molecular geometry. For this reason, each lone pair directly cancels the impact of the other on the bond angles. As such, square planar molecules exhibit the expected value of 90° for all of its bond angles.

Example Problem 8.12

What are the electronic and molecular geometries of the compound PCl_3.	
Solution:	
We first must construct the correct Lewis structure of the compound in question as we have done previously in example problems 8.3 through 8.11.	
Because there are three bonds and one lone pair, we conclude that the central atom must accommodate four electron groups.	
The electronic geometry which corresponds to four electron groups is Tetrahedral.	4 Electron Groups; **$EG = 4$** Electronic Geometry = Tetrahedral
Because there is one lone pair, the molecular geometry is a derivative of the electronic geometry. In other words, only three of the four electron groups are bonding groups. As such, we expect the molecule to adopt a Pyramidal shape. Additionally, the presence of the lone pair exerts greater repulsion on the bonding groups resulting in a bond angle less than the characteristic tetrahedral angle of 109.5°.	4 Electron Groups; $EG = 4$ **Electronic Geometry = Tetrahedral** 1 Lone Pair ($EG = 4$): **Molecular Geometry = Pyramidal**

Example Problem 8.13

What are the electronic and molecular geometries of the compound, XeF_4.	
Solution:	
We first must construct the correct Lewis structure of the compound in question as we have done previously in example problems 8.3 through 8.12.	
Because there are four bonds and two lone pairs, we conclude that the central atom must accommodate six electron groups.	
The electronic geometry which corresponds to six electron groups is octahedral.	6 Electron Groups; **EG = 6** Electronic Geometry = Octahedral
Because there are two lone pairs, the molecular geometry is a derivative of the electronic geometry. In other words, only four of the six electron groups are bonding groups. As such, we expect the molecule to adopt a square planar shape. Additionally, in an octahedral electronic geometry, two lone pairs adopt positions directly opposite each other (balancing their repulsive impact on the neighboring electron groups). As such, we expect characteristic bond angle of 90° in the square planar molecular geometry.	v6 Electron Groups; $EG = 6$ **Electronic Geometry = Octahedral** 2 Lone Pair ($EG = 6$): **Molecular Geometry = Square Planar**

Section 8.9 Bond and Molecular Polarity

Even as Lewis theory provides a simple, straightforward approach to predicting bonding structure in molecules, there are some things that the theory does not handle very well. For instance, we know from our discussion of electronegativities that bonding electron pairs are not evenly shared between all pairs of bonding atoms. Nevertheless, Lewis theory treats all bonding electron pairs as though they are evenly distributed across a covalent bond. In other words, Lewis theory seems to make the assumption that all covalent bonds are "perfectly" covalent. Just as in the case of resonance, in this instance we will have to compensate for the limitations of the theory. Let's consider an example, *HF*. The Lewis dot structure is as follows:

The bonding electron pair between these two atoms, according to the Lewis depiction, seems equally shared. There is nothing to indicate otherwise. However, we know from experimental observation that *HF* molecules, when an external electric field is applied, will orient themselves according to positive and negative poles as shown here.

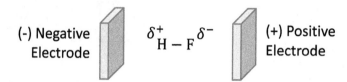

Such alignment informs us that there must be a positive charge (however slight) on the hydrogen side of the bond and negative charge on the fluorine side. We indicate this with a δ^+ or δ^- (δ is the Greek letter delta), each indicating a partial positive or negative charge. This does NOT mean that we have an ionic bond but rather that the bonding electrons are not evenly distributed over the bonding pair of atoms. As such, a "partial" charge imbalance or separation is set up. Separation of electric charge over a given distance is called an **electric dipole**. Covalent bonds which exhibit a measurable electric dipole (due to uneven sharing of bonding electron pairs) are referred as **polar covalent bonds**. When the sharing of electrons in a covalent bond is equal or close to equal, such that no appreciable electric dipole is observed, these bonds are referred to as **nonpolar covalent bonds**. We quantify the polarity of a bond by its *dipole moment*. The **dipole moment** (μ) is defined as the product of the distance (r) over which two opposite charges of equal magnitude are separated and the magnitude of those charges (q):

$$\mu = q \cdot r$$

It will not be necessary at this point to calculate the dipole moment of a bond. Rather, we will utilize this concept in a more qualitative manner for the time being. With this in mind, there are two notations which are commonly used to indicate a polar bond in a molecule. The first is with the use of the "delta" notation (shown below). The second is with a vector notation as follows:

$$\overset{\delta^+}{H} - \overset{\delta^-}{F} \qquad \text{or} \qquad \overset{+\!\longrightarrow}{H - F}$$

The positive sign on the end of the arrow indicates the positive "pole" is located on the hydrogen atom, and the arrow points always toward the negative end of the bond.

Because it would seem that any combination of two dissimilar atoms should realize an unequal sharing of bonding electrons, we need a method for determining the nature of a covalent bond. For this we return to the Pauling Scale of Electronegativities (see Figure 8.2). Recall that we learned in a previous section that **electronegativity** refers to the relative attraction that a bonded atom has for shared, "bonding" electrons. As such, the difference in electronegativity (ΔEN) between two covalently bonded atoms determines the relative degree of charge separation that can be expected. In other words, atoms with large differences in electronegativity (when engaged in a covalent bond) will result in a larger dipole moment than atoms with little to no difference in electronegativity. Generally, we can label bonds as *covalent*, *polar covalent*, and *ionic* according to the following ranges in ΔEN:

Covalent- $0 \leq \Delta EN \leq 0.4$
Polar Covalent- $0.4 < \Delta EN < 2.0$
Ionic- $2.0 \leq \Delta EN$

Let's apply this to our example of *HF*. If we examine Figure 8.2, we see that the electronegativities for *H* and *F* are:

$$EN_H = 2.1$$

$$EN_F = 4.0$$

Therefore the difference in electronegativities is:

$$\Delta EN = EN_F - EN_H = 4.0 - 2.1 = 1.9$$

Because 0.4 < (ΔEN = 1.9) < 2.0, we would conclude that the *H–F* bond in this molecule is a polar covalent bond. Further, because fluorine is the more electronegative atom, we also conclude that the negative pole will be located at the fluorine end of the bond. It is in this way we can determine relative polarity between various bonds. The following example problems provide some additional practice at establishing relative bond polarities.

Example Problem 8.14

Determine whether each of the following bonds are covalent, polar covalent, or ionic.
$H-C \qquad N-C \qquad O-C \qquad F-C$

Solution:

In order to determine bond polarity, we must look to the electronegativities given in Figure 8.2. In the case of the carbon – hydrogen bond, we calculate a difference in electronegativities between hydrogen and carbon. Carbon has an electronegativity of 2.5 and hydrogen 2.1. The difference ΔEN is 0.4.	$\Delta EN = EN_C - EN_H = 2.5 - 2.1 = 0.4$ $0.0 < (\Delta EN = 0.4) \leq 0.4$ Therefore, the bond is **covalent**.
In the case of the nitrogen – carbon bond, ΔEN = 0.5 and therefore we would consider the bond to be polar covalent.	$\Delta EN = EN_N - EN_C = 3.0 - 2.5 = 0.5$ $0.4 < (\Delta EN = 0.5) \leq 1.9$ Therefore, the bond is **polar covalent**.
For the carbon – oxygen bond, ΔEN = 1.0 and we therefore know that the bond is polar covalent.	$\Delta EN = EN_O - EN_C = 3.5 - 2.5 = 1.0$ $0.4 < (\Delta EN = 1.0) \leq 1.9$ Therefore, the bond is **polar covalent**.

For the carbon − fluorine bond, $\Delta EN = 1.5$ and we therefore know that the bond is polar covalent.	$\Delta EN = EN_F - EN_C = 4.0 - 2.5 = 1.5$ $0.4 < (\Delta EN = 1.5) \leq 1.9$ Therefore, the bond is **polar covalent**.

Notice that the difference in ΔEN in this series of bonds tracks with increasing electronegativity of the other atoms. We expect that the dipole moment of each bond will increase as ΔEN increases. As such, it is fair to conclude that the $C-F$ bond is much more polar than the $C-N$ or $C-O$ bonds.

Molecular Polarity

With what we have just learned regarding bond polarity, let's apply this concept to an entire molecule. To do this, let's begin with a common example, CO_2. If we begin with the Lewis structure, we have:

$$: O\!\!=\!\!C\!\!=\!\!O :$$

We see immediately from the structure that there is only one type of bond in this molecule, $C=O$. If we look to the electronegativity difference for C and O, we find:

$$EN_c = 2.5$$

$$EN_o = 3.5$$

$$\Delta EN = 3.5 - 2.5 = 1.0$$

Because $0.4 < (\Delta EN = 1.0) < 2.0$, we can say that both carbon-oxygen double bonds in CO_2 are polar covalent bonds. Further, we know that in each case, the negative pole is centered on the more electronegative atoms as follows:

$$\overset{\delta^-}{:}\overset{\delta^+}{O}\!\!=\!\!\overset{\delta^-}{C}\!\!=\!\!O :$$

However, if we are to answer the question as to whether there is a molecular dipole, we need to consider the molecular geometry of CO_2. Since there are two electron groups on the central atom in the Lewis structure, we know the molecular geometry is linear. Further, it is helpful when considering the molecular polarity to use the vector notation as follows:

$$\overset{\delta^-}{:}\overset{\delta^+}{O}\!\!=\!\!\overset{\delta^-}{C}\!\!=\!\!O :$$

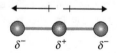

Here we see that each electric dipole is canceling the other. Think of each dipole as a vector quantity with a magnitude (defined by ΔEN) and a direction (defined by the relative position of positive and negative charges). In this case of CO_2, we have two vector quantities of equal magnitude with precisely opposing directions. As such, the net sum of these two vectors is zero, and therefore, we expect CO_2 to behave as a nonpolar molecule, which it does.

Let's contrast this with another common example, water. If we construct a Lewis structure, and determine the polarity of all the bonds as well as the molecular geometry of H_2O, we get the following:

  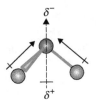

In this case, the two dipoles are not oriented in completely opposing directions. As such, they sum to a "net" molecular dipole that bisects the $H-O-H$ bond angle, placing the negative pole on the oxygen atom while the positive pole resides at the hydrogen end of the molecule. It is for this reason that water is said to be, and indeed is, a polar molecule. Additionally, the charge separation that is inherent in polar molecules sets up electrostatic attractive forces between the oppositely charged poles of neighboring molecules. This will be discussed further in Chapter 9 regarding intermolecular forces.

Example Problem 8.15

Determine whether PF_3 is polar or nonpolar.

Solution:	
Draw the Lewis structure of the molecule and determine its geometry. In this case we see that there are four electron groups (including one lone pair) around the central phosphorus atom.	(Lewis structure of PF_3 with central P, lone pair, and three F atoms)
Since we know that $EG = 4$ and there is one lone pair, the molecular geometry is pyramidal.	(Ball-and-stick pyramidal geometry model with lone pair)
Determine if the molecule contains polar bonds. In this case there are three $P-F$ bonds for which we find $\Delta E = 1.9$.	$\Delta EN = EN_F - EN_P = 4.0 - 2.1 = 1.9$ $0.4 < (\Delta EN = 1.9) \leq 1.9$ Polar covalent bond

Determine whether the dipole moments of the polar bonds cancel each other or sum together for a resulting molecular dipole moment. In this case they sum together for a net molecular dipole moment for which the negative pole resides between the fluorine atoms and the positive pole at the phosphorus atom.	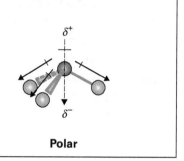 **Polar**

Example Problem 8.16

Determine whether CCl_4 is polar or nonpolar.	
Solution:	
Draw the Lewis structure of the molecule and determine its geometry. In this case, we see that there are four electron groups (no lone pairs) around the central carbon atom.	$$\ddot{\underset{\cdot\cdot}{Cl}}-\underset{\underset{\ddot{\underset{\cdot\cdot}{Cl}}}{\overset{\cdot\cdot}{\overset{\ddot{Cl}}{\vert}}}}{\overset{\overset{\cdot\cdot}{\ddot{Cl}}}{\vert}}{C}-\ddot{\underset{\cdot\cdot}{Cl}}$$
Since we know that $EG = 4$ and there are no lone pairs, the molecular geometry is tetrahedral.	109.5°
Determine if the molecule contains polar bonds. In this case, there are four $C-Cl$ bonds for which we find $\Delta E = 0.5$.	$\Delta EN = EN_{Cl} - EN_C = 3.0 - 2.5 = 0.5$ $0.4 < (\Delta EN = 0.5) \le 1.9$ Polar Covalent bond
Determine whether the dipole moments of the polar bonds cancel each other or sum together for a resulting molecular dipole moment. In this case, the four dipole moments cancel each other. As such, the molecule is nonpolar.	**Nonpolar**

Section 8.10 Valence Bond Theory

As bond theories go, it should be fairly obvious that Lewis theory is somewhat simple in its treatment of the electronic structure of atoms and the chemical bonding which arises from it. In fact, despite its utility, Lewis theory fails to adequately describe many observed properties of even the simplest of elements and compounds. For example, because Lewis theory pairs all electrons, it is largely incapable of predicting magnetic properties, paramagnetism, and diamagnetism, in many cases. For this and other reasons, more complex theories have been developed which are based on the quantum mechanical model of the atom. One of these is called **valence bond (VB) theory**. The basic idea in valence bond theory is that electrons reside in quantum mechanical orbitals localized on individual atoms. These are the standard *s*, *p*, *d*, and *f* orbitals we learned in Chapter 7 and their

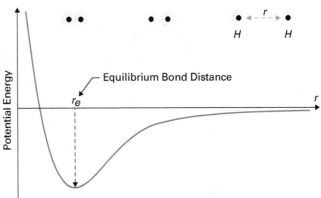

Figure 8.5 The potential energy curve for the formation of a *H*—*H* bond. At large separations (large *r*) the potential energy of interaction is zero. As the atoms approach, the electrostatic attraction between electrons and the two nuclei results in a reduction of potential energy until a minimum is reached. This is the lowest energy, most stable distance between the atoms and, as such, this defines the bond distance for the *H*—*H* bond.

derivatives (hybrid orbitals) which we will discuss in more detail shortly. When two atoms approach each other, the electrons and nucleus from each atom interact with the electrons and nucleus of the other. The effect of such interactions on the energies of the electrons in the atoms can be calculated (such calculations are too complex and beyond the scope of this text). If the energy of the system is lowered by these interactions, a bond forms, and if the energy is raised, no bond forms. Essentially, bonds stabilize chemical systems and will form spontaneously for this reason whenever possible. Figure 8.5 depicts the calculated potential energy of two hydrogen atoms as function of the distance between their nuclei.

To put this in somewhat simpler terms, when two atoms approach, their valence atomic orbitals will overlap, and this can be a stabilizing or a destabilizing interaction. Generally, if two orbitals on neighboring atoms are of appropriate symmetry such that they can overlap, and they collectively contain two electrons that can **spin-pair,** a bond will form. In other words, two atomic orbitals on neighboring atoms can overlap and form a new bonding or molecular orbital which is occupied by a pair of electrons with opposite spin states (Pauli exclusion still applies in VB theory). With this in mind, the following points summarize VB theory:

1. Valence electrons of atoms reside in atomic orbitals (such as those we learned about in Chapter 7).

2. A chemical bond forms from overlap of two half-filled atomic orbitals, allowing these two electrons to spin-pair (localized on two neighboring or bonding atoms).

3. Molecular geometry is determined by the orientation and geometry of the overlapping orbitals.

Let's consider H_2 as an example. If we imagine two free hydrogen atoms approaching each other, the question is will they form a bond. Lewis theory said yes because they had unpaired electrons and, further, required an additional electron each to realize a duet. In VB theory, we will say yes if the valence orbitals occupied by the single electron on each atom can overlap and the electrons can spin-pair.

Figure 8.6 The hydrogen atom has an electron configuration which contains a half-filled 1*s* orbital capable of overlap with another half-filled orbital located on a neighboring hydrogen atom. This produces a single σ-bond with a spin-paired set of electrons occupying it.

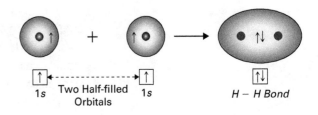

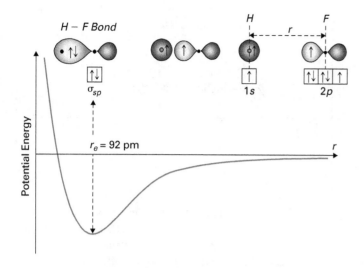

Figure 8.7 In the case of the formation of an *HF* molecule, the fluorine has an electron configuration which contains a half-filled 2*p* orbital. It is this 2*p* orbital, therefore, which is available for overlap with the 1*s* on the hydrogen atom.

To illustrate this, let's consider the orbital diagram of each of the hydrogen atoms as shown in Figure 8.6.

Here we see that because there are two half-filled valence orbitals capable of overlap and formation of new bonding orbital with spin-paired electrons, then a new molecular orbital is formed. Further, this orbital addition results in the bulk of the bonding electron density residing in the inter-nuclear region, where electrons can interact with both nuclei. This type of direct orbital overlap along the bond axis is referred to as a **sigma bond (σ-bond)**.

Let's consider another example, *HF*. Here the hydrogen will again use its 1*s* electron in bond formation; however, in the fluorine atom, it is one of the valence 2*p* orbitals which is half-filled and available for bonding. The hydrogen 1*s* orbital approaches and then overlaps with the 2*p* of fluorine, and the two electrons spin-pair, forming a σ-bond (direct head-to-head overlap). The optimum distance of interaction is where the energy of the system is lowest. This defines the bond length (92 *pm* in the case of *HF*).

Orbital Hybridization

What happens when dealing with molecules with symmetries other than that of linear diatomic molecules? How does VB theory predict the molecular geometries we have been discussing? These are good questions and can be addressed again, with an example, CH_4. If we examine the valence orbital diagram of hydrogen and carbon, we find the following:

H: $1s^1$

$$\boxed{\uparrow}$$
$$1s$$

C: $1s^2 2s^2 2p^2$

$$\boxed{\uparrow\downarrow} \quad \boxed{\uparrow}\ \boxed{\uparrow}\ \boxed{\ }$$
$$2s \qquad\quad 2p$$

Therefore, we would conclude that carbon can make two bonds with two hydrogen atoms. This is because we see it has two half-filled valence orbitals in the 2*p* subshell. This suggests that the compound that would naturally form between carbon and hydrogen would be CH_2. Further, we know that the *p* orbitals are oriented 90° from each other (recall from Chapter 7), and therefore, this model would predict a bond angle of 90°. Nevertheless, we know from our previous work (Lewis theory) that carbon and hydrogen form methane, CH_4, with bond angles of 109.5°. We have apparently reached an impasse — until we consider another idea. In VB theory, orbitals from the same atom can mix to form new orbitals from one another. This is a phenomenon called *orbital hybridization*. **Orbital hybridization** is the mixing of *s*, *p*, and *d* orbitals on a particular atom to form a new set of atomic orbitals called **hybrid orbitals**. The idea is that since bonding interactions are stabilizing, the atomic orbitals will spontaneously hybridize in order to maximize bonding. In the case of carbon, there are four valence electrons.

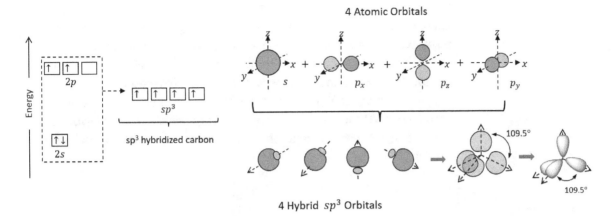

4 Atomic Orbitals

4 Hybrid sp^3 Orbitals

If, through hybridization, the carbon atom can realize four bonds from these four electrons (rather than two), that is energetically favored, and the atomic orbitals will hybridize to accomplish this. To understand this, let's examine an orbital energy diagram (see Figure 8.8).

As shown here, if the 2s orbital and the three 2p orbitals can mix to form four **degenerate** hybrids, each composed of 25% s-character and 75% p-character, we have four half-filled hybrid orbitals available for bonding with four hydrogen 1s electrons. These hybrids are referred to as **sp^3 orbitals** because they are composed of one "s" and three "p" orbitals. Additionally, if we calculate four such hybrids, we find that the major lobe of each orbital is oriented toward the vertices of a four-sided tetrahedron. *As such, we associate the sp^3 hybrid orbitals with the **tetrahedral electronic geometry*** from VSEPR theory. Further, since all of the molecular geometries we have encountered are derivatives of the five basic electronic geometries of linear, trigonal, tetrahedral, trigonal bipyramidal, and octahedral, we should expect five hybridization schemes that account for these electronic geometries in VB theory as well.

Figure 8.8 Hybridization of the 2s with the three 2p orbitals of carbon results in four degenerate hybrid sp^3 orbitals. These hybrid orbitals are oriented such that their major lobes are directed along axes at angles of 109.5° from one another.

Orbital Hybridization and Double Bonds

sp^2-Hybrid Orbitals – While methane is an example of the hybridization of one s-orbital and three p-orbitals, we can also consider other combinations. For example, hybridization of an s-orbital with two p-orbitals (three atomic orbitals) produces three sp^2 hybrid orbitals and one remaining unhybridized p-orbital (as shown in Figure 8.9).

Figure 8.9 Hybridization of the 2s with two of the three 2p orbitals of carbon results in three degenerate hybrid sp^2 orbitals. These hybrid orbitals are oriented such that their major lobes are directed along axes at angles of 120° from one another.

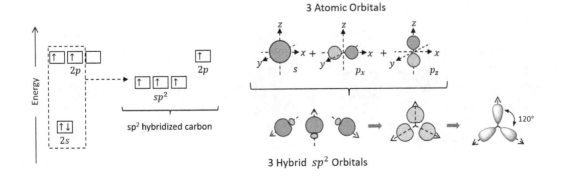

3 Atomic Orbitals

3 Hybrid sp^2 Orbitals

Notice the orientation of the three hybrids relative to each other. They are arranged in a trigonal geometry with 120° angles between them. At this point, we may ask, "Why should an atom hybridize in an sp^2 configuration rather than an sp^3 or any other combination?" The answer again is simply to achieve the lowest energy state, which is accomplished through maximum bonding. If an sp^2 configuration best achieves this, then it is the natural result according to VB theory. To illustrate this, let's consider formaldehyde, CH_2O. Recall that we have already predicted the Lewis structure in a previous section:

Here we see that the central atom, carbon, has three electron groups according to VSEPR theory, which means, in terms of VB theory, we will need to produce three hybrid orbitals. If we wish to make three hybrid orbitals, we must mix three (valence) atomic orbitals (the $2s$ and two $2p$ orbitals). Therefore, we leave one of the three $2p$ orbitals un-hybridized. Additionally, sp^2 hybridization allows carbon to form four bonds in this case: a single σ-bond with each of the two H atoms and a double bond with the O atom, as shown in Figure 8.10.

Notice that in VB theory a double bond consists of a σ-bond through direct head-to-head overlap of an sp^2 hybrid orbital on carbon and another sp^2 hybrid orbital on the oxygen atom and a π-bond between the unhybridized p-orbitals on the carbon and the oxygen atoms. A **pi-bond (π-bond)** is one in which two p-orbitals overlap in a side-to-side fashion. The combination of a σ- and π-bond is how VB theory accounts for double bonds. Nevertheless, we can clearly see that with three σ-bonds (three electron groups in VSEPR), we establish a trigonal geometry regarding electron distribution around the central atom. In this way we see that the VB model of formaldehyde corresponds to the Lewis model in that we have a trigonal electronic geometry and molecular geometry, and we have two single bonds and one double bond, just as is predicted by Lewis and VSEPR theories.

***sp* – Hybrid Orbitals: Triple Bonds** – Mixing of one *s*- and one *p*-orbital results in the formation of two hybrid *sp* orbitals (leaving two *p*-orbitals

Figure 8.10 In describing the bonding pattern in formaldehyde, the hybridization of the $2s$ with two of the three $2p$ orbitals of carbon and oxygen atoms results in three degenerate hybrid sp^2 orbitals on each atom, leaving one un-hybridized $2p$ orbital available for π-bond formation. In valence bond theory a double bond consists of a single σ-bond and a single π-bond.

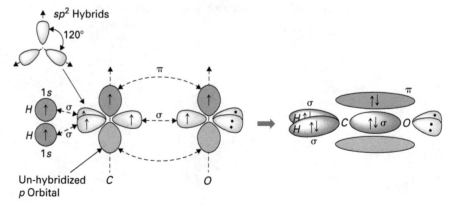

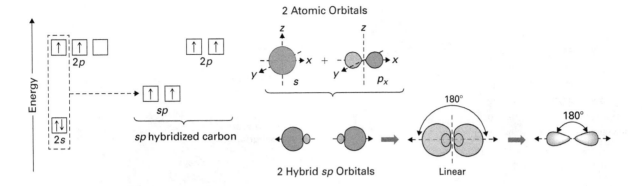

2 Atomic Orbitals

sp hybridized carbon

2 Hybrid *sp* Orbitals

Linear

unhybridized). The relative orientation of these orbitals is depicted in Figure 8.11.

A simple and common example of *sp* hybridization is the linear molecule acetylene, C_2H_2:

$$H—C≡C—H$$

Again, two electron groups (according to VSEPR) indicate the need for two hybrid orbitals (VB theory). As such, we invoke *sp* hybridization as follows:

In this case we see that carbon is able to form a maximum of four bonds, a single σ-bond with a hydrogen atom and a triple bond with the other carbon atom. Additionally, just as a double bond consists of a σ- and a π-bond, a triple bond consists of a σ- and two π-bonds.

***sp³d* and *sp³d²* Hybrid Orbitals: Expanded Octets** – Recall that we learned that elements in the third row or higher on the periodic table could engage an expanded octet if necessary. This was explained on the basis that these elements had empty *d* orbitals in their valence shells that could be involved in bonding, thus expanding the number of electrons they could accommodate. VB theory explicitly does this when dealing with such elements. For example recall PCl_5 and SeF_6:

Figure 8.11 Hybridization of the 2*s* with one of the three 2*p* orbitals results in two degenerate hybrid *sp* orbitals. These hybrid orbitals are oriented such that their major lobes are directed along axes at angles of 180° from one another.

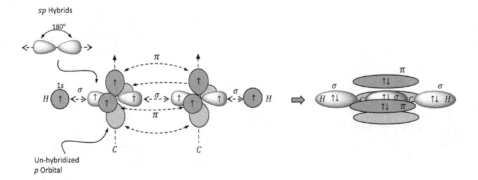

sp Hybrids

180°

1*s*

σ

π

σ

π

H

H

σ

σ

π

π

σ

H

H

Un-hybridized
p Orbital

C

C

Figure 8.12 In describing the bonding pattern in acetylene, the hybridization of the 2*s* with one of the three 2*p* orbitals of both carbon atoms results in two degenerate hybrid *sp* orbitals on each atom, leaving two un-hybridized 2*p* orbitals available for π-bond formation. In valence bond theory a triple bond consists of a single σ-bond and two π-bonds.

Figure 8.13 Hybridization of the 3*s* with three 3*p* orbitals and one 3*d* orbital on Phosphorus results in five degenerate hybrid *sp³d* orbitals. These hybrid orbitals are oriented such that their major lobes are directed along axes at angles of 120° from one another in a trigonal equatorial plane which are at an angle of 90° from two "axial" lobes (Trigonal Bipyramidal). Likewise, hybridization of an *s*, three *p*, and two *d* orbitals results in six degenerate *sp³d²* hybrids (angles = 90°; Octahedral).

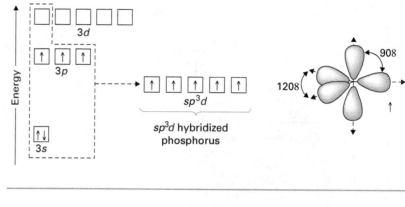

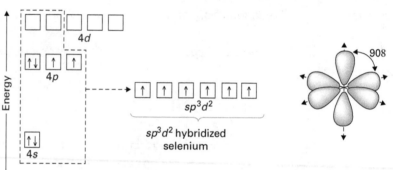

In the case of PCl_5 we see there are five electron groups around phosphorus and therefore, we require five hybrid orbitals which must be derived from five atomic orbitals. These are the 3*s*, the three 3*p*, and one of the five 3*d* orbitals. The resulting hybrid orbitals are referred to as **sp³d hybrid orbitals**. Likewise, SeF_6 requires six hybrids derived from six atomic orbitals; one 4*s*, three 4*p*, and two 4*d* orbitals. These are referred to as **sp³d² hybrid orbitals**. Figure 8.13 depicts the orientation of these hybrids relative to each other. Figure 8.14 summarizes everything we have learned regarding molecular structure and bonding patterns from VSEPR and VB theories.

Example Problem 8.17

Determine the electronic and molecular geometries as well as the hybridization on the central atom of SO_3^{2-}.	
Solution:	
First, we determine the Lewis structure of the sulfite ion.	$$\begin{bmatrix} :\overset{..}{O}: \\ \vert \\ :\overset{..}{O}=S-\overset{..}{O}: \\ ^{..} \quad ^{..} \end{bmatrix}^{2-}$$
We see from the Lewis structure that the central atom has four electron groups, three bonds, and one lone pair. We can clearly see from Figure 8.14 that four electron groups give an electronic geometry of tetrahedral.	*EG* = 4 **Electronic Geometry = Tetrahedral**

We also see from Figure 8.14 that a tetrahedral electronic geometry corresponds to a hybridization in VB theory of sp^3.	**Hybridization = SP^3**
With a **tetrahedral electronic geometry** containing one lone pair, we will therefore have a **pyramidal molecular geometry**.	

Figure 8.14 Summary of hybridization, and electronic and molecular geometries.

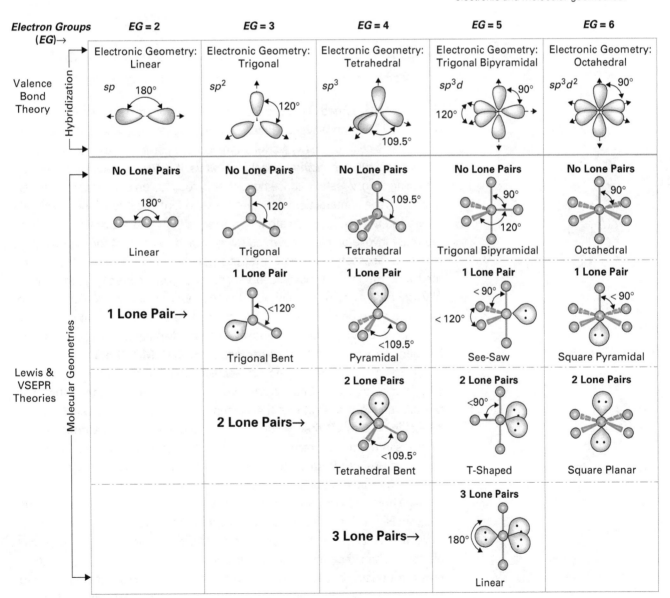

Example Problem 8.18

Given the Lewis structure of sulfur tetrafluoride shown below, determine hybridization of the central sulfur atom.

Solution:

We see immediately upon inspection of the Lewis structure that the central sulfur atom has five electron groups. This means that S has an expanded octet with ten valence electrons. We will need five hybrid orbitals to accommodate five σ-bonding pairs. This requires that we include one d orbital in our hybridization. As such, sulfur must adopt an sp^3d hybridization scheme.

Sulfur = sp^3d

Section 8.11 Molecular Orbital Theory

Recall that we learned in the previous chapter that orbitals are regions of space defined by electron wave-functions. Further, we learned in the previous sections of this chapter that wave-functions can be combined to produce hybrid orbitals as well as *bonding molecular orbitals*. It is this last point that another prevailing theory rests. Valence bond theory focuses on purely atomic orbitals and the overlap (interaction) between these to form localized bonding orbitals between the two individual atoms involved in the bond. However, even here we must invoke an idea known as hybridization to account for the observed molecular geometries. A more sophisticated theory should alleviate the need for hybridization to explain observations and, also, correctly predict many physical properties of compounds that VB theory still misses. For example, O_2 is known to be paramagnetic due to its observed attraction to a magnetic field; however, VB theory still predicts it to be diamagnetic. To address such deficiencies, we now introduce **molecular orbital (MO) theory**.

In molecular orbital theory, molecular orbitals are created from combinations of atomic orbitals from two or more different atoms such that the orbital and the electrons that occupy it are delocalized over the entire molecule. Where VB theory combines wave-functions from atomic orbitals on the same atom to form hybrid orbitals, MO theory combines orbitals in the same way but from all of the atoms within a molecule. Let's consider a simple diatomic example, H_2 (Figure 8.15).

Again, when waves interact, they can do so constructively or destructively. In Figure 8.15 we see the combination of two $1s$ orbitals in a hydrogen molecule. Notice that there are two possible combinations of these two orbitals. When they are in phase, they interact constructively, building up electron density in the region between the two atomic nuclei. This is referred to as a **bonding molecular orbital** or simply a **bonding orbital**, in

MO theory. Likewise, when the wave functions are out of phase they interact destructively, reducing the probability of finding an electron in the region between the nuclei. This is referred to as an **antibonding orbital** and is characterized by a nodal plane perpendicular to the inter-nuclear axis. Note: the number of orbitals is always conserved. Interaction of two atomic orbitals produces two molecular orbitals, one bonding and one antibonding. Additionally, antibonding orbitals are always destabilizing (higher in energy) and bonding orbitals are always stabilizing (lower in energy) relative to the original atomic orbitals. This is depicted in the molecular orbital energy diagram (simply referred to as the **MO diagram**) of the H_2 molecule in Figure 8.15. Also note that the MO diagram labels each of the molecular orbitals as σ and σ*(sigma and sigma-star). The sigma designation in MO theory indicates the orbital is cylindrically symmetric relative to the inter-nuclear axis, while the "star" superscript is reserved for antibonding orbitals.

Since we have covered the combination of s-orbitals in the formation of an MO diagram, let's turn our attention to p-orbital overlap in MO theory. If we assume another diatomic example such as O_2 we can visualize this scenario quite readily. In Figure 8.16, we see the MO diagram of the O_2 molecule. The two 2s orbitals combine just as the 1s orbitals described previously; however, the 2p orbitals will be a bit more complex. If we imagine our coordinate system such that the x-coordinate is collinear with the inter-nuclear axis, we can imagine the $2p_x$ orbitals from the two oxygen atoms overlapping in a "head-on" fashion. This results in the σ_{2p} and the σ_{2p}^* orbitals depicted in Figure 8.16. However, the $2p_y$ and the $2p_z$ orbitals from each atom must overlap in a "side-on" fashion, and, as such, these interactions result in two sets of π-orbitals, two π_{2p} orbitals, and two π_{2p}^* orbitals. In MO theory, orbitals which are not cylindrically symmetric relative to the inter-nuclear axis are referred to as π orbitals. Therefore, Figure 8.16 depicts all possible MOs resulting from the combination of the 2p orbitals in the O_2 molecule.

In an MO diagram, once we have identified the possible MOs and their relative energies, we then sequentially occupy these orbitals according to Pauli, Hund, and Aufbau, just as we would for atomic orbitals. For O_2 there are a total of 16 electrons, eight for each oxygen atom. Also, note that in the MO diagram of O_2, the highest energy orbitals occupied by electrons are the π_{2p}^* orbitals (one electron each according to Hund's rule). This accurately accounts for oxygen's observed paramagnetism (a failing of both Lewis and VB theories). Additionally, the π_{2p}^* orbitals are referred to in this case as the **highest occupied molecular orbital(s)** or **HOMO** for short. While the σ_{2p}^* orbital is the **lowest unoccupied molecular orbital** or **LUMO**.

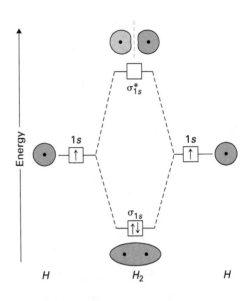

Figure 8.15 The MO energy diagram for the H_2 molecule.

SUMMARY:

1. Orbitals are conserved – the number of atomic orbitals combined equals the number of MOs formed.

2. When two atomic orbitals combine, the result is one molecular orbital which is lower in energy, a **bonding orbital**, and another molecular orbital which is higher in energy, an **anti-bonding orbital**.

Figure 8.16 The MO energy diagram for the O_2 molecule.

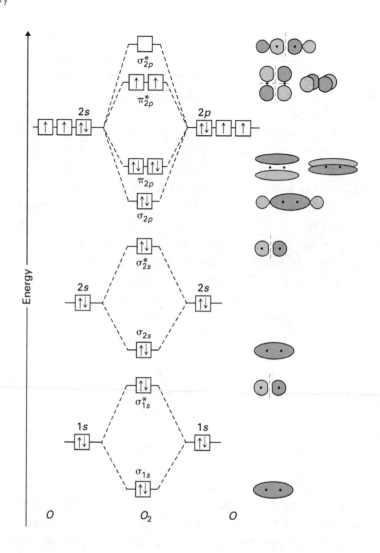

Homonuclear Diatomic Molecules

So far, our examples have been simple homonuclear diatomic molecules. As such, you could imagine that the MO diagram would be essentially the same for all such molecular elements of the second row of the periodic table, and you would be right. However, calculations have shown that the π_{2p} bonding orbitals are actually higher in energy than the σ_{2p} only for the elements O_2, F_2, and Ne_2. All other second-row, homo-nuclear, diatomic elements realize a lower energy for the π_{2p} orbitals than for the σ_{2p}. This last point also raises a strange question. Does MO theory predict there should be a bond between two Ne atoms? The truth is we could construct an MO diagram which describes just that. However, we know that no such molecular form of Ne exists. As such, we need a method to determine the stability of a molecule which is described by a given MO diagram. Once we have filled the energy-level diagram with the correct number of electrons, we can calculate a *bond order* for the molecule. The **bond order (BO)** is a number which describes whether a given set of occupied MOs is collectively lower in energy (stabilized) relative to the free (unbonded) atoms. It usually corresponds to the number (or multiplicity) of bonds between atoms (one for a single bond, two for a double bond, and three for a triple bond). However, fractional bond orders are possible. Nevertheless, the greater the bond order, the shorter the bond length and the stronger the bond. Essentially, the greater the bond order, the more stable the molecule. The bond order of a molecule is calculated as follows:

$$BO = \frac{(no.\ of\ bonding\ electrons) - (no.\ of\ antibonding\ electrons)}{2}$$

A bond order of zero predicts just as many electrons in bonding orbitals as are in anti-bonding orbitals; therefore, no net stabilization is realized from the formation of a molecule. In such a case we would predict that the particular molecule does not exist. Figure 8.17 summarizes the electron distributions in molecular orbitals for the second-row elements. *Note that a bond order of zero is predicted for the Ne_2 molecule.* Also, we see that the electrons occupy the molecular orbitals in the same fashion they would atomic orbitals, according to the Aufbau principle, the Pauli exclusion principle, and Hund's rule. As such, we can write electron configurations using molecular orbitals just as we have learned previously. Example problem 8.19 provides some practice regarding this.

Example Problem 8.19

Determine the electron configurations and bond orders and predict whether the O_2^+ or O_2^- ions exist or not. Which is most stable?	
Solution:	
	O_2 $(\sigma_{2s})^2 (\sigma_{2s}^*)^2 (\sigma_{2p})^2 (\pi_{2p})^4 (\pi_{2p}^*)^2$
Let's focus first on O_2^+. We can use the MO diagrams in Figure 8.17 to help us. We see that the configuration of O_2 is: If we remove an electron from this configuration to form the O_2^+ ion, we see that there are now fewer electrons in antibonding orbitals; therefore, the bond order increases from 2 to 2.5	O_2^+ $(\sigma_{2s})^2 (\sigma_{2s}^*)^2 (\sigma_{2p})^2 (\pi_{2p})^4 (\pi_{2p}^*)^1$ $BO = \frac{(8-3)}{2} = 2.5$
If we perform the same analysis with O_2^-, we find the bond order decreases because the additional electron is added to an antibonding orbital, π_{2p}^*. In this case the bond order is 1.5	O_2^- $(\sigma_{2s})^2 (\sigma_{2s}^*)^2 (\sigma_{2p})^2 (\pi_{2p})^4 (\pi_{2p}^*)^3$ $BO = \frac{(8-5)}{2} = 1.5$
We, therefore, predict that each ion will exist, as each has a nonzero bond order. However, O_2^+ would be most stable, given its higher bond order.	

Heteronuclear Diatomic Molecules

When two atoms of the same element form a diatomic molecule, the corresponding atomic orbitals are of precisely the same energy. However, this is not the case when two different elements interact. For example, in the *HF*

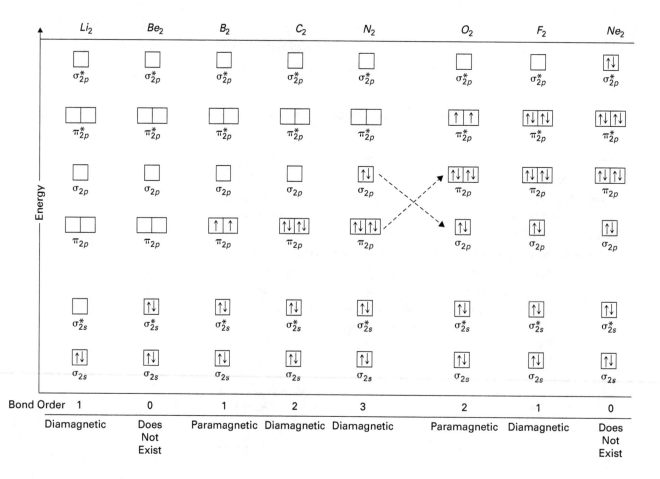

Figure 8.17 Molecular Orbital Diagrams for the second row diatomic elements along with bond orders and magnetic properties.

molecule, the 1s orbital of the hydrogen atom is similar in energy, not to the 1s or even the 2s orbital on the fluorine atom, but rather it is closest to the energy of the fluorine 2p orbital. In fact, atomic orbitals of the more electronegative elements are lower in energy than the corresponding orbitals of less electronegative elements. Further, orbitals that are closest in energy are those which are most likely to have the strongest interaction in MO theory. As such, we expect the 1s of hydrogen and one of the 2p orbitals of fluorine to combine and form molecular orbitals in the HF molecule as depicted in the MO diagram in Figure 8.18.

Here we see how the ten electrons (1 from H and 9 from F) are distributed in the HF molecule according to MO theory. Notice how there are three "non-bonding" orbitals in the valence shell of fluorine, occupied by six electrons. These correspond to the three lone pairs of electrons predicted by Lewis theory. However, unlike Lewis theory, MO theory handles polar covalent bonding quite well. For example, in the MO diagram of HF we see that the bonding σ_{sp} molecular orbital is much closer in energy to the 2p orbital of fluorine than it is to the 1s of hydrogen. As such, we would expect this bonding orbital to have much more 2p (fluorine) "character." In other words, the closer in energy a molecular orbital is to one of the atomic orbitals which constitute it, the more of that atomic orbital's character is prevalent in the resulting MO. As such, the σ_{sp} in the case of HF would be centered more toward the fluorine atom than the hydrogen. The opposite is true for the σ_{sp}^*, which is closer in energy to the hydrogen 1s. As such, MO theory correctly predicts the bonding electrons will be located closer to fluorine than to hydrogen, resulting in a polar bond.

Key Terms

1. Antibonding orbital
2. Bond angle
3. Bond order
4. Bond polarity
5. Bonding electron pair
6. Bonding orbital (MO)
7. Bonding pair
8. Covalent bonding
9. Dipole moment
10. Double bond
11. Duet
12. Electron group
13. Electronegativity
14. Electronic geometry
15. Expanded octet
16. Formal charge
17. Free radical
18. Highest occupied molecular orbital (HOMO)
19. Hybrid orbitals
20. Incomplete octet
21. Ionic bonding
22. Lewis dot structure
23. Lewis theory
24. Lone pair
25. Lowest unoccupied molecular orbital (LUMO)
26. Metallic bonding
27. Molecular geometry
28. Molecular orbital diagram
29. Molecular orbital theory
30. Molecular polarity

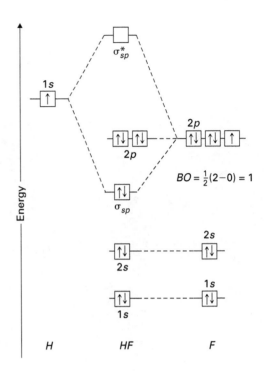

Figure 8.18 MO energy diagram for the *HF* molecule.

31. Nonbonding electron pair

32. Octahedral

33. Octet rule

34. Orbital hybridization

35. Pi bond

36. Polar covalent bond

37. Resonance

38. Resonance hybrid

39. Resonance structures

40. See-saw

41. Sigma bond

42. sp

43. sp^2

44. sp^3

45. sp^3d

46. sp^3d^2

47. Spin-pair

48. Triple bond

49. Valence bond theory

50. Valence Shell Electron Pair Repulsion Theory (VSEPR)

Problems

CHEMICAL BONDS AND ELECTRONEGATIVITY

1. Why do elements form chemical bonds with other elements?

2. What type of bond forms between metals?

3. What type of bond will form between a metal and a nonmetal?

4. What type of bond will form between two nonmetals?

5. Describe covalent bonding.

6. Describe ionic bonding.

7. Describe metallic bonding.

8. What is meant by the term electronegativity?

9. Which element has a greater attraction for bonding electrons, oxygen or magnesium?

10. Which element has a greater attraction for bonding electrons, aluminum or chlorine?

LEWIS THEORY – LEWIS SYMBOLS AND STRUCTURES

11. Write the Lewis symbol for the following elements.

    a. *Mg*

    b. *P*

    c. *As*

    d. *B*

12. Write the Lewis symbol for the following elements.

    a. *Li*

    b. *He*

    c. *Ne*

    d. *Se*

13. Write the Lewis symbol for the following elements.

    a. *N*

    b. *F*

    c. *Br*

    d. *Ba*

14. Write the Lewis symbol for the following elements.

    a. *O*

    b. *Si*

    c. *I*

    d. *Rb*

15. Write the Lewis symbol for each of the following monatomic ions.

    a. Ca^{2+}

    b. Rb^+

    c. S^{2-}

    d. N^{3-}

16. Write the Lewis symbol for each of the following monatomic ions.

    a. Na^+

    b. Al^{3+}

    c. Cl^-

    d. O^{2-}

17. Write the correct Lewis structure for the binary ionic compounds formed from the following pairs of elements.

    a. Barium and bromine

    b. Potassium and chlorine

    c. Aluminum and oxygen

18. Write the correct Lewis structure for the binary ionic compounds formed from the following pairs of elements.

    a. Calcium and nitrogen

    b. Lithium and fluorine

    c. Rubidium and oxygen

19. Explain why it is possible to have diatomic molecules with fewer than 16 valence electrons (total).

20. What is meant by the term resonance hybrid?

21. Which of the following elements can never be a central atom when writing Lewis structures? Explain.

    a. P

    b. Se

    c. H

    d. F

22. Draw the Lewis structure for the following:

    a. SiF_4

    b. CS_2

    c. $COCl_2$

23. Draw the Lewis structure for the following:

    a. NF_3

    b. ClF_4^-

    c. NH_4^+

24. Draw the Lewis structure for the following:

    a. $SeCl_4$

    b. NO_2^+

    c. $SnCl_3^-$

25. Draw the Lewis structure for the following:

    a. GeH_4

    b. NCl_3

    c. BF_4^-

26. Draw the Lewis structure for the following:

    a. $CHClF_2$

    b. Cl_2SO

    c. XeO_2F_2

27. Draw all possible resonance structures of sulfite, SO_3^{2-}.

28. Draw the resonance structures of phosphate, PO_4^{3-}.

29. Draw the resonance structures and the resonance hybrid of ozone, O_3.

30. Draw the Lewis structure of the following oxyacids:

    a. Sulfuric acid, H_2SO_4

    b. Nitric Acid, HNO_3

31. Draw the Lewis structure of the following oxyacids:

    a. Boric Acid, H_3BO_3

    b. Carbonic Acid, H_2CO_3

32. Draw the following compounds which exhibit exceptions to the octet rule:

    a. BeH_2

    b. SiF_5^-

    c. XeO_3

33. Draw the following compounds which exhibit exceptions to the octet rule:

    a. PF_5

    b. SiF_6^{2-}

    c. BrF_5

34. Draw the following compounds which exhibit exceptions to the octet rule:

    a. ClF_3

    b. SF_4

    c. BF_3

35. Draw the following compounds which exhibit exceptions to the octet rule:

    a. XeF_2

    b. ClF_5

    c. ClO_3^-

36. Write the Lewis structures and assign formal charges to the atoms in the following compounds:

   a. N_2H_4

   b. PO_4^{3-}

   c. HNO_3

37. Write the Lewis structures and assign formal charges to the atoms in the following compounds:

   a. BF_4^-

   b. IF_5

   c. AlH_4^-

38. Write Lewis structures for the following and assign formal charges to all atoms. Expand octets where necessary to lower formal charges:

   a. BrO_3^-

   b. AsO_4^{3-}

   c. ClO_3^-

39. Write Lewis structures for the following and assign formal charges to all atoms. Expand octets where necessary to lower formal charges:

   a. $SeOF_2$

   b. SO_4^{2-}

   c. ClO_2^-

40. Using formal charge as a guide, determine which Lewis structure in each of the following set is more likely to be correct for HN_3:

   H—N=N=N :   H—N≡N—N :

41. Using formal charge as a guide, determine which Lewis structure in each of the following set is more likely to be correct for SCN:

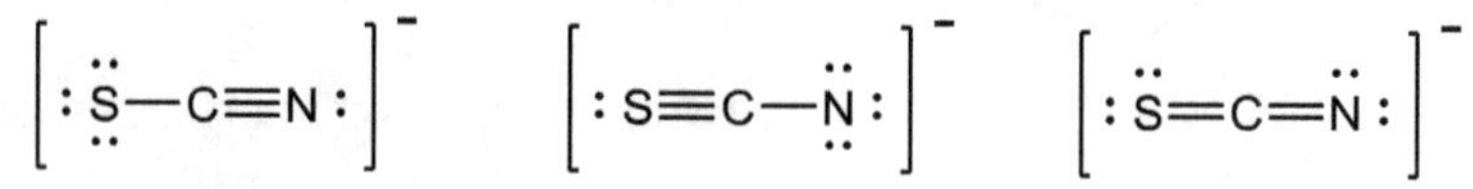

   [: S—C≡N :]⁻   [: S≡C—N :]⁻   [: S=C=N :]⁻

42. Using formal charge as a guide, determine which Lewis structure in each of the following set is more likely to be correct for CH_2N_2:

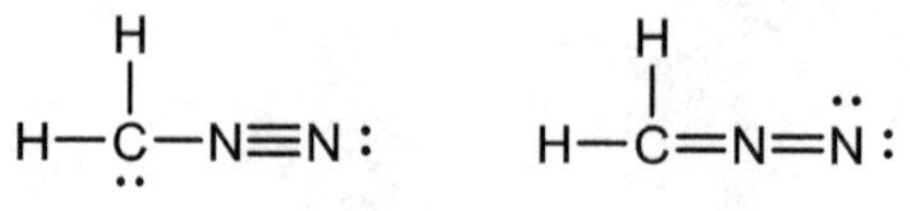

   H   H
   | |
   H—C—N≡N :   H—C=N=N :

43. Using formal charge as a guide, determine which Lewis structure in each of the following set is more likely to be correct for ClO_4^-:

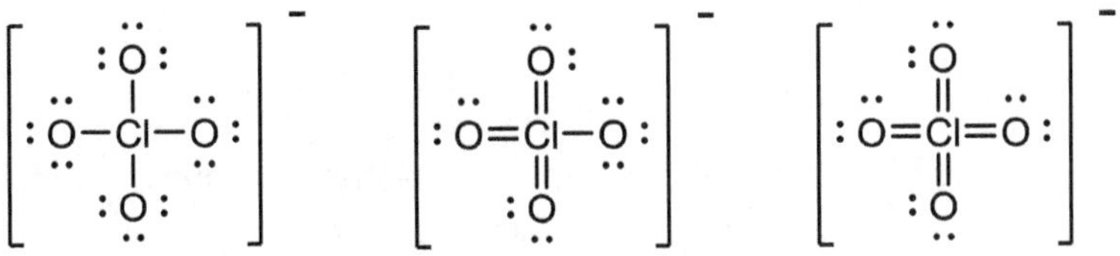

VALENCE SHELL ELECTRON PAIR REPULSION THEORY (VSEPR)

44. What are the five basic electronic geometries and the number of electron groups which correspond to each?

45. What is the difference between electronic and molecular geometry? When are they the same? When are they different?

46. How many bonding groups and lone pairs are on the central atom of a molecule with a tetrahedral molecular geometry?

47. How many bonding groups and lone pairs are on the central atom of a molecule with a see-saw molecular geometry?

48. How many bonding groups and lone pairs are on the central atom of a molecule with a bent molecular geometry for which the bond angle is < 120°?

49. How many bonding groups and lone pairs are on the central atom of a molecule with a square planar molecular geometry?

50. How many bonding groups and lone pairs are on the central atom of a molecule with a square pyramidal molecular geometry?

51. How many bonding groups and lone pairs are on the central atom of a molecule with a pyramidal molecular geometry?

52. How many bonding groups and lone pairs are on the central atom of a molecule with a T-shaped molecular geometry?

53. How many bonding groups and lone pairs are on the central atom of a molecule with a bent molecular geometry for which the bond angle is < 109.5°?

54. Determine the molecular, electronic geometry, and characteristic bond angle for each of the following:

    a. PF_3

    b. PF_5

    c. PF_6^-

55. Determine the molecular, electronic geometry, and characteristic bond angle for each of the following:

    a. CH_2Cl_2

    b. $COCl_2$

    c. H_2S

56. Determine the molecular, electronic geometry, and characteristic bond angle for each of the following:

    a. SiF_4

    b. SiF_5^-

    c. SiF_6^{2-}

57. Sketch the 3-dimensional representations of the following using the solid and hatched wedge notation:

    a. BrF_5

    b. PF_5

    c. SF_4

58. Sketch the 3-dimensional representations of the following using the solid and hatched wedge notation:

    a. SCl_6

    b. BrF_3

    c. CH_2Cl_2

59. Arrange the following in order of increasing bond angle:

    a. SO_2

    b. SO_3

    c. SO_3^{2-}

    d. SO_4^{2-}

60. Arrange the following in order of increasing bond angle:

    a. ClO_2^-

    b. ClO_3^-

    c. ClO_4^-

BOND AND MOLECULAR POLARITY

61. What is meant by the term polar covalent bond?

62. Is a $H-C$ bond covalent, polar covalent, or ionic? Why?

63. Is a $H-N$ bond covalent, polar covalent, or ionic? Why?

64. Arrange the following bind types in order of increasing polarity:

    a. $Cl-O$

    b. $Cl-C$

    c. $Cl-P$

    d. $Cl-B$

65. Arrange the following bind types in order of increasing polarity:

    a. $H-O$

    b. $Al-H$

    c. $Al-F$

    d. $Al-O$

66. Categorize the following compounds as polar or nonpolar:

    a. SF_6

    b. SF_4

    c. NCl_3

    d. NF_3

67. Categorize the following compounds as polar or nonpolar:

    a. CH_2Cl_2

    b. $CHCl_3$

    c. CCl_4

    d. CH_3Cl

68. Categorize the following compounds as polar or nonpolar:

    a. BCl_3

    b. $AsCl_3$

    c. SO_3

69. Categorize the following compounds as polar or nonpolar:

    a. CH_4

    b. $SiCl_4$

    c. BrF_5

    d. PCl_5

VALENCE BOND THEORY

70. What hybridization is associated with each of the five electronic geometries?

71. What characteristic bond angles are produced from the following orbital hybridizations:

    a. sp

    b. sp^2

    c. sp^3

    d. sp^3d

    e. sp^3d^2

72. What is the hybridization on the central atom in each of the following compounds:

    a. BCl_3

    b. SiF_5^-

    c. SO_3

    d. SF_4

73. What is the hybridization on the central atom in each of the following compounds:

    a. PF_6^-

    b. $AsCl_3$

    c. $COCl_2$

    d. $AlCl_3$

74. What is the hybridization on each carbon atom in ethylene, C_2H_4? Describe the bonding arrangement. How many π-bonds are present in this molecule? Where are they located?

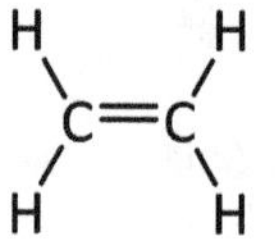

75. What is the hybridization on each carbon atom in acetone, C_3H_6O? Describe the bonding arrangement. How many π-bonds are present in this molecule? Where are they located?

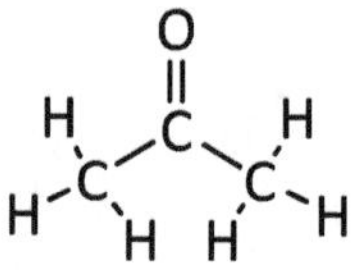

76. What is the hybridization on each carbon atom in isopropyl alcohol, C_3H_7OH? Describe the bonding arrangement. How many π-bonds are present in this molecule? Where are they located?

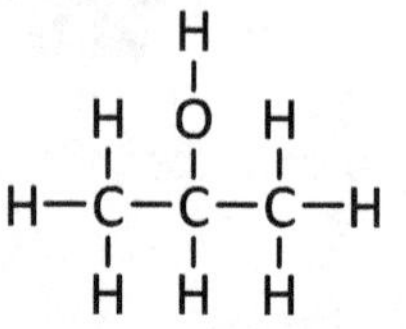

77. Predict the hybridization of each non-hydrogen atom in the following compounds:

    a.

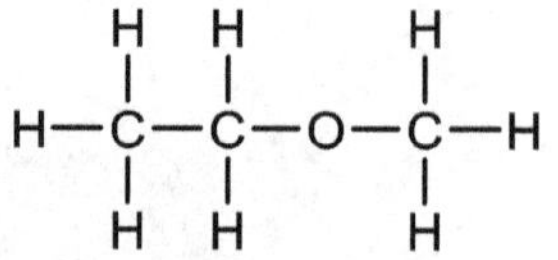

    b.

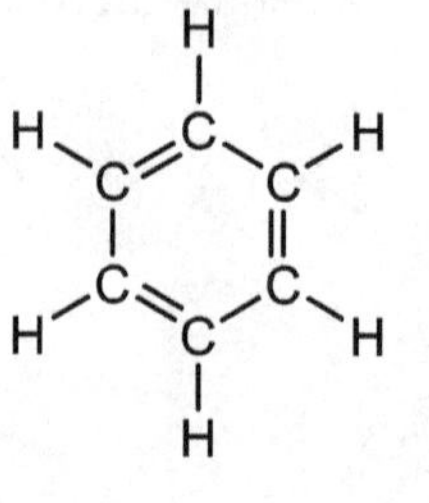

    c.

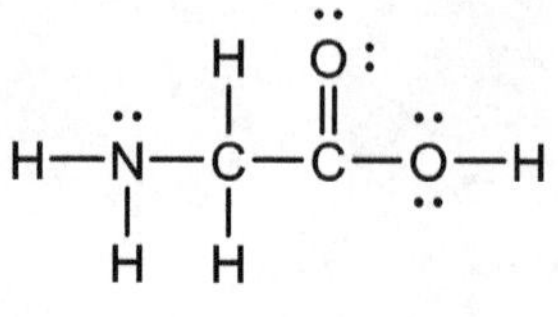

MOLECULAR ORBITAL THEORY

78. Describe the principal difference between MO theory and VB Theory.

79. What are bonding and antibonding orbitals and how do they arise in MO theory?

80. What is bond order and what does it tell us?

81. Construct an MO diagram for the homonuclear diatomic molecule H_2. Use this diagram to determine the bond order of the following species and predict whether each will exist:

    a. H_2

    b. H_2^+

    c. H_2^-

    d. He_2^+

    e. He_2

82. Determine the electron configurations of the following:

    a. Li_2

    b. Li_2^+

    c. Li_2^-

83. Determine the electron configurations of the following:

    a. B_2

    b. B_2^+

    c. B_2^-

84. Determine the electron configurations of the following:

    a. N_2

    b. N_2^+

    c. N_2^-

85. Determine the electron configurations of the following:

    a. F_2

    b. F_2^+

    c. F_2^-

86. What are the bond orders for the species in problem 82? Arrange those that exist in order of increasing stability.

87. What are the bond orders for the species in problem 83? Arrange those that exist in order of increasing stability.

88. What are the bond orders for the species in problem 84? Arrange those that exist in order of increasing stability.

89. What are the bond orders for the species in problem 85? Arrange those that exist in order of increasing bond length.

90. Use the following generic MO diagram to assess the following:

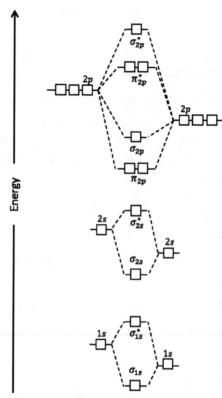

a. What is the bond order of *CO*? What is the HOMO? What is the LUMO? Is it paramagnetic?

b. What is the bond order of the hypothetical compound *BO*? Is it paramagnetic? What is the HOMO? What is the LUMO? Is it paramagnetic?

c. What is the bond order of *CN⁻*? What is the HOMO? What is the LUMO? Is it paramagnetic?

d. What is the bond order of *NF*? What is the HOMO? What is the LUMO? Is it paramagnetic?

e. What is the bond order of *NF⁻*? What is the HOMO? What is the LUMO? Is it paramagnetic?

Image Credits

Intermolecular Forces and Phase Diagrams

After reading this chapter, you should be able to do the following:

- Know what intermolecular forces are and what causes them.

- Be able to identify which of the intermolecular forces are present in different atoms and molecules.

- Have an understanding of the relative strengths of each of these types of intermolecular forces.

- Describe how these intermolecular forces influence various properties of substances.

- Describe a phase diagram and the types of information it contains.

- Define each of the Key Terms listed at the end of the chapter dealing with these concepts.

Changes in the states of matter from solid, liquid, and gas. A solid iceberg is observed in surrounding liquid water.

Section 9.1 Introduction

Have you ever wondered what intermolecular forces hold matter together and what happens to these forces with changes in the states of matter? For example, if you look at an iceberg sitting in the ocean, why is the iceberg solid while the surrounding water is liquid? In this chapter, we answer this and many more questions regarding intermolecular forces and changes in the states of matter. If you recall from chapter 2, we characterized the three states of matter as solid, liquid, or gas. Remember that the particles that make up a particular substance get further and further apart from one another as you go from a solid, to a liquid, and then to the gas state as illustrated in Figure 9.1. Notice that this can be accomplished by the application of heat in going from a solid to liquid and either heat or reduced pressure from a liquid to a gas. In fact, as we saw with gases in Chapter 6, the molecules are spread so far apart that most of what is contained in a gas is "empty space," and therefore we could make some

Figure 9.1 Changes in the states of matter.

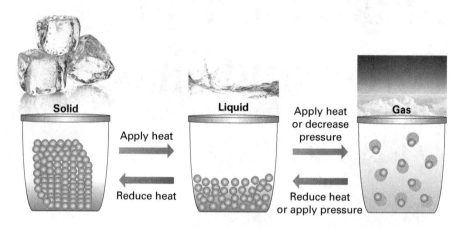

assumptions. For example, under standard conditions, we could assume little to no interactions among the gas particles owing to the large distances between them. As a result of some of these assumptions, we could relate various properties of gases (i.e. volume, pressure, and temperature) using the "ideal" gas law equation. However, when studying matter in the condensed state, namely liquids and solids, it is somewhat more complicated by the fact that the molecules are now closer to one another and interacting with each other. Notice again from Figure 9.1 that this can be accomplished by cooling or increased pressure in going from a gas to a liquid, and further cooling to get a solid from the liquid state. Thus, we do not have an "ideal" equation for liquids and solids as the assumptions that we could make with gases cannot be used here with liquids and solids. In fact, as discussed in Chapter 2, the relatively strong intermolecular forces holding the molecules close together in a solid result in a definite shape. This is in contrast to liquids or gases which have an indefinite shape. Notice from Figure 9.2

Figure 9.2 Solids with atoms or molecules arranged in either a well-ordered manner resulting in a crystalline solid, or randomly organized as observed in amorphous solids.

SiO$_2$ Crystalline Solid Structure (Quartz)   SiO$_2$ Amorphous Solid Structure (Glass)

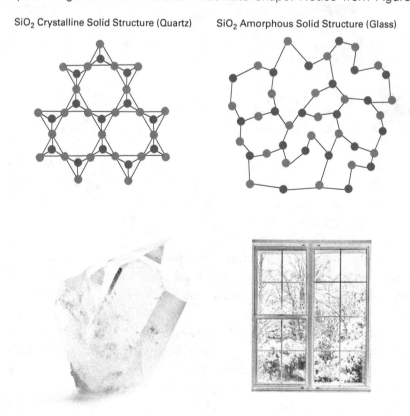

that the definite shape observed in solids can either be very organized or not. The atoms or molecules in a solid can be arranged in a well-ordered manner resulting in a **crystalline solid** or can be randomly organized as is the case with **amorphous solids**. Quartz and glass are great examples of crystalline and amorphous solids, respectively. In this chapter, we will further investigate the types of intermolecular forces that hold atoms and molecules together in matter, as well as the numerous properties of liquids attributed to intermolecular forces. We will then conclude this chapter with a brief discussion on phase diagrams.

Section 9.2 Intermolecular Forces

Intermolecular forces are essentially responsible for holding condensed matter together and occur between atoms and molecules and are essentially electrostatic forces arising from differences in ionic charges, temporary charges, and permanent partial charges. In chemistry, it is very important for us to understand why these forces exist and how strong these forces are in order to appreciate various properties of matter. For example, the energy required to overcome the different specific types of intermolecular forces is directly responsible for the various physical properties discussed in this chapter such as boiling point, melting point, and viscosity to name a few. Furthermore, this is an important concept when it comes to understanding the solubility of matter in various solvents, as well as determining the structure of various biological molecules such as DNA. Therefore, we must first examine the four different types of intermolecular forces.

Dispersion Forces

Fritz Wolfgang London was a Jewish-German physicist born in 1900 in Breslau, Germany. His significant scientific contributions to our current understanding of dispersion forces (also commonly referred to as "London dispersion forces") were critical. **Dispersion forces** are present in all atoms and molecules and occur based on slight fluctuations in electron distribution. In other words, based on probability given any point in time, the electrons will be unevenly distributed throughout the atom or molecule resulting in an electron-rich region, leaving another region of the atom or molecule electron deficient. This unsymmetrical distribution of electrons results in an instantaneous, temporary dipole (with slightly negative and positive regions), which can then induce temporary dipoles in neighboring atoms or molecules as depicted in Figure 9.3. As with all intermolecular forces, the magnitude of dispersion forces is very important as it affects various physical properties such as the boiling point of atoms or molecules. For example, weaker forces result in lower boiling points, while stronger forces result in higher boiling points. The magnitude of dispersion forces can in part depend on how easily

Fritz Wolfgang London (1900–1954) made significant scientific contributions with respect to intermolecular forces present in atoms and molecules which have led to our current understanding of dispersion forces.

Figure 9.3 Dispersion forces. All atoms and molecules have dispersion forces, which result based on temporary instantaneous fluctuations in electron distribution.

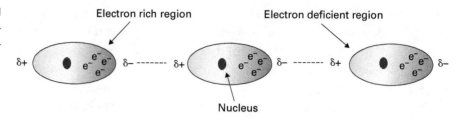

the electrons can be polarized, which in turn depends on the size of the electron cloud. Larger electron clouds are more easily polarized when compared to smaller ones; thus, they have higher boiling points. For example, helium with a molar mass of 4.00 *g/mol* has a boiling point of about 4 K, while xenon is much larger with a molar mass of 131.30 *g/mol* and a boiling point of 165 K. If you recall our discussion in Chapter 4 involving the various types of hydrocarbons, you will remember that the molecular weight increases from 30.08 *g/mol* for ethane to 114.26 *g/mol* for octane. Therefore, it should not be surprising to now learn that the boiling point is much lower for the smaller ethane molecule when compared to the much larger octane molecule, as we can see from Table 9.1. However, it is important to note that size alone is not the sole predictor of determining relative boiling points. For example, if we compare *n*-pentane and isopentane as illustrated in Figure 9.4, we notice that while they have the same molecular weight of 72.17 *g/mol*, *n*-pentane has a slightly higher boiling point than isopentane. Why? Well the answer has to do with the shape of the molecules and the larger surface area available to interact with neighboring molecules associated with *n*-pentane versus isopentane. A larger surface area allows for greater interactions, which translate into a higher boiling point. In any event, much of what we know today regarding dispersion forces can be traced back to the very significant scientific contributions involving intermolecular forces made by Fritz London (nominated for the Noble Prize in Chemistry on five separate occasions).

Figure 9.4 Comparison of the different shapes associated with *n*-pentane (left) and isopentane (right) and how this affects the boiling points of the two.

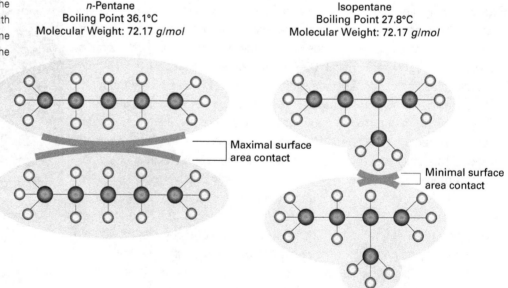

Table 9.1 List of various hydrocarbons along with their molecular weights and boiling points.

Chemical Name	Molecular Weight (*g/mol*)	Boiling Point (°C)
Ethane	30.08	−88.6
Propane	44.11	−42.1
Butane	58.14	−0.5
Pentane	72.17	36.1
Hexane	86.20	68.7
Heptane	100.23	98.4
Octane	114.26	125.8

Dipole-Dipole Forces

While all atoms and molecules have relatively weak dispersion forces, not all molecules necessarily have dipole-dipole intermolecular forces, which is a stronger intermolecular force. In order to determine whether a particular molecule experiences this type of intermolecular force, it is necessary for us to be able to determine if the molecule in question is polar (recall our discussion of molecular polarity from Chapter 8). **Dipole-dipole forces** exist in all polar molecules. Polar molecules have a dipole, in which the molecule contains permanent electron-rich and electron-deficient regions, which gives rise to partially negative and partially positive "poles" on the molecule. Therefore, polar molecules have both dispersion forces as well as dipole-dipole interactions. As a result, they have considerably higher boiling and melting points when compared to nonpolar molecules due to this additional stronger intermolecular force. For example, let's take a look at two molecules of comparable molar masses, the nonpolar molecule butane and the polar molecule acetone (Figure 9.5).

Notice that while both molecules have dispersion forces, only acetone experiences additional dipole-dipole forces as a result of the more electronegative oxygen atom present on the molecule, which is not present on the nonpolar butane molecule. Therefore, it should not surprise us to learn that the boiling and melting point of acetone is much higher than butane. This concept is really based on the electron distribution around the molecule and

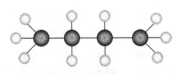

n-Butane
Boiling Point: −0.5 °C
Melting Point: −138 °C
Molecular Weight: 58.14 *g/mol*

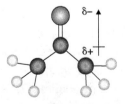

Acetone (2-propanone)
Boiling Point: 56 °C
Melting Point: −95 °C
Molecular Weight: 58.08 *g/mol*

Figure 9.5 Comparison of boiling and melting points between the nonpolar butane molecule (left) and the polar acetone (2-propanone) molecule (right).

whether or not there are factors that would influence heavy electron concentration in a particular region of the molecule over another. In other words, if we consider the symmetrical molecule butane, notice that there is really no reason to believe that most of the electron density would permanently reside at one end of the molecule over the other, and therefore it is nonpolar. However, if we look at acetone on the other hand, most of the electron density would permanently reside around the highly electronegative oxygen atom, resulting in an uneven electron distribution, making this molecule polar in nature (recall Chapter 8). Knowing whether a molecule is polar or not can also help us determine the **miscibility** of a substance, which is the ability to mix with another substance without separating into two separate liquid phases. Generally speaking, polar molecules mix with other polar molecules, while nonpolar molecules mix with other nonpolar molecules. Liquids that are not miscible with each other are referred to as **immiscible** liquids. For example, we are familiar with what happens if we combine oil (nonpolar) and vinegar (polar) in salad dressing, which clearly separate from one another into two very distinctive phases. These two liquids are therefore said to be immiscible with one another. Incidentally, the reason we use soap when we shower is due to the fact that the oils present on our skin are nonpolar while water is polar, thus they do not mix well. Soap contains **amphiphilic molecules**, which are molecules that possess both nonpolar and polar properties. Thus, the nonpolar region can trap oils, while the polar region mixes quite well with water as the soap is washed away from the body, taking the dirt with it.

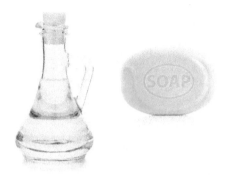

Oil (nonpolar) and vinegar (polar) are immiscible liquids that do not mix and form two distinctive different states of liquid. Soap contains amphiphilic molecules that are capable of removing oils present on the body.

Hydrogen Bonding

Hydrogen bonding occurs when polar molecules contain hydrogen directly bound to very electronegative atoms, specifically nitrogen, oxygen, or fluorine. This intermolecular force is stronger than a regular dipole-dipole interaction and can be thought of as an exceptionally strong dipole-dipole interaction. This occurs due to the large electronegativity difference between hydrogen and any of these highly electronegative atoms. The result of such interactions is that hydrogen has a relatively large partial positive charge, while the nitrogen, oxygen, or fluorine atoms have a large partial negative charge (Figure 9.6). **Note:** Despite the name, hydrogen bonding should not be confused as a type of chemical bond, which are much stronger than intermolecular forces.

Therefore, the boiling and melting points of molecules that experience this type of intermolecular force go up quite dramatically when compared to molecules that do not. For example, if we were to compare two molecules of similar molar masses such as fluoromethane (34.03 *g/mol*) and hydrogen peroxide (34.02 *g/mol*), we would see a dramatic difference in their respective boiling points (Figure 9.7). The boiling point of fluoromethane is only −78.4°C, while the extrapolated boiling point of hydrogen peroxide is 150.2°C. This is an extrapolated temperature because in practice hydrogen peroxide can potentially undergo explosive thermal decomposition if heated to this temperature. In any event, notice that while both molecules experience

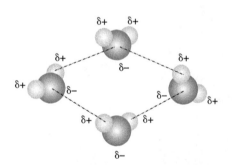

Figure 9.6 Hydrogen bonding occurs with polar molecules that contain hydrogen directly bonded to very electronegative atoms (nitrogen, oxygen or fluorine).

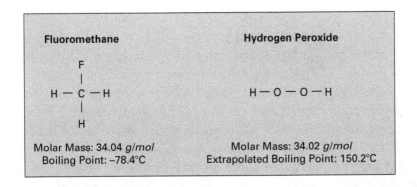

Fluoromethane	Hydrogen Peroxide
F | H — C — H | H	H — O — O — H
Molar Mass: 34.04 *g/mol* Boiling Point: −78.4°C	Molar Mass: 34.02 *g/mol* Extrapolated Boiling Point: 150.2°C

Figure 9.7 Comparison of boiling points between fluoromethane (left) and hydrogen peroxide (right). While both molecules are of comparable size, the hydrogen bonding that occurs in hydrogen peroxide dramatically increase its boiling point relative to that of fluoromethane.

dispersion forces and dipole-dipole interactions (both molecules are polar), hydrogen peroxide also contains additional hydrogen bonding intermolecular forces as hydrogen is directly bound to oxygen.

To illustrate how powerful hydrogen bonding can be, we can examine a truly remarkable substance, water. Water is important to sustain life, and its behavior is so unique that almost no other substance behaves quite like it. Recall from Chapter 8 that water has a bent geometry, and the highly polar *O–H* bonds give water a significant dipole moment. In fact, these two *O–H* bonds present in water allow for one water molecule to hydrogen bond with four other water molecules. The result is that they tenaciously cling to each other to form a uniquely intricate network. In fact, it has been estimated based on molecules of similar size that without hydrogen bonding, the predicted boiling point of water would be approximately −90°C! This is a difference of almost 200°C from the true boiling point of water, 100°C. Thus, water is a liquid at room temperature, which is obviously very important to sustain life as it is the main solvent in living organisms, allowing for nutrients to readily travel throughout the body. Water is also a very unique substance in that it is less dense in the solid phase than in the liquid phase, which is not the case with most substances. This is because as water cools, it actually becomes more dense until about 4°C, and then it expands as it freezes due to this unique hydrogen bonding pattern which allows water molecules to be regularly arranged resembling an "open-cage" structure containing a great deal of empty space. This is why ice floats on top of liquid water on a frozen lake, and your ice cubes float in your drink. This is also an important fact as it relates to sustaining life because if solid ice sank to the bottom of a lake every time it froze, it would essentially eliminate all aquatic life living in the lake.

Water is less dense in the solid state than in the liquid state, which is why ice floats on top of liquid water.

Did you know how chemistry might relate to your job as a non-chemist? As a biologist, or possibly a biochemist, working in a forensics lab, it may in fact be your job to identify a suspect based on DNA left at a crime scene. If you recall from Chapter 2, DNA is our genetic code and is very unique to each individual. Often when a crime is committed, there are trace amounts of DNA left at the crime scene that can be retrieved and then taken back to the laboratory for analysis. However, it is very common that the amount of DNA left at the crime scene may not be enough to accurately acquire a DNA profile of the perpetrator. Therefore, it becomes necessary for scientists to be able to amplify small amounts of DNA in the laboratory in order to make an accurate match to the DNA profiles of possible suspects. The polymerase chain reaction (PCR) is a technique that can be used to accomplish this goal. During this procedure, the double stranded DNA helix is repeatedly heated and cooled during amplification. Why? Well, the double stranded DNA helix is held together by hydrogen bonds between what we call base pairs, or the building blocks of DNA. Heat is needed to separate the strands, essentially breaking the hydrogen bonds holding the complex together, so that an enzyme can gain access to each strand and make more DNA. Cooling is then required during a process called annealing so that the hydrogen bonds can be reformed between base pairs in order to restore the double stranded helix. We will discuss DNA in much further detail in chapter 16.

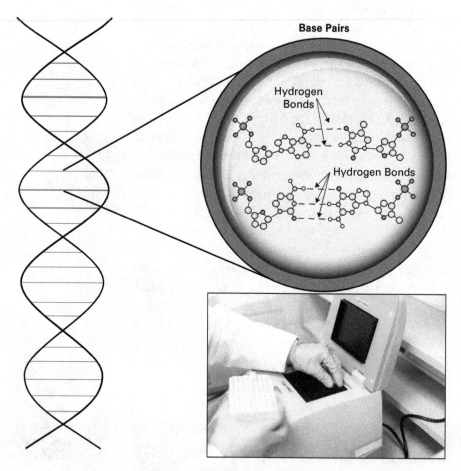

Structure of deoxyribonucleic acids (DNA) depicted in a double stranded helix held together by hydrogen bonds between base pairs.

Example Problem 9.1

Arrange the following in order of increasing boiling points:
Kr, He, Ne, Xe
Solution:

As with all atoms, all of the noble gases have dispersion forces. The trend in predicting boiling points among these atoms is based on size, with the larger atoms having higher boiling points.	*He < Ne < Kr < Xe*

Example Problem 9.2

For each of the following, determine which intermolecular forces are present:
1. *Ne*
2. *HF*
3. *HBr*
4. *H_2O*
Solution:

1. *Ne* is a noble gas and has dispersion forces like all atoms.	**Dispersion forces.**
2. *HF* has not only dispersion forces as with all molecules, but it is also polar and has dipole-dipole interactions. Furthermore, because hydrogen is directly bound to fluorine, it also has hydrogen bonding.	**Dispersion forces, dipole-dipole forces, and hydrogen bonding.**
3. *HBr* has not only dispersion forces as with all molecules, but it is also polar and therefore it also has dipole-dipole interactions.	**Dispersion forces and dipole-dipole forces.**
4. *H_2O* has not only dispersion forces as with all molecules, but it is also polar and has dipole-dipole interactions. Furthermore, because hydrogen is directly bound to oxygen, it also has hydrogen bonding.	**Dispersion forces, dipole-dipole forces, and hydrogen bonding.**

Example Problem 9.3

For each of the following, determine which intermolecular forces are present:
1. *CH_3CH_3*
2. *CH_4*
3. *CH_3CH_2OH*
4. *CH_3CH_2F*
Solution:

1. *CH_3CH_3* is nonpolar and has dispersion forces as with all molecules.	**Dispersion forces.**
2. *CH_4* is nonpolar and has dispersion forces as with all molecules.	**Dispersion forces.**
3. *CH_3CH_2OH* has not only dispersion forces as with all molecules, but it is also polar, so it also has dipole-dipole interactions. Furthermore, because hydrogen is directly bound to oxygen, it also has hydrogen bonding.	**Dispersion forces, dipole-dipole forces, and hydrogen bonding.**
4. *CH_3CH_2F* has not only dispersion forces as with all molecules, but it is also polar and has dipole-dipole interactions. However, notice that the fluorine atom is not directly bound to hydrogen (it is bound to carbon in this case), so this molecule does not have hydrogen bonding.	**Dispersion forces and dipole-dipole forces.**

Ion-Dipole Forces

Ion-dipole forces occur between an ionic compound and a polar compound. This particular intermolecular force involves interactions between two "un-like" things and is very different from any of the other types of intermolecular forces discussed so far in this chapter. For example, when we looked at water, we discussed the dispersion forces, dipole-dipole forces, and the hydrogen bonding that occurs between one water molecule and another water molecule. We now turn our attention to an intermolecular force that occurs between two different entities, such as a water molecule and anions and cations, rather than neighboring water. For example, if we were to mix sodium chloride in water, there are relatively strong interactions that would occur between these two entities. If you recall from Chapter 5, as the salt dissolves in the water in a process known as solvation, ion-dipole forces take over as the positively charged sodium cations interact with the partially negatively charged oxygen atoms of water molecules, and the negatively charged chloride ions interact with the partially positively charged hydrogen atoms in water. Of the four intermolecular forces discussed in this chapter, this intermolecular force is the strongest.

Figure 9.8 Ion-dipole forces occur between an ionic compound such as sodium chloride and a polar compound such as water.

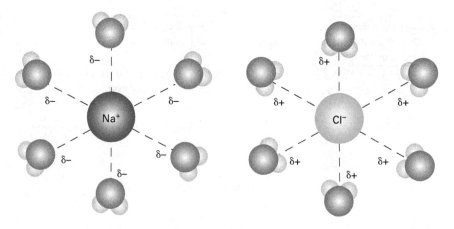

Section 9.3 Properties of Liquids Attributed to Intermolecular Forces

As mentioned in the introduction of this chapter, matter in the condensed liquid or solid state is somewhat more complicated to study when compared to gases. Under normal conditions, molecules in the gas state are so far apart from one another that they tend to behave somewhat independently from one another. This makes studying gases somewhat easier, largely because of the various assumptions that can be made as we have already thoroughly discussed in Chapter 6. Of the two condensed states of matter, however, the liquid state is a little more complicated than the solid state. In the solid state, the molecules are a lot closer together and form rather rigid ordered arrangements, as we have examined earlier with crystalline and amorphous solids. The molecules in liquids, on the other hand, do, in fact, interact with their neighbors, but unlike solids, there is not much order to their arrangement as they do have some freedom of motion. In this section, we now focus our attention to the properties associated with liquids. Specifically, we will first discuss vaporization, condensation, boiling point, and critical properties. We will then focus on other properties pertaining to liquids, including surface tension, capillary action, meniscus, and viscosity.

Evaporation, Condensation, Boiling Point, and Critical Properties of Liquids

The process of **evaporation** involves a substance changing from the liquid state to the gas state. **Condensation** would be the opposite of this process in which a substance changes from the gas state to the liquid state. As you can see, these are opposite processes whereby evaporation is an endothermic process, and condensation is an exothermic process. In fact, in order to better understand these concepts we must look at this in terms of molecular energies. Notice from Figure 9.9 that there is a range of energies that molecules in the liquid state have with only a few of the molecules having enough energy to escape the liquid phase and enter the gas phase. In **volatile liquids**, the intermolecular forces tend to be weak, and liquids vaporize more readily, while in **nonvolatile liquids** the intermolecular forces are stronger and fewer molecules escape the liquid phase. Also, notice from Figure 9.9 that the number of molecules able to escape the liquid state increases with increasing temperature, as we would expect. The circumstances must be favorable for this to happen; in other words, molecules in a liquid must have enough energy and be moving in the right direction in order to break free from the intermolecular forces holding them to neighboring molecules and escape the liquid state. The **heat of vaporization ($\Delta H°_{vap}$)** is the amount of heat energy required to vaporize one mole of a liquid to the gas state under standard conditions, and the units are generally given in *kJ/mol*. As mentioned earlier, the reverse of this process is condensation in which the gas molecules slowly transfer some of their kinetic energy to other cooler molecules or solid objects surrounding them in an exothermic process as

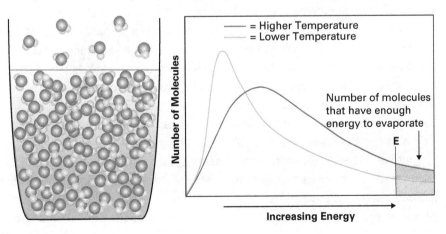

Figure 9.9 There is a range of energies that molecules have in a liquid, with only a few able to escape the liquid and go into the gas state. The number of molecules able to do this increases with increasing temperature.

they return to the liquid state. In fact, if we have a sealed container containing a liquid in which gas molecules are not allowed to escape, gaseous molecules would eventually return back to the liquid state. At constant temperature, eventually the rate of condensation and evaporation will become equal, at which point **dynamic equilibrium** is reached. Chemists generally depict dynamic equilibrium with two arrows pointing in opposite directions. Thus, in this case we could illustrate this point as follows:

$$Liquid \rightleftarrows Vapor$$

This means that the two processes are happening at the same time and at the same rate. The **vapor pressure** is defined as the pressure of the vapor in dynamic equilibrium with its liquid and is dependent on the intermolecular forces of the liquid at a given temperature. To put it simply, vapor pressure is essentially a measure of how easily molecules can escape the liquid state and go in to the gas state. Qualitatively, the propensity of the molecules of a liquid to do this is referred to as the **volatility** of a liquid; thus, liquids with higher vapor pressures at a given temperature are more volatile liquids. Quantitatively, the vapor pressure of a given liquid can be calculated using the **Clausius-Clapeyron equation**, which technically gives a linear relationship between the natural log of the vapor pressure and the inverse of the temperature (as seen in the margin). In any event, as we noted earlier, the number of molecules able to escape the liquid state increases with increasing temperature, and now we know that is because the vapor pressure increases. In fact, the **boiling point** of a liquid is defined as the temperature at which a liquid's vapor pressure is equal to the external pressure. The **normal boiling point** of a liquid is the temperature at which a liquid's vapor pressure is 1 *atm* (atmospheric pressure at sea level). Notice that the external pressure is specified (1 *atm*) in the definition of the normal boiling point; therefore, this number is standardized and does not change with geographical location, which is not the case with the boiling points of liquids. For example, the normal boiling point of water is 100°C, but the boiling point of water can change depending on geography and, more specifically, altitude. In San Francisco, California, where the elevation is practically at sea level (1 *atm*), the boiling point of water is 100°C, but in Denver, Colorado, where the elevation is closer to a mile above sea level (~0.82 *atm*), the boiling point of water is only 94°C. Table 9.2 lists the boiling points of water at different geographical locations varying in altitude.

So far in this section we have discussed liquids and gases in terms of two very distinctive states with respect to both temperature and pressure. However, it should be noted that there are specific temperature and pressure conditions at which the gas and liquid states comingle to form a **supercritical fluid**, which have properties of both liquids and gases. Supercritical fluids can be very useful and are used for various reasons. For example, supercritical CO_2 is an excellent solvent and is used to extract caffeine from coffee beans. Furthermore, the temperature and pressure conditions needed to reach the supercritical state for carbon dioxide is relatively easy to obtain. For a given liquid, the temperature at which this occurs is referred to as the **critical temperature**, and the pressure at which this occurs is called the **critical pressure**.

$$\ln P_{vap} = -\frac{\Delta H_{vap}}{R}\left(\frac{1}{T}\right) + \ln \beta$$

The Clausius-Clapeyron Equation – Where P_{vap} is the vapor pressure, ΔH_{vap} is the heat of vaporization, R is the gas constant (8.314 $J/(mol \cdot K)$), T is the absolute temperature (K) and β is a constant that depends on the gas in question.

Table 9.2 List of the boiling points of water at different geographical locations varying in altitude.

Geographical Location	Elevation above sea level (feet)/Pressure (*atm*)	Approximate Boiling Point of Water (°C)
San Francisco, California (sea level)	0/1.0	100
Boston, Massachusetts (sea level)	20/1.0	100
Denver, Colorado	5,280/0.83	94
Mt. McKinley, Alaska (highest mountain peak in North America)	20,320/0.46	83
Mt. Everest, Tibet (highest mountain peak on Earth)	29,035/0.32	78

Surface Tension, Capillary Action, Meniscus, and Viscosity

The molecules present at the surface of a liquid tend to behave very differently from interior molecules. In part, this is due to the fact that surface molecules have fewer neighbors to interact with when compared to those present in the interior of the liquid (Figure 9.10). The effect of this on molecules present on the surface is an inward force of attraction between surface molecules that can act like an elastic skin layer. This gives rise to **surface tension**, which is the energy required to break through this layer and to increase the surface area by a unit amount while spreading the material out as a film. **Capillary action**, which is somewhat related to surface tension, is the ability of a liquid to flow up a narrow tube against gravity. This is due to the attraction between the liquid and the tube, known as **adhesive forces**. Capillary action results when these adhesive forces are strong enough to overcome the **cohesive forces** of the liquid, which are the forces between the liquid molecules themselves. Notice when you put water in a graduated cylinder, for example, that the top of the water makes a "U" or concave shape. This is due to the adhesive forces between the water molecules and the cylinder, resulting in a **meniscus**. It is important to note that when measuring liquid such as water in a graduated cylinder that we take the measurement from the bottom of the meniscus in order to get an accurate measurement. It also important to note that some liquids such as mercury form an inverted "U" or convex shape. This is because the cohesive forces of mercury are strong (thus, surface tension is high) when compared to the adhesive forces. Another very important property as it relates to liquids is **viscosity**, which is the resistance of liquids to flow. Notice that if you spill a glass of water, the water flows out of the glass quite quickly. However, if you try to get honey out of its container, it is much more difficult. In this example, honey is much more viscous than water. Viscosity is obviously dependent on the strength of the intermolecular forces and, therefore, temperature, but also on the shape on the molecule. Longer molecules, even those with weaker intermolecular forces, can, in fact, be more viscous than much smaller molecules with stronger intermolecular forces as they can become entangled with each other contributing to an increase in

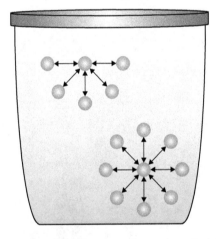

Figure 9.10 Surface molecules in a liquid have fewer neighbors with which to interact when compared to interior molecules, resulting in surface tension.

The adhesive properties of the water (left) molecules contribute to the concave meniscus, while the cohesive properties of the mercury atoms (right) contribute to the convex meniscus.

viscosity. For example, the long hydrocarbon chain molecules in olive oil make it much more viscous than water, which is a much smaller molecule, even though water experiences strong hydrogen bonding. Another important point related to viscosity is that it can be measured, and the unit is often expressed as either poise (P) or centipoise (cP). While poise is defined as $1 \frac{g}{cm \cdot s}$, centipoise is commonly defined as water at room temperature or approximately 1 cP.

Section 9.4 **Phase Diagrams**

As we have seen in this chapter, the state a substance is dependent on both temperature and pressure. Whether a substance exists as a solid, liquid, or gas depending on both temperature and pressure can be summarized in a **phase diagram**. For example, Figure 9.11 is the phase diagram for water. Notice that pressure is on the y-axis, and temperature is on the x-axis with the three main regions of the diagram representing the three states of matter: solid, liquid, and gas. Also, the lines on a phase diagram represent the temperature and pressure conditions in which two phases exist at equilibrium. In fact, the **triple point** represents the temperature and pressure conditions in which all three states coexists at equilibrium. For water, this occurs at a pressure of 0.006 *atm* and a temperature of 0.01°C. The **fusion curve** is the line that separates solids and liquids, the **sublimation curve** is the line that separates solids and gases, while the **vapor pressure curve** is the line that separates gases and liquids. Also, notice that the **critical point** represents the temperature and pressure conditions above which a supercritical fluid exists, and that at temperatures above this point, gases cannot be condensed into a liquid no matter how high the pressure gets.

Figure 9.11 Phase diagram for water.

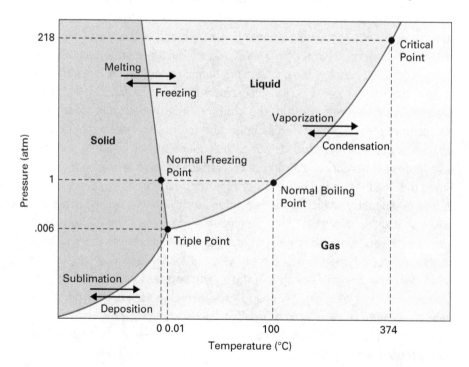

Key Terms

1. Adhesive forces
2. Amorphous solids
3. Amphiphilic molecules
4. Boiling point
5. Capillary action
6. Clausius-Clapeyron Equation
7. Cohesive forces
8. Condensation
9. Critical point
10. Critical pressure
11. Critical temperature
12. Crystalline solid
13. Dipole-dipole forces
14. Dispersion forces
15. Dynamic equilibrium
16. Evaporation
17. Fusion curve
18. Heat of vaporization (ΔH°_{vap})
19. Hydrogen bonding
20. Immiscible
21. Intermolecular forces
22. Ion-dipole forces
23. Meniscus
24. Miscible
25. Nonvolatile liquids
26. Normal boiling point
27. Phase diagram
28. Sublimation curve
29. Supercritical fluid
30. Surface tension
31. Triple point
32. Vapor pressure
33. Vapor pressure curve
34. Viscosity
35. Volatile liquids
36. Volatility

Problems

INTERMOLECULAR FORCES

1. What are intermolecular forces, and why are they important?

2. What are the major types of intermolecular forces discussed in this chapter?

3. What are dispersion forces? Can you give an example of a molecule that experiences this type of intermolecular force?

4. Order the following noble gases in terms of increasing boiling points:

   Xe, Ne, Kr and Ar.

5. Order the following hydrocarbons in terms of increasing boiling points:

   CH_4, $CH_3CH_2CH_2CH_3$, CH_3CH_3, and $CH_3CH_2CH_3$.

6. Which of the following molecules would you expect to have a higher boiling point and why?

7. What are dipole-dipole forces? Can you give an example of a molecule that experiences this type of intermolecular force?

8. Which of the following molecules would you expect to have a higher boiling point and why?

9. What are miscible substances? Can you give an example?

10. What are immiscible substances? Can you give an example?

11. What are amphiphilic molecules? Can you give an example?

12. What is hydrogen bonding? Can you give an example of a molecule that experiences this type of intermolecular force?

13. Which of the following molecules would you expect to have a higher boiling point and why?

14. What are ion-dipole forces? Can you give an example of an ion(s) and molecule that experiences this type of intermolecular force?

15. Which kind of intermolecular forces are present in *He*?

16. Which kind of intermolecular forces are present in NH_3?

17. Which kind of intermolecular forces are present in *Kr*?

18. Which kind of intermolecular forces are present in *HCL*?

19. Which kind of intermolecular forces are present in CH_3OH?

20. Which kind of intermolecular forces are present in $CH_3CH_2CH_3$

21. Which kind of intermolecular forces are present in H_2Se?

22. Which kind of intermolecular forces are present in *CO*?

23. Which kind of intermolecular forces are present in CCl_4?

24. Which kind of intermolecular forces are present in H_2O?

25. What are some of the characteristics that make water a rather unique substance necessary to sustain life, and how is this related to intermolecular forces?

PROPERTIES OF LIQUIDS ATTRIBUTED TO INTERMOLECULAR FORCES

26. Describe the process of vaporization (evaporation).

27. Describe the process of condensation.

28. In volatile liquids, the intermolecular forces tend to be (weaker/stronger) and vaporize more readily, whereas nonvolatile liquids tend to have (weaker/stronger) intermolecular forces and fewer molecules escape the liquid phase.

29. Define heat of vaporization (ΔH°_{vap}).

30. Define dynamic equilibrium.

31. Define vapor pressure.

32. What is a volatile liquid? What is a nonvolatile liquid?

33. What is the difference between the boiling point and normal boiling point of a liquid?

34. What is a supercritical fluid? What is the critical temperature and critical pressure?

35. What causes surface tension in a liquid?

36. What is capillary action?

37. What is the difference between adhesive and cohesive forces?

38. What causes a meniscus to form when a liquid is placed in a graduated cylinder?

39. What is the viscosity of a liquid?

40. Define miscibility, and describe the difference between miscible and immiscible liquids.

For questions 41-44, consider the following two substances:

41. Which of the two liquids above would have stronger intermolecular forces?

42. Which of the two liquids above would you expect to have a higher vapor pressure?

43. Which of the two liquids above would you expect to be more volatile?

44. Which of the two liquids above would you expect to have a higher boiling point?

For questions 45-48, consider the following two substances:

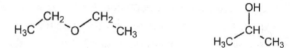

45. Which of the two liquids above would have stronger intermolecular forces?

46. Which of the two liquids above would you expect to have a higher vapor pressure?

47. Which of the two liquids above would you expect to be more volatile?

48. Which of the two liquids above would you expect to have a higher boiling point?

49. Are the vapor pressure of a particular liquid and temperature related? If so, what is the relationship?

50. Consider two beakers of water, one containing 100 ml of water with a diameter of 8 cm and the other containing the same amount of water but with a diameter of 14 cm. From which beaker will the water evaporate faster? Is there a difference in the vapor pressure of the water between the two beakers?

51. Consider two beakers with identical diameters (8 cm) containing the same amount of liquid (100 ml), one filled with water and the other containing acetone. Which liquid will evaporate faster? Is there a difference in the vapor pressure between the two liquids?

52. One of the tubes below contains water and the other mercury. Based on the shape of the meniscus, can you tell which one contains the water versus the mercury?

53. Shelby and Rusty are lab partners in their General Chemistry Laboratory class. As part of their experiment, they are required to fill a graduated cylinder with 25 *ml* of water. Shelby grabs a clean graduated cylinder, fills it with the required amount of water and notices a nice concave meniscus. Rusty, on the other hand, unknowingly grabs a dirty graduated cylinder which has an oily residue lining on the inside of the cylinder. He fills it with the required amount of water and notices that the shape of his meniscus is not the same as Shelby's. What would you expect Rusty's meniscus to look like and why?

54. Are ethanol (CH_3CH_2OH) and water miscible substances? Explain.

55. Are carbon tetrachloride (CCl_4) and water miscible substances? Explain.

56. Are *NaCl* and water miscible substances? Explain.

PHASE DIAGRAMS

57. What is a phase diagram?

58. What is the significance of crossing a line in a phase diagram?

Using the phase diagram depicted below, consider the following questions:

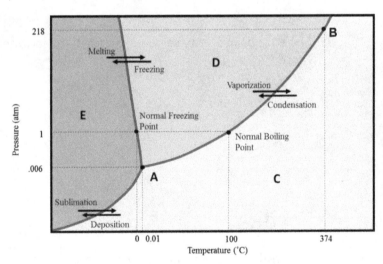

59. The gas phase is represented by which of the following letters?

    a. A

    b. B

    c. C

    d. D

    e. E

60. The solid phase is represented by which of the following letters?
    a. A
    b. B
    c. C
    d. D
    e. E
61. The liquid phase is represented by which of the following letters?
    a. A
    b. B
    c. C
    d. D
    e. E
62. The critical point is represented by which of the following letters?
    a. A
    b. B
    c. C
    d. D
    e. E
63. The triple point is represented by which of the following letters?
    a. A
    b. B
    c. C
    d. D
    e. E

Image Credits

- Fig. 9.Aa: Copyright © Depositphotos/edesignua.
- Fig. 9.Ab: Copyright © Depositphotos/the_lightwriter.
- Fig. 9.1a: Copyright © Depositphotos/Valentyn_Volkov.
- Fig. 9.1b: Copyright © Depositphotos/fisher.photostudio.
- Fig. 9.1c: Copyright © Depositphotos/Paulpaladin.
- Fig. 9.2a: Copyright © Depositphotos/de-kay.
- Fig. 9.2b: Copyright © Depositphotos/elenathewise.
- Fig. 9.B: Copyright © 1928 by Gerhard Hund, (CC BY 3.0) at https://commons.wikimedia.org/wiki/File:London,Fritz_1928_M%C3%BCnchen.jpg.
- Fig. 9.Ca: Copyright © Depositphotos/MidoSemsem.
- Fig. 9.Cb: Copyright © Depositphotos/gcpics.
- Fig. 9.Da: Copyright © Depositphotos/Taden1.
- Fig. 9.Db: Copyright © Depositphotos/belchonock.
- Fig. 9.E : Copyright © Depositphotos/macor.

Chemical Equilibrium

CHAPTER
10

LEARNING OBJECTIVES AND OUTCOMES

After reading this chapter you should be able to do the following:

- Understand and explain the nature of chemical equilibrium.

- Define and properly write the equilibrium constant, K, expression for a chemical reaction.

- Distinguish "product-favored" and "reactant-favored" reactions on the basis of the value of K.

- Understand how K changes as chemical equations are reversed, amplified, and added together.

- Determine the equilibrium constant for gases in terms of partial pressures, K_p, and understand the relationship between K_p and K_c.

- Calculate equilibrium constants, K_c, from reactant and product concentrations at equilibrium.

- Calculate equilibrium concentrations of reactants and products using an equilibrium constant, K_c, for a given reaction.

- Calculate the reaction quotient, Q, and determine whether a reaction is either "at equilibrium" ($Q = K$) or whether there will be a net conversion toward products or reactants in order to achieve equilibrium.

- Use Le Châtelier's Principle to predict the effect on chemical equilibrium of a reaction resulting from changes in concentrations of reactants and products, temperature as well as volume (or pressure) of reactions involving gases.

- Calculate molar solubility from K_{sp}.

- Calculate molar solubility in the presence of a common ion.

- Define and apply the Key Terms listed at the end of this chapter.

Section 10.1 Introduction

So far we have learned a great deal about chemical reactions. However, in our discussions we have treated chemical reactions as being described by one of two states, the reactants (the initial state) and the products (the final state). In other words, we have considered reactions as proceeding to complete conversion to products, with little examination as to how this is accomplished. We will now begin to examine the nature of chemical reactions from a more nuanced perspective. We begin by understanding reactions according to two main characteristics. These are the rate (speed) of reaction and the extent of reaction. The **reaction rate** refers to the velocity at which a reaction proceeds from the reactants to products and is defined as the change in concentration of reactants and/or products per unit time. The study of the rate of chemical reactions is called **Chemical Kinetics** and is the topic of Chapter 14 of this text. For the purposes of our current topic, suffice to say that the rate of reaction will vary from one reaction to the next, depending on the nature of the reactants and products as well as other variables such as concentration and temperature. In other words, some reactions simply proceed more quickly than others.

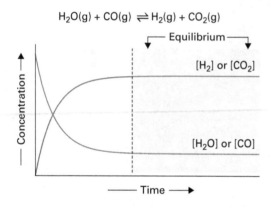

$$H_2O(g) + CO(g) \rightleftharpoons H_2(g) + CO_2(g)$$

Figure 10.1 When the rates of the forward and reverse reactions are same, the concentrations of the reactants and products cease to change. A dynamic steady state is reached at this point where the rate of consumption and production of each component of the reaction mixture is perfectly balanced.

The topic of the current chapter will be concerned primarily with the *extent* of chemical reactions. The *extent of reaction* is a measure of the progress of the reaction. In other words, it refers to how completely the reactants have been converted to products. As it turns out, after a sufficient period of time has elapsed, the concentrations of the reactants and products in a given reaction will cease to change. This is a state referred to as **chemical equilibrium** and arises from the fact that chemical reactions are **reversible.** To understand this a little better, let's consider the example in Figure 10.1. Here we see the evolution of the concentrations of reactants and products in a reaction commonly referred to as the water-gas-shift reaction. In this reaction, water and carbon monoxide are converted (catalytically) to hydrogen gas and carbon dioxide at high temperature.

Notice that initially, the concentrations of the products are zero (red line) and that the reaction proceeds rapidly at first as reactant concentrations decrease (blue line). This is because, as we will learn in Chapter 14, reaction rates are often directly dependent on the concentrations of the reactants. However, as the reaction progresses, the reaction rate slows until it reaches zero at which point it appears that the reaction has ceased altogether. However, this is not the case. What is actually happening is that the reaction is proceeding in both the forward and the reverse directions simultaneously. Initially, because there are no products, the reverse reaction rate is nonexistent (zero). However, as the concentration of the products increases, the rate of the reverse reaction also increases. Meanwhile, the rate of the forward reaction continuously decreases with depletion of the reactant concentrations. Eventually, the two rates reach a point at which they are perfectly equal and balanced and at this point *dynamic equilibrium* is said to have been reached. As such, we define the term **dynamic equilibrium** in a chemical reaction as that state in which the rate of the forward reaction is equal to the rate of the reverse reaction. *Note: just because the rate of the forward and reverse reactions are equal at equilibrium, this does not imply that the concentrations of reactants and products are equal.* Indeed, depending on the reaction in question, most of the reactants may have been converted to product by

Chemical equilibrium is essentially the state in a reaction characterized by a precise balance of reaction rates in the forward and reverse reactions.

the time equilibrium is achieved. On the other hand, other reactions may have only converted a small fraction of the reactants to product at equilibrium. As such, it is important to quantify the concentrations of reactants and products at equilibrium, and this is the subject of the next section.

Did you know how chemistry might relate to your job as a non-chemist? Nitrogen containing compounds are used as fertilizers the world over. For centuries, farmers have used animal manure for this purpose. However, in the late 1800s a German chemist named Fritz Haber developed a method for producing ammonia, a key ingredient in the industrial production of nitrogenous fertilizers. The process essentially relies on the reaction of nitrogen gas and hydrogen to form ammonia and requires an iron oxide catalyst:

Fitz Haber (1868–1934) was a German chemist most noted for his development of an economically viable method of nitrogen fixation in the production of ammonia, known as the Haber Process.

$$N_2(g) + 3H_2(g) \rightleftharpoons 2NH_3(g)$$

At room-temperature, this reaction favors the forward direction quite readily. Unfortunately the rate of reaction at this temperature is too slow to be economically viable. If the temperature is increased (600–700 K), the reaction proceeds faster, but because the reaction is exothermic, high temperatures shift the position of the equilibrium back toward the reactants. For this reason, the equilibrium is manipulated by increasing the pressure (approximately 200 atm). As we will learn in this chapter, because there are fewer gas molecules on the product side of this equilibrium, high pressure will shift the reaction in this direction, enhancing the production of ammonia. It is this careful manipulation of the equilibrium between the reactant and product which makes the Haber process possible. Currently, the Haber process produces about 450 million tons of fertilizer annually and has nearly quadrupled agricultural output since

the turn of the twentieth century. Additionally, even today, the Haber process is the most cost-effective method of "fixing" atmospheric nitrogen. Without it, feeding the global population of seven billion people would present an enormous problem.

Section 10.2 Equilibrium Constant

It is possible to restate or summarize the information in the previous section as follows:

> *In a chemical system, at a given temperature, a state is, or will be, reached in which the ratio of the reactant and product concentrations maintains a constant value.*—**The Law of Mass Action.**

The law of mass action can be given mathematical expression for a generic chemical equation as follows:

$$aA + bB \rightleftharpoons cC + dD$$

$$Equilibrium\,Constant = K = \frac{[C]^c[D]^d}{[A]^a[B]^b}$$

Where K is known as the **equilibrium constant**, [A], [B], [C] and [D] are the various reactant and product concentrations and the lower case a, b, c, and d are the stoichiometric coefficients in the balanced chemical equation. (Because we use molar concentrations to express the equilibrium constant, it is often denoted as K_c as well.) Therefore, we can write such an expression for the equilibrium constant for any chemical reaction if we have the balanced chemical equation. Let's consider an example. Suppose we are interested in the reaction of hydrogen gas with gaseous iodine:

$$H_2(g) + I_2(g) \rightleftharpoons 2HI(g)$$

We can express the equilibrium constant, K_c, in terms of the molar concentrations of the reactants and products at equilibrium as shown here:

$$K_c = \frac{[HI]^2}{[H_2][I_2]}$$

Notice that the stoichiometric coefficients, 1, 1, and 2 from the balanced chemical reaction equation become the exponents in the equilibrium constant expression.

Example Problem 10.1 — The Equilibrium Constant Expression

Write the equilibrium constant expression for the following reaction:
$$4\,NH_3(g) + 3\,O_2(g) \rightleftharpoons 2\,N_2(g) + 6\,H_2O(g)$$
Solution:
The equilibrium constant, K_c, is expressed as the ratio of the molar concentrations of the products over reactants each raised to the power of its respective stoichiometric coefficients. $$K_c = \frac{[N_2]^2[H_2O]^6}{[NH_3]^4[O_2]^3}$$

The Meaning of the Equilibrium Constant

You may be wondering what all of this tells us. We have learned to derive an expression for the equilibrium constant of a reaction. That's great, but what does it mean? What is the difference if K_c is large ($K_c \gg 1$) or small ($K_c \ll 1$)? Close examination of the expression tells us that if $K_c \gg 1$, then the numerator in our expression is larger than the denominator, indicating that, at equilibrium, the "forward" reaction is dominant or favored. In other words, most of the reactants have been converted to products. Likewise, when

$K_c \ll 1$, the reverse reaction is favored, and most of the reactants remain as such. If $K_c = 1$, neither the forward nor the reverse reaction is dominant, and the extent of reaction at equilibrium is approximately "halfway." Note: the equilibrium constant says nothing regarding the rate of reaction in either the forward or the reverse directions; it merely provides a quantitative description of the extent of reaction at equilibrium.

Regarding the Relationship between K_c and Balanced Equations

There a number of ways to write chemical reactions. As we shall learn in various places in this text, the coefficients in a chemical reaction equation can be amplified by a multiplication factor, or the reaction equation can be written in the reverse direction. Whatever the case may be, if the chemical equation is in some way manipulated or modified, the equilibrium constant will also change as a consequence. There are three such modifications we will discuss here:

1. If an equation is reversed, then the equilibrium constant is inverted. For example, consider the generic reaction equation:

$$aA + bB \rightleftharpoons cC + dD$$

We express K_c for this reaction as:

$$K_{forward} = \frac{[C]^c [D]^d}{[A]^a [B]^b}$$

If we reverse this reaction:

$$cC + dD \rightleftharpoons aA + bE$$

Then the equilibrium constant is given as:

$$K_{reverse} = \frac{[A]^a [B]^b}{[C]^c [D]^d} = \frac{1}{K_{forward}}$$

2. Because the reaction coefficients are exponents in the equilibrium constant expression, if you multiply a reaction equation by a factor, n, you must raise K_c to that power. Again, let's consider K_c for a generic reaction:

$$aA + bB \rightleftharpoons cC + dD \qquad K_1 = \frac{[C]^c [D]^d}{[A]^a [B]^b}$$

If the equation is multiplied by n, then:

$$na\,A + nb\,B \rightleftharpoons nc\,C + nd\,D \qquad K_2 = \frac{[C]^{nc} [D]^{nd}}{[A]^{na} [B]^{nb}} = \left(\frac{[C]^c [D]^d}{[A]^a [B]^b} \right)^n = K_1^n$$

3. If two or more reaction equations are summed to generate a net or overall equation, then simply multiply the individual equilibrium constants to generate an overall constant. Consider the following generic reaction equations:

$$aA \rightleftharpoons bB \quad K_1 = \frac{[B]^b}{[A]^a}$$

$$bB \rightleftharpoons cC + dD \quad K_2 = \frac{[C]^c[D]^d}{[B]^b}$$

If we are to take the sum of these two reactions, we arrive at a net overall reaction equation as follows:

$$aA \rightleftharpoons bB$$
$$+ \quad bB \rightleftharpoons cC + dD$$
$$\overline{\qquad aA \rightleftharpoons cC + dD \qquad}$$

Therefore, K_{net} is the product of K_1 and K_2 and is entirely consistent with the Law of Mass Action:

$$K_{net} = K_1 \times K_2 = \frac{[B]^b}{[A]^a} \times \frac{[C]^c[D]^d}{[B]^b} = \frac{[C]^c[D]^d}{[A]^a}$$

Example Problem 10.2—Relationship between K_c and Changes in Chemical Reaction Equation.

At a particular temperature, $K_c = 4.50$ for the following reaction:
$$H_2O(g) + CO(g) \rightleftharpoons H_2(g) + CO_2(g)$$
Given this information, what is the value of K_c' for the following:
$$2H_2(g) + 2CO_2(g) \rightleftharpoons 2H_2O(g) + 2CO(g)$$

Solution:	
First, since the reaction has been reversed, we will invert K_c.	$K_c' = \dfrac{1}{K_c}$
Also, since we have multiplied the coefficients by a factor of two, we must also raise our equilibrium constant to the second power.	$K_c' = \left(\dfrac{1}{K_c}\right)^2$
Therefore, the value of K_c' is 0.0494.	$K_c' = \left(\dfrac{1}{4.50}\right)^2 = \mathbf{0.0494}$

Example Problem 10.3—Relationship between K_c and Changes in Chemical Reaction Equation.

Given the Following reactions:

$$N_2(g) + O_2(g) \rightleftharpoons 2NO(g) \quad K_c'$$

$$2NO(g) + O_2(g) \rightleftharpoons 2NO_2(g) \quad K_c''$$

a.) Show how the equilibrium constant (K_c) of the formation of NO_2 from N_2 and O_2 is expressed in terms of K_c' and K_c''.

b.) What is the value of K_c if $K_c' = 4.5 \times 10^{-25}$ and $K_c'' = 6.4 \times 10^9$?

Solution:	
a.) First, we determine how the given equations sum to the equation of interest.	$N_2(g) + O_2(g) \rightleftharpoons 2NO(g)$ $+ \quad 2NO(g) + O_2(g) \rightleftharpoons 2NO_2(g)$ _____ $N_2(g) + 2O_2(g) \rightleftharpoons 2NO_2(g)$
We can therefore express K_c as the product of K_c' and K_c''.	$K_c' \times K_c'' = \dfrac{[NO]^2}{[N_2][O_2]} \times \dfrac{[NO_2]^2}{[NO]^2[O_2]} = \dfrac{[NO_2]^2}{[N_2][O_2]^2} = K_c$
b.) Given the values of K_c' and K_c'', we can calculate K_c.	$K_c = K_c' \times K_c'' = (4.5 \times 10^{-25})(6.4 \times 10^9)$ $K_c = 2.88 \times 10^{-15}$

Section 10.3 Equilibrium Constant in Terms of Partial Pressures– K_p vs. K_c

For reactions which take place in the gaseous state, it is possible to express the equilibrium constant in terms of partial pressures. Recall from Chapter 6 (gases) that mixtures of gases exert a total pressure which is essentially the sum of the contributions (partial pressures) of each of the individual component gases which make up the mixture. Further, according to the ideal gas law, the concentration of a gas is proportional to its partial pressure. To illustrate this, let's consider an example reaction for which all reactants and products are in the gaseous state, the formation of ammonia:

$$3H_2(g) + N_2(g) \rightleftharpoons 2NH_3(g)$$

If we express the equilibrium constant of this reaction according to the law of mass action as we have learned, we arrive at the following:

$$K_c = \frac{[NH_3]^2}{[H_2]^3[N_2]}$$

However, because all of these compounds are in the gaseous state, we can express their molar concentrations in terms of partial pressures. Consider the ideal gas law:

$$PV = nRT$$

If the molar concentration of a compound is defined as moles per liter, then we can calculate this for a gas by isolating the term n/V as shown here:

$$\frac{n}{V} = \frac{P}{RT}$$

If we apply this to a single component, gas A, of a mixture, we can express its molar concentration as follows:

$$[A] = \frac{n_A}{V} = \frac{P_A}{RT}$$

Where P_A is the partial pressure of compound A in a mixture of gases. If we apply this to our expression of the equilibrium constant for the formation reaction of ammonia, we can arrive at a new expression of K in terms of partial pressures, which we will refer to as K_p:

$$K_c = \frac{[NH_3]^2}{[H_2]^3[N_2]} = \frac{\left(\dfrac{P_{NH_3}}{RT}\right)^2}{\left(\dfrac{P_{H_2}}{RT}\right)^3\left(\dfrac{P_{N_2}}{RT}\right)} = \frac{P^2_{NH_3}}{P^3_{H_2} \cdot P_{N_2}} \cdot \left(\frac{1}{RT}\right)^{2-3-1} = K_p \cdot \left(\frac{1}{RT}\right)^{-2}$$

Therefore:

$$K_p = K_c(RT)^{-2}$$

Hence, the equilibrium constant, K_p, takes the same form as the expression for K_c, except in terms of partial pressures rather than molar concentrations. We can represent this relation for any given reaction. Consider the generic reaction equation here:

$$aA + bB \rightleftharpoons cC + dD$$

We will express K_c as:

$$K_c = \frac{[C]^c[D]^d}{[A]^a[B]^b} = \frac{\left(\dfrac{P_C}{RT}\right)^c\left(\dfrac{P_D}{RT}\right)^d}{\left(\dfrac{P_A}{RT}\right)^a\left(\dfrac{P_B}{RT}\right)^b} = \frac{P^c_C \cdot P^d_D}{P^a_A \cdot P^b_B} \cdot \left(\frac{1}{RT}\right)^{c+d-(a+b)}$$

Hence:

$$K_c = K_p\left(\frac{1}{RT}\right)^{\Delta n} \qquad \Delta n = c + d - (a+b)$$

where Δn is the sum of the stoichiometric coefficients of the products in our reaction equation minus that of the reactants. Therefore, it is obvious that:

$$K_p = K_c(RT)^{\Delta n}$$

Note that *when there is no net change in the number of moles of gaseous species due to the reaction ($\Delta n = 0$), K_p and K_c are equivalent.*

Example Problem 10.4

If the following reaction has a value of $K_p = 4.55 \times 10^{-13}$ at a temperature of 25°C, what is the value of K_c at this temperature?

$$2\,NO_2(g) \rightleftharpoons O_2(g) + 2\,NO(g)$$

Solution:	
We know that the relationship between K_c and K_p is given by the equation here.	$K_p = K_c(RT)^{\Delta n}$
Rearrange the equation to solve for K_c.	$K_c = \dfrac{K_p}{(RT)^{\Delta n}}$
Calculate Δn.	$\Delta n = (1 + 2) - 2 = 1$
Therefore, the equation is simply K_p over RT. As such, we find the value of $K_c = 1.86 \times 10^{-14}$	$K_c = \dfrac{K_p}{(RT)^1} = \dfrac{4.55 \times 10^{-13}}{\left(0.08206\,\dfrac{atm \cdot L}{mol \cdot K}\right)(298\,K)}$ $K_c = 1.86 \times 10^{-14}$

Section 10.4 Heterogeneous Equilibria– Solids and Liquids

In the previous section, we saw a special case where the idea of the molar concentration of gases held some interesting implications in the way in which the equilibrium constant can be expressed. In contrast to gases, however, liquids and solids do not lend themselves readily to descriptions in terms of molar concentrations. This is because solids and liquids do not expand to fill the containers in which they are held. In other words, if I have a gaseous sample contained in a reactor, the gas will expand to fill the entire volume of the reactor. Further, as the gas is consumed due to a reaction, its concentration in the reactor will change with time. Solids and liquids, on the other hand, do not expand to fill a reactor (container), and, as such, we would say their concentration is largely a function of their density, which is essentially invariant under most reaction conditions. Therefore, as long as any quantity of a liquid or solid is present, its concentration remains constant. For this reason, liquids and solids which may be involved as reactants or products in a reaction are not included in the equilibrium constant expression, K_c. Consider the following example, the ionization of acetic acid in water:

$$HC_2H_3O_2(aq) + H_2O(l) \rightleftharpoons C_2H_3O_2^-(aq) + H_3O^+(aq)$$

We might think that there would be a [H_2O] term in the expression for the equilibrium constant. However, since water is a pure liquid it is omitted and we would express K_c as follows:

$$K_c = \frac{[C_2H_3O_2^-][H_3O^+]}{[HC_2H_3O_2]}$$

Example Problem 10.5

Write the expression for K_c for the following reactions:

a.) $2H_2S(g) + SO_2(g) \rightleftharpoons 3S(s) + 2H_2O(g)$

b.) $CO_2(g) + C(s) \rightleftharpoons 2CO(g)$

Solution:	
a.) Since sulfur in this case is a solid, we omit it from the expression for K_c.	$2H_2S(g) + SO_2(g) \rightleftharpoons 3S(s) + 2H_2O(g)$ $$K_c = \frac{[H_2O]^2}{[H_2S]^2[SO_2]}$$
b.) Since carbon in this case is a solid, we omit it from the expression for K_c.	$CO_2(g) + C(s) \rightleftharpoons 2CO(g)$ $$K_c = \frac{[CO]^2}{[CO_2]}$$

Section 10.5 Determining the Equilibrium Constant

If the concentrations of the reactants and products in a given reaction are known at equilibrium, the equilibrium constant can be calculated. This is accomplished simply by placing these concentrations into the expression for K_c and calculating the result. Let's consider the following reaction of hydrogen with iodine to form hydrogen iodide gas:

$$H_2(g) + I_2(g) \rightleftharpoons 2HI(g)$$

If we know, for the reaction above at a temperature of 425°C, that the empirically determined equilibrium concentrations of the reactants and products are [H_2] = 0.2105 M, [I_2] = 0.2105 M and [HI] = 1.579 M, we can substitute these values into the expression for K_c and determine the equilibrium constant.

$$K_c = \frac{[HI]^2}{[H_2][I_2]} = \frac{(1.579\,M)^2}{(0.2105\,M)(0.2105\,M)} = 56.27$$

Hence, at 425°C the equilibrium constant for this reaction is 56.27. While this seems reasonable enough, it is an uncommon scenario to have access to the equilibrium concentrations of all compounds involved in a reaction. It is much more common experimentally that the initial concentrations are known, and only one of the reactant's (or product's) concentration at equilibrium is ascertained empirically. This is usually adequate, however, because with a balanced chemical equation, the concentrations of the remaining reactants and products can be calculated stoichiometrically. With this in mind, let's consider our previous example from a slightly different angle. Let's imagine that 0.100 moles H_2 and 0.100 *mols* I_2 are delivered into a 1.000-*L* flask at 425°C. After equilibrium is realized, it is determined empirically that 0.1579 *mols* of *HI* has been produced. In this case we need to calculate, or infer, the equilibrium concentrations of the reactants as well if we are to calculate K_c for this reaction. To do this, we construct a *reaction table* which details, or provides expressions for, the initial concentrations, changes in those concentrations, and the resulting equilibrium concentrations as follows:

Concentration	$H_2(g)$	+	$I_2(g)$	$\rightleftharpoons$	$2\ HI(g)$
Initial	0.100		0.100		0
Change	$-x$		$-x$		$+2x$
Equilibrium	$0.100-x$		$0.100-x$		$+2x$

Here we use the stoichiometric coefficients to make certain inferences. For instance, we expect the reactants to realize a diminished concentration due to reaction, as these must be consumed to some degree in order to produce the product. We are not sure to what degree the initial reactant concentrations are reduced, so we represent this quantity as $-x$. Further, we expect that the increase in the product concentration should be twice this quantity, $2x$. This stems from the 2:1 stoichiometric ratio between the product and each of the reactants (as described by the reaction co-efficients). Because 0.1579 moles of *HI* were present at equilibrium in a 1-*L* volume, we know that the equilibrium concentration of the product is 0.1579 *M*. Therefore:

$$2x = 0.1579\,M$$

And x is easily determined:

$$x = \frac{0.1579\,M}{2} = 0.07895\,M$$

Having ascertained that $x = 0.07895\,M$, we can calculate our equilibrium constant. Again, we arrive at $K_c = 56.27$ (@ 425°C) just as before:

$$K_c = \frac{[HI]^2}{[H_2][I_2]} = \frac{(2x)^2}{(0.100-x)(0.100-x)} = \frac{(0.1579\,M)^2}{(0.02105\,M)(0.02105\,M)} = 56.27$$

Example Problem 10.6

A 0.250-L reactor at 250°C initially contains 0.500 moles Cl_2 and 0.500 moles of PCl_3. The reaction is allowed to reach equilibrium (according to the following reaction equation) and it is empirically determined that the equilibrium concentration of PCl_3 is 1.061 M. Determine the equilibrium constant K_c.

$$PCl_3(g) + Cl_2(g) \rightleftharpoons PCl_5(g)$$

	Solution:
First, we determine the initial concentrations of the reactants.	$$[PCl_3] = \frac{0.500\,moles}{0.250\,L} = 2.00\,M$$ $$[Cl_2] = \frac{0.500\,moles}{0.250\,L} = 2.00\,M$$

Now, we are able to establish expressions for the equilibrium concentrations of the components of the reaction mixture using the tabular format.

Concentration	$PCl_3(g)$	$+ Cl_2(g)$	$\rightleftharpoons PCl_5(g)$
Initial	2.00	2.00	0
Change	$-x$	$-x$	$+x$
Equilibrium	**2.00 – x**	**2.00 – x**	**x**

We can now substitute these expressions into the expression for K_c.	$$K_c = \frac{[PCl_5]}{[PCl_3][Cl_2]}$$ $$K_c = \frac{x}{(2.00 - x)^2}$$
Since we know the equilibrium concentration of PCl_3 is 1.061 M, we can solve for x. (Note: The last significant figure is denoted in red font.)	$$1.061\,M = 2.00 - x$$ $$x = 2.00 - 1.061 = 0.939$$
We can substitute this value into our expression and solve for K_c. Therefore, we find that at 250°C, the value of K_c for this reaction is 0.834.	$$K_c = \frac{x}{(2.00 - x)^2} = \frac{0.939}{(2.00 - 0.939)^2}$$ $$K_c = \frac{0.939}{1.125721} = 0.834$$ $$\mathbf{K_c = 0.834}$$

Example Problem 10.7

If a quantity of pure NO gas is contained in a reactor at a certain temperature with a total pressure of 5.000 atm and when the reaction reaches equilibrium the partial pressure of O_2 (P_{O_2}) is 2.4495 atm, what is the value of K_p?

$$2\,NO(g) \rightleftharpoons O_2(g) + N_2(g)$$

	Solution:

	Concentration	$2\,NO(g)$	$\rightleftharpoons$ $O_2(g)$	$+ N_2(g)$
First, we must establish expressions for the equilibrium pressures of the components of the reaction mixture.	Initial	5.0000	0	0
	Change	$-2x$	$+x$	$+x$
	Equilibrium	**5.000 – x**	**x**	**x**

Next, we substitute these expressions into our expression for K_p.	$$K_p = \frac{P_{O_2} \cdot P_{N_2}}{P_{NO}^2} = \frac{(x)(x)}{(5.000 - 2x)^2}$$
Additionally, we know that the equilibrium pressure of O_2 is expressed as x, and further, it is given as 2.4495 atm.	$$x = 2.4495\,atm$$

We now substitute this value for x and find the value of K_p = 588.2	$K_p = \dfrac{x^2}{(5.000-2x)^2} = \dfrac{(2.4495)^2}{(5.0000-2(2.4495))^2}$ $K_p = \dfrac{6.00005025}{0.010201} = \mathbf{588.2}$

Section 10.6 The Reaction Quotient

Sometimes we are observing reactions which are not yet at equilibrium and for which there is a nonzero concentration of products. In such a circumstance, it is often useful, or necessary, to be able to predict the net direction in which the reaction must proceed to achieve equilibrium. In other words, will the reaction proceed toward the left (toward reactants) or toward the right (toward products)? This question can be answered using a quantity referred to as the *reaction quotient, Q*. The reaction quotient takes the same form as the expression for the equilibrium constant, K, but does not necessarily reflect equilibrium conditions. Therefore, we express Q for a generic reaction equation as follows:

$$aA + bB \rightleftharpoons cC + dL$$

$$Q_c = \frac{[C]^c[D]^d}{[A]^a[B]^b} \; ; \; Q_p = \frac{P_C^c \cdot P_D^d}{P_A^a \cdot P_B^b}$$

The key here is to understand that Q need not refer to equilibrium. As such, we define the **reaction quotient** as the ratio of the product and reactant molar concentrations (or partial pressures) each raised to their respective stoichiometric coefficient—*at any point in a chemical reaction*. While K_c (or K_p) is constant at a given temperature for a given reaction, Q_c (or Q_p) depends on the state of the reaction at any given time and changes as the reaction proceeds toward equilibrium. As such, Q provides a quantitative assessment of the progress of a chemical reaction, and when the value of Q is considered relative to the value of the equilibrium constant, it provides an indication of the direction the reaction must take to achieve equilibrium. *At equilibrium Q is equal to K.*

Let's consider the generic example in Figure 10.2. For the reaction, $A \rightleftharpoons B$, wherein compounds A and B are either in solution or in the gaseous state, we can express the reaction quotient as:

$$Q_c = \frac{[B]}{[A]}$$

If we plot Q_c as a function of $[B]$ or $[A]$ (Figure 10.2), we can visualize some basic points. First, for all values of $Q > 1$, then $[B] > [A]$. Likewise, when $Q < 1$, then $[B] < [A]$. Further, understanding that all reactions are progressing toward equilibrium, we see that when $Q < K$, there will need to be a net production of the product B in order to reach equilibrium ($Q = K$). In other words, Q

Figure 10.2 The reaction quotient, Q, is the ratio of the product and reactant molar concentrations each raised to their respective stoichiometric coefficients at any point in a chemical reaction. When $Q = K$ the reaction is at equilibrium. When $Q > K$, the reaction will proceed to the left as it approaches equilibrium. When $Q < K$, the reaction proceed to the right as it approaches equilibrium.

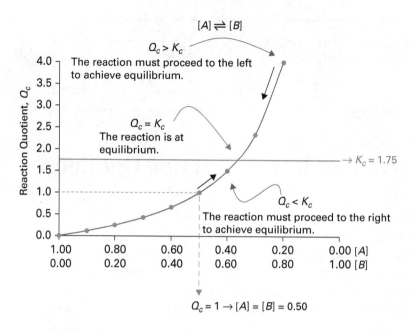

must increase in order to reach equilibrium. For Q to increase, the reactant concentration must decrease ($[A] \downarrow$), and the product concentration must increase ($[B] \uparrow$). Another way to say this is that the reaction will proceed to the right. Likewise, when $Q > K$, the reaction quotient must decrease in order to achieve equilibrium. Therefore, the reactant concentration must increase while the product concentration decreases. That is, the reaction will proceed to the left. If $Q = K$, we say the reaction is at equilibrium. In this way, we can predict the direction in which a reaction will proceed as it moves toward equilibrium if we understand the relative values of K and Q at any point during a reaction.

Example Problem 10.8 — Using the Reaction Quotient to Determine the Direction of Reaction.

Consider the following reaction:

$$H_2(g) + I_2(g) \rightleftharpoons 2\,HI(g) \qquad K_p = 56.26$$

The current status of the reaction mixture is characterized by the following:

$$P_{H_2} = 0.119\,atm$$

$$P_{I_2} = 0.107\,atm$$

$$P_{HI} = 0.750\,atm$$

Is this reaction at equilibrium? If not, will the product or the reactants have to be depleted in order to reach equilibrium?

Solution:	
In order to answer this question, we will need to calculate Q_p from the given partial pressures.	$Q_p = \dfrac{P_{HI}^{\,2}}{P_{H_2} P_{I_2}} = \dfrac{(0.750)^2}{(0.119)(0.107)} = 44.2$
We see immediately that Q_p is less than K_p.	$(Q_p = 44.2) < (K_p = 56.26)$

When $Q_p < K_p$, we know that the reaction must proceed to the right to achieve equilibrium. As such, we would expect the reactants to be further depleted in order to reach equilibrium.

Section 10.7 Determining Equilibrium Concentrations

If you recall from Chapter 4, we were singularly concerned with stoichiometric calculations and, in particular, the calculation of yields. It is obvious that, as chemists, the ability to predict how much product can be formed in a given reaction is an important skill. However, the concept of equilibrium would seem, in many cases, to complicate this process. For this, as well as other reasons, it is often desirable to calculate equilibrium concentrations of reactants and products, using known values for K_c or K_p, along with initial concentrations of the reactants and products. Let's consider again our example of the water-gas-shift reaction (Figure 10.1). Under certain conditions, it is known that $K_c = 4.24$ for this reaction. Further, recall the balanced chemical equation:

$$H_2O(g) + CO(g) \rightleftharpoons H_2(g) + CO_2(g)$$

If 0.500 moles each of water and carbon monoxide are placed in a 1.00 *L* reaction vessel and allowed to react and come to equilibrium, what will the equilibrium concentrations be? First we will determine the initial concentrations:

$$[H_2O]_i = \frac{n_{H_2O}}{V} = \frac{0.500 \ mol \ H_2O}{1.00 \ L} = 0.500 \ M$$

$$[CO]_i = \frac{n_{CO}}{V} = \frac{0.500 \ mol \ CO}{1.00 \ L} = 0.500 \ M$$

$$[H_2]_i = [CO_2]_i = 0 \ M$$

Next, constructing a reaction table, we develop an expression for the equilibrium concentrations of the reactants and products. Since the reaction quotient, Q_c, will initially equal zero in this case, we know the reaction will proceed to the right, and, as such, the reactant concentrations will decrease by a quantity, x, and the products will increase, as shown:

Concentration	H_2O(g)	+ CO(g)	$\rightleftharpoons$ H_2(g)	+ CO_2(g)
Initial	0.500	0.500	0	0
Change	$-x$	$-x$	$+x$	$+x$
Equilibrium	0.500 − x	0.500 − x	x	x

Because we do not know the precise numerical value of the change in concentration of the reactants, we must express the equilibrium concentrations in terms of the unknown change, x, as shown in the table above. Therefore:

$$K_c = \frac{[H_2][CO_2]}{[H_2O][CO]} = \frac{(x)(x)}{(0.500 - x)(0.500 - x)} = 4.24$$

In this case the expression takes on the form of a perfect square, and, as such, we can solve for x by, first, taking the square root of both sides of the equation:

$$\sqrt{4.24} = \frac{x}{0.500 - x}$$

Thus:

$$2.059 = \frac{x}{0.500 - x}$$

$$(2.059)(0.500 - x) = x$$

$$1.0296 - 2.059x = x$$

$$1.0296 = x(1 + 2.059)$$

Therefore:

$$x = \frac{1.0296}{1 + 2.059} = 0.3366$$

Since we now have determined the numeric value of x, we also know the numeric values of our equilibrium concentrations:

$$[H_2O]_{eq} = [CO]_{eq} = 0.500 - x = 0.500 - 0.3366 = \textbf{0.1634 M}$$

$$[H_2]_{eq} = [CO_2]_{eq} = x = \textbf{0.3366 M}$$

Let's consider another example. Suppose we are conducting an experiment wherein we place 0.250 moles of NO_2 gas into a 0.500-L flask. The gas is then allowed to reach equilibrium according to the following reaction equation:

$$N_2O_4(g) \rightleftharpoons 2\,NO_2(g) \qquad K_c = 0.350$$

In this case, since the initial concentration of the "reactant" is zero, $Q_c = \infty$, and, therefore, the reaction will proceed to the left. In other words, because $Q_c > K_c$, the reactant concentration will increase by a quantity, while the product will decrease as shown:

Concentration	$N_2O_4(g)$	$\rightleftharpoons$	$2\,NO_2(g)$
Initial	0		0.500
Change	+x		−2x
Equilibrium	x		0.500 − 2x

If we substitute these results into our expression for K_c, we arrive at the following:

$$K_c = \frac{[NO_2]^2}{[N_2O_4]} = \frac{(0.500 - 2x)^2}{x} = 0.350$$

Rearrangement of this expression presents us with a quadratic equation:

$$4x^2 - 2.00x + 0.250 = 0.350x$$

$$4x^2 - 2.350x + 0.250 = 0$$

Therefore, we must solve the quadratic equation to determine the value of x. The following represents a generic solution to quadratic equations:

$$ax^2 + bx + c = 0; \quad then \quad x = \frac{-b \pm \sqrt{b^2 - 4ac}}{2a}$$

If we apply this solution to our quadratic, we get the following:

$$x = \frac{+2.350 \pm \sqrt{(-2.350)^2 - 4(4)(0.250)}}{2(4)} = \frac{2.350 \pm \sqrt{5.523 - 4}}{8}$$

Therefore:

$$x = \frac{2.350 \pm \sqrt{1.523}}{8} = 0.4480 \, M \quad or \quad 0.1395 \, M$$

Since the first solution $(x = 0.4480 \, M)$ will result in a negative equilibrium concentration for NO_2, we dispense with it. As such, we find that $x = 0.1395 \, M$ and our equilibrium concentrations are as follows:

$$[NO_2]_{eq} = 0.500 - 2x = 0.500 - 2(0.1395) = \mathbf{0.2210 \, M}$$

$$\left[N_2O_4 \right]_{eq} = x = \mathbf{0.1395 \, M}$$

Example Problem 10.9 provides further practice calculating the equilibrium concentrations of reactants and products.

Example Problem 10.9

Consider the following reaction:

$$2 \, NO_2(g) \rightleftharpoons N_2O_4(g) \quad K_c = 2.75$$

If the reaction mixture initially contained pure NO_2 with a concentration of $[NO_2] = 0.350 \, M$, what are the concentrations of NO_2 and N_2O_4 at equilibrium?

Solution:	
First, we will establish the direction the reaction must proceed. Because $[N_2O_4]=0$, Q_c is also zero. Therefore, we expect depletion of the reactant and formation of the product as the reaction achieves equilibrium.	$Q_c < K_c$

Next we employ our tabular approach to develop expressions for the equilibrium concentrations.	Concentration	$2 \, NO_2(g)$	$\rightleftharpoons$	$N_2O_4(g)$
	Initial	0.350		0
	Change	$-2x$		$+x$
	Equilibrium	**0.350 − 2x**		**x**

We can now substitute this in our expression for K_c.	$$K_c = \frac{[N_2O_4]}{[NO_2]^2} = \frac{x}{(0.350 - 2x)^2} = 2.75$$
We can now rearrange the equation to solve for x.	$$11.0x^2 - 4.85x + 0.3369 = 0$$
Since we have arrived at a quadratic equation, we determine the possible solutions as shown.	$$ax^2 + bx + c = 0; \quad then \quad x = \frac{-b \pm \sqrt{b^2 - 4ac}}{2a}$$ $$x = \frac{4.85 \pm \sqrt{(-4.85)^2 - 4(11.0)(0.3369)}}{2(11.0)}$$ $$x = 0.3545 \quad or \quad 0.08639$$
Since the first solution (0.3545) would produce a negative value for the equilibrium concentration of NO_2, we can dispense with it. Therefore, if we substitute the second solution into our expressions for the equilibrium concentrations we arrive at our solution.	$$[NO_2] = 0.350 - 2(0.08639) = \mathbf{0.177 \; M}$$ $$[N_2O_4] = 0.08639 = \mathbf{0.0864 \; M}$$

Section 10.8 Le Châtelier's Principle

So far we have learned that chemical reactions progress toward equilibrium. This was the general principle behind our use of the reaction quotient, Q, to predict the net direction a reaction will undergo as it proceeds to equilibrium. This principle has an interesting additional consequence. What if we were to change the conditions of a chemical system after equilibrium was already established. In such a case, the reaction would shift in a direction to re-establish equilibrium under the new set of conditions. This concept was formalized in what is known as *Le Châtelier's principle*.

Le Châtelier's principle: *When a chemical system at equilibrium is perturbed, the system will shift in the direction which minimizes the perturbation.*

There are three main ways in which a chemical system at equilibrium can experience a perturbation. These include changes in concentrations of reactants or products, changes in volume or pressure, and changes in temperature. We will examine each of these in turn.

Henry L. Le Châtelier (1850–1936) was a French chemist most noted for his principle of chemical equilibrium.

Changes in Concentration

Consider the following system at equilibrium:

$$PCl_3(g) + Cl_2(g) \rightleftharpoons PCl_5(g)$$

$$Q_c = K_c = \frac{[PCl_5]}{[PCl_3][Cl_2]}$$

Suppose that we interrupt or disturb the equilibrium by the addition of more $PCl_5(g)$ to the reaction mixture. According to Le Châtelier, the reaction will shift to the left such as to re-establish its equilibrium. We can see why if we consider the effect on Q. At equilibrium $Q_c = K_c$. When more product (PCl_5) is added, Q_c is now greater than K_c. As we have already learned in a previous section, when $Q_c > K_c$, the reaction will proceed to the left (depletion of product and increase in reactants) as equilibrium is "re-established" in this case. Essentially, changes to the concentration of any of the reactants or products will necessarily alter the reaction quotient, breaking equilibrium and setting up an inequality with the equilibrium constant. The system then responds just as we have learned:

1. Changes in concentration which result in the inequality $Q > K$ will cause the reaction to shift left in order to re-establish equilibrium. (Product concentration decreases; reactant concentration increases.)

2. Changes in concentration which result in the inequality $Q < K$ will cause the reaction to shift right in order to re-establish equilibrium. (Product concentration increases; reactant concentration decreases.)

Let's consider another change. Suppose we increase the concentration of the reactants, PCl_3 and Cl_2. In this case, an increase in the reactant concentration will result in a decrease in the value of the reaction quotient, such that Q_c is now lower than K_c. This will result in a shift right to re-establish the equality, $Q_c = K_c$. Essentially, adding more of one of the products shifts the reaction left (toward reactants) while decreasing one of the products shifts the reaction right (toward the products). The same logic applies to the reactants. Adding reactant shifts the reaction right (toward the products) while decreasing one of the reactants shifts the reaction left (toward the reactants).

Example Problem 10.10

Consider the following reaction:
$$N_2(g) + 3H_2(g) \rightleftharpoons 2NH_3(g)$$
Having established equilibrium, what is the effect of adding additional NH_3 to the reaction mixture?
Solution:
According to Le Châtelier, if additional product is added to the reaction mixture (at equilibrium), the reaction will shift to minimize this change. As such, the reaction will shift to the left, depleting the product (NH_3), resulting in an increase in the concentrations of the reactants.

Changes in Pressure (Volume)

Recall from Chapter 6 that, for gases, pressure and volume are inversely related (Boyle's Law, Section 6.3). In other words, all things being equal, if the volume of a gas is decreased, the pressure increases and vice versa. As such, when the volume of a reaction at equilibrium is changed, the pressure will change as well. According to Le Châtelier, when the volume of chemical reaction at equilibrium is altered, the reaction will shift in a direction to minimize the resulting change in pressure. Let's again consider our example:

$$PCl_3(g) + Cl_2(g) \rightleftharpoons PCl_5(g)$$

In this case, we can see that all of the reactants and products are in the gaseous state. Also, let's imagine this reaction taking place inside a cylinder which has a moveable piston on one side that can be manipulated to increase or decrease the volume of the system. In other words, we can easily compress or expand the volume. If we compress the system by pushing the piston inward such that the volume of the reactor is decreased by one half, we know from the ideal gas law ($PV = nRT$) that the partial pressure of each gaseous component will increase. How then will the reaction at equilibrium respond to minimize this increase in pressure? We can answer this question, again, by examining the reaction quotient, Q_p. If we express Q_p for the initial conditions, we have the following:

$$Q_p = \frac{P_{PCl_5}}{P_{PCl_3} \cdot P_{Cl_2}}$$

If we reduce the volume of the reaction vessel by a half, we know this will alter the partial pressures of the components because partial pressures vary inversely with volume as expressed by the ideal gas law:

$$P_A = \frac{n_A RT}{V_i}$$

When the final volume (V_f) is half the initial volume (V_i), the resulting partial pressure (P_A') is twice the initial partial pressure (P_A) for component A:

$$P_A' = \frac{n_A RT}{V_f} = \frac{n_A RT}{\frac{V_i}{2}} = \frac{2n_A RT}{V_i} = 2P_A$$

Therefore, the new reaction quotient (Q_p') is:

$$Q_p' = \frac{P_{PCl_5}'}{P_{PCl_3}' \cdot P_{Cl_2}'} = \frac{2P_{PCl_5}}{2P_{PCl_3} \cdot 2P_{Cl_2}} = \frac{1}{2}Q_p$$

Figure 10.3 A reactor consists of a piston and cylinder assembly, in which a reaction is at equilibrium. If we compress the system by pushing the piston inward such that the volume of the reactor is decreased by ½, we know from the ideal gas law ($PV = nRT$) that the partial pressure of each gaseous component will increase. Le Châtelier says that the reaction at equilibrium will respond by shifting in the direction which decreases the total number of gaseous particles in the system, mitigating the increase in pressure due to the compression.

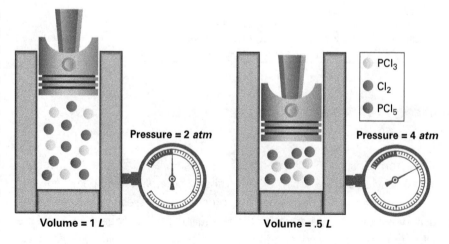

PCl₃
Cl₂
PCl₅

Pressure = 2 atm   Pressure = 4 atm

Volume = 1 L   Volume = .5 L

Therefore, since $Q_p < (Q_p = K_p)$, we know that the reaction will proceed to the right (increase of products and decrease of reactants) in order to re-establish equilibrium.

How is this consistent with the language of Le Châtelier's principle? In other words, how does this shift to the right serve to minimize the change in pressure of the system? Isn't the volume still halved? Would not the pressure still be twice as much? The answer lies in the balanced chemical reaction equation. Note that if the reaction proceeds to the right, the total number of moles of gas molecules is reduced by a half. In other words, one mole of PCl_3 reacts with one mole of Cl_2 (two moles total) to produce just one mole of PCl_5. Since we know (according to the ideal gas law) that pressure varies directly with the number of moles of gas particles in a sample, a shift to the right in this case will reduce the pressure of the system, minimizing the increase due to compression. In any event, just as in the case of changes in concentration, changes to the volume alter the reaction quotient, Q_p, breaking equilibrium and setting up an inequality with the equilibrium constant, K_p. The system then responds just as we have learned in the previous section:

1. Changes in volume which result in the inequality $Q_p > K_p$ will cause the reaction to shift left in order to re-establish equilibrium.

2. Changes in concentration which result in the inequality $Q_p < K_p$ will cause the reaction to shift right in order to re-establish equilibrium.

Example Problem 10.11

Consider the following reaction:

$$N_2(g) + 3H_2(g) \rightleftharpoons 2NH_3(g)$$

Having established equilibrium, would the compression of the reaction mixture (reduction in volume) favor the formation or depletion of product (NH_3)? Why or why not?

Solution:

The compression of the reaction mixture would result in increased partial pressures of all components. According to Le Châtelier, the reaction will respond to minimize this increase in partial pressures. Since the right side of the equation has fewer moles of gas particles than the left, *the reaction will shift right resulting in the formation of more product.* This would diminish the number of gaseous molecules in the system which reduces the pressure.

Changes in Temperature

Another variable which will disturb or stress the equilibrium of a reaction is temperature. Have you noticed throughout this chapter that we often specify a temperature which is associated with a given value of K_c? This is because the equilibrium constant itself is dependent on temperature. In other words, for a given reaction the equilibrium constant is different at different temperatures. Let's again consider our example.

$$PCl_3(g) + Cl_2(g) \rightleftharpoons PCl_5(g) \quad \Delta H_{rxn}^o = -92.5\,kJ$$

In this case, we include the **enthalpy of reaction**, ΔH^o, also referred to as the "heat" of reaction. We will learn more about quantifying heats of reaction in Chapter 12. For now, suffice to say that chemical reactions will either absorb (require) heat, or they will give off (release) heat. Reactions which release heat are said to be **exothermic reactions**, and they have a value of $\Delta H^o < 0$. In such cases, we can think of the heat as an additional product of the reaction. Likewise, chemical reactions that absorb heat are referred to as **endothermic reactions** and have a value of $\Delta H^o > 0$. In this case, we can consider heat as a reactant. The main difference in applying Le Châtelier's principle in cases of changing temperature is that variation in temperature changes the value of K rather than Q. Nevertheless, the reasoning is similar. We will cover the temperature dependence of K in more detail in Chapter 12 (Thermochemistry) and Chapter 14 (Chemical Kinetics), but for now it is important to simply understand a couple of guidelines:

1. For exothermic reactions ($\Delta H^o < 0$), K decreases as temperature increases and vice versa.

2. For endothermic reactions ($\Delta H^o > 0$), K increases as temperature increases and vice versa.

Let's apply these guidelines to our example. Suppose that following the establishment of equilibrium, we increase the temperature of the reaction mixture described by the reaction equation above. Since the heat of reaction is less than zero, we know the reaction is exothermic. As such, increasing the temperature would result in a decrease in the value of K. Since at equilibrium $Q = K$, a decrease in K results in the inequality $Q > K$. We know in this case that if Q is greater than K, the reaction will then shift left (decreasing the product concentration and increasing the reactant concentration). In other words, a lower K value results in the formation of less product at equilibrium. Likewise, if we had reduced the temperature, K would increase, resulting in $Q < K$, shifting the reaction to the right favoring the formation of product. The effect is reversed when dealing with endothermic reactions.

Example Problem 10.12

Consider the exothermic reaction described here:

$$2\,SO_2(g) + O_2(g) \rightleftharpoons 2\,SO_2(g) \qquad \Delta H^O < 0$$

Having established equilibrium, what is the effect of increasing the reaction temperature?

Solution:

Since the reaction is exothermic, we can think of heat as a product. Therefore, heating the reaction mixture will result in a shift to the left (away from the product) according to Le Châtelier. Alternatively, we can also see this in terms of the relative values of K and Q. Since increasing the temperature will cause the value of K to decrease, Q will also have to decrease in order to re-establish equilibrium. This will require the product concentration to decrease while that of the reactants will increase. That is to say the reaction must shift to the left.

Section 10.9 Solubility Equilibria

The phenomenon of equilibrium is not strictly relegated to chemical reactions only. This should not be surprising inasmuch as equilibrium is essentially the establishment of balance between the rates of competing processes. With this in mind, let's consider another such pair of related, or competing, processes. These are dissolution and precipitation. In Chapter 5 we learned about the solubility of different compounds, and, in fact, we established some empirical rules for predicting the solubility of various compounds in water. In these cases, we treated the solubility of compounds as somewhat of a black-and-white (an either-or) question. Compounds were either soluble or not. The truth is that many compounds have varying degrees of solubility. Let's consider an example. We could describe the dissolution of strontium sulfate in water according to the following equation:

$$SrSO_4(s) \rightleftharpoons Sr^{2+}(aq) + SO_4^{2-}(aq)$$

The expression of an equilibrium in this case suggests a limited solubility for strontium sulfate and, further, a dynamic interplay between rates of dissolution and precipitation. This is a much more accurate picture of the solubility of compounds. For solutions at saturation, we can express an equilibrium constant for this process according to the law of mass action as follows:

$$K_{sp} = [Sr^{2+}][SO_4^{2-}]$$

Notice, we exclude the $[SrSO_4]$ term from the expression as the undissolved strontium sulfate is a solid. Recall that we exclude solids and liquids from the equilibrium constant expression. Additionally, **K_{sp}** is the equilibrium constant for this process, which we refer to as the **solubility product**. The K_{sp} for strontium sulfate at 25°C is 3.4×10^{-7}. Appendix III of this text gives some common K_{sp} values. These can be used to determine or predict the "molar solubility" of various compounds. Let's consider our example. Suppose I would like to know the molar solubility of strontium sulfate in pure water at 25°C. We begin by constructing a reaction table to develop expressions for the equilibrium concentrations of the dissolved ions as follows:

Concentration	$SrSO_4(s) \rightleftharpoons$	$Sr^{2+}(aq) +$	$SO_4^{2-}(aq)$
Initial	N/A	0 M	0 M
Change	N/A	+x	+x
Equilibrium	N/A	x	x

Therefore we can express K_{sp} as follows:

$$K_{sp} = [Sr^{2+}][SO_4^{2-}] = (x)(x) = x^2 = 3.44 \times 10^{-7}$$

Further, it is obvious:

$$\sqrt{3.4 \times 10^{-7}} = x$$

$$x = 5.8 \times 10^{-4} \ M$$

Therefore the molar solubility of strontium sulfate is 5.8×10^{-4} moles per liter.

Example 10.13—Calculating Molar Solubility from K_{sp}.

Calculate the molar solubility of $Ca(OH)_2$ at 25°C.	
Solution:	
We first look up the value of K_{sp} of calcium hydroxide in Appendix III and write a balanced equation describing the dissolution.	$Ca(OH)_2(s) \rightleftharpoons Ca^{2+}(aq) + 2OH^-(aq)$ $$K_{sp} = 4.7 \times 10^{-6}$$

Stoichiometrically determine expressions for the equilibrium concentrations of the calcium and hydroxide ions using the tabular format.	Concentration	$Ca(OH)_2(s)$	$\rightleftharpoons$	$Ca^{2+}(aq)$	$+2OH^-(aq)$
	Initial	N/A		0	0
	Change	N/A		+x	+2x
	Equilibrium	**N/A**		**x**	**2x**

Substitute these expressions into the K_{sp} expression and solve for x.	$$K_{sp} = [Ca^{2+}][OH^-]^2 = (x)(2x)^2$$ $$K_{sp} = 4x^3 = 4.7 \times 10^{-6}$$
	$$x = \sqrt[3]{\frac{4.7 \times 10^{-6}}{4}} = 1.06 \times 10^{-2}$$

Therefore the **molar solubility of calcium hydroxide at 25°C is 1.06×10^{-2} moles per liter.**

The Common Ion Effect

When a compound is dissolved in a solution which already contains one of its constituent ions, its solubility in that solution will be diminished to a degree dictated by the value of K_{sp} and the initial concentration of the common ion. This is a phenomenon known as the Common Ion Effect and is stated as follows:

The Common Ion Effect: *The solubility of an ionic compound will be lower in a solution which contains a common ion than it otherwise would be in pure water.*

In order to clearly understand this concept, consider the following example problem.

Example 10.14—The Common Ion Effect

Calculate the molar solubility of $Ca(OH)_2$ in a solution which is 0.100 M in $NaOH$ at 25°C.	
Solution:	
We first look up the value of K_{sp} of calcium hydroxide in Appendix III and write a balanced equation describing the dissolution.	$Ca(OH)_2(s) \rightleftharpoons Ca^{2+}(aq) + 2OH^-(aq)$ $$K_{sp} = 4.7 \times 10^{-6}$$

Stoichiometrically determine expressions for the equilibrium concentrations of the calcium and hydroxide ions using the tabular format. Because the hydroxide ion is already present in the solution, we acknowledge this by indicating an initial concentration for hydroxide of 0.100.	Concentration	$Ca(OH)_2(s)$	$\rightleftharpoons Ca^{2+}(aq) + 2\ OH^-(aq)$	
	Initial	N/A	0	0.100
	Change	N/A	$+x$	$+2x$
	Equilibrium	**N/A**	**x**	**0.100 + 2x**
Substitute these expressions into the K_{sp} expression.	$$K_{sp} = [Ca^{2+}][OH^-] = (x)(0.100 + 2x)^2$$ $$K_{sp} = (x)(0.100 + 2x)^2 = 4.7 \times 10^{-6}$$			
In solving this expression for x, we arrive at a third order polynomial, which is difficult to solve. In such a circumstance, we can take advantage of the fact that K_{sp} is negligibly small compared to the initial hydroxide ion concentration. As such, we can make the assumption shown here. **(This assumption is valid any time x is 5% of the ion concentration or less.)**	$$0.100 + 2x \approx 0.100$$ Therefore: $$(x)(0.100 + 2x)^2 \approx (x)(0.100)^2 = 4.7 \times 10^{-6}$$ $$0.0100x = 4.7 \times 10^{-6}$$ $$x = 4.7 \times 10^{-4}\ M$$			

Therefore the **molar solubility in this case will be 4.7×10^{-4} moles per liter**. Compare this result to the molar solubility of calcium hydroxide in pure water which was determined in Example Problem 10.13. The solubility in this case is diminished by two orders of magnitude.

Key Terms

1. Chemical equilibrium

2. Chemical kinetics

3. Common Ion Effect

4. Dynamic equilibrium

5. Endothermic reaction

6. Exothermic reaction

7. Law of Mass Action

8. Le Châtelier's principle

9. Reaction quotient

10. Reaction rate

11. Reversible reaction

12. Solubility product

Problems

EQUILIBRIUM CONSTANT

1. When a reaction is at equilibrium, there is no change in the concentrations of the reactants or products. Why is this state considered dynamic?

2. If a reaction proceeds to near completion, is K_c large or small?

3. Write the equilibrium constant expression in terms of concentrations of reactants and products (K_c) as well as in terms of partial pressures (K_p) for the following reaction:

$$CH_4(g) + 4\,F_2(g) \rightleftharpoons CF_4(g) + 4\,HF(g)$$

4. Write the equilibrium constant expression in terms of concentrations of reactants and products (K_c) as well as in terms of partial pressures (K_p) for the following reaction:

$$2\,N_2(g) + 4\,H_2O(g) \rightleftharpoons 4\,H_2(g) + 4\,NO(g)$$

5. Write the equilibrium constant expression in terms of concentrations of reactants and products (K_c) as well as in terms of partial pressures (K_p) for the following reaction:

$$4\,NH_3(g) + 3\,O_2(g) \rightleftharpoons 2\,N_2(g) + 6\,H_2O(g)$$

6. Write the equilibrium constant expression in terms of concentrations of reactants and products (K_c) as well as in terms of partial pressures (K_p) for the following reaction:

$$2\,N_2(g) + 4\,H_2O(g) \rightleftharpoons 4\,H_2(g) + 4\,NO(g)$$

7. Write the equilibrium constant expression in terms of concentrations of reactants and products (K_c):

$$H_2O(l) + SO_3(g) \rightleftharpoons H_2SO_4(aq)$$

8. Write the equilibrium constant expression in terms of concentrations of reactants and products (K_c) as well as in terms of partial pressures (K_p) for the following reaction:

$$2\,C(s) + O_2(g) \rightleftharpoons 2\,CO(g)$$

9. Classify the following reactions as product-favored or reactant-favored:

a. $C_2H_2(g) + H_2O(g) \rightleftharpoons CH_3CHO(g)$ $K_c = 4.0 \times 10^{-4}$

b. $PCl_3(g) + Cl_2(g) \rightleftharpoons PCl_5(g)$ $K_c = 23.0$

10. Classify the following reactions as product-favored or reactant-favored:

    a. $C(s) + 2Cl_2(g) \rightleftharpoons CCl_4(g)$ $\qquad$ $K_c = 8.3 \times 10^{10}$

    b. $CCl_4(g) + CH_4(g) \rightleftharpoons 2CH_2Cl_2(g)$ $\qquad$ $K_c = 0.95$

11. At a particular temperature, $K_c = 3.45 \times 10^{-9}$ for the following reaction:

    $$C_2H_4(g) \rightleftharpoons C_2H_2(g) + H_2(g)$$

    Given this information, what is the value of K_c for the following:

    $$3C_2H_4(g) \rightleftharpoons 3C_2H_2(g) + 3H_2(g)$$

12. At a particular temperature, $K_c = 3.45 \times 10^{-9}$ for the following reaction:

    $$C_2H_4(g) \rightleftharpoons C_2H_2(g) + H_2(g)$$

    Given this information, what is the value of K_c for the following:

    $$C_2H_2(g) + H_2(g) \rightleftharpoons C_2H_4(g)$$

13. At a particular temperature, $K_c = 7.15 \times 10^{27}$ for the following reaction:

    $$2CO(g) + O_2(g) \rightleftharpoons 2CO_2(g)$$

    Given this information, what is the value of K_c for the following:

    $$6CO_2(g) \rightleftharpoons 6CO(g) + 3O_2(g)$$

14. At a particular temperature, $K_c = 7.15 \times 10^{27}$ for the following reaction:

    $$2CO(g) + O_2(g) \rightleftharpoons 2CO_2(g)$$

    Given this information, what is the value of K_c for the following:

    $$CO_2(g) \rightleftharpoons CO(g) + \frac{1}{2}O_2(g)$$

15. Given the following (@298 K):

    $$C(s) + 2H_2(g) \rightleftharpoons CH_4(g) \qquad K_1 = 7.1 \times 10^8$$

    $$C(s) + 2Cl_2(g) \rightleftharpoons CCl_4(g) \qquad K_2 = 8.3 \times 10^{10}$$

    $$H_2(g) + Cl_2(g) \rightleftharpoons 2HCl(g) \qquad K_3 = 5.1 \times 10^{16}$$

    Calculate the equilibrium constant, K_c, for the following reaction.

    $$CH_4(g) + 4Cl_2(g) \rightleftharpoons CCl_4(g) + 4HCl(g) \quad K_c = ?$$

16. Given the following (@2000 K):

$$N_2O_4(g) \rightleftharpoons 2\,NO_2(g) \qquad K_1 = 4.80 \times 10^4$$

$$N_2(g) + 2\,O_2(g) \rightleftharpoons 2\,NO_2(g) \qquad K_2 = 7.59 \times 10^{-9}$$

Calculate the equilibrium constant, K_c, for the following reaction.

$$N_2(g) + 2\,O_2(g) \rightleftharpoons N_2O_4(g) \quad K_c = ?$$

EQUILIBRIUM CONSTANT IN TERMS OF PARTIAL PRESSURES

17. Find K_c for the following reaction:

$$2\,NO(g) + O_2(g) \rightleftharpoons 2\,NO_2(g) \quad K_p = 1.95 \times 10^{12}\,(@\,298\,K)$$

18. Find K_c for the following reaction:

$$2\,CO(g) + O_2(g) \rightleftharpoons 2\,CO_2(g) \quad K_p = 1.38 \times 10^{90}\,(@\,298\,K)$$

19. Find K_c for the following reaction:

$$CH_4(g) + H_2O(g) \rightleftharpoons CO(g) + 3\,H_2(g) \quad K_p = 1.98 \times 10^{32}\,(@\,375\,K)$$

20. Find K_p for the following reaction:

$$N_2(g) + 3\,H_2(g) \rightleftharpoons 2\,NH_3(g) \quad K_c = 3.78\,(@\,600\,K)$$

21. Find K_p for the following reaction:

$$2\,SO_2(g) + O_2(g) \rightleftharpoons 2\,SO_3(g) \quad K_c = 3.71 \times 10^8\,(@\,600\,K)$$

22. For which of the following equilibria are the values of K_c and K_p the same?

    a. $H_2(g) + Cl_2(g) \rightleftharpoons 2\,HCl(g)$

    b. $C(s) + 2\,H_2(g) \rightleftharpoons CH_4(g)$

    c. $C_2H_4(g) \rightleftharpoons C_2H_2(g) + H_2(g)$

23. For which of the following equilibria are the values of K_c and K_p the same?

    a. $H_2O(g) + CO(g) \rightleftharpoons CO_2(g) + H_2(g)$

    b. $CCl_4(g) + CH_4(g) \rightleftharpoons 2\,CH_2Cl_2(g)$

    c. $4\,NH_3(g) + 3\,O_2(g) \rightleftharpoons 2\,N_2(g) + 6\,H_2O(g)$

HETEROGENEOUS EQUILIBRIA—SOLIDS AND LIQUIDS

24. Write the expression K_c associated with the following reaction:

$$2\,HCl(aq) + CaCO_3(s) \rightleftharpoons CaCl_2(aq) + H_2O(l) + CO_2(g)$$

25. Write the expressions for K_p and K_c associated with the following reaction:

$$P_4(s) + 5\,O_2(g) \rightleftharpoons P_4O_{10}(s)$$

26. Write the expressions for K_p and K_c associated with the following reaction:

$$SnO_2(s) + 2H_2(g) \rightleftharpoons Sn(s) + 2H_2O(g)$$

27. Write the expressions for K_p and K_c associated with the following reaction:

$$CaCO_3(s) \rightleftharpoons CaO(s) + CO_2(g)$$

DETERMINING THE EQUILIBRIUM CONSTANT

28. A pure sample of ammonia gas is contained in a sealed reactor and heated to a particular temperature.

$$2NH_3(g) \rightleftharpoons N_2(g) + 3H_2(g)$$

At equilibrium, $[NH_3] = 0.418$ M, $[N_2] = 0.282$ M and $[H_2] = 0.846$ M. What is the value of K_c for this reaction?

29. A pure sample of PCl_5 gas is contained in a sealed reactor and heated to a particular temperature.

$$PCl_5(g) \rightleftharpoons Cl_2(g) + PCl_3(g)$$

At equilibrium, $[PCl_5] = 0.0333$ M, $[Cl_2] = 0.167$ M and $[PCl_3] = 0.167$ M. What is the value of K_c for this reaction?

30. A pure sample of SO_2Cl_2 gas is contained in a sealed reactor and heated to a particular temperature.

$$SO_2Cl_2(g) \rightleftharpoons SO_2(g) + Cl_2(g)$$

Initially, $[SO_2Cl_2] = 0.500$ M. However, having established equilibrium, $[Cl_2] = 0.4075$ M. Calculate the value of K_c for this reaction.

31. Consider the following reaction equation:

$$2H_2S(g) \rightleftharpoons 2H_2(g) + S_2(g)$$

The initial partial pressure of H_2S is 0.345 *atm*, while the partial pressures of the products are zero initially. Having established equilibrium, $P_{S_2} = 0.00632$ *atm*. Calculate the value of K_p for this reaction.

32. Consider the following reaction equation:

$$SO_2(g) + NO_2(g) \rightleftharpoons SO_3(g) + NO(g)$$

If 0.350 moles of SO_2 and 0.350 moles of NO_2 are delivered into a 1.00-L reactor at a particular temperature and having established equilibrium, calculate the value of K_c for this reaction, if it is determined that $[SO_3] = 0.214$ M at equilibrium.

33. Consider the following reaction equation:

$$CO(g) + H_2O(g) \rightleftharpoons CO_2(g) + H_2(g)$$

If 0.410 moles of CO_2 and 0.240 moles of H_2 are delivered into a 0.500-L reactor at a particular temperature and having established equilibrium, calculate the value of K_c for this reaction, if it is determined that $[CO] = 0.0960\ M$ at equilibrium.

THE REACTION QUOTIENT

34. Consider the following hypothetical reaction:

$$A(g) \rightleftharpoons 2\,B(g)$$

If the value of K_c at a particular temperature is 15, is the reaction at equilibrium if the concentrations of the gases A and B are $[A] = 0.10\ M$ and $[B] = 1.50\ M$? If not, which direction will the reaction proceed to establish equilibrium?

35. Consider the following hypothetical reaction:

$$A(g) + B(g) \rightleftharpoons 2\,C(g)$$

If the value of K_c at a particular temperature is 2.3×10^{-2}, is the reaction at equilibrium if the concentrations of the gases A, B, and C are $[A] = 0.250\ M$, $[B] = 0.377\ M$ and $[C] = 0.0652\ M$? If not, which direction will the reaction proceed to establish equilibrium?

36. Consider the following reaction:

$$2\,SO_2(g) + O_2(g) \rightleftharpoons 2\,SO_3(g)$$

Calculate the value of Q_c if the reaction mixture contains 3.25 g SO_2, 4.87 g O_2, and 3.70 g SO_3 in a 0.500-L reactor. If $K_c = 250$, is the reaction at equilibrium? If not, which direction will the reaction proceed in order to establish equilibrium?

37. Consider the following reaction:

$$I_2(g) + Cl_2(g) \rightleftharpoons 2\,ICl(g) \qquad K_p = 82$$

If the reaction mixture is described by the partial pressures $P_{I_2} = 0.210\ atm$, $P_{Cl_2} = 0.185\ atm$, and $P_{ICl} = 2.01\ atm$, is the reaction at equilibrium? If not, will the product need to be depleted or produced in order to establish equilibrium?

DETERMINING EQUILIBRIUM CONCENTRATIONS

38. Consider the following hypothetical reaction:

$$A(g) \rightleftharpoons 2\,B(g)$$

The value of K_c at a particular temperature for this reaction is 15. Assuming the initial concentration of A was $[A] = 0.200\ M$, construct a reaction table and determine the equilibrium concentration of B.

39. Consider the following hypothetical reaction:

$$A(g) + B(g) \rightleftharpoons 2C(g)$$

If the value of K_c at a particular temperature is 2.3×10^{-2} and the initial concentrations of reactants are $[A] = 0.100 \, M$ and $[B] = 0.100 \, M$, what is the equilibrium concentration of C?

40. Consider the following reaction (@ 925 K):

$$CO(g) + H_2O(g) \rightleftharpoons CO_2(g) + H_2(g) \quad K_c = 1.34$$

If 0.250 moles of CO and 0.250 moles of H_2O are initially placed in a 0.500-L reactor and allowed to reach equilibrium, what are the equilibrium concentrations of the products and reactants?

41. Consider the following reaction (@ 800 K):

$$COCl_2(g) \rightleftharpoons CO(g) + Cl_2(g) \quad K_c = 6.16 \times 10^{-2}$$

If 0.350 moles of $COCl_2$ is initially placed in a 0.250-L reactor, heated to 800 K, and allowed to reach equilibrium, what are the equilibrium concentrations of the products and the reactant?

42. Consider the following reaction (@ 375 K):

$$C_2H_2(g) + H_2O(g) \rightleftharpoons CH_3CHO(g) \quad K_c = 4.0 \times 10^{-4}$$

If 0.100 moles of C_2H_2 and 0.250 moles of H_2O are initially placed in a 0.300-L reactor and allowed to reach equilibrium, what are the equilibrium concentrations of the product and the reactants?

43. Consider the following reaction (@ 1100 K):

$$CO(g) + H_2O(g) \rightleftharpoons CO_2(g) + H_2(g) \quad K_c = 0.458$$

If 14.01 g of CO and 4.504 g of H_2O are initially placed in a 1.00-L reactor and allowed to reach equilibrium, what are the equilibrium concentrations of the products and the reactants?

44. Consider the following reaction (@ 1000 K):

$$COCl_2(g) \rightleftharpoons CO(g) + Cl_2(g) \quad K_c = 1.59$$

If initially the reactor contains $COCl_2$ at a partial pressure of $P_{COCl_2} = 0.880 \, atm$, what are the equilibrium partial pressures of the products and the reactant? (Hint: You will need to know K_p for this problem.)

45. Consider the following reaction (@ 800 K):

$$COCl_2(g) \rightleftharpoons CO(g) + Cl_2(g) \quad K_c = 6.16 \times 10^{-2}$$

Assuming a reactor contained all three gaseous components, all with partial pressures of 0.250 *atm*, what partial pressures will the reactant and products have at equilibrium? (Hint: You will need to know K_p for this problem.)

46. Consider the following reaction (@ 425 K):

$$NH_3(g) + H_2S(g) \rightleftharpoons NH_4HS(g) \quad K_c = 323$$

If 1.703 g NH_3, 3.408 g H_2S, and 25.05 g NH_4HS are initially placed in a 1.00-L reactor and allowed to reach equilibrium, what is the concentration of H_2S at equilibrium?

LE CHÂTELIER'S PRINCIPLE

47. Consider the following endothermic reaction:

$$CH_4(g) + 2H_2S(g) \rightleftharpoons CS_2(g) + 4H_2(g) \quad \Delta H > 0$$

Assuming the reaction is at equilibrium, in which direction will the reaction shift in response to each of the following stresses?

   a. Increase in P_{CS_2}

   b. Decrease in $[H_2S]$

   c. Increased temperature

   d. Increased volume

48. Consider the following endothermic reaction:

$$COCl_2(g) \rightleftharpoons CO(g) + Cl_2(g) \quad \Delta H > 0$$

Assuming the reaction is at equilibrium, in which direction will the reaction shift in response to each of the following stresses?

   a. Increase in P_{COCl_2}

   b. Decrease in P_{Cl_2}

   c. Decreased temperature

   d. Decreased volume

49. Consider the following exothermic reaction:

$$CO(g) + H_2O(g) \rightleftharpoons CO_2(g) + H_2(g) \quad \Delta H < 0$$

Assuming the reaction is at equilibrium, in which direction will the reaction shift in response to each of the following stresses?

   a. Increase in $[H_2O]$

   b. Decrease in P_{CO}

   c. Decreased temperature

   d. Increased volume

50. Consider the following exothermic reaction:

$$CO(g) + 2H_2(g) \rightleftharpoons CH_3OH(l) \qquad \Delta H < 0$$

Assuming the reaction is at equilibrium, in which direction will the reaction shift in response to each of the following stresses?

a. Decrease in $[H_2]$

b. Increase in P_{CO}

c. Decreased temperature

d. Decreased volume

SOLUBILITY PRODUCT - K_{SP}

51. Write the expression for the solubility product K_{sp} for each of the following compounds:

a. $Al(OH)_3$

b. CaF_2

c. $PbCl_2$

d. $CoCO_3$

52. Write the expression for the solubility product K_{sp} for each of the following compounds:

a. $BaCrO_4$

b. $Ca_3(PO_4)_2$

c. $Mg(OH)_2$

d. $SrSO_4$

53. Use the K_{sp} values in Appendix III to determine the molar solubilities of the following compounds in pure water.

a. $Al(OH)_3$

b. CaF_2

c. $PbCl_2$

d. $CaCO_3$

54. Use the K_{sp} values in Appendix III to determine the molar solubilities of the following compounds in pure water.

a. $BaCro_4$

b. $Ca_3(PO_4)_2$

c. $Mg(OH)_2$

d. PbI_2

55. Determine the molar solubility of calcium sulfate in the following solvents or solutions:

    a. Pure water

    b. 0.100 M $Ca(NO_3)_2$

    c. 0.200 M Na_2SO_4

56. Determine the molar solubility of magnesium fluoride in the following solvents or solutions:

    a. Pure water

    b. 0.200 M $Mg(NO_3)_2$

    c. 0.270 M NaF

Image Credits

- Fig. 10.A: Copyright © Depositphotos/Wavebreakmedia.
- Fig. 10.B: Copyright © Depositphotos/flytosky11.
- Fig. 10.C: Source: https://commons.wikimedia.org/wiki/File:Fritz_Haber.png.
- Fig. 10.D: Copyright © 2009 by Pauline Eccles, (CC BY-SA 2.0) at https://commons.wikimedia.org/wiki/File:Crop_spraying,_Bromsash_-_geograph.org.uk_-_1367703.jpg.
- Fig. 10.E: Source: https://commons.wikimedia.org/wiki/File:Lechatelier.jpg.
- Fig. 10.3a: Copyright © Depositphotos/Alex_Leo.
- Fig. 10.3b: Copyright © Depositphotos/jakkarin_rongkankeaw.

Acids, Bases, and Buffers

CHAPTER
11

After reading this chapter, you should be able to do the following:

- Define and distinguish between Arrhenius, Brønsted-Lowry, and Lewis acids and bases.

- Identify and define acid-base conjugate pairs.

- Name acids and bases.

- Understand the pH and pOH scales, as well as be able to perform calculations involving hydronium and hydroxide ion concentrations.

- Understand and perform acid-base titration calculations.

- Understand and interpret titration curves.

- Distinguish between strong and weak acids and bases.

- Be familiar with acid and base ionization constants (K_a and K_b), and know how to use them in calculations.

- Perform calculations involving polyprotic acids.

- Know what a buffer is and be familiar with all calculations involving both acidic and basic buffer systems with respect to pH and pOH, as well as hydronium and hydroxide ion concentrations.

- Perform calculations involving disturbing a buffer system with either added acid or base.

- Understand and identify the characteristics of an effective buffer system.

- Define each of the Key Terms listed at the end of the chapter dealing with these concepts.

Section 11.1 Introduction

Heartburn, also known as acid indigestion, occurs when hydrochloric acid from the stomach enters the esophagus. Hydrochloric acid, which is found in the stomach and used to facilitate food digestion, is normally prevented from entering the esophagus by the esophageal sphincter. However, a weakened esophageal sphincter cannot prevent at least some of the acid from entering the esophagus resulting in a burning sensation in the chest area which can

Acid reflux

Esophagus

Esophageal sphincter weakened passes the gastric juices

Stomach

Gastric juices

Heartburn occurs when hydrochloric acid from the stomach enters the esophagus. The pain associated with heartburn can often times be alleviated by taking an "antacid".

be very painful. Many times people who experience this take an "antacid" to alleviate the pain. The reason this works is because the antacid pills contain a base (i.e. sodium bicarbonate) which can neutralize the acid. Recall from Chapter 5 that a neutralization reaction combines H^+ and OH^- ions to form neutral water. In this chapter, we further explore various aspects of acid/base chemistry while applying equilibrium concepts discussed in Chapter 10. We will further use these concepts and apply them to buffer solutions.

Section 11.2 Acids and Bases Definitions

Recall from Chapter 5 that an **acid** is a molecular compound that undergoes ionization when dissolved in water to form H^+ ions, and a **base** is any substance that increases the concentration of OH^- ions when dissolved in water. In fact, according to the **Arrhenius definition** of acids and bases, an **Arrhenius acid** produces H^+ ions in aqueous solution while an **Arrhenius base** produces OH^- ions in aqueous solution. Therefore, under this definition HCl is an Arrhenius acid, and $NaOH$ is an Arrhenius base (Figure 11.1).

This can be depicted as follows:

$$HCl\ (aq) \rightarrow H^+\ (aq) + Cl^-\ (aq)$$

$$NaOH\ (aq) \rightarrow Na^+\ (aq) + OH^-\ (aq)$$

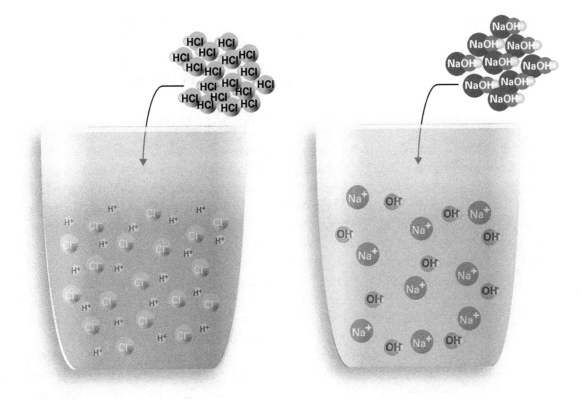

Figure 11.1 Hydrochloric acid produces H^+ ions in aqueous solution and is an Arrhenius acid, while $NaOH$ produces OH^- ions in aqueous solution and is therefore considered an Arrhenius base.

Notice that HCl is a covalent compound, and therefore does not contain ions. How does it ionize then? Well, recall that acids by definition are dissolved in water. As such, all acids are given the "(aq)" aqueous designation. Further, H^+ ions are very reactive and can react with water to form the **hydronium ion** (H_3O^+) in the following manner:

$$H^+ + H_2O \rightarrow H_3O^+$$

As acids are always dissolved in water by definition, chemists often use the term "hydronium ion" to describe both H^+ as well as H_3O^+. It is understood in this way that the acid is solvated in water. On the other hand, $NaOH$ is an ionic compound containing Na^+ and OH^- ions; therefore, one can easily see that it disassociates into these ions when dissolved in water. In some bases, however, it becomes less obvious where the OH^- ions are coming from, and they do not technically fall under the Arrhenius definition of a base. For example, we know that ammonia (NH_3) is a base, but where do the OH^- ions come from if Arrhenius bases produce these ions? Well, it is a little difficult to see how this could be the case under this definition of bases. Thus, we have a second and more inclusive definition for acids and bases known as the **Brønsted-Lowry definition**, which focuses on the proton (H^+) ion. H^+ cations are essentially protons and are often referred to as such. Using this definition, we can say that a **Brønsted-Lowry acid** is a proton donor while a **Brønsted-Lowry base** is a proton acceptor. Notice that this is a much more widely applicable definition. For example, if we now look again at both the acid (HCl) and the base ammonia (NH_3), we can see that they both clearly fit into this definition. That is, *HCl* is a proton donor, and *NH$_3$* is a proton acceptor as illustrated in the following equations:

$$HCl\ (aq) + H_2O\ (l) \rightarrow Cl^-\ (aq) + H_3O^+\ (aq)$$

$$NH_3\ (aq) + H_2O\ (l) \rightleftharpoons NH_4^+(aq) + OH^-\ (aq)$$

Note that we express this process as an equilibrium for weak acids and bases (hence, the double arrow). We will discuss weak acids and bases in greater detail later in this chapter. Nevertheless, we can now see that ammonia, in accepting a proton from water, generates the ammonium polyatomic ion (NH_4^+) and the *OH$^-$* ion, clearly making this a base under the Brønsted-Lowry definition. *Also, notice how water under this definition is acting like either a base (proton acceptor) when combined with HCl or an acid (proton donor) when mixed with ammonia.* This is an example of an **amphoteric** substance, which is defined as any substance that can act like either an acid or a base. Also, notice that while *HCl* is acting as an acid (proton donor) in the forward direction, the resulting *Cl$^-$* anion that it produces now, in theory, act as a base (proton acceptor). The same can be said with ammonia. That is, while *NH$_3$* is acting as a base (proton acceptor) in the forward direction, the resulting ammonium ion (NH_4^+) that it produces now acts as an acid (proton donor) in the reverse direction. These are examples of **conjugate acid-base pairs**, which are two substances that are related to one another by the simple transfer of a proton. Thus, we have the following:

Figure 11.2 Conjugate acid-base pairs, related to one another by the simple transfer of a proton.

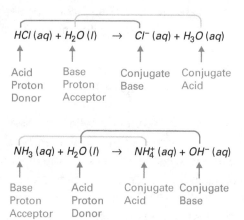

While the Brønsted-Lowry definition of acids and bases will be the most useful to us in this course, and particularly in this chapter, it should also be noted that there is a third even more inclusive definition of acids and bases known as the Lewis definition. If you recall from Chapter 8, G.N. Lewis is most commonly known for the development of the electron dot representation of chemical bonding. This third model is named after him in which a **Lewis acid** is defined as an electron pair acceptor, and a **Lewis base** is an electron pair donor. While you may find the Lewis definition of acids and bases incredibly useful in more advanced chemistry courses, the Brønsted-Lowry definition is the most appropriate for our current discussion.

Johannes Brønsted (1879-1947) was a Danish physical chemist and professor of inorganic and physical chemistry at the University of Copenhagen. With Thomas Martin Lowry, he introduced the protonic theory of acid-base reactions in 1923.

Example Problem 11.1

Identify the Brønsted-Lowry acid and base, as well as the conjugate acid and base in each of the following reactions:

a. $HI\ (aq) + H_2O\ (l) \rightarrow I^-\ (aq) + H_3O^+\ (aq)$

b. $HNO_3\ (aq) + H_2O\ (l) \rightarrow NO_3^-\ (aq) + H_3O^+\ (aq)$

c. $NH_3\ (aq) + H_2O\ (l) \rightleftharpoons NH_4^+(aq) + OH^-\ (aq)$

d. $CH_3NH_2\ (aq)\ H_2O\ (l) \rightleftharpoons CH_3NH_3^+\ (aq) + OH^-\ (aq)$

Solution:	
a. $HI\ (aq) + H_2O\ (l) \rightarrow I^-\ (aq) + H_3O^+\ (aq)$ *HI* is the acid because it donates a proton to water, making water the base because it accepts the proton. After *HI* donates its proton, the resulting I^- is then the conjugate base because it can now, accept a proton. After H_2O accepts a proton, the resulting H_3O^+ becomes the conjugate acid because it can now donate a proton.	Brønsted-Lowry Acid: **HI** Brønsted-Lowry Base: **H_2O** Conjugate Acid: **H_3O^+** Conjugate Base: **I^-**
b. $HNO_3\ (aq) + H_2O\ (l) \rightarrow NO_3^-\ (aq) + H_3O^+\ (aq)$ HNO_3 is the acid because it donates a proton to water, making water the base because it accepts the proton. After HNO_3 donates its proton, the resulting NO_3^- is then the conjugate base because it can now, accept a proton. After H_2O accepts a proton, the resulting H_3O^+ becomes the conjugate acid because it can now donate a proton.	Brønsted-Lowry Acid: **HNO_3** Brønsted-Lowry Base: **H_2O** Conjugate Acid: **H_3O^+** Conjugate Base: **NO_3^-**
c. $NH_3\ (aq) + H_2O\ (l) \rightleftharpoons NH_4^+(aq) + OH^-\ (aq)$ H_2O is the acid because it donates a proton to ammonia (NH_3), making NH_3 the base because it accepts the proton. After H_2O donates its proton, the resulting OH^- is then the conjugate base because it can now, accept a proton. After NH_3 accepts a proton, the resulting NH_4^+ becomes the conjugate acid because it can now donate a proton.	Brønsted-Lowry Acid: **H_2O** Brønsted-Lowry Base: **NH_3** Conjugate Acid: **NH_4^+** Conjugate Base: **OH^-**
d. $CH_3NH_2\ (aq) + H_2O\ (l) \rightleftharpoons CH_3NH_3^+(aq) + OH^-\ (aq)$ H_2O is the acid because it donates a proton to methylamine (CH_3NH_2), making CH_3NH_2 the base because it accepts the proton. After H_2O donates its proton, the resulting OH^- is then the conjugate base because it can now accept a proton. After CH_3NH_2 accepts a proton, the resulting $CH_3NH_3^+$ becomes the conjugate acid because it can now donate a proton.	Brønsted-Lowry Acid: **H_2O** Brønsted-Lowry Base: **CH_3NH_2** Conjugate Acid: **$CH_3NH_3^+$** Conjugate Base: **OH^-**

Thomas Martin Lowry (1874–1936) was an English physical chemist and founder-member and president of the Faraday Society from 1928 to 1930. He also assisted in the development of the Bronsted-Lowry acid-base theory with Johannes Nicolaus Brønsted.

Example Problem 11.2

Write the formula for the conjugate acid of each of the following:

a. ClO_4^-

b. HCO_3^-

Write the formula for the conjugate base of each of the following:

c. $HCHO_2$

d. HF

Solution:	
a. If ClO_4^- were to act like a base and accept a proton, then the conjugate acid would be $HClO_4$.	**Conjugate Acid: $HClO_4$**
b. If HCO_3^- were to act like a base and accept a proton, then the conjugate acid would be H_2CO_3.	**Conjugate Acid: H_2CO_3**
c. If $HCHO_2$ were to act like an acid and donate a proton, then the conjugate base would be CHO_2^-.	**Conjugate Base: CHO_2^-**
d. If HF were to act like an acid and donate a proton, then the conjugate base would be F^-.	**Conjugate Base: F^-**

Section 11.3 Acids and Bases Nomenclature

Now that we have covered some basic definitions of acids and bases, we will discuss nomenclature. As we have seen, an acid is a proton donor, and this acidic hydrogen is generally written first in the formula, while the nonmetal(s) is/are written second. In order to name a particular acid, we must first be able to determine whether the acid is a binary acid or an oxyacid. A **binary acid** contains hydrogen and a nonmetal, while an **oxyacid** is composed of hydrogen and an oxyanion, or an anion containing a nonmetal and oxygen. Thus, HCl is a binary acid, while H_2SO_4 is an oxyacid. It is important to determine whether we are dealing with a binary acid or an oxyacid first because the rules for naming each of these two types of acids are different as illustrated in Figure 11.3. For example, if we have a binary acid, we use the prefix "hydro-", then add the suffix "-ic" to the base name of the nonmetal followed by the word "acid." Therefore, HCl is hydrochloric acid, HF is hydrofluoric acid, HI is hydroiodic acid, and so on. If, however, we have an oxyacid, we must first determine whether the base name of the oxyanion ends in "-ite" or "-ate." If the oxyanion ends in "-ite," then we simply replace it with "-ous" and add the word "acid." Thus, HNO_2 is nitrous acid because it is hydrogen with the nitrite polyatomic ion (NO_2^-). However, if the oxyanion ends in "-ate," then we simply replace it with "-ic" and add the word "acid." Therefore, HNO_3 is nitric acid because it is hydrogen with the nitrate polyatomic ion (NO_3^-). Notice that we do not use the prefix "hydro-" on oxyacids. It is also important to point out that there are some exceptions to these rules. For example, H_2SO_4 is sulfuric acid, not "sulfic" acid, which is what we would get if we were to follow these rules (i.e. replace the "-ate" in sulfate with "-ic"). This is done essentially because sulfuric acid sounds better, and the same can be said about H_2SO_3, which is sulfurous acid not "sulfous" acid, which is what we would once again get if we were to follow these rules (i.e. replace "-ite" in sulfite with "-ous"). With respect to naming bases, we simply follow the rules as outlined in

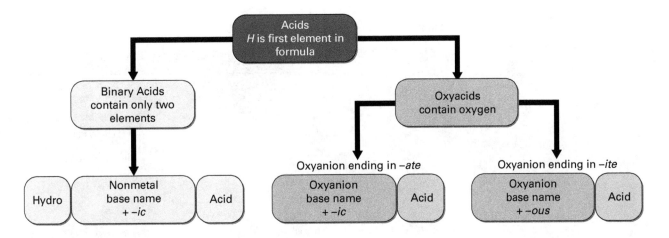

Figure 11.3 Rules for naming binary and oxyacids.

Chapter 3 regarding naming ionic compounds. Thus, *NaOH* is sodium hydroxide, $Ca(OH)_2$ is calcium hydroxide, *KOH* is potassium hydroxide, and so on. Table 11.1 summarizes some commonly used acids and bases. In any event, let us now practice with some examples.

Example Problem 11.3

Write the names of the following acids:
a. *HCl*
b. H_2CO_3
c. *HI*
d. H_3PO_4

Write the formulas for the following acids:
e. Hydrosulfuric acid
f. Sulfuric acid
g. Hydrofluoric acid
h. Chlorous acid

Solution:	
a. Binary acid, therefore we use the "hydro" prefix and add "ic" to the base name of the nonmetal.	**Hydrochloric acid**
b. Oxyacid, therefore we do not use "hydro," and in this case we replace "ate" in carbonate (CO_3^{2-}) with "ic."	**Carbonic acid**
c. Binary acid, therefore we use the "hydro" prefix and add "ic" to the base name of the nonmetal.	**Hydroiodic acid**
d. Oxyacid, therefore we do not use "hydro," and in this case we replace "ate" in phosphate (PO_4^{3-}) with "ic". Note, this is another exception because "phosphoric acid" sounds better than "phosphic acid" (see also explanation for H_2SO_4 and H_2SO_3 above).	**Phosphoric acid**
e. Binary acid because of the "hydro" prefix and the "ic" on the end of the base name of the nonmetal.	H_2S
f. Oxyacid (no "hydro" prefix) and the "ic" indicates that the polyatomic ion ends in "ate" or sulfate (SO_4^{2-}) in this case.	H_2SO_4
g. Binary acid because of the "hydro" prefix and the "ic" on the end of the base name of the nonmetal.	*HF*
h. Oxyacid (no "hydro" prefix) and the "ous" indicates that the polyatomic ion ends in "ite" or chlorite (ClO_2^-) in this case.	$HClO_2$

Table 11.1 Some commonly used acids and bases.

List of Common Acids and Bases			
Acids		Bases	
Formula	Name	Formula	Name
HCl	Hydrochloric Acid	$NaOH$	Sodium Hydroxide
HBr	Hydrobromic acid	$LiOH$	Lithium Hydroxide
HI	Hydroiodic Acid	KOH	Potassium Hydroxide
HNO_3	Nitric acid	$RbOH$	Rubidium Hydroxide
H_2SO_4	Sulfuric Acid	$CsOH$	Cesium Hydroxide
$HClO_4$	Perchloric Acid	$Ca(OH)_2$	Calcium Hydroxide
HF	Hydrofluoric Acid	$Sr(OH)_2$	Strontium Hydroxide
H_3PO_4	Phosphoric Acid	$Ba(OH)_2$	Barium Hydroxide
$HC_2H_3O_2$	Acetic Acid	NH_3	Ammonia

Example Problem 11.4

a. Write the names of the following bases: $NaOH$, KOH and $Ca(OH)_2$.
b. Write the formulas for ammonia, barium hydroxide, and cesium hydroxide.

Solution:	
a. When writing the names for bases, we simply use the rules for naming ionic compounds as discussed in Chapter 3.	**Sodium hydroxide ($NaOH$), Potassium hydroxide (KOH) and Calcium hydroxide ($Ca(OH)_2$).**
b. When writing the formulas for bases, we simply use the rules as outlined for ionic compounds as discussed in Chapter 3 (cation first, then the negatively charged polyatomic OH^- ion second). Ammonia is also a very common base that we should be familiar with.	**NH_3 (ammonia), $Ba(OH)_2$ (barium hydroxide) and $CsOH$ (cesium hydroxide).**

Section 11.4 Autoionization of Water and Scales Used to Quantify Acidity and Basicity

Now that we have covered some basic qualitative definitions of acids and bases as well as nomenclature, we turn our attention to a more quantitative approach to acids and bases and apply what we have learned from Chapter 10 regarding equilibrium constants. In other words, now that we know that acidic solutions have more hydronium ions in solution compared to hydroxide ions and that basic solutions have more hydroxide ions in solution than hydronium ions, the question now becomes to what *extent* is this the case, and can this be quantified? Well, in order to understand this, we first need to discuss the autoionization of water. Recall that water is an amphoteric substance, meaning that it can act as an acid or a base in a process called **autoionization**. Thus, we have water acting as both acid and base in the following equation:

$$H_2O\ (l) + H_2O\ (l) \rightleftharpoons H_3O^+\ (aq) + OH^-\ (aq)$$

Note that while one of the water reactants is acting like an acid (proton donor), the other water reactant is acting like a base (proton acceptor). This can then be simplified, and we can write the equilibrium constant for water, which is denoted as K_w and is called **the ion product for water** as follows:

$$H_2O\ (l) \rightleftharpoons H^+\ (aq) + OH^-\ (aq)$$

$$K_w = [H^+][OH^-]$$

Note again, you will often see H^+ and H_3O^+ used interchangeably. At 25°C, $K_w = 1.0 \times 10^{-14}$ (recall from Chapter 10 that equilibrium constants are temperature dependent). This means that in pure neutral water, we have equal concentrations of H^+ and OH^- ions in solution, or $1.0 \times 10^{-7}\ M$ of each in pure neutral water at 25°C. Therefore, under these conditions we can write the following:

$$[H^+] = [OH^-] = 1.0 \times 10^{-7}\ M$$

Therefore, if we know that the concentration of H^+ ions multiplied by the concentration of OH^- ions always equals 1.0×10^{-14} at 25°C, then the following must be true for acidic and basic solutions:

$$\textit{In acidic solutions, } [H^+] > [OH^-]$$

$$\textit{In basic solutions, } [H^+] < [OH^-]$$

This makes sense because, as mentioned earlier, we expect that as the hydronium ions increase in acidic solutions when compared to a neutral solution, the hydroxide ions decrease. Thus, it follows that as hydroxide ions increase in basic solutions when compared to a neutral solution, the hydronium ions decrease. In other words, when one goes up the other must go down for this to be true. Now that we understand the process of the autoionization of water, we can begin to tackle some of the quantification aspects of acid/base chemistry by looking at a few examples.

Example Problem 11.5

Calculate the hydronium ion concentration for each solution at 25°C and determine whether it is acidic, basic, or neutral:

a. $[OH^-] = 8.4 \times 10^{-8}\ M$

b. $[OH^-] = 1.0 \times 10^{-7}\ M$

c. $[OH^-] = 3.4 \times 10^{-4}\ M$

d. $[OH^-] = 4.8 \times 10^{-9}\ M$

Solution:	
a. $[H^+] > [OH^-]$, therefore the solution is acidic.	$K_w = [H^+][OH^-] = 1.0 \times 10^{-14}$ $[H^+] = \dfrac{1.0 \times 10^{-14}}{[OH^-]}$ $[H^+] = \dfrac{1.0 \times 10^{-14}}{8.4 \times 10^{-8}} = 1.2 \times 10^{-7} \ M$ **Acidic (slightly)**
b. $[H^+] = [OH^-]$, therefore the solution is neutral.	$K_w = [H^+][OH^-] = 1.0 \times 10^{-14}$ $[H^+] = \dfrac{1.0 \times 10^{-14}}{[OH^-]}$ $[H^+] = \dfrac{1.0 \times 10^{-14}}{1.0 \times 10^{-7}} = 1.0 \times 10^{-7} \ M$ **Neutral**
c. $[OH^-] > [H^+]$, therefore the solution is basic.	$K_w = [H^+][OH^-] = 1.0 \times 10^{-14}$ $[H^+] = \dfrac{1.0 \times 10^{-14}}{[OH^-]}$ $[H^+] = \dfrac{1.0 \times 10^{-14}}{3.4 \times 10^{-4}} = 2.9 \times 10^{-11} \ M$ **Basic**
d. $[H^+] > [OH^-]$, therefore the solution is acidic.	$K_w = [H^+][OH^-] = 1.0 \times 10^{-14}$ $[H^+] = \dfrac{1.0 \times 10^{-14}}{[OH^-]}$ $[H^+] = \dfrac{1.0 \times 10^{-14}}{4.8 \times 10^{-9}} = 2.1 \times 10^{-6} \ M$ **Acidic**

Now, we can calculate the concentration of both the hydronium and hydroxide ions in solution, and then use this information in order to determine whether a solution is acidic, basic, or neutral. While this is very useful, there are more convenient scales that can be used in order to determine acidity/basicity of a solution without dealing with these types of concentration numbers. Specifically, the pH and pOH scales can be used to determine this type of information in a far more convenient manner. The **pH** and **pOH** scales are defined as the negative log of either the hydronium ion concentration or the hydroxide ion concentration, respectively:

$$pH = -\log[H_3O^+]$$

$$pOH = -\log[OH^-]$$

These scales are convenient as they run from 0 to 14 with 7 being neutral. In general, at 25°C solutions that have a pH less than 7 on the pH scale are acidic, and those with a pH of greater than 7 are basic. The numbers run opposite on the pOH scale (see Figure 11.4).

Acidic   **Basic**

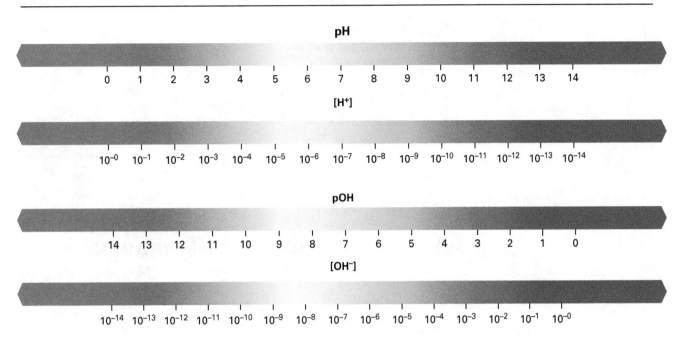

Figure 11.4 The pH (top) and pOH (bottom) scales.

It is important to note that the p-scale (referring to the negative log of something) can also be used for other values. For example, we also have the pK_w, which is the negative log of the K_w, which we can see in the following equation:

$$pK_w = -\log K_w = -\log(1.0 \times 10^{-14}) = 14.00$$

Another important point here when using the p-scale and logarithms is significant figures. Notice that only the numbers to the right of the decimal are significant in a logarithm. Thus, we report the pK_w here as 14.00 (2 decimal places) because K_w is given to two significant figures (1.0×10^{-14}). *Also, note that pH, pOH, and pK_w are all related to each other by the following expression at 25°C:*

$$pK_w = pH + pOH = 14.00$$

Let us now look at an example of how we can apply all of this quantitatively.

Example Problem 11.6

Calculate the pH, pOH, and the hydroxide ion concentration of a solution that has a hydronium ion concentration of 2.1×10^{-3} M at 25°C.	
Solution:	
To calculate the pH, we simply take the negative log of the hydronium ion concentration. To find the pOH, we can then subtract the pH from the pK_w. The hydroxide	$pH = -\log[H_3O^+] = -\log[2.1 \times 10^{-3}] = \mathbf{2.68}$ **(acidic solution)**

ion concentration can be determined by dividing K_w by the hydronium ion concentration. Note that another way to calculate the hydroxide ion concentration if we know the pOH is as follows:

$$pOH = -\log[OH^-]$$

$$[OH^-] = antilog(-pOH)$$

$$[OH^-] = 4.8 \times 10^{-12} \; M$$

$$pOH = 14.00 - pH = 11.32$$

$$[OH^-] = \frac{1.0 \times 10^{-14}}{[H^+]} = \frac{1.0 \times 10^{-14}}{2.1 \times 10^{-3}} = 4.8 \times 10^{-12} \; M$$

Section 11.5 Acid-Base Titrations: A Common Laboratory Technique

A common laboratory technique involving acids and bases is **titration** (Figure 11.5) in which a solution of known concentration called the **titrant** is reacted with another substance of unknown concentration, known as the **analyte**. This is an example of an **acid-base reaction**, or **neutralization reaction**, and is generally done in order to determine an unknown concentration of either an acid or a base. For example, let's say we know that we have 10.0 *ml* of *HCl* in a bottle, but do not know the concentration. One way to determine this information is to make a solution of base (i.e. *NaOH*) of known concentration and perform a titration. For example, we can make a 0.100 *M* solution of *NaOH*, and then add it to a **burette**, which is a device used in chemistry to dispense precise volumes of chemical solutions (Figure 11.5). As we slowly add our *NaOH* solution to the *HCl*, we notice that we have added a total of 13.8 *ml* of our basic solution to the acid to reach the **equivalence point**. Equivalence point is the volume in a titration at which the number of moles of added OH^- ions from the *NaOH* solution equals the number of H^+ ions present in the *HCl* solution. We know that we are close to the equivalence point because we added a few drops of an indicator to the *HCl* solution prior to the titration. An **indicator** is a dye that changes color based on the acidity/basicity of the solution (Figure 11.6), so that we know when we have reached the **endpoint**, which is the point at which a color change is observed. In theory, the equivalence point and endpoint should be very close to one another, but as you can see from Figure 11.6, the pH at which different indicators undergo a color change varies from one indicator to another. In any event, from this information we can now calculate the unknown *HCl* concentration as follows:

$$HCl \; (aq) + NaOH \; (aq) \rightarrow H_2O \; (l) + NaCl \; (aq)$$

$$13.8 \; ml \; NaOH \times \frac{1 \; L}{1,000 \; ml} \times \frac{0.100 \; mols \; NaOH}{1 \; L \; Sol'n} \times \frac{1 \; mol \; HCl}{1 \; mol \; NaOH} \times \frac{1}{0.0100 \; L \; Sol'n} = 0.138 \; M \; HCl$$

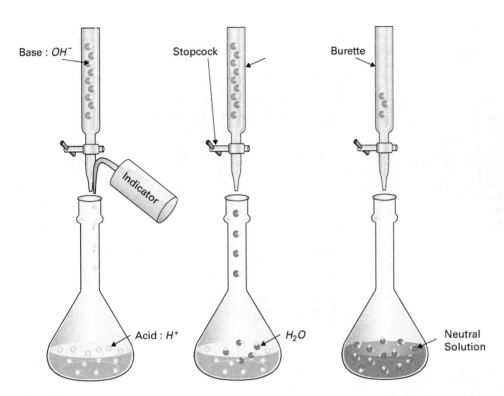

Figure 11.5 Titration of an acid with a base in an acid-base neutralization reaction.

Common pH Indicators

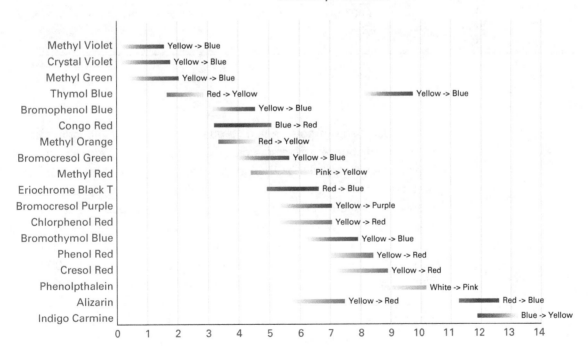

Figure 11.6 Several common pH indicators used in titrations.

Example Problem 11.7

A 25.0 ml sample of H_2SO_4 (unknown concentration) is titrated with a 0.100 M $NaOH$ solution. The equivalence point is reached after 32.5 ml of the $NaOH$ solution is added. What is the concentration of the H_2SO_4 sample?

Solution:	
First, we need to write out the balanced equation for this neutralization reaction.	$$H_2SO_4 \ (aq) + 2NaOH \ (aq) \rightarrow 2H_2O \ (l) + Na_2SO_4 \ (aq)$$
Now that we know the stoichiometric ratio between the acid and base (1:2), we can carry out our calculations. Note that if your answer to this question is 0.130 M (~twice the correct value of 0.0650 M), then you probably overlooked the correct acid: base ratio (1:2).	$32.5 \ ml \ NaOH \times \dfrac{1 \ L}{1,000 \ ml} \times \dfrac{0.100 \ mols \ NaOH}{1 \ L \ Sol'n} \times \dfrac{1 \ mol \ H_2SO_4}{2 \ mols \ NaOH} \times \dfrac{1}{0.0250 \ L \ Sol'n}$ $= 0.0650 \ M \ H_2SO_4$

Example Problem 11.8

A 38.5 ml sample of H_3PO_4 (unknown concentration) is titrated with a 0.100 M $Ba(OH)_2$ solution. The equivalence point is reached after 29.5 ml of the $Ba(OH)_2$ solution is added. What is the concentration of the H_3PO_4 sample?

Solution:	
First, we need to write out the balanced equation for this neutralization reaction.	$2H_3PO_4 \ (aq) + 3Ba(OH)_2 \ (aq) \rightarrow 6H_2O \ (l) + Ba_3(PO_4)_2 \ (s)$
Now that we know the stoichiometric ratio between the acid and base (2:3), we can carry out our calculations.	$29.5 \ ml \ Ba(OH)_2 \times \dfrac{1 \ L}{1,000 \ ml} \times \dfrac{0.100 \ mols \ Ba(OH)_2}{1 \ L \ Sol'n} \times \dfrac{2 \ mols \ H_3PO_4}{3 \ mols \ Ba(OH)_2} \times \dfrac{1}{0.0385 \ L \ Sol'n}$ $= 0.0511 \ M \ H_3PO_4$

One nice thing to note regarding questions involving titrations is that you will quickly notice with a little practice that they are all very similar. For example, they all involve four variables (concentrations and volumes for both the acid and the base), three of which you will be given in the question, and you solve for the fourth. That being said, the other nice aspect is that you can quickly check your work to make sure that you have the right answer. For example, let's take a look at the last Example Problem that we worked (11.8). Notice that in the question you are given the base concentration (0.100 M of barium hydroxide), base volume (29.5 ml of barium hydroxide), and the acid volume (38.5 ml of phosphoric acid). Again, like all titration questions, here we have these three variables, and we are left to solve for the fourth variable, in this case the acid concentration. Once we have solved the problem and determined that the acid concentration is 0.0511 M, we can then double check our answer by selecting three different variables from the original question (one of which is our answer of 0.0511 M for the acid concentration from problem 11.8). We then solve for the fourth variable, for which we already know the answer because it was given to us in the original question. For example, if we were to take the acid concentration that we solved for in problem 11.8 (0.0511 M), as well as the acid volume and base concentration from the original question (38.5 *ml* and 0.100 *M*, respectively), would we get a volume of 29.5 *ml* of the $Ba(OH)_2$ solution as given in the original question? Let's see by working Example Problem 11.9.

Example Problem 11.9

A 38.5 *ml* sample of 0.0511 *M* H_3PO_4 is titrated with a 0.100 *M* $Ba(OH)_2$ solution. What volume of the $Ba(OH)_2$ solution is needed to reach the equivalence point?
Solution:

First, we need to write out the balanced equation for this neutralization reaction.	$2H_3PO_4\ (aq) + 3Ba(OH)_2\ (aq) \rightarrow 6H_2O\ (l) + Ba_3(PO_4)_2\ (s)$
Now, using the correct stoichiometric ratio between the acid and base (2:3), we can carry out our calculations to see if we in fact arrive at 29.5 *ml* of the barium hydroxide solution. In this case, we have more information on the acid (both concentration and volume) than the base (concentration only), so we start our calculations with the acid volume.	$38.5\ ml\ H_3PO_4 \times \dfrac{1\ L}{1{,}000\ ml} \times \dfrac{0.0511\ mols\ H_3PO_4}{1\ L\ Sol'n} \times \dfrac{3\ mols\ Ba(OH)_2}{2\ mols\ H_3PO_4} \times \dfrac{1\ L\ Sol'n}{0.100\ mols\ Ba(OH)_2}$ $\times \dfrac{1{,}000\ ml}{1\ L} = \textbf{29.5 ml } Ba(OH)_2$ ✔

Titration Curves

Titration curves, or pH curves, are plots in which pH values are generally depicted on the *y*-axis of the graph, while increasing amounts of either acid or base added to the analyte appear on the *x*-axis (Figure 11.7). Notice in Figure 11.7 that we have two titration curves, one with a strong base (i.e. *NaOH*) being added to a strong acid (left), and a strong base being added to a weak acid (right). In both cases we see the characteristic "S" shape common to titration curves, with the equivalence point appearing at the inflection point of the curve. However, there are subtle differences between

Figure 11.7 Titration curves of a strong base added to a strong acid (left) and a strong base added to a weak acid (right).

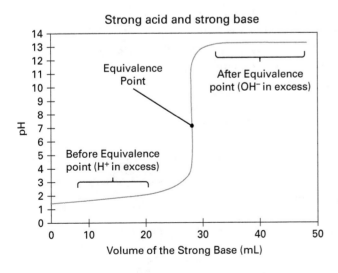

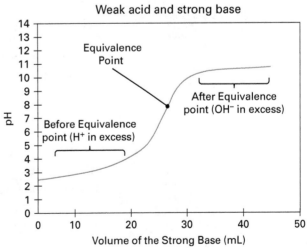

these two plots. Strong acids tend to have a low starting pH value (< 2.00) as we would expect, while weaker acids have higher pH values prior to the titration (> 2.00). Also, notice that strong acids being titrated with a strong base have an equivalence point of approximately 7.00 and a relatively steeper curve, while weaker acids being titrated with a strong base have a slightly basic equivalence point (~8.00) and a more gradual curve. Incidentally, titration curves can also be constructed with acids (titrant) being added to the base (analyte), in which the curve would essentially be flipped with high pH values prior to the titration, which would then decrease with added acid. Acid strength is discussed further in the next section.

Section 11.6 Acid Strength

Perhaps you have noticed so far in our discussions involving acids and bases that what really matters in acid/base chemistry is essentially how many H^+ ions and OH^- ions are in solution and available to react. In other words, does the acid or base that we are dealing with ionize completely to produce a lot of these ions, or only partially, in which case a lot fewer H^+ and OH^- ions are available to react in solution? Well, the answer to that question is that it depends on the strength of the particular acid or base of interest. If you recall from Chapter 5, **strong acids** completely dissociate into ions when dissolved in water and are therefore strong electrolytes, while **weak acids** only partially ionize when dissolved in water and are therefore weak electrolytes. Table 11.2 lists some examples of commonly used strong and weak acids. Hydrochloric acid is an example of a strong acid which undergoes complete ionization indicated by the single arrow below:

$$HCl\ (aq) + H_2O\ (l) \rightarrow H_3O^+\ (aq) + Cl^-\ (aq)$$

The single arrow indicates that almost no intact HCl exists because it has essentially completely disassociated in H_3O^+ (H^+) and Cl^- ions as a result of it being a strong acid. Therefore, if we have a 0.10 M HCl solution, we can easily calculate the pH of this because we know that there are 0.10 M H_3O^+ (H^+) ions in solution due to the complete ionization of this strong acid. Thus, the pH is of this solution is as follows:

$$pH = -\log 0.10 = 1.00$$

In contrast, acetic acid is considered a weak acid and only partially ionizes when dissolved in water as indicated by the double (or equilibrium) arrow as depicted in the following equation:

$$HC_2H_3O_2\ (aq) + H_2O\ (l) \rightleftharpoons H_3O^+\ (aq) + C_2H_3O_2^-\ (aq)$$

Table 11.2 Some examples of commonly used strong and weak acids. A more extensive list of weak acids with associated K_a values can be found in Appendix III.

Some Common Strong Acids		Some Common Weak Acids		
Formula	**Name**	**Formula**	**Name**	**K_a (25°C)**
HCl	Hydrochloric acid	HF	Hydrofluoric acid	3.5×10^{-4}
HBr	Hydrobromic acid	$HC_2H_3O_2$	Acetic acid	1.8×10^{-5}
HI	Hydroiodic acid	$HCHO_2$	Formic acid	1.8×10^{-4}
HNO_3	Nitric acid	HNO_2	Nitrous acid	4.6×10^{-4}
H_2SO_4	Sulfuric acid	H_2SO_3	Sulfurous acid	$1.2 \times 10^{-2} (K_{a1})$

In this case, there are plenty of intact $HC_2H_3O_2$ molecules and relatively few H_3O^+ (H^+) and $C_2H_3O_2^-$ ions in solution due to the partial ionization that occurs with weak acids. Therefore, pH calculations are not as straightforward as they are with strong acids. For example, we cannot assume that a 0.10 M $HC_2H_3O_2$ solution contains 0.10 M H_3O^+ (H^+) ions in solution because that would be incorrect with only partial ionization occurring. Thus, when dealing with weak acids, we must know the equilibrium constant for the ionization reaction in order to determine the hydronium ion concentration and ultimately the pH of the solution.

The Acid Ionization Constant (K_a)

The **acid ionization constant (K_a)** is the equilibrium constant for the ionization reaction of acids, which is very useful for calculations involving weak acids (Table 11.2). A more extensive list of weak acids along with their associated K_a values can also be found in Appendix III. If we apply what we learned in Chapter 10 regarding equilibrium constants, we can then define K_a as follows for a generic acid (HA):

$$HA \ (aq) \rightleftharpoons H^+ \ (aq) + A^- \ (aq)$$

$$K_a = \frac{[H^+][A^-]}{[HA]}$$

It is important to remember that equilibrium constants are given by [products]/[reactants], which means that a smaller K_a value is a weaker acid (less ionization) and a large K_a value is a stronger acid (more ionization). Thus, if we know that acetic acid has a K_a value of 1.8×10^{-5} as listed in Table 11.2, we can now calculate the pH of a 0.10 M $HC_2H_3O_2$ solution by constructing a reaction table as follows:

$$\text{Concentration} \quad HC_2H_3O_2(aq) \rightleftharpoons H^+(aq) + C_2H_3O_2^-(aq)$$

Initial	0.10	0.00	0.00
Change	$-x$	$+x$	$+x$
Equilibrium	$0.10 - x$	x	x

$$K_a = \frac{[H^+][A^-]}{[HA]}$$

$$1.8 \times 10^{-5} = \frac{[x][x]}{[0.10-x]}$$

As first mentioned in Chapter 10, we would now normally apply the quadratic formula in order to solve for x. However, in many cases when x (or the change) is very small when compared to the weak acid concentration (<5%), we can make the following assumption:

$$1.8 \times 10^{-5} = \frac{[x][x]}{[0.10-x]} \approx \frac{[x]^2}{[0.10]}$$

$$x = \sqrt{(1.8 \times 10^{-5}) \times (0.10)} = 1.3 \times 10^{-3} \ M$$

Now, to make sure that our assumption was valid:

$$\frac{1.3 \times 10^{-3} \ M}{0.10 \ M} \times 100\% = 1.3 \ \%$$

Notice that this number also represents the **percent ionization**, which is the ratio of the ionized acid concentration to the initial acid concentration multiplied by 100%. Here, we find that the change (or percent ionization) is less than 5%, therefore the assumption was valid, and the quadratic equation is not needed. If this was not the case, and the change was greater than 5%, then we would simply use the solution to the quadratic equation as follows:

$$x = \frac{-b \pm \sqrt{b^2 - 4ac}}{2a}$$

In any event, because that is not the case here in this example, we can now simply take the negative log of x to get the pH because x represents the hydronium ion concentration.

$$pH = -\log(1.3 \times 10^{-3}) = 2.87$$

We will now work Example Problem 11.10 which is similar to this one in which the approximation will be valid (x is small and less than 5%), and also Example Problem 11.11 in which the approximation will not be valid (x is greater than 5%) and the quadratic formula must be used.

Example Problem 11.10

What is the pH of a 0.10 M solution of formic acid (K_a of $HCHO_2 = 1.8 \times 10^{-4}$)?	

	Solution:
First, let's write our equation for ionization of formic acid and set up our table as follows:	$HCHO_2(aq) \rightleftharpoons H^+(aq) + CHO_2^-(aq)$ Concentration $\quad HCHO_2(aq) \rightarrow H^+(aq) + CHO_2^-(aq)$ Initial $\qquad\qquad$ 0.10 $\qquad$ 0.00 $\qquad$ 0.00 Change $\qquad\qquad$ $-x$ $\qquad$ $+x$ $\qquad$ $+x$ Equilibrium $\qquad$ 0.10 $-x$ $\qquad$ x $\qquad$ x
Now, we set up our K_a expression. For now we will assume that the assumption, $x \ll 0.10$, is valid, but will have to check the percent ionization at the end to make sure that this is true. If not, we will have to come back to this step and apply the quadratic formula.	$K_a = \dfrac{[H^+][CHO_2^-]}{[HCHO_2]}$ $1.8 \times 10^{-4} = \dfrac{[x][x]}{[0.10-x]}$ $1.8 \times 10^{-4} \approx \dfrac{[x]^2}{[0.10]}$
Now we solve for x.	$x = \sqrt{(1.8 \times 10^{-4}) \times (0.10)} = 4.2 \times 10^{-3}\ M$
Before we move on to find the pH, we must first make sure that our assumption made in the previous step is valid. Thus, we now determine the percent ionization to make sure that it is less than 5% of the original acid concentration.	Percent Ionization = $\dfrac{x}{0.10\ M} \times 100 = \dfrac{4.2 \times 10^{-3}\ M}{0.10\ M} \times 100\% = 4.2\ \%$
Now that we have determined that our assumption is valid (albeit barely), we can now calculate the pH by taking the negative log of x (which represents the hydronium ion concentration).	$pH = -\log(4.2 \times 10^{-3}) = \textbf{2.38}$

Example Problem 11.11

What is the pH of a 0.10 M solution of chlorous acid (K_a of $HClO_2 = 1.1 \times 10^{-2}$)?	

	Solution:
First, let's write our equation for ionization of formic acid and set up our table as follows:	$HClO_2(aq) \rightleftharpoons H^+(aq) + ClO_2^-(aq)$ Concentration $\quad HClO_2(aq) \rightarrow H^+(aq) + ClO_2^-(aq)$ Initial $\qquad\qquad$ 0.10 $\qquad$ 0.00 $\qquad$ 0.00 Change $\qquad\qquad$ $-x$ $\qquad$ $+x$ $\qquad$ $+x$ Equilibrium $\qquad$ 0.10 $-x$ $\qquad$ x $\qquad$ x

Now, we set up our K_a expression. For now we will assume that the assumption is valid, but will have to check the percent ionization at the end to make sure that this is true. If not, we will have to come back to this step and apply the quadratic formula.	$K_a = \dfrac{[H^+][ClO_2^-]}{[HClO_2]}$ $1.1 \times 10^{-2} = \dfrac{[x][x]}{[0.10-x]}$ $1.1 \times 10^{-2} \approx \dfrac{[x]^2}{[0.10]}$
Now we solve for x.	$x = \sqrt{(1.1 \times 10^{-2}) \times (0.10)} = 3.3 \times 10^{-2}\ M$
Before we move on to find the pH, we must first make sure that the assumption made in the previous step is valid. Thus, we now determine the percent ionization to make sure that it is less than 5% of the original acid concentration.	Percent Ionization $= \dfrac{x}{0.10\ M} \times 100 = \dfrac{3.3 \times 10^{-2}\ M}{0.10\ M} \times 100\% = 33\ \%$
In this case, the assumption is **NOT** valid. Thus, we must now apply the quadratic formula to solve for x.	$1.1 \times 10^{-2} = \dfrac{[x]^2}{[0.10-x]}$ $1.1 \times 10^{-2}(0.10 - x) = x^2$ $1.1 \times 10^{-3} - (1.1 \times 10^{-2})x = x^2$ $x^2 + (1.1 \times 10^{-2})x - 1.1 \times 10^{-3} = 0$ $x = \dfrac{-b \pm \sqrt{b^2 - 4ac}}{2a}$ $x = \dfrac{-(1.1 \times 10^{-2}) \pm \sqrt{(1.1 \times 10^{-2})^2 - 4(1)(-1.1 \times 10^{-3})}}{2(1)}$ $x = \dfrac{-(1.1 \times 10^{-2}) \pm 0.067}{2(1)}$ $x = -0.039\ or\ x = 0.028$
Since the hydronium concentration cannot be a negative number, 0.028 is the correct answer here.	*Thus, $x = 0.028$* $pH = -\log 0.028 = \mathbf{1.55}$

Polyprotic Acids and Acid Ionization Constants

Most of the acids discussed thus far have only one ionizable proton, commonly referred to as **monoprotic acids** (i.e. HCl, HF, $HClO_2$ etc.). On the other hand, **polyprotic acids** have more than one ionizable proton. For example, **diprotic acids** have two ionizable protons (i.e. H_2SO_4) and **triprotic acids** have three ionizable protons (i.e. H_3PO_4). For the most part, polyprotic acids ionize in successive steps, and therefore have more than one K_a value. For example, let's take a look at the triprotic acid, phosphoric acid:

$$H_3PO_4\ (aq) + H_2O\ (l) \rightleftharpoons H_3O^+\ (aq) + H_2PO_4^-\ (aq) \qquad K_{a1} = 7.5 \times 10^{-3}$$

$$H_2PO_4^- \ (aq) + H_2O \ (l) \rightleftharpoons H_3O^+ \ (aq) + HPO_4^{2-} \ (aq) \qquad K_{a2} = 6.2 \times 10^{-8}$$

$$HPO_4^{2-} \ (aq) + H_2O \ (l) \rightleftharpoons H_3O^+ \ (aq) + PO_4^{3-} \ (aq) \qquad K_{a3} = 4.2 \times 10^{-13}$$

Notice that K_{a1} is much larger than either K_{a2} or K_{a3}, which is generally the case with polyprotic acids. This is in part due to the fact that the formation of hydronium ions in the first step inhibits their formation in the second and third steps as Le Châtelier's principle would predict (see Chapter 10). Therefore, when dealing with polyprotic acids, we can generally focus on K_{a1} only as K_{a2} and K_{a3} generally tend to be negligible (not always the case, such as dilute solutions of certain acids). Therefore, we can determine the pH of most solutions of polyprotic acids as we have done in previous sections involving just one K_a value.

Example Problem 11.12

What is the pH of a 0.125 M solution of carbonic acid ($K_{a1} = 4.3 \times 10^{-7}$ and $K_{a2} = 5.6 \times 10^{-11}$)?

Solution:

<table>
<tr>
<td>First, let's write our equation for ionization of carbonic acid (first step) and set up our table as follows:</td>
<td>

$$H_2CO_3(aq) \rightleftharpoons H^+ \ (aq) + HCO_3^- \ (aq)$$

Concentration	$H_2CO_3(aq) \rightarrow$	$H^+ \ (aq) +$	$HCO_3^- \ (aq)$
Initial	0.125	0.00	0.00
Change	$-x$	$+x$	$+x$
Equilibrium	$0.125 - x$	x	x

</td>
</tr>
<tr>
<td>Now, we set up our K_a expression. Note that we will only focus on K_{a1} here because this value is much larger than K_{a2} (5.6 × 10⁻¹¹), which is negligible. We will assume that the assumption is valid but will have to check the percent ionization at the end to make sure that this true. If not, we will have to come back to this step and apply the quadratic formula.</td>
<td>

$$K_a = \frac{[H^+][HCO_3^-]}{[H_2CO_3]}$$

$$4.3 \times 10^{-7} = \frac{[x][x]}{[0.125 - x]}$$

$$4.3 \times 10^{-7} = \frac{[x][x]}{[0.125 - x]}$$

$$4.3 \times 10^{-7} \approx \frac{[x]^2}{[0.125]}$$

</td>
</tr>
<tr>
<td>Now we solve for x.</td>
<td>

$$x = \sqrt{(4.3 \times 10^{-7}) \times (0.125)} = 2.3 \times 10^{-4} \ M$$

</td>
</tr>
<tr>
<td>Before we move on to find the pH, we must first make sure that our assumption made in the previous step is valid. Thus, we now determine the percent ionization to make sure that it is less than 5% of the original acid concentration.</td>
<td>

Percent Ionization =

$$\frac{x}{0.125 \ M} \times 100 = \frac{2.3 \times 10^{-4} \ M}{0.125 \ M} \times 100\% = 0.18 \ \%$$

</td>
</tr>
<tr>
<td>Now that we have determined that our assumption is valid, we can now calculate the pH by taking the negative log of x (which represents the hydronium ion concentration).</td>
<td>

$$pH = -\log 2.3 \times 10^{-4} = \mathbf{3.64}$$

</td>
</tr>
</table>

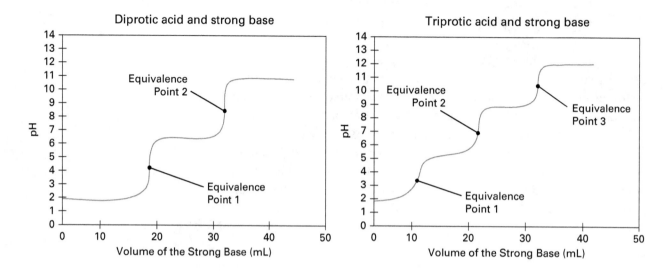

Figure 11.8 Titration curve of a diprotic acid (left) and a triprotic acid (right) with a strong base.

Titration curves can also be constructed for polyprotic acids. As we can see in Figure 11.8, this is the titration of either a diprotic acid with two inflection or equivalence points (left) as well as a triprotic acid with three inflection points (right).

Molecular Structure and Acid Strength

In this section, we will explore the possibility of determining the relative strengths of acids based on their molecular structure. Remember, that an acid according to the Brønsted-Lowry definition is a proton donor. Therefore, it follows that a strong acid should be able to donate a proton much more easily than a weak acid, which should then be able to donate a proton much more readily than a nonacid. This is essentially dependent on the polarity as well as the strength of the bond holding the hydrogen to the acidic molecule. For example, consider the ionization of the following generic acid (HA):

$$HA \rightarrow H^+ + A^-$$

What makes this an acid depends on the ability of the hydrogen to "escape" the intact HA molecule acquiring a positive charge while leaving behind the conjugate base with a negative charge. This is readily accomplished with polar bonds where the hydrogen has a partial positive charge and the rest of the molecule a partial negative charge as follows (recall bond polarity from Chapter 8):

$$\delta^+ H \longrightarrow A \; \delta^-$$

Thus, it follows that HF is a stronger acid than H_2O due to the presence of the very electronegative fluorine atom which results in a very polarized bond.

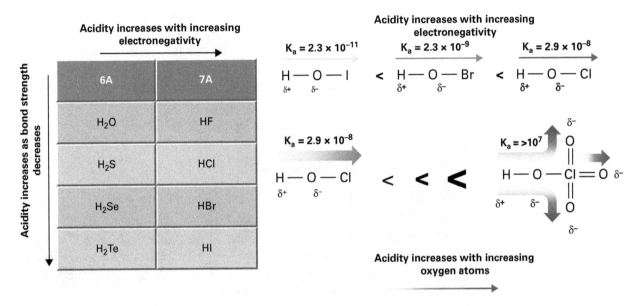

Figure 11.9 Trends for binary acid strengths (left) and oxyacid strengths (right).

This would also explain why the hydrogens in methane (CH_4) are not acidic because the carbon hydrogen bond is essentially nonpolar. In addition to polarity, bond strength is also a factor. The easier the hydrogen can come off (the weaker the bond), the stronger the acid. Therefore, it is really a combination of these two factors that ultimately determines relative acid strength. That being said, the trend for binary acid strength is depicted in Figure 11.9 (left). Notice that the acidic strength increases as you go down columns 6A and 7A, even though electronegativity decreases. This is because the hydrogen is released more easily with larger atoms because it is less tightly held. As a result, *HF* is considered a weak acid while *HCl* and *HBr* are considered strong acids. With respect to oxyacids containing the same number of oxygen atoms, acid strength increases with increasing electronegativity (Figure 11.9-top, right). Thus, hypochlorous acid is stronger than hypoiodous acid. For oxyacids with different numbers of oxygen atoms, acid strength increases with the number of oxygen atoms (Table 11.9-bottom, right). Thus, perchloric acid is much stronger than hypochlorous acid.

Section 11.7 Base Strength

Determining base strength is similar to acids in that we are interested in the extent to which they ionize. However, with bases we are interested in the OH^- ions that are produced rather than H^+ ions. Therefore, we can conclude that **strong bases** completely ionize when dissolved in water, while **weak bases** undergo only partial ionization. Table 11.3 lists some commonly used strong and weak bases. Sodium hydroxide is an example of a strong base which undergoes complete ionization, again indicated by the single arrow below:

$$NaOH\ (aq) \rightarrow Na^+\ (aq) + OH^-\ (aq)$$

As we saw with acids, the single arrow here indicates that almost no intact *NaOH* exists because it has essentially completely disassociated in *Na⁺* and *OH⁻* ions as a result of it being a strong base. Therefore, if we have a 0.10 *M* *NaOH* solution, we can easily calculate the pH of this because we know that there are 0.10 *M OH⁻* ions in solution due to the complete ionization of this strong base. Thus, the pH is of this solution is as follows:

$$pOH = -\log 0.10 = 1.00$$

$$pH = 14.00 - 1.00 = 13.00$$

As you can see, a pH of 13.00 makes sense as this is expected to be a very basic solution. It is important to note, however, that unlike polyprotic acids which ionize in a series of steps, bases containing two *OH⁻* ions dissociate in one step. Therefore, we handle this a little bit differently than we did with polyprotic acids. For example, let's consider a 0.10 *M* solution of strong base *Ca(OH)₂*. We would calculate the pH as follows:

$$[OH^-] = 2(0.10 \ M) = 0.20 \ M$$

$$pOH = -\log 0.20 = 0.70$$

$$pH = 14.00 - 0.70 = 13.30$$

As expected, we get a slightly higher pH value (more basic) for a 0.10 *M* solution of *Ca(OH)₂* than a 0.10 *M* solution of *NaOH* due to the presence of two *OH⁻* ions in calcium hydroxide. In contrast to strong bases, ammonia is considered a weak base with only partial ionization occurring when dissolved in water as indicated by the double (or equilibrium) arrow as depicted in the following equation:

$$NH_3 \ (aq) + H_2O \ (l) \rightleftharpoons NH_4^+ \ (aq) + OH^- \ (aq)$$

Table 11.3 Some examples of commonly used strong and weak bases. A more extensive list of weak bases with associated K_b values can be found in Appendix III.

Some Common Strong Bases		Some Common Weak Bases		
Formula	Name	Formula	Name	K_b (25°C)
NaOH	Sodium hydroxide	NH_3	Ammonia	1.8×10^{-5}
CaOH	Calcium hydroxide	HCO_3^-	Hydrogen carbonate	2.3×10^{-8}
KOH	Potassium hydroxide	$C_6H_5NH_2$	Aniline	3.9×10^{-10}
LiOH	Lithium hydroxide	C_5H_5N	Pyridine	1.7×10^{-9}
Ba(OH)₂	Barium hydroxide	$HONH_2$	Hydroxylamine	1.1×10^{-8}

In this case, there are plenty of intact NH_3 molecules and relatively few NH_4^+ and OH^- ions in solution due to the partial ionization that occurs with weak bases. Therefore, pH calculations are not as straightforward as they are with strong bases. For example, we cannot assume that a 0.10 M NH_3 solution contains 0.10 M OH^- ions in solution because that would be incorrect with only partial ionization occurring. Thus, when dealing with weak bases, we must again know the equilibrium constant for the ionization reaction in order to determine the hydroxide ion concentration in this case, and ultimately the pH of the solution.

The Base Ionization Constant (K_b)

The **base ionization constant (K_b)** is the equilibrium constant for the ionization reaction of bases, which is very useful for weak bases (Table 11.3). A more extensive list of weak bases along with their associated K_b values can also be found in Appendix III. If we apply what we learned in Chapter 10 regarding equilibrium constants with acid ionization constants, we can then define K_b as follows for a generic base (B):

$$B\ (aq) + H_2O\ (l) \rightleftharpoons BH^+\ (aq) + OH^-\ (aq)$$

$$K_b = \frac{[BH^+][OH^-]}{[B]}$$

Once again, it is important to note that equilibrium constants are given by [products]/[reactants], which means that a smaller K_b value is a weaker base (less ionization) and a large K_b value is a stronger base (more ionization). Thus, if we know that ammonia has a K_b value of 1.8×10^{-5} as listed in Table 11.3, we can now calculate the pH of a 0.10 M NH_3 solution by constructing a reaction table as follows:

Concentration	$NH_3\ (aq) + H_2O\ (l) \rightleftharpoons NH_4^+\ (aq) + OH^-\ (aq)$		
Initial	0.10	0.00	0.00
Change	$-x$	$+x$	$+x$
Equilibrium	$0.10 - x$	x	x

$$K_b = \frac{[NH_4^+][OH^-]}{[NH_3]}$$

$$1.8 \times 10^{-5} = \frac{[x][x]}{[0.10 - x]}$$

As we saw with acids, we would now normally apply the quadratic formula in order to solve for x. However, in many cases when x (or the change) is very small when compared to the weak base concentration (<5%), we can make the following assumption:

$$1.8 \times 10^{-5} = \frac{[x][x]}{[0.10 - x]} \approx \frac{[x]^2}{[0.10]}$$

$$x=\sqrt{(1.8\times10^{-5})\times(0.10)}=1.3\times10^{-3}\ M$$

Now, to make sure that our assumption was valid:

$$\frac{1.3\times10^{-3}\ M}{0.10\ M}\times100\%=1.3\%$$

Here, we find that the change (or percent ionization) is less than 5%; therefore, the assumption was valid, and the quadratic equation is not needed. We can now simply take the negative log of x to get the pOH because x represents the hydroxide ion concentration. From there we can calculate the pH as follows:

$$pOH=-\log1.3\times10^{-3}=2.87$$

$$pH=14.00-2.87=11.13$$

We will now work Example Problem 11.13 involving strong bases and Example Problem 11.14 involving a weak base.

Example Problem 11.13

What is the $[OH^-]$, $[H^+]$, pOH and pH of a 0.011 M solution of barium hydroxide?	
Solution:	
First, let's write our equation for ionization of barium hydroxide (first step) and also recognize that this is a strong base (complete ionization).	$Ba(OH)_2(aq)\rightleftharpoons Ba^{2+}(aq)+2\ OH^-(aq)$ $[OH^-]=2[Ba(OH)_2]=2(0.011)=\mathbf{0.022\ M}$
Now, to find the hydronium ion concentration we can use the ion product for water equation (K_w) and solve for $[H^+]$.	$K_w=[H^+][OH^-]$ $[H^+]=\dfrac{K_w}{[OH^-]}=\dfrac{1.0\times10^{-14}}{0.022}=\mathbf{4.545\times10^{-13}\ M}$
We can now determine the pOH and pH.	$pOH=-\log[OH^-]=-\log(0.022)=\mathbf{1.66}$ $pH=-\log[H^+]=-\log(4.545\times10^{-13})=\mathbf{12.34}$
Notice that the pOH and pH correctly add up to 14.00, or the pK_w.	$pK_w=pH+pOH=12.34+1.66=14.00$ ✔

Example Problem 11.14

What is the $[OH^-]$, $[H^+]$, pOH, and pH of a 0.125 M solution of the weak base hydrogen carbonate ($K_b=2.3\times10^{-8}$)?	
Solution:	
First, let's write our equation for hydrogen carbonate (first step) and set up our table as follows:	$HCO_3^-(aq)+H_2O(l)\rightarrow H_2CO_3(aq)+OH^-(aq)$

Concentration	$HCO_3^-(aq)+H_2O(l)\rightarrow$	$H_2CO_3(aq)+$	$OH^-(aq)$
Initial	0.125	0.00	0.00
Change	$-x$	$+x$	$+x$
Equilibrium	$0.125-x$	x	x

Now, we set up our K_b expression. We will assume that the assumption is valid, but will have to check the percent ionization at the end to make sure that this is true. If not, we will have to come back to this step and apply the quadratic formula.	$K_b = \dfrac{[H_2CO_3][OH^-]}{[HCO_3^-]}$ $2.3 \times 10^{-8} = \dfrac{[x][x]}{[0.125 - x]}$ $2.3 \times 10^{-8} \approx \dfrac{[x][x]}{[0.125]}$ $2.3 \times 10^{-8} = \dfrac{[x]^2}{[0.125]}$
Now we solve for x.	$x = [OH^-] = \sqrt{(2.3 \times 10^{-8}) \times (0.125)} = \mathbf{5.4 \times 10^{-5}\ M}$
Before we move on to find the $[H^+]$, pOH, and pH, we must first make sure that our assumption made in the previous step is valid. Thus, we now determine the percent ionization to make sure that it is less than 5% of the original acid concentration.	Percent Ionization $= \dfrac{x}{0.125\ M} \times 100\% = \dfrac{5.4 \times 10^{-5}\ M}{0.125\ M} \times 100\% = 0.043\%$
Now that we have determined that our assumption is valid, we can now calculate the hydronium ion concentration using the ion product for water equation (K_w).	$K_w = [H^+][OH^-]$ $[H^+] = \dfrac{K_w}{[OH^-]} = \dfrac{1.0 \times 10^{-14}}{5.4 \times 10^{-5}} = \mathbf{1.852 \times 10^{-10}\ M}$
We can now calculate the pOH and pH values.	$pOH = -\log[OH^-] = -\log(5.4 \times 10^{-5}) = \mathbf{4.27}$ $pH = -\log[H^+] = -\log(1.852 \times 10^{-10}) = \mathbf{9.73}$
Notice that the pOH and pH correctly add up to 14.00, or the pK_w.	$pK_w = pH + pOH = 9.73 + 4.27 = 14.00$ ✔

Section 11.8 Buffers

Buffers are solutions that resist changes in pH by neutralizing added acid or base, which is somewhat unique as the pH in most solutions will change quite dramatically when even the smallest amounts of acid or base are added to them. In fact, buffers play a key role in biological systems, where it is very important that a certain pH is maintained as dramatic shifts in pH would be detrimental to life. Your blood is a good example of a buffer where it is necessary that a very narrow pH range is maintained (~7.26 – 7.42). As you can imagine, dramatic shifts in our blood pH would be absolutely catastrophic for us as human beings. In fact, our blood contains a mixture of the relatively weak carbonic acid and the bicarbonate ion. In doing so, it has the ability to resist changes in pH, whether acidic or basic products enter the blood stream. For example, the carbonic acid can neutralize added base as follows:

$$H_2CO_3\ (aq) + OH^-\ (aq) \rightarrow HCO_3^-\ (aq) + H_2O\ (l)$$

Similarly, the bicarbonate ion can neutralize added acid:

$$HCO_3^-\ (aq) + H^+\ (aq) \rightarrow H_2CO_3\ (aq)$$

Notice that the pH maintained in our blood is slightly basic, which is essentially due to the fact that numerous acidic byproducts are metabolically produced in our bodies every day and released into our blood streams. As is the case with all buffers, the ability to maintain a desired pH relies on the fact that both the weak acid (or weak base) is present along with the conjugate base (or conjugate acid), respectively. In this case, notice we have the weak carbonic acid as well as the conjugate base, or the bicarbonate ion. By both being present, the carbonic acid ionizes less (thereby resulting in a slightly higher pH) than it would normally ionize without the conjugate base present as Le Châtelier's principle would predict because the equilibrium is shifted to the left as shown below:

$$H_2CO_3\ (aq) + H_2O\ (l) \rightleftharpoons HCO_3^-\ (aq) + H_3O^+\ (aq)$$

This is an example of the **common ion effect** (discussed in Chapter 10) in which a solution contains two substances that share a common ion (in this case, HCO_3^-). It is also important to point out that here we have an example of an **acidic buffer** composed of a weak acid and its conjugate base, but it is also possible to have a **basic buffer** in which you have both the weak base as well as the conjugate acid. Figure 11.10 illustrates how an acidic buffer can be made by combining the weak acid acetic acid and its conjugate base, sodium acetate. In any event, now that we have established some basic definitions regarding buffers and their purpose, we now focus our attention on pH calculations involving buffers.

Figure 11.10 Example of an acidic buffer composed of acetic acid and its conjugate base sodium acetate.

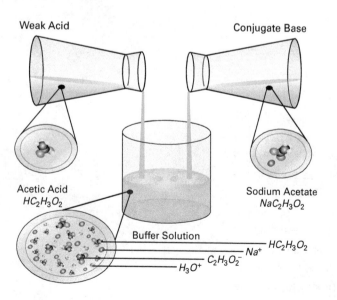

Weak Acid

Conjugate Base

Acetic Acid
$HC_2H_3O_2$

Sodium Acetate
$NaC_2H_3O_2$

Buffer Solution

$HC_2H_3O_2$

Na^+

$C_2H_3O_2^-$

H_3O^+

Calculating the pH of a Buffer

The pH calculations involving buffer solutions are very similar to those already discussed in this chapter. The major difference here, however, is the fact that we now have to account for the presence of the conjugate acid or base. For example, let's look at an acidic buffer solution composed of 0.10 *M* acetic acid and 0.10 *M* of the conjugate base sodium acetate.

Concentration	$HC_2H_3O_2(aq) \rightleftharpoons C_2H_3O_2^-(aq) + H^+(aq)$		
Initial	0.10	0.10	0
Change	$-x$	$+x$	$+x$
Equilibrium	$0.10 - x$	$0.10 + x$	x

$$K_a = \frac{[H^+][C_2H_3O_2^-]}{[HC_2H_3O_2]}$$

$$1.8 \times 10^{-5} = \frac{[x][0.10+x]}{[0.10-x]}$$

Now we will simplify the equation for now and check to make sure that our assumption is valid later:

$$1.8 \times 10^{-5} = \frac{[x][0.10+x]}{[0.10-x]} \approx \frac{x(0.10)}{[0.10]}$$

$$x = \frac{(1.8 \times 10^{-5}) \times (0.10)}{0.10} = 1.8 \times 10^{-5} \ M$$

Now, to make sure that our assumption was valid:

$$\frac{1.8 \times 10^{-5} \ M}{0.10 \ M} \times 100\% = 0.018\%$$

Since this value is less than 5%, our assumption was valid and we can continue working on this problem to find the pH.

$$pH = -\log 1.8 \times 10^{-5} = 4.74$$

Notice that this value is slightly higher than the pH of a 0.01 M solution of acetic acid alone, which we worked out to be 2.87 in the "Acid Ionization Constant (K_a)" section of this chapter. Knowing what we now know regarding buffer solutions, this answer makes sense. Let us now look at another very useful equation that we can use when it comes to calculations involving buffers.

The Henderson-Hasselbalch Equation

Lawrence Henderson was born in Lynn, Massachusetts, in 1878 and died in Cambridge, Massachusetts, in 1942 at the age of 63. He was a biochemist whose early work involved acid-base regulation as it relates to buffer systems in the human body. He wrote the Henderson equation involving carbonic acid as a buffer solution in 1908, which was later modified by Karl Hasselbalch who expressed the equation in logarithmic terms. Karl Hasselbalch was a physician and chemist born in 1874 in Aastrup, Denmark, and he died in 1962. His modified equation is now known as the **Henderson-Hasselbalch equation**, which is commonly used to calculate pH as a measure of acidity.

This equation can be derived if we consider the ionization of a generic buffer containing a weak acid (HA) and its conjugate base (A^-) as follows:

$$HA\ (aq) \rightleftharpoons H^+\ (aq) + A^-\ (aq)$$

$$K_a = \frac{[H^+][A^-]}{[HA]}$$

$$[H^+] = \frac{K_a\,[HA]}{[A^-]}$$

$$-\log[H^+] = -\log\left(\frac{K_a\,[HA]}{[A^-]}\right)$$

$$-\log[H^+] = -\log K_a - \log\frac{[HA]}{[A^-]}$$

$$-\log[H^+] = -\log K_a + \log\frac{[A^-]}{[HA]}$$

Thus, we arrive at the Henderson-Hasselbalch equation:

$$pH = pK_a + \log\frac{[A^-]}{[HA]}$$

If we now return to our previous example involving a buffer solution containing 0.10 M acetic acid and 0.10 M sodium acetate, we can use this equation to see if we arrive at the same pH value of 4.74:

$$pH = pK_a + \log\frac{[A^-]}{[HA]}$$

$$pH = -\log(1.8 \times 10^{-5}) + \log\frac{[0.10]}{[0.10]}$$

$$pH = 4.74 + 0.00$$

$$\mathbf{pH = 4.74}$$

Let's work another example using both methods.

Example Problem 11.15

Using both the tabular format as well as the Henderson-Hasselbalch equation, calculate the pH of a buffer solution containing 0.025 M benzoic acid ($HC_7H_5O_2$) and 0.50 M sodium benzoate ($NaC_7H_5O_2$). According to Appendix III, the K_a value for benzoic acid is 6.5×10^{-5}.

Solution:	
First, we will solve this problem using the tabular format by writing the ionization of benzoic acid (first step) and set up our table as follows:	$HC_7H_5O_2(aq) \rightleftharpoons C_7H_5O_2^-\ (aq) + H^+\ (aq)$

Concentration	$HC_7H_5O_2(aq) \rightleftharpoons$	$C_7H_5O_2^-\ (aq) +$	$H^+\ (aq)$
Initial	0.025	0.50	0.00
Change	$-x$	$+x$	$+x$
Equilibrium	$0.025 - x$	$0.50 + x$	x

	$$K_a = \frac{[H^+][C_7H_5O_2^-]}{[HC_7H_5O_2]}$$ $$6.5 \times 10^{-5} = \frac{[x][0.50+x]}{[0.025-x]}$$
Now, we will solve for x, or the hydronium ion concentration. Also, we will assume that the assumption is valid, but will have to check the percent ionization at the end to make sure that this is true. If not, we will have to come back to this step and apply the quadratic formula.	$$6.5 \times 10^{-5} = \frac{[x][0.50+x]}{[0.025-x]} \approx \frac{x(0.50)}{[0.025]}$$ $$x = \frac{(6.5 \times 10^{-5}) \times (0.025)}{0.50} = 3.25 \times 10^{-6} \ M$$
Now let's make sure that our assumption was valid.	Percent Ionization $$= \frac{x}{0.025 \ M} \times 100 = \frac{3.25 \times 10^{-6} \ M}{0.025 \ M} \times 100\% = 0.013\%$$
Now that we have verified that our assumption was valid (<5%), we can calculate the pH.	$$pH = -\log(3.25 \times 10^{-6}) = \mathbf{5.49}$$
Now we will use the Henderson-Hasselbalch equation to verify our answer.	$$pH = pK_a + \log \frac{[C_7H_5O_2^-]}{[HC_7H_5O_2]}$$ $$pH = -\log(6.5 \times 10^{-5}) + \log \frac{[0.50]}{[0.025]}$$ $$pH = 4.187 + 1.301$$ $$pH = \mathbf{5.49}$$

It should also be noted that the Henderson-Hasselbalch equation can also be modified for use with weak base buffer systems. For example, consider the following generic basic buffer system:

$$B \ (aq) + H_2O \ (l) \rightleftharpoons BH^+ \ (aq) + OH^- \ (aq)$$

The Henderson-Hasselbalch equation can be modified as follows:

$$pOH = pK_b + \log \frac{[BH^+]}{[B]}$$

Calculations Involving Changes in the pH of a Buffer

Now that we have used various methods to calculate the pH of a buffer solution, we will now look at calculations involving additional acid or base added to buffers, and how buffers are able to resist dramatic changes in pH. While the pH does, in fact, change as we will see under these circumstances, these are only slight fluctuations when compared to other solutions with no buffering capabilities. When we work these types of problems, we must first take into account the amount of added acid or base to the buffer solution when we calculate our initial concentration. From there, we can work the problem using either the tabular format or Henderson-Hasselbalch equation as we have already done in this chapter. Let's look at Example 11.16 where we have a strong acid being added to a buffer system and then Example 11.17 where we have a strong base being added to the buffer solution.

Example Problem 11.16

Calculate the pH of a buffer solution containing 0.10 M acetic acid and 0.10 M sodium acetate if 0.010 $mols$ of HCl were added to the buffer system. Assume a 1.0 liter total solution, and ignore any small changes in volume that might occur upon acid addition. The K_a value for acetic acid according to Appendix III is 1.8×10^{-5}. For comparison purposes, calculate how the pH of 1.0 L of pure water changes following the addition of the same amount of HCl (again, ignore any small changes in volume that might occur upon acid addition).

Solution:	
First, we need to determine the initial concentrations of both the acetic acid and the conjugate base, sodium acetate. This is due to the fact that the additional number of $mols$ of HCl added to the buffer needs to be subtracted from the original sodium acetate concentration, and added to the acetic acid concentration. In other words, added acid will react with the conjugate base to make more acid. Then we can set up our table as follows:	Initial concentration calculations: $HC_2H_3O_2 = 0.10 \; mols + 0.01 \; mols \; HCl \; added = 0.11 \; M$ $C_2H_3O_2^- = 0.10 \; mol - 0.01 \; mols \; HCl \; added = 0.090 \; M$ Concentration $HC_2H_3O_2(aq) \rightleftharpoons C_2H_3O_2^- (aq) + H^+ (aq)$ Initial ⠀⠀⠀⠀⠀0.11⠀⠀⠀⠀⠀0.090⠀⠀⠀⠀⠀0.00 Change ⠀⠀⠀⠀$-x$⠀⠀⠀⠀⠀$+x$⠀⠀⠀⠀⠀$+x$ Equilibrium ⠀$0.11 - x$⠀⠀$0.090 + x$⠀⠀x $K_a = \dfrac{[H^+][C_2H_3O_2^-]}{[HC_2H_3O_2]}$ $1.8 \times 10^{-5} = \dfrac{[x][0.090+x]}{[0.11-x]}$
Now, we will solve for x, or the hydronium ion concentration. Also, we will assume that the assumption is valid, but will have to check the percent ionization at the end to make sure that this is true. If not, we will have to come back to this step and apply the quadratic formula.	$1.8 \times 10^{-5} = \dfrac{[x][0.090+x]}{[0.11-x]} \approx \dfrac{x(0.090)}{[0.11]}$ $x = \dfrac{(1.8 \times 10^{-5}) \times (0.11)}{0.090} = 2.2 \times 10^{-5} \; M$
Now let's make sure that our assumption was valid.	Percent Ionization $= \dfrac{x}{0.11 \; M} \times 100 = \dfrac{2.2 \times 10^{-5} \; M}{0.11 \; M} \times 100\% = 0.020\%$
Now that we have verified that our assumption was valid (<5%), we can calculate the pH. This pH value makes sense because it dropped upon acid addition from 4.74, which is the pH of this buffer solution prior to HCl addition (see example calculation in "Calculating the pH of a Buffer" section).	$pH = -\log(2.2 \times 10^{-5}) = \mathbf{4.66}$

Incidentally, the Henderson-Hasselbalch equation can be used to verify our answer.	$pH = pK_a + \log\dfrac{[C_2H_3O_2^-]}{[HC_2H_3O_2]}$
	$pH = -\log(1.8 \times 10^{-5}) + \log\dfrac{[0.090]}{[0.11]}$
	$pH = 4.745 + (-8.715 \times 10^{-2})$
	$pH = \textbf{4.66}$ ✔
Now let's see how the pH changes if we were to add 0.010 *mols* HCl to 1.0 *L* of pure water initially at pH = 7.00.	$[H^+] = \dfrac{0.010\ mols\ HCl}{1.0\ L} = 0.010\ M$ $pH = -\log 0.010 = \textbf{2.00}$

Notice how the pH changed by only a very small amount with the buffer (from 4.74 to 4.66), while a dramatic drop in pH was observed with pure water. This is a good example of how effective a buffer can be against dramatic changes in pH.

Example Problem 11.17

Calculate the pH of a buffer solution containing 0.10 *M* acetic acid and 0.10 *M* sodium acetate if 0.010 *mols* of *NaOH* were added to the buffer system. Assume a 1.0 liter total solution, and ignore any small changes in volume that might occur upon base addition. The K_a value for acetic acid according to Appendix III is 1.8×10^{-5}. For comparison purposes, calculate how the pH of 1.0 *L* of pure water changes following the addition of the same amount of *NaOH* (again, ignore any small changes in volume that might occur upon base addition).

Solution:	
First, we need to determine the initial concentrations of both the acetic acid and the conjugate base, sodium acetate. This is due to the fact that the additional number of *mols* of *NaOH* added to the buffer needs to be subtracted from the original acetic acid concentration and added to the sodium acetate concentration. In other words, added base will react with the acid to make more conjugate base. Then we can set up our table as follows:	Initial concentration calculations: $HC_2H_3O_2 = 0.10\ mols - 0.01\ mols\ NaOH\ added = 0.090\ M$ $C_2H_3O_2^- = 0.10\ mols + 0.01\ mols\ NaOH\ added = 0.11\ M$

Concentration	$HC_2H_3O_2 (aq) \rightleftharpoons$	$C_2H_3O_2^-\ (aq) +$	$H^+\ (aq)$
Initial	0.090	0.11	0.00
Change	$-x$	$+x$	$+x$
Equilibrium	$0.090 - x$	$0.11 + x$	x

$K_a = \dfrac{[H^+][C_2H_3O_2^-]}{[HC_2H_3O_2]}$

$1.8 \times 10^{-5} = \dfrac{[x][0.11 + x]}{[0.090 - x]}$

Now, we will solve for *x*, or the hydronium ion concentration. Also, we will assume that the assumption is valid, but will have to check the percent ionization at the end to make sure that this is true. If not, we will have to come back to this step and apply the quadratic formula.	$1.8 \times 10^{-5} = \dfrac{[x][0.11 + x]}{[0.090 - x]} \approx \dfrac{x(0.11)}{[0.090]}$ $x = \dfrac{(1.8 \times 10^{-5}) \times (0.090)}{0.11} = 1.47 \times 10^{-5}\ M$
Now let's make sure that our assumption was valid.	Percent Ionization $=$ $\dfrac{x}{0.090\ M} \times 100 = \dfrac{1.47 \times 10^{-5}\ M}{0.090\ M} \times 100\% = .016\%$

Now that we have verified that our assumption was valid (<5%), we can calculate the pH. This pH value makes sense because it increased upon base addition from 4.74, which is the pH of this buffer solution prior to *NaOH* addition (see example calculation in "Calculating the pH of a Buffer" section).	$pH = -\log(1.47 \times 10^{-5}) = \mathbf{4.83}$ ✓
Incidentally, the Henderson-Hasselbalch equation can be used to verify our answer.	$pH = pK_a + \log \dfrac{[C_2H_3O_2^-]}{[HC_2H_3O_2]}$ $pH = -\log(1.8 \times 10^{-5}) + \log \dfrac{[0.11]}{[0.090]}$ $pH = 4.745 + 8.715 \times 10^{-2}$ $pH = \mathbf{4.83}$ ✓
Now let's see how the pH changes if we were to add 0.010 *mols NaOH* to 1.0 *L* of pure water initially at pH = 7.00.	$[OH^-] = \dfrac{0.010 \; mols \; NaOH}{1.0 \; L} = 0.010 \; M$ $pOH = -\log 0.010 = 2.00$ $pH = 14.00 - 2.00 = \mathbf{12.00}$
Notice how the pH changes by only a very small amount with the buffer (from 4.74 to 4.83), while a dramatic increase in pH is observed with pure water. This is another good example of how effective a buffer can be against dramatic changes in pH.	

Buffer Effectiveness

Recall at the beginning of this chapter that we had mentioned that buffers have the capability to neutralize small amounts of acids and bases, as we have just seen with Examples 11.16 and 11.17. The question now becomes how much added acid or base can a buffer neutralize? In other words, how effective is a particular buffer? The answer to that question essentially depends on two major factors. First, the relative concentrations of the weak acid and conjugate base (or weak base and conjugate acid) are an important consideration. Buffers tend to be more effective when the relative concentrations of weak acid and conjugate base (or weak base and conjugate acid) are equal or in a 1:1 ratio. Second, the absolute concentrations of each are also important, with higher concentrations being more effective. Another important consideration with respect to buffers involves the **buffer range**, which is the pH range in which a particular acid and its conjugate base (or weak base and its conjugate acid) are effective. Generally speaking, the effective range for a given buffer is within one pH unit on either side (one unit lower and one unit higher) than its pK_a or pK_b value. For example, if you wanted to make a solution buffered at a pH of 4.50, formic acid ($pK_a = 3.74$) would be a much better choice for you to use in your buffer system than, for example, hypochlorus acid ($pK_a = 7.54$).

Key Terms

1. Acid
2. Acid-base reactions
3. Acidic buffer
4. Acid ionization constant (K_a)
5. Amphoteric
6. Analyte
7. Arrhenius acid
8. Arrhenius base
9. Arrhenius definition
10. Autoionization
11. Base
12. Base ionization constant (K_b)
13. Basic buffer
14. Binary acid
15. Brønsted-Lowry acid
16. Brønsted-Lowry base
17. Brønsted-Lowry definition
18. Buffer range
19. Buffers
20. Burette
21. Common ion effect
22. Conjugate acid-base pairs
23. Diprotic acids
24. Endpoint
25. Equivalence point
26. Henderson-Hasselbalch equation
27. Hydronium ion
28. Indicator
29. Ion product for water (K_w)
30. Lewis acid
31. Lewis base
32. Monoprotic acids
33. Neutral
34. Neutralization reaction
35. Oxyacid

36. Percent ionization

37. pH

38. pH curves

39. pOH

40. Polyprotic acids

41. Strong acids

42. Strong bases

43. Titrant

44. Titration curves

45. Titrations

46. Weak acids

47. Weak bases

Problems

ACIDS AND BASES DEFINITIONS

1. What is the definition of an Arrhenius acid and an Arrhenius base?

2. For each of the following, identify which are Arrhenius acids and which are Arrhenius bases.

    a. HCl

    b. $NaOH$

    c. $HC_2H_3O_2$

    d. KOH

3. What is the definition of a Brønsted-Lowry acid and a Brønsted-Lowry base?

4. Identify the Brønsted-Lowry acid and Brønsted-Lowry base in each of the following reactions.

    a. $HBr\ (aq) + H_2O\ (l) \rightarrow H_3O^+\ (aq) + Br^-\ (aq)$

    b. $NH_3\ (aq) + H_2O\ (l) \rightleftharpoons NH_4^+\ (aq) + OH^-\ (aq)$

    c. $HI\ (aq) + H_2O\ (l) \rightarrow H_3O^+\ (aq) + I^-\ (aq)$

    d. $CH_3NH_2\ (aq) + H_2O\ (l) \rightleftharpoons CH_3NH_3^+\ (aq) + OH^-\ (aq)$

5. What is an amphoteric substance? Give an example.

6. What are conjugate acid-base pairs?

7. What are the conjugate acids for each of the following bases?

    a. ClO_4^-

    b. HCO_3^-

    c. NH_3

    d OH^-

8. What are the conjugate bases for each of the following acids?

    a. H_3O^+

    b. H_2SO_4

    c. HCl

    d HI

ACIDS AND BASES NOMENCLATURE

9. What is a binary acid?

10. What is an oxyacid acid?

11. What are the names of the following acids?

    a. $HClO$

    b. HCl

    c. H_2SO_3

    d HBr

12. What are the names of the following acids?

    a. $HClO_4$

    b. HF

    c. H_2SO_4

    d $HClO_2$

13. Write the formulas for each of the following acids.

    a. Phosphoric acid

    b. Hydroiodic acid

    c. Chloric acid

    d Acetic acid

14. What are the names of the following bases?

    a. $NaOH$

    b. $Ba(OH)_2$

    c. KOH

    d. $RbOH$

15. Write the formulas for each of the following bases.

    a. Magnesium hydroxide

    b. Lithium hydroxide

    c. Ammonia

    d. Calcium hydroxide

AUTOIONIZATION OF WATER AND SCALES USED TO QUANTIFY ACIDITY AND BASICITY

16. What is the autoionization of water?

17. What is the ion product constant for water?

18. In an acidic solution at 25°C, which of the following is true?

    a. $[H^+] < [OH^-]$

    b. $[H^+] = [OH^-]$

    c. $[H^+] > [OH^-]$

    d. $[H^+] = [OH^-] = 1.0 \times 10^{-14}\ M$

19. In a basic solution at 25°C, which of the following is true?

    a. $[H^+] < [OH^-]$

    b. $[H^+] = [OH^-]$

    c. $[H^+] > [OH^-]$

    d. $[H^+] = [OH^-] = 1.0 \times 10^{-14}\ M$

20. In neutral solution at 25°C, which of the following is true?

    a. $[H^+] < [OH^-]$

    b. $[H^+] = [OH^-]$

    c. $[H^+] > [OH^-]$

    d. $[H^+] = [OH^-] = 1.0 \times 10^{-14}\ M$

21. Calculate the hydronium ion concentration for each solution at 25°C and determine whether it is acidic, basic, or neutral:

    a. $[OH^-] = 1.0 \times 10^{-7}\ M$

    b. $[OH^-] = 6.3 \times 10^{-8}\ M$

    c. $[OH^-] = 4.1 \times 10^{-2}\ M$

    d. $[OH^-] = 2.3 \times 10^{-10}\ M$

22. Calculate the hydroxide ion concentration for each solution at 25°C and determine whether it is acidic, basic, or neutral:

    a. $[H^+] = 3.4 \times 10^{-4}\ M$

    b. $[H^+] = 8.5 \times 10^{-11}\ M$

    c. $[H^+] = 5.2 \times 10^{-3}\ M$

    d. $[H^+] = 9.8 \times 10^{-5}\ M$

23. Define pH and pOH.

24. Calculate the pH and pOH for each of the solutions listed in question #21.

25. Calculate the pH and pOH for each of the solutions listed in question #22.

ACID AND BASE TITRATIONS: A COMMON LABORATORY TECHNIQUE

26. What is a titration reaction? Define titrant and analyte.

27. What is a burette?

28. What is the difference between the equivalence and endpoints in an acid-base neutralization reaction during titration? What is an indicator, and why is it used in these types of reactions?

29. Complete and balance the following acid-base equation:

$$HCl\ (aq) + NaOH\ (aq) \rightarrow$$

30. Complete and balance the following acid-base equation:

$$H_2SO_4\ (aq) + LiOH\ (aq) \rightarrow$$

31. Complete and balance the following acid-base equation:

$$H_3PO_4\ (aq) + NaOH\ (aq) \rightarrow$$

32. Complete and balance the following acid-base equation:

$$HCl\ (aq) + Ca(OH)_2\ (aq) \rightarrow$$

33. A 30.0 *ml* sample of *HCl* (unknown concentration) is titrated with a 0.100 *M NaOH* solution. The equivalence point is reached after 38.2 *ml* of the *NaOH* solution is added. What is the concentration of the *HCl* sample?

34. What is the volume of a 0.127 *M HCl* solution if it requires 38.2 *ml* of a 0.100 *M NaOH* solution to reach the equivalence point?

35. A 19.3 *ml* sample of H_2SO_4 (unknown concentration) is titrated with a 0.320 *M NaOH* solution. The equivalence point is reached after 24.6 *ml* of the *NaOH* solution is added. What is the concentration of the H_2SO_4 sample?

36. What is the volume of a 0.204 *M* H_2SO_4 solution if it requires 24.6 *ml* of a 0.320 *M NaOH* solution to reach the equivalence point?

37. A 12.8 *ml* sample of H_3PO_4 (unknown concentration) is titrated with a 0.250 *M KOH* solution. The equivalence point is reached after 28.7 *ml* of the *KOH* solution is added. What is the concentration of the H_3PO_4 sample?

38. What is the volume of a 0.187 *M* H_3PO_4 solution if it requires 28.7 *ml* of a 0.250 *M KOH* solution to reach the equivalence point?

39. A 22.0 *ml* sample of $HClO_4$ (unknown concentration) is titrated with a 0.200 *M NaOH* solution. The equivalence point is reached after 34.2 *ml* of the *NaOH* solution is added. What is the concentration of the $HClO_4$ sample?

40. A 25.0 *ml* sample of *HCl* (unknown concentration) is titrated with a 0.150 *M* $Ca(OH)_2$ solution. The equivalence point is reached after 22.5 *ml* of the $Ca(OH)_2$ solution is added. What is the concentration of the *HCl* sample?

41. Below are the titration curves of a strong base being added to either a strong or a weak acid. Which one is which, and why?

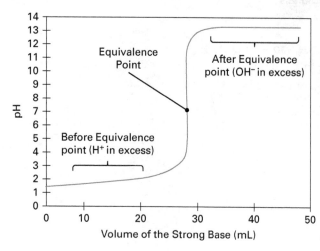

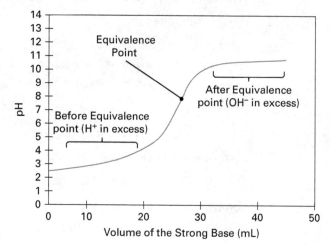

ACID STRENGTH

42. What is the major distinction between strong and weak acids?

43. What is the pH of a 0.25 M solution of the strong acid HCl?

44. What is the pH of a 0.10 M solution of the strong acid $HClO_4$?

45. What is the pH of a 0.02 M solution of the strong acid HNO_3?

46. What is the hydronium ion concentration in a HCl solution (strong acid) with a pH value of 1.55?

47. What is the hydronium ion concentration in a HI solution (strong acid) with a pH value of 2.59?

48. What mass (grams) of the strong acid HCl is present in a 0.35 L solution with a pH value of 1.85?

49. What mass (grams) of the strong acid HI is present in a 0.20 L solution with a pH value of 1.26?

50. What is the acid ionization constant (K_a)?

51. Write the K_a expression for the generic weak acid HA.

52. What is percent ionization, and how do we calculate it when dealing with weak acids?

53. When doing calculations involving weak acids and acid ionization constants, when can you use the "simplifying" assumption (i.e. assume that the change, or x is small), and when can you not?

54. Calculate the pH of a 0.50 M nitrous acid solution ($K_a = 4.6 \times 10^{-4}$).

55. Calculate the pH of a 0.30 M hydrofluoric acid solution ($K_a = 3.5 \times 10^{-4}$).

56. Calculate the pH of a 0.25 M acetic acid solution ($K_a = 1.8 \times 10^{-5}$).

57. Calculate the pH of a 0.65 M formic acid solution ($K_a = 1.8 \times 10^{-4}$).

58. Calculate the pH of a 0.80 M nitrous acid solution ($K_a = 4.6 \times 10^{-4}$).

59. Calculate the pH of a 0.50 M hydrofluoric acid solution ($K_a = 3.5 \times 10^{-4}$).

60. Calculate the pH of a 0.10 M nitrous acid solution ($K_a = 4.6 \times 10^{-4}$).

61. Calculate the pH of a 0.050 M hydrofluoric acid solution ($K_a = 3.5 \times 10^{-4}$).

62. Calculate the pH of a 0.010 M nitrous acid solution ($K_a = 4.6 \times 10^{-4}$).

63. Calculate the percent ionization of a 1.0 M solution of acetic acid ($K_a = 1.8 \times 10^{-5}$).

64. Calculate the percent ionization of a 1.0 M solution of formic acid ($K_a = 1.8 \times 10^{-4}$).

65. Calculate the percent ionization of a 0.10 M solution of acetic acid ($K_a = 1.8 \times 10^{-5}$).

66. What are polyprotic acids?

67. For the most part, what assumption can we generally make when dealing with polyprotic acids and why?

68. Define monoprotic, diprotic, and triprotic acids. Give an example for each.

69. Calculate the pH of a 0.20 M carbonic acid solution ($K_{a1} = 4.3 \times 10^{-7}$ and $K_{a2} = 5.6 \times 10^{-11}$).

70. Below are titration curves of a diprotic and triprotic acid titrated with a strong base. Which one is which, and how can you tell?

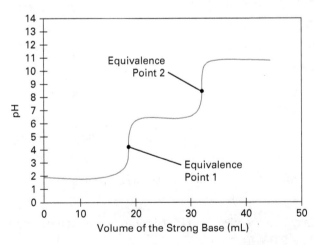
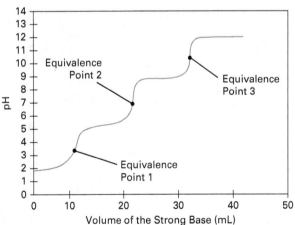

71. Which acid would you expect to be stronger, H_2S or HCl?

72. Which acid would you expect to be stronger, H_2Se or HBr?

73. Which acid would you expect to be stronger, *HF* or *HI*?

74. Which acid would you expect to be stronger, *HClO* or *HClO$_4$*?

BASE STRENGTH

75. What is the major distinction between strong and weak bases?

76. What is the pH of a 0.20 *M* solution of the strong base *NaOH*?

77. What is the pH of a 0.15 *M* solution of the strong base *KOH*?

78. What is the pH of a 0.050 *M* solution of the strong base *Sr(OH)$_2$*?

79. What is the hydroxide ion concentration in a *NaOH* solution with a pH value of 11.25?

80. What is the hydroxide ion concentration in a *LiOH* solution with a pH value of 9.10?

81. What is the hydroxide ion concentration *Ca(OH)$_2$* solution with a pH value of 12.25?

82. What is the hydroxide ion concentration *Ba(OH)$_2$* solution with a pH value of 13.15?

83. What is the pH of a solution that is 2.8% *NaOH* by mass and has a density of 1.02 *g/ml*?

84. What is the pH of a solution that is 1.5% *LiOH* by mass and has a density of 1.02 *g/ml*?

85. What is the base ionization constant (K_b)?

86. Write the K_b expression for the generic base *B*.

87. Calculate the pH of a 0.50 *M* ammonia solution ($K_b = 1.8 \times 10^{-5}$).

88. Calculate the pH of a 0.25 *M* hydrogen carbonate solution ($K_b = 2.3 \times 10^{-8}$).

89. Calculate the pH of a 0.30 *M* methylamine solution ($K_b = 4.4 \times 10^{-4}$).

90. Calculate the pH of a 0.45 *M* carbonate solution ($K_b = 1.8 \times 10^{-4}$).

91. Calculate the pH of a 1.0 *M* ethylamine solution ($K_b = 5.6 \times 10^{-4}$).

92. Calculate the pH of a 1.5×10^{-2} *M* ammonia solution ($K_b = 1.8 \times 10^{-5}$).

93. Calculate the pH of a 0.85 *M* hydrogen carbonate solution ($K_b = 2.3 \times 10^{-8}$).

94. Calculate the pH of a 0.50 *M* ethylamine solution ($K_b = 5.6 \times 10^{-4}$).

95. Calculate the pH of a 0.35 M carbonate solution ($K_b = 1.8 \times 10^{-4}$).

96. Morphine is a narcotic pain reliever commonly used to treat moderate to severe pain and is a weak base ($K_b = 1.6 \times 10^{-6}$). What is the pH of a 0.25 M solution of morphine?

97. Nicotine is a highly addictive drug and is a weak base ($K_b = 1.0 \times 10^{-6}$). What is the pH of a 0.85 M solution of nicotine?

98. Calculate the percent ionization of a 0.10 M solution of ammonia ($K_b = 1.8 \times 10^{-5}$).

99. Calculate the percent ionization of a 1.5 M solution of ammonia ($K_b = 1.8 \times 10^{-5}$).

100. Calculate the percent ionization of a 0.45 M solution of methylamine ($K_b = 4.4 \times 10^{-4}$).

BUFFERS

101. What are buffers? Give an example of a buffer.

102. What is the normal pH range of human blood? How is this pH range maintained?

103. What are acidic and basic buffers and how are they made?

104. What is the common ion effect?

105. Explain why you would NOT use strong acids or bases to make a buffer.

106. Consider the following generic acidic buffer system containing approximately equal amounts of acid (HA) and conjugate base (A^-):

$$HA\ (aq) \rightleftharpoons H^+(aq) + A^-\ (aq)$$

Based on Le Châtelier's principle, describe how added acid would affect this equilibrium and how this buffer system would minimize a dramatic change in pH. Does the pH go up or down?

107. Consider the following generic acidic buffer system containing approximately equal amounts of acid (HA) and conjugate base (A^-):

$$HA\ (aq) \rightleftharpoons H^+(aq) + A^-\ (aq)$$

Based on Le Châtelier's principle, describe how added base would affect this equilibrium and how this buffer system would minimize a dramatic change in pH. Does the pH go up or down?

108. What is the pH of a buffer system containing 0.25 M $HCHO_2$ and 0.20 M $NaCHO_2$? The K_a value for formic acid is 1.8×10^{-4}.

109. What is the pH of a buffer system containing 0.10 M $HC_2H_3O_2$ and 0.15 M $NaC_2H_3O_2$? The K_a value for acetic acid is 1.8×10^{-5}.

110. What is the pH of a buffer system containing 0.17 M HF and 0.23 M NaF? The K_a value for hydrofluoric acid is 3.5×10^{-4}.

111. What is the pH of a buffer system containing 0.10 M $HCHO_2$ and 0.10 M $NaCHO_2$? The K_a value for formic acid is 1.8×10^{-4}.

112. What is the pH of a buffer system containing 0.18 M NH_3 and 0.26 M NH_4Cl? The K_b value for ammonia is 1.8×10^{-5}.

113. What is the pH of a buffer system containing 0.24 M CH_3NH_2 and 0.13 M CH_3NH_3Br? The K_b value for methylamine is 4.4×10^{-4}.

114. What is the pH of a buffer system containing 0.28 M $C_2H_5NH_2$ and 0.37 M $C_2H_5NH_3Br$? The K_b value for ethylamine is 5.6×10^{-4}.

115. What is the pH of a buffer system containing 0.10 M NH_3 and 0.10 M NH_4Cl? The K_b value for ammonia is 1.8×10^{-5}.

116. What is the Henderson-Hasselbalch equation? Show how it is derived.

117. According to the Henderson-Hasselbalch equation, the pH = pK_a when which of the following is true?

$$HA\ (aq) \rightleftharpoons H^+\ (aq) + A^-\ (aq)$$

a. $[A^-]/[HA] = 0$

b. $log\ ([A^-]/[HA]) = 1$

c. $[A^-] \gg [HA] = 0$

d. $[A^-] = [HA]$

118. Calculate the pH of the solution in Question # 108 using the Henderson-Hasselbalch equation and compare your answers.

119. Calculate the pH of the solution in Question # 109 using the Henderson-Hasselbalch equation and compare your answers.

120 Calculate the pH of the solution in Question # 110 using the Henderson-Hasselbalch equation and compare your answers.

121. Calculate the pH of the solution in Question # 111 using the Henderson-Hasselbalch equation and compare your answers.

122. How can the Henderson-Hasselbalch equation be modified when working with basic buffers?

123. Calculate the pH of the solution in Question # 112 using the modified Henderson-Hasselbalch equation for basic buffers and compare your answers.

124. Calculate the pH of the solution in Question # 113 using the modified Henderson-Hasselbalch equation for basic buffers and compare your answers.

125. Calculate the pH of the solution in Question # 114 using the modified Henderson-Hasselbalch equation for basic buffers and compare your answers.

126. Calculate the pH of the solution in Question # 115 using the modified Henderson-Hasselbalch equation for basic buffers and compare your answers.

127. Calculate the pH of a solution that is composed of 305 ml of 0.50 M HF and 445 ml of 0.60 M NaF. The K_a value for hydrofluoric acid is 3.5×10^{-4}.

128. Calculate the pH of a solution that is composed of 225 ml of 0.10 M CH_3NH_2 and 175 ml of 0.25 M CH_3NH_3Br. The K_b value for methylamine is 4.4×10^{-4}.

129. Calculate the ratio of $NaC_2H_3O_2$ to $HC_2H_3O_2$ needed in order to generate a buffer system with a pH = 4.25. The K_a value for acetic acid is 1.8×10^{-5}.

130. Calculate the ratio of NaF to HF needed in order to generate a buffer system with a pH = 3.74. The K_a value for hydrofluoric acid is 3.5×10^{-4}.

131. Calculate the ratio of NH_4Cl to NH_3 needed in order to generate a buffer system with a pH = 9.75. The K_b value for ammonia is 1.8×10^{-5}.

132. Calculate the ratio of CH_3NH_3Br to CH_3NH_2 needed in order to generate a buffer system with a pH = 10.25. The K_b value for methylamine is 4.4×10^{-4}.

133. Calculate the pH of a buffer solution containing 0.20 M acetic acid and 0.15 M sodium acetate if 0.010 $mols$ of **HCl** were added to the buffer system. Assume a 1.0 liter total solution, and ignore any small changes in volume that might occur upon **acid** addition. The K_a value for acetic acid is 1.8×10^{-5}.

134. Calculate the pH of a buffer solution containing 0.20 M acetic acid and 0.15 M sodium acetate if 0.010 $mols$ of **NaOH** were added to the buffer system. Assume a 1.0 liter total solution, and ignore any small changes in volume that might occur upon **base** addition. The K_a value for acetic acid is 1.8×10^{-5}.

135. Calculate the pH change of 1.0 L of neutral water when 0.010 $mols$ of **HCl** is added. Ignore any small changes in volume that might occur upon **acid** addition. Compare your answer to Question #133 where the same amount of acid is added to an acidic buffer system.

136. Calculate the pH change of 1.0 L of neutral water when 0.010 $mols$ of **NaOH** is added. Ignore any small changes in volume that might occur upon **base** addition. Compare your answer to Question #134 where the same amount of base is added to an acidic buffer system.

137. Calculate the pH of a buffer solution containing 0.20 M methylamine and 0.15 M methylammonium chloride if 0.010 *mols* of **HCl** were added to the buffer system. Assume a 1.0 liter total solution, and ignore any small changes in volume that might occur upon **acid** addition. The K_b value for methylamine 4.4 x 10^{-4}. Compare your answer to Question # 135 where the same amount of acid is added to pure neutral water.

138. Calculate the pH of a buffer solution containing 0.20 M methylamine and 0.15 M methylammonium chloride if 0.010 *mols* of **NaOH** were added to the buffer system. Assume a 1.0 liter total solution, and ignore any small changes in volume that might occur upon **base** addition. The K_b value for methylamine 4.4 × 10^{-4}. Compare your answer to Question # 136 where the same amount of base is added to pure neutral water.

139. What two major factors are important to consider when determining how effective a particular buffer is at neutralizing either added acid or base?

140. What is the buffer range of a particular buffer system?

141. Would formic acid ($K_a = 1.8 \times 10^{-4}$) or hypochlorus acid ($K_a = 2.9 \times 10^{-8}$) be a better choice for a buffer solution with a pH of 7.20? Why?

142. Would formic acid ($K_a = 1.8 \times 10^{-4}$) or hypochlorus acid ($K_a = 2.9 \times 10^{-8}$) be a better choice for a buffer solution with a pH of 4.00? Why?

Image Credits

Thermodynamics and Thermochemistry

CHAPTER 12

After reading this chapter, you should be able to do the following:

- Define energy and distinguish between kinetic and potential energy.
- Define and apply the First Law of Thermodynamics.
- Calculate changes in Internal Energy for a reaction.
- Calculate heat transferred in a process from changes in temperature.
- Calculate work from changes in volume.
- Calculate enthalpy changes for a reaction.
- Identify exothermic and endothermic processes.
- Perform stoichiometric calculations involving enthalpy and thermochemical equations.
- Calculate internal energy changes and enthalpy changes from calorimetry experiments.
- Define and write balanced formation reaction equations.
- Use standard heats of formation to calculate estimated reaction enthalpies.
- Use bond energies to calculate reaction enthalpies.
- Use the Born-Haber cycle to calculate lattice energies of ionic solids.
- Define and apply the Second Law of Thermodynamics.
- Define entropy.
- Recognize positive and negative changes in entropy for spontaneous and nonspontaneous chemical and physical processes.
- Calculate entropy changes for chemical reactions from standard molar entropies of substances.
- Define and explain Gibbs free energy.
- Calculate standard free energy changes for chemical reactions.
- Predict spontaneity of a chemical reaction on the basis of its free energy change.
- Predict spontaneity of a chemical reaction as function of temperature.
- Calculate free energy changes for reactions under nonstandard conditions.
- Calculate the equilibrium constant of a reaction from its standard free energy of reaction.
- Define each of the Key Terms listed at the end of the chapter dealing with these concepts.

Section 12.1 Introduction

Recall from Chapter 7 that the universe is composed of two components, matter and energy. Further, we defined **matter** as anything with mass and volume, and **energy** was defined as the capacity to do *work*. While these definitions seem to describe two very disparate concepts, the truth is that all matter contains energy. Further, any chemical or physical change that matter might undergo will necessarily carry with it corresponding changes in energy. For example, just as we saw with electronic transitions in the hydrogen atom (the Bohr Model, Chapter 7), matter can absorb energy from its surroundings in order to adopt a higher energy state or it can release energy to its surroundings to adopt a lower energy state. The exchange of energy between matter and its surroundings is extremely important to each of us and society as a whole. Indeed, this economy of energy is at the foundation of our very existence. Food that we consume transfers energy to our bodies, allowing us to move, think, interact, and work (Chapter 16). Fossil fuels as well as solar, nuclear, wind, and hydroelectric power are the sources of energy which drive our modern society, whether we are looking at manufacturing, communications, transportation, or just lighting and heating our homes. The scientific discipline that is concerned with the transfer of energy from one system to another and its transformation from one form to another is called **thermodynamics**. The field of thermodynamics which deals with the energy changes associated with chemical change is called **thermochemistry**. This relationship between chemical reactions and their corresponding energy changes will be the subject of the current chapter. To accommodate the quantitative elements of such a discussion, it is important here to review the relevant units of measure related to energy.

The Joule

In Chapter 7 we defined *energy* as the capacity to do *work* and we defined **work** as a force acting over a distance. As such, units of energy and work are both derived in terms of force by distance. A common unit of force is the newton, N, which is defined as:

$$1\,N = 1\,\frac{kg \cdot m}{s^2}$$

This can be thought of as the force required to move a 1 *kg* mass at an acceleration of 1 *m/s²*. With this in mind, we therefore define the joule, J, as a unit of work (force in newtons times distance in meters):

$$1\,J = 1\,N \cdot m = 1\,\frac{kg \cdot m^2}{s^2}$$

$$1\,J = \frac{kg \cdot m^2}{s^2}$$

Recall from Chapter 7, we already defined the joule as the unit of measure for energy. Here we now show that a joule is indeed a measure of force acting over a distance and that work and energy are therefore measured in the same units. Additionally, the joule is the standard SI unit of measure for quantifying energy and work. Another commonly used unit of energy is the calorie. A **calorie** is defined as the energy required to raise the temperature of 1 gram of water by 1°C. Table 12.1 lists the common units of energy.

Table 12.1 Common Units of Energy

Unit	Energy Required to Increase the Temperature of 1 gram of Water by 1°C.
Calorie (cal)	1.00 *cal*
Joule (J)	4.184 *J*
Kilojoule (kJ)	4.184×10^{-3} *kJ*

Section 12.2 The First Law of Thermodynamics and the Nature of Energy

One of the most important characteristics of energy is that it is conserved. In other words, energy can neither be created nor destroyed. This is what is referred to as **the first law of thermodynamics** (also called **the law of conservation of energy**). It essentially tells us that the total energy in the universe is a constant and cannot be altered due to any process. Put differently, the following expression always holds:

$$\Delta E_{universe} = 0$$

where the symbol Δ indicates a change. If this is true, why are we so concerned with "generating" energy? If it cannot be destroyed, how is it so easily depleted? In other words, what happens to energy when we use it, if it isn't destroyed? The answer is quite simple. Think of energy as a kind of currency, just like the money in your bank account. There is a finite amount of money in circulation, but at any given point in time, you possess only some portion of it. As you spend, you deplete your account and are forced to replenish it by earning more money. But even as you spend your money, you do not add, or take away, one dollar from the total amount of money in circulation. It is simply transferred to another person or entity. Energy is very much like this. It is a zero-sum game, and with each action you take, you deplete or spend some stored energy. To understand this analogy precisely, it is instructive here to discuss how energy is stored and spent.

Recall that energy is categorized as either potential energy or kinetic energy. **Potential energy** is the energy associated with, or due to, composition or position. This is stored energy, like the money "stored" in your bank account. **Kinetic energy** is the energy associated with, or due to, motion. The kinetic energy of an object with a mass, m, is given as:

$$KE = \frac{1}{2}mv^2$$

where v is the velocity (m/s) of a particle with a mass, m, in kg. Energy can be converted from one of these forms to the other, but total energy is always conserved. To illustrate this idea, let's consider a common, yet simple, example (Figure 12.1). Let's suppose we have a weight, such as a bowling ball, which we raise to a certain height above the ground. As you lift the ball, your body is applying a force (to counter gravity) over a distance (up to the final height of the ball). Recall that force acting over a distance is work. Therefore, in lifting, your body transfers energy to the ball in the form of work. As the ball is lifted, its potential energy increases due its position above the ground within the gravitational field of the Earth. If we use the ball as our point of reference, we would say the ball gained energy from its surroundings in the form of work, which is now stored or potential energy. If the ball is then released, this potential energy is converted to kinetic energy due to its motion. When the ball strikes the ground, all of its potential energy has been converted to kinetic energy. Some of this kinetic energy will be transferred to the ground in the form of work, for instance if the ball causes some rocks, dirt, or vegetation to be moved, while some of the kinetic energy is transferred to the ground as heat. The ground is slightly warmed due to impact. In this example, we see a complex interplay between the bowling ball and its surroundings. We see

Figure 12.1 The transformation of kinetic energy to potential energy. As the ball rises its velocity slows as the kinetic energy is converted to potential energy. As the ball stops rising and begins to fall, potential energy is converted back to kinetic energy.

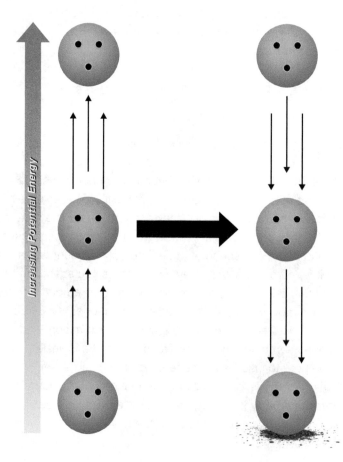

kinetic and potential energy are interconverted but we also see transfer of energy between the ball and its surroundings, manifested as either heat or work. The relationship between heat, work, and the energy of a system will be the subject of the following sections.

The System and Surroundings

In order to adequately study and quantify the exchange of energy which occurs due a physical or chemical change, it is necessary at this point to introduce the concept of the *system*. For the purposes of this discussion, the **system** will be defined as the specific portion of the universe which we are observing or investigating. Further, we will define everything else in the universe as the **surroundings**. From a practical point of view, it will be useful to think of the surroundings a little more narrowly, as anything which is capable of exchanging energy with the *system*. Nevertheless, since the system and the surroundings (as we have just defined them) constitute the entire universe, we now understand the first law of thermodynamics in terms of these concepts as follows:

$$\Delta E_{universe} = \Delta E_{sys} + \Delta E_{surr} = 0$$

In other words, any change in energy realized by the system due to a chemical or physical process must be accompanied by an equal but opposite change in the surroundings in order that total energy is conserved.

$$\Delta E_{sys} = -\Delta E_{surr}$$

Therefore, if the system gains energy, the surroundings must lose an equal amount of energy (to the system). Likewise if the system loses energy, the surroundings must gain an equal amount of energy (from the system). This is a fundamental concept in thermochemistry and will be essential in understanding the remainder of this chapter.

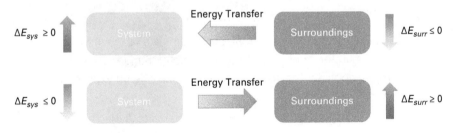

Internal Energy

In order to more clearly understand the idea of system and surroundings as it relates to thermochemistry, it is helpful to say a few words about what constitutes the *system*. Any system that we can define can be thought of as consisting of a collection of particles. For instance, in our previous example we would have defined the bowling ball as the system. The bowling ball consists of a collection of atoms and molecules (particles) held together in the solid state by a collection of strong intermolecular forces (Chapter 9). Therefore, at any point in time, the total energy of our system would simply be the sum total of all the energies of all the particles constituting the system (the bowling ball). This idea of the sum-total energy of the system is contained in a new concept we will now define called the *internal energy*, denoted *E*. **The internal energy (*E*)** of a system is defined as the sum of all of the potential and kinetic energies of all the particles which constitute the system. It is not practically possible to measure, directly, all energies of all the particles of a system. However, we are able to readily measure **changes** in the internal energy of a system. With this in mind, we begin by recognizing that the internal energy is an example of what is referred to as a *state function*. A **state function** is a property that depends only on the current state of the system in question. Therefore, any change in a state function due to a process or event under investigation is simply a function of the initial and final states of the system before and after the event or process. As such, we can define the change in internal energy as follows:

$$\Delta E_{sys} = E_{final} - E_{initial}$$

where $E_{initial}$ and E_{final} are the internal energies of the system in its initial and final states. The Greek letter Δ indicates a change in any variable and will be explicitly defined as *the final state minus the initial state*. If the final value of the internal energy of a system is larger than the initial, $\Delta E > 0$. *A positive value for ΔE indicates a net gain of energy by the system. However, if the system loses energy to the surroundings, the final value of the internal energy will be smaller than the initial and ΔE will be negative.* For a chemical reaction, the system is defined as all of the particles (molecules, ions, or atoms) which constitute the reactants and the products involved in the reaction in question. The *state* of a chemical system is a function of parameters such as temperature, pressure, concentration, and physical state (solid, liquid, or gas). Further, the initial state of a chemical system is represented by the reactants and the final state by the products. Therefore:

$$\Delta E_{rxn} = E_{prod} - E_{react}$$

where E_{react} and E_{prod} are the internal energies of the reactants (initial state) and products (final state) before and after a chemical change (reaction = "rxn"). As an example, consider the combustion of octane (the principal component of gasoline):

$$2\,C_8H_{18}(l) + 25\,O_2(g) \rightarrow 16\,CO_2(g) + 18\,H_2O(g)$$

When octane (C_8H_{18}) reacts with oxygen, it produces carbon dioxide, water, and energy. This energy is then used to power cars and other forms of transportation. Where does this energy come from? It is stored (potential) energy associated with the composition of the octane and oxygen molecules. This is what is referred to as *chemical energy*. **Chemical energy** is the potential energy associated with chemical composition, the relative distributions of electrons and nuclei in atoms and molecules. When the reactants in our example (octane and oxygen) undergo a chemical reaction, the chemical composition of the system changes. New substances (products: CO_2 and H_2O)

are formed with new compositions. Therefore, a chemical change carries with it a corresponding change in chemical energy. We can represent this diagrammatically for the current example as shown in Figure 12.2.

Here we see that the reactants (initial state), octane and oxygen, have greater internal energy than do the products (final state), carbon dioxide and water. As such, we find that the internal energy change associated with this reaction is negative, $\Delta E_{rxn} < 0$. In other words, because the final state is lower in energy than the initial, the system realizes a net loss of internal energy due to this process (reaction). Therefore, we can interpret the sign of the internal energy change of a reaction, ΔE_{rxn}, as follows:

1. If the internal energy of the reactants is greater than that of the products ($E_{react} > E_{prod}$), then $\Delta E_{rxn} < 0$, and the reaction releases energy to the surroundings.

2. If the internal energy of the reactants is less than that of products ($E_{react} < E_{prod}$), then $\Delta E_{rxn} > 0$, and the reaction absorbs energy from the surroundings.

There is an additional consequence of the fact that internal energy is a state function. Recall from Chapter 10 that reactions are reversible. If we reverse a reaction, then the resulting change in internal energy for the reaction is equal in magnitude but opposite in sign. Notice, as shown in Figure 12.3, that if we reverse the combustion of octane, ΔE_{rxn} is now positive and energy is transferred into the system from the surroundings.

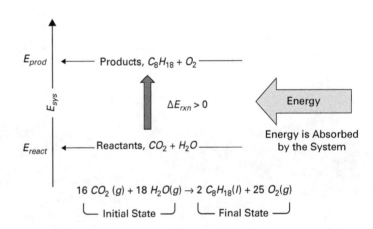

Figure 12.2 Energy diagram for the combustion of octane. Because the internal energy of the reactants is greater than that of the products, the system realizes a net loss of internal energy. Energy is transferred from the system to the surroundings.

Figure 12.3 Energy diagram for the formation of octane. Because the internal energy of the reactants is less than that of the products, the system realizes a net gain of internal energy. Energy must be transferred from the surroundings to the system for the reaction to proceed.

Heat and Work—The Two Modes of Energy Transfer

Given our definition of internal energy, it should be somewhat intuitive that direct measurement of the internal energy of a system is impractical. As such, it is the relative change in energy that we are most concerned with. Further, as we have already alluded to in previous sections, the two mechanisms by which energy is transferred between the system and the surroundings are as *heat* and *work*. We can describe this mathematically with the following expression:

$$\Delta E_{sys} = q + w$$

where q is heat and w is work. **Heat (q)** is the transfer of thermal energy (measured in joules) between the system and surroundings. This is not to be confused with *temperature* itself, which is a measure of the average kinetic energy of the particles that make up an object or system. On the other hand, we can think of work in this context as the energy transferred between the system and surroundings due to a force moving an object or objects. With this in mind, we can define **energy** a little more precisely and say that it is the capacity to do work *or produce heat*. As we will see in the following sections, heat and work can be empirically quantified for a chemical reaction, providing an experimental basis for the determination of ΔE_{rxn}.

In Summary

In this section, we defined the concepts of heat, work, and internal energy. Keeping these concepts in mind, we can invoke the first law of thermodynamics which says that the total energy of the universe is conserved:

$$\Delta E_{universe} = 0$$

Further, since we know that the internal (or total) energy of any given system is not constant, it therefore holds that:

$$\Delta E_{universe} = \Delta E_{sys} + \Delta E_{surr} = 0$$

Thus:

$$\Delta E_{sys} = -\Delta E_{surr}$$

In other words, any energy lost by the system in question, in the form of either heat or work, is gained by the surroundings and vice versa. *A negative sign for ΔE indicates a loss of energy and a positive sign indicates a gain of energy.* Further, as we have seen, the change in internal energy for any system is manifested by two mechanisms, heat and work:

$$\Delta E_{sys} = q + w$$

Therefore, the following sign convention is established for the internal energy change, heat, and work:

	Positive Values (+) $(\Delta E, q, w) > 0$	**Negative Values (−)** $(\Delta E, q, w) < 0$
Internal Energy, ΔE	The internal energy change (ΔE) is positive (+) when the system gains energy.	The internal energy change (ΔE) is negative (−) when the system releases energy
Heat, q	Heat (q) is positive (+) when the system absorbs heat from the surroundings.	Heat (q) is negative (−) when the system loses heat to the surroundings.
Work, w	Work (w) is positive (+) when the system gains energy from work done on it by the surroundings.	Work (w) is negative (−) when the system loses energy by doing work on the surroundings.

Example Problem 12.1

In a chemical reaction, 596 J of thermal energy is transferred to the surroundings, and 342 J of work is done. What is the internal energy change (ΔE_{sys}) due to this reaction?	
Solution:	
In this case, we know that energy is transferred to the surroundings as heat. Therefore, q is negative because it represents a loss of energy for the system.	$q = -596\ J$
Also, since work was done on the system, the system realizes a gain of energy, and, therefore, work is a positive term.	$w = +342\ J$
The internal energy change is simply the sum of these terms.	$\Delta E_{sys} = q + w = (-596\ J) + (342\ J)$ $\Delta E_{sys} = -254\ J$
Therefore, the system realized a total loss of 254 J of internal energy.	

Section 12.3 Quantifying Heat

Imagine you have prepared hot soup for dinner. Once you have ladled out a portion of soup into a bowl and placed it on the table, how long will you wait to eat it? Chances are you would not wait too long because it will very quickly cool to an unappetizing temperature. The reason for this illustrates clearly the distinction between heat and temperature. We have already learned that heat is the transfer of thermal energy due to a difference in temperature between a system and its surroundings. *Further, thermal energy is always spontaneously transferred from matter of higher temperature to that of lower temperature.* If we understand the soup is warmer than its surroundings (which includes the bowl, the table, the air, etc.), we would expect thermal energy to flow from the soup to the surroundings until our system (the soup) and surroundings both reach the same temperature. In other words, our soup is now at the same temperature as the surrounding room. This is referred to as **thermal equilibrium**. At *thermal equilibrium* the system and surroundings have reached the same temperature and there is no longer any net transfer of thermal energy or heat.

Temperature Change ($\triangle T$) and Heat Capacity

As we have just seen in our previous example, when an object absorbs or releases heat, its temperature changes. If it gives off heat, it gets cooler. If it absorbs heat, it gets warmer. Mathematically, this is represented by the following proportionality:

$$q \propto \Delta T$$

where q is the heat absorbed or released by the system and ΔT is its corresponding change in temperature, which we define as follows:

$$\Delta T = T_f - T_i$$

where T_f and T_i are the final and initial temperatures of the system (before and after the specified transfer of thermal energy). As such, when the system heats up ($T_f > T_i$), then heat is absorbed and $q > 0$. When the system cools ($T_f < T_i$), heat is released and $q < 0$. Further, we can define a constant of proportionality between the temperature change and heat as follows:

$$q = C \times \Delta T$$

where C is defined as the **heat capacity** of the system which represents the amount of energy required to raise the temperature of the system by 1°C (assuming ΔT is measured in °C). Therefore, the higher the heat capacity, the more energy is required to increase the temperature of the system. As such, we can think of *heat capacity* as a measure of the resistance of the system to temperature change. If we rearrange the equation to isolate heat capacity, we find that it is given in units of joules per °C as follows:

$$C = \frac{q(J)}{\Delta T(°C)}$$

Further, heat capacity is an *extensive property*. This means that it depends on the mass or amount of matter in the system. This should be somewhat intuitive in that it reasonably follows from common experience that it takes longer to bring one gallon of water to a boil (raise the temperature to the boiling point) than it does one cup of water given the same setting on the stove. In other words, it will require more heat to increase the temperature of a gallon of water by 1°C than it does for one cup of water. This is another way of saying that the heat capacity of a substance is proportional to its mass:

$$C \propto m$$

Again, as with any proportionality, we can define another proportionality constant (C_s), as follows:

$$C = m \cdot C_s$$

By substitution, we arrive at the following equation:

$$q = m \cdot C_s \cdot \Delta T$$

where q is the heat in J, ΔT is the change in temperature in °C, m is the mass of a substance in grams, and we define C_s as the **specific heat capacity** of that substance (also referred to a **specific heat**), which is an *intensive property* and given in units of $\frac{J}{g \cdot °C}$. In other words, the specific heat capacity is the amount of heat (in joules) required to raise the temperature of 1 gram of a substance by 1°C. This relationship is of importance because it allows us to determine the direction and magnitude of heat transfer due to a process simply by measuring a change in temperature (assuming we know the specific heat of the substance in question). Table 12.2 lists some common substances along with their specific heat capacities.

Table 12.2 Specific Heat Capacities of Some Common Substances

Substance	C_s ($J/g \cdot °C$)
Elements	
Lead	0.129
Gold	0.129
Silver	0.235
Copper	0.385
Iron	0.449
Aluminum	0.900
Compounds	
Ethanol	2.42
Water	4.184
Materials	
Glass (Pyrex)	0.750
Granite	0.790
Sand	0.840

*At 298 K

To illustrate the application of this concept, let's consider an example. Assume we have a copper sample which weighs 4.32 *g* and has been heated to a temperature of 43.0°C. If the copper sample is allowed to cool to room temperature (23.2°C), how much heat ($q = ?$) is lost by the copper sample in this process? To answer this question, we will first recognize that our system is the copper sample. Having done so, we can unambiguously identify the change in temperature for our system as follows:

$$\Delta T = T_f - T_i = 23.2°C - 43.0°C = -19.8°C$$

Note that, because the temperature of the system has decreased, we quite naturally arrive at a negative value for ΔT. Additionally, we then can look up the specific heat of copper from Table 12.2 and calculate q as follows:

$$q = m \cdot C_s \cdot \Delta T = (4.32\ g)\left(0.385\ \frac{J}{g \cdot °C}\right)(-19.8°C) = -32.9\ J$$

Therefore, a copper sample with mass of 4.32 *g* which cools from 43.0°C to 23.2°C will have released 32.9 *J* of heat upon reaching thermal equilibrium. (We know that the heat is transferred to the surroundings because we arrive at a negative value of q.) The following example problems provide more practice with calculations involving heat capacity and specific heat.

Example Problem 12.2

Suppose a 3.76-*g* sample of ethanol is heated to 35.0°C and is allowed to cool to room temperature (21.3°C). How much heat (in joules) is gained or lost by the ethanol due to cooling?	
Solution:	
In order to calculate q, we need a sample mass, specific heat capacity, and a change in temperature. The specific heat capacity of ethanol is found in Table 12.2. ($C_S = 2.42\frac{J}{g \cdot °C}$) All other given information is as shown here.	$m = 3.76\ g$ $T_i = 35.0°C$ $T_f = 21.3°C$ $C_s = 2.42\frac{J}{g \cdot °C}$
The relationship between heat (q) and mass, specific heat, and temperature change of a substance is as shown:	$q = m \cdot C_s \cdot \Delta T$ $(\Delta T = T_f - T_i)$
Assuring all quantities are in the correct/consistent units, we substitute into the equation and solve for q.	$q = m \cdot C_s \cdot \Delta T$ $q = (3.76\ g)\left(2.42\frac{J}{g \cdot °C}\right)(21.3°C - 35.0°C)$ $q = -125\ J$
Therefore, because we calculate a negative value for q, we conclude that the sample lost 125 *J* of thermal energy as it cooled to room temperature.	

Example Problem 12.3

A 3.80-*g* sample of metal has been labeled pure aluminum. The sample was heated to 42.62°C from an initial temperature of 21.00°C. If this required 73.7 *J* of heat to raise its temperature as described here, calculate the specific heat capacity of the metal. Is this consistent with the sample being pure aluminum?

Solution:	
Collect the given information and relationships. We are given the heat (q) and the mass of the sample as well as its initial and final temperatures.	$m = 3.80\ g$ $T_i = 21.00°C$ $T_f = 42.62°C$ $q = 73.7\ J$ $q = m \cdot C_s \cdot \Delta T$ $\Delta T = T_f - T_i$
We are asked to determine the specific heat capacity of the sample from the given data. This will require that we isolate the C_s in our equation for q.	$q = m \cdot C_s \cdot \Delta T$ $C_s = \dfrac{q}{m \cdot \Delta T}$
Assuring all quantities are in the correct/consistent units we substitute into the expression and solve for C_s.	$C_s = \dfrac{q}{m \cdot \Delta T}$ $C_s = \dfrac{(73.7\ J)}{(3.80\ g)(42.62°C - 21.00°C)}$ $C_s = 0.897\ \dfrac{J}{g \cdot °C}$

Reference to table 12.2 provides $0.900\ \frac{J}{g\cdot°C}$ as the specific heat of aluminum. Since this is very nearly the specific heat we calculate form the given data, we conclude that the data are indeed consistent with a sample of aluminum.

Heat Transfer Experiments

Let's assume that we have a substance for which a temperature change (ΔT) has been measured experimentally. As we have already seen, if we know the specific heat and the mass of our sample, we can quantify the heat associated with this temperature change according to the following:

$$q = m \cdot C_s \cdot \Delta T$$

However, if we find that heat is given off by our sample ($\Delta T < 0$), then where has the heat gone? We know from the first law of thermodynamics, that it is absorbed by the surroundings. In other words, any heat lost by the system must be absorbed by the surroundings and vice versa. Therefore, the following expression holds:

$$q_{sys} = -q_{surr}$$

Let's consider an example. Suppose we have a metal sample of unknown specific heat capacity with a mass of 23.7 g. If the metal is heated to a temperature of 78.25°C and then submerged in 45.0 g of water in an insulated container at a temperature of 23.21°C, then the two substances would necessarily engage in an exchange of heat. Heat transfer would continue until both the metal and the water reached *thermal equilibrium* (the same "final" temperature), which we determine experimentally to be 26.15°C in this case. If we wish to know the specific heat capacity of the metal, we begin with the following expression:

$$q_{metal} = -q_{water}$$

Therefore:

$$m_{metal} \cdot C_{s,\,metal} \cdot \Delta T_{metal} = -(m_{water} \cdot C_{s,\,water} \cdot \Delta T_{metal})$$

Here we are simply assuming that all heat is transferred between the water and the metal sample only, so we treat the water as though it is the surroundings and our metal sample is the system. Further, since we know from Table 12.2 that the specific heat of water is 4.184 $\frac{J}{g \cdot °C}$, we can isolate the specific heat of the metal and determine its value as follows:

$$m_{metal} \cdot C_{s,\,metal} \cdot \Delta T_{metal} = -(m_{water} \cdot C_{s,\,water} \cdot \Delta T_{water})$$

Thus:

$$C_{s,\,metal} = \frac{-(m_{water} \cdot C_{s,\,water} \cdot \Delta T_{water})}{m_{metal} \cdot \Delta T_{metal}}$$

Substituting the values for these variables:

$$C_{s,\,metal} = \frac{-(45.0\,g)\left(4.184\frac{J}{g \cdot °C}\right)(2.94°C)}{(23.7\,g)(-52.10°C)} = 0.448\,\frac{J}{g \cdot °C}$$

Therefore, the metal which comprises the sample has a specific heat capacity of 0.448 $\frac{J}{g \cdot °C}$. Notice, in Table 12.2 the specific heat of iron is listed as 0.449 $\frac{J}{g \cdot °C}$, and, as such, we can reasonably assert that this sample is likely composed primarily of iron. The following example problem provides additional practice with heat exchange problems.

Example Problem 12.4

A 12.3-*g* sample of iron at room temperature of 21.00°C is placed in a sample of pure water, initially at a temperature of 45.31°C, in a thermally insulated container. If thermal equilibrium is reached at a temperature of 41.17°C, what is the mass of the sample of water.
Solution:

Collect the given information of the initial temperatures and final temperature of the iron and water, the mass of iron, and the specific heat of iron and water (Table 12.2).	$m_{Fe} = 12.3\,g$ $m_w = ?\,g$ $T_f = 41.17°C$ $T_{i_{Fe}} = 21.00°C$ $T_{i_w} = 45.31°C$ $C_{s,\,Fe} = 0.449\frac{J}{g \cdot °C}$ $C_{s,\,w} = 4.184\frac{J}{g \cdot °C}$
Next, we assume all heat is exchanged between the iron sample and water only. With this in mind, we write the equation which describes the relation between heat absorbed by iron and that released by the water.	$q_{Fe} = -q_w$ $m_{Fe} \cdot C_{s,\,Fe} \cdot \Delta T_{Fe} = -(m_w \cdot C_{s,\,w} \cdot \Delta T_w)$

Next, we isolate the mass term for water.	$$m_w = -\left[\frac{m_{Fe} \cdot C_{s,Fe} \cdot \Delta T_{Fe}}{C_{s,w} \cdot \Delta T_w}\right]$$
We now substitute our given information into this equation and calculate the mass of water.	$$m_w = -\left[\frac{(12.3\,g)\left(0.449\frac{J}{g \cdot °C}\right)(41.17°C - 21.00°C)}{\left(4.184\frac{J}{g \cdot °C}\right)(41.17°C - 45.31°C)}\right]$$ $$m_w = -[-6.43\,g]$$ $$m_w = \mathbf{6.43\ g}$$

Section 12.4 Quantifying Work

We have already established that energy is exchanged between system and surroundings through two mechanisms, heat and work. In the previous section we learned how measured changes in temperature for the system can be used to quantify heat. We now turn our attention to quantifying work. While there are many different types of work which can be associated with chemical reactions, we will limit our discussion here to work done through expansion or compression of gases. This type of work is referred to as **Pressure-Volume Work**.

Let's consider an example. Suppose a reaction is taking place in a cylinder with a weightless, movable, frictionless piston on one side (with an area *A*) as shown in Figure 12.4. Further, we see that there is an external pressure of 1 *atm* applied to the piston. As such, the pressure in the system is maintained at 1 *atm*. With this in mind, we can derive an expression for pressure-volume work. If we begin with the definition of work as a force acting over a distance we have the following:

$$w = F \times D$$

Figure 12.4 Piston moving within a cylinder due to expansion or compression of the system.

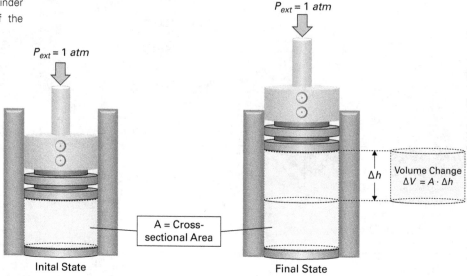

If the piston in the cylinder expands, it pushes against an external force. Recall from Chapter 6 that we defined pressure as force divided by area:

$$P = \frac{F}{A}$$

Therefore, in this case, force can be expressed as:

$$F = P \times A$$

Substituting this expression into our definition of work, we arrive at the following:

$$w = F \times D = P \times A \times D$$

In this equation, work is now given as the product of pressure times area times distance. The distance, D, in this case, is the change in position (or height) of the piston, Δh. Since the product of area, A, and distance (length) is volume, it follows that:

$$w = P \times A \times \Delta h = P \times \Delta V$$

where ΔV is the change in volume due to this hypothetical reaction. However, since ΔV is positive when the volume expands against an external pressure ($V_f > V_i$), we must include a negative sign in the equation for work.

$$w = -P\Delta V$$

In other words, the negative sign in this equation accommodates the sign convention for work described in section 12.2. When the system expands against an external pressure ($\Delta V > 0$), energy is lost due to work ($w < 0$), because work is done on the surroundings by the system. Likewise, if the system is compressed ($\Delta V < 0$), the system gains energy due to work ($w > 0$), because work is done on the system by the surroundings.

1. When $\Delta V > 0$, work is done on the surroundings by the system and $w < 0$.

2. When $\Delta V < 0$, work is done on the system by the surroundings and $w > 0$.

If we apply the equation we have just derived to a particular system, it should be obvious that we will calculate work in units of liter-atmospheres ($L \cdot atm$). The conversion between joules and $L \cdot atm$ is as follows:

$$101.3 \, J = 1 \, L \cdot atm$$

Example Problem 12.5

A fuel is burned in a cylinder-piston assembly and expands against an external pressure of 1.07 *atm* from an initial volume of 0.521 *L* to a final volume of 1.132 *L*. How much work is done due to this expansion?	
Solution:	
Collect given information. We are given the pressure as well as the initial and final volumes of the system.	$P = 1.07 \, atm$ $V_i = 0.521 \, L$ $V_f = 1.132 \, L$

Next, we write the expression for work in terms of the pressure and change in volume.	$w = -P\Delta V$ $\Delta V = V_f - V_i$
Substitute the pressure and volume data into the equation.	$w = -(1.07\,atm)(1.132\,L - 0.521\,L)$ $w = -0.654\,atm \cdot L$
We now convert units of atmosphere-liters to joules. ($101.3\,J = 1\,atm \cdot L$)	$w = -0.654\,atm \cdot L \times \dfrac{101.3\,J}{1\,atm \cdot L}$ $w = -66.2\,J$

Because we arrive at a negative value for work, we conclude that 66.2 J of work is done on the surroundings by the system.

Section 12.5 Enthalpy

So far, we have learned about the change in total energy of a system, which we termed the change in internal energy, ΔE. Further, the internal energy change can be expressed as the sum of two contributions, heat and work. However, as chemists we are often concerned only with the *heat* exchanged due to a chemical reaction and not the *work* done. For this reason we define an additional quantity, *enthalpy*. **Enthalpy** is defined as the sum of the internal energy of a system plus the product of its pressure and volume *under conditions of constant pressure*.

$$H = E + PV$$

Recall the ideal gas law from Chapter 6 ($PV = nRT$). Here we learned that the product of pressure and volume (PV) of a gas is purely a function of its current state as defined by temperature and the moles of gas particles in the system. *In other words, PV is a state function and an extensive property.* Additionally, we have already established that the internal energy (E) is state function and an extensive property. Therefore, **enthalpy (H) is also a state function and an extensive property of the system.**

Further, why do we define enthalpy only for conditions of constant pressure? The reason is a practical one. If we carry out a reaction in a sealed container, the volume of the system is held constant ($\Delta V = 0$). In such a case, the internal energy change for a system is entirely manifested as heat (q). The reason for this is that when $\Delta V = 0$, work is also zero (recall that, $w = -P\Delta V$). In other words, under conditions of constant volume, $\Delta E_{sys} = q_{sys}$. This is a fact that will be of importance in the following section on calorimetry. However, many chemical processes are carried out in containers which are open to the atmosphere. In such cases, the pressure is held constant (atmospheric pressure) but the system is free to expand against or be compressed by the atmosphere (this is exactly the scenario in the previous example concerning the weightless, frictionless piston). Nevertheless, as chemists, we are often interested only in the heat associated with a process and not the work. Enthalpy, as it is defined here, is a quantity which allows us to essentially disregard the work done on or by the system. To see this, let's consider the expression for the change in enthalpy for a process taking place under conditions of constant pressure:

$$\Delta H = \Delta E + \Delta(PV)$$

Note that because pressure is constant, there is no change in pressure (ΔP) for the system. Therefore:

$$\Delta(PV) = P\Delta V$$

Further, we have already defined the change in internal energy as the sum of heat and work:

$$\Delta E = q + w$$

Therefore:

$$\Delta H = (q + w) + P\Delta V$$

Since work is defined as the opposite of the product of pressure and the change in volume ($w = -P\Delta V$), we arrive at the following:

$$\Delta H = q + (-P\Delta V) + P\Delta V$$

Therefore:

$$\Delta H = q$$

In other words, we have shown that under conditions of constant pressure, the enthalpy of a process is simply the heat exchanged between the system and the surroundings. It is because of this that the enthalpy change for a reaction is often simply referred to as the heat of reaction.

Section 12.6 Thermochemical Equations and Stoichiometry

The enthalpy change for a chemical reaction is referred to as the **enthalpy of reaction** or the **heat of reaction**. In order to understand how this quantity is expressed, we must also define another concept, the **thermochemical equation**. A thermochemical equation is simply a balanced chemical equation which includes the enthalpy change which corresponds to the chemical change described by the equation. For example, let's again consider the combustion of octane. The balanced thermochemical equation which describes this reaction is as follows:

$$2\,C_8H_{18}(l) + 25\,O_2(g) \rightarrow 16\,CO_2(g) + 18\,H_2O(g) \qquad \Delta H_{rxn} = -10{,}148.2\,kJ \cdot mol^{-1}$$

The first point to understand in interpreting this equation is that the sign convention is the same for enthalpy as it is for the internal energy change. As such, we interpret the negative sign for the heat of reaction in this case to indicate that heat is released. Reactions which give off heat ($\Delta H_{rxn} < 0$) are referred to as **exothermic reactions**. Likewise, those which absorb heat ($\Delta H_{rxn} > 0$) are referred to as **endothermic reactions**. In this case, we conclude that the combustion of octane is an exothermic process, which is consistent with common experience. Additionally, recall that enthalpy is an *extensive property*. In other words, the more octane that is burned in this case, the more heat is generated. As such, the amount of heat absorbed or released is dependent on the amounts of reactants which actually undergo reaction. *Therefore, we understand the value reported for the enthalpy of reaction to correspond to the stoichiometric quantities as written in the balanced thermochemical equation.* With this in mind, we understand the equation for the combustion of octane to indicate that for every two moles of C_8H_{18} and 25 moles of O_2 consumed or 16 moles of CO_2 and 18 moles of H_2O produced, 10,148.2 kJ of heat is generated or released by the reaction (the system). In fact, this is just another stoichiometric relationship. From this equation we can construct the following stoichiometric ratios:

$$2\,mol\,C_8H_{18} : -10,148.2\,kJ$$

$$25\,mol\,O_2 : -10,148.2\,kJ$$

$$16\,mol\,CO_2 : -10,148.2\,kJ$$

$$18\,mol\,H_2O : -10,148.2\,kJ$$

Each of these ratios can now serve as a conversion factor in a stoichiometric calculation which relates the heat released from this reaction to the relative quantities of reactants and products which are consumed or produced, respectively. Figure 12.5 depicts a flow chart of stoichiometric relationships which we have covered so far in this text.

To illustrate this, let's consider a specific example. Suppose we are to burn 50.0 g of octane and we wish to determine the amount of heat this will generate in kJ, given the balanced thermochemical equation above. If we follow the flow chart in Figure 12.5, we see that we can convert the mass

Figure 12.5 Flow-chart summary of the relevant stoichiometric relationships.

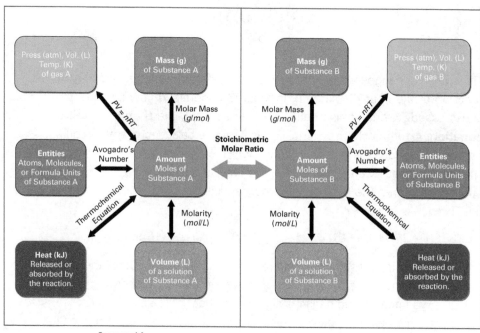

of octane to moles (using molar mass as a conversion) and this quantity can be directly converted to heat (kJ) as shown here (the molar mass of octane is 114.26 g/mol):

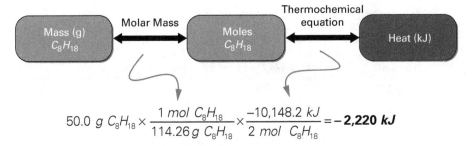

$$50.0 \ g \ C_8H_{18} \times \frac{1 \ mol \ C_8H_{18}}{114.26 \ g \ C_8H_{18}} \times \frac{-10{,}148.2 \ kJ}{2 \ mol \ C_8H_{18}} = \mathbf{-2{,}220 \ kJ}$$

Therefore, we conclude that the combustion of 50.0 g of octane will generate or release 2,220 kJ of heat. The following example problems will provide additional practice with stoichiometric calculations involving enthalpies of reaction.

Example Problem 12.6

Identify the following as either an endothermic or an exothermic process.
a.) Fuel burning
b.) Water freezing
c.) Water evaporating

Solution:
a.) When fuel is burned (such as gasoline in your automobile), energy is released from the system in the form of heat. Therefore, the process is exothermic ($\Delta H < 0$).
b.) When water freezes, it releases energy, lowering the thermal motion of the water molecules; therefore, heat is transferred from the water to the surroundings, constituting an exothermic process ($\Delta H < 0$).
c.) When water evaporates, the water molecules proceed from low thermal energy to higher thermal energy. This requires the system to gain energy as heat. Therefore, this is an endothermic process ($\Delta H > 0$).

Example Problem 12.7

Consider the reaction depicted in the following thermochemical equation at 25°C:

$$Mg \ (s) + 2 \ HCl \ (aq) \rightarrow MgCl_2(aq) + H_2(g) \quad \Delta H^{\circ}_{rxn} = -467 \ kJ$$

Calculate the amount of heat (in kJ) released by the reaction of 250.0 ml of a 0.650 M HCl(aq) solution.

Solution:

Step 1: Establish a strategy for solution of this problem (Figure 12.5 can be useful here). We see from the balanced thermochemical equation, that for every two moles of HCl consumed, 467 kJ of heat is released. Therefore, we first establish the number of moles of HCl are in the specified volume of the solution.

Starting with the volume of the HCl solution, we can use the molar concentration to convert this quantity to moles of HCl. From here we use the enthalpy of reaction given in the thermochemical equation to convert to heat. The following relationships will be used as conversion factors:

$$0.650 \ mol \ HCl = 1 \ L \ HCl \ Solution$$
$$-467 \ kJ = 2 \ mol \ HCl$$

Step 2: Using the strategy we established in the previous step, begin with the given volume of the *HCl* solution and apply the conversion factors as follows (note: we must always convert to units of liters when dealing with molar concentrations, see Chapter 5):

$$250.0 \; ml \; HCl \times \frac{1 \; L}{1000 \; ml} \times \frac{0.650 \; mol \; HCl}{1 \; L} \times \frac{-467 \; kJ}{2 \; mol \; HCl} = -37.9 \; kJ$$

Therefore, we find that 37.9 *kJ* of heat is released when 250.0 *ml* of a 0.650 *M HCl* solution is consumed according to the reaction described in the thermochemical equation above.

Section 12.7 Calorimetry

We have now learned how to use a thermochemical equation to make predictions about heat exchange due to a reaction and the relative amounts of reactants and products involved, but how do we determine the heat associated with a particular reaction? We do so using a device called a *calorimeter*. **Calorimetry** is the scientific discipline directed toward the measurement of heat. A **calorimeter** is an apparatus which is used to perform chemical reactions under controlled conditions such that temperature changes can be carefully measured. Recall that for a chemical reaction we define the system as all of the atoms, molecules, and/or ions that constitute the reactants and products. Owing to this, it is not possible to measure temperature changes of the system directly. Therefore, in calorimetry experiments, temperature measurements are made for the surroundings. The temperature change for the surroundings will be dependent on ΔE_{rxn} and the heat capacity of the surroundings, which will have to be carefully defined. With this in mind, there are two types of calorimetry experiments we will be concerned with. These are referred to as **constant-volume calorimetry** (also called **bomb calorimetry**) and **constant-pressure calorimetry** (also called **coffee cup calorimetry**). We will describe each in the following subsections.

Constant-Volume (Bomb) Calorimetry

In *constant-volume calorimetry*, measurements are made using an apparatus commonly referred to as a bomb calorimeter. A **bomb calorimeter** is a piece of equipment specifically designed to measure ΔE, most commonly for combustion reactions. It consists of a sealed reaction chamber, called a bomb, in which there is a sample pan or cup which is connected to ignition wires. The reactor is submerged in a larger, well-insulated tank filled with water and equipped with a stirring mechanism and a thermometer to measure temperature (see Figure 12.6).

In a typical experiment, a sample of known mass is placed in the pan and sealed in the reactor. Which is filled with oxygen gas (to facilitate combustion). The reactor is completely submerged in the water, and an initial temperature is recorded. The sample is then ignited, and the reaction proceeds.

The temperature is monitored until it reaches a final, maximum value. Because the reaction is carried out in a sealed reactor, its volume is held constant. In other words, $\Delta V = 0$ and therefore, work is also zero.

$$w = -P\Delta V = -P(0) = 0$$

Owing to this, we need only quantify the heat released by the reaction to determine the change in internal energy.

$$\Delta E_{rxn} = q_{rxn} + w = q_{rxn} + (0) = q_{rxn}$$

Further, notice in the description of the experimental setup, we did not measure the temperature change (ΔT) of the system (the reaction) but rather the water. Therefore, the temperature change is associated with the surroundings, not the system directly. *In a bomb calorimetry experiment, the surroundings are defined as the calorimeter itself.* Therefore, we can assume that the following expression holds:

$$\Delta E_{rxn} = q_{rxn} = -q_{cal}$$

In other words, any heat gained by the surroundings (the calorimeter) must be heat released by the system (the reaction). Further, in order to convert the empirically determined change in temperature of the calorimeter to heat, we need the heat capacity of the entire instrument (the water and other components of the calorimeter) which we will denote as C_{cal}.

$$q_{cal} = C_{cal} \times \Delta T$$

Therefore:

$$\Delta E_{rxn} = q_{rxn} = -q_{cal} = -(C_{cal} \times \Delta T)$$

Additionally, because the internal energy change is an extensive property, it is customary to report it in units of *kJ/mol*. Therefore, the sample mass is converted to moles, and ΔE is calculated as follows:

$$\Delta E_{rxn} = \frac{q_{rxn}}{n} = \frac{-(C_{cal} \times \Delta T)}{n}$$

where n is the amount (moles) of sample as calculated from the sample mass. Let's return to our example of the combustion of octane. Suppose a 0.5323-g sample of octane is placed in a bomb calorimeter which is known to have a heat capacity of 12.71 *kJ/°C*. The octane is ignited and the temperature of the calorimeter rises from 20.00°C to 21.86°C. We can determine the heat released by the reaction and, therefore, the internal energy change of this combustion reaction as follows:

$$\Delta E_{rxn} = \frac{-(C_{cal} \times \Delta T)}{n_{octane}}$$

First we calculate the change in temperature.

$$\Delta T = T_f - T_i = 21.86°C - 20.00°C = 1.86°C$$

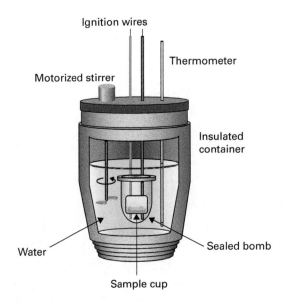

Figure 12.6 A Bomb Calorimeter measures changes in temperature under conditions of constant volume. Bomb Calorimeters are used to determine internal energy changes (ΔE_{rxn}) for combustion reactions.

Next we calculate the moles of octane consumed in the reaction (the molar mass of C_8H_{18} is 114.26 g/mol).

$$n_{octane} = 0.5323\,g\,C_8H_{18} \times \frac{1\,mol\,C_8H_{18}}{114.26\,g\,C_8H_{18}} = 0.004659\,mol\,C_8H_{18}$$

Since we are given the heat capacity of the calorimeter, we calculate ΔE_{rxn} as follows.

$$\Delta E_{rxn} = \frac{-(C_{cal} \times \Delta T)}{n_{octane}} = \frac{-\left(12.71\frac{kJ}{°C}\right)(1.86°C)}{0.004659\,mol} = -5.074 \times 10^3\,kJ \cdot mol^{-1}$$

Therefore, the internal energy change (ΔE_{rxn}) for the combustion of octane (C_8H_{18}) is −5074 kJ per mole of octane consumed. The following example problem provides further practice.

Example Problem 12.8

If 1.378 grams of naphthalene ($C_{10}H_8$) are burned in a bomb calorimeter known to have a heat capacity of 11.73 $\frac{kJ}{°C}$, what is the internal energy change for this reaction if the temperature of the calorimeter rises from 20.251°C to a final temperature of 24.970°C?
Solution:

Step 1: Collect the given data. In this case, we are given a sample mass, the heat capacity of the calorimeter as well as initial and final temperatures of the calorimeter before and after combustion.	$m = 1.378\,g$ $C_{cal} = 11.73\frac{kJ}{°C}$ $T_i = 20.251°C$ $T_f = 24.970°C$
Step 2: Derive the equation for the reaction in terms of the given data. i. In the first place, we are measuring the temperature change of the calorimeter not the reaction. As such, we define the calorimeter as the surroundings. ii. Second, we understand (according to the First Law) that q_{rxn} is simply the opposite of q_{cal}. ($q_{surr} = q_{cal}$) iii. Third, when $\Delta V = 0$, then $\Delta E_{rxn} = q_{rxn}$. iv. Finally, since ΔE_{rxn} is an extensive property, we customarily report it in kJ/mol. (where n is moles of the sample, naphthalene)	i. $q_{cal} = C_{cal} \cdot \Delta T$ ii. $q_{rxn} = -q_{surr} = -q_{cal}$ iii. $\Delta E_{rxn} = q_{rxn} = -q_{cal}$ $\Delta E_{rxn} = q_{rxn} = -(C_{cal} \cdot \Delta T)$ iv. $\Delta E_{rxn} = \frac{q_{rxn}}{n} = \frac{-(C_{cal} \cdot \Delta T)}{n}$
Step 3: Substitute our given data into the equation for ΔE_{rxn} and calculate its value. (The molar mass of $C_{10}H_8$ is 128.2 g/mol.)	$\Delta E_{rxn} = \frac{-(C_{cal} \cdot \Delta T)}{n} = \frac{-(C_{cal})(T_f - T_i)}{n}$ $\Delta E_{rxn} = \dfrac{-\left(11.73\frac{kJ}{°C}\right)(24.970°C - 20.251°C)}{\left(1.378\,g\,C_{10}H_8 \times \frac{1\,mol\,C_{10}H_8}{128.2\,g\,C_{10}H_8}\right)}$ $\Delta E_{rxn} = -5.15 \times 10^3\,kJ \cdot mol^{-1}$

Therefore, we conclude that the internal energy change for the combustion of naphthalene is −5,150 kJ per mole of naphthalene.

Constant-Pressure (Coffee Cup) Calorimetry

Even as the calorimeter described in the previous section represents a fairly sophisticated piece of equipment, this is not always necessary. In fact, if you think about it, a calorimeter is essentially an insulted container, a thermometer, and a stirrer. Indeed, another type of calorimetry requires a container consisting of nothing more than two styrofoam coffee cups nested together, an insulating lid or cover, a simple thermometer, and a stirring rod (see Figure 12.7). This is an example of a *constant-pressure calorimeter* (also referred to as a coffee cup calorimeter for obvious reasons).

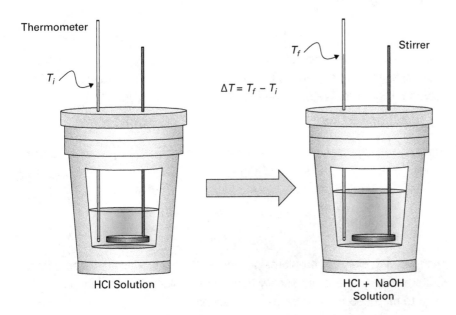

Figure 12.7 A Coffee Cup Calorimeter measures changes in temperature under conditions of constant pressure. Coffee Cup Calorimeters are used to determine enthalpy changes (ΔH_{rxn}) for reactions in aqueous solution.

Although it is fairly rudimentary, such an apparatus is perfectly adequate for the determination of heat transfer due to chemical reactions in solution (usually aqueous solution). In a typical experiment, reactants are delivered into the reactor (all reactant solutions are at the same initial temperature). The reaction mixture is stirred, and the temperature is monitored, and a final temperature is recorded. Again, we are not directly measuring a temperature change for the system, but for the surroundings. Also, *because such experiments are carried out under constant pressure (atmospheric pressure), coffee cup calorimetry experiments are used to determine the enthalpies of reaction (ΔH_{rxn}).* For approximate results the following two assumptions are made:

1. Because there are no significant components of the calorimeter submerged in the solution, the surroundings in this case are defined simply as the solution. In other words, we are assuming no heat is leaked or lost to the styrofoam cups, the stirrer, or the thermometer.

2. Having defined the solution as the surroundings, we further assume aqueous solutions have a specific heat equal to that of water ($4.184 \frac{J}{g \cdot °C}$).

As we have already learned in a previous section, the enthalpy of reaction is simply the heat of reaction at constant pressure:

$$\Delta H_{rxn} = q_{rxn}$$

Further, since we are defining the solution as the surroundings for the reaction (the system) we also know that:

$$\Delta H_{rxn} = q_{rxn} = -q_{soln}$$

In this case, we can use the empirically determined change in temperature of the solution (ΔT), along with the solution mass and specific heat capacity of water to calculate the heat absorbed or released by the solution (surroundings) as follows:

$$q_{soln} = m_{soln} \cdot C_{s, water} \cdot \Delta T$$

where m_{soln} is the mass of the solution in grams, $C_{s, water}$ is the specific heat capacity of water, and ΔT is the measured temperature change of the solution. Therefore, we have the following:

$$\Delta H_{rxn} = q_{rxn} = -q_{soln} = -(m_{soln} \cdot C_{s, water} \cdot \Delta T)$$

Again, as was the case in bomb calorimetry, we report the enthalpy of reaction in units of kJ per mole of one of the reactants. Therefore, our experimental data can be used to calculate the enthalpy of reaction as follows:

$$\Delta H_{rxn} = \frac{-(m_{soln} \cdot C_{s, water} \cdot \Delta T)}{n}$$

The following example problems provide additional practice and also demonstrate how to use this empirically determined value of the reaction enthalpy to write balanced thermochemical equations.

Example Problem 12.9

As depicted in Figure 12.7, suppose that 25.00 ml of a 0.250 M HCl (aq) solution is delivered to a coffee cup calorimeter containing 50.00 ml of a 0.450 M $NaOH$ (aq) solution with stirring. As a result, the temperature of the reaction solution rises from 24.000°C to a final temperature of 25.103°C. Calculate the enthalpy of reaction in kilojoules per mole of $NaCl$ and write the balanced thermochemical equation for this acid-base neutralization reaction. Assume that the density of the reaction solution is 1.01 g/ml and also that the specific heat of the solution is the same as that of water, 4.184 $\frac{J}{g \cdot °C}$.

$$HCl(aq) + NaOH(aq) \rightarrow NaCl(aq) + H_2O(l)$$

Solution:	
Step 1: Collect the given information. We are given the concentrations of both reactant solutions along with their volumes. This provides a total volume of the resulting solution. We are also given the density of the reaction solution (d_{soln}) and specific heat as well as the final and initial temperatures of the solution.	$[HCl] = 0.250\,M$ $[NaOH] = 0.450\,M$ $V_{HCl} = 25.00\,ml \times \dfrac{1\,L}{1000\,ml} = 0.02500\,L$ $V_{NaOH} = 50.00\,ml \times \dfrac{1\,L}{1000\,ml} = 0.05000\,L$ $V_{soln} = 25.00\,ml + 50.00\,ml = 75.00\,ml$ $T_f = 25.103°C$ $T_i = 24.000°C$

	$\Delta T_{soln} = 25.103°C - 24.000°C = 1.103°C$
	$d_{soln} = 1.01\,g/ml$
	$C_{s,soln} = 4.184\,\dfrac{J}{g\cdot°C}$
Step 2: Derive the equation for the heat of reaction in terms of the given data. i. In the first place, we are measuring the temperature change of the reaction solution (soln), not the reaction itself. As such, we define the solution as the surroundings in constant-pressure calorimetry experiments. ii. Second, we understand (according to the First Law) that q_{rxn} is simply the opposite of q_{soln}. iii. Third, when the pressure is constant, then $\Delta H_{rxn} = q_{rxn}$. iv. Finally, since ΔH_{rxn} is an extensive property, we are asked to report it in *kJ/mol NaCl*. (Where n_{NaCl} is moles of the product, sodium chloride)	i. $q_{surr} = q_{soln} = m_{soln}\cdot C_{s,soln}\cdot\Delta T_{soln}$ ii. $q_{rxn} = -q_{surr} = -q_{soln}$ iii. $\Delta H_{rxn} = q_{rxn} = -q_{soln}$ $\Delta H_{rxn} = q_{rxn} = -(m_{soln}\cdot C_{s,soln}\cdot\Delta T_{soln})$ iv. $\Delta H_{rxn} = \dfrac{q_{rxn}}{n} = \dfrac{-(m_{soln}\cdot C_{s,soln}\cdot\Delta T_{soln})}{n}$ $\Delta H_{rxn} = \dfrac{-(m_{soln}\cdot C_{s,soln}\cdot\Delta T_{soln})}{n_{NaCl}}$
Step 3: Before substituting our given data into the equation for ΔH_{rxn} and calculating its value, we first need to determine the moles of *NaCl* produced. This will require determining a limiting reagent (see Chapter 4 for review). We begin with the given volumes and concentrations of the individual reactant solutions and calculate a yield in moles of *NaCl* from each. We find here that the limiting reagent is *HCl*, and 0.00625 *mol NaCl* is the theoretical yield.	$V_{HCl} = 25.00\,ml \times \dfrac{1\,L}{1000\,ml} = 0.02500\,L$ $[HCl] = 0.250\,M$ $0.02500\,L\,HCl \times \dfrac{0.250\,mol\,HCl}{1\,L} \times \dfrac{1\,mol\,NaCl}{1\,mol\,HCl}$ $= \mathbf{0.00625\,mol\,NaCl}$ $V_{NaOH} = 50.00\,ml \times \dfrac{1\,L}{1000\,ml} = 0.05000\,L$ $[NaOH] = 0.450\,M$ $0.05000\,L\,NaOH \times \dfrac{0.450\,mol\,NaOH}{1\,L}$ $\times \dfrac{1\,mol\,NaCl}{1\,mol\,NaOH} = 0.0225\,mol\,NaCl$
Step 4: Substitute our given data into the equation for ΔH_{rxn} and calculate its value.	$\Delta H_{rxn} = \dfrac{-(m_{soln}\cdot C_{s,soln}\cdot\Delta T_{soln})}{n_{NaCl}}$ $= \dfrac{-\left(75.00\,ml \times \dfrac{1.01\,g}{ml}\right)\left(4.184\,\dfrac{J}{g\cdot°C}\right)(1.103°C)}{0.00625\,mol\,NaCl}$ $\Delta H_{rxn} = -5.59\times10^4\,\dfrac{J}{mol\,Nacl}$ $= \mathbf{-55.9\,\dfrac{kJ}{mol\,NaCl}}$

Therefore, because sodium chloride has a stoichiometric coefficient of 1 in the balanced chemical equation, the balanced thermochemical equation is simply:

$$HCl(aq) + NaOH(aq) \rightarrow NaCl(aq) + H_2O(l) \qquad \Delta H_{rxn} = -55.9 \ kJ \cdot mol^{-1}$$

Note: Because sodium cations and chloride anions are spectators (Chapter 5), we expect the heat of reaction for the neutralization of strong acids and bases to always be the same. In other words, for strong acids and bases, the heat of neutralization will always be approximately -55.9 kJ per mole of water formed according to the balanced chemical equation. This is because the **_net_** ionic equation is always the same for such reactions:

$$H^+(aq) + OH^-(aq) \rightarrow H_2O(l) \qquad \Delta H_{rxn} = -55.9 \ kJ \cdot mol^{-1}$$

Indeed, calculation of the heat of reaction for this net ionic equation using heats of formation in Appendix II gives the same result. _Calculations involving standard heats of formation will be discussed in detail in Section 12.9._

$$\Delta H^\circ_{rxn} = \sum \left(n\Delta H^\circ_f \right)_{prod} - \sum \left(n\Delta H^\circ_f \right)_{react}$$

$$\Delta H^\circ_{rxn} = \Delta H^\circ_{f,H_2O(l)} - \left[\Delta H^\circ_{f,H^+(aq)} + \Delta H^\circ_{f,OH^-(aq)} \right]$$

$$\Delta H^\circ_{rxn} = (-285.8 \ kJ) - [(0) + (-229.9 \ kJ)] = -55.9 \ kJ$$

Section 12.8 Hess's Law

In the previous sections, we learned a number of things regarding enthalpy, and, in particular, the enthalpy of reaction for a chemical process. Two very important points regarding the enthalpy of a chemical reaction are these:

1. **The enthalpy of reaction is an extensive property of that reaction.** As such, the greater the amount of reactants undergoing a reaction, the more heat will be released or absorbed due to that reaction. Further, recall that ΔH_{rxn}, in a thermochemical equation, is given according to the precise stoichiometric ratios in the chemical equation in question. Consider the following generic example:

$$A + 2B \rightarrow 3C + 2D \qquad \Delta H_1$$

Suppose we multiplied the reaction coefficients in this equation by a factor of two. If we did so, there would be a new value for the enthalpy of reaction because ΔH is an extensive property. In fact, because we amplified the quantities of the reactants by 2, the enthalpy would also be twice as much as it was previously. This is the nature of extensive properties, and, therefore, **_if a chemical equation is multiplied by some value, the reaction enthalpy is also multiplied by that value._**

$$2A + 4B \rightarrow 6C + 4D \qquad \Delta H_2 = 2 \times \Delta H_1$$

2. **The enthalpy of reaction is a state function.** Recall that we defined a state function as a property that depends only on the current state of the system, irrespective of its history. Therefore, the change in a state function, due to a process, is simply dependent on the initial and final states of the system before and after the process in question. Further, we use the Greek letter delta to denote the change in a state function and define it (for enthalpy in this case) as follows:

$$\Delta H_{rxn} = H_{final} - H_{initial}$$

In a chemical reaction, the initial state is represented by the reactants and the final state is represented by the products. As such, we can express this function as:

$$\Delta H_{rxn} = H_{products} - H_{reactants}$$

Understanding the enthalpy of reaction in these terms has a very important implication; if a reaction is reversed, the products become the reactants, and the reactants become the products. This has the effect of changing the sign of the enthalpy of reaction according to the expression above. Let's look at an example. Consider the generic reaction equation below:

$$A \rightarrow B \quad \Delta H_{A \rightarrow B}$$

The enthalpy of this reaction ($\Delta H_{A \rightarrow B}$) can be expressed as follows, since A is the reactant (initial state) and B is the product (final state):

$$\Delta H_{A \rightarrow B} = H_B - H_A$$

However, if we reverse the reaction as shown here:

$$B \rightarrow A \quad \Delta H_{B \rightarrow A}$$

In this case, B is now the reactant (initial state) and A the product (final state). Thus:

$$\Delta H_{B \rightarrow A} = H_A - H_B$$

It follows therefore, that $\Delta H_{A \rightarrow B}$ is the opposite of $\Delta H_{B \rightarrow A}$.

$$H_B - H_A = -(H_A - H_B)$$
$$\Delta H_{A \rightarrow B} = -\Delta H_{B \rightarrow A}$$

This is always true of state functions and, as such, *if a chemical equation is reversed, the enthalpy of reaction changes sign*. In other words, if a reaction is exothermic in the forward direction (as written), it is endothermic by the same magnitude in the reverse direction and vice versa.

Hess's Law

Keeping these last two points in mind, let's walk through another example. Suppose a chemical process is represented not by one reaction but two reactions. For instance, assume we wish to convert hypothetical compound A to compound C, but this will require two distinct reactions (or steps) as shown here:

$$A \rightarrow B \quad \Delta H_{A \rightarrow B} = H_B - H_A$$

$$B \rightarrow C \quad \Delta H_{B \rightarrow C} = H_C - H_B$$

In this process, compound B is merely an intermediate on the path to our desired product, C. Nevertheless, each step will have its own enthalpy of reaction which we define as a function of the final and initial states of the systems, just as before. However, *because enthalpy is a state function, it is not dependent on any particular path between the final and initial states.* As such, we could sum these two equations together and develop an overall equation that describes the entire process, and the overall enthalpy would simply be defined by the reactants and products in this new, overall reaction equation as shown here:

$$\begin{array}{c} A \rightarrow B \\ + \ B \rightarrow C \\ \hline A \rightarrow C \end{array}$$

Because B is present on both the left and right sides of the reaction arrow, it will be cancelled and we are left with the overall reaction, $A \rightarrow C$. Further, the enthalpy of this new equation will be defined by the following expression:

$$\Delta H_{A \rightarrow C} = H_C - H_A$$

where A and C are the reactant and the product of our overall reaction, representing the initial and final states of our system. Additionally, it can be easily shown that $\Delta H_{A \rightarrow C}$ is simply the sum of $\Delta H_{A \rightarrow B}$ and $\Delta H_{B \rightarrow C}$:

$$(H_B - H_A) + (H_C - H_B) = H_C - H_A$$

$$\Delta H_{A \rightarrow B} + \Delta H_{B \rightarrow C} = \Delta H_{A \rightarrow C}$$

Therefore, *the enthalpy change of an overall chemical process is equal to the sum of the enthalpy changes for individual steps in that process.* This is referred to as **Hess's Law**.

Germain Henri Hess (1802–1850) was a Russian-Swiss chemist who is most famous for development of the thermochemical principle which bears his name, Hess's Law.

Estimating Unknown Enthalpies of Reaction— Application of Hess's Law

In many circumstances the empirical determination of reaction enthalpy is impractical. This can be due to the complexity of a particular chemical process or simply that a reaction occurs under conditions which are not amenable to calorimetry experiments. When such instances arise, and it is necessary to determine the change in enthalpy, we rely on the three quantitative relationships described in the previous sections, to calculate the desired reaction enthalpy. These three relationships are summarized below:

1. If a chemical equation is multiplied by some value, the reaction enthalpy is also multiplied by that value.

2. If a chemical equation is reversed, the enthalpy of reaction changes sign.

3. Hess's Law: The enthalpy change of an overall chemical process is equal to the sum of the enthalpy changes for individual steps in that process.

As it turns out, any reaction equation can be expressed as the sum of any number of theoretical or actual steps. As such, we can apply Hess's Law by defining an overall reaction (a reaction equation of interest) as the sum of a series of steps (chemical reactions) for which the enthalpy of reaction is already known. Steps must be chosen, however, such that when added together, they will sum up to the reaction equation of interest. Let's consider an example. Suppose we wished to determine the enthalpy change for the following reaction:

$$2\,C_4H_{10}(g) + 13\,O_2(g) \rightarrow 8\,CO_2(g) + 10\,H_2O(g) \quad \Delta H_{rxn} = ?$$

We know the enthalpies of reaction for the following:

1. $CO_2(g) \rightarrow C(s) + O_2(g)$ $\qquad \Delta H = +393.5\ kJ$

2. $4\,C(s) + 5\,H_2(g) \rightarrow C_4H_{10}(g)$ $\qquad \Delta H = -125.6\ kJ$

3. $2\,H_2(g) + O_2(g) \rightarrow 2\,H_2O(g)$ $\qquad \Delta H = -483.6\ kJ$

If we can arrange these three reactions such that they add up to the reaction equation of interest, then, according to Hess's Law, we can sum their enthalpies to arrive at the value of our unknown enthalpy. This is done by manipulating each equation with respect to its direction and through multiplication. However, each manipulation must include manipulation of the corresponding enthalpy. Let's begin with equation 1 in our example. Here we see that CO_2 is a reactant but is written as a product in the reaction of interest. Therefore, we will reverse this reaction such that CO_2 is now a product, making sure to change the sign of its enthalpy. Recall that if a chemical equation is reversed, the enthalpy of reaction changes sign.

1. $C(s) + O_2(g) \rightarrow CO_2(g)$ $\qquad \Delta H = -393.5\ kJ$

Additionally, CO_2 has a coefficient of 8 in the reaction of interest but a coefficient of 1 in equation 1. Therefore, in addition to reversing the reaction, we also multiply it by a factor of 8, which places a coefficient of 8 on CO_2 in equation 1:

1. $8\,C(s) + 8\,O_2(g) \rightarrow 8\,CO_2(g)$ $\qquad \Delta H = 8(-393.5\ kJ) = -3{,}148\ kJ$

Having repositioned CO_2 as a product and adjusted its coefficient to match that of CO_2 in our equation of interest, we now examine equation 2. Here we find that C_4H_{10} is a product with a coefficient of 1, but in the reaction interest, it is a reactant with a coefficient of 2. Therefore we reverse equation 2 and multiply it by a factor of 2. This requires that we also change the sign of the enthalpy and multiply it by a factor of 2 as well.

$$2. \quad 2C_4H_{10}(g) \rightarrow 8C(s) + 10H_2(g) \quad \Delta H = 2(+125.6\,kJ) = +251.2\,kJ$$

Further, we find equation 3 depicts water as a product with a coefficient of 2. The reaction interest also has water as a product, but it has a coefficient of 10 rather than 2. Therefore we simply multiply equation 3 by a factor of 5, which requires we also multiply the corresponding enthalpy by 5 as well.

$$3. \quad 10H_2(g) + 5O_2(g) \rightarrow 10H_2O(g) \quad \Delta H = 5(-483.6\,kJ) = -2{,}418\,kJ$$

If we have now manipulated our equations along with their corresponding enthalpies properly, Hess's Law says we simply add them together to arrive at our equation of interest along with its corresponding enthalpy of reaction as follows:

$$8C(s) + 8O_2(g) \rightarrow 8CO_2(g) \qquad \Delta H = -3{,}148\,kJ$$
$$2C_4H_{10}(g) \rightarrow 8C(s) + 10H_2(g) \qquad \Delta H = +251.2\,kJ$$
$$+ \quad 10H_2(g) + 5O_2(g) \rightarrow 10H_2O(g) \qquad + \quad \Delta H = -2{,}418\,kJ$$

$$\overline{2C_4H_{10}(g) + 13O_2(g) \rightarrow 8CO_2(g) + 10H_2O(g)} \qquad \overline{\Delta H_{rxn} = -5{,}315\,kJ}$$

We see here that the C and H_2 terms cancel perfectly. Additionally, note that the $8O_2$ term from equation 1 and the $5O_2$ term from equation 3 add up to $13O_2$ in the desired equation, leaving us with a resulting equation which is identical to our reaction of interest. Owing to this, we can assume we have manipulated our equations properly and, by extension, the enthalpies as well. Therefore, by summation, we find that the enthalpy of reaction for the combustion of butane is $\Delta H_{rxn} = -5{,}315\,kJ$. The following example problem provides further practice with the application of Hess's Law.

Example Problem 12.10

Consider the following reaction:

$$3N_2(g) + 4H_2(g) + C(s) + 6O_2(g) \rightarrow 6NO(g) + 4H_2O(g) + CO_2(g)$$

Use the thermochemical equations below to estimate the enthalpy of the above reaction equation:

1. $2NO(g) \rightarrow N_2(g) + O_2(g)$ $\qquad \Delta H = -182.6\,kJ$
2. $2H_2(g) + O_2(g) \rightarrow 2H_2O(g)$ $\qquad \Delta H = -483.6\,kJ$
3. $C(s) + O_2(g) \rightarrow CO_2(g)$ $\qquad \Delta H = -393.5\,kJ$

Solution:

The manner of solution to Hess's Law problems is always the same. We manipulate the equations with known enthalpies such that their summation gives us the reactants and products of interest. Let's begin with equation 1. Here we see that NO is written as a reactant with coefficient of 2. However, in our reaction of interest we see it is a product with a coefficient of 6. Therefore, we reverse equation 1 and multiply it by a factor of three. This requires that we also manipulate enthalpy by changing sign and multiplying it by 3 as well.

1. $3N_2(g) + 3O_2(g) \rightarrow 6NO(g)$ $\qquad \Delta H = 3(+182.6\,kJ) = +547.8\,kJ$

Equation 2 has H_2O written as a product (just as our equation of interest) with a coefficient of 2. In the equation of interest H_2O has a coefficient of 4. Therefore, we multiply equation 2 and its enthalpy by a factor of 2.

2. $4 H_2(g) + 2 O_2(g) \rightarrow 4 H_2O(g)$ $\Delta H = 2(-483.6\,kJ) = -967.2\,kJ$

Equation 3 has CO_2 written as a product with a coefficient of 1, just as with the reaction of interest. As such, no change is required for equation 3.

3. $C(s) + O_2(g) \rightarrow CO_2(g)$ $\Delta H = -393.5\,kJ$

We now show that the equations, properly manipulated according to direction and through multiplication, will sum to the reaction equation of interest. In this case, no terms cancel.

$$3 N_2(g) + 3 O_2(g) \rightarrow 6 NO(g)$$
$$4 H_2(g) + 2 O_2(g) \rightarrow 4 H_2O(g)$$
$$+ \qquad C(g) + O_2(g) \rightarrow CO_2(g)$$
$$\overline{3 N_2(g) + 4 H_2(g) + C(s) + 6 O_2(g) \rightarrow 6 NO(g) + 4 H_2O(g) + CO_2(g)}$$

Since, the three equations sum to the reaction of interest, we can assume proper manipulation. Further, ΔH for the reaction of interest is the sum of the three enthalpies for equations 1, 2, and 3.

$$\Delta H = +547.8\,kJ$$
$$\Delta H = -967.2\,kJ$$
$$\underline{\Delta H = -393.5\,kJ}$$
$$\Delta H_{rxn} = -812.9\,kJ$$

Therefore, we find the enthalpy of reaction for the reaction interest is $-812.9\,kJ$.

$3 N_2(g) + 4 H_2(g) + C(s) + 6 O_2(g) \rightarrow 6 NO(g) + 4 H_2O(g) + CO_2(g)$ $\mathbf{\Delta H_{rxn} = -812.9\,kJ}$

Section 12.9 Standard Conditions and Enthalpies of Formation

In the previous section, we used known enthalpies of reaction to estimate an unknown overall enthalpy for a reaction which we expressed as a series of steps. However, a more generally applicable procedure for this is the calculation of unknown enthalpies of reaction from tabulated *standard enthalpies of formation*. To understand how this is done, we must first explore three concepts: the standard state, standard enthalpy of reaction (ΔH_{rxn}^{o}), and the standard enthalpy of formation (ΔH_f^{o}) for a compound.

The Standard State. The enthalpy associated with a particular chemical reaction will vary somewhat depending on the conditions as well as the state of the reactants and products. For example, consider the following reaction equations:

$$C(s) + 2 Cl_2(g) \rightarrow CCl_4(l) \quad \Delta H = -139\,kJ$$

$$C(s) + 2 Cl_2(g) \rightarrow CCl_4(g) \quad \Delta H = -96.0\,kJ$$

Notice that each of these essentially depicts the same reaction. However, in one case conditions are such that a liquid product forms and in the other, a gaseous product forms. This is a minor difference, but enough to realize a significantly different enthalpy of reaction. Indeed, conditions of pressure, concentration, and temperature along with the physical state of the reactants and products will all have an impact on the observed enthalpy of reaction. For this reason, chemists have established a standard set of conditions which defines the standard state for a given substance (compound or element). These are listed below:

1. For a gas, the standard state is a constant pressure of 1 *bar*. (**Note:** For the purposes of the textbook, 1 *bar* will be considered equivalent to 1 *atm*. 1 bar =1.013 *atm*.)

2. For a substance in aqueous solution, the standard state is defined as a concentration of 1 *M*.

3. For a pure substance (solid or liquid), the standard state is defined as the most stable form of that substance at 1 *atm* pressure and the temperature of interest. There is no universally accepted standard temperature (when defining standard states); however, in most thermodynamic tables, the temperature of interest is 25°C (298 K).

The Standard Enthalpy of Reaction, ΔH°_{rxn}. The standard enthalpy of reaction, denoted as ΔH°_{rxn}, is defined as the enthalpy change corresponding to a reaction at constant pressure (1 *bar*) wherein all reactants and products are in their respective standard states. The "$^{\circ}$" superscript indicates the "standard" enthalpy of reaction.

Standard Enthalpy of Formation, ΔH°_{f}, also called the **standard heat of formation**. The standard enthalpy of formation is the enthalpy change associated with the standard formation reaction of a substance. The **standard formation reaction** is defined as the formation of *1 mole* of a compound from its constituent elements in their standard states. *For elements in their standard states, $\Delta H^{\circ}_{f} = 0\ kJ$, by definition.* This serves as the reference point, against which all other standard enthalpies are quantified. It is in this way that we can identify from thermodynamic tables the standard state for an element (its most stable form). Table 12.3 lists some common elements and compounds along with their standard heats of formation. A more comprehensive list is in Appendix II of this text.

Writing Balanced Equations for Standard Formation Reactions

We have just learned that a standard formation reaction for a compound is defined as the formation of *1 mole* of a compound from its constituent elements in their standard states. With this definition in mind, we can write

Table 12.3 Standard Heats of Formation, ΔH_f° at 298 K

Formula	$\Delta H_f^o (kJ/mol)$	Formula	$\Delta H_f^o (kJ/mol)$
Aluminum		**Chlorine**	
Al(s)	0	Cl(g)	121.3
Al(g)	330.0	Cl₂(g)	0
AlCl₃(s)	−704.2	HCl(g)	−92.3
Al₂O₃(s)	−1675.7	HCl(aq)	−167.2
Bromine		**Fluorine**	
Br(g)	111.9	F(g)	78.9
Br₂(g)	30.9	F₂(g)	0
Br₂(l)	0	HF(g)	−273.3
HBr(g)	−36.3	**Hydrogen**	
Br⁻(aq)	−120.9	H(g)	218.0
Calcium		H₂(g)	0
Ca(s)	0	**Nitrogen**	
Ca(g)	177.8	N₂(g)	0
CaC₂(s)	−59.8	NH₃(g)	−45.9
CaCO₃(s)	−1207.6	NH₄NO₃(s)	−365.6
CaCl₂(s)	−795.4	NO(g)	91.3
CaF₂(s)	−1228.0	NO₂(g)	33.2
Carbon		**Oxygen**	
C(s, diamond)	1.9	O₂(g)	0
C(s, graphite)	0	O₃(g)	142.7
C(g)	716.7	H₂O(g)	−241.8
CBr₄(s)	18.8	H₂O(l)	−285.8
CH₄(g, methane)	−74.4	**Sodium**	
C₂H₅OH(l, ethanol)	−277.7	Na(s)	0
C₂H₅OH(g, ethanol)	−235.1	NaCl(s)	−411.1
C₂H₆(g, ethane)	−83.8	NaCl(aq)	−407.2
C₃H₈(g, propane)	−104.7	Na₂CO₃(s)	−1130.8
C₄H₁₀(l, butane)	−146.6	NaF(s)	−575.4
C₄H₁₀(g, butane)	−125.6	NaI(s)	−287.8
C₅H₁₂(l, pentane)	−173.5	NaNO₃(s)	−467.9
C₅H₁₂(g, pentane)	−146.9	**Sulfur**	
C₆H₆(l, benzene)	49.0	S(s, monoclinic)	0.3
C₆H₁₂O₆(s, glucose)	−1273.3	S(s, rhombic)	0
C₈H₁₈(l, octane)	−250.1	SO₂(g)	−296.8
CO(g)	−110.5	SO₃(g)	−396.0
CO₂(g)	−393.5	H₂SO₄(l)	−814.0
CO₂(aq)	−413.8	H₂SO₄(aq)	−909.3

balanced equations describing the formation of any compound. Let's consider the example of liquid methanol, $CH_3OH(l)$. We see from its formula that it consists of three elements. These are carbon, hydrogen, and oxygen. Therefore, we begin by writing a skeletal equation as follows:

$$C + H + O \rightarrow CH_3OH(l)$$

Because we have not yet determined the standard state for each element, we are not yet able to attribute formulas or physical states to the reactants. To do this, we refer to Table 12.3. Note here, that we first find elemental carbon listed as having two possible states, solid graphite or solid diamond. We also see that it is the solid graphite form which carries a standard heat of formation of zero, $\Delta H_f^\circ = 0\ kJ$. Therefore, we know that graphite is the most stable form (standard state) for elemental carbon. The equation is then updated accordingly:

$$C(s, graphite) + H + O \rightarrow CH_3OH(l)$$

Likewise, we find the diatomic gas as the standard states for both elemental hydrogen and oxygen on Table 12.3. As such, the equation is again updated to reflect this:

$$C(s, graphite) + H_2(g) + O_2(g) \rightarrow CH_3OH(l)$$

Having established the standard states for our constituent elements, we can now balance the equation. We begin here by recognizing the definition of the formation reaction requires the coefficient for the product be 1. Recall that the standard formation reaction is characterized by the formation of 1 mole of the compound in question. This may sometimes require fractional coefficients, as it does for O_2 in this case.

$$C(s, graphite) + 2\,H_2(g) + \frac{1}{2}O_2(g) \rightarrow CH_3OH(l)$$

Further, the standard heat of formation listed for liquid methanol in Appendix II ($\Delta H_f^\circ = -239.1\ kJ$) is the standard enthalpy change associated with this reaction equation as written. Therefore, we have a balanced thermochemical equation for the standard formation reaction of liquid methanol:

$$C(s, graphite) + 2\,H_2(g) + \frac{1}{2}O_2(g) \rightarrow CH_3OH(l) \quad \Delta H_f^\circ = -239.1\ kJ$$

Example Problem 12.11

Write the balanced standard formation reaction for naphthalene, $C_{10}H_8$. Note: the standard heat of formation for naphthalene is $\Delta H_f^\circ = 78.5\ kJ \cdot mol^{-1}$.	
Solution:	
Step 1: Write the skeletal equation. This is done by identifying all constituent elements in the compound of interest and writing them as reactants.	$C + H \rightarrow C_{10}H_8(s)$
Step 2: Identify the standard states of the elements. This is done by identifying the state of each element with a $\Delta H_f^\circ = 0\ kJ$, from Appendix II. In this case, we find that standard state of carbon is solid graphite and that of hydrogen is diatomic hydrogen gas.	$C_{(s, graphite)} + H_2(g) \rightarrow C_{10}H_8(s)$
Step 3: Balance the equation. By definition, the product compound must have a coefficient of 1. $$10\,C_{(s, graphite)} + 4\,H_2(g) \rightarrow C_{10}H_8(s) \quad \Delta H_f^\circ = 78.5\ kJ \cdot mol^{-1}$$	

Determining Standard Enthalpies of Reaction from Standard Heats of Formation

Having defined the standard formation reaction and its associated standard enthalpy of formation, we can now use these values to predict the standard enthalpy of any reaction. This is accomplished in two theoretical steps along with application of Hess's Law.

1. First, we imagine that all of the reactants in any particular reaction are "decomposed" into their constituent elements in their standard states. The point here is that we understand decomposition of a compound to be the precise reverse of its formation reaction. As such, the enthalpy change associated with this step is equal in magnitude but opposite in sign to the standard heat of formation.

$$\Delta H^o_{decomp} = -\Delta H^o_f$$

2. Second, the formation of the product compounds can now take place from their constituent elements (formed from the decomposition of the reactants in step 1).

Let's look at an example. Suppose we wished to determine the standard enthalpy of reaction for the combustion of octane.

$$2\,C_8H_{18}(l) + 25\,O_2(g) \rightarrow 16\,CO_2(g) + 18\,H_2O(g) \quad \Delta H^o_{rxn} = ?$$

First, we note that elemental oxygen is a reactant and already in its standard state; as such, it can be ignored. However, if we were to write the standard formation reactions for each **compound** in this equation along with its corresponding standard heat of formation (Table 12.3 or Appendix II), we arrive at the following:

1. $8\,C(s, graphite) + 9\,H_2(g) \rightarrow C_8H_{18}(l)$ $\Delta H^o_f = -250.1\,kJ$

2. $C(s, graphite) + O_2(g) \rightarrow CO_2(g)$ $\Delta H^o_f = -393.5\,kJ$

3. $H_2(g) + \frac{1}{2}O_2(g) \rightarrow H_2O(g)$ $\Delta H^o_f = -241.8\,kJ$

Let's examine the formation reaction depicted by equation 1. This is the formation reaction of liquid octane, C_8H_{18}. Note that although octane is the product in equation 1 with a coefficient of 1, it is a reactant in our reaction of interest with a coefficient of 2. Therefore, as we learned previously, we must reverse equation 1 and multiply it by a factor of 2. This will require that we also change the sign of its enthalpy and multiply it by a factor of 2 also:

1. $2\,C_8H_{18}(l) \rightarrow 16\,C(s, graphite) + 18\,H_2(g)$ $\Delta H^o_f = +500.2\,kJ$

This now describes the decomposition of the reactant octane into its constituent elements in their standard states. As we examine equation 2, we see that CO_2 is written as a product with a coefficient of 1 (as the definition of the standard formation reaction requires). CO_2 is a product in our reaction of interest as well, but it has a coefficient of 16. Therefore, we simply amplify the formation reaction and standard enthalpy of formation of CO_2 by a factor of 16 as shown here:

1. $2C_8H_{18}(l) \rightarrow 16\,C(s, graphite) + 18\,H_2(g)$ $\Delta H_f^o = +500.2\,kJ$

2. $16\,C(s, graphite) + 16\,O_2(g) \rightarrow 16\,CO_2(g)$ $\Delta H_f^o = -6{,}296.0\,kJ$

A similar analysis of equation 3, gives the following:

3. $18\,H_2(g) + 9\,O_2(g) \rightarrow 18\,H_2O(g)$ $\Delta H_f^o = -4{,}352.4\,kJ$

With application of Hess's Law, we arrive at the following result:

$$
\begin{aligned}
2\,C_8H_{18}(l) &\rightarrow 16\,C(s, graphite) + 18\,H_2(g) &\quad \Delta H_f^o &= +500.2\ kJ\\
16\,C(s, graphite) + 16\,O_2(g) &\rightarrow 16\,CO_2(g) &\quad \Delta H_f^o &= -6{,}296.0\ kJ\\
+\quad 18\,H_2(g) + 9\,O_2(g) &\rightarrow 18\,H_2O(g) &\quad +\ \Delta H_f^o &= -4{,}352.4\ kJ\\
\hline
2\,C_8H_{18}(l) + 25\,O_2(g) &\rightarrow 16\,CO_2(g) + 18\,H_2O(g) &\quad \Delta H_{rxn}^o &= -10{,}148.2\ kJ
\end{aligned}
$$

Here we find that the elemental carbon (graphite) and hydrogen gas all canceled perfectly, leaving us with a resulting equation which is identical to the reaction of interest. Based on this, we can assume proper manipulation of the equations, and, therefore, we sum the resulting enthalpies to arrive at a value for the standard enthalpy of reaction for the combustion of octane, $\Delta H_{rxn}^o = -10{,}148.2\,kJ$. This pattern can be repeated for any reaction equation of interest, as long as the standard heats of formation of the compounds involved in the reaction are known. This pattern can also be generalized into the following equation:

$$\Delta H_{rxn}^o = \sum \left(n\Delta H_f^o\right)_{prod} - \sum \left(n\Delta H_f^o\right)_{react}$$

where n is the amount (in moles) of each reactant or product as described by the coefficients in the balanced chemical equation. In other words, *the standard enthalpy of reaction is equal to the sum of the standard enthalpies of formation of the products minus the sum of the standard enthalpies of formation of the reactants.* Let's apply this equation to the previous example. The following is the balanced chemical reaction equation along with the heats of formation for the reactants and products for the combustion of octane (as listed in Table 12.3).

$2C_8H_{18}(l) + 25\,O_2(g) \rightarrow 16\,CO_2(g) + 18\,H_2O(g)$

1. $C_8H_{18}(l)$ $\Delta H_f^o = -250.1\,kJ$

2. $O_2(g)$ $\Delta H_f^o = 0\,kJ$

3. $CO_2(g)$ $\Delta H_f^o = -393.5\,kJ$

4. $H_2O(g)$ $\Delta H_f^o = -241.8\,kJ$

If we now expand our equation, it takes the following form:

$$\Delta H^o_{rxn} = \left[16\left(\Delta H^o_{f,CO_2}\right) + 18\left(\Delta H^o_{f,H_2O}\right)\right]_{prod} - \left[2\left(\Delta H^o_{f,C_8H_{18}}\right) + 25\left(\Delta H^o_{f,O_2}\right)\right]_{react}$$

Substituting the values from Table 12.3:

$$\Delta H^o_{rxn} = \left[16(-393.5\,kJ) + 18(-241.8\,kJ)\right]_{prod} - \left[2(-250.1\,kJ) + 25(0\,kJ)\right]_{react}$$

Therefore:

$$\Delta H^o_{rxn} = \left[(-6,296.0\,kJ) + (-4,352.4\,kJ)\right]_{prod} - \left[(-500.2\,kJ) + (0\,kJ)\right]_{react}$$

$$\Delta H^o_{rxn} = -6,296.0\,kJ - 4,352.4\,kJ + 500.2\,kJ = \textbf{-10,148.2\,kJ}$$

The following example problem provides some additional practice calculating enthalpies of reaction from standard heats of formation.

Example Problem 12.12

Use the standard heats of formation in Appendix II to calculate ΔH^o_{rxn} for the following reaction. $$3\,CO(g) + Fe_2O_3(s) \rightarrow 3\,CO_2(g) + 2\,Fe(s)$$	
Solution:	
Gather the standard enthalpies of formation for each product and each reactant from Appendix II.	Reactants: $$\Delta H^o_{f,CO} = -110.5\,kJ$$ $$\Delta H^o_{f,Fe_2O_3} = -824.2\,kJ$$ Products: $$\Delta H^o_{f,CO_2} = -393.5\,kJ$$ $$\Delta H^o_{f,Fe} = 0\,kJ$$
ΔH^o_{rxn} can be calculated by subtracting the heats of formation of the reactants from those of the products. (Note: Each ΔH^o_f term is amplified by the corresponding coefficient (n) from the balanced chemical equation.)	$$\Delta H^o_{rxn} = \sum\left(n\Delta H^o_f\right)_{prod} - \sum\left(n\Delta H^o_f\right)_{react}$$ $$\Delta H^o_{rxn} = \left[3\Delta H^o_{f,CO_2} + 2\Delta H^o_{f,Fe}\right]_p - \left[3\Delta H^o_{f,CO} + \Delta H^o_{f,Fe_2O_3}\right]_r$$
Substitute the ΔH^o_f values from Appendix II into the equation and calculate ΔH^o_{rxn}	$$\Delta H^o_{rxn} = \left[3\Delta H^o_{f,CO_2} + 2\Delta H^o_{f,Fe}\right]_p - \left[3\Delta H^o_{f,CO} + \Delta H^o_{f,Fe_2O_3}\right]_r$$ $$= \left[3(-393.5\,kJ) + 2(0\,kJ)\right]_p - \left[3(-110.5\,kJ) + (-824.2\,kJ)\right]_r$$ $$\Delta H^o_{rxn} = \textbf{-24.8\,kJ}$$

Section 12.10 The Enthalpy of Bonding

Recall from Chapter 8 we discussed bonding theories. In our discussions, we established two main types of bonding, ionic and covalent. Further, we established the idea that bonding occurs primarily as a path to greater stability, and this was justified in terms of potential energy. We now give quantitative expression to this concept by introducing a new term, *bond energy*. A *bond energy* is defined as the enthalpy change associated with the breaking of a covalent bond for 1 mole of molecules in the gaseous state. Because it always requires an input of energy to break a chemical bond, bond energies are endothermic ($\Delta H > 0\ kJ$). With this in mind, the definition can be refined to state that, **bond energy** (also called **bond strength**) *is the energy required to homolytically break a particular bond in 1 mole of a molecule in the gaseous state*. The term homolytically simply means that the bonding electrons are evenly divided between the bonding atoms when the bond is broken. Generally, the stability of a particular covalent bond, and by extension a particular molecule, is measured by its bond energy. Stronger bonds have higher bond energies and are more chemically inert. For example, consider the two diatomic molecules chlorine and nitrogen. Both are gaseous, diatomic molecular elements with the following bond energies:

$$Cl_2(g) \rightarrow 2\,Cl(g) \qquad \Delta H = 243\,kJ$$

$$N_2(g) \rightarrow 2\,N(g) \qquad \Delta H = 946\,kJ$$

This tells us that nearly 4 times as much energy is required to break the nitrogen bond as is required for chlorine. Based on these data, we can conclude that chlorine gas is much more reactive (less stable) than nitrogen, which is indeed the case. In fact, nitrogen is known to be an exceptionally stable, chemically inert substance, which is reflected in its bond energy. Additionally, while bond energies in diatomic molecules are relatively unambiguous, the bond energy for a particular type of bond in a polyatomic molecule is a little more complex. Indeed, bond energies will vary somewhat as a function of their chemical environment. Therefore, when we speak of bond energies, these are average bond energies taken over a large number of different compounds. Table 12.4 provides a selected list of average bond energies.

Table 12.4 Average Bond Energies

Bond Type	Energy ($kJ \cdot mol^{-1}$)	Bond Type	Energy ($kJ \cdot mol^{-1}$)	Bond Type	Energy ($kJ \cdot mol^{-1}$)
$Br - Br$	193	$Cl - F$	253	$N = N$	418
$Br - Cl$	218	$F - F$	159	$N \equiv N$	946
$Br - F$	250	$H - Br$	366	$N - O$	222
$C - Br$	280	$H - C$	414	$N = O$	590
$C - C$	347	$H - Cl$	431	$O - Br$	235
$C = C$	611	$H - F$	570	$O - Cl$	203
$C \equiv C$	837	$H - H$	436	$O - F$	190
$C - Cl$	339	$H - I$	297	$O - I$	234
$C - F$	485	$H - N$	389	$O - O$	142
$C - I$	240	$H - O$	464	$O = O$	498
$C - N$	305	$I - Br$	175	$S - Br$	218
$C = N$	615	$I - Cl$	208	$S - Cl$	253
$C \equiv N$	891	$I - I$	151	$S - F$	327
$C - O$	360	$N - Br$	276	$S - O$	265
$C = O$	736	$N - Cl$	200	$S = O$	523
$C \equiv O$	1072	$N - F$	272	$S - S$	266
$Cl - Cl$	243	$N - N$	163	$S = S$	418

Trends in Bond Energies

Notice in Table 12.4, that some trends in bond energies are based on the type of bond in question. In other words, bond energies for triple bonds are stronger than double bonds which are in turn, stronger than single bonds. For example, the following bond energies are reported for carbon-carbon single, double, and triple bonds:

$$C-C \quad \Delta H = 347 \, kJ$$

$$C=C \quad \Delta H = 611 \, kJ$$

$$C\equiv C \quad \Delta H = 837 \, kJ$$

In addition to bond order, bond energies also trend with bond length. Recall from Chapter 7 that **bond length** is defined as the distance between nuclei in two atoms mutually engaged in a covalent bond. Generally, bond energies are greater for bonds with shorter bond length. Consider the following series of bond lengths and bond energies:

	Bond Length (*pm*)	Bond Energy (*kJ/mol*)
$H-F$	92	570
$H-Cl$	127	431
$H-Br$	141	366
$H-I$	161	297

Here we see the bond energy decreases with increasing bond length (as a function of the increasing atomic radii of the halogens).

Estimating Standard Enthalpies of Reaction from Bond Energies

It is possible to use tables of average bond energies to estimate the enthalpy of reaction. To illustrate this, let's consider the example of the reaction of hydrogen and oxygen to form water, as depicted in the following equation:

$$2\,H_2(g) + O_2(g) \rightarrow 2\,H_2O(g)$$

Here it is instructive to visualize the reactants and products according to their bonding patterns as described by Lewis structures:

$$2 \;\; H-H \; + \; :\ddot{O}=\ddot{O}: \;\; \rightarrow \;\; 2 \;\; H-\ddot{O}-H$$

In this way, it is possible to more easily visualize the reaction taking place as a series of bond-breaking and bond-forming steps. For instance, we can imagine that 2 moles of $H-H$ single bonds must be broken along with 1 mole of $O=O$ double bonds. This is because 2 moles of hydrogen molecules are consumed for every 1 mole of oxygen according to the stoichiometric coefficients in the balanced equation (Figure 12.8). Further, we imagine that 4 moles of O—H single bonds are formed (2 moles of O—H bonds for each mole of water formed). The enthalpies of this series of bond breaking and forming steps can now be summed to realize an overall enthalpy of reaction. However, we must keep in mind that, because bond formation is the reverse of bond breaking, this process is, therefore, exothermic, and the enthalpy change for such a step will be the negative of the bond energy for a particular bond. As such, we apply the following equation:

$$\Delta H_{rxn} = \sum \left(n\Delta H_{BE} \right)_{bonds\ broken} - \sum \left(n\Delta H_{BE} \right)_{bonds\ formed}$$

where n is the number of moles of each particular bond type which is formed or broken. For our current example, and using bond energies taken from Table 12.4, this equation takes the following form:

$$\Delta H_{rxn} = [(2 \times 436\ kJ) + (1 \times 498\ kJ)] - [4 \times 464\ kJ]$$

Thus:

$$\Delta H_{rxn} = [(872\ kJ) + (498\ kJ)] - [1856\ kJ]$$

$$\Delta H_{rxn} = 1370\ kJ - 1856\ kJ$$

$$\Delta H_{rxn} = -486\ kJ$$

Therefore, we estimate the enthalpy of reaction for the formation of 2 moles of water from 2 moles of hydrogen and 1 mole of oxygen to be $\Delta H_{rxn} = -486\ kJ$.

$$2\ H_2(g) + O_2(g) \rightarrow 2\ H_2O(g) \qquad \Delta H_{rxn} = -486\ kJ$$

We would expect this value to be roughly twice the standard heat of formation, ΔH_f°, of water, given the stoichiometric coefficients in the balanced chemical equation. If we locate the heat of formation of gaseous water in Table 12.3, we find it to be −241.8 kJ. Twice this value gives −483.6 kJ. As such, we find that a reasonable estimate for the heat of reaction in this case can be achieved from average bond energies. The following example provides further practice.

Figure 12.8 We can sum enthalpies of bond breaking and bond formation to estimate reaction enthalpies.

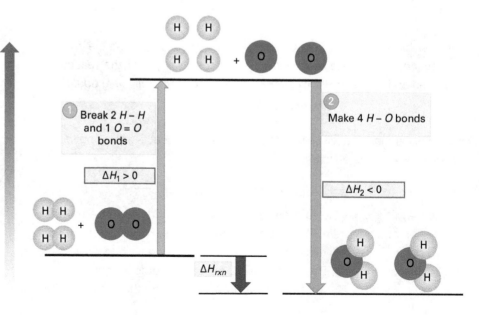

Example Problem 12.13

Use the bond energies given in Table 12.4 to estimate the enthalpy of reaction for the following:
$$H_2(g) + Cl_2(g) \rightarrow 2\,HCl(g)$$

Solution:	
Recall that it is easier to visualize and "count" the various bond types if we first rewrite the equation using the Lewis structures of the reactants and products (Chapter 8).	H–H + :C̈l–C̈l: → 2 H–C̈l:
Identify which "existing" bonds are broken in the reaction and the sum of their bond energies. These are identified in the reactants.	H–H + :C̈l–C̈l: $$\sum \left(n\Delta H_{BE}\right)_{broken}$$ $$1\left(\Delta H_{H-H}\right) + 1\left(\Delta H_{Cl-Cl}\right) =$$ $$1(436\,kJ) + 1(243\,kJ) = 679\,kJ$$
Identify which "new" bonds are formed in the reaction and take the sum of their bond energies. These are identified in the products.	2 H–C̈l: $$\sum \left(n\Delta H_{BE}\right)_{formed}$$ $$2\left(\Delta H_{H-Cl}\right) = 2(431\,kJ) = 862\,kJ$$
Calculate ΔH_{rxn} by subtracting the sum of the bond energies of the bonds formed from that of the bonds broken.	$$\Delta H_{rxn} = \sum \left(n\Delta H_{BE}\right)_{broken} - \sum \left(n\Delta H_{BE}\right)_{formed}$$ $$\Delta H_{rxn} = 679\,kJ - 862\,kJ$$ $$\Delta H_{rxn} = -183\ \textbf{kJ}$$

Lattice Energy

We now turn our attention to the energetics of ionic bonds. Recall from Chapters 2 and 3, we learned that ionic bonds form through the complete transfer of one or more electrons from a metal to a nonmetal. When this occurs, the resulting ions are then bonded together by virtue of the electrostatic attraction which exists between particles of opposite charge. We can break this down into two distinct steps, one in which a metal loses electrons and another in which a nonmetal gains electrons. For example, sodium and chlorine undergo such a process to form sodium chloride (table salt). The following equations represent these two steps:

1. $Na(g) \rightarrow Na^+(g) + e^-$

2. $\frac{1}{2}Cl_2(g) + e^- \rightarrow Cl^-(g)$

In step 1, we have depicted the loss of an electron from sodium in the gaseous state. Recall from Chapter 7 that the energy required to remove 1 mole of electrons from 1 mole of an element in the gaseous state is called its *ionization energy*. Further, the energy released when a mole of atoms in the gaseous state gains a mole of electrons is called its *electron affinity*. If we look up the first ionization energy of sodium and the electron affinity of chlorine, we can represent these as enthalpies as follows:

1. $Na(g) \rightarrow Na^+(g) + e^-$ $\qquad \Delta H_{IE} = +496\,kJ$

2. $\frac{1}{2}Cl_2(g) + e^- \rightarrow Cl^-(g)$ $\qquad \Delta H_{EA} = -349\,kJ$

If we sum these steps together, we get an enthalpy of reaction for the formation of sodium chloride of +147 *kJ/mol*, suggesting an endothermic process. However, we know from the heat of formation of *NaCl* that this is an exothermic process:

$$Na(s) + \frac{1}{2}Cl_2(g) \rightarrow NaCl(s) \qquad \Delta H^o_f = -411.2\,kJ$$

How do we understand this discrepancy? First of all, the ionization energy and the electron affinity are defined for atoms and ions in the gaseous state. However, we know that ionic solids exist in the solid state, and it is the solid state structure of ionic compounds that is the answer to our question. Within an ionic solid, each anion is surrounded by a specific number of cations in a very specific arrangement. Likewise, each cation is surrounded by a specific number of anions. Because these are ions, they will each realize a certain potential energy due to their proximity to one another and their respective charges. Further, because ionic compounds do not form discrete molecules but rather three dimension arrays or lattices of ions, the overall stability (energy) of the array depends on the interactions between a large number of ions as opposed to a simple pair-wise, discrete interaction between an individual cation and an individual anion. Therefore, we measure the stability of an ionic compound based on the potential energy associated with the specific arrangements and charges of ions in the entire crystalline lattice. This is referred to as the *lattice energy*. In covalent bonding the bond energy was defined as the energy required to homolytically break a bond in the gaseous state. The analogous quantity in ionic bonding is the **lattice energy** which is defined as the energy required to separate one mole of an ionic solid into ions in the gaseous state. Just as with bond energies, lattice energy is a quantitative measure of the relative stability of an ionic compound.

As it turns out, however, we cannot measure lattice energy directly. It is possible to ascertain the lattice energy if the correct thermodynamic quantities are known for a given ionic solid. The calculation is carried out using a method known as the **Born-Haber cycle**. The method takes its name from its developers, Max Born (Chapter 7) and Fritz Haber, and is based on Hess's Law. For any given ionic solid, a series of theoretical steps can be defined which precede the formation of the solid lattice from gaseous ions. To illustrate how this is accomplished, let's consider the example of magnesium chloride, $MgCl_2$.

$$Mg(s) + Cl_2(g) \rightarrow MgCl_2(s) \qquad \Delta H^o_f = -641.3\,kJ$$

This equation, as written, represents the standard formation reaction of this salt, and, as such, its heat of formation is the standard enthalpy change for

Fritz Haber (1868–1934) was a German chemist who is noted for his invention of the Haber-Bosch process for which he received a Nobel Prize in Chemistry in 1918.

the reaction in question. In the Born-Haber cycle, the overall reaction enthalpy is taken as the sum of the enthalpy changes for a series of five theoretical steps which are outlined as follows:

1. Because the lattice energy describes the interconversion between gaseous ions and a solid compound, we begin by moving all solid reactants into the gaseous state. In the current example, chlorine already exists in the gaseous state, but magnesium solid will have to be converted to magnesium vapor.

    $$Mg(s) \rightarrow Mg(g) \quad \Delta H_1 = +147.1 \, kJ \qquad \text{(The heat of sublimation)}$$

    The energy of sublimation for magnesium is 147.1 *kJ/mol*. **Sublimation** refers to the change in state of a substance directly from a solid to a gas (Chapter 9).

2. Because we are moving toward free gaseous ions (as required by the definition of lattice energy), we must break the Cl_2 bond, converting it to free atomic chlorine gas.

    $$Cl_2(g) \rightarrow 2\,Cl(g) \quad \Delta H_2 = +243 \, kJ \qquad \text{(The bond energy)}$$

    The energy required to accomplish this is the *bond energy* of Cl_2, which is known from Table 12.4 as 243 *kJ*.

3. Next we ionize 1 mole of the gaseous magnesium atoms. This will require the first and the second *ionization energies* for magnesium since it will adopt a charge of +2. In other words, 2 electrons will have to be removed from each magnesium atom.

    $$Mg(g) + e^- \rightarrow Mg^+(g) \quad \Delta H_3' = 738.0 \, kJ \qquad \text{(The first ionization energy)}$$

    $$Mg^+(g) + e^- \rightarrow Mg^{2+}(g) \quad \Delta H_3'' = 1{,}450 \, kJ \qquad \text{(The second ionization energy)}$$

4. Next we add 2 moles of electrons to the 2 moles of Cl atoms. 2 moles because when we broke the bonds in 1 mole of Cl_2 gas, we formed 2 moles of gaseous Cl atoms (see step 2). This requires that we double the electron affinity of chlorine.

    $$2\,Cl(g) + 2e^- \rightarrow 2Cl^-(g) \quad \Delta H_4 = 2(-348.6 \, kJ) \qquad \text{(The electron affinity)}$$

5. We can now combine 1 mole of gaseous magnesium cations with 2 moles of gaseous chloride anions to form a solid ionic lattice.

    $$Mg^{2+}(g) + 2\,Cl^-(g) \rightarrow MgCl_2(s) \quad \Delta H_5 = ?$$

This last step is precisely the reverse of the definition of the lattice energy and therefore:

$$\text{Lattice Energy} = -\Delta H_5$$

Further, although we do not know this quantity, we can calculate it. This is because Hess's Law tells us that the overall enthalpy of this reaction (the standard heat of formation of magnesium chloride) is the sum of all the enthalpies for steps 1 through 5. As such:

$$\Delta H_f^o(MgCl_2) = \Delta H_1 + \Delta H_2 + \Delta H_3' + \Delta H_3'' + \Delta H_4 + \Delta H_5$$

Thus:

$$\Delta H_5 = \Delta H_f^o - (\Delta H_1 + \Delta H_2 + \Delta H_3' + \Delta H_3'' + \Delta H_4)$$

If we substitute the values for each step as follows:

$$\Delta H_5 = -641.3\,kJ - (147.1\,kJ) - (243\,kJ) - (738.0\,kJ) - (-1,450\,kJ) - (-697.2\,kJ)$$
$$\Delta H_5 = -2,522\,kJ$$

Therefore:

$$\textbf{\textit{Lattice Energy}} = -\Delta H_5 = +2,522\,kJ$$

Figure 12.9 illustrates the Born-Haber cycle for this example graphically.

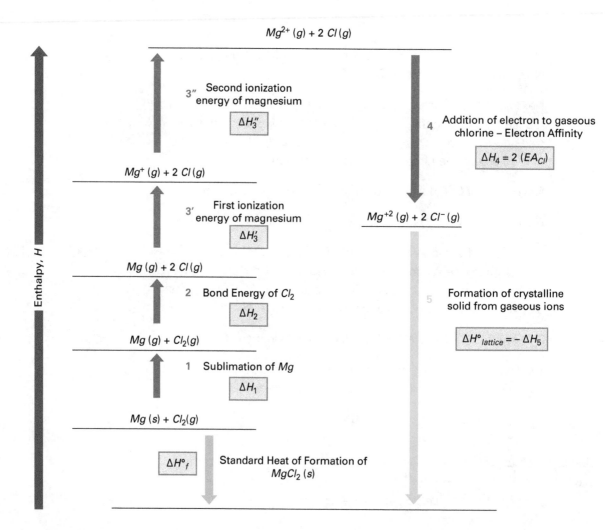

Figure 12.9 The Born-Haber cycle for the formation of magnesium chloride.

Trends in Lattice Energy

Recall Coulomb's Law from Chapter 7, which stated that the potential energy between two charged particles was proportional to the product of the charges of the two particles in question and inversely proportional to the distance between them:

$$E \propto \frac{q_1 q_2}{r}$$

Because lattice energy is a function of this electrostatic potential energy, it exhibits trends according to these two variables of ionic charge ($q_1 q_2$) and distance (r). Let's examine both trends separately.

Ionic Radius. The distance between two ions in an ionic solid is a function of the ionic radii of the ions in question. *We expect that the greater the magnitude of this coulombic potential energy (E), the greater the lattice energy.* For example, consider the following:

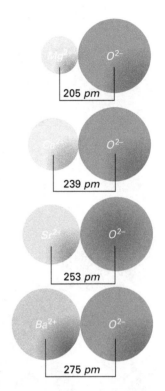

Metal Oxide	Lattice Energy (kJ/mol)
MgO	3,926
CaO	3,540
SrO	3,220
BaO	3,081

Bond Lengths (pm) of Group 2A metal oxides.

Notice that as we examine the lattice energies of the metal oxides of the Group 2A metals, we see a steady decrease in lattice energy as we move down the column (Group 2A on the periodic table) from magnesium oxide to barium oxide. We can explain this according to Coulomb's law. As the ionic radius of the metal cation increases, so does its distance from the oxide anion. Recall trends in ionic radii from Chapter 7. Coulomb's Law tells us that the potential energy of interaction between two oppositely charged particles becomes less negative (the magnitude decreases) as the distance between the two ions increases. *In other words, as the sum of the ionic radii of the ions which constitute an ionic compound increases, the lattice energy decreases and vice versa.*

Ionic Charge. In order to examine the effect of ionic charges on lattice energy, let's consider another comparison.

Metal Oxide	Lattice Energy (kJ/mol)
NaCl	751
BaO	3,081

Bond Lengths (pm) of sodium chloride and barium oxide.

In this case we have two ionic compounds with roughly the same inter-nuclear distance, 276 *pm* for *NaCl* and 275 *pm* for *BaO*. However, we see that the lattice energies are very different. Recall that according to Coulomb's Law, the potential energy between charged particles is directly proportional to the product of their charges. In the case of *NaCl*, we see that $E \propto -\frac{1}{r}$ because each ion in this compound is singly charged (either positive or negative 1) as shown here:

$$E \propto \frac{q_1 q_2}{r} = \frac{(+1)(-1)}{r} = \frac{-1}{r}$$

In the case of *BaO*, each ion is doubly charged, and, therefore, we see that $E \propto \frac{-4}{r}$:

$$E \propto \frac{q_1 q_2}{r} = \frac{(+2)(-2)}{r} = \frac{-4}{r}$$

As we have already learned, the more negative the potential energy, according to Coulomb, the greater the magnitude of the lattice energy. Hence, the lattice energy of *BaO* is approximately four times that of *NaCl* since *r* is essentially the same for both compounds ($4 \times 751 \frac{kJ}{mol} = 3{,}004 \frac{kJ}{mol}$). In other words, we conclude that *the magnitude of the lattice energy trends directly with the product of the ionic charges*. Additionally, we can clearly see that ionic charge has a much greater impact on the magnitude of the lattice energy than do variations in ionic radii.

In Summary

1. Lattice energy decreases with increasing ionic radius.

2. Lattice energy increases with increasing ionic charge.

Example Problem 12.14

Arrange the following in order of increasing lattice energy: 1. *NaCl* 2. *KCl* 3. *SrS* 4. *BaS*	
Solution:	
Recall that ionic charge has a greater impact on the magnitude of lattice energy than does ionic radius. As such, we know that *SrS* and *BaS* have greater lattice energies than do *NaCl* and *KCl*, due to their ionic charges.	$(NaCl, KCl) < (SrS, BaS)$
Because barium has a larger ionic radius than strontium, we expect the lattice energy of *SrS* to be greater than *BaS* due to the inverse relationship between lattice energy and ionic radius.	$(NaCl, KCl) < BaS < SrS$
Similar analysis of *NaCl* and *KCl* predicts a greater lattice energy for *NaCl* than *KCl*. Therefore the compounds are arranged in order of increasing lattice energy as shown.	$KCl < NaCl < BaS < SrS$

The Heat of Solution

Recall from Chapter 5, we discussed the chemistry of solutions. As it happens, lattice energy finds use in understanding the thermodynamics of the formation of solutions. As in any process, when a solute is dissolved into a solvent, there is an associated change in energy. In many cases this change in energy is due to the formation of a solution is manifested as heat exchange.

At constant pressure, this is referred to as the *enthalpy of solution*. The **enthalpy of solution, ΔH_{soln}** (also called **heat of solution**) is the heat (absorbed or released) when a solute is dissolved in a solvent. Again, we can rely on Hess's Law in understanding this process. To do this for an ionic compound, we imagine two steps in the formation of a solution, described as follows:

1. Completely separate the solute (ionic compound) into its constituent ions. This is essentially the process we used in defining the lattice energy for ionic compound. Therefore, if we invoke an example, *NaCl*, we can represent this as follows:

$$NaCl(s) \rightarrow Na^+(g) + Cl^-(g) \qquad \Delta H_{Lattice} = 751 \, kJ$$

We know the lattice energy of sodium chloride is 751 *kJ* from the previous section.

2. Next, the gaseous ions, formed in the previous step, enter the solvent and become solvated (or hydrated in aqueous solutions). The enthalpy change associated with this process in an aqueous system is called the **heat of hydration, ΔH_{hydr}**. We will focus our discussion on aqueous systems for the remainder of this section.

$$Na^+(g) + Cl^-(g) \rightarrow Na^+(aq) + Cl^-(aq) \qquad \Delta H_{hydr} = ?$$

The enthalpy change associated with this second step is the *heat of hydration* for sodium chloride: the energy released or absorbed due to dissolution of gaseous sodium and chloride ions into water. We expect this to be an exothermic step due to the strong intermolecular ion-dipole interactions between the water molecules and the individual sodium and chloride ions (described in Chapter 9 of this text). Nevertheless, direct measurement of the heat of hydration is not practical. However, heats of solution, ΔH_{soln}, are routinely measured using *constant-pressure calorimetry* experiments. With an empirically determined value for ΔH_{soln}, application of Hess's Law provides a method for determination of ΔH_{hydr} as follows:

$$
\begin{array}{ll}
NaCl(s) \rightarrow Na^+(g) + Cl^-(g) & \Delta H_{Lattice} = 751 \, kJ \\
+ \quad Na^+(g) + Cl^-(g) \rightarrow Na^+(aq) + Cl^-(aq) & + \quad \Delta H_{hydr} = ? \\
\hline
NaCl(s) \rightarrow Na^+(aq) + Cl^-(aq) & \Delta H_{soln} = +4 \, kJ
\end{array}
$$

Here see the overall enthalpy of solution for sodium chloride is +4 *kJ/mol*, as determined through calorimetry. Hess's Law tells us:

$$\Delta H_{soln} = \Delta H_{Lattice} + \Delta H_{hydr}$$

Thus, the heat of hydration is simply the difference between the heat of solution and the lattice energy.

$$\Delta H_{hydr} = \Delta H_{soln} - \Delta H_{Lattice}$$

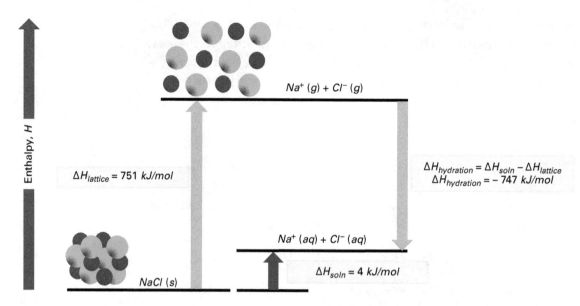

Figure 12.10 The sum of the lattice energy and the heat of hydration is the heat of solution.

Substituting our known values for ΔH_{soln} and $\Delta H_{Lattice}$ gives:

$$\Delta H_{hydr} = 4\ kJ - 751\ kJ$$

$$\Delta H_{hydr} = -747\ kJ$$

As expected, we find that the hydration of the sodium and chloride ions is decidedly exothermic. This example is depicted graphically in Figure 12.10. The following example problem provides further practice at calculating the heat of hydration.

Example Problem 12.15

If the heat of solution of KCl(aq) is determined to be 17.2 kJ via constant-pressure calorimetry, what is the heat of hydration for KCl if its lattice energy is determined to be 699 kJ/mol?	
Solution:	
Recall that the heat of solution is the sum of the lattice energy and the heat of hydration for a compound dissolved in water.	$\Delta H_{soln} = \Delta H_{Lattice} + \Delta H_{hydr}$
We rearrange the equation to isolate the heat of hydration.	$\Delta H_{hydr} = \Delta H_{soln} - \Delta H_{Lattice}$
Substituting the given values, we can now calculate the heat of hydration as shown.	$\Delta H_{hydr} = 17.2\ kJ - 699\ kJ$ $\Delta H_{hydr} = -682\ kJ$

Section 12.11 Spontaneity, Entropy, and the Second Law of Thermodynamics

Another characteristic of chemical reactions that chemists are interested in is spontaneity. A **spontaneous** process is one which proceeds without any outside intervention. For instance, let's return to the example of the bowling ball raised above the ground (Section 12.2). When it is released, we are not surprised to see the ball spontaneously fall. Nor are we surprised to see water flowing downhill. We explain these observations according to a tendency of systems to move toward states of lower potential energy. In terms of chemical reactions, we learned in Chapter 10 that a reaction will spontaneously tend toward equilibrium. Further, we can predict the direction of this tendency in any particular chemical system based on the relative values of Q (the reaction quotient) and K (the equilibrium constant). In other words, chemical reactions are similar to flowing water and bowling balls in that they, too, will spontaneously proceed in a direction, and to an extent dictated by their *potential* to do so. What drives a reaction to equilibrium? What factors determine the chemical "potential" to undergo spontaneous change?

Regarding this last question, one might be tempted to suggest spontaneous processes proceed from higher energy states to lower energy states. However, the first law of thermodynamics tells us that the total energy of the universe is conserved, and, therefore, any energy gained or lost by the system is accompanied with an equal and opposite change in energy for the surroundings:

$$\Delta E_{univ} = \Delta E_{sys} + \Delta E_{surr} = 0$$

This provides an accounting for energy, but it in no way determines or dictates any direction that a process must proceed. In other words, for the system to lower its energy, its immediate surroundings must increase in energy. For example, a piece of ice will spontaneously melt on a table top at room temperature. The first law will tell us that energy from the table is transferred to the ice as heat which increases the kinetic energy of the water molecules, converting it to a liquid. An equally acceptable process according to the first law would be the transfer of energy from the (now melted) water back to the table, causing the water to freeze. However, we know from common experience that water at room temperature will not spontaneously freeze. This is even more interesting when you consider that in this case, water melting (which is spontaneous) is an *endothermic* process while water freezing (not spontaneous) is an *exothermic* process. Therefore, we must accept that the first law can make no prediction of spontaneity, and, as such, there must be another criterion for this beyond the relative change in internal energy or enthalpy.

Why is this so? Why should the ice spontaneously gain kinetic energy? The answer to this question is contained in a new concept that we will now define called entropy. **Entropy (S)** is defined as the measure of the distribution or dispersal of energy within a system at a given temperature. This can be understood a little more informally as a measure of the "disorder" of a system. Additionally, we now also introduce **the second law of thermodynamics** which states that entropy of the universe increases due to a spontaneous process. In other words, *the second law says that there is a natural progression of circumstances toward increasing disorder or randomness (from lower entropy to higher entropy).* We can express this with the following inequality respecting spontaneous processes:

$$\Delta S_{univ} > 0$$

Because the universe can be defined by two parts, the system and the surroundings:

$$\Delta S_{univ} = \Delta S_{sys} + \Delta S_{surr} > 0$$

Therefore, we understand that a process is spontaneous, according to the second law, if the sum of the entropy change for the system and the surroundings is positive. This brings us back to our question of the ice melting, or the more general question, why should thermal energy spontaneously flow from matter with higher temperature to matter of lower temperature? The answer generally is that the sum of the entropy changes for this process is positive. In other words, it increases the entropy of the universe.

Entropy and Changes in Physical State

With our definition of entropy in mind, we can further generalize its application to our example of the melting ice. Indeed, respecting changes in the physical states of matter, the following general guideline regarding entropy applies:

$$S_{solid} < S_{liquid} \ll S_{gas}$$

In other words, we will generally understand that the entropy of a substance is minimized in the solid state and increases with transition to the liquid state. This is because the solid state is much more ordered, and particles in the solid state have a correspondingly low freedom of kinetic motion. As such, it is intuitive that the liquid state is less ordered than the solid state. Further, because molecules in the gaseous state enjoy much greater freedom of motion, we acknowledge a significantly greater entropy (disorder) associated with the gaseous state relative to liquids and solids. Therefore, we will expect the entropy to increase ($\Delta S > 0$) for each of the following circumstances:

1. A transition of a substance from the solid to the liquid state.

2. A transition of a substance from the solid to the gaseous state.

3. A transition of a substance from the liquid to the gaseous state.

4. A chemical reaction for which there is a net increase in the number of moles of gaseous molecules or ions.

The last point refers to chemical reactions. However, when there is no net increase in the moles of gaseous species in a reaction, determining whether ΔS is positive or negative may be less obvious. In such cases, *entropy is expected to increase when there is a net increase in the number of moles of ions or molecules due to chemical reaction or other process.*

Example Problem 12.16

Determine whether the following chemical reactions will have a positive or a negative entropy of reaction:

1. $2\,Na(s)+Cl_2(g)\rightarrow 2\,NaCl(s)$

2. $C_3H_8(g)+5\,O_2(g)\rightarrow 3CO_2(g)+4\,H_2O(g)$

3. $H_2O(l)\rightarrow H_2O(g)$

Solution:	
Equation 1: In this case, we expect the entropy to decrease due to the conversion of gaseous chlorine into chloride ions in the solid state.	$\Delta S<0$
Equation 2: In this case we expect the entropy to increase due to the greater number of molecules in the gaseous state on the right side of the equation (7 moles of gas in the products vs. 6 moles of gas in the reactants).	$\Delta S>0$
Equation 3: A substance changing from liquid to gas will have a positive entropy change.	$\Delta S>0$

Entropy and Chemical Reactions

To illustrate these concepts a little more clearly, let's consider an example reaction equation (at 298 K):

$$2\,CO(g)+O_2(g)\rightarrow 2\,CO_2(g)$$

In this case, we expect this reaction to exhibit a negative ΔS, given the guidelines we have just learned. However, if we are to understand whether this reaction is spontaneous, we need to know whether ΔS_{univ} is positive or negative. To do this, we need to know ΔS_{sys} and ΔS_{surr}. In this case, ΔS_{sys} is ΔS_{rxn}, and this is where we will begin. Entirely analogous to the standard enthalpy of reaction, we can define a **standard entropy of reaction, ΔS°_{rxn}**:

$$\Delta S^\circ_{rxn} = \sum (nS^\circ)_{prod} - \sum (nS^\circ)_{react}$$

Where, S° is the **standard molar entropy** (also called the **standard entropy**) of each element or compound constituting the reactants and products, and n is the number of moles of each species (its stoichiometric coefficient in the balanced equation). The *standard molar entropy* of a substance is defined as the absolute entropy of one mole of substance in its standard state. Table 12.5 (and Appendix II) provides a list of standard molar entropies for a number of compounds. Note: Unlike enthalpies, we can discuss absolute entropies for a given substance, a point that is further clarified in Section 12.12. Therefore, to calculate ΔS°_{rxn} we look up the standard entropy values of our reactants and products in Table 12.5 and apply this equation as follows:

$$\Delta S^\circ_{rxn} = \left[2\times S^\circ_{CO_2}\right]_{prod} - \left[2\times S^\circ_{CO} +1\times S^\circ_{O_2}\right]_{react}$$

Then, substituting standard entropies from Table 12.5:

$$\Delta S^\circ_{rxn} = \left[2\times\left(213.8\,\frac{J}{mol\cdot K}\right)\right]_{prod} - \left[2\times\left(197.7\,\frac{J}{mol\cdot K}\right)+\left(205.2\,\frac{J}{mol\cdot K}\right)\right]_{react}$$

Table 12.5 Standard Molar Entropies, $S°$, at 298 K

Formula	$S°$ $(J/mol \cdot K)$	Formula	$S°$ $(J/mol \cdot K)$
Bromine		**Hydrogen**	
$Br(g)$	175.0	$H(g)$	114.6
$Br_2(g)$	245.5	$H_2(g)$	130.7
$Br_2(l)$	152.2	**Nitrogen**	
$HBr(g)$	198.7	$N_2(g)$	191.6
$Br_-(aq)$	80.71	$NH_3(g)$	192.8
Carbon		$NO(g)$	210.8
$CO(g)$	197.7	$NO_2(g)$	239.9
$CO_2(g)$	213.8	**Oxygen**	
$CO_2(aq)$	117.6	$O_2(g)$	205.2
$C(s, diamond)$	2.4	$O_3(g)$	238.9
$C(s, graphite)$	5.7	$H_2O(g)$	188.8
$C(g)$	158.1	$H_2O(l)$	69.9
$CH_4(g, methane)$	186.3	**Sulfur**	
$C_2H_5OH(l, ethanol)$	160.7	$SO_2(g)$	248.2
$C_2H_5OH(g, ethanol)$	282.7	$SO_3(g)$	256.7
$C_2H_6(g, ethane)$	229.6	$H_2SO_4(l)$	156.9
$C_6H_{12}O_6 (s, glucose)$	212.1	$H_2SO_4(aq)$	18.5

and

$$\Delta S°_{rxn} = \left(427.6 \, \frac{J}{mol \cdot K}\right) - \left(395.4 \, \frac{J}{mol \cdot K}\right) - \left(205.2 \, \frac{J}{mol \cdot K}\right)$$

$$\Delta S°_{rxn} = -173.0 \, \frac{J}{mol \cdot K}$$

Therefore, we find the entropy change for the reaction described in the above equation is $-173.0 \frac{J}{mol \cdot K}$. A negative value is just as we would have predicted, given the guidelines we learned in the previous section. The following example problem will provide further practice predicting the sign of $\Delta S°_{rxn}$ as well as calculating its value.

Example Problem 12.17

Using standard entropies listed in Appendix II, calculate the entropy of reaction ($\Delta S°_{rxn}$) for the following reaction:

$$2 \, SO_2(g) + O_2(g) \rightarrow 2 \, SO_3(g)$$

	Solution:
Gather the standard entropies for each product and reactant from Appendix II.	Reactants: $$S°_{SO_2} = 248.2 \, \frac{J}{mol \cdot K}$$ $$S°_{O_2} = 205.2 \, \frac{J}{mol \cdot K}$$ Products: $$S°_{SO_3} = 256.7 \, \frac{J}{mol \cdot K}$$

Standard entropies of reaction are calculated as the difference of the sum of the standard entropies of the products minus those of the reactants.	$$\Delta S^o_{rxn} = \sum (nS^o)_{prod} - \sum (nS^o)_{react}$$
Substitute the standard entropies of the reactants and products into the equation and calculate ΔS^o_{rxn}.	$$\Delta S^o_{rxn} = \left[2S^o_{SO_3}\right]_p - \left[2S^o_{SO_2} + S^o_{O_2}\right]_r$$ $$= \left[2\left(256.7\,\frac{J}{mol \cdot K}\right)\right]_p - \left[2\left(248.2\,\frac{J}{mol \cdot K}\right) + \left(205.2\,\frac{J}{mol \cdot K}\right)\right]_r$$ $$\Delta S^o_{rxn} = -188.2\,\frac{J}{mol \cdot K}$$

Entropy and the Surroundings

Let's now turn our attention to quantifying ΔS for the surroundings. To do this, we begin by recognizing some relationships concerning the exchange of energy between the system and the surroundings. If a reaction is exothermic, for instance ($\Delta H^o_{rxn} < 0$), this means heat is transferred to the surroundings from the reaction ($\Delta H_{surr} > 0$). This will cause an increase in the molecular motion (the kinetic energy) of the particles constituting the surroundings. In other words, entropy increases. For endothermic reactions ($\Delta H^o_{rxn} > 0$), the opposite is true. As such, we begin by acknowledging that the change in entropy of the surroundings due to a reaction is proportional to its enthalpy change:

$$\Delta S_{surr} \propto \Delta H_{surr}$$

In other words, the entropy change for the surroundings tracks according to how much heat it either gains or loses due to a reaction. Additionally, we have already established the following relationship from the first law:

$$\Delta H_{surr} = -\Delta H_{rxn}$$

Therefore:

$$\Delta S_{surr} \propto -\Delta H_{rxn}$$

Further, the impact that a given enthalpy (amount of heat) may have on the entropy of surroundings also depends on the temperature. For example, if the temperature is very low, then it will not require much heat to cause a relatively large change in the molecular motion of the particles constituting the surroundings. Likewise, if the temperature is already high, then a given quantity of heat will have a more diminished effect on molecular motion. Put differently, the higher the temperature, the lower the change in entropy (positive or negative) for a given value of ΔH_{rxn}. We can express this as follows:

$$\Delta S_{surr} = \frac{-\Delta H_{rxn}}{T}$$

where T is temperature in kelvins. Let's now apply this to our current example and determine the spontaneity of the reaction (at 298 K). We can calculate the enthalpy of reaction from standard heats of formation (Appendix II):

$$2\,CO(g) + O_2(g) \rightarrow 2\,CO_2(g) \qquad \Delta H^o_{rxn} = -566.0\,kJ \cdot mol^{-1}$$

Given this, we can determine the entropy change for the surroundings (ΔS_{surr}) as well:

$$\Delta S_{surr} = \frac{-\Delta H_{rxn}}{T} = \frac{-(-566.0\,kJ \cdot mol^{-1})}{298\,K} \times \frac{1000\,J}{1\,kJ}$$

$$\Delta S_{surr} = 1,899\,\frac{J}{mol \cdot K}$$

Further, we have already determined the value for ΔS^o_{rxn} in the previous section:

$$\Delta S^o_{rxn} = -173\,\frac{J}{mol \cdot K}$$

We can now determine ΔS_{univ} as follows:

$$\Delta S_{univ} = \Delta S_{rxn} + \Delta S_{surr} = \left(-173\,\frac{J}{mol \cdot K}\right) + \left(1,899\,\frac{J}{mol \cdot K}\right)$$

$$\Delta S_{univ} = 1,726\,\frac{J}{mol \cdot K}$$

Because, $\Delta S_{univ} > 0$, we expect this reaction to proceed spontaneously. Note that this is true, even though the entropy change for the reaction is negative. This is because the reaction is very exothermic, and, therefore, it causes a large positive change in entropy for the surroundings which more than offsets the negative contribution from ΔS^o_{rxn}.

Example Problem 12.18

Using Table 12.3 and ΔS^o_{rxn} calculated in the previous example problem, calculate ΔS_{surr} and ΔS_{univ} for the following reaction at 298 K and indicate whether it will proceed spontaneously as written. $$2\,SO_2(g) + O_2(g) \rightarrow 2\,SO_3(g) \qquad \Delta S^o_{rxn} = -188.2\,\frac{J}{mol \cdot K}$$	
Solution:	
Since ΔS_{univ} is the sum of ΔS^o_{rxn} and ΔS_{surr}, we must first determine the entropy change for the surroundings, the equation for which is shown here.	$$\Delta S_{univ} = \Delta S_{sys} + \Delta S_{surr}$$ $$\Delta S_{surr} = \frac{-\Delta H_{rxn}}{T}$$
Therefore, we need to calculate ΔH_{rxn} using standard heats of formation in Table 12.3 (Section 12.9).	$$\Delta H^o_{rxn} = \sum \left(n\Delta H^o_f\right)_{prod} - \sum \left(n\Delta H^o_f\right)_{react}$$ $$\Delta H^o_{rxn} = \left[2\Delta H^o_{f,SO_3}\right]_p - \left[2\Delta H^o_{f,SO_2} + \Delta H^o_{f,O_2}\right]_r$$ $$\Delta H^o_{rxn} = \left[2(-396.0\,kJ)\right]_p - \left[2(-296.8\,kJ) + (0\,kJ)\right]_r$$ $$\Delta H^o_{rxn} = -198.4\,kJ \cdot mol^{-1}$$

Having established the standard enthalpy of formation, we can now calculate the entropy change for the surroundings at 298 K.	$$\Delta S_{surr} = \frac{-\Delta H_{rxn}}{T}$$ $$\Delta S_{surr} = \frac{-\left(-198.4\,kJ \cdot mol^{-1}\right)}{298\,K} \times \frac{1000\,J}{1\,kJ}$$ $$\Delta S_{surr} = +665.8\,\frac{J}{mol \cdot K}$$
Having calculated ΔS_{surr} we can now determine ΔS_{univ}.	$$\Delta S_{univ} = \Delta S_{sys} + \Delta S_{surr}$$ $$= \left(-188.2\,\frac{J}{mol \cdot K}\right) + \left(665.8\,\frac{J}{mol \cdot K}\right)$$ $$\Delta S_{univ} = 477.6\,\frac{J}{mol \cdot K}$$

Therefore, because $\Delta S_{univ} > 0$ for this reaction at 298 K, we conclude *this reaction is spontaneous as written.*

Section 12.12 The Third Law of Thermodynamics and Absolute Entropy

As we have just seen in the previous section, unlike with enthalpy or internal energy, we actually have direct measurements of the entropy of various compounds and elements. To understand this distinction, we now introduce the **third law of thermodynamics** which states that *the entropy of perfect crystalline substance is zero at a temperature of 0 K, absolute zero.* This allows for the determination of absolute entropies of substances (as in the case of the standard molar entropies in Table 12.5). We show this by beginning with what was implicitly recognized in the previous discussion over the determination of ΔS°_{rxn}, which is that *entropy is a state function.* As such, the following holds:

$$\Delta S_{sys} = S_f - S_i$$

If we initially have a crystalline substance at absolute zero, then the third law says, $S_i = 0$. If we allow the substance to heat up to a higher temperature (we most commonly reference 298 K), then $\Delta S_{sys} = S_f$ or the absolute entropy of that substance at that particular temperature. Table 12.5 lists *standard molar entropies* (S°) for various compounds at 298 K.

Section 12.13 The Gibbs Free Energy

In Section 12.11 we defined the parameters for the determination of spontaneity of a reaction in terms of the entropy change of the universe, ΔS_{univ}. The second law tells us that for a spontaneous reaction:

$$\Delta S_{univ} = \Delta S_{rxn} + \Delta S_{surr} > 0$$

However, we are often interested in ascertaining spontaneity by consideration of only the reaction (the system) itself. This can be accomplished through a minor manipulation of the above equation. Recall that we defined ΔS_{surr} as follows:

$$\Delta S_{surr} = \frac{-\Delta H_{rxn}}{T}$$

Therefore, by substitution:

$$\Delta S_{univ} = \Delta S_{rxn} - \frac{\Delta H_{rxn}}{T} > 0$$

If we then multiply both sides by $-T$ we arrive at the following:

$$-T\Delta S_{univ} = \Delta H_{rxn} - T\Delta S_{rxn} < 0$$

We now have a function which describes the condition for spontaneity entirely in terms of the system only ($\Delta H_{rxn} - T\Delta S_{rxn} < 0$). Further, the product of temperature and entropy is energy. As such, this equation is the basis for a new thermodynamic term we will now introduce known as *Gibbs free energy*. **Gibbs free energy (G)** (also called simply **free energy**) is defined as the enthalpy of a system minus the product of temperature (in Kelvin) and the entropy at constant temperature:

$$G = H - TS$$

Just as enthalpy and entropy are state functions and extensive properties, so is the free energy. As such, it is customarily reported in units of $\frac{kJ}{mol}$. Additionally, we express the change in free energy as:

$$\Delta G = \Delta H - T\Delta S$$

Therefore, for a reaction at constant temperature, $\Delta G_{rxn} < 0$ for a spontaneous process. Additionally, we further define the free energy change of a reaction as a measure of the useful energy released by the system and available to do work.

Interpreting ΔG°_{rxn}

It is important to remember the free energy is simply another expression for the change in entropy of the universe ($\Delta G_{sys} = -T\Delta S_{univ}$). We have simply manipulated the expression to provide a quantity which can be determined solely from changes occurring for the system. Therefore, as we have just noted, ΔG for a chemical reaction contains within it the conditions for spontaneity, according to the second law of thermodynamics. Owing to this, we can summarize the conditions for spontaneity of a chemical reaction in terms of ΔG as follows:

1. A reaction is spontaneous (in the forward direction as written): $\Delta G < 0$

2. A reaction is nonspontaneous (in the forward direction as written): $\Delta G > 0$

3. A reaction is at equilibrium: $\Delta G = 0$

Additionally, just as its definition implies, ΔG *is a state function and an extensive property* and, therefore, subject to the same set of relationships to the balanced chemical reaction equation as ΔH°_{rxn}. These include Hess's Law and are summarized as follows (for a review, see section 12.8):

1. The free energy of reaction is an extensive property of that reaction. Therefore, *if a chemical equation is multiplied by some value, the free energy is also multiplied by that value.*

$$A + 2B \rightarrow 3C + 2D \qquad \Delta G_1$$

Then:

$$2A + 4B \rightarrow 6C + 4D \qquad \Delta G_2 = 2 \times \Delta G_1$$

2. The free energy of reaction is a state function. Therefore, *if a chemical equation is reversed, the free energy of reaction changes sign, and accordingly, if a reaction is spontaneous in the forward direction, it will be nonspontaneous in the reverse direction and vice versa.*

$$\Delta G_{forward} = -\Delta G_{reverse}$$

In other words, the free energy determines the spontaneous direction of a reaction. Recall from Chapter 10 that reactions are reversible, and the spontaneous direction of a reaction at any point in time (forward or reverse) will depend on whether ΔG is positive or negative in either direction. We explore the relation between ΔG, the reaction quotient, Q, and the equilibrium constant, K, later in this chapter.

3. *The free energy change of an overall chemical process is equal to the sum of the free energy changes for individual steps in that process.*

Standard Conditions

It should be fairly intuitive that the free energy change (as we have just defined it) is very analogous to enthalpy. For example, just like enthalpy, we have no defined reference (or zero point) and, therefore, no absolute value for free energy. Consequently, we are interested in relative changes in free energy due to chemical processes and, just as the case with enthalpy changes, we are free to define the zero point for free energy change as conveniently as possible. To do this we, again, invoke the concept of standard states and conditions as described in section 12.9. With this in mind, we define the following terms (entirely analogous to our discussion of ΔH):

1. The **standard free energy of reaction, ΔG^o_{rxn},** is defined as the change in free energy for a reaction under standard conditions wherein reactants and products are in their standard states (as defined in section 12.9).

$$\Delta G^o_{rxn} = \Delta H^o_{rxn} - T\Delta S^o_{rxn}$$

2. The **standard free energy of formation, ΔG^o_f,** is the free energy change associated with the standard formation reaction of a substance. Recall that the *standard formation reaction* is defined as the formation of *1 mole* of a compound from its constituent elements in their standard states. *For elements in their standard states, $\Delta G^o_f = 0$ kJ by definition.* Additionally, free energies of formation can be used to calculate the standard free energy of reaction, just as standard enthalpies of reaction can be calculated from standard enthalpies of formation, according to the following general equation:

$$\Delta G^o_{rxn} = \sum (n\Delta G^o_f)_{prod} - \sum (n\Delta G^o_f)_{react}$$

Table 12.6 (and Appendix II) list standard free energies of formation for various compounds at 298 K. The following example problem demonstrates methods for calculating ΔG^o_{rxn}.

Table 12.6 Standard Free Energies of Formation, ΔG^o_f, at 298 K

Formula	$\Delta G^o_f (kJ/mol)$	Formula	$\Delta G^o_f (kJ/mol)$
Bromine		Hydrogen	
Br(g)	82.4	H(g)	203.3
Br$_2$(g)	3.1	H$_2$(g)	0
Br$_2$(l)	0	**Nitrogen**	
HBr(g)	−53.4	N$_2$(g)	0
Br⁻(aq)	−102.82	NH$_3$(g)	16.4
Carbon		NO(g)	87.6
CO(g)	−137.2	NO$_2$(g)	51.3
CO$_2$(g)	−394.4	**Oxygen**	
CO$_2$(aq)	−368.0	O$_2$(g)	0
C(s, diamond)	2.9	O$_3$(g)	163.2
C(s, graphite)	0	H$_2$O(g)	−228.6
C(g)	671.3	H$_2$O(l)	−237.2
CH$_4$(g, methane)	−50.3	**Sulfur**	
C$_2$H$_5$OH(l, ethanol)	−174.8	SO$_2$(g)	−300.1
C$_2$H$_5$OH(g, ethanol)	−168.5	SO$_3$(g)	−371.0
C$_2$H$_6$(g, ethane)	−31.9	H$_2$SO$_4$(l)	−690.0
C$_6$H$_{12}$O$_6$ (s, glucose)	−910.4	H$_2$SO$_4$(aq)	−744.6

Example Problem 12.19

Consider the following reaction equation:

$$C_{12}H_{22}O_{11}(s) + 12\,O_2(g) \rightarrow 12\,CO_2(g) + 11\,H_2O(g)$$

Show that the following equations produce the same result for the free energy of this reaction at 298 K (to at least three significant figures):

1. $\Delta G^o_{rxn} = \Delta H^o_{rxn} - T\Delta S^o_{rxn}$

2. $\Delta G^o_{rxn} = \sum (n\Delta G^o_f)_{prod} - \sum (n\Delta G^o_f)_{react}$

Equation 1: This equation requires that we determine ΔH^o_{rxn} and ΔS^o_{rxn} using data in Appendix II (as described in the Sections 12.9 & 12.11) and making sure we have consistent units. ($\Delta H^o_{f,C_{12}H_{22}O_{11}} = -2{,}226.1\,kJ$ and $S^o_{C_{12}H_{22}O_{11}} = 360.24\,\frac{J}{mol \cdot K}$)	$\Delta H^o_{rxn} = \sum (n\Delta H^o_f)_{prod} - \sum (n\Delta H^o_f)_{react}$ $\Delta H^o_{rxn} = [12(-393.5\,kJ) + 11(-241.8\,kJ)]_p - [-2{,}226.1\,kJ]_r$ $\Delta H^o_{rxn} = -5{,}155.7\,kJ \cdot mol^{-1}$
	$\Delta S^o_{rxn} = \sum (nS^o)_{prod} - \sum (nS^o)_{react}$ $\Delta S^o_{rxn} = \left[12\left(213.8\,\frac{J}{mol \cdot K}\right) + 11\left(188.8\,\frac{J}{mol \cdot K}\right)\right]_p - \left[\left(360.24\,\frac{J}{mol \cdot K}\right) + 12\left(205.2\,\frac{J}{mol \cdot K}\right)\right]_r$ $\Delta S^o_{rxn} = 1{,}819.8\,\frac{J}{mol \cdot K} \times \frac{1\,kJ}{1000\,J} = 1.8198\,\frac{kJ}{mol \cdot K}$
Having determined ΔH^o_{rxn} and ΔS^o_{rxn}, we can now calculate ΔG^o_{rxn} according to equation 1.	$\Delta G^o_{rxn} = \Delta H^o_{rxn} - T\Delta S^o_{rxn}$ $\Delta G^o_{rxn} = (-5{,}155.7\,kJ \cdot mol^{-1}) - (298\,K)\left(1.8198\,\frac{kJ}{mol \cdot K}\right)$ $\Delta G^o_{rxn} = -5.70 \times 10^3\,kJ \cdot mol^{-1}$
Equation 2: This equation requires that we use ΔG^o_f data listed in Appendix II and calculate ΔG^o_{rxn} as the difference of the sum of the standard free energies of formation of the products minus those of the reactants. ($\Delta G^o_{f,C_{12}H_{22}O_{11}} = -1544.3\,kJ$)	$\Delta G^o_{rxn} = \sum (n\Delta G^o_f)_{prod} - \sum (n\Delta G^o_f)_{react}$ Reactants: $\Delta G^o_{f,C_{12}H_{22}O_{11}} = -1{,}544.3\,kJ$ $\Delta G^o_{f,O_2} = 0\,kJ$ Products: $\Delta G^o_{f,CO_2} = -394.4\,kJ$ $\Delta G^o_{f,H_2O} = -228.6\,kJ$
Substituting our values for ΔG^o_f into the equation, we calculate ΔG^o_{rxn} as shown.	$\Delta G^o_{rxn} = \left[12\Delta G^o_{f,CO_2} + 11\Delta G^o_{f,H_2O}\right]_p - \left[\Delta G^o_{f,C_{12}H_{22}O_{11}} + \Delta G^o_{f,O_2}\right]_r$ $\Delta G^o_{rxn} = \left[12(-394.4\,kJ) + 11(-228.6\,kJ)\right]_p - \left[(-1{,}544.3\,kJ) + (0\,kJ)\right]_r$ $\Delta G^o_{rxn} = -5.70 \times 10^3\,kJ \cdot mol^{-1}$
	Therefore, we demonstrate that each equation provides the same value for the free energy of reaction in this case (to within three significant figures).

ΔS_{rxn}, ΔH_{rxn}, Temperature and Spontaneity

Here it is instructive to take a moment to consider the relationship between ΔS_{rxn}, ΔH_{rxn}, absolute temperature, and spontaneity (the sign of ΔG_{rxn}) in a given direction. In this context, let's consider the equation for the free energy of a reaction according to a series of scenarios:

$$\Delta G_{rxn} = \Delta H_{rxn} - T\Delta S_{rxn}$$

1. First, let's consider a scenario in which a reaction will always be expected to be spontaneous no matter the temperature. A reaction is always spontaneous under all conditions when $\Delta H_{rxn} < 0$ and $\Delta S_{rxn} > 0$. This will always produce a negative free energy change ($\Delta G_{rxn} < 0$).

2. When $\Delta H_{rxn} > 0$ and $\Delta S_{rxn} < 0$, the reaction will always be nonspontaneous because $\Delta G_{rxn} > 0$ under any circumstance.

3. When ΔH_{rxn} and ΔS_{rxn} are of the same sign, ΔG_{rxn} will carry the same sign as ΔH_{rxn} unless the following condition holds:

$$\left| T\Delta S_{rxn} \right| > \left| \Delta H_{rxn} \right|$$

In other words, when the enthalpy and entropy of reaction are of the same sign, spontaneity is dependent on temperature. When ΔH_{rxn} is negative, the reaction is spontaneous at lower temperature but reverses and becomes nonspontaneous at high temperatures. Likewise, if ΔH_{rxn} is positive, so is ΔG_{rxn} (nonspontaneous), but it reverses and becomes spontaneous again at high temperature. In other words, ΔG_{rxn} has the same sign as ΔH_{rxn} except at high temperature. (These relationships are summarized in Table 12.7.)

Table 12.7 Reaction Spontaneity and Sign of ΔH, ΔS, and ΔG.

ΔH	ΔS	ΔG	Comment
−	+	−	Always Spontaneous
+	−	+	Always Nonspontaneous
−	−	+/−	Spontaneous at Low Temperature Nonspontaneous at High Temperature
+	+	+/−	Nonspontaneous at Low Temperature Spontaneous at High Temperature

The relationships in Table 12.7 above can be summarized in two statements. First, *when the enthalpy and entropy change for a reaction are of different signs, ΔG_{rxn} has the same sign as ΔH_{rxn} under all circumstances. However, when the enthalpy and entropy change for a reaction are of the same sign, ΔG_{rxn} has the same sign as ΔH_{rxn} except at high temperature.* What is this temperature? The answer is the temperature where $\Delta G = 0$. Let's consider the example of the formation of hydrogen iodide. Is this reaction spontaneous at 298 K, and, if so, will this condition be reversed at a particular temperature? We will answer this question in the following step-wise fashion:

$$H_2(g) + I_2(g) \rightarrow 2HI(g)$$

1. If we wish to determine the spontaneity of this reaction, we first determine the standard enthalpy of reaction, which, in this case, is twice the standard heat of formation of $HI(g)$ (see section 12.9):

$$H_2(g) + I_2(g) \rightarrow 2\,HI(g) \qquad \Delta H^o_{rxn} = 51.8\,kJ \cdot mol^{-1}$$

2. Next we determine the ΔS^o_{rxn} using absolute standard entropies of the reactants and products, as given in Table 12.5 and Appendix II. This is accomplished as follows:

$$\Delta S^o_{rxn} = \sum (nS^o)_{prod} - \sum (nS^o)_{react}$$

Thus:

$$\Delta S^o_{rxn} = \left[2 \times S^o_{HI}\right]_{prod} - \left[1 \times S^o_{H_2} + 1 \times S^o_{I_2}\right]_{react}$$

Substitution gives:

$$\Delta S^o_{rxn} = \left[2 \times \left(206.3\,\frac{J}{mol \cdot K}\right)\right]_{prod} - \left[\left(130.7\,\frac{J}{mol \cdot K}\right) + \left(260.6\,\frac{J}{mol \cdot K}\right)\right]_{react}$$

$$\Delta S^o_{rxn} = \left(412.6\,\frac{J}{mol \cdot K}\right) - \left(130.7\,\frac{J}{mol \cdot K}\right) - \left(260.6\,\frac{J}{mol \cdot K}\right)$$

$$\Delta S^o_{rxn} = 21.3\,\frac{J}{mol \cdot K}$$

3. Since ΔS^o_{rxn} and ΔH^o_{rxn} are both positive, we expect the reaction to be nonspontaneous at room temperature (298 K). To verify this we calculate ΔG^o_{rxn} at 298 K:

$$\Delta G^o_{rxn} = \Delta H^o_{rxn} - T\Delta S^o_{rxn}$$

$$\Delta G^o_{rxn} = \left(51.8\,\frac{kJ}{mol}\right) - (298\,K)\left(21.3\,\frac{J}{mol \cdot K} \times \frac{1\,kJ}{1000\,J}\right)$$

$$\Delta G^o_{rxn} = 45.5\,\frac{kJ}{mol}$$

4. From this, we conclude that the Gibbs free energy of reaction is positive as expected, and the reaction is nonspontaneous when carried out under standard conditions at 298 K. However, at what temperature will this trend reverse? What is the minimum temperature above which we expect this reaction to proceed spontaneously? To answer this, we must simply find the temperature at which $\Delta G^o_{rxn} = 0$ as follows:

$$\Delta G_{rxn} = \Delta H_{rxn} - T\Delta S_{rxn} = 0$$

Thus, we find that when $\Delta G^o_{rxn} = 0$:

$$\Delta H_{rxn} = T\Delta S_{rxn}$$

From here we simply isolate temperature:

$$T = \frac{\Delta H_{rxn}}{\Delta S_{rxn}}$$

This is a condition which is met at equilibrium ($\Delta G_{rxn}^o = 0$). Therefore, we understand that this is the temperature at which the reaction will be at equilibrium with all reactants and products otherwise in their standard states ($Q = K = 1$ for the current reaction). At temperatures above this, the reaction is spontaneous in the forward direction (Chapter 10; $Q > K$). In our current example, we now substitute the reaction enthalpy and entropy as follows:

$$T = \frac{\left(51.8 \dfrac{kJ}{mol}\right)}{\left(21.3\dfrac{J}{mol \cdot K} \times \dfrac{1\,kJ}{1000\,J}\right)} = 2{,}432\,K$$

Therefore, we conclude that this reaction will proceed spontaneously at temperatures above 2,432 K. There is one acknowledgement worth noting here. We used values for ΔH_{rxn} and ΔS_{rxn} measured at 298 K in the context of an entirely different (significantly higher) temperature. As such, the result is an approximation which is reasonably good for the stated purpose. The following example problem provides further practice.

Example Problem 12.20

The following reaction has a negative ΔH_{rxn} and a negative ΔS_{rxn}. Therefore, we expect this reaction to be spontaneous except at high temperatures. At what temperature (in Kelvins) will it become nonspontaneous?

$$Cu(s) + Cl_2(g) \rightarrow CuCl_2(s) \qquad \Delta H_{rxn}^o = -220.1\,kJ \cdot mol^{-1}$$
$$\Delta S_{rxn}^o = -148.2\,J \cdot (mol \cdot K)^{-1}$$

Solution:	
Set ΔG_{rxn}^o to zero and isolate T.	$\Delta G_{rxn}^o = \Delta H_{rxn}^o - T\Delta S_{rxn}^o = 0$ $\Delta H_{rxn}^o = T\Delta S_{rxn}^o$ $T = \dfrac{\Delta H_{rxn}^o}{\Delta S_{rxn}^o}$
We now simply substitute the given values of ΔH_{rxn}^o and ΔS_{rxn}^o (adjusting for units) and calculate T.	$T = \dfrac{\Delta H_{rxn}^o}{\Delta S_{rxn}^o}$ $T = \dfrac{\left(-220.1\dfrac{kJ}{mol}\right)}{\left(-148.2\dfrac{J}{mol \cdot K}\right)\left(\dfrac{1\,kJ}{1000\,J}\right)}$ $T = 1{,}485\,K$

Therefore, we expect this reaction to become spontaneous at temperatures below 1,485 K.

What Is Meant by the Term "Free Energy"?

When we use chemical reactions to generate energy, such as burning octane to drive automobiles, we are using energy generated by the reaction to do some kind of work. As we have already defined it, the free energy of reaction represents the maximum limit of energy released that can be used for this purpose. The reason for this is that in any reaction, some energy must be used to satisfy the second law of thermodynamics. To illustrate this, consider the example reaction below:

$$2\,CO(g) + O_2(g) \rightarrow 2\,CO_2(g)$$

If we calculate the standard enthalpy, entropy, and free energy of reaction for this equation at 298 K, we have the following:

$$\Delta H^o_{rxn} = -566.0\, kJ \cdot mol^{-1}$$

$$\Delta S^o_{rxn} = -173 \times 10^{-3}\, kJ \cdot mol^{-1}$$

$$\Delta G^o_{rxn} = -514.5\, kJ \cdot mol^{-1}$$

In this case, the entropy of reaction is negative, and, as such, the reaction will proceed spontaneously only if some of the heat given off by this exothermic process is used to raise the entropy of the surroundings by a quantity sufficient to satisfy the second law:

$$\Delta S_{univ} = \Delta S^o_{rxn} + \Delta S_{surr} > 0$$

The amount of energy "free" to do work, due to this reaction, is the remaining heat given off after accounting for the heat required to increase the entropy of the surroundings ($T\Delta S^o_{rxn}$).

Section 12.14 Gibbs Free Energy and Nonstandard Conditions

In the previous section we saw that even though the standard free energy of reaction is positive, and the reaction is therefore nonspontaneous, this is only true under standard conditions at a given temperature (298 K). In other words, if we change the conditions of the reaction (such as temperature), the value of ΔG_{rxn} changes as well and may even reverse sign. The equation used to calculate the **free energy of reaction (at nonstandard conditions),** ΔG_{rxn}, from the standard free energy of reaction, ΔG^o_{rxn}, is given as follows:

$$\Delta G_{rxn} = \Delta G^o_{rxn} + RT\ln Q$$

where Q is the reaction quotient which we described in Chapter 10 and R is the gas constant. Recall that:

$$101.3\, J = 1\, atm \cdot L$$

Therefore, in this case we utilize the gas constant in terms of joules instead of atmosphere-liters:

$$R = 0.08206 \frac{atm \cdot L}{mol \cdot K} \times \frac{101.3\, J}{atm \cdot L} = 8.314 \frac{J}{mol \cdot K}$$

The following example problem demonstrates the calculation of the free energy of a reaction under nonstandard conditions.

Example Problem 12.21

Consider the reaction depicted in the following chemical equation at 298 K:

$$H_2(g) + I_2(g) \rightarrow 2\,HI(g) \qquad \Delta G^o_{rxn} = 2.60\,kJ \cdot mol^{-1}$$

If the initial partial pressures of the reactants and products are as listed below, calculate ΔG_{rxn} under these conditions and predict whether the reaction will be expected to proceed spontaneously in the forward direction as written.

$$P_{H_2} = 3.76\,atm$$

$$P_{I_2} = 0.024\,atm$$

$$P_{HI} = 0.573\,atm$$

Solution:	
The problem asks us to calculate the free energy change of this reaction under nonstandard conditions, the equation for which is shown here.	$$\Delta G_{rxn} = \Delta G^o_{rxn} + RT \ln Q$$
Therefore, we will first need to calculate the reaction quotient (since all other variables are given in the problem) (See Chapter 10 for a review.)	$$Q_p = \frac{[0.573]^2}{[0.024][3.76]} = 3.64$$
Next we substitute our calculated value for Q along with the given data into the equation for ΔG_{rxn}.	$$\Delta G_{rxn} = \Delta G^o_{rxn} + RT \ln Q$$ $$\Delta G_{rxn} = (2.60\,kJ \cdot mol^{-1}) + \left(8.314\,\frac{J}{mol \cdot K} \times \frac{1\,kJ}{1000\,J}\right)(298\,K)\ln 3.64$$ $$\Delta G_{rxn} = 5.80\ kJ \cdot mol^{-1}$$

Therefore, because the free energy of reaction is positive, we predict this reaction to be nonspontaneous in the forward direction under the given conditions.

Section 12.15 Gibbs Free Energy and Equilibrium

Recall from Chapter 10 that we defined equilibrium as the point at which the forward and reverse reaction rates are equal. Now we define equilibrium from a thermodynamic point of view. Here we say that **equilibrium** *is the point with the lowest possible free energy available to the reaction (system).* At this point, there is no further driving force for a reaction to proceed in either direction. For this reason, we say $\Delta G = 0$ at equilibrium. With this in mind, let's examine the equation for the free energy of reaction under nonstandard conditions:

$$\Delta G_{rxn} = \Delta G^o_{rxn} + RT \ln Q$$

If we do so, we come to the following general conclusions:

1. When ΔG°_{rxn} is large and positive (at a given temperature), then ΔG_{rxn} will only become negative when $RT\ln Q$ is sufficiently negative to counter the large positive ΔG°_{rxn}. In this case, Q is very small, and little to no product has been formed.

2. When ΔG°_{rxn} is large and negative (at a given temperature), then ΔG_{rxn} will only become positive when $RT\ln Q$ is sufficiently positive to counter a large negative ΔG°_{rxn}. In this case, Q is large and significant product has been formed.

3. When the reaction is at equilibrium, $Q = K$ (the equilibrium constant) and as we have already learned $\Delta G_{rxn} = 0$. Therefore:

$$0 = \Delta G^{\circ}_{rxn} + RT\ln K$$

Thus:

$$\Delta G^{\circ}_{rxn} = -RT\ln K$$

This last point shows that the standard free energy of reaction and the equilibrium constant are directly related (at the same given temperature). Further, this also implies that when $Q < K$, the reaction is spontaneous in the forward direction, and when $Q > K$, the reaction is spontaneous in the reverse direction. We can demonstrate this by the following derivation:

$$\Delta G_{rxn} = \Delta G^{\circ}_{rxn} + RT\ln Q$$

By substitution ($\Delta G^{\circ}_{rxn} = -RT\ln K$):

$$\Delta G_{rxn} = (-RT\ln K) + RT\ln Q$$

Thus:

$$\Delta G_{rxn} = RT\ln Q - RT\ln K$$

If we collect common terms:

$$\Delta G_{rxn} = RT\left(\ln \frac{Q}{K}\right)$$

Therefore, we conclude that, at a given temperature, if $Q > K$ then $\Delta G_{rxn} > 0$, and when $Q < K$ then $\Delta G_{rxn} < 0$. In other words, at any point in time, a chemical reaction at a given temperature (in Kelvins) will spontaneously tend toward equilibrium, just as we learned in Chapter 10.

This is graphically depicted in Figure 12.11. Here we see how the free energy of a system evolves in a chemical reaction as a function of the composition of the reaction mixture. As we have established, a spontaneous process is one which results in a decrease in Gibbs free energy ($\Delta G < 0$). Therefore, at any point on this curve the reaction spontaneously proceeds in the direction with a negative slope ($\Delta G < 0$). In other words, the reaction proceeds from higher free energy to lower. When the free energy reaches a minimum, ΔG is zero. From this point, free energy will increase ($\Delta G > 0$) in either the forward or the reverse direction (toward products or reactants),

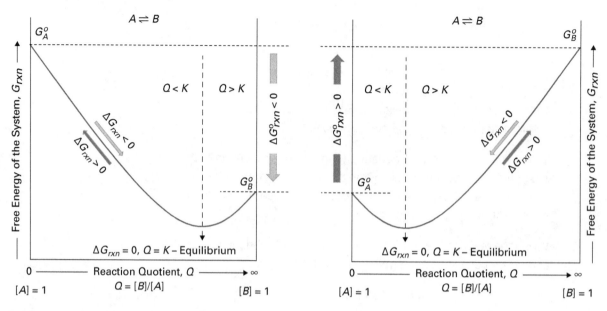

Figure 12.11 Free Energy vs. the Extent of Reaction – for generic reactions $A \rightleftharpoons B$. In each case depicted here the reaction proceeds spontaneously along the free energy (G) curve until the reaction mixture is reached which represents the lowest free energy available to the system. This is the equilibrium mixture, here ΔG is positive in either direction, and, as such, there is no driving force for the concentrations of A or B to change. a.) In a product favored reaction $K > 1$, $G_A^o > G_B^o$ and, therefore, $\Delta G_{rxn}^o < 0$. b.) In a reactant favored reaction, $K < 1$, $G_A^o < G_B^o$ and, therefore, $\Delta G_{rxn}^o > 0$.

indicating there is no driving force for the concentrations of the reactants or products to change. As such, the value for Q where the free energy reaches a minimum represents the equilibrium position of a reaction ($Q = K$). For this reason, free energy is also called the *chemical potential* of a reaction, as all reactions spontaneously proceed toward minimum free energy. For negative values of ΔG_{rxn}^o, the equilibrium lies to the right, $K = [B]/[A] > 1$, and these are *product-favored reactions*. For positive values of ΔG_{rxn}^o, the equilibrium lies to the left, $K = [B]/[A] < 1$, and these are *reactant-favored reactions*.

Example Problem 12.22

If the following reaction takes place at 298 K, calculate its equilibrium constant at that temperature.
$$2\,H_2(g) + O_2(g) \rightleftharpoons 2\,H_2O(g)$$

Solution:	
ΔG_{rxn}^o and the equilibrium constant, K, are related according to the equation shown here.	$$\Delta G_{rxn}^o = -RT \ln K$$
Therefore, we first calculate ΔG_{rxn}^o according to free energy of formation data in Appendix II (Section 12.13).	$$\Delta G_{rxn}^o = \sum (n\Delta G_f^o)_{prod} - \sum (n\Delta G_f^o)_{react}$$ Reactants: $$\Delta G_{f,H_2}^o = 0\,kJ$$ $$\Delta G_{f,O_2}^o = 0\,kJ$$ Products: $$\Delta G_{f,H_2O}^o = -228.6\,kJ$$ $$\Delta G_{rxn}^o = [2(-228.6\,kJ)]_p - [(0\,kJ)+(0\,kJ)]_r$$ $$\Delta G_{rxn}^o = -457.2\,kJ \cdot mol^{-1}$$

Using the equation for ΔG^o_{rxn}, we now isolate K, substitute the values for each variable and calculate the equilibrium constant as shown.	$\Delta G^o_{rxn} = -RT \ln K$ $\ln K = \dfrac{\Delta G^o_{rxn}}{-RT} = -\dfrac{(-457.2\,kJ \cdot mol^{-1})}{\left(8.314\dfrac{J}{mol \cdot K} \times \dfrac{1\,kJ}{1000\,J}\right)(298\,K)}$ $\ln K = 184.54$ $K = e^{184.54} = 1.39 \times 10^{80}$

The Dependence of K on Temperature

We can now use the equation for ΔG^o_{rxn} in terms of the equilibrium constant to derive a quantitative expression for K in terms of temperature.

$$\Delta G^o = -RT \ln K$$

If $\Delta G^o = \Delta H^o - T\Delta S^o$, then:

$$-RT \ln K = \Delta H^o - T\Delta S^o$$

Therefore:

$$\ln K = -\frac{\Delta H^o}{R}\left(\frac{1}{T}\right) + \frac{\Delta S^o}{R}$$

Therefore, a plot of $\ln K$ vs T^{-1} will show a linear behavior with a slope of $-\frac{\Delta H^o}{R}$ and an intercept of $\frac{\Delta S^o}{R}$. This is only an approximation as it relies on the assumption that ΔH^o and ΔS^o are independent of temperature. This is only reasonable over a limited temperature interval. We can re-express in such a way as to be able to determine the equilibrium constant at another temperature when it is known for a given temperature:

$$\ln\frac{K_2}{K_1} = -\frac{\Delta H^o}{R}\left(\frac{1}{T_2} - \frac{1}{T_1}\right)$$

Additionally, this equation can also be used to determine the enthalpy of reaction if the equilibrium constant is known at two different temperatures.

Example Problem 12.23

Consider the following generic equation:	
$A(g) \rightleftharpoons 2B(g)$ $\Delta H^o = 55.00\,kJ \cdot mol^{-1}$	
If a vessel initially contains only A with a partial pressure of $P_A = 0.950$ *atm* and at equilibrium $P_A = 0.368$ *atm*. What is the equilibrium constant at 400 K?	
Solution:	
As we just learned, the equation which relates equilibrium constants at different temperatures is as shown here.	$\ln\dfrac{K_2}{K_1} = -\dfrac{\Delta H^o}{R}\left(\dfrac{1}{T_2} - \dfrac{1}{T_1}\right)$

Next we determine the expression for the initial equilibrium constant, K_1. (See Chapter 10 for a review.)	Concentration $\quad A(g) \quad \rightleftharpoons \quad 2B(g)$ Initial $\qquad$ 0.950 $\qquad$ 0 Change $\qquad$ $-x$ $\qquad$ $+2x$ **Equilibrium** $\qquad$ **0.950 − x** $\qquad$ **2x** $x = 0.950\,atm - 0.368\,atm = 0.582\,atm$ $$K_1 = \frac{[2 \times 0.582]^2}{[0.950 - 0.582]} = 3.68$$
We now rearrange to isolate K_2.	$$\ln\frac{K_2}{K_1} = -\frac{\Delta H^o}{R}\left(\frac{1}{T_2} - \frac{1}{T_1}\right)$$ $$\ln K_2 - \ln K_1 = -\frac{\Delta H^o}{R}\left(\frac{1}{T_2} - \frac{1}{T_1}\right)$$ $$\ln K_2 = \ln K_1 - \frac{\Delta H^o}{R}\left(\frac{1}{T_2} - \frac{1}{T_1}\right)$$
Substituting the values for K_1, ΔH^o, T_1 and T_2, we calculate K_2.	$$\ln K_2 = \ln 3.68 - \frac{\left(55.00\frac{kJ}{mol} \times \frac{1000\,J}{1\,kJ}\right)}{\left(8.314\frac{J}{mol \cdot K}\right)}\left(\frac{1}{(400\,K)} - \frac{1}{(298\,K)}\right)$$ $$\ln K_2 = 6.96$$ $$K_2 = e^{6.96} = 1.058 \times 10^3$$

Key Terms

1. Bomb calorimetry

2. Bond energy

3. Bond strength

4. Born-Haber Cycle

5. Calorie

6. Calorimeter

7. Calorimetry

8. Chemical energy

9. Coffee cup calorimetry

10. Constant-pressure calorimetry

11. Constant-volume calorimetry

12. Endothermic

13. Energy

14. Enthalpy

15. Enthalpy of reaction

16. Enthalpy of solution

17. Entropy

18. Exothermic

19. Extensive property

20. First Law of Thermodynamics

21. Formation reaction

22. Gibbs Free Energy

23. Heat

24. Heat capacity

25. Heat of hydration

26. Heat of reaction

27. Heat of solution

28. Heat of solvation

29. Hess's Law

30. Intensive property

31. Internal energy

32. Joule

33. Kinetic energy

34. Lattice energy

35. Potential energy

36. Pressure-volume work

37. Second Law of Thermodynamics

38. Specific heat capacity

39. Spontaneous

40. Standard conditions

41. Standard enthalpy of formation

42. Standard enthalpy of reaction

43. Standard entropy reaction

44. Standard free energy of formation

45. Standard free energy of reaction

46. Standard heat of formation

47. Standard heat of reaction

48. Standard molar entropy

49. Standard state

50. State function

51. Surroundings

52. System

53. Thermochemical equation

54. Thermochemistry

55. Thermodynamics

56. Thermal equilibrium

57. Third Law of Thermodynamics

58. Work

Problems

THE FIRST LAW OF THERMODYNAMICS AND THE NATURE OF ENERGY

1. Define thermodynamics and thermochemistry.

2. Define the first law of thermodynamics (also known as the law of conservation of energy).

3. Define potential and kinetic energy.

4. A ball with a mass of 2 *kg* is thrown straight up in the air with an initial velocity of 2 *m/s*. At the ball's highest point, what is the kinetic energy of the ball?

5. An object is in motion with a velocity of 3.24 *m/s*. If the object has a mass of 5.31 *kg*, what is its kinetic energy?

6. If a particular system gains energy, the _____ must lose an equal amount of energy (to the system). Likewise if the _____ loses energy, the surroundings must gain an equal amount of energy (from the system).

7. Define internal energy.

8. The internal energy of a system has a net gain/loss of energy if $\Delta E > 0$.

9. The internal energy of a system has a net gain/loss of energy if $\Delta E < 0$.

10. What are the two mechanisms by which energy can be transferred between the system and the surroundings?

11. What is heat? What is the difference between heat and temperature?

12. Is q_{sys} positive or negative if the temperature of the system increases due to an event or process?

13. Is q_{sys} positive or negative if the temperature of the system decreases due to an event or process?

14. If work is done on the system by the surroundings due to an event or process, will the work term be a positive or a negative contribution to the internal energy change?

15. What is a state function?

16. Define chemical energy.

17. If the $E_{react} > E_{prod}$, then the ΔE for the reaction (ΔE_{rxn}) is _____ zero and the reaction _____ to/from the surroundings.

    a. less than/releases energy

    b. greater than/releases energy

    c. less than/absorbs energy

    d. greater than/absorbs energy

18. If the $E_{react} < E_{prod}$, then the ΔE for the reaction (ΔE_{rxn}) is _____ zero and the reaction _____ to/from the surroundings.

    a. less than/releases energy

    b. greater than/releases energy

    c. less than/absorbs energy

    d. greater than/absorbs energy

19. A chemical system produces 155 kJ of heat and does 140.5 kJ of work. What is its internal energy change?

20. A chemical system absorbs 155 kJ of heat and does 140.5 kJ of work. What is its internal energy change?

21. A chemical system produces 155 kJ of heat and has 140.5 kJ of work done on it by the surroundings. What is its internal energy change?

22. A chemical system absorbs 155 kJ of heat and has 140.5 kJ of work done on it by the surroundings. What is its internal energy change?

QUANTIFYING HEAT

23. Define the heat capacity of a substance.

24. Define the specific heat capacity of a substance.

25. Suppose an object is allowed to cool to room temperature (23.2°C). How much heat (in joules) is lost if the object had an initial temperature of 56.5°C? The sample weighs 5.45 g and has a specific heat capacity of 0.790 $\frac{J}{g \cdot {}^\circ C}$.

26. Ethanol is heated to 40.1°C and is allowed to cool to 23.2°C. The sample has a mass of 9.87 g and a specific heat capacity of 2.42 $\frac{J}{g \cdot {}^\circ C}$. How much heat is lost?

27. What is the identity of a substance that weighs 2.81 g if it takes 34.7 J of energy to heat it from 5.00°C to 37.1°C (hint-see Table 12.2).

28. What is the identity of a substance that weighs 15.2 *g* if it takes 86.5 *J* of energy to heat it from 24.8°C to 32.0°C (hint-see Table 12.2).

29. If 49.4 *J* of energy is required to heat a certain volume of liquid bromine from 25.0°C to 28.5°C, what volume (*ml*) of liquid bromine is present? The specific heat capacity and density of liquid bromine are 0.226 $\frac{J}{g \cdot °C}$ and 3.12 *g/ml*, respectively.

30. With a 45.8 *g* sample of water, how much heat is required to heat the water from 22.3°C to 35.8°C?

31. Given that mercury has a specific heat of 0.140 $\frac{J}{g \cdot °C}$, what is the mass of a sample of pure mercury if 550.0 *J* of energy was required to heat the sample from 22.3 °C to 78.5°C?

32. Calculate the specific heat of gold if a 56.8-*g* sample of gold underwent an elevation in temperature of 36.0°C and absorbed 593.0 *J* of energy.

33. If 1.65 *L* of pure water with an initial temperature of 22.00°C is heated and absorbs 219.4 *kJ* of heat, assuming the density of water is 1.00 *g/ml*, what is the final temperature of the water?

34. Suppose a metal sample with an unknown specific heat capacity has a mass of 34.3 *g*. The metal is heated to 72.3°C and then submerged in 100.0 *g* of water (with an initial temperature of 23.2°C) in an insulated container. The transfer of heat between the metal and water causes the temperature of the water to increase to 24.7°C. What is the heat capacity of the metal?

35. Suppose you have a metal sample of unknown mass with a specific heat capacity of 0.329 $\frac{J}{g \cdot °C}$. The metal is heated to 47.4°C and then submerged in 5.00 *g* of water (with an initial temperature of 23.2°C) in an insulated container. The transfer of heat between the metal and water causes the temperature of the water to increase to 28.9°C. What is the mass of the metal?

36. A 35.7 *g* sample of an unknown metal is heated to 123.7°C and is then placed into a coffee cup calorimeter with 100.0 *g* of water at 22.3°C. After the metal has cooled, the temperature of the water changed to 26.04°C.

    a. What released heat?

    b. What absorbed heat?

    c. Calculate the heat absorbed by the solution.

    d. Calculate the specific heat of the iron.

37. A 50.0 *g* sample of an unknown metal is heated to 350.0°C and is then placed into a coffee cup calorimeter with 400.0 *g* of water at 22.3°C. After the metal has cooled, the temperature of the water changed to 30.85°C.

a. What released heat?

b. What absorbed heat?

c. Calculate the specific heat of the metal.

QUANTIFYING WORK

38. What is the type of work done through the expansion or compression of gases?

39. Is work positive or negative when the system expands against an external pressure?

40. Is work positive or negative when the system is compressed by an external pressure?

41. A balloon expands by 0.55 L against an external pressure of 1.05 atm. Calculate the work done by this expansion in joules.

42. If a chemical system absorbs 450 kJ of heat and expands from an initial volume of 0.750 L to a final volume of 1.250 L against an external pressure of 1.10 atm, calculate the internal energy change due to this process.

43. A chemical system is compressed by an external pressure of 1.75 atm from an initial volume of 3.27 L to a final volume of 1.75 L. If the system absorbed 225 J of heat, what is the internal energy change for this process?

ENTHALPY

44. Define enthalpy.

45. Is enthalpy an extensive or intensive property?

46. Define the term exothermic in the context of chemical reactions.

47. Define the term endothermic in the context of chemical reactions.

48. If the ΔH_{rxn} for a thermochemical reaction is less than zero, then is the reaction an endothermic or exothermic process?

49. If the ΔH_{rxn} for a thermochemical reaction is greater than zero, then is the reaction an endothermic or exothermic process?

50. Indicate whether each of the following processes is endothermic or exothermic.

    a. Propane burning in a gas barbeque grill.

    b. Water boiling on a stove top.

    c. Condensation of water vapor from the air onto an ice-cold soda can.

51. Indicate whether each of the following processes is endothermic or exothermic.

    d. Wood burning.

    e. A liquid freezing.

    f. Acetone (nail polish remover) evaporating.

52. If a chemical reaction takes place at constant pressure wherein one mole of a compound is consumed, and the reaction gives off 2,786 kJ of heat and does 17 kJ of work, what are ΔE and ΔH for the reaction?

53. If 1 mole of propane (C_3H_8) undergoes a combustion reaction at a pressure of 1 atm and has an internal energy change of $-2,049$ kJ, how much work is done if the enthalpy of the reaction is $\Delta H = -2,044$ kJ?

54. According to the following reaction, determine the amount of heat (kJ) that will be generated from the complete consumption of the following amounts of each reactant.

$$CH_4(g) + 2O_2(g) \rightarrow CO_2(g) + 2H_2O(l) \quad \Delta H_{rxn} = -882.0\ kJ\ /\ mol$$

a. 17.0 g CH_4 (g)

b. 16.9 g O_2 (g)

55. According to the following reaction, determine the amount of heat (kJ) that will be generated from the production of the following amounts of each product.

$$CH_4(g) + 2O_2(g) \rightarrow CO_2(g) + 2H_2O(l) \quad \Delta H_{rxn} = -882.0\ kJ\ /\ mol$$

a. 46.7 g CO_2 (g)

b. 9.50 g H_2O (l)

56. According to the following reaction, determine the amount of heat (kJ) that will be generated from the complete consumption of the following amounts of each reactant.

$$2C_2H_6(g) + 7O_2(g) \rightarrow 4CO_2(g) + 6H_2O(l) \quad \Delta H_{rxn} = 2,856.6\ kJ\ /\ mol$$

a. 5.00 g C_2H_6 (g)

b. 9.30 g O_2 (g)

57. According to the following reaction, determine the amount of heat (kJ) that will be generated from the production of the following amounts of each product.

$$2C_2H_6(g) + 7O_2(g) \rightarrow 4CO_2(g) + 6H_2O(l) \quad \Delta H_{rxn} = 2,856.6\ kJ\ /\ mol$$

a. 14.6 g CO_2 (g)

b. 9.00 g H_2O (l)

58. What mass of octane (C_8H_{18}) must be burned to generate 2,375 kJ of heat according to the following thermochemical reaction?

$$2C_8H_{18}(l) + 25O_2(g) \rightarrow 16CO_2(g) + 18H_2O(g) \quad \Delta H_{rxn} = -10,148.2\ kJ \cdot mol^{-1}$$

59. Consider the following thermochemical reaction. If this reaction is carried out with 45.00 ml of a 0.475 M HCl (aq) solution, and the resulting reaction produces 3.87 kJ of heat, is HCl the limiting reagent?

$$Mg(s) + 2HCl(aq) \rightarrow MgCl_2(aq) + H_2(g) \quad \Delta H°_{rxn} = -467\ kJ$$

CALORIMETRY

60. Define calorimetry.

61. What is a calorimeter?

62. Suppose 5.0 g of octane is placed in a bomb calorimeter with a known heat capacity of 12.71 kJ°C. The octane is ignited, and the temperature of the calorimeter rises from 22.3°C to 27.8°C. Determine the internal energy change of this combustion reaction.

63. Suppose 1.013 g of naphthalene ($C_{10}H_8$) is placed in a bomb calorimeter with a known heat capacity of 11.67 kJ°C. The naphthalene is ignited, and the temperature of the calorimeter rises from 25.00°C to 28.50°C. Determine the internal energy change of this combustion reaction.

64. 0.1573 g of Zn is delivered to a coffee cup calorimeter containing 50.00 ml of an aqueous solution. Write the balanced thermochemical equation for the reaction which ensues if the temperature of the solution rises from 21.31°C to 23.06°C, assuming the zinc is completely consumed. (Assume the density of the solution is 1.00 g/ml and the specific heat of the solution is that of water 4.184 $\frac{J}{g \cdot °C}$.)

$$Zn(s) + 2HCl(aq) \rightarrow ZnCl_2(aq) + H_2(g) \quad \Delta H_{rxn} = ?$$

HESS'S LAW

65. What is Hess's Law?

66. How does multiplying an equation by a certain factor affect ΔH?

67. How does dividing an equation by a certain factor affect ΔH?

68. How does reversing a reaction equation affect ΔH?

69. Given the following equation:

$$3 O_2(g) \rightarrow 2 O_3(g) \quad \Delta H = +285.4 \ kJ,$$

what is the value of ΔH for the following reaction?

$$\frac{3}{2} O_2(g) \rightarrow O_3(g)$$

70. Given the following equation:

$$2Ag_2S(s) + 2H_2O(l) \rightarrow 4Ag(s) + 2H_2S(g) + O_2(g) \quad \Delta H = +595.5 \ kJ,$$

calculate ΔH for the following reaction.

$$Ag(s) + \frac{1}{2}H_2S(g) + \frac{1}{4}O_2(g) \rightarrow \frac{1}{2}Ag_2S(s) + \frac{1}{2}H_2O(l)$$

71. Given the following reactions and their associated enthalpies:

1. $2 NO(g) + O_2(g) \rightarrow 2 NO_2(g) \quad \Delta H = -116.2 \ kJ$

2. $2NO(g) \rightarrow N_2(g) + O_2(g)$ $\Delta H = -182.6 \text{ kJ}$

calculate the enthalpy of the following reaction.

$$N_2(g) + 2O_2(g) \rightarrow 2NO_2(g)$$

72. Given the following reactions and their associated enthalpies:

1. $2CaCO_3(s) \rightarrow 2Ca(s) + 2CO_2(g) + O_2(g)$ $\Delta H = +1628.2 \text{ kJ}$

2. $2CaO(s) \rightarrow 2Ca(s) + O_2(g)$ $\Delta H = +1269.8 \text{ kJ}$

calculate the enthalpy of the following reaction.

$$CaCO_3(s) \rightarrow CaO(s) + CO_2(g)$$

73. Given the following reactions and their associated enthalpies:

1. $S(s) + O_2(g) \rightarrow SO_2(g)$ $\Delta H = -296.8 \text{ kJ}$

2. $2S(s) + 3O_2(g) \rightarrow 2SO_3(g)$ $\Delta H = -792.0 \text{ kJ}$

calculate the enthalpy of the following reaction.

$$2SO_2(g) + O_2(g) \rightarrow 2SO_3(g)$$

74. Given the following reactions and their associated enthalpies:

1. $2CO(g) + O_2(g) \rightarrow 2CO_2(g)$ $\Delta H = -566.0 \text{ kJ}$

2. $2Fe(s) + O_2(g) \rightarrow 2FeO(s)$ $\Delta H = -544.0 \text{ kJ}$

calculate the enthalpy of the following reaction.

$$FeO(s) + CO(g) \rightarrow Fe(s) + CO_2(g)$$

75. Given the following reactions and their associated enthalpies:

1. $2NO(g) \rightarrow N_2(g) + O_2(g)$ $\Delta H = -182.6 \text{ kJ}$

2. $2H_2(g) + O_2(g) \rightarrow 2H_2O(g)$ $\Delta H = -483.6 \text{ kJ}$

3. $C(s) + O_2(g) \rightarrow CO_2(g)$ $\Delta H = -393.5 \text{ kJ}$

calculate the enthalpy of the following reaction.

$$3N_2(g) + 4H_2(g) + C(s) + 6O_2(g) \rightarrow 6NO(g) + 4H_2O(g) + CO_2(g)$$

STANDARD CONDITIONS AND ENTHALPIES OF FORMATION

76. Define the standard enthalpy of reaction.

77. Define the standard enthalpy of formation.

78. Use standard enthalpies of formation (Appendix II) to calculate ΔH°_{rxn} for each of the following reactions:

a. $CH_4(g) + 2O_2(g) \rightarrow CO_2(g) + 2H_2O(g)$

b. $2CH_3OH(l) + 3O_2(g) \rightarrow 2CO_2(g) + 4H_2O(l)$

79. Calculate the ΔH°_{rxn} for the following reaction using the data presented in Appendix II:

$$C(s) + H_2O(g) \rightarrow CO(g) + H_2(g)$$

80. Calculate the ΔH°_{rxn} for the following reaction using the data presented in Appendix II:

$$N_2(g) + O_2(g) \rightarrow 2NO(g)$$

81. Calculate the ΔH°_{rxn} for the following reaction using the data presented in Appendix II:

$$CaCO_3(s) \rightarrow CaO(s) + CO_2(g)$$

82. Calculate the ΔH°_{rxn} for the following reaction using the data presented in Appendix II:

$$2H_2S(g) + 3O_2(g) \rightarrow 2SO_2(g) + 2H_2O(l)$$

THE ENTHALPY OF BONDING

83. Use bond energies from Table 12.4 to estimate the enthalpy of reaction for the following:

$$H_2(g) + O_2(g) \rightarrow H_2O_2(g)$$

84. Use bond energies from Table 12.4 to estimate the enthalpy of reaction for the following:

$$N_2(g) + 3H_2(g) \rightarrow 2NH_3(g)$$

85. Arrange the following in order of increasing lattice energy:

    a. *MgO*

    b. *CaO*

    c. *RbBr*

    d. *CsBr*

86. Arrange the following in order of increasing lattice energy:

    a. *MgO*

    b. *SrS*

    c. *NaF*

    d. *RbBr*

87. Use the Born-Haber cycle to calculate the lattice energy of *KCl*. The heat of sublimation and the first ionization energy of potassium are 89.1 *kJ/mol* and 418.8 *kJ/mol*, respectively. The standard heat of formation of KCl is -436.7 *kJ/mol*, the bond energy of Cl_2 is 242.6 *kJ/mol* and the electron affinity of Cl is -348.6 *kJ/mol*.

88. Use the Born-Haber cycle and data from Appendix II and Chapter 7 to calculate the lattice energy of MgF_2 ($\Delta H^\circ_f = -1,123.8\ kJ$). The heat of sublimation of magnesium is 147.1 *kJ/mol* and the electron affinity of fluorine is –328.1 *kJ/mol*. The first and second ionization energies of *Mg* are 737.5 *kJ/mol* and 1,451 *kJ/mol*, respectively. Additionally, diatomic fluorine has a bond energy of 159.0 *kJ/mol*.

SPONTANEITY, ENTROPY, AND THE SECOND LAW OF THERMODYNAMICS

89. Indicate the sign of ΔS_{rxn} for each of the following:

    a. $2KCl(s) + 3O_2(g) \rightarrow 2KClO_3(s)$

    b. $CaCO_3(s) \rightarrow CaO(s) + CO_2(g)$

90. Indicate the sign of ΔS_{rxn} for each of the following:

    a. $NH_4Cl(s) \rightarrow HCl(g) + NH_3(g)$

    b. $N_2(g) + 3 H_2(g) \rightarrow 2 NH_3(g)$

91. Calculate ΔS_{surr} for each of the following reactions at 298 K.

    a. $\Delta H^o_{rxn} = -165.7\ kJ$

    b. $\Delta H^o_{rxn} = -14.23\ kJ$

    c. $\Delta H^o_{rxn} = +165.7\ kJ$

    d. $\Delta H^o_{rxn} = +14.23\ kJ$

92. Calculate ΔS_{surr} for each of the following reactions at 100 K.

    a. $\Delta H^o_{rxn} = -165.7\ kJ$

    b. $\Delta H^o_{rxn} = -14.23\ kJ$

    c. $\Delta H^o_{rxn} = +165.7\ kJ$

    d. $\Delta H^o_{rxn} = +14.23\ kJ$

93. Calculate ΔS_{univ} for each of the following reactions and indicate whether the reaction will proceed spontaneously.

    a. $\Delta H^o_{rxn} = +120.0\ kJ; \Delta S^o_{rxn} = -310 J/K; T = 298\ K$

    b. $\Delta H^o_{rxn} = -120.0\ kJ; \Delta S^o_{rxn} = +310 J/K; T = 298\ K$

    c. $\Delta H^o_{rxn} = -120.0\ kJ; \Delta S^o_{rxn} = -310 J/K; T = 100\ K$

    d. $\Delta H^o_{rxn} = -120.0\ kJ; \Delta S^o_{rxn} = -310 J/K; T = 500K$

94. Calculate the ΔS^o_{rxn} for the following reaction using the data presented in Appendix II:

$$C(s) + H_2O(g) \rightarrow CO(g) + H_2(g)$$

95. Calculate the ΔS^o_{rxn} for the following reaction using the data presented in Appendix II:

$$N_2(g) + O_2(g) \rightarrow 2NO(g)$$

96. Calculate the ΔS^o_{rxn} for the following reaction using the data presented in Appendix II:

$$CaCO_3(s) \rightarrow CaO(s) + CO_2(g)$$

97. Calculate the ΔS^o_{rxn} for the following reaction using the data presented in Appendix II:

$$2H_2S(g) + 3O_2(g) \rightarrow 2SO_2(g) + 2H_2O(l)$$

GIBBS FREE ENERGY

98. What is meant by "free" energy?

99. Would you predict whether or not a particular reaction would be spontaneous if you knew that it had a negative ΔH and a positive ΔS?

100. Would you predict whether or not a particular reaction would be spontaneous if you knew that it had a negative ΔH and a negative ΔS?

101. Would you predict whether or not a particular reaction would be spontaneous if you knew that it had a positive ΔH and a positive ΔS?

102. Would you predict whether or not a particular reaction would be spontaneous if you knew that it had a positive ΔH and a negative ΔS?

103. A particular reaction carried out at 298 K has a $\Delta H = -108$ kJ and $\Delta S = +286$ J/K. What is the Gibbs free energy of the reaction? Is the reaction spontaneous? If not, at what temperature would this reaction be spontaneous?

104. A particular reaction has a $\Delta H = -108$ kJ and $\Delta S = -286$ J/K and is carried out at 298 K. What is the Gibbs free energy of the reaction? Is the reaction spontaneous? If not, at what temperature would this reaction be spontaneous?

105. A particular reaction has a $\Delta H = +108$ kJ and $\Delta S = +286$ J/K and is carried out at 298 K. What is the Gibbs free energy of the reaction? Is the reaction spontaneous? If not, at what temperature would this reaction be spontaneous?

106. Calculate the Gibbs free energy for the following reaction at 298 K:

$$C(s) + H_2O(g) \rightarrow CO(g) + H_2(g)$$
$$\Delta H^o_{rxn} = 131.3 \, kJ; \Delta S^o_{rxn} = 133.9 \, J/K$$

107. Calculate the Gibbs free energy for the following reaction at 298 K:

$$N_2(g) + O_2(g) \rightarrow 2NO(g)$$
$$\Delta H^o_{rxn} = 182.6 \, kJ; \Delta S^o_{rxn} = 24.8 \, J/K$$

108. Calculate the Gibbs free energy for the following reaction at 298 K:

$$CaCO_3(s) \rightarrow CaO(s) + CO_2(g)$$
$$\Delta H^o_{rxn} = 179.2 \, kJ; \Delta S^o_{rxn} = 160.2 \, J/K$$

109. Calculate the Gibbs free energy for the following reaction at 298 K:

$$2H_2S(g) + 3O_2(g) \rightarrow 2SO_2(g) + 2H_2O(l)$$
$$\Delta H^o_{rxn} = -1124.0 \, kJ; \Delta S^o_{rxn} = -391.0 \, J/K$$

GIBBS FREE ENERGY AND NONSTANDARD CONDITIONS

110. Consider the reaction depicted in the following chemical equation at 298 K:

$$N_2(g) + O_2(g) \rightarrow 2\,NO(g) \qquad \Delta G^o_{rxn} = 175.2 \, kJ \cdot mol^{-1}$$

   a. Calculate the equilibrium constant for this reaction at 298 K.

   b. If the initial partial pressures of the reactants and products are as listed below, calculate ΔG_{rxn} under these conditions and predict whether the reaction will be expected to proceed spontaneously in the forward direction as written.

$$P_{N_2} = 0.650 \, atm$$

$$P_{O_2} = 0.150 \, atm$$

$$P_{NO} = 0.450 \, atm$$

111. Consider the reaction depicted in the following chemical equation at 298 K:

$$C(s) + H_2O(g) \rightarrow CO(g) + H_2(g) \qquad \Delta G^o_{rxn} = 91.4 \, kJ \cdot mol^{-1}$$

a. Calculate the equilibrium constant for this reaction at 298 *K*.

b. If the initial partial pressures of the reactants and products are as listed below, calculate ΔG_{rxn} under these conditions and predict whether the reaction will be expected to proceed spontaneously in the forward direction as written.

$$P_{H_2O} = 0.250 \, atm$$

$$P_{H_2} = 0.250 \, atm$$

$$P_{CO} = 0.450 \, atm$$

112. Consider the reaction depicted in the following chemical equation at 298 K:

$$Br_2(g) + Cl_2(g) \rightarrow 2 \, BrCl(g) \qquad \Delta G^o_{rxn} = -1.1 \, kJ \cdot mol^{-1}$$

a. Calculate the equilibrium constant for this reaction at 298 K.

b. If the initial partial pressures of the reactants and products are as listed below, calculate ΔG_{rxn} under these conditions and predict whether the reaction will be expected to proceed spontaneously in the forward direction as written.

$$P_{Br_2} = 0.500 \, atm$$

$$P_{Cl_2} = 0.100 \, atm$$

$$P_{BrCl} = 1.00 \, atm$$

113. The enthalpy (ΔH^o_{rxn}) for a reaction is –20.5 *kJ/mol*. If the equilibrium constant of this reaction is 3.2×10^3 at 298 K, what is the equilibrium constant at 400 K?

114. A reaction has an equilibrium constant of 30.2 at 298 K, what is ΔH^o_{rxn} if the equilibrium constant at 800 K is 1455?

Image Credits

Oxidation-Reduction and Electrochemistry

CHAPTER 13

After reading this chapter, you should be able to do the following:

- Explain what is meant by the term oxidation-reduction.

- Explain and assign oxidation numbers to elements under various circumstances.

- Identify redox reactions using oxidation number assignments.

- Identify the oxidizing and reducing agents in redox reactions.

- Balance redox reactions under acidic and basic conditions using the half-reaction method.

- Describe a galvanic cell and its components.

- Describe galvanic cells using cell notation (also called cell diagrams).

- Use standard reduction potentials to identify the cathode and anode in a galvanic cell and calculate the cell potential.

- Use the standard cell potential to calculate equilibrium constants and Gibbs free energy for redox reactions and predict spontaneity.

- Calculate the cell potential of galvanic cells under nonstandard conditions, using the Nernst equation.

- Describe the process of electrolysis and distinguish electrolytic cells from galvanic cells.

- Predict the products in an electrolytic cell and stoichiometrically determine yields.

- Define each of the Key Terms listed at the end of the chapter dealing with these concepts.

Section 13.1 Introduction

So far, we have dealt with a variety of chemical reaction types. In the current chapter, we will be exploring a field of chemistry which is concerned with reactions characterized by *the exchange of electrons*. Such reactions are referred to as **Oxidation-Reduction** reactions, or **Redox** reactions for short. The importance of understanding such reaction types becomes apparent at a fundamental level. For example, consider the following net ionic equation carried out in aqueous solution:

$$Cu(s) + Ag^+(aq) \rightarrow Ag(s) + Cu^{2+}(aq)$$

At first glance, this equation appears to be perfectly balanced. However, as we execute this reaction in a laboratory, we find that there are two moles of Ag^+ consumed for each mole of Cu. This is inconsistent with the stoichiometric coefficients in our balanced equation. Why is this so? The answer is that this is a redox reaction; therefore, we must account for the exchange of electrons to properly depict this reaction. It is easiest to understand this if we look at this reaction as two separate but simultaneous processes. First, we have the copper metal losing electrons to form copper(II) cations as shown here:

$$Cu(s) \rightarrow Cu^{2+}(aq) + 2e^-$$

This is referred to as a **half-reaction** and depicts the *oxidation of copper* in this case. **Oxidation** is defined as the loss of electrons. The second process consists in silver cation gaining electrons to form neutral silver metal:

$$Ag^+(aq) + e^- \rightarrow Ag(s)$$

The gain of electrons is referred to as **reduction**. In this case, we would describe this process as the reduction of silver ion to form silver metal. Upon careful examination of these two reactions, we see that the reduction of 1 mole of silver cations *consumes* 1 mole of electrons while the oxidation of 1 mole of copper *produces* 2 moles of electrons. We can easily conclude, therefore, that twice as many moles of silver cations will be reduced than moles of copper oxidized, and our equation is properly balanced as follows:

$$Cu(s) + 2\ Ag^+(aq) \rightarrow 2\ Ag(s) + Cu^{2+}(aq)$$

Another way of understanding this is that when dealing with redox reactions, we must balance these according to both mass and charge. Notice that our properly balanced equation not only is balanced according to mass (equal numbers of each element on both sides of the arrow) but is also balanced according to charge. In other words, the net charge on both sides of the reaction arrow must be the same (in our current example there is a net charge of 2+ on the reactant and product side of the reaction arrow).

The exchange of electrons in chemical reactions is the basis for a major application of thermodynamics: the field of electrochemistry. **Electrochemistry** is defined as the study of electrical work and its relation to chemical change. Electrochemistry has many important implications for everyday life. Every time you drive your car, use your smartphone, turn on your computer, or just listen to music over the radio, you are relying on electricity produced through chemical means. Such energy is generated by use of **electrochemical cells**, devices that rely on redox reactions to generate electrical current. In this chapter, we will be primarily concerned with redox reactions, electrochemical cells, and electrolytic cells. **Electrolytic**

cells are systems which use electric current to produce chemical changes. To facilitate our exploration of these and many ancillary subjects, we will first introduce the concept of the *oxidation number* (also referred to as the *oxidation state*).

Section 13.2 Oxidation Numbers and Identifying Redox Reactions

In the example we discussed in the introduction section of this chapter, we dealt with a redox reaction involving ionic species. However, with covalent species, redox reactions are less obvious. As such, it is necessary to have a method for keeping track of the "flow" of electrons in such redox reactions. To facilitate this, chemists employ the application of the concept of *oxidation number*, also referred to as *oxidation state*. We define **oxidation numbers** as imaginary charges which are assigned based on a set of rules. These are determined by assigning shared (bonding) electrons in covalent species to the atoms with greatest electronegativity. The rules are summarized below:

General rules (in order of priority):
1. Free elements have an oxidation number of 0.
2. Monatomic ions have an oxidation number equal to their charge.
3. The sum of oxidation numbers in a neutral compound must be 0.
4. The sum of the oxidation numbers of the elements in a polyatomic ion must equal the charge on the ion.

Specific Rules (in order of priority):
1. Group 1A metals have an oxidation number of +1 in all of their compounds.
2. Group 2A metals have an oxidation number of +2 in all of their compounds.
3. Fluorine has an oxidation number of −1 in all of its compounds.
4. Hydrogen has an oxidation number of +1 in its compounds with other nonmetals.
   a. Hydrogen has an oxidation number of −1 in compounds with boron and metals.
5. Oxygen has an oxidation number of −2 in its compounds.
   a. Oxygen has an oxidation number of −1 in peroxides.
6. Group 7A elements (Halogens) have an oxidation number of −1 in their compounds.
7. Group 6A elements have an oxidation number of −2 in their compounds.
8. Group 5A elements have an oxidation number of −3 in their compounds.

The rules outlined here are written in order of priority. In other words, when applying the rules there may be instances when two rules appear to be in conflict, or it may not be obvious which of two rules applies in a particular instance. In such cases, we apply the rule with priority—that is, the rule which is listed first (general rules have priority over specific rules). Example problem 13.1 illustrates how the rules should be applied in determining the oxidation numbers of elements in ions and compounds.

Example Problem 13.1 – Assigning Oxidation Numbers

Assign an oxidation number to the highlighted element in each of the following:

   a. Br_2
   b. H_2SO_4
   c. PO_4^{3-}
   d. $CaCl_2$
   e. Mg^{2+}

Solution:	
a. The first general rule states that free elements have an oxidation number of zero. As such, the O.N. of bromine in Br_2 is zero.	Br_2 **O.N. = 0**; For Bromine
b. Since this is a compound, we apply the third general rule. The third general rule states that the sum of the oxidation numbers in this compound will be zero. The rules state that hydrogen has an O.N. of +1 in combination with nonmetals. Further, we know oxygen always has an O.N. of −2 (except in peroxides or in combination with fluorine). Since we know O.N.s for hydrogen and oxygen, we can solve for that of sulfur, and we find it to be +6.	H_2SO_4 General rule 3: $2(O.N.^H) + O.N.^S + 4(O.N.^O) = 0$ $O.N.^H = +1$ $O.N.^O = -2$ $O.N.^S = x$ Therefore: $2(+1) + x + 4(-2) = 0$ $2 + x - 8 = 0$ $x = +6$ **O.N.^{S} = +6**
c. Since this is a polyatomic ion, we apply the fourth general rule. The fourth general rule states that the sum of the oxidation numbers will equal the charge on the ion, which is −3. The rules also state that oxygen always has an O.N. of −2 (except in peroxides or in combination with fluorine). Therefore we find the O.N. of phosphorus to be +5.	PO_4^{3-} General rule 4: $(O.N.^P) + 4(O.N.^O) = -3$ $O.N.^P = x$ $O.N.^O = -2$ Therefore: $x + 4(-2) = -3$ $x - 8 = -3$ $x = +5$ **O.N.^{P} = +5**

d. The rules tell us that all Group 2A metals have an O.N. of +2 in their compounds. As such, calcium has an O.N. of +2. The third general rule requires, then, that we assign chlorine an O.N. of −1.	$CaCl_2$ General rule 3: $$O.N.^{Ca} + 2\,(O.N.^{Cl}) = 0$$ $O.N.^{Ca} = +2$ $O.N.^{Cl} = -1$ Therefore: $$+2 + 2\,(-1) = 0$$
e. The second general rule states that monatomic ions have an O.N. equal to their charge.	Mg^{2+} $O.N.^{Mg} = +2$

Non-integer (Fractional) Oxidation Numbers

There is one additional point we should make regarding the assignment of oxidation numbers. It is possible to have non-integer oxidation numbers. This should not cause any concern. Non-integer oxidation numbers are used in the same fashion as integer oxidation numbers. For example, consider butane, C_4H_{10}. If we apply the rules as we have just learned, we arrive at an oxidation number of +1 for the hydrogen atoms. However, general rule 3 will require that we assign an oxidation number of −2.5 to the carbon atoms. This is entirely appropriate, even if it is somewhat uncomfortable. Recall the basis for our rules. In the butane molecule, two carbon atoms are bonded to three hydrogen atoms while the remaining two are bonded to only two hydrogen atoms. It is not necessary to require these different carbon atoms (exhibiting different bonding patterns) to have the same oxidation number. We can assign an oxidation number of −2 to the carbons bonded to two hydrogens while assigning an oxidation of −3 to those bonded to three hydrogens. This is attributed to the fact that it is appropriate to distribute shared, bonding electrons equally to the identical atoms involved in a carbon-carbon bond. Nevertheless, on average, the oxidation number of carbon in butane is −2.5, and, for all purposes in this text, we should use these values in the same fashion as we do oxidation numbers which adopt integer values. This last point will be clearer in the next section on identifying redox reactions.

Butane

Oxidation Number = −3

Oxidation Number = −2

Identifying Redox Reactions

Redox reactions are characterized by the transfer of electrons from one element to another. However, it is not always obvious whether this is occurring. In these cases, we can use oxidation numbers to identify redox reactions. Consider the combustion of methane:

$$CH_4(g) + 2\,O_2(g) \rightarrow CO_2(g) + 2\,H_2O(l)$$

If we determine the oxidation number of each element in this reaction equation, we can determine whether redox is occurring. First, we know that according to general rule 1, the oxidation number of O_2 is 0. In methane, we see that hydrogen has an oxidation number of +1 and general rule 3 requires assignment of an oxidation number of –4 to carbon. Respecting the products, carbon has an oxidation number of +4 in CO_2 while oxygen has an oxidation number of –2. Likewise, we see that in water, hydrogen and oxygen have oxidation numbers of +1 and –2, respectively.

Oxidation Number

$$\underset{\text{Oxidation}}{\underset{-4\;\;+1}{CH_4(g)}} + \underset{0}{2\,O_2(g)} \rightarrow \underset{+4\;-2}{CO_2(g)} + \underset{+1\;-2}{2\,H_2O(l)}$$

Oxidation

Reduction

Note that the change in oxidation state of carbon from –4 to +4 must be accounted for by a loss of eight electrons. In other words, when the oxidation number for a given element increases, it has undergone a loss of electrons. As such, we can define **oxidation** as an increase in oxidation number for a given element. Likewise, we identify **reduction** as a decrease in oxidation number of a given element due to a chemical reaction. We can clearly see in our example that the oxidation number of oxygen decreases from 0 to –2. From this assignment, we identify oxygen as being reduced in this reaction. There is no change in the oxidation number of hydrogen. An important point to realize when identifying oxidation and reduction is that each process occurs simultaneously with the other. In other words, in order for an element to be oxidized, another element must be reduced and vice versa. Let's consider another simple reaction, the formation reaction of magnesium chloride.

Oxidation Number

$$\underset{0}{Mg(s)} + \underset{0}{Cl_2(g)} \rightarrow \underset{+2\;\;-1}{MgCl_2(s)}$$

Oxidation

Reduction

We see that magnesium is oxidized (loses electrons) while chlorine is reduced (gains electrons). In a sense, we understand that the magnesium donates the electrons which then reduce the chlorine. In such a case, we would label the reactant containing the element which is oxidized (magnesium) as the

reducing agent (electron donor). Likewise, the reactant which contains the element which is reduced is referred to as the **oxidizing agent** (electron acceptor). Example problems 13.2 and 13.3 provide practice at identifying redox reactions as well as oxidizing and reducing agents.

Example Problem 13.2 – Identifying Redox Reactions

Consider the following reaction. Is this a redox reaction? If so identify the oxidizing and reducing agents.

$$Na_2CO_3(aq) + 2\ HClO_4(aq) \rightarrow CO_2(g) + H_2O(l) + 2\ NaClO_4(aq)$$

Solution:

First we must assign oxidation numbers to all of the elements in each reactant and product. This is accomplished by applying the rules for assigning oxidation numbers.

$$\overset{+1\ +4\ -2}{Na_2CO_3}(aq) + 2\ \overset{+1\ +7\ -2}{HClO_4}(aq) \rightarrow \overset{+4\ -2}{CO_2}(g) + \overset{+1\ -2}{H_2O}(l) + 2\ \overset{+1\ +7\ -2}{NaClO_4}(aq)$$

Because there is no change in the oxidation states of any of the elements due to the reaction, we would say this is not a redox reaction, and, as such, there is no oxidizing or reducing agent.

Example Problem 13.3 – Identifying Redox Reactions

Consider the following reaction. Is this a redox reaction? If so identify the oxidizing and reducing agents.

$$4\ Fe(OH)_2(aq) + 2\ H_2O(l) + O_2(g) \rightarrow 4\ Fe(OH)_3(aq)$$

Solution:

First, we must assign oxidation numbers to all of the elements in each reactant and product. This is accomplished by applying the rules for assigning oxidation numbers.

$$4\ \overset{+2\ -2\ +1}{Fe(OH)_2}(aq) + 2\ \overset{+1\ -2}{H_2O}(l) + \overset{0}{O_2}(g) \rightarrow 4\ \overset{+3\ -2\ +1}{Fe(OH)_3}(aq)$$

We can clearly see that the oxidation number of iron increases due to this reaction from +2 to +3 and also that of oxygen decreases from 0 to −2. As such, we would say the iron is oxidized and the oxygen is reduced.

$$4\ \overset{+2\ \ -2\ +1}{Fe(OH)_2}(aq) + 2\ \overset{+1\ \ -2}{H_2O}(l) + \overset{0}{O_2}(g) \rightarrow 4\ \overset{+3\ \ -2\ +1}{Fe(OH)_3}(aq)$$

Oxidation ——

Reduction ——

Since the oxidizing agent is the reactant which contains the element which is reduced (thereby facilitating the oxidation of another element), we identify oxygen (O_2) as the oxidizing agent. Likewise, the reducing agent is the reactant which contains the element that is oxidized. Therefore the reducing agent is identified as iron(II) hydroxide ($Fe(OH)_2$).

$$\textbf{\textit{Oxidizing Agent}} = O_2$$

$$\textbf{\textit{Reducing Agent}} = Fe(OH)_2$$

Section 13.3 Balancing Redox Reactions: The Half-Reaction Method

When dealing with redox reactions taking place in aqueous solution, it is often difficult to balance such reactions by inspection. For this reason, chemists employ the half-reaction method of balancing redox reactions. In this method, we first separate the reaction into two **half-reactions**, one depicting the oxidation process and the other depicting the reduction process, just as we did in the example offered in the introductory section of this chapter (Section 13.1). We then balance each half-reaction separately according to both mass and charge. Following this, we then sum the two balanced half-reactions back together. The steps involved will differ depending on whether the reaction is taking place under acidic or basic conditions. Example problems 13.4 and 13.5 illustrate the steps involved in balancing redox reactions according to the half-reaction method.

Example Problem 13.4 – Balancing Redox Reactions Using the Half-Reaction Method Under Acidic Conditions

The reaction represented by the following ionic equation takes place under acidic conditions. Use the half-reaction method to write a balanced net ionic equation for this redox process. $$Fe^{2+}(aq) + MnO_4^-(aq) \rightarrow Fe^{3+}(aq) + Mn^{2+}(aq)$$
Solution:
Step 1: To be complete, we should acknowledge that the first step is to recognize the reaction is a redox reaction. We can clearly see the oxidation numbers for iron change due to reaction from +2 to +3. Also, we can see the manganese is reduced from an O.N. of +7 to +2.
Step 2: Separate the reaction into half-reactions representing the oxidation of iron(II) and the reduction of manganese in the permanganate ion: Oxidation half-reaction: $$Fe^{2+}(aq) \rightarrow Fe^{3+}(aq)$$ Reduction half-reaction: $$MnO_4^-(aq) \rightarrow Mn^{2+}(aq)$$
Step 3: Balance the half-reactions according to mass. To accomplish this, we first balance all "non-hydrogen" and "non-oxygen" elements. In this case, these are already balanced. Oxidation half-reaction: $$Fe^{2+}(aq) \rightarrow Fe^{3+}(aq)$$ Reduction half-reaction: $$MnO_4^-(aq) \rightarrow Mn^{2+}(aq)$$

Step 4: Add water to balance the oxygen atoms, and, because we are in acidic conditions, use H^+ cations to balance hydrogen atoms as follows:

Oxidation half-reaction:

$$Fe^{2+}(aq) \rightarrow Fe^{3+}(aq)$$

Reduction half-reaction:

$$8\ H^+(aq) + MnO_4^-(aq) \rightarrow Mn^{2+}(aq) + 4\ H_2O(l)$$

Because the oxidation half-reaction is already balanced according to mass, we need not alter it in this step.

Step 5: Balance the half-reactions according to charge. Add electrons such that the net charge is conserved on both sides of the reaction arrow as shown here:

Oxidation half-reaction:

$$Fe^{2+}(aq) \rightarrow Fe^{3+}(aq) + 1e^-$$

Reduction half-reaction:

$$8\ H^+(aq) + MnO_4^-(aq) + 5e^- \rightarrow Mn^{2+}(aq) + 4\ H_2O(l)$$

In this case, the addition of one electron to the right side of the oxidation half-reaction effectively balances the charge to +2 on both sides of the reaction equation. Likewise, addition of five electrons to the left side of the reduction half-reaction balances the charge to +2 on both sides of the equation.

Step 6: Multiply each equation by an appropriate factor such that there are equal numbers of electrons produced in the oxidation half-reaction as consumed in the reduction half-reaction:

Oxidation half-reaction:

$$5\ Fe^{2+}(aq) \rightarrow 5\ Fe^{3+}(aq) + 5e^-$$

Reduction half-reaction:

$$8\ H^+(aq) + MnO_4^-(aq) + 5e^- \rightarrow Mn^{2+}(aq) + 4\ H_2O(l)$$

In this case, we multiply the oxidation half-reaction by a factor of five.

Step 7: Sum the half-reactions together to generate the balanced net equation and, if necessary, eliminate any species that appear on both sides of the reaction arrow:

$$5\ Fe^{2+}(aq) \rightarrow 5\ Fe^{3+}(aq) + 5e^-$$
$$+ \quad 8\ H^+(aq) + MnO_4^-(aq) + 5e^- \rightarrow Mn^{2+}(aq) + 4\ H_2O(l)$$
$$\overline{8\ H^+(aq) + MnO_4^-(aq) + 5\ Fe^{2+}(aq) \rightarrow 5\ Fe^{3+}(aq) + Mn^{2+}(aq) + 4\ H_2O(l)}$$

Step 8: Double-check that the elements are balanced.

Reactants		Products	
Element	Number	Element	Number
Mn	1	Mn	1
O	4	O	4
H	8	H	8
Fe	5	Fe	5

Also, double-check that the net charge on both sides of the reaction is balanced.

$$8(+1)+1(-1)+5(+2)=+17 \rightarrow 5(+3)+1(+2)=+17$$

Therefore, the balanced net ionic equation for this reaction is:

$$8\,H^+(aq)+MnO_4^-(aq)+5\,Fe^{2+}(aq) \rightarrow 5\,Fe^{3+}(aq)+Mn^{2+}(aq)+4\,H_2O(l)$$

When redox reactions are carried out under basic conditions, the half-reaction procedure for balancing redox reaction equations is the same as under acidic conditions with a single additional step. We simply neutralize any H^+ cations with an appropriate quantity of hydroxide ions (to be added in equal quantity to both sides of the reaction equation).

Example Problem 13.5 – Balancing Redox Reactions Using the Half-Reaction Method Under Basic Conditions

The reaction represented by the following ionic equation takes place under basic conditions. Use the half-reaction method to write a balanced net ionic equation for this redox process.

$$CN^-(aq)+MnO_4^-(aq) \rightarrow MnO_2(aq)+CNO^-(aq)$$

Solution:

Step 1: The first step is to recognize the reaction is a redox reaction. We can clearly see the oxidation numbers change due to reaction for carbon, from +2 to +4. Also, we can see the manganese is reduced from an O.N. of +7 to +4.

$$\overset{+2\ -3}{CN^-}(aq) + \overset{+7\ -2}{MnO_4^-}(aq) \rightarrow \overset{+4\ -2}{MnO_2}(aq) + \overset{+4\ -3\ -2}{CNO^-}(aq)$$

Oxidation

Reduction

Step 2: Separate the reaction into half-reactions representing the oxidation of CN^- and the reduction of manganese in the permanganate ion.

Oxidation half-reaction:

$$CN^-(aq) \rightarrow CNO^-(aq)$$

Reduction half-reaction:

$$MnO_4^-(aq) \rightarrow MnO_2(aq)$$

Step 3: Balance the half-reactions according to mass. To accomplish this we first balance all "non-hydrogen" and "non-oxygen" elements. In this case, these are already balanced.

Oxidation half-reaction:

$$CN^-(aq) \rightarrow CNO^-(aq)$$

Reduction half-reaction:

$$MnO_4^-(aq) \rightarrow MnO_2(aq)$$

Step 4: Even though we are in basic conditions, proceed as we did under acidic conditions. Therefore, add water to balance for oxygen atoms and use H^+ cations to balance hydrogen atoms as follows:

Oxidation half-reaction:

$$CN^-(aq) + H_2O(l) \rightarrow CNO^-(aq) + 2\ H^+(aq)$$

Reduction half-reaction:

$$MnO_4^-(aq) + 4\ H^+(aq) \rightarrow MnO_2(aq) + 2\ H_2O(l)$$

Step 5: Balance the half-reactions according to charge. Add electrons such that the net charge is conserved on both sides of the reaction arrow as shown here:

Oxidation half-reaction:

$$CN^-(aq) + H_2O(l) \rightarrow CNO^-(aq) + 2\ H^+(aq) + 2\ e^-$$

Reduction half-reaction:

$$MnO_4^-(aq) + 4\ H^+(aq) + 3\ e^- \rightarrow MnO_2(aq) + 2\ H_2O(l)$$

Step 6: Multiply each equation by an appropriate factor such that there are equal numbers of electrons produced in the oxidation half-reaction as consumed in the reduction half-reaction:

Oxidation half-reaction:

$$3\ CN^-(aq) + 3\ H_2O(l) \rightarrow 3\ CNO^-(aq) + 6\ H^+(aq) + 6\ e^-$$

Reduction half-reaction:

$$2\ MnO_4^-(aq) + 8\ H^+(aq) + 6\ e^- \rightarrow 2\ MnO_2(aq) + 4\ H_2O(l)$$

In this case, we multiply the oxidation half-reaction by a factor of three and the reduction half-reaction by a factor of two, resulting in the production and consumption of six electrons in these two half-reactions, respectively.

Step 7: Sum the half-reactions together to generate the balanced net equation and, if necessary, eliminate any species that appear on both sides of the equation:

$$3\ CN^-(aq) + 3\ H_2O(l) \rightarrow 3\ CNO^-(aq) + 6H^+(aq) + 6\ e^-$$
$$+\ 2\ MnO_4^-(aq) + 8\ H^+(aq) + 6e^- \rightarrow 2\ MnO_2(aq) + 4\ H_2O(l)$$
$$\overline{2\ MnO_4^-(aq) + 2H^+(aq) + 3\ CN^-(aq) \rightarrow 3\ CNO^-(aq) + 2\ MnO_2(aq) + H_2O(l)}$$

Step 8: Since we are under basic conditions, we will now neutralize all H^+ cations with OH^- anions forming water. Be sure to add the same number of hydroxide anions to both sides of the equation.

$$2\ MnO_4^-(aq) + 2\ H_2O(l) + 3\ CN^-(aq) \rightarrow 3\ CNO^-(aq) + 2\ MnO_2(aq) + H_2O(l) + 2\ OH^-(aq)$$

Eliminate any waters that appear on both sides of the reaction.

$$2\ MnO_4^-(aq) + H_2O(l) + 3\ CN^-(aq) \rightarrow 3\ CNO^-(aq) + 2\ MnO_2(aq) + 2\ OH^-(aq)$$

Step 9: Double-check that the elements are balanced.

Reactants		Products	
Element	Number	Element	Number
Mn	2	Mn	2
O	9	O	9
H	2	H	2
C	3	C	3
N	3	N	3

Also, double-check that the net charge on both sides of the reaction is balanced.

$$2(-1) + 3(-1) = -5 \quad \rightarrow \quad 3(-1) + 2(-1) = -5$$

Therefore the balanced net ionic equation for this reaction is:

$$2\ MnO_4^-(aq) + H_2O(l) + 3\ CN^-(aq) \rightarrow 3\ CNO^-(aq) + 2\ MnO_2(aq) + 2\ OH^-(aq)$$

Section 13.4 Galvanic (Voltaic) Cells

There are two types of electrochemical cells. These are galvanic cells and electrolytic cells. The principal difference between these two types of cells rests on whether the redox reaction upon which a cell is based is spontaneous or not. Recall from Chapter 12 that a reaction with a negative ΔG value is spontaneous, and those with a positive ΔG value are not spontaneous. **Galvanic cells** (also referred to as **voltaic cells**) are devices which use spontaneous redox reactions to generate an electric current which is then used to do work. **Electrolytic cells** are devices which use an external electric current to drive redox reactions which are not spontaneous. These will be the subject of later sections of this chapter. We will concern ourselves currently with galvanic cells.

Let's consider a common example of a redox reaction. Suppose we placed a solid piece of zinc metal into a beaker that contained a blue solution of copper(II) sulfate. In such a scenario, we would observe the blue color of the solution fade as the zinc metal would reduce the Cu^{2+} to copper metal.

Likewise, the zinc would be simultaneously oxidized to form Zn^{2+} according to the following net ionic equation.

$$Cu^{2+}(aq) + Zn(s) \rightarrow Zn^{2+}(aq) + Cu(s)$$

In this case, there is clearly a transfer of electrons from the zinc metal to the copper(II) cation. However, the electrons are transferred directly from the reducing agent to the oxidizing agent in solution. In order to take advantage of this reaction, we need to physically separate the two half-reactions and allow the electrons to transfer through some conductive material such as wire. With this in mind, let's imagine we place a solution of zinc sulfate in a beaker and a solution of copper(II) sulfate in another separate beaker. In the first beaker, we also place a strip of zinc metal which is connected by a wire to a strip of copper metal which is then submerged in the copper(II) sulfate solution in the second beaker. We would expect then that it is now possible for these two half-reactions to occur in separate containers, and the electrons would travel through the wire from the oxidation half-reaction to the reduction half-reaction as shown in Figure 13.1.

This is an example of galvanic (voltaic) cell. The two metal strips act as electrodes. **Electrodes** are conductive materials which facilitate the flow of electrons to and from each of the half-cells. **Half-cells** are the two separate compartments of the galvanic cell, one containing the oxidation half-reaction and the other containing the reduction half-reaction. In this case, each electrode is participating in the following half-reactions:

$$Zn^{2+}(aq) + 2\ e^- \rightleftharpoons Zn(s)$$

$$Cu^{2+} + 2\ e^- \rightleftharpoons Cu(s)$$

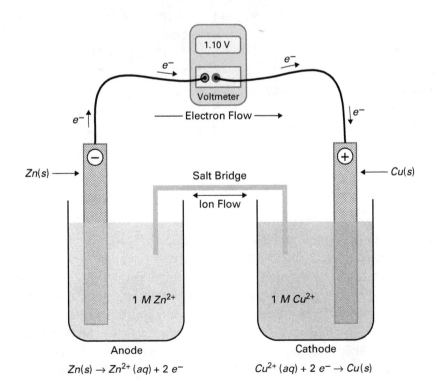

Figure 13.1 A Galvanic (Voltaic) Cell. The greater tendency to reduction exhibited by zinc relative to copper results in an electron flow from the zinc half-cell to the copper half-cell. The flow of ions across the salt bridge counters the charge buildup due to electron flow and allows the reaction to proceed.

Notice each of these is written as a reduction reaction. Depending on which of these equilibria lies more to the right, the flow of electrons will be determined. In other words, because the reduction of copper(II) lies farther to the right than does the reduction of zinc cations, reduction will preferentially occur in the copper(II) half-cell, and oxidation will occur in the zinc sulfate half-cell. As a result, the zinc electrode will be the source of electrons which will flow toward the copper electrode. This means the zinc electrode is negatively charged (relative to the copper electrode), and we refer to this as the anode. The **anode** is the electrode where oxidation occurs in all electrochemical cells. Likewise, the more positive electrode is the cathode. The **cathode** is the electrode where reduction occurs in all electrochemical cells. In order to avoid the buildup of positive charge at the anode and negative charge at the cathode due to electron flow, we also include a **salt bridge** which allows the free flow of counter-ions between the two half-cells. In the absence of a salt bridge there would be a buildup of opposite charges in the half-cells which would halt the reaction almost instantaneously. A salt bridge typically contains an electrolyte in solution and held between two permeable plugs or discs which allow free flow of counter ions between each half-cell while maintaining their separation.

Having described the components of a generic galvanic cell, it is instructive at this point to define some units of measure. First, recall that we measure electric charge in units of coulombs (C). For example, the charge on an electron is -1.602×10^{-19} C. As such, we measure electric current through a medium in units of charge per unit time. The commonly used unit of current is the **ampere** (*amp*), which is defined as 1 C/s.

$$1\ amp = 1\ \frac{C}{s}$$

The driving force which is responsible for the flow of electrons through a wire is similar to that responsible for water flowing downhill. It is a function of a difference in potential energy. Just as water flows from higher potential energy to lower potential energy within the gravitational field of the planet, so do electrons flow from higher to lower potential energy within the electric field set up by the different charges on the electrodes in an electrochemical cell. We measure the potential energy difference in units of joules per unit charge and define a **volt** as the following:

$$1\ volt\ (V) = 1\frac{J}{C}$$

The volt takes its name from Alessandro Volta, an eighteenth-century chemist who is credited with the invention of the battery. A potential difference of 1 volt means that for a charge of 1 coulomb, there is an energy difference of 1 joule between the two electrodes. Therefore, the greater the potential difference (potential for short) between two electrodes, the greater the tendency for electron flow to occur. This is also referred to as the **electromotive force (emf)**. When referring to the potential between two electrodes in an electrochemical cell, we refer to this specifically as the **cell potential** and

Alessandro Volta (1745–1827) was an Italian chemist who is widely credited with the invention of the battery. Owing to this the unit used in the measurement of electric potential energy bears his name (the Volt).

give it the symbol E_{cell}. Additionally, there is a standard cell notation (also referred to as a cell diagram) which is used as a shorthand in describing a galvanic cell. The notation defines oxidation (anode) on the left and reduction (cathode) on the right. The following is the cell diagram describing our current example cell:

$$Zn(s)\big|Zn^{2+}(aq)\big\|Cu^{2+}(aq)\big|Cu(s)$$

Note the two half-cells are separated by a double line while the single lines represent the boundary between the electrodes in the solid phase and the ions in aqueous solution.

Section 13.5 Standard Electrode Potentials

As we have just learned, the force which drives the electric current in a galvanic cell is the potential difference which exists between the anode and the cathode, or rather, the oxidation and reduction half-cells. In this context, we can imagine that each half-reaction has its own **standard reduction potential** (also called a **standard electrode potential**). Further, we can relate these two standard potentials to the cell potential as follows:

$$E^o_{cell} = E^o_{cathode} - E^o_{anode}$$

Here the superscript "o" denotes that these are measured under standard conditions. We understand, therefore, that standard electrode potentials are those which are determined for half-cells in which all solutes are at a concentration of 1 M and all gases are at a pressure of 1 atm at a temperature of 25°C. *Also, when performing this calculation, it is important to remember that the standard reduction potentials are intensive properties of the half-reactions and should never be multiplied by any factor, regardless of the coefficients in the balanced chemical equation.* Nevertheless, even as we carefully define standard reduction potentials and the conditions under which they are determined, we cannot measure such potentials directly. We can only measure the overall potential difference due to the "whole" redox reaction on which an electrochemical cell is based. Therefore, we must define a zero point, a reference half-reaction for which we define the standard reduction potential to be zero and against which all other standard reduction potentials can be measured. The half-cell electrode chosen for this role is the **standard hydrogen electrode** (**SHE**). The standard hydrogen electrode is characterized by an inert metal electrode (platinum) submerged in a 1 M HCl solution, bathed in hydrogen gas at a pressure of 1 atm (hydrogen gas is bubbled over the electrode) (Figure 13.2). When employed in a galvanic cell, the SHE is described by the following balanced half-reaction:

$$2H^+(aq)+2e^- \rightarrow H_2(g) \qquad E^o_{cathode}=0.00\ V$$

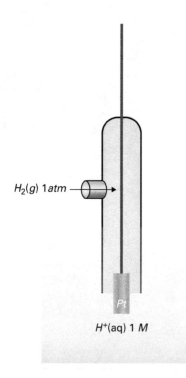

$H_2(g)$ 1atm

Pt

$H^+(aq)$ 1 M

Figure 13.2 The Standard Hydrogen Electrode (SHE). The standard hydrogen electrode is chosen as the standard reference against which all other reduction potentials are measured. It consists of an inert platinum electrode, submerged in a 1 M HCl solution and bathed in H_2 gas at a pressure of 1 atm.

Notice that the electrode in the SHE is platinum. This is an example of an **inert electrode**. *Inert electrodes* are used when a half-cell consists of a half-reaction wherein all species are in either the aqueous or the gaseous state (as is the case in the SHE). Platinum and graphite are commonly used examples of inert electrodes.

To better understand how we might use the SHE as a reference in the determination of standard reduction potentials, let's consider an example. Suppose we connect a SHE to a copper electrode and submerge the copper electrode into a 1 M solution of copper(II) sulfate (Figure 13.3) with a salt bridge placed between the two half-cells. A couple of things are observed experimentally. First, we notice that the mass of the copper electrode increases due to operation of the cell. This is a result of additional copper metal accumulating onto the electrode and therefore must be a product in this reaction. In other words, reduction is occurring at the copper(II) half-cell, which means that the copper electrode is the cathode. Additionally, we experimentally determine the cell potential using a voltmeter that gives a reading of 0.34 V.

The half-cell reactions are:

Oxidation (anode): $\qquad H_2(g) \rightarrow 2\,H^+(aq) + 2\,e^-$

Reduction (cathode): $\qquad Cu^{2+}(aq) + 2\,e^- \rightarrow Cu(s)$

The overall cell reaction is the sum of these two, with electrons consumed and produced at the cathode and anode (respectively), properly balanced as follows:

$$H_2(g) + Cu^{2+}(aq) \rightarrow 2\,H^+(aq) + Cu(s)$$

Further, since the cell potential (0.34 V) is the difference between the standard reduction potentials of the two half-cells, we now determine the standard reduction potential of copper(II) half-cell:

$$E^o_{cell} = E^o_{cathode} - E^o_{anode} = E^0_{Cu^{2+}/Cu} - E^o_{H^+/H_2} = 0.34\ V$$

Since we have defined the standard reduction potential of the SHE as zero, we have:

$$E^0_{Cu^{2+}/Cu} = 0.34\ V - E^o_{H^+/H_2} = 0.34\ V - 0.00\ V = 0.34\ V$$

Therefore, the standard reduction potential of the Cu^{2+}/Cu half-reaction is 0.34 V. Additionally, it is in this fashion that the standard reduction potential can be empirically determined for any half-reaction in question. Table 13.1 lists some selected standard reduction potentials for common half-reactions. A more comprehensive list is given in Appendix IV of this text.

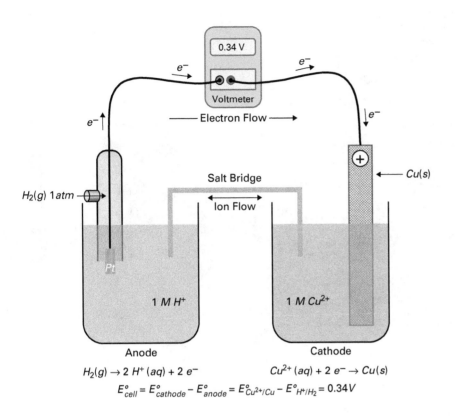

Figure 13.3 The Standard Hydrogen Electrode (SHE) is arbitrarily assigned a reduction potential of zero. As such, an empirically determined cell potential of 0.34 V gives the standard electrode potential of the cathode in this case.

Calculating the Standard Cell Potential from Standard Reduction Potentials

Let's return to our previous example of the copper-zinc electrochemical cell depicted in Figure 13.1. Suppose we wish to know the expected cell potential for an electrochemical cell composed of these two half-cells. We can calculate this quantity and identify the anode and cathode simply by examination of the standard reduction potentials of the two half-reactions in question (as listed in Table 13.1).

$$Cu^{2+} + 2e^- \rightleftharpoons Cu(s) \qquad E^o_{Cu^{2+}/Cu} = 0.34 \ V$$

$$Zn^{2+}(aq) + 2e^- \rightleftharpoons Zn(s) \qquad E^o_{Zn^{2+}/Zn} = -0.76 \ V$$

However, when we examine Table 13.1, we see that all half-reactions are listed as reductions. Even so, we know that in any oxidation-reduction reaction, one of these half-reactions must be reversed and undergo oxidation instead. Therefore, the first question to ask is which of these half-reactions will be more likely to proceed in the reverse direction and undergo oxidation rather than reduction. We can correctly identify this in any pair of half-reactions by understanding that the greater the value of the standard reduction potential, the more likely the half-reaction will proceed as written. In other words, copper(II) is more likely to undergo reduction (more likely to proceed in the forward direction, as written in Table 13.1) because it has a higher standard reduction potential ($E^o_{Cu^{2+}/Cu} > E^o_{Zn^{2+}/Zn}$). Therefore, the zinc half-reaction is more likely to proceed in the reverse direction. Note also, that Table 13.1

Table 13.1 Selected Standard Reduction Potentials

Reduction Half-Reaction	$E°(V)$
$F_2(g) + 2\,e^- \rightarrow 2\,F^-(aq)$	2.87
$H_2O_2(l) + 2\,H^+(aq) + 2\,e^- \rightarrow 2\,H_2O(l)$	1.76
$MnO_4^-(aq) + 4\,H^+(aq) + 3e^- \rightarrow MnO_2(s) + 2\,H_2O(l)$	1.67
$Au^{3+}(aq) + 3e^- \rightarrow Au(aq)$	1.52
$MnO_4^-(aq) + 8\,H^+(aq) + 5\,e^- \rightarrow Mn^{2+}(aq) + 4\,H_2O(l)$	1.51
$PbO_2(s) + 4\,H^+(aq) + 2\,e^- \rightarrow Pb^{2+}(aq) + 2\,H_2O(l)$	1.46
$Cl_2(g) + 2\,e^- \rightarrow 2\,Cl^-(aq)$	1.36
$Cr_2O_7^{2-}(aq) + 14\,H^+(aq) + 6\,e^- \rightarrow 2\,Cr^{3+}(aq) + 7\,H_2O(l)$	1.23
$O_2(g) + 4\,H^+(aq) + 4\,e^- \rightarrow 2\,H_2O(l)$	1.23
$MnO_2(s) + 4\,H^+(aq) + 2e^- \rightarrow Mn^{2+}(aq) + 2\,H_2O(l)$	1.22
$Br_2(aq) + 2\,e^- \rightarrow 2\,Br^-(aq)$	1.09
$NO_3^-(aq) + 4H^+(aq) + 3\,e^- \rightarrow NO(g) + 2\,H_2O(l)$	0.96
$ClO^-(aq) + H_2O(l) + 2\,e^- \rightarrow Cl^-(aq) + 2\,OH^-(aq)$	0.81
$Ag^+(aq) + e^- \rightarrow Ag(s)$	0.80
$Fe^{3+}(aq) + e^- \rightarrow Fe^{2+}(aq)$	0.77
$O_2(g) + 2\,H^+(aq) + 2\,e^- \rightarrow H_2O_2(aq)$	0.70
$MnO_4^-(aq) + 2\,H_2O(l) + 3\,e^- \rightarrow MnO_2(s) + 4\,OH^-(aq)$	0.60
$Cu^+(aq) + e^- \rightarrow Cu(s)$	0.52
$O_2(g) + 2\,H_2O(l) + 4\,e^- \rightarrow 4\,OH^-(aq)$	0.40
$Cu^{2+}(aq) + 2\,e^- \rightarrow Cu(s)$	0.34
$Cu^{2+}(aq) + e^- \rightarrow Cu^+(aq)$	0.15
$2\,H^+(aq) + 2\,e^- \rightarrow H_2(g)$	0.00
$Fe^{3+}(aq) + 3\,e^- \rightarrow Fe(s)$	−0.036
$Pb^{2+}(aq) + 2\,e^- \rightarrow Pb(s)$	−0.13
$Sn^{2+}(aq) + 2\,e^- \rightarrow Sn(s)$	−0.14
$N_2(g) + 5\,H^+(aq) + 4\,e^- \rightarrow N_2H_5^+(aq)$	−0.23
$Ni^{2+}(aq) + 2\,e^- \rightarrow Ni(s)$	−0.26
$Cd^{2+}(aq) + 2\,e^- \rightarrow Cd(s)$	−0.40
$Fe^{2+}(aq) + 2\,e^- \rightarrow Fe(s)$	−0.45
$Cr^{3+}(aq) + 3\,e^- \rightarrow Cr(s)$	−0.74
$Zn^{2+}(aq) + 2\,e^- \rightarrow Zn(s)$	−0.76
$2\,H_2O(l) + 2\,e^- \rightarrow H_2(g) + 2\,OH^-(aq)$	−0.83
$Mn^{2+}(aq) + 2\,e^- \rightarrow Mn(s)$	−1.19
$Al^{3+}(aq) + 3\,e^- \rightarrow Al(s)$	−1.66
$Mg^{2+}(aq) + 2\,e^- \rightarrow Mg(s)$	−2.37
$Na^+(aq) + e^- \rightarrow Na(s)$	−2.71
$Ca^{2+}(aq) + 2\,e^- \rightarrow Ca(s)$	−2.87
$Ba^{2+}(aq) + 2\,e^- \rightarrow Ba(s)$	−2.91
$K^+(aq) + e^- \rightarrow K(s)$	−2.93
$Li^+(aq) + e^- \rightarrow Li(s)$	−3.04

Oxidizing Strength

Reducing Strength

is arranged in order of decreasing standard reduction potential; therefore, whichever one of any two half reactions is lower down the list in Table 13.1, that is the half-reaction which should be reversed. In our current example, we find that zinc's lower reduction potential requires that it be oxidized (reversed) when paired with the Cu^{2+}/Cu half-cell. As such, we now write the overall cell reaction equation as the sum of oxidation and reduction as shown here:

Oxidation (anode): $\qquad Zn(s) \rightarrow Zn^{2+}(aq) + 2e^{-}$

Reduction (cathode): $\qquad Cu^{2+}(aq) + 2e^{-} \rightarrow Cu(s)$

Overall: $\qquad Cu^{2+}(aq) + Zn(s) \rightarrow Zn^{2+}(aq) + Cu(s)$

Having established the identity of the anode and cathode half-cells, we can now easily determine the cell potential as follows:

$$E^{o}_{cell} = E^{o}_{cathode} - E^{o}_{anode} = E^{o}_{Cu^{2+}/Cu} - E^{o}_{Zn^{2+}/Zn}$$

Therefore:

$$E^{o}_{cell} = 0.34 \ V - (-0.76 \ V) = 1.10V$$

Spontaneous Redox (Cell) Reactions

What we have just learned is that when two half-cells are brought together, the overall reaction will naturally (spontaneously) favor the reduction in the half-cell with the higher reduction potential. In other words, *the half-cell with the most positive reduction potential will spontaneously undergo reduction and act as the cathode in a galvanic cell. Because of this, all spontaneous redox reactions will naturally exhibit positive cell potentials ($E^{o}_{cell} > 0$).* This is an important concept in understanding the distinction between galvanic cells and electrolytic cells. We will discuss spontaneity and the relationship between ΔG, K, and E^{o}_{cell} in the next section, but first, let's practice this concept in a couple of example problems.

Example Problem 13.6 – Calculating Standard Potentials of Electrochemical Cells

Use the standard electrode potentials in Table 13.1 to calculate the standard cell potential for a galvanic cell based on the reaction described by the following balanced equation at 25°C.

$$MnO_2(s) + 2 \ Ag(s) + 4 \ H^{+}(aq) \rightleftharpoons Mn^{2+}(aq) + 2Ag^{+}(aq) + 2 \ H_2O(l)$$

Solution:

Step 1: Identify the oxidation and reduction half-reactions. We first identify that silver is oxidized and manganese is reduced. As such:

Oxidation half-reaction (**anode**):

$2 \ Ag(s) \rightarrow 2 \ Ag^{+}(aq) + 2 \ e^{-}$

Reduction half-reaction (**cathode**):

$MnO_2(s) + 4 \ H^{+} + 2 \ e^{-} \rightarrow Mn^{2+}(aq) + 2 \ H_2O(l)$

Step 2: Look up the standard reduction potentials for each half-reaction (Table 13.1):

Oxidation half-reaction (**anode**): $E^o_{anode} = 0.80\ V$

$$2\ Ag(s) \rightarrow 2\ Ag^+(aq) + 2\ e^-$$

Reduction half-reaction (**cathode**): $E^o_{cathode} = 1.22\ V$

$$MnO_2(s) + 4\ H^+ + 2\ e^- \rightarrow Mn^{2+}(aq) + 2\ H_2O(l)$$

Step 3: Calculate the cell potential by taking the difference between the standard reduction potentials of the cathode and anode:

$$E^o_{cell} = E^o_{cathode} - E^o_{anode} = (1.22\ V) - (0.80\ V) = \mathbf{0.42\ V}$$

Therefore, the following represents the balanced cell reaction equation complete with the resulting standard cell potential, E^o_{cell}:

$$MnO_2(s) + 2\ Ag(s) + 4\ H^+(aq) \rightleftharpoons Mn^{2+}(aq) + 2Ag^+(aq) + 2\ H_2O(l) \qquad \mathbf{E^o_{cell} = 0.42\ V}$$

Example Problem 13.7 – Calculating Standard Potentials of Electrochemical Cells

Use the standard electrode potentials in Table 13.1 to calculate the standard cell potential for a galvanic cell based on the reaction described by the following unbalanced equation at 25°C. Assume acidic conditions and that all solutes are 1 M, and all partial pressures are 1 atm.

$$Cr^{3+}(aq) + Cl_2(g) \rightleftharpoons Cr_2O_7^{2-}(aq) + Cl^-(aq)$$

Solution:

Step 1: Identify the oxidation and reduction half-reactions. We first identify that chromium is oxidized and chlorine is reduced. As such:

Oxidation half-reaction:

$$Cr^{3+}(aq) \rightarrow Cr_2O_7^{2-}(aq)$$

Reduction half-reaction:

$$Cl_2(g) \rightarrow Cl^-(aq)$$

Step 2: Next, we balance all "non-hydrogen" and "non-oxygen" elements:

Oxidation half-reaction:

$$2\ Cr^{3+}(aq) \rightarrow Cr_2O_7^{2-}(aq)$$

Reduction half-reaction:

$$Cl_2(g) \rightarrow 2\ Cl^-(aq)$$

Step 3: Balance all oxygen and hydrogen atoms under acidic conditions as described in the previous section:

Oxidation half-reaction:

$$2\ Cr^{3+}(aq)+7H_2O(l)\rightarrow Cr_2O_7^{2-}(aq)+14\ H^+(aq)$$

Reduction half-reaction:

$$Cl_2(g)\rightarrow 2\ Cl^-(aq)$$

Step 5: Balance the half-reactions according to charge. Add electrons that the net charge is conserved on both sides of the reaction arrow as shown here. Additionally, we can look up the standard **reduction** potentials for these two half-reactions:

Oxidation half-reaction (**Anode**):
$$2\ Cr^{3+}(aq)+7H_2O(l)\rightarrow Cr_2O_7^{2-}(aq)+14\ H^+(aq)+6\ e^- \qquad E^o=1.23\ V$$

Reduction half-reaction (**Cathode**):
$$Cl_2(g)+2\ e^-\rightarrow 2\ Cl^-(aq) \qquad\qquad E^o=1.36\ V$$

Step 6: Multiply both half-reactions by the appropriate multiple and sum them to arrive at the balanced cell reaction (as we learned in the previous section).

$$2\ Cr^{3+}(aq)+7H_2O(l)+3\ Cl_2(g)\rightarrow Cr_2O_7^{2-}(aq)+14\ H^+(aq)+6\ Cl^-(aq)$$

Additionally, we find the difference in the standard reduction potentials of the two half-reactions (remembering the standard reduction potential is an intensive property, requiring no multiplication).

$$E^o_{cell}=E^o_{cathode}-E^o_{anode}=1.36\ V-1.23\ V=\textbf{0.13}\ \textbf{V}$$

Therefore, the following represents the balanced cell reaction equation complete with the resulting standard cell potential, E^o_{cell}.

$$2\ Cr^{3+}(aq)+7H_2O(l)+3\ Cl_2(g)\rightarrow Cr_2O_7^{2-}(aq)+14\ H^+(aq)+6\ Cl^-(aq)\quad \boldsymbol{E^o_{cell}=0.13\ V}$$

Example Problem 13.8 – Writing Spontaneous Redox Reactions

Combine the following half-reactions into the balanced equation for a spontaneous redox reaction and calculate E^o_{cell}.

$$NO_3^-(aq)+4\ H^+(aq)+3\ e^-\rightarrow NO(g)+2\ H_2O(l) \qquad E^o=0.96\ V$$
$$N_2(g)+5\ H^+(aq)+4\ e^-\rightarrow N_2H_5^+(aq) \qquad\qquad E^o=-0.23\ V$$

Solution:

Step 1: In order to arrive at the balanced equation, we identify which half-reaction will serve as the anode (oxidation). Because the half-reactions are written as reductions, the reducing agents are written as reactants, and oxidizing agents are written as products in all cases. As such, we reverse the half-reaction that has the lowest (least positive, most negative) reduction potential. This will represent the oxidation process in this reaction:

Oxidation half-reaction:

$$N_2H_5^+(aq) \rightarrow N_2(g) + 5\ H^+(aq) + 4\ e^-$$

Reduction half-reaction:

$$NO_3^-(aq) + 4\ H^+(aq) + 3\ e^- \rightarrow NO(g) + 2\ H_2O(l)$$

Step 2: In order to balance the electrons consumed (reduction) with the number produced (oxidation), we multiply the oxidation half-reaction by 3 and the reduction half-reaction by 4:

Oxidation half-reaction:

$$3\ N_2H_5^+(aq) \rightarrow 3\ N_2(g) + 15\ H^+(aq) + 12\ e^-$$

Reduction half-reaction:

$$4\ NO_3^-(aq) + 16\ H^+(aq) + 12\ e^- \rightarrow 4\ NO(g) + 8\ H_2O(l)$$

Step 3: We now sum the two half-reactions to arrive at the balanced cell reaction equation:

$$3\ N_2H_5^+(aq) \rightarrow 3\ N_2(g) + 15\ H^+(aq) + 12\ e^-$$
$$4\ NO_3^-(aq) + 16\ H^+(aq) + 12\ e^- \rightarrow 4\ NO(g) + 8\ H_2O(l)$$
$$\overline{4\ NO_3^-(aq) + 3\ N_2H_5^+(aq) + H^+(aq) \rightarrow 3\ N_2(g) + 4\ NO(g) + 8\ H_2O(l)}$$

Additionally, we find the difference in the standard reduction potentials of the two half-reactions (remembering the standard reduction potential is an intensive property, requiring no multiplication).

$$E^o_{cell} = E^o_{cathode} - E^o_{anode} = 0.96\ V - (-0.23\ V) = \mathbf{1.19\ V}$$

Therefore,

$$4\ NO_3^-(aq) + 3\ N_2H_5^+(aq) + H^+(aq) \rightarrow 3\ N_2(g) + 4\ NO(g) + 8\ H_2O(l) \qquad E^o_{cell} = \mathbf{1.19\ V}$$

$E^o_{cell} > 0\ V,$ therefore, the reaction is spontaneous under standard conditions.

Section 13.6 Gibbs Free Energy, Equilibrium, and Cell Potential

We now turn our attention to the relationship between E^o_{cell} and thermodynamic quantities. To begin this discussion, we should understand that what an electrochemical cell essentially does is facilitate the interconversion of chemical and electrical energy. In order to quantify this, it is instructive to define a few concepts and equations. First, electrical energy in a cell is the product of the cell potential, E^o_{cell}, which dictates the total charge that passes through the cell. Recall that we measure charge in **coulombs** and potential in **volts**, which is defined as joules per coulomb (J/C). As such:

$$Elect.\ Energy\ (J) = E^o_{cell} \left(\frac{J}{C} \right) \times total\ charge\ (C)$$

We already have learned how to determine E^o_{cell}. However, we now need a method to determine the total charge. This is done by determining the total number of moles of electrons which pass through the cell.

$$total\ charge\ (C) = nF = n \left(96,486\ \frac{C}{mol} \right)$$

where F is the **Faraday constant**, which is essentially the total charge of 1 mole of electrons. The Faraday constant takes its name from the nineteenth-century English scientist Michael Faraday, who is credited with many accomplishments related to electrochemistry, among which was the discovery of electrolysis. Therefore, we can calculate the electrical energy of an electrochemical cell as follows:

$$Elect.\ Energy = nFE^o_{cell}$$

Recall from Chapter 12 that we defined the free energy of a reaction (ΔG) as the energy available to do work. Since the E^o_{cell} sets the upper limit on the amount of electrical energy generated by an electrochemical cell, it therefore defines the maximum available electrical energy to do work. As such:

$$\Delta G^o = w = -nFE^o_{cell}$$

Here, the negative sign indicates that work is done by the system on the surroundings. Therefore, when E^o_{cell} is positive, ΔG^o is negative. In other words, we again demonstrate that E^o_{cell} is positive for spontaneous redox reactions. Additionally, since we know the relation between ΔG^o and the equilibrium constant, K, we can further derive the relation between E^o_{cell} and K. Recall from Chapter 12 that:

$$\Delta G^o = -RT \ln K$$

Therefore:

$$-nFE^o_{cell} = -RT \ln K$$

$$E^o_{cell} = \frac{RT \ln K}{nF}$$

At standard conditions, $T = 298\ K$ and $\frac{RT}{F}$ is simply 0.0257 V.

$$E^o_{cell} = \frac{0.0257 \text{ } V}{n} \ln K$$

We can also express this in terms of the base-10 log of K:

$$E^o_{cell} = \frac{0.0592 \text{ } V}{n} \log K$$

Example Problem 13.9 – Calculating ΔG° From E°cell.

Michael Faraday (1791–1867) was an English scientist who is credited with many accomplishments related to electromagnetism and electrochemistry. Among his most notable contributions was the discovery of electrolysis.

Use standard reduction potentials to calculate $\Delta G°$ for the following reaction:
$$2 \text{ } Fe^{3+}(aq) + Zn(s) \rightleftharpoons 2 \text{ } Fe^{2+}(aq) + Zn^{2+}(aq)$$

Solution:	
Identify the oxidation and reduction half-reactions and look up the standard reduction potentials for each in Table 13.1.	Oxidation half-reaction: $Zn(s) \rightleftharpoons Zn^{2+}(aq) + 2 \text{ } e^-$ $\qquad E^o = -0.76 \text{ } V$ Reduction half-reaction: $2 \text{ } Fe^{3+}(aq) + 2 \text{ } e^- \rightleftharpoons 2 \text{ } Fe^{2+}(aq)$ $\qquad E^o = 0.77$
Use the standard reduction potentials to determine E^o_{cell}.	$E^o_{cell} = E^o_{cathode} - E^o_{anode} = 0.77 \text{ } V - (-0.76 \text{ } V) = \mathbf{1.53 \text{ } V}$
Then calculate $\Delta G°$ keeping in mind there is an exchange of 2 moles of electrons in this particular case.	$$\Delta G^o = -nFE^o_{cell}$$ $$\Delta G^o = -(2 \text{ } mol \text{ } e^-)\left(\frac{96,485 \text{ } C}{mol \text{ } e^-}\right)\left(1.53\frac{J}{C}\right) = \mathbf{-2.95 \times 10^5 \text{ } J}$$ **$\Delta G^o < 0 \text{ } J$, therefore, the reaction is spontaneous under standard conditions.**

Example Problem 13.10 – Calculating K from E°cell.

Use standard reduction potentials to calculate K for the following reaction:
$$2 \text{ } Fe^{3+}(aq) + Zn(s) \rightleftharpoons 2 \text{ } Fe^{2+}(aq) + Zn^{2+}(aq)$$

Solution:	
Identify the oxidation and reduction half-reactions and look up the standard reduction potentials for each in Table 13.1.	Oxidation half-reaction: $Zn(s) \rightleftharpoons Zn^{2+}(aq) + 2 \text{ } e^-$ $\qquad E^o = -0.76 \text{ } V$ Reduction half-reaction: $2 \text{ } Fe^{3+}(aq) + 2 \text{ } e^- \rightleftharpoons 2 \text{ } Fe^{2+}(aq)$ $\qquad E^o = 0.77$
Use the standard reduction potentials to determine E^o_{cell}.	$E^o_{cell} = E^o_{cathode} - E^o_{anode} = 0.77 \text{ } V - (-0.76 \text{ } V) = \mathbf{1.53 \text{ } V}$

Then calculate, keeping in mind there is an exchange of 2 moles of electrons in this particular case.	$$E^o_{cell} = \frac{0.0592\ V}{n}\log K$$ $$\log K = \frac{nE^o_{cell}}{0.0592\ V} = \frac{(2)(1.53\ V)}{0.0592\ V} = 51.6892$$ $$K = 10^{51.6892} = \mathbf{4.89 \times 10^{51}}$$

Calculating the Cell Potential Under Non-Standard Conditions

Again, recalling from Chapter 12, the free energy of a reaction under non-standard conditions is related to $\Delta G°$ as follows:

$$\Delta G = \Delta G^o + RT\ln Q$$

where Q is the reaction quotient (Chapter 10). As we learned in the previous derivations:

$$\Delta G^o = -nFE^o_{cell}$$

Therefore, it follows that:

$$-nFE_{cell} = -nFE^o_{cell} + RT\ln Q$$

$$E_{cell} = E^o_{cell} - \frac{RT}{nF}\ln Q$$

If we assume again that T = 298 K, we have the following equation:

$$E_{cell} = E^o_{cell} - \frac{0.0257\ V}{n}\ln Q$$

The log-10 analogue is again,

$$E_{cell} = E^o_{cell} - \frac{0.0592\ V}{n}\log Q$$

This is referred to as the **Nernst equation** and allows the determination of E^o_{cell} from non-standard reactant and product concentrations in redox reactions.

Walter Hermann Nernst (1864–1931) was a German chemist and Nobel laureate. He is considered a founding father of the field of Physical Chemistry and is noted for, among many accomplishments, the development of the equation which bears his name, the Nernst equation.

Example Problem 13.11 – Calculating E°_{cell} Under Non-standard Conditions–The Nernst Equation.

Determine the cell potential for the following:

Oxidation half-reaction:

$$Fe\ (s) \rightleftharpoons Fe^{2+}(aq) + 2\ e^- \qquad\qquad E^o = -0.45\ V$$

Reduction half-reaction:

$$MnO_4^-(aq) + 8\ H^+(aq) + 5\ e^- \rightleftharpoons Mn^{2+}(aq) + 4\ H_2O(l) \qquad E^o = 1.51\ V$$

At 25°C and :

$$[MnO_4^-] = 2.0\ M$$

$$[H^+] = 0.75\ M$$

$$[Mn^{2+}] = 1.66 \times 10^{-2}\ M$$

$$[Fe^{2+}] = 1.50 \times 10^{-1}\ M$$

Solution:

Balance (by the half-reaction method) the overall redox reaction equation and, using the standard reduction potentials for the two half-reactions, calculate the standard cell potential, E^o_{cell}.

$$5\ Fe(s) + 2\ MnO_4^-(aq) + 16\ H^+(aq) \rightleftharpoons 5\ Fe^{2+}(aq) + 2\ Mn^{2+}(aq) + 8\ H_2O(l)$$

$$E^o_{cell} = E^o_{cathode} - E^o_{anode} = 1.51\ V - (-0.45\ V) = \mathbf{1.96\ V}$$

Next use the balanced cell reaction equation to determine the value for the reaction quotient, Q.	$Q = \dfrac{[Fe^{2+}]^5 [Mn^{2+}]^2}{[MnO_4^-]^2 [H^+]^{16}} = \dfrac{[0.150]^5 [0.0166]^2}{[2.00]^2 [0.75]^{16}} = 5.22 \times 10^{-7}$
Calculate E_{cell} from E^o_{cell} using the Nerst equation. Recall that the number of electrons exchanged in this balanced equation is 10.	$E_{cell} = E^o_{cell} - \dfrac{0.0592\ V}{n} \log Q$ $E_{cell} = (1.96\ V) - \dfrac{0.0592\ V}{10} \log 5.22 \times 10^{-7}$ $E_{cell} = \mathbf{2.00\ V}$

Concentration Cells

Because, as we have just seen, the concentration of ions in solution determines reduction potentials of half-cells, it is possible to construct what is referred to as a concentration cell. A **concentration cell** is an electrochemical cell wherein both half-cells consist of the same half-reaction, but the solutes are present in different concentrations. Let's consider the copper(II) half-reaction as our example in this case. Suppose we have two half-cells consisting of a copper electrode in a solution of copper(II) sulfate. In one

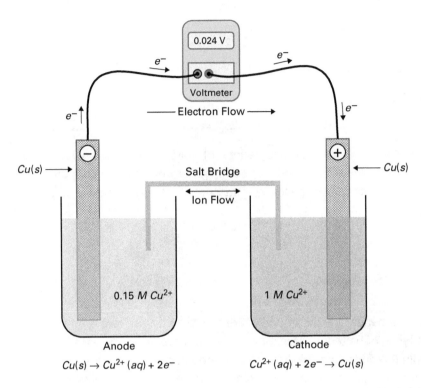

A concentration cell relies on the dependence of the half-cell potential on ion concentration to realize a measurable electromotive force.

half-cell, we have a copper(II) concentration of 0.15 M and in the other 1.0 M. Because the two half-reactions are occurring in separate containers, it is reasonable to represent this cell as follows:

$$Cu(s)\left|Cu^{2+}(0.15\ M)\right|\left|Cu^{2+}(1.0\ M)\right|Cu(s)$$

where the copper(II) ion concentrations are noted separately for the cathode and anode half-cells. Because the concentrations are different, each of these half-cells will exhibit different potentials, with the cell potential given to us according to the Nernst Equation as follows:

$$E_{cell} = E^o_{cell} - \frac{0.0592\ V}{2}\log\frac{[Cu^{2+}]_{dilute}}{[Cu^{2+}]_{conc.}}$$

Here we have the more dilute half-cell depicted as the anode. This is because the more concentrated solution will always represent reduction (cathode) in a concentration cell. Also, we see that $n = 2$ as the number of moles of electrons exchanged in the overall cell reaction is two moles of electrons. Additionally, because each half-cell is the same half-reaction, the standard cell potential is zero by definition ($E^0_{cell} = 0\ V$). Therefore, we calculate the cell potential (at 25°C) as:

$$E_{cell} = (0\ V) - \frac{0.0592\ V}{2}\log\frac{(0.15\ M)}{(1.0\ M)} = \textbf{0.024\ V}$$

Section 13.7 Application of Electrochemistry: Batteries and Fuel Cells

One of the most common applications of voltaic cells in everyday use is batteries. **Batteries** are essentially nothing more than voltaic cells connected in series. The following is a brief description of some common types of batteries.

Primary Batteries

Primary batteries are those which are not able to be "re-charged." Once these types of batteries reach equilibrium, they are generally discarded.

Alkaline Batteries. Alkaline batteries are a subset of batteries collectively known as *dry-cell batteries* and are constructed with no fluid components, hence the name. These include the common AAA, AA, C, and D batteries used in small handheld or mobile devices such as flashlights, radios, etc. The anode is typically solid zinc, which also serves as a container. The cathode is usually a carbon (graphite) rod which runs down the center of the battery in contact with a mixture of MnO_2 in an electrolyte paste consisting of KOH and water (see Figure 13.4).

Oxidation (anode): $Zn(s) + 2\ OH^-(aq) \rightarrow Zn(OH)_2(s) + 2\ e^-$

Reduction (cathode): $2\ MnO_2(s) + 2\ H_2O(l) + 2\ e^- \rightarrow 2\ MnO(OH)(s) + 2\ OH^-(aq)$

Overall: $Zn(s) + 2\ MnO_2(s) + 2\ H_2O(l) \rightarrow Zn(OH)_2(s) + 2\ MnO(OH)(s)$

Mercury batteries are commonly used to power small electronic devices such as watches.

Mercury Batteries. These batteries are typically characterized by a stainless steel can in which a zinc-mercury amalgam anode lines the can. Additionally there is usually either a silver or a mercury cathode in contact with an alkaline electrolyte which usually consists of ZnO and HgO. These are typically used in small electronic devices like watches. The cell reactions are as follows:

Oxidation (anode): $Zn(Hg)(s) + 2\ OH^-(aq) \rightarrow ZnO(s) + H_2O(l) + 2\ e^-$

Reduction (cathode): $HgO(s) + H_2O(l) + 2\ e^- \rightarrow Hg(l) + 2\ OH^-(aq)$

Overall: $Zn(Hg)(s) + HgO(s) \rightarrow ZnO(s) + Hg(l)$

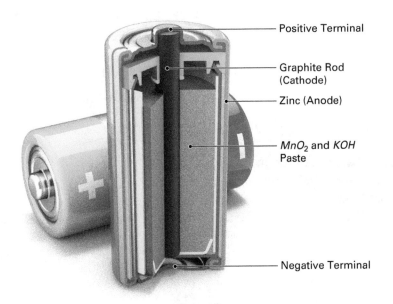

Positive Terminal

Graphite Rod
(Cathode)

Zinc (Anode)

MnO_2 and *KOH*
Paste

Negative Terminal

Figure 13.4 An Alkaline battery consists of a graphite cathode in contact with a basic MnO_2 paste.

Re-Chargeable Batteries

Lead-Acid Storage Batteries. Lead-acid storage batteries are those typically found in automobiles. These consist of six individual cells connected in series. Within each cell, there is a lead grid which supports a grade of porous lead which serves as the anode, and another lead grid upon which lead(IV) oxide, $PbO_2(s)$, is packed and which serves as the cathode. Both of these electrodes are submerged in an electrolyte fluid consisting of a 30% sulfuric acid solution. The cell reactions are as follows:

Oxidation (anode): $Pb(s) + SO_4^{2-}(aq) \rightarrow PbSO_4(s) + 2\ e^-$

Reduction (cathode): $PbO_2(s) + 4\ H^+(aq) + SO_4^{2-}(aq) + 2\ e^- \rightarrow PbSO_4(s) + 2\ H_2O(l)$

Overall: $Pb(s) + PbO_2(s) + 4\ H^+(aq) + 2\ SO_4^{2-}(aq) \rightarrow 2\ PbSO_4(s) + 2\ H_2O(l)$

During operation, these reactions can be reversed (the battery is re-charged) by application of an electric current from an external source such as the alternator in a car engine.

Fuel Cells

Fuel cells are like batteries. However, the reactant components of the redox reaction are continuously fed into the cell like a fuel. The most common example of a fuel cell is the hydrogen-oxygen fuel cell. Here hydrogen gas is continuously fed and allowed to flow past a platinum anode where it is

Lead-Acid Storage batteries are commonly used in automobiles.

oxidized. Likewise, oxygen gas is fed through a similar cathode where it is reduced. The cell reactions are as follows:

Oxidation (anode): $2 H_2(g) + 4 OH^-(aq) \rightarrow 4 H_2O(l) + 4 e^-$

Reduction (cathode): $O_2(g) + 2 H_2O(l) + 4 e^- \rightarrow 4 OH^-(aq)$

Overall: $2 H_2(g) + O_2(g) \rightarrow 2 H_2O(l)$

Notice that in this case hydrogen and oxygen are continuously fed into the cell, undergoing redox which generates an electric current. As such, fuel cells do not "die" as we expect batteries to. As long as fuel is provided, electric current can be produced. In the case of our example, the only byproduct of this process is water.

Section 13.8 Electrolysis

In the previous section, we learned that hydrogen and oxygen can be fed into a fuel cell to generate electric current from the spontaneous redox reaction between these two elements for which the product is pure water. Further, we described this process by the following equations:

HYDROGEN-OXYGEN FUEL CELL (SPONTANEOUS):

Oxidation (anode): $2 H_2(g) + 4 OH^-(aq) \rightarrow 4 H_2O(l) + 4 e^-$

Reduction (cathode): $O_2(g) + 2 H_2O(l) + 4 e^- \rightarrow 4 OH^-(aq)$

Overall: $2 H_2(g) + O_2(g) \rightarrow 2 H_2O(l)$

However, if a source of an external electric current can be inserted into this process, it could drive the reverse reaction, separating water into its constituent elements. This is an example of what is referred to as electrolysis. **Electrolysis** is the use of electrical energy to force a redox reaction which is otherwise not spontaneous. The following half-reactions depict the anode and cathode half-cells for the electrolysis of water.

ELECTROLYSIS OF WATER (NON-SPONTANEOUS):

Oxidation (anode): $2 H_2O(l) \rightarrow O_2(g) + 4 H^+(aq) + 4 e^-$

Reduction (cathode): $4 H_2O(l) + 4 e^- \rightarrow 2 H_2(g) + 4 OH^-(aq)$

Overall: $2 H_2O(l) \rightarrow 2 H_2(g) + O_2(g)$

Notice that the half-cells have now switched roles. The anode in the spontaneous process has become the cathode and vice versa. Additionally, where hydrogen and oxygen were reactants in the fuel cell, they are now the products in the *electrolytic cell*. This effect is demonstrated by placing two inert electrodes into a container of water, each of which is connected to either the positive or the negative terminals of a battery with a potential of a few volts. Assuming the presence of electrolytes in solution to allow for conduction of electric current, oxygen gas and hydrogen gas can be collected as products at the anode and cathode, respectively.

In fact, we can expect that any spontaneous redox reaction can be reversed within an electrochemical cell if an external power source of sufficient voltage is supplied. Let's return to our familiar example of the copper-zinc electrochemical cell (Figure 13.1). The galvanic cell depicted in Figure 13.1 consists of the following half-reactions:

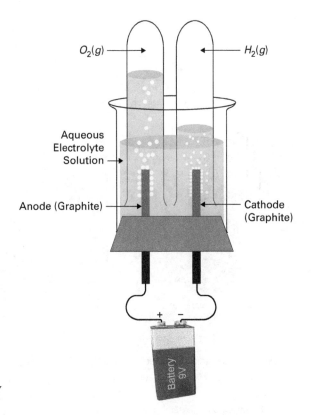

Electrolysis of water.

Oxidation (anode): $Zn(s) \rightarrow Zn^{2+}(aq) + 2\ e^-$

Reduction (cathode): $Cu^{2+}(aq) + 2\ e^- \rightarrow Cu(s)$

Overall: $Cu^{2+}(aq) + Zn(s) \rightarrow Zn^{2+}(aq) + Cu(s)$

$$E^o_{cell} = E^o_{cathode} - E^o_{anode} = E^0_{Cu^{2+}/Cu} - E^o_{Zn^{2+}/Zn} = 0.34\ V - (-0.76\ V) = 1.10\ V$$

Here, we determined that this particular electrochemical cell will spontaneously reduce copper(II) and oxidize zinc with a cell potential of $E^0_{cell} = 1.10\ V$. If, however, we connected the zinc electrode to the negative terminal of a battery and, likewise, the copper electrode to the positive terminal, this would force electron flow in the direction opposite to that of the galvanic cell, assuming the battery potential (voltage) is greater than 1.10 V. In other words, the negative terminal would push electrons toward the zinc electrode causing it to be negatively charged. The zinc electrode now serves as the effective source of electrons; therefore, Zn^{2+} ions in solution are reduced while the positive terminal would draw electrons away from the copper electrode, which is now positively charged, causing copper metal to be oxidized to Cu^{2+} ions (Figure 13.5). As such, this electrolytic cell is characterized by the following half-reactions:

Oxidation (anode): $Cu(s) \rightarrow Cu^{2+}(aq) + 2\ e^-$

Reduction (cathode): $Zn^{2+}(aq) + 2\ e^- \rightarrow Zn(s)$

Overall: $Zn^{2+}(aq) + Cu(s) \rightarrow Cu^{2+}(aq) + Zn(s)$

$$E^o_{cell} = E^o_{cathode} - E^o_{anode} = E^o_{Zn^{2+}/Zn} - E^0_{Cu^{2+}/Cu} = -0.76\ V - (+0.34\ V) = -1.10\ V$$

Notice in this case, the cell potential is now negative (but of equal magnitude to that of the galvanic cell). Since this reaction is not spontaneous, our external power source will have to apply a potential greater than

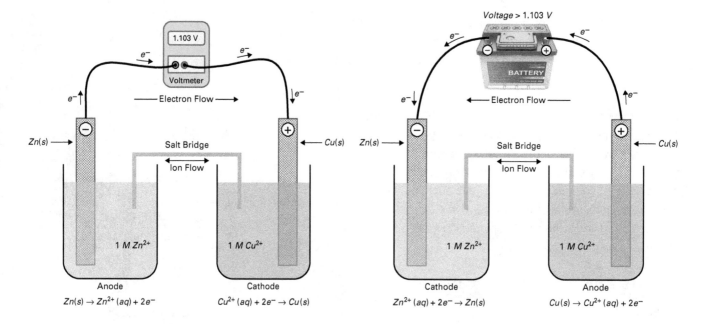

Figure 13.5 A galvanic cell and its electrolytic counterpart. In an electrolytic cell, an otherwise nonspontaneous chemical change is driven by an external electric power source. Further, the external power source acts as the source of electrons and, therefore, the cathode is negatively charged, while the anode is positively charged. In a galvanic cell, the anode is the source of electrons and, therefore, negatively charged, while the cathode is positively charged.

1.10 V in order to drive this electrolytic reaction. The following summarizes the difference between galvanic and electrolytic cells.

In Summary

1. In a galvanic cell the anode is the source of electrons and therefore, negatively charged, while the cathode is positively charged.

2. In an electrolytic cell the external electric power source is the source of electrons and therefore, the cathode is negatively charged, while the anode is positively charged.

Predicting the Products of Electrolysis

Predicting the outcome of an electrolytic process can be fairly obvious but not always. Owing to this, we begin with the simple case of molten salts. Let's consider the example of molten sodium chloride. Here, we imagine only a single vessel (as in the example of the electrolysis of water) and, further, there are only two species present, Na^+ and Cl^-. If we submerge two inert electrodes into our molten salt, each connected to one of the two terminals of a battery, we know that reduction must occur at the negatively charged cathode and oxidation at the anode. The only question is, which of the two species in our sample will be oxidized and which will be reduced? If we recognize that Na^+ cannot be further oxidized, we must conclude that it will be preferentially reduced at the cathode. Likewise, we note the Cl^- anion cannot be further reduced and, therefore, could only be oxidized. Another way to understand this is, *in the electrolysis of a salt, the cation is reduced, and the anion is oxidized.* As such, we predict the following half-reactions at each electrode:

Oxidation (anode): $\qquad 2\ Cl^-\ (l) \rightarrow Cl_2(g) + 2\ e^-$

Reduction (cathode): $\qquad Na^+(l) + e^- \rightarrow Na(s)$

Overall: $\qquad 2\ Cl^-(l) + 2\ Na^+(l) \rightarrow Cl_2(g) + 2\ Na(s)$

In the case of molten, binary salts, this is a straightforward prediction since there are no other species to complicate the issue. This, however, is not the case for salts in aqueous solution, as we will see in the next section.

Overvoltage: Electrolysis of Aqueous Salt Solutions

Let's keep going with the sodium chloride example but consider electrolysis in aqueous solution rather than the molten state. In contrast to our previous situation, electrolysis of aqueous *NaCl* consists of a redox reaction occurring in a mixture of water and ions, rather than a sample of pure sodium chloride. Indeed, we have already learned that water will undergo electrolysis. As such, when predicting the nature of the half-reaction at the cathode as well as the anode, we must consider the possibility that water, too, is either reduced or oxidized. With this in mind, let's begin with the cathode. Here, there is the possibility that either *Na*$^+$ or water is reduced. We know this because, as we have just learned, cations are reduced in the electrolysis of salts. Therefore, we have the following possibilities from which to choose:

Reduction: $\quad Na^+(aq) + e^- \rightarrow Na(s)$ $\qquad\qquad E^o = -2.71\ V$

$\quad 2\ H_2O(l) + 2\ e^- \rightarrow H_2(g) + 2\ OH^-(aq)$ $\qquad E = -0.42\ V \qquad (E^o = -0.83\ V)$

Likewise, at the anode, either water or chloride will be oxidized as shown below:

Oxidation: $\quad 2\ Cl^-(aq) \rightarrow Cl_2(g) + 2\ e^-$ $\qquad\qquad E^o = 1.36\ V$

$\quad 2\ H_2O(l) \rightarrow O_2(g) + 4\ H^+(aq) + 4\ e^-$ $\qquad E = 0.82\ \ V \qquad (E^o = 1.23\ V)$

Notice that the electrode potentials for the oxidation and reduction of water are not the standard potentials listed in Appendix IV or Table 13.1. This is because the reaction is taking place at neutral pH where the concentrations of H^+ and OH^- are essentially zero ($[H^+] = [OH^-] = 10^{-7}M \approx 0\ M$). Nevertheless, having established the appropriate reduction potentials for the half-reactions in question, the general guidelines are as follows:

1. *For reduction (cathode)*, the half-reaction with the highest (most positive) reduction potential is preferred.

2. *For oxidation (anode)*, the half-reaction with the lowest (most negative) reduction potential is preferred.

Based on these guidelines, and upon examination of the reduction potentials listed above, we would conclude the following:

1. Since the reduction potential of water is more positive than that of sodium, water will be preferentially reduced at the cathode.

2. Likewise, since the reduction potential for the half-reaction depicting the oxidation of water is more negative than that of chloride, water will be preferentially oxidized at the anode.

In other words, we predict, based solely on the reduction potentials alone, that electrolysis of aqueous sodium chloride will merely be the preferential electrolysis of water with H_2 gas and O_2 gas as the products at the cathode and anode, respectively. However, this is not what is observed experimentally. While H_2 gas is indeed the product observed at the cathode, Cl_2 gas is the observed product of oxidation at the anode, rather than O_2. In other words, even though we find that the electrode potential for the oxidation of water is 0.82 V, it requires more than 0.82 V to actually cause the oxidation reaction to occur. This is referred to as overvoltage. **Overvoltage** is the voltage, over and above that which is otherwise expected based on the standard electrode potentials, which is required to drive a nonspontaneous redox reaction in an electrolytic process. The reasons for this phenomenon are beyond the scope of this text. Nevertheless, for the oxidation and reduction of water as described by the half-reactions above, the overvoltage in each case increases the voltage required by approximately 0.4 to 0.6 V in magnitude. This would place the apparent electrode potential for the oxidation of water at around 1.4 V, making Cl_2 gas the preferred product of oxidation in this cell. Therefore, in the electrolysis of aqueous sodium chloride, we expect the products to be chlorine gas at the anode and hydrogen gas, as well as hydroxide, at the cathode.

Oxidation (anode):	$2\ Cl^-(aq) \rightarrow Cl_2(g) + 2\ e^-$	$E^o = 1.36\ V$
Reduction (cathode):	$2\ H_2O(l) + 2\ e^- \rightarrow H_2(g) + 2\ OH^-(aq)$	$E = -0.42\ V$
Overall:	$2\ Cl^-(aq) + 2\ H_2O(l) \rightarrow Cl_2(g) + H_2(g) + 2\ OH^-(aq)$	

Example problem 13.12 provides further practice in predicting the products of electrolysis.

Example Problem 13.12 – Electrolysis Reactions

Predict the half-reactions occurring at the anode and cathode for the electrolysis of potassium iodide. Write the balanced cell reaction equation and thereby predict the products.	
Solution:	
There are two different possibilities for the half-reaction occurring at the cathode. These are the reduction of K^+ or the reduction of water. We would settle on the one with the most positive reduction potential as shown here. Overvoltage is not an issue in the case.	Reduction: $K^+(aq) + 1\ e^- \rightarrow K(s)$ $\qquad$ $E^o = -2.93\ V$ Reduction: $2\ H_2O(l) + 2\ e^- \rightarrow H_2(g) + 2\ OH^-(aq)$ $\qquad$ $E = -0.42\ V$ $([OH^-] = 10^{-7}\ M)$

There are two different possibilities for the half-reaction occurring at the anode. These are the oxidation of I^- or the oxidation of water. We will settle on the one with the most negative reduction potential. In this case, this is the reduction of iodide as shown here.	Oxidation: $2\ I^-(aq) \rightarrow I_2(aq) + 2\ e^- \qquad E^o = 0.54\ V$ Oxidation: $2\ H_2O(l) \rightarrow O_2(g) + 4\ H^+(aq) + 4\ e^- \qquad E = 0.82\ V$ $([H^+] = 10^{-7}\ M)$

We now combine the two half-reactions and balance the equation as described in previous sections.

$$2\ H_2O(l) + 2\ I^-(aq) \rightarrow H_2(g) + 2\ OH^-(aq) + I_2(aq)$$

Again, the cell potential is the difference between the standard reduction potentials for the half-reactions at the cathode and the anode.

$$E^o_{cell} = E^o_{cathode} - E^o_{anode} = -0.42\ V - (0.54\ V) = \mathbf{-0.96\ V}$$

Stoichiometry in Electrolysis

We now turn our attention to stoichiometric considerations. Because the externally applied current in an electrolytic cell directly drives the rate of the redox reaction, we can include considerations of current in the stoichiometric determination of theoretical yields. Again, let's continue to use the copper-zinc electrochemical cell as our example. Suppose we are using this cell to generate zinc metal (such cells are often used in metal-plating procedures wherein various metals are coated or plated with other metals). The half-reaction in which zinc is produced and deposited as a solid neutral metal is as follows:

$$Zn^{2+}(aq) + 2\ e^- \rightarrow Zn(s)$$

The half-reaction provides a stoichiometric ratio between the number of moles of electrons consumed and the number of moles of zinc metal produced.

$$1\ mol\ Zn(s) = 2\ moles\ e^-$$

Additionally, the current applied to the electrolytic cell can be used in concert with a specific time interval to calculate the precise quantity of charge which has passed through the cell. Recall that one ampere is defined as 1 coulomb of charge per second:

$$1\ amp = 1\frac{C}{s}$$

Therefore:

$$Current\left(\frac{C}{s}\right) \times time\ (s) = total\ charge\ (C)$$

From here we can apply the Faraday constant to determine the total number of moles of electrons consumed in this half-reaction, which in turn gives us the moles and expected mass of the product, zinc metal. Let's apply this approach to determine the mass of zinc produced from this electrolytic cell over a time interval of 3.0 minutes with a current of 3.5 *amp*.

We first convert current and time to total charge.

$$3.0 \; min \times \frac{60 \; s}{1 \; min} \times \frac{3.5 \; C}{s}$$

We then convert total charge to moles of electrons consumed using the Faraday constant.

$$3.0 \; min \times \frac{60 \; s}{1 \; min} \times \frac{3.5 \; C}{s} \times \frac{1 \; mol \; e^-}{96,485 \; C}$$

From here it is a matter of conversion to moles of zinc then to mass.

$$3.0 \; min \times \frac{60 \; s}{1 \; min} \times \frac{3.5 \; C}{s} \times \frac{1 \; mol \; e^-}{96,485 \; C} \times \frac{1 \; mol \; Zn}{2 \; mol \; e^-} \times \frac{65.38 \; g \; Zn}{1 \; mol \; Zn} = \textbf{0.21} \; \textit{\textbf{g}}$$

Therefore, in this particular cell 0.21 *g* of zinc can be produced in a 3.0-minute interval at a current of 3.5 *amp*. Example problem 13.13 provides additional practice with the application of stoichiometry to electrolysis.

Example Problem 13.13 – Stoichiometry in Electrolysis Reactions

How many minutes would it take to plate out (produce) 10.0 *g* of silver using a current of 2.5 *amps*?
$$Ag^+(aq) + e^- \rightarrow Ag(s)$$
Solution:
We convert the mass (10.0*g*) to moles silver, which is converted to moles electrons using the stoichiometric coefficients in our equation. We can convert this quantity to coulombs using Faraday's constant, which is converted to time in seconds using the given value of the current $\left(1 \; amp = \frac{1C}{s}\right)$.
$$10.0 \; g \; Ag \times \frac{1 \; mol \; Ag}{107.87 \; g \; Ag} \times \frac{1 \; mol \; e^-}{1 \; mol \; Ag} \times \frac{96,485 \; C}{1 \; mol \; e^-} \times \frac{1 \; s}{2.50 \; C} \times \frac{1 \; min.}{60 \; s} = \textbf{59.6} \; \textit{\textbf{min.}}$$

Did you know how chemistry might relate to you as a non-chemist? While we have learned a great deal regarding electrochemical cells and how they power our cars, watches, and a myriad of other devices and processes, spontaneous redox reactions can often work against us as well. Every year, billions of dollars are lost due to damage caused by **corrosion** of buildings, cars, boats, equipment, etc. Corrosion is the unwanted oxidation of metals caused by oxidizing agents present in nearly all natural environments. The main culprit, however, is oxygen in the presence of water. We can see clearly from Table 13.1 that oxygen (under acidic conditions) has a reduction potential of +1.23 V. Most common metals (such as iron) are much lower on the list, meaning that, when in contact with oxygen and water, most metals will spontaneously undergo oxidation. In fact, a huge part of the iron industry exists to replace iron which has corroded (rusted). Iron oxidizes according to the following half-reaction:

$$Fe(s) \rightarrow Fe^{2+}(aq) + 2 \; e^- \qquad E^o = -0.45 \; V$$

If an iron surface is in contact with a drop of water, then oxygen can act as an oxidizing agent and will undergo reduction:

$$O_2(g) + 4\ H^+(aq) + 4\ e^- \rightarrow 2\ H_2O(l) \qquad E^o = +1.23\ V$$

The overall reaction is this case is written as follows:

$$2\ Fe(s) + O_2(g) + 4\ H^+(aq) \rightarrow 2\ H_2O(l) + 2\ Fe^{2+}(aq)$$

$$E^o_{cell} = +1.68\ V$$

Acidic conditions are usually realized as water can react with carbon dioxide in the air to form carbonic acid. Additionally, the very positive cell potential portends of a reaction that is spontaneous and unavoidable. The iron(II) ions will continue to oxidize in the presence of oxygen and water to form iron(III) oxide, Fe_2O_3, which is the compound with the characteristic "rust" appearance.

Based on this description, water must be present in addition to iron and oxygen in order for rust to occur. For this reason, one of the main ways in which corrosion is prevented is by application of moisture-impermeable coatings such as the paint on automobiles. Have you ever noticed that cars only tend to rust in places where the paint has been scratched or chipped away? Another method, commonly in use, is the placement of another metal which is more prone to oxidation in contact with the iron. In other words, the placement of a metal which has a more negative reduction potential (listed lower on Table 13.1) in contact with iron. This creates a situation where this other metal will preferentially oxidize in place of the iron. This is referred to as a **sacrificial electrode**. The same effect is accomplished by coating iron with such an "other" metal. This is what is done with galvanized metal tools or parts, such as galvanized nails for instance. Galvanized nails are iron nails coated with a layer of zinc, which has a more negative reduction potential than does iron and, therefore, oxidizes in place of the iron nail. Further, even as the zinc oxidizes, the resulting zinc oxide remains and acts as a protective coating just like the paint on your car.

Sacrificial Electrodes are commonly used in marine applications to prevent corrosion. Here we see a sacrificial zinc anode affixed to the underside of a boat, to prevent oxidation of the hull and the screw/prop assembly.

Key Terms

1. Alkaline battery
2. Ampere
3. Anode
4. Battery
5. Cathode
6. Cell diagram
7. Cell notation
8. Cell potential
9. Concentration cell
10. Corrosion
11. Coulomb
12. Electrochemical cells
13. Electrochemistry
14. Electrode
15. Electrolysis
16. Electrolytic cells
17. Electromotive force
18. Faraday constant
19. Fuel cells
20. Galvanic cells
21. Half-cell
22. Half-reaction
23. Inert electrode
24. Nernst equation
25. Overvoltage
26. Oxidation
27. Oxidation number
28. Oxidation state
29. Oxidation-reduction reaction
30. Oxidizing agent
31. Redox reactions
32. Reducing agent
33. Reduction

34. Sacrificial electrode

35. Salt bridge

36. Standard cell potential

37. Standard electrode potential

38. Standard hydrogen electrode (SHE)

39. Standard reduction potential

40. Volt

41. Voltaic cells

Problems

OXIDATION-REDUCTION (REDOX) REACTIONS

1. What is reduction?

2. What is oxidation?

3. What is an oxidation number?

4. How do we use oxidation numbers to identify redox reactions?

5. Define the term reducing agent.

6. Define the term oxidizing agent.

7. Assign oxidation numbers to the elements in the following:

   a. $CsBr$

   b. H_2CO_3

   c. Na_2O_2

8. Assign oxidation numbers to the elements in the following:

   a. $SrBr_2$

   b. H_2SO_4

   c. $KMnO_4$

9. Assign oxidation numbers to the elements in the following:

   a. Cl_2

   b. Mg^{2+}

   c. NO_2

10. Assign oxidation numbers to the elements in the following:

    a. PCl_5

    b. BrO_3^-

    c. H_3BO_3

11. Determine whether the following reaction is a redox reaction. If so, identify the oxidizing and reducing agents.

$$2\ Na(s) + Cl_2(g) \rightarrow 2NaCl(s)$$

12. Determine whether the following reaction is a redox reaction. If so, identify the oxidizing and reducing agents.

$$Mg(s) + 2\ H_2O(l) \rightarrow Mg(OH)_2(aq) + H_2(g)$$

13. Determine whether the following reaction is a redox reaction. If so, identify the oxidizing and reducing agents.

$$2\ NaOH(aq) + H_2SO_4(aq) \rightarrow Na_2SO_4(aq) + 2\ H_2O(l)$$

14. Determine whether the following reaction is a redox reaction. If so, identify the oxidizing and reducing agents.

$$C_3H_8(g) + 5\ O_2(g) \rightarrow 3\ CO_2(g) + 4\ H_2O(g)$$

BALANCING REDOX REACTIONS

15. Define the term half-reaction.

16. Balance the following half-reactions:
    a. $NiO_2(s) \rightarrow Ni^{2+}(aq)$ (Acidic Conditions)
    b. $N_2H_4(aq) \rightarrow N_2(g)$ (Basic Conditions)

17. Balance the following half-reactions:
    a. $IO_3^-(aq) \rightarrow I^-(aq)$ (Acidic Conditions)
    b. $ClO^-(aq) \rightarrow Cl^-(aq)$ (Basic Conditions)

18. Balance the following half-reactions:
    a. $Ag(s) \rightarrow Ag_2O(s)$ (Basic Conditions)
    b. $H_2O_2(aq) \rightarrow H_2O(l)$ (Acidic Conditions)

19. Balance the following half-reactions:
    a. $Cr(s) \rightarrow Cr^{3+}(aq)$ (Acidic Conditions)
    b. $MnO_4^-(aq) \rightarrow MnO_2(s)$ (Basic Conditions)

20. Balance the following redox reactions using the half-reaction method under acidic conditions.
    a. $Al^{3+}(aq) + Cu(s) \rightarrow Al(s) + Cu^{2+}(aq)$
    b. $Ag(s) + Fe^{3+}(aq) \rightarrow Ag^+(aq) + Fe(s)$
    c. $NO_3^-(aq) + Cd(s) \rightarrow NO(g) + Cd^{2+}(aq)$

21. Balance the following redox reactions using the half-reaction method under acidic conditions.

    a. $H_2O_2(aq) + Zn(s) \rightarrow H_2O(l) + Zn^{2+}(aq)$

    b. $BrO_3^-(aq) + Fe(s) \rightarrow Br_2(l) + Fe^{2+}(aq)$

    c. $Cu^{2+}(aq) + N_2H_5^+(aq) \rightarrow N_2(g) + Cu(s)$

22. Balance the following redox reactions using the half-reaction method under acidic conditions.

    a. $MnO_4^-(aq) + Ca(s) \rightarrow MnO_2(s) + Ca^{2+}(aq)$

    b. $PbO_2(s) + I^-(aq) \rightarrow Pb^{2+}(aq) + I_2(s)$

    c. $Cr_2O_7^{2-}(aq) + Fe(s) \rightarrow Cr^{3+}(aq) + Fe^{3+}(aq)$

23. Balance the following redox reactions using the half-reaction method under basic conditions.

    a. $MnO_2(s) + Cl_2(g) \rightarrow MnO_4^-(aq) + Cl^-(aq)$

    b. $ClO^-(aq) + Fe(s) \rightarrow Cl^-(aq) + Fe^{3+}(aq)$

24. Balance the following redox reactions using the half-reaction method under basic conditions.

    a. $MnO_4^-(aq) + I^-(aq) \rightarrow MnO_2(s) + I_2(g)$

    b. $Mn^{2+}(aq) + H_2O_2(aq) \rightarrow MnO_2(s) + H_2O(l)$

25. Balance the following redox reactions using the half-reaction method under basic conditions.

    a. $ClO^-(aq) + Cr(OH)_4^-(aq) \rightarrow CrO_4^{2-}(aq) + Cl^-(aq)$

    b. $Br_2(l) \rightarrow BrO_3^-(aq) + Br^-(aq)$

GALVANIC (VOLTAIC) CELLS

26. What is an electrode?

27. Define the terms anode and cathode.

28. Define the terms half-cell.

29. Describe the difference between a galvanic (voltaic) cell and an electrolytic cell.

30. What is the standard hydrogen electrode? What is its significance?

31. What is the relation between the spontaneity of a redox reaction and the cell potential, E_{cell}°?

32. Use a cell diagram to describe a cell consisting of a silver electrode submerged in a 1 M solution of silver nitrate and a copper electrode submerged in a 1 M solution of copper(II) sulfate.

33. Use a cell diagram to describe a cell consisting of a zinc electrode submerged in a 1 M solution of zinc sulfate and a magnesium electrode submerged in a 1 M solution of magnesium nitrate.

34. Arrange the following in order of increasing reducing strength:

    a. *Cu*

    b. *Zn*

    c. *Fe*

    d. *Pb*

35. Arrange the following in order of increasing oxidizing strength:

    a. Li^+

    b. Cr^{2+}

    c. Ti^{2+}

    d. Sn^{2+}

36. Use the standard electrode potentials in Table 13.1 to calculate the standard cell potential for a Galvanic cell based on the reaction described by the following balanced equation at 25°C.

$$2\ ClO_2(g)+2\ I^-(aq)\rightarrow 2\ ClO_2^-(aq)+I_2(s)$$

37. Use the standard electrode potentials in Table 13.1 to calculate the standard cell potential for a Galvanic cell based on the reaction described by the following balanced equation at 25°C.

$$Zn(s)+2\ H^+(aq)\rightarrow Zn^{2+}(aq)+H_2(g)$$

38. Use the standard electrode potentials in Table 13.1 to calculate the standard cell potential and write the overall balanced equation for a Galvanic cell based on the reaction described by the following cell diagram at 25°C. Assume acidic conditions and that all solutes are 1 *M* and all partial pressures are 1 *atm*.

$$Zn(s)\big|Zn^{2+}(aq)\big\|Ni^{2+}(aq)\big|Ni(s)$$

39. Use the standard electrode potentials in Table 13.1 to calculate the standard cell potential and write the overall balanced equation for a Galvanic cell based on the reaction described by the following cell diagram at 25°C. Assume acidic conditions and that all solutes are 1 *M* and all partial pressures are 1 *atm*.

$$Pb(s)\big|Pb^{2+}(aq)\big\|Ag^+\ (aq)\big|Ag(s)$$

40. Use the standard electrode potentials in Table 13.1 to calculate the standard cell potential for a Galvanic cell based on the reaction described by the following cell diagrams at 25°C (acidic conditions).

    a. $Cu(s)\big|Cu^{2+}(aq)\big\|MnO_4^-\ (aq)\big|MnO_2(aq)|Pt(s)$

    b. $Cr(s)\big|Cr^{3+}(aq)\big\|Fe^{3+}\ (aq)\big|Fe(s)$

    c. $Mg(s)\big|Mg^{2+}(aq)\big\|Ni^{2+}\ (aq)\big|Ni(s)$

41. Use the standard electrode potentials in Table 13.1 to calculate the standard cell potential for a Galvanic cell based on the reaction described by the following cell diagrams at 25°C (acidic conditions) .

    a. $Fe(s)|Fe^{2+}(aq)\|H^+(aq)|H_2(g)|Pt(s)$

    b. $Zn(s)|Zn^{2+}(aq)\|Sn^{2+}(aq)|Sn(s)$

    c. $Al(s)|Al^{3+}(aq)\|Fe^{2+}(aq)|Fe(s)$

42. Determine E^o_{cell} for the following balanced reaction equations and indicate whether they will proceed spontaneously as written.

    a. $MnO_2(s)+4\ H^+(aq)+Zn(s)\rightarrow Mn^{2+}(aq)+2\ H_2O(l)+Zn^{2+}(aq)$

    b. $Ca(s)+Cd^{2+}(aq)\rightarrow Ca^{2+}+Cd(s)$

    c. $5\ Fe^{2+}(aq)+2\ Mn^{2+}(aq)+8\ H_2O(l)\rightarrow 5\ Fe(s)+2\ MnO_4^-(aq)+16\ H^+(aq)$

43. Balance the following reaction equations and determine E^o_{cell} for each reaction. Indicate whether they will proceed spontaneously as written.

    a. $Fe(s)+Cr_2O_7^{2-}(aq)\rightarrow Fe^{2+}(aq)+Cr^{3+}(aq)$ (acidic)

    b. $MnO_2(s)+Ag^+(aq)\rightarrow MnO_4^-(aq)+Ag(s)$ (basic)

    c. $Ni^{2+}(aq)+H_2O_2(aq)\rightarrow O_2(g)+Ni(s)$ (acidic)

44. Combine the following half-reactions into the balanced equation for a spontaneous redox reaction and calculate E^o_{cell}.

    $N_2O(g)+2\ H^+(aq)+2\ e^-\rightarrow N_2(g)+H_2O(l)$ $E^o=1.73\ V$

    $I_2(s)+2\ e^-\rightarrow 2\ I^-(aq)$ $E^o=0.54\ V$

45. Combine the following half-reactions into the balanced equation for a spontaneous redox reaction and calculate E^o_{cell}.

    $MnO_4^-(aq)+4\ H^+(aq)+3\ e^-\rightarrow MnO_2(s)+2\ H_2O(l)$ $E^o=1.67\ V$

    $Fe^{2+}(aq)+2\ e^-\rightarrow Fe(s)$ $E^o=-0.45$

GIBBS FREE ENERGY, EQUILIBRIUM, AND CELL POTENTIAL

46. Use standard reduction potentials to calculate ΔG^o for the following reactions:

    a. $Br_2(l)+2\ I^-(aq)\rightarrow 2\ Br^-(aq)+I_2(s)$

    b. $Cu^{2+}(aq)+Pb(s)\rightarrow Pb^{2+}(aq)+Cu(s)$

47. Use standard reduction potentials to calculate ΔG^o for the following unbalanced reactions:

    a. $2\ Al(s)+Ni^{2+}(aq)\rightarrow 2\ Al^{3+}(aq)+Ni(s)$

    b. $Ca(s)+Pb^{2+}(aq)\rightarrow Ca^{2+}(aq)+Pb(s)$

48. Use standard reduction potentials to calculate $\Delta G°$ for the following unbalanced reactions:

    a. $MnO_2(s)+4\ H^+(aq)+Sn(s)\rightarrow Mn^{2+}(aq)+2\ H_2O(l)+Sn^{2+}(aq)$

    b. $Co(s)+Fe^{3+}(aq)\rightarrow Co^{2+}(aq)+Fe(s)$

49. Use standard reduction potentials to calculate $\Delta G°$ for the following unbalanced reactions:

    a. $O_2(g)+2\ H_2O(l)+2\ Sn\ (s)\rightarrow 4\ OH^-(aq)+2\ Sn^{2+}(aq)$

    b. $2\ H^+(aq)+Sn(s)\rightarrow H_2(g)+Sn^{2+}$

50. Determine the equilibrium constant, K, for the reactions in problem 46.

51. Determine the equilibrium constant, K, for the reactions in problem 47.

52. Determine the equilibrium constant, K, for the reactions in problem 48.

53. Determine the equilibrium constant, K, for the reactions in problem 49

54. Calculate $E°_{cell}$ for the following reaction at 25°C under the given sets of conditions:

$$Pb^{2+}(aq)+Mn(s)\rightarrow Pb(s)+Mn^{2+}(aq)$$

    a. Standard Conditions: $[Pb^{2+}]=1.00\ M;[Mn^{2+}]=1.00\ M$

    b. $[Pb^{2+}]=0.0150\ M;[Mn^{2+}]=1.50\ M$

    c. $[Pb^{2+}]=1.50\ M;[Mn^{2+}]=0.0150\ M$

55. Calculate $E°_{cell}$ for the following reaction at 25°C under the given sets of conditions:

$$2\ Fe^{3+}(aq)+3\ Zn(s)\rightarrow 2\ Fe(s)+3\ Zn^{2+}(aq)$$

    a. Standard Conditions: $[Fe^{3+}]=1.00\ M;[Zn^{2+}]=1.00\ M$

    b. $[Fe^{3+}]=0.00100\ M;[Zn^{2+}]=3.00\ M$

    c. $[Fe^{3+}]=2.25\ M;[Zn^{2+}]=0.00320\ M$

56. At 25°C, one of the half-cells in a galvanic cell consists of a copper electrode submerged into a $3.75 \times 10^{-3}\ M$ aqueous solution of copper(II) nitrate, while the other half-cell consists of a zinc electrode in a 0.375 M solution of zinc nitrate. Calculate $E°_{cell}$ for this galvanic cell.

57. At 25°C, one of the half-cells in a galvanic cell consists of a lead electrode submerged into a 0.0350 M aqueous solution of lead(II) nitrate, while the other half-cell consists of a silver electrode in a 0.375 M solution of silver nitrate. Calculate $E°_{cell}$ for this galvanic cell.

ELECTROLYSIS

58. Consider the following generic electrolytic cell:

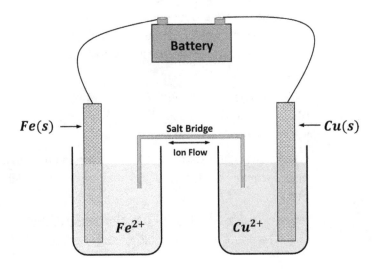

Sketch this cell and:

a. Write the balanced half-reaction for the cathode.

b. Write the balanced half-reaction for the anode.

c. Label the battery terminals as positive or negative and draw the flow of electrons.

59. Sketch a cell similar to that in problem 59 except replace the $Cu^{2+}(aq) / Cu(s)$ cell with $Mg^{2+}(aq) / Mg(s)$.

a. Write the balanced half-reaction for the cathode.

b. Write the balanced half-reaction for the anode.

c. Label the battery terminals as positive or negative and draw the flow of electrons.

60. Write the half-reactions that occur at the anode and cathode during electrolysis of molten sodium iodide.

61. Write the half-reactions that occur at the anode and cathode during electrolysis of molten potassium chloride.

62. In the electrolysis of aqueous potassium chloride, is chlorine gas or oxygen more likely to evolve from the anode? Why?

63. In the electrolysis of aqueous magnesium chloride, is magnesium metal or hydrogen gas more likely to evolve from the cathode? Why?

64. Write the half-reactions that occur at the anode and cathode during electrolysis of aqueous copper(II) chloride.

65. Write the half-reactions that occur at the anode and cathode during electrolysis of aqueous copper(II) bromide.

66. Write the half-reactions that occur at the anode and cathode during electrolysis of aqueous nickel(II) iodide.

67. Write the half-reactions that occur at the anode and cathode during electrolysis of aqueous calcium chloride.

68. Electrolysis and electroplating is the chemical means by which many metals are produced. If electrolysis of a solution of a silver salt is carried out with a current of 2.0 amps, what mass of silver metal will be produced over a time interval of 1.50 hours?

69. If electrolysis of a solution of Zn^{2+} is carried out with a current of 1.35 amps, what mass of zinc will be produced over a time interval of 45.25 minutes?

70. If electrolysis of a solution of Fe^{3+} is carried out with a current of 1.75 amps, how long would it take to produce 4.35 g of iron metal?

71. If electrolysis of a solution of Na^+ is carried out with a current of 2.00 amps, how long would it take to produce 10.00 g of sodium metal?

Image Credits

Chemical Kinetics

LEARNING OBJECTIVES AND OUTCOMES

After reading this chapter, you should be able to do the following:

- Perform simple chemical reaction rate calculations based on depletion of reactants and production of products with respect to two different time points.

- Perform calculations involving instantaneous rate at one point in time.

- Describe the reactant concentration effects on chemical reaction rates.

- Determine the rate law equation for a given chemical reaction from experimental data and be able to perform calculations using this equation.

- Perform calculations involving the integrated rate laws.

- Calculate reaction half-lives.

- Describe temperature effects on chemical reactions and apply the Arrhenius equation.

- Describe catalytic effects on chemical reactions.

- Recognize the difference between an overall chemical reaction and the reaction mechanism.

- Define each of the Key Terms listed at the end of the chapter dealing with these concepts.

Section 14.1 Introduction

Thus far, we have studied the basics of Chemistry and the structure of matter, among numerous other topics. We have learned about nomenclature and how to write various formulas of molecules as well as balanced chemical equations. We have seen how these balanced chemical equations can give us a wealth of information to include the ability to calculate product yields. In Chapters 10 and 11 we have also examined concepts associated with equilibrium and how far reactions will proceed towards completion, while in Chapter 12 we looked at whether reactions require energy or, in fact, release energy. While we have already covered a vast array of chemical concepts, we have yet to discuss another important aspect of chemical reactions, and that is reaction rates. **Reaction rates** involve the change in either reactant or product concentrations as a function of time. In order to understand the importance of this concept, let us, for example, consider how reaction rates

A rates of the chemical reactions that safely and successfully launch the space shuttle must be carefully controlled.

affect a space shuttle launch. If the chemical reaction that propels the shuttle ultimately into orbit is too slow, then the shuttle will not launch. If, however, the reaction rate is too fast, this might then put the lives of the astronauts onboard in danger. Therefore, the rates of these chemical reactions must be understood and carefully controlled in order to safely and successfully launch the space shuttle. In this chapter, we examine rates of reactions and the factors that affect the rate, as well as theories that explain these effects.

Section 14.2 Overview of Chemical Reaction Rates

Chemical Kinetics is the study of how fast reactants change into products by examining reaction rates. During a given chemical reaction, reactants decrease as products increase with time. The reaction rate refers to how fast this occurs and is usually expressed as a change in some quantity per unit of time. This is very similar to the speed limit at which we drive in our cars. For example, when you drive 60 miles per hour you cover 60 miles in one hour. In the same way, we can either measure the disappearance of a reactant or the appearance of product with respect to time. In fact, we can use several tools to measure reaction rates, some of which have already been discussed in previous chapters. For example, titration, mass spectroscopy, gas chromatography (for analysis of gas formation during a chemical reaction), and measurement of pressure fluctuations have all been used to accomplish this goal. In some cases, an **aliquot**, or a sample, can be taken at various time points for analysis using some of these methods. One technique, however, that we have not yet discussed but will examine much further in Chapter 15 involves polarimetry (involving the use of plane polarized light). In fact, one of the very first well-documented experiments involving measuring the rate of a chemical reaction was performed by Ludwig Wilhelmy using this very technique. Wilhelmy was a German scientist born in 1812 who would later publish his work involving the chemical kinetics of the breakdown of sucrose into glucose and fructose (these saccharides will be discussed further in Chapter 16). Wilhelmy died in Berlin in 1864, but not before being credited with having the first quantitative study in chemical kinetics for his work. In any event, now that we are aware of some techniques that can be used to monitor the rates of chemical reactions, let us now turn our attention to how these rates can be mathematically expressed by considering the following generic chemical equation below:

$$A \rightarrow B$$

We can express the rate of this reaction with respect to the disappearance of our reactant (A) or the production of product (B) as follows where is the change in time (time interval):

$$Rate\,of\,reaction = -\frac{\Delta[A]}{\Delta t} = \frac{\Delta[B]}{\Delta t}$$

Notice that the change in the reactant concentration is assigned a negative sign because it is decreasing with time, while the change in the product concentration gets a positive sign (usually left out and understood to be positive in the rate expression) because it increases with time. Either way, the rate of reaction will always be a positive number. How can this be? Well, let's consider Figure 14.1.

If we were to calculate the rate of reaction during the first 20 seconds with respect to the reactant (A), we would get the following:

$$Rate\,of\,reaction = -\frac{\Delta[A]}{\Delta t} = -\frac{([A]_2 - [A]_1)}{(t_2 - t_1)} = -\frac{(3M - 5M)}{(20s - 0s)} = 0.1\,M/s$$

Recall that Δx is defined as the final value minus the initial value (where x is any given variable of interest). If we were to calculate the rate of reaction during the first 20 seconds with respect to the product (B), we would get the following:

$$Rate\,of\,reaction = \frac{\Delta[B]}{\Delta t} = \frac{([B]_2 - [B]_1)}{(t_2 - t_1)} = \frac{(2M - 0M)}{(20s - 0s)} = 0.1\,M/s$$

It is important to note that, in both cases, whether we determine the rate with respect to reactant or product, we get the same positive number (0.1 M/s) within a given time frame. Similarly, if we chose to determine the rate of reaction during the second 20 seconds (i.e. the time period between 20 seconds and 40 seconds) with respect to the reactant (A), we would get the following:

$$Rate\,of\,reaction = -\frac{\Delta[A]}{\Delta t} = -\frac{([A]_2 - [A]_1)}{(t_2 - t_1)} = -\frac{(2M - 3M)}{(40s - 20s)} = 0.05\,M/s$$

If we again were to calculate the rate of reaction during this same time period with respect to the product (B), we would get the following:

$$Rate\,of\,reaction = \frac{\Delta[B]}{\Delta t} = \frac{([B]_2 - [B]_1)}{(t_2 - t_1)} = \frac{(3M - 2M)}{(40s - 20s)} = 0.05\,M/s$$

Again, notice that in both cases, whether we determine the rate with respect to reactant or product, we get the same positive number (0.05 M/s) within the given time frame (between 20 seconds and 40 seconds). It is also important to point out here that in this example, we have a 1:1 stoichiometric ratio between reactant and product A:B, which makes things relatively easy. However, this is not usually the case. The question becomes, how do we set up our rate expression when the stoichiometric ratio is not 1:1 such that we get the same reaction rate regardless of whether we monitor the disappearance of reactants or production of products? In other words, we need a single rate for the entire reaction regardless of the coefficients in the balanced chemical

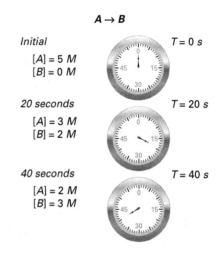

A → B

Initial
[A] = 5 M
[B] = 0 M
T = 0 s

20 seconds
[A] = 3 M
[B] = 2 M
T = 20 s

40 seconds
[A] = 2 M
[B] = 3 M
T = 40 s

Figure 14.1 Reactant and product concentrations with respect to time for a generic reaction $A \rightarrow B$.

equation. How is this done? Well, let's look at a specific example involving cyclobutane in order to clarify the question being asked here.

$$C_4H_8 \rightarrow 2C_2H_4$$

In this example, 1 *mol* of C_4H_8 produces 2 *mols* of C_2H_4. How is it that we can get a single rate for the entire reaction if C_2H_4 is being produced twice as fast as C_4H_8 disappears? Well, in order to account for this fact, the rate expression definition has to be reflective of the coefficients in the balanced chemical equation which can be accomplished as follows:

$$Rate\,of\,reaction = -\frac{\Delta[C_4H_8]}{\Delta t} = \frac{1}{2}\frac{\Delta[C_2H_4]}{\Delta t}$$

Notice that here we have included a "1 over 2" term in front of the rate of the appearance of products. In this case, the "2" is the stoichiometric coefficient for C_2H_4 from the balanced reaction equation. More generally, we can now define the rate of reaction of a generic equation while accounting for differences in the stoichiometric coefficients as follows:

$$aA + bB \rightarrow cC$$

$$Rate\,of\,reaction = -\frac{1}{a}\frac{\Delta[A]}{\Delta t} = -\frac{1}{b}\frac{\Delta[B]}{\Delta t} = \frac{1}{c}\frac{\Delta[C]}{\Delta t}$$

Note, that it is very important at this time that we become familiar with the various rate definitions and their associated mathematical expressions, all of which are summarized in Table 14.1 for the above generic equation.

Table 14.1 The various rate definitions and their associated mathematical expressions for the generic reaction $aA + bB \rightarrow cC$.

$aA + bB \rightarrow cC$	
Rates	**Mathematical Expressions of Various Rates**
Rate of Disappearance of "A"	$Rate = \dfrac{\Delta[A]}{\Delta t}$
Rate of Reaction with respect to the Disappearance of "A"	$Rate = -\dfrac{1}{a}\dfrac{\Delta[A]}{\Delta t}$
Rate of Disappearance of "B"	$Rate = \dfrac{\Delta[B]}{\Delta t}$
Rate of Reaction with respect to the Disappearance of "B"	$Rate = -\dfrac{1}{b}\dfrac{\Delta[B]}{\Delta t}$
Rate of Appearance of "C"	$Rate = \dfrac{\Delta[C]}{\Delta t}$
Rate of Reaction with respect to the Appearance of "C"	$Rate = -\dfrac{1}{c}\dfrac{\Delta[C]}{\Delta t}$

Example Problem 14.1

Consider the following chemical reaction:

$$2N_2O\,(g) \rightarrow 2N_2\,(g) + O_2\,(g)$$

What is the rate of reaction if 2.1 *mols* of O_2 is produced in a 0.50 *L* container in the first 20.0 seconds of the reaction? What is the rate of depletion of N_2O and rate of production of N_2 during this same time period?

Solution:	
First, let's express the rate of reaction in terms of the change in concentrations of all reactants and products.	$$Rate\ of\ reaction = -\frac{1}{2}\frac{\Delta[N_2O]}{\Delta t} = \frac{1}{2}\frac{\Delta[N_2]}{\Delta t} = \frac{\Delta[O_2]}{\Delta t}$$
Now, let's calculate the rate of reaction in terms of the rate of appearance of O_2.	$$Concentration\ of\ O_2 = \frac{2.1\ mols\ O_2}{0.50\ L} = 4.2\ M$$ $$Rate\ of\ reaction = \frac{\Delta[O_2]}{\Delta t} = \frac{\left([O_2]_2 - [O_2]_1\right)}{\left(t_2 - t_1\right)}$$ $$= \frac{(4.2M - 0.0M)}{(20.0s - 0.0s)} = 2.1 \times 10^{-1}\frac{M}{s}$$
Now that we know the rate of reaction, we can now solve for the rate of depletion of $N_2O\left(\frac{\Delta[N_2O]}{\Delta t}\right)$ and the rate of production of $N_2\left(\frac{\Delta[N_2]}{\Delta t}\right)$ this same time period.	Rate of depletion of $N_2O\left(\frac{\Delta[N_2O]}{\Delta t}\right)$: $$Rate\ of\ reaction = 2.1 \times 10^{-1}\frac{M}{s} = -\frac{1}{2}\frac{\Delta[N_2O]}{\Delta t}$$ Thus, $\frac{\Delta[N_2O]}{\Delta t} = -4.2 \times 10^{-1}\frac{M}{s}$ *Notice that this value is negative because it is a reactant, which makes sense. Rate of production of $N_2\left(\frac{\Delta[N_2]}{\Delta t}\right)$: $$Rate\ of\ reaction = 2.1 \times 10^{-1}\frac{M}{s} = \frac{1}{2}\frac{\Delta[N_2]}{\Delta t}$$ Thus, $\frac{\Delta[N_2]}{\Delta t} = 4.2 \times 10^{-1}\frac{M}{s}$ *Notice that this value is positive because it is a product, which makes sense.

Example Problem 14.2

Consider the following chemical reaction:

$$C_4H_8(g) \rightarrow 2C_2H_4(g)$$

This reaction was monitored and the following data were collected:

Time (seconds)	$[C_4H_8]$ (M)
0.0	1.00
20.0	0.81
40.0	0.67
60.0	0.59

Calculate the rate of reaction between 20.0 and 40.0 seconds, as well as between 40.0 and 60.0 seconds. Also, calculate the rate of production of C_2H_4 during these time periods.

Solution:	
First, let's express the rate of reaction in terms of the change in concentrations of all reactants and products.	$Rate\ of\ reaction = -\dfrac{\Delta[C_4H_8]}{\Delta t} = \dfrac{1}{2}\dfrac{\Delta[C_2H_4]}{\Delta t}$
Now, let's calculate the rate of reaction in terms of the rate of depletion of C_4H_8 between 20.0 and 40.0 seconds.	$Rate\ of\ reaction = -\dfrac{\Delta[C_4H_8]}{\Delta t}$ $= -\dfrac{\left([C_4H_8]_2 - [C_4H_8]_1\right)}{(t_2 - t_1)}$ $= -\dfrac{\left(0.67M - 0.81M\right)}{(40.0s - 20.0s)}$ $= 7.0 \times 10^{-3}\dfrac{M}{s}$
Now that we know the rate of reaction, we can now solve for the rate of production of $C_2H_4\left(\frac{\Delta[C_2H_4]}{\Delta t}\right)$ during this same time period (20.0 – 40.0 s).	Rate of production of $C_2H_4\left(\frac{\Delta[C_2H_4]}{\Delta t}\right)$: $Rate\ of\ reaction = 7.0 \times 10^{-3}\dfrac{M}{s} = \dfrac{1}{2}\dfrac{\Delta[C_2H_4]}{\Delta t}$ Thus, $\frac{\Delta[C_2H_4]}{\Delta t} = 1.4 \times 10^{-2}\frac{M}{s}$ *Notice that this value is positive because it is a product, which makes sense.
Now, let's calculate the rate of reaction in terms of the rate of depletion of C_4H_8 between 40.0 and 60.0 seconds.	$Rate\ of\ reaction = -\dfrac{\Delta[C_4H_8]}{\Delta t}$ $= -\dfrac{\left([C_4H_8]_2 - [C_4H_8]_1\right)}{(t_2 - t_1)}$ $= -\dfrac{\left(0.59M - 0.67M\right)}{(60.0s - 40.0s)}$ $= 4.0 \times 10^{-3}\dfrac{M}{s}$
Now that we know the rate of reaction, we can now solve for the rate of production of $C_2H_4\left(\frac{\Delta[C_2H_4]}{\Delta t}\right)$ during this same time period (40.0 – 60.0 s).	Rate of production of $C_2H_4\left(\frac{\Delta[C_2H_4]}{\Delta t}\right)$: $Rate\ of\ reaction = 4.0 \times 10^{-3}\dfrac{M}{s} = \dfrac{1}{2}\dfrac{\Delta[C_2H_4]}{\Delta t}$ Thus, $\frac{\Delta[C_2H_4]}{\Delta t} = 8.0 \times 10^{-3}\frac{M}{s}$ *Notice that this value is positive because it is a product, which makes sense.

So far, we have calculated the rate of chemical reactions between two different time points. It is also important to point out that we can actually calculate the instantaneous rate of a reaction at any one time point. This can be done by calculating the slope of the line tangent to the point of interest on a graph of concentration versus time. For example, consider Figure 14.2 and the oxidation reaction of nitrogen monoxide to produce nitrogen dioxide.

$$2\ NO(g) + O_2(g) \rightarrow 2NO_2(g)$$

If we wanted to know what the instantaneous rate was at a particular given point in time (in this case at precisely 4,475 seconds after the reaction

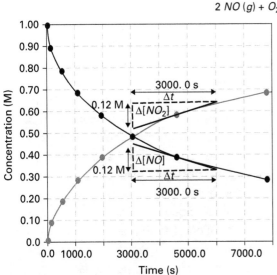

$$2\ NO\ (g) + O_2\ (g) \rightarrow 2\ NO_2\ (g)$$

Time (s)	[NO] (M)	[NO₂] (M)
0.0	1.00	0.0
210	0.90	0.10
570	0.80	0.20
1010	0.70	0.30
1925	0.60	0.40
3005	0.50	0.50
4475	0.40	0.60
7925	0.30	0.70

Instantaneous Rate (Reactant):

$$Rate_{4475\ seconds} = -\frac{\Delta[NO]}{\Delta t} = -\frac{-0.12\ M}{3000.0\ s} = 4.0 \times 10^{-5}\ M/s$$

Instantaneous Rate (Product):

$$Rate_{4475\ seconds} = \frac{\Delta[NO_2]}{\Delta t} = \frac{0.12\ M}{3000.0\ s} = 4.0 \times 10^{-5}\ M/s$$

begins) with respect to the depletion of reactants, we can calculate that as follows:

Figure 14.2 The instantaneous rate can be calculated by finding the slope of the line that is tangent to the point of interest.

$$Rate_{4475\ seconds} = -\frac{\Delta[NO]}{\Delta t} = -\frac{-0.12\ M}{3000.0\ s} = 4.0 \times 10^{-5}\ M/s$$

Incidentally, we can also calculate the instantaneous rate at the same time point with respect to the production of products as follows:

$$Rate_{4475\ seconds} = \frac{\Delta[NO_2]}{\Delta t} = \frac{0.12\ M}{3000.0\ s} = 4.0 \times 10^{-5}\ M/s$$

Now that we have looked at an overview of chemical reaction rates, we will now further our understanding of this concept by examining how different factors influence chemical reaction rates. Specifically, over the next three sections we will discuss concentration effects, temperature effects as well catalytic effects on the overall chemical reaction rates.

Section 14.3 Concentration Effects on Chemical Reaction Rates

In this section, we will discuss how varying the concentration of reactants in a chemical reaction affects the overall reaction rate. For example, if we look at the reactant concentration changes with respect to time in Figure 14.2, we notice that the most rapid changes occur at the beginning of the reaction and then taper off toward the end. In fact, as the tangent line to the curve reaches zero, there are essentially no more changes to the reactant concentration because it is now completely depleted. Additionally, there are no more changes to the product concentration at this point as we have produced all we can. In this example, we can see how the rate is fastest at the beginning of the reaction when we have the highest concentration of reactants and slows dramatically as the reactant concentration decreases with time. Thus, we can see the parallel between concentration and reaction rates. However, these observations do not tell us the extent to which concentration affects reaction rates. For example, if we were to double the concentration of reactants, does the rate also double, quadruple, or even do nothing? In order to address these questions, we need to consider what is referred to as the reaction order. The **reaction order** tells us how the reaction rate depends on the reactant concentrations. In order to determine this particular parameter for a given chemical reaction, we generally need to conduct a series of experiments in which we vary the concentration of each reactant and determine how this in fact influences (if at all) the overall reaction rate. For example, let us consider the following generic reaction and experimental data:

$$A + B \rightarrow C$$

Experiment	$[A]$	$[B]$	Initial Reaction Rate (M/s)
1	1.0	1.0	1.0×10^{-3}
2	1.0	0.50	5.0×10^{-4}
3	0.50	1.0	2.5×10^{-4}

From this experimental data, we look for two different experiments that we can compare where just one of the reactant concentrations is changing, while the other remains constant. Thus, if we compare Experiment #2 and #1, we see that while $[A]$ remains constant in both experiments at 1.0 M, $[B]$ changes from 0.50 M in Experiment #2 to 1.0 M in Experiment #1. We also notice that the reaction rate is doubled when $[B]$ is doubled in going from Experiment #2 to Experiment #1. Thus, we can conclude that the initial reaction rate is directly proportional to $[B]$. That is:

$$Rate \propto [B]$$

Now that we have determined how the concentration of B affects the reaction rate, we now look for two different experiments in which $[B]$ remains constant and $[A]$ changes. Thus, if we compare Experiment #3 and #1, we see that while $[B]$ remains constant, $[A]$ is doubled. When $[A]$ is doubled, we also notice that the reaction rate goes up by a factor of 4. Therefore, the reaction rate is proportional to the square of the concentration of A as follows:

$$Rate \propto [A]^2$$

If we now want to combine these two to get an overall rate expression we get the following:

$$Rate \propto [A]^2[B]$$

Notice that we have multiplied these two together in the rate expression because increasing the concentrations of reactants produces increasing numbers of collision between the two, which are proportional to product of the number of molecules of each reactant. Now, we can further modify this equation to generate the **rate law equation**, which defines the mathematical relationship between the reactant concentrations (in this case A and B) to the reaction rate as follows:

$$Rate = k[A]^2[B]$$

where k is defined as the **rate constant** or proportionality constant (related to the slope of the line in a graph of concentration versus time). Also, notice that each reactant is raised to their respective orders. That is, [A] is second-order and [B] is first-order. It would also follow that if increasing the concentration of a particular reactant in a chemical reaction had no effect on the rate, it would be zero-order. The **overall reaction order** is defined as the sum of the powers in the rate equation. Thus, the overall reaction order in the above example would be third-order overall. Now that we have determined the rate expression for this reaction, we can pick any of the three experiments above and calculate the value of k as follows:

If we pick Experiment #1:

$$k = \frac{Rate}{[A]^2[B]} = \frac{1.0 \times 10^{-3} M \cdot s^{-1}}{(1.0M)^2 \times (1.0M)} = 1.0 \times 10^{-3} \ M^{-2} \cdot s^{-1}$$

If we pick Experiment #2:

$$k = \frac{Rate}{[A]^2[B]} = \frac{5.0 \times 10^{-4} M \cdot s^{-1}}{(1.0M)^2 \times (0.50M)} = 1.0 \times 10^{-3} \ M^{-2} \cdot s^{-1}$$

If we pick Experiment #3:

$$k = \frac{Rate}{[A]^2[B]} = \frac{2.5 \times 10^{-4} M \cdot s^{-1}}{(0.50M)^2 \times (1.0M)} = 1.0 \times 10^{-3} \ M^{-2} \cdot s^{-1}$$

Thus, we can write the following rate equation:

$$Rate = k[A]^2[B] = (1.0 \times 10^{-3} \ M^{-2} \cdot s^{-1})[A]^2[B]$$

Notice that no matter which experiment we pick, we get the same correct answer for the value of k (1.0 $\times 10^{-3}$ $M^{-2} \cdot s$. Also, notice the units for k here are $M^{-2} \cdot s$. In fact, the units for k will vary depending on the overall reaction

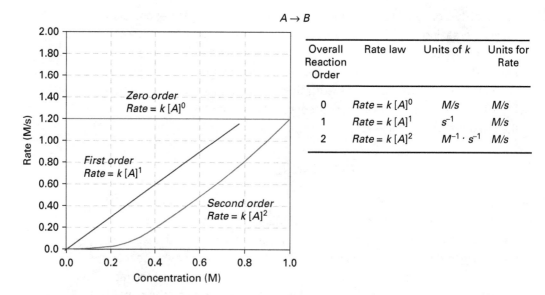

Figure 14.3 Demonstration of how changing the concentration of reactants affects the initial reaction rates when reactants are either zero-, first-, or second-order (left). Also, the various units for k are dependent upon the overall reaction order (right). These units will vary such that the units for the rate are M/s.

order such that the units for the rate always works out to M/s. Thus, in this example (overall third-order) we get the following:

$$Rate = k[A]^2[B] = \underbrace{\frac{k}{\frac{1}{M^2 \cdot s}}}_{} \underbrace{M^2 M}_{[A]^2[B]} = \frac{M}{s}$$

Figure 14.3 summarizes how changing the concentration of reactants affects the initial reaction rates when reactants are either zero-, first- or second-order, as well as various units for k depending on the overall reaction order.

Example Problem 14.3

Consider the following generic chemical reaction and experimental data:

$$A + B \rightarrow C$$

Experiment	[A]	[B]	Initial Reaction Rate (M/s)
1	0.25	0.25	2.4×10^{-3}
2	0.50	0.25	9.6×10^{-3}
3	0.25	0.50	2.4×10^{-3}
4	0.50	0.50	9.6×10^{-3}

Determine the reaction rate law expression. What is the overall reaction order? What is the value of the rate constant k?

Solution:	
First, let's write a general rate law using x and y for the orders of [A] and [B].	$Rate = k[A]^x[B]^y$

Now, we look for two experiments above in which [A] changes, but [B] remains constant. Notice if we compare Experiments #1 and #2 (or #3 and #4), we see that [A] doubles, while [B] remains constant. Also, notice that the rate also quadruples when [A] doubles, so [A] must be second-order (substitute 2 in for x).	$$Rate = k[A]^2[B]^y$$
Now, we look for two other experiments above in which [B] changes but [A] remains constant. Notice if we compare Experiments #1 and #3 (or #2 and #4), we see that [B] doubles, while [A] remains constant. Also, notice that the rate is unaffected and does not change. Therefore, [B] must be zero-order as it has no effect on the rate (substitute 0 in for y). Thus, [B] is left out of the overall rate expression.	$$Rate = k[A]^2[B]^0$$ or $$\mathbf{Rate = k[A]^2}$$ Thus, the overall reaction order is **second-order**.
Now, we can pick any one of the four experiments, plug in the rate and concentration values for [A], and solve for k. Notice that no matter what experiment you pick, you will get the same correct answer. Also notice the units for k in this case (second-order overall reaction order = $M^{-1} \cdot s^{-1}$).	$$Rate = k[A]^2$$ If we pick Experiment #1 or #3: $$k = \frac{Rate}{[A]^2} = \frac{2.4 \times 10^{-3} M \cdot s^{-1}}{(0.25M)^2} = 3.8 \times 10^{-2}\ M^{-1} \cdot s^{-1}$$ If we pick Experiment #2 or #4: $$k = \frac{Rate}{[A]^2} = \frac{9.6 \times 10^{-3} M \cdot s^{-1}}{(0.50M)^2} = 3.8 \times 10^{-2}\ M^{-1} \cdot s^{-1}$$ Thus, we can write the following rate equation: $$\mathbf{Rate = (3.8 \times 10^{-2}\ M^{-1} \cdot s^{-1})[A]^2}$$

Example Problem 14.4

Consider the following chemical reaction and experimental data acquired at a particular temperature:
$$2NO_2\ (g) + F_2(g) \rightarrow 2NO_2F\ (g)$$

Experiment	[NO_2]	[F_2]	Initial Reaction Rate (M/s)
1	0.50	0.50	0.13
2	0.50	1.0	0.26
3	1.0	1.0	0.52

Determine the reaction rate law expression. What is the overall reaction order? What is the value of the rate constant k?
Solution:

First, let's write a general rate law using x and y for the orders of [NO_2] and [F_2].	$$Rate = k[NO_2]^x[F_2]^y$$

Now, we look for two experiments above in which $[NO_2]$ changes but $[F_2]$ remains constant. Notice if we compare Experiments #2 and #3, we see that $[NO_2]$ doubles, while $[F_2]$ remains constant. Also, notice that the rate also doubles when $[NO_2]$ doubles, so $[NO_2]$ must be first-order (substitute 1 in for x).	$Rate = k[NO_2]^1[F_2]^y$
Now, we look for two other experiments above in which $[F_2]$ changes, but $[NO_2]$ remains constant. Notice if we compare Experiments #1 and #2, we see that $[F_2]$ doubles, while $[NO_2]$ remains constant. Also, notice that the rate also doubles when $[F_2]$ doubles, so $[F_2]$ must also be first-order (substitute 1 in for y).	$Rate = k[NO_2]^1[F_2]^1$ or $Rate = k[NO_2][F_2]$ Thus, the overall reaction order is **second-order**.
Now, we can pick any one of the three experiments, plug in the rate and concentration values for $[NO_2]$ and $[F_2]$, and solve for k. Notice that no matter what experiment you pick, you will get the same correct answer. Also notice the units for k in this case (second-order overall reaction order = $M^{-1} \cdot s^{-1}$).	$Rate = k[NO_2][F_2]$ If we pick Experiment #1: $k = \dfrac{Rate}{[NO_2][F_2]} = \dfrac{0.13 M \cdot s^{-1}}{(0.50M) \times (0.50M)} = 0.52\, M^{-1} \cdot s^{-1}$ If we pick Experiment #2: $k = \dfrac{Rate}{[NO_2][F_2]} = \dfrac{0.26 M \cdot s^{-1}}{(0.50M) \times (1.0M)} = 0.52\, M^{-1} \cdot s^{-1}$ If we pick Experiment #3: $k = \dfrac{Rate}{[NO_2][F_2]} = \dfrac{0.52 M \cdot s^{-1}}{(1.0M) \times (1.0M)} = 0.52\, M^{-1} \cdot s^{-1}$ Thus, we can write the following rate equation: $Rate = (0.52\ M^{-1} \cdot s^{-1})[NO_2][F_2]$

Integrated Rate Laws

Notice in Figure 14.3 that we have a plot of rate versus various reactant concentrations acquired by doing several experiments. However, what if we wanted to determine the rate law and calculate the rate constant with a single experiment by looking at the relationship between reactant concentration and time? In other words, is it possible to do this in a single experiment by following the decreasing concentrations of a particular reactant with respect to time? The answer to this question is yes; we can do this by using the **integrated rate law**, which utilizes the relationship between the concentrations of the reactants and time. For example, let us consider a single reactant (*A*) for simplicity decomposing into products (B and C), and consider zero-order, first-order, and second-order integrated rate laws:

$$A \rightarrow B + C$$

Zero-Order Integrated Rate Law

Since the decomposition of $[A]$ is $= -\frac{\Delta[A]}{\Delta t}$, we can write the following:

$$Rate = -\frac{\Delta[A]}{\Delta t} = k$$

Upon integration (individual steps not shown here), we get the zero-order integrated rate law in the form of an equation of a straight line as follows:

$$[A]_t = -kt + [A]_0$$

where $[A]_t$ is the concentration of A at any time (t), k is the rate constant, and $[A]_0$ is the initial concentration of A.

First-Order Integrated Rate Law

Since the decomposition of $[A]$ is $= -\frac{\Delta[A]}{\Delta t}$, we can write the following:

$$Rate = -\frac{\Delta[A]}{\Delta t} = k[A]$$

Upon integration (individual steps not shown here), we get the first-order integrated rate law in the form of an equation of a straight line as follows:

$$ln[A]_t = -kt + ln[A]_0$$

where $[A]_t$ is the concentration of A at any time (t), k is the rate constant, and $[A]_0$ is the initial concentration of A.

Second-Order Integrated Rate Law

Since the decomposition of $[A]$ is $= -\frac{\Delta[A]}{\Delta t}$, we can write the following:

$$Rate = -\frac{\Delta[A]}{\Delta t} = k[A]^2$$

Upon integration (individual steps not shown here), we get the second-order integrated rate law in the form of an equation of a straight line as follows:

$$\frac{1}{[A]_t} = kt + \frac{1}{[A]_0}$$

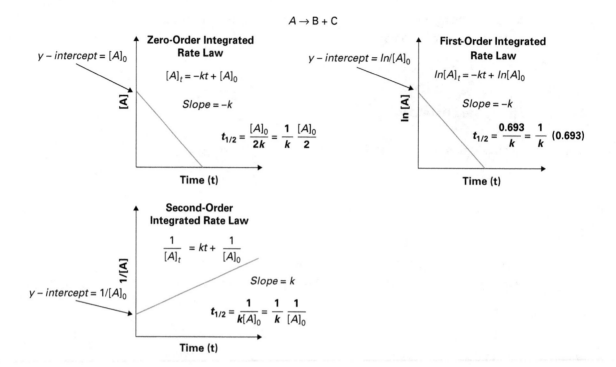

$$A \rightarrow B + C$$

Zero-Order Integrated Rate Law

$y - intercept = [A]_0$

$$[A]_t = -kt + [A]_0$$

$Slope = -k$

$$t_{1/2} = \frac{[A]_0}{2k} = \frac{1}{k}\frac{[A]_0}{2}$$

First-Order Integrated Rate Law

$y - intercept = ln/[A]_0$

$$ln[A]_t = -kt + ln[A]_0$$

$Slope = -k$

$$t_{1/2} = \frac{0.693}{k} = \frac{1}{k}(0.693)$$

Second-Order Integrated Rate Law

$y - intercept = 1/[A]_0$

$$\frac{1}{[A]_t} = kt + \frac{1}{[A]_0}$$

$Slope = k$

$$t_{1/2} = \frac{1}{k[A]_0} = \frac{1}{k}\frac{1}{[A]_0}$$

Figure 14.4 Plots of zero–order, first–order, and second–order integrated rate law equations. Zero-Order Reaction Half-Life, First-Order Reaction Half-Life, and Second-Order Reaction Half-Life Expressions are depicted within each plot.

where $[A]_t$ is the concentration of A at any time (t), k is the rate constant, and $[A]_0$ is the initial concentration of A. Figure 14.4 graphically depicts the equations above for zero-order, first-order, and second-order integrated rate laws.

Reaction Half-Lives

Reaction half-life refers to the time in which the concentration of a reactant decreases by half and is commonly discussed in chemical kinetics. It is important to keep in mind that the half-life of a reaction is inversely related to the rate constant, which is to say that higher reaction rates translate into shorter half-lives. The mathematical relationship between the rate constants and half-lives are dependent on the overall order of the reaction and are therefore derived below.

Zero-Order Reaction Half-Life—The half-life for a zero-order reaction can be calculated as follows:

$$[A]_t = -kt + [A]_0$$

$$t_{1/2} = \frac{[A]_0}{2k} = \frac{1}{k}\frac{[A]_0}{2}$$

First-Order Reaction Half-Life—The half-life for a first-order reaction can be calculated as follows:

$$ln[A]_t = -kt + ln[A]_0$$

$$t_{1/2} = \frac{0.693}{k} = \frac{1}{k}(0.693)$$

Second-Order Reaction Half-Life—The half-life for a second-order reaction can be calculated as follows:

$$\frac{1}{[A]_t} = kt + \frac{1}{[A]_0}$$

$$t_{1/2} = \frac{1}{k[A]_0} = \frac{1}{k}\frac{1}{[A]_0}$$

Example Problem 14.5

Consider the following generic chemical reaction and experimental data:

$$A \rightarrow B + C$$

Time (s)	[A]
0	0.94
25	0.62
50	0.46
75	0.36
100	0.30
125	0.26
150	0.23
175	0.20
200	0.18

Determine the order of the reaction. What is the value of the rate constant k? What is the half-life of the reaction?

Solution:

First, we will generate all three plots for zero-order, first-order, and second-order. The plot that yields a straight line will tell us the order of this reaction.

Time	[A]	ln [A]	1/[A]
0	0.94	−0.06	1.06
25	0.62	−0.48	1.61
50	0.46	−0.78	2.17
75	0.36	−1.02	2.78
100	0.30	−1.20	3.33
125	0.26	−1.35	3.85
150	0.23	−1.47	4.35
175	0.20	−1.61	5.00
200	0.18	−1.71	5.56

If we apply the zero-order integrated rate law:

$$[A]_t = -kt + [A]_0$$

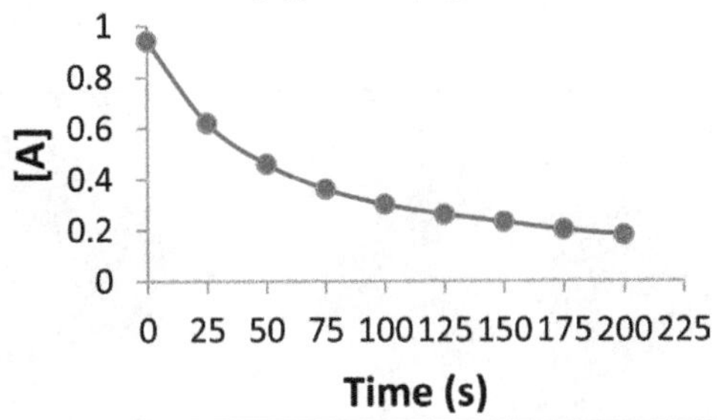

If we apply the first-order integrated rate law:

$$ln\,[A]_t = -kt + ln\,[A]_0$$

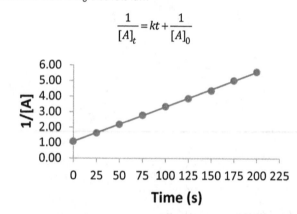

If we apply the second-order integrated rate law:

$$\frac{1}{[A]_t} = kt + \frac{1}{[A]_0}$$

Thus, we can conclude that this reaction is **second-order,** since this fits the data linearly.

Now that we know this is a second-order reaction, we can calculate k. While we can pick any time point to do this, here we will use the concentration of A at 25 s.	$$\frac{1}{[A]_t} = kt + \frac{1}{[A]_0}$$ $$k = \frac{\left(\dfrac{1}{[A]_t} - \dfrac{1}{[A]_0}\right)}{t}$$ $$k = \frac{\left(\dfrac{1}{(0.62M)} - \dfrac{1}{(0.94M)}\right)}{25s} = 0.022\,M^{-1} \cdot s^{-1}$$ Thus, the rate expression can be written as follows: $$Rate = (0.022\ M^{-1} \cdot s^{-1})\,[A]^2$$
Now, we can calculate the half-life for the reaction. If we wanted to, we could also calculate the y-intercept value and write out the equation of the line.	$$t_{1/2} = \frac{1}{k[A]_0} = \frac{1}{k}\frac{1}{[A]_0} = \frac{1}{0.022\,M^{-1} \cdot s^{-1}}\frac{1}{0.94\,M} = 48\,s$$ $$y - intercept = \frac{1}{[A]_0} = \frac{1}{(0.94M)} = 1.06$$ $$y = 0.022x + 1.06$$

Section 14.4 Temperature Effects on Chemical Reaction Rates

In order for most reactions to occur, essentially two basic criteria must be met according to the **collision theory of kinetics.** According to this theory, reactant molecules must collide with sufficient energy and proper orientation for the reaction to take place. **Effective collisions** result when both of these conditions are met, which can then lead to the formation of an **activated complex** or **transition state** (Figure 14.5). This complex is a temporary high energy and unstable complex. The **activation energy** (E_a) is defined as the energy barrier (or activation barrier) which must be overcome in order to temporarily form the activated complex as reactants are used to produce products. Based on our understanding of effective collisions leading to product formation, it should be no surprise that reaction rates are very dependent on temperature. In other words, higher temperatures can produce a higher frequency of effective collisions, which, in turn, results in faster reaction rates. If, however, temperature has such a profound effect on reaction rates, then why does this variable not appear in the rate expression (i.e. Rate = $k[A]^x$)? The short answer to this question is that it does. The effect of temperature on the reaction rate is contained within the rate constant (k), which is therefore really only constant at a constant temperature. We can clearly see this correlation by taking a look at the **Arrhenius equation** as follows:

Svante Arrhenius (1859–1927) was a developed the Arrhenius equation,and was awarded the Nobel Prize for Chemistry in 1903.

$$k = Ae^{\frac{-E_a}{RT}}$$

where k is the rate constant, A is the pre-exponential factor (or frequency factor), $e^{\frac{-E_a}{RT}}$ is the exponential factor (explained in further detail below), E_a is the activation energy, R is the gas constant $\left(8.314 \frac{J}{mol \cdot K}\right)$, and T is the Kelvin temperature. The **pre-exponential or frequency factor (A)** in the Arrhenius equation represents the number of times that reactants approach the activation barrier, while the **exponential factor** $\left(e^{\frac{-E_a}{RT}}\right)$ represents the number of molecules that have enough energy to make it over the activation barrier on a given approach. Svante Arrhenius was a Swedish scientist born in 1859 who developed this equation and was awarded the Nobel Prize for Chemistry in 1903, becoming the first Swedish Nobel laureate.

Figure 14.5 Energy diagram of uncatalyzed and catalyzed reactions.

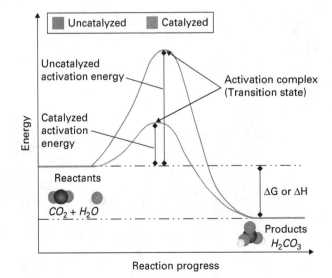

Section 14.5 Catalytic Effects on Chemical Reaction Rates

We have so far discussed chemical reaction rates and how changing the concentration or temperature can affect them. However, this is not always possible from a practical point of view. There are limits as to how concentrated a sample can be and how high the temperature can go before unwanted side-reactions start to occur. An alternative to these methods involves using a **catalyst** to increase reaction rates, which can do this without itself being consumed in the reaction. Catalysts work by lowering the activation energy of a particular reaction (Figure 14.5). It is important to point out that while they increase the rates of chemical reactions by lowering the activation energy, catalysts do not affect ΔG or ΔH of the reaction as discussed in Chapter 12. A good example of a catalyst is found in the catalytic converters present in our cars. Catalytic converters are emission-control devices which contain a mixture of precious metals (i.e. platinum) that catalyzes reactions involving the conversion of toxic gases and pollutants in our exhaust to less toxic pollutants. For example, nitrogen monoxide and carbon monoxide can be converted to nitrogen and carbon dioxide using this solid catalyst as follows:

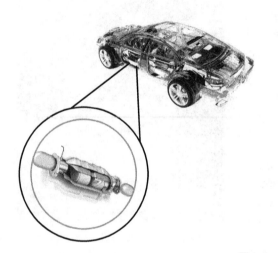

$$2NO\,(g) + 2CO\,(g) \rightarrow N_2\,(g) + 2CO_2\,(g)$$

This is an example of a **heterogeneous catalyst**, in which the catalyst (solid) is in a different phase from the reactants (gases). A **homogeneous catalyst** would be one in which the catalyst is in the same phase as the reactants. **Enzymes** are biological catalysts that increase the rates of biochemical reactions. For example, hexokinase (Figure 14.6) is an enzyme that catalyzes the

Figure 14.6 Hexokinase is an enzyme that phosphorylates hexoses (6 carbon sugars) forming hexose phosphate. *Indicates a phosphate group.

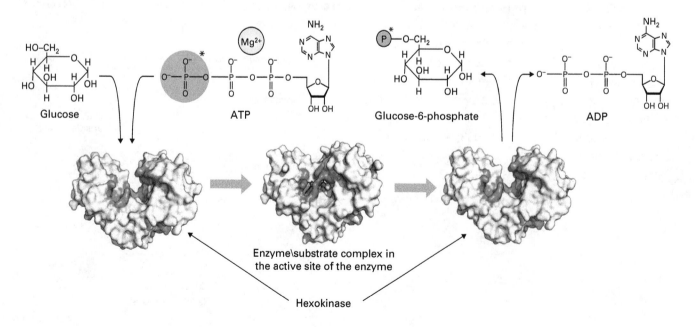

Glucose   ATP   Glucose-6-phosphate   ADP

Enzyme\substrate complex in the active site of the enzyme

Hexokinase

first step in glycolysis in which glucose is converted to glucose-6-phosphate (discussed in further detail below).

Section 14.6 Reaction Mechanisms

Most of what we have discussed in this chapter has been the rates of single-step or overall chemical reactions. However, most reactions (i.e. biochemical reactions) occur as a series of steps. For example, glycolysis is the metabolic pathway that converts glucose ultimately into pyruvate, a process in which organisms acquire biochemical energy (generally in the form of adenosine triphosphate or *ATP*. The whole process is ten metabolic steps. However, if we were to only consider the first five steps in the metabolic pathway (i.e. the "preparatory or investment stage" of glycolysis), we get the following overall reaction:

Glucose + 2 ATP → 2 Glyceraldehyde – 3 – phosphate + 2 ADP

While this is the overall reaction for this particular stage of glycolysis, we can write out the five individual series of steps that contribute to this overall reaction as seen in Figure 14.7. This is known as the **reaction mechanism**, which is the series of individual steps that contribute to the overall chemical reaction. Notice that the reaction mechanism contains **reaction intermediates** (crossed out in red), which are produced in one step and consumed in another. As such, the reaction intermediates do not appear in overall reaction. It is also important to point out that reaction mechanisms generally contain

Figure 14.7 The first five reactions of Glycolysis with reaction intermediates crossed out in red, and highlighted species that appear in the overall reaction.

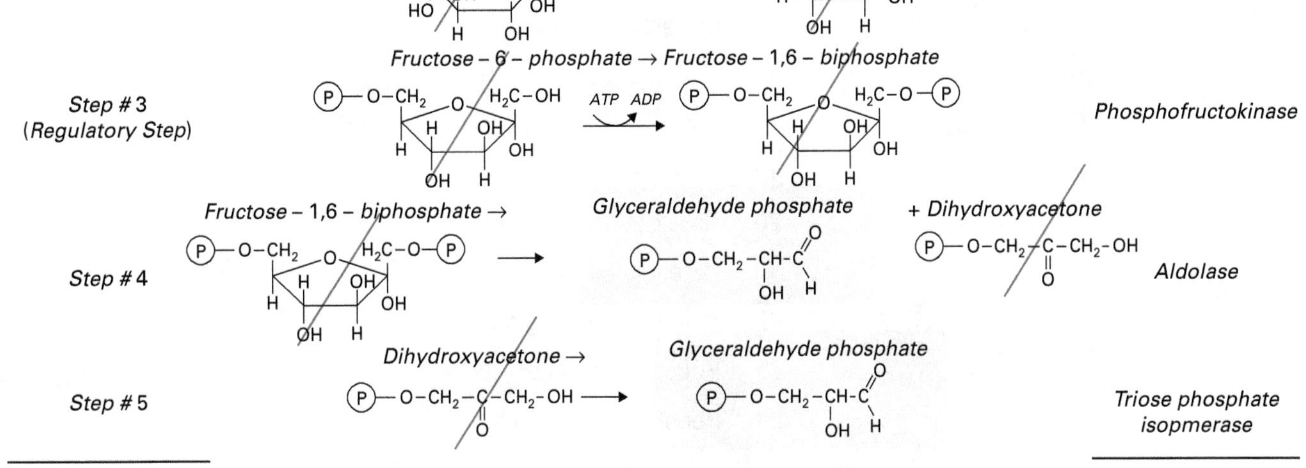

Step		Enzyme
Step # 1	*Glucose → Glucose – 6 – phosphate*	Hexokinase
Step # 2	*Glucose – 6 – phosphate → Fructose – 6 – phosphate*	Phosphoglucose Isomerase
Step # 3 (*Regulatory Step*)	*Fructose – 6 – phosphate → Fructose – 1,6 – biphosphate*	Phosphofructokinase
Step # 4	*Fructose – 1,6 – biphosphate →* *Glyceraldehyde phosphate* *+ Dihydroxyacetone*	Aldolase
Step # 5	*Dihydroxyacetone →* *Glyceraldehyde phosphate*	Triose phosphate isopmerase

a **rate-determining or rate-limiting step**, which has a much slower rate than the others in the mechanism and is often a point of regulatory control of the whole reaction mechanism. As the rate-determining step is the slowest step, it limits the overall rate of the reaction and is therefore generally used to determine the rate law for the whole reaction mechanism. For example, in glycolysis step #3 involving the enzyme phosphofructokinase is one of the rate-limiting steps and is a major point of regulation in this process. In any event, while the naming and drawing of these individual structures may seem a bit complicated at this point, we will now get into more detail regarding nomenclature and classification of various molecules as it relates to both Organic Chemistry and Biochemistry in the next two chapters.

Key Terms

1. Activated complex
2. Activation energy
3. Aliquot
4. Arrhenius equation
5. Catalyst
6. Chemical kinetics
7. Collision theory of kinetics
8. Effective collisions
9. Enzymes
10. Exponential factor (Arrhenius equation)
11. First-order integrated rate law
12. First-order reaction half-life
13. Frequency factor (*A*) (Arrhenius equation)
14. Heterogeneous catalyst
15. Homogenous catalyst
16. Integrated rate law
17. Overall reaction order
18. Pre-exponential factor (*A*) (Arrhenius equation)
19. Rate constant
20. Rate-determining step
21. Rate law equation
22. Rate-determining step
23. Reaction half-lives
24. Reaction intermediates

Problems

OVERVIEW OF CHEMICAL REACTION RATES

1. What are chemical reaction rates?

2. Define chemical kinetics.

3. Why are the rates of reactions defined as the negative of the change of reactant concentrations with respect to time, and positive of the change of product concentrations with respect to time?

4. Express the rate of reaction with respect to each reactant and product given the following hypothetical generic chemical equation:

$$A + B \rightarrow C + D$$

5. Express the rate of reaction with respect to each reactant and product given the following hypothetical generic chemical equation:

$$A + 3B \rightarrow 2C + 2D$$

6. Express the rate expression with respect to the reactant or product in **bold** in the balanced chemical equations listed below.

    a. $\mathbf{CH_4(g)} + 2O_2(g) \rightarrow CO_2(g) + 2H_2O(g)$

    b. $P_4(s) + \mathbf{3O_2(g)} \rightarrow 2P_2O_3(s)$

    c. $2Fe_2O_3(s) + 3C(s) \rightarrow \mathbf{4Fe(s)} + 3CO_2(g)$

    d. $2H_2(g) + V_2O_5(s) \rightarrow V_2O_3(s) + \mathbf{2H_2O(l)}$

7. Express the rate expression with respect to the reactant or product in **bold** the balanced chemical equations listed below.

   a. **$4NH_3(g)$** + $5O_2(g)$ → $4NO(g)$ + $6H_2O(g)$

   b. $3Cl_2(g)$ + **$6NaOH(aq)$** → $5NaCl(aq)$ + $NaClO_3(aq)$ + $3H_2O(l)$

   c. $2Fe(s)$ + $O_2(g)$ + $2H_2O(l)$ → **$2Fe(OH)_2(s)$**

   d. $C_6H_6(l)$ + $15H_2O_2(l)$ → $6CO_2(g)$ + **$18H_2O(l)$**

8. Using the data table below, calculate the rate of reaction with respect to reactant x in the first 10 seconds.

$$X \rightarrow Y + Z$$

Time (s)	X concentration (M)	Y concentration (M)	Z concentration (M)
0.0	3.00	0.00	0.00
10.0	2.70	0.30	0.30
20.0	2.40	0.60	0.60
30.0	2.20	0.80	0.80

9. Using the data table in Question # 8, calculate the rate of reaction with respect to product Y in the last 10.0 seconds.

10. Consider the following chemical reaction:

$$2SO_2(g) + O_2(g) \rightarrow 2SO_3(g)$$

What is the rate of this reaction if 0.15 *mols* of SO_3 are produced in a 0.50 *L* container in the first 25.0 *s*?

11. Based on your answer from Question # 10, what is the rate of depletion of $O_2\left(\frac{\Delta O_2}{\Delta t}\right)$ in that reaction during the same time period?

12. Consider the following chemical reaction:

$$2N_2O(g) \rightarrow 2N_2(g) + O_2(g)$$

What is the rate of this reaction if 0.25 *mols* of O_2 are produced in a 0.50 *L* container in the first 35.0 *s*?

13. Based on your answer from Question # 12, what is the rate of depletion of $N_2O\left(\frac{\Delta N_2O}{\Delta t}\right)$ in that reaction during the same time period?

For Questions #14–17, consider the following chemical equation:

This reaction was monitored and the following data were collected:

$$C_4H_8 \rightarrow 2C_2H_4$$

Time (seconds)	$[C_4H_8]$ (M)
0.0	1.00
20.0	0.72
40.0	0.61
60.0	0.55

14. Given the data above, what is the reaction rate between 0.0 *s* and 20.0 *s*?

15. Given the data above, what is the rate of production of C_2H_4 $\left(\frac{\Delta[C_2H_4]}{\Delta t}\right)$ between 0.0 *s* and 20.0 *s*?

16. Given the data above, what is the reaction rate between 20.0 *s* and 40.0 *s*?

17. Given the data above, what is the rate of production of C_2H_4 $\left(\frac{\Delta[C_2H_4]}{\Delta t}\right)$ between 20.0 *s* and 40.0 *s*?

18. What is the difference between the average rate of a reaction and the instantaneous rate of a reaction?

CONCENTRATION EFFECTS ON CHEMICAL REACTION RATES

19. What is the reaction order?

20. What is the rate law equation?

21. Define the rate constant (*k*).

22. What is the overall reaction order?

23. What is the rate law if reactant "*A*" in the following generic equation is determined to be zero-order?

$$A \rightarrow B$$

24. What is the rate law if reactant "*A*" in the following generic equation is determined to be first-order?

$$A \rightarrow B$$

25. What is the rate law if reactant "*A*" in the following generic equation is determined to be second-order?

$$A \rightarrow B$$

26. What are the units for the rate constant (*k*) in an overall zero-order reaction?

27. What are the units for the rate constant (k) in an overall first-order reaction?

28. What are the units for the rate constant (k) in an overall second-order reaction?

For Questions #29–31, consider the following graph:

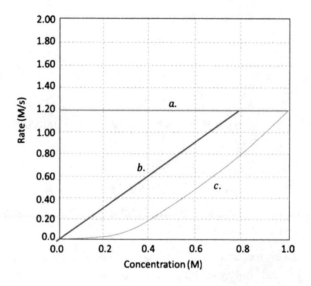

29. The line labeled "*a*" in the above graph represents what reaction order?

    a. Zero-order

    b. First-order

    c. Second-order

    d. Third-order

30. The line labeled "*b*" in the above graph represents what reaction order?

    a. Zero-order

    b. First-order

    c. Second-order

    d. Third-order

31. The line labeled "*c*" in the above graph represents what reaction order?

    a. Zero-order

    b. First-order

    c. Second-order

    d. Third-order

For Questions #32–36, consider the following hypothetical generic chemical reaction and experimental data acquired at a particular temperature:

$$A + B \rightarrow C$$

Experiment	[A]	[B]	Initial Reaction Rate (M/s)
1	0.23	0.23	0.13
2	0.23	0.46	0.26
3	0.46	0.23	0.26

32. What is the order of "A"?

33. What is the order of "B"?

34. What is the overall order of the reaction?

35. What is the value of the rate constant (k) for the reaction?

36. Write the rate law expression for this generic chemical reaction.

For Questions #37–41, consider the following chemical reaction and experimental data acquired at a particular temperature:

$$2NO\left(g\right) + O_2\left(g\right) \rightarrow 2NO_2\left(g\right)$$

Experiment	[NO]	[O$_2$]	Initial Reaction Rate (M/s)
1	0.48	0.48	1.0×10^{-5}
2	0.96	0.48	4.1×10^{-5}
3	0.48	0.96	2.1×10^{-5}

37. What is the order of NO?

38. What is the order of O_2?

39. What is the overall order of the reaction?

40. What is the value of the rate constant (k) for the reaction?

41. Write the rate law expression for this chemical reaction.

42. What is the integrated rate law?

43. Write the mathematical expression for the zero-order integrated rate law given the following generic equation:

$$A \rightarrow B + C$$

44. Write the mathematical expression for the first-order integrated rate law given the following generic equation:

$$A \rightarrow B + C$$

45. Write the mathematical expression for the second-order integrated rate law given the following generic equation:

$$A \rightarrow B + C$$

For Questions #46–48, consider the following generic equation and various graphs:

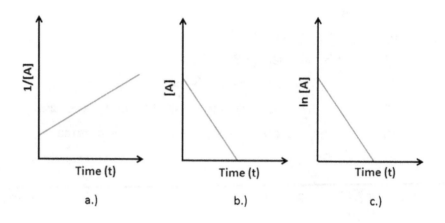

a.)   b.)   c.)

46. Which of the above plots represents the zero-order integrated rate law?

47. Which of the above plots represents the first-order integrated rate law?

48. Which of the above plots represents the second-order integrated rate law?

49. What are reaction half-lives?

50. Write the mathematical expression for the half-life of a zero-order reaction given the following generic equation:

$$A \rightarrow B + C$$

51. Write the mathematical expression for the half-life of a first-order reaction given the following generic equation:

$$A \rightarrow B + C$$

52. Write the mathematical expression for the half-life of a second-order reaction given the following generic equation:

$$A \rightarrow B + C$$

For Questions #53–55, consider the following generic equation and experimental data:

$$A \rightarrow B + C$$

Time (s)	[A]
0	0.98
25	0.88
50	0.79
75	0.69
100	0.59
125	0.50
150	0.40
175	0.30
200	0.20

53. Determine the order of the above reaction.

54. Given the data above, what is the value of the rate constant (k) for the reaction?

55. Write the rate expression for this reaction.

56. Given the data above, what is the half-life of the reaction?

For Questions #57–60, consider the following generic equation and experimental data:

$$A \rightarrow B + C$$

Time (s)	[A]
0	0.98
25	0.79
50	0.64
75	0.53
100	0.43
125	0.35
150	0.29
175	0.24
200	0.20

57. Determine the order of the above reaction.

58. Given the data above, what is the value of the rate constant (k) for the reaction?

59. Write the rate expression for this reaction.

60. Given the data above, what is the half-life of the reaction?

61. What is the collision theory of kinetics?

62. What is an activated complex?

63. What is the activation energy?

64. If temperature has such a profound effect on reaction rates, why is it not present in the rate equation (i.e. *Rate = k*[*A*]ˣ)? Write out the Arrhenius equation.

65. What is the pre-exponential factor in the Arrhenius equation and what does it tell you?

66. What is the exponential factor in the Arrhenius equation and what does it tell you?

67. What are catalysts?

68. What is a heterogeneous catalyst?

69. What is a homogeneous catalyst?

70. What are enzymes? Give an example.

71. What is a reaction mechanism?

72. What are reaction intermediates?

73. What is a rate-limiting step?

Image Credits

Introduction to Organic Chemistry

CHAPTER 15

LEARNING OBJECTIVES AND OUTCOMES

After reading this chapter, you should be able to do the following:

- Demonstrate a basic understanding of organic chemistry and explain why carbon is so important.

- Explain the differences between various hydrocarbons, to include both aliphatic and aromatic compounds.

- Define basic properties and explain the nomenclature of aliphatic compounds, to include alkanes, alkenes, alkynes, and cyclic compounds.

- Identify the various types of alkyl groups, as well as functional groups, and be able to name these compounds.

- Define isomerism in organic compounds and be able to differentiate between different kinds of isomers.

- Define the basic properties and explain the nomenclature of aromatic compounds.

- Define each of the Key Terms listed at the end of the chapter dealing with these concepts.

Section 15.1 Introduction

When students think of organic chemistry, many things may come to mind such as the organic compounds responsible for the pleasant odors associated with perfumes and colognes or extraction of various organic compounds from plants and leaves such as tobacco leaves. Maybe you think of the manufacturing of clothing and organic dyes. In fact, William Henry Perkin was a famous organic chemist who discovered the first synthetic, organic dye in 1856, mauveine. This is a purple dye, which was significant at the time because purple was the color preferred by royalty. Up until its discovery in 1856, purple dyes used for clothing were obtained by natural resources such as mollusks, and consequently were very expensive. Mauveine was the first mass-produced dye, and, as a result, Perkin was a very wealthy man by his mid-thirties, proving that organic chemistry can in fact be a very worthy subject for a scientist to devote an entire career. Since that time, this area of chemistry has grown into the large field of study that it is today with

Organic chemistry may bring to mind organic compounds found in perfumes and colognes or organic compounds from plants and tobacco leaves. For some, the thought of organic chemistry may bring to mind the anxiety of studying vast amounts of material for exams.

"Is it too late to drop the course?"

many widely used applications. In fact, for some students the very thought of organic chemistry may bring to mind the anxiety of studying vast amounts of material in preparation for challenging and infamous organic chemistry exams! Indeed, of the millions of known compounds, most of them are, in fact, organic molecules. Why is that? Well, let's take a look at the definition of organic chemistry. **Organic chemistry** is the study of carbon-containing compounds, which may also contain various other elements such as hydrogen, nitrogen, and oxygen, to name a few. The next obvious question is why does the carbon framework provide for such a vast array of diverse compounds? First, if you recall from Chapter 8, carbon prefers four bonds, which allows it to adopt an octet. This relatively large number of bonds allows carbon to form more complex structures than do other elements like nitrogen, oxygen, or the halogens, which prefer only three, two, or even just one bond(s), respectively. The four bonds formed by carbon can also exist in various combinations. For example, carbon can have four single bonds to four other atoms, one double bond and two single bonds, two double bonds, or a triple bond and a single bond, thus providing for numerous possible combinations. In other words, as we also saw in Chapter 8, carbon can adopt sp^3, sp^2 as well as sp hybridization. Furthermore, carbon has the ability to **catenate**, which is to say it can bond to itself to form long chains in more ways and combinations than any other element on the periodic table. For example, as we saw in Chapter 2 when we discussed Mendeleev and the periodic law, we would expect silicon to be chemically and physically similar to carbon, which to some degree it is. However, unlike carbon, silicon has a higher binding affinity to oxygen than itself, which is particularly problematic with respect to catenation in oxygen-rich environments (such as the planet Earth). Moreover, silicon is much larger than carbon, and therefore its ability to form double and triple bonds is extremely limited, further restricting its ability to generate large families of diverse compounds, which is a necessity for life. In this chapter, we will explore the basics of Organic Chemistry to include both the nomenclature as well as various properties of the different types of organic molecules.

William Henry Perkin (1838–1907) was an English chemist who is best known for his discovery of mauveine, which is an aniline purple dye.

Section 15.2 **Hydrocarbons**

If you recall from Chapter 4, we briefly introduced **hydrocarbons**, which are organic compounds that contain only carbon and hydrogen. Most hydrocarbons found on this planet result from decomposed organic matter in crude oil, and they are, in fact, the simplest form of organic compounds. However, as we saw in the introduction to this chapter, many different hydrocarbons are possible due to the unique character of carbon, and therefore hydrocarbons have many uses. For example, hydrocarbons are found in gasoline, jet fuel, candle wax, and aerosol sprays (volatile hydrocarbons), to name a few. Thus, we can classify hydrocarbons essentially into two major groups. These are aliphatic and aromatic hydrocarbons. While the aromatic hydrocarbons are very unique in nature and will be addressed later on, the **aliphatic hydrocarbons** can be further broken down into the alkanes, alkenes, and alkynes. **Alkanes** are hydrocarbons that contain all single bonds, while **alkenes** and **alkynes** have either a double or a triple bond, respectively (Table 15.1). We will now focus our attention on the properties and nomenclature of aliphatic hydrocarbons and then address aromatic hydrocarbons.

Oil refineries are one way in which to process hydrocarbons for use from crude oil.

Table 15.1 Propane, Propene, and Propyne are common examples of the three different types of aliphatic hydrocarbons.

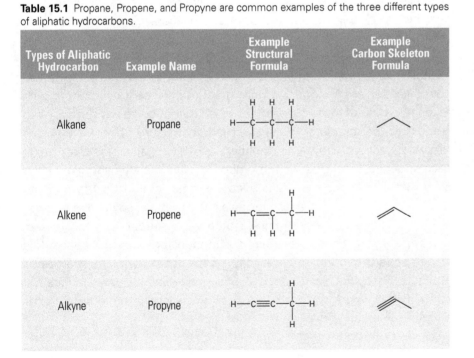

Types of Aliphatic Hydrocarbon	Example Name	Example Structural Formula	Example Carbon Skeleton Formula
Alkane	Propane		
Alkene	Propene		
Alkyne	Propyne		

Properties and Nomenclature of Aliphatic Hydrocarbons

The term "aliphatic" is derived from the Greek word "aleiphar," meaning "fat or oil." In fact, most aliphatic compounds are flammable, and one of the most common types of reactions involving aliphatic compounds is a combustion reaction, or the burning of these compounds in the presence of oxygen. These reactions are exothermic, and thus are ideal energy sources that drive our way of life to include warming our homes and transporting us from one point to another (i.e. cars, planes, trains, etc.). For example, let us revisit the examples outlined in Table 15.1—propane, propene, and propyne—and look at the following combustion reactions:

$$C_3H_8 \ (g) + 5O_2 \ (g) \rightarrow 3CO_2 \ (g) + 4H_2O \ (l) \qquad \Delta H° = -2220 \ kJ/mol$$

$$2C_3H_6 \ (g) + 9O_2 \ (g) \rightarrow 6CO_2 \ (g) + 6H_2O \ (l) \qquad \Delta H° = -2058 \ kJ/mol$$

$$C_3H_4 \ (g) + 4O_2 \ (g) \rightarrow 3CO_2 \ (g) + 2H_2O \ (l) \qquad \Delta H° = -1850 \ kJ/mol$$

Notice that they are all exothermic reactions. Now that we have established some basic properties associated with aliphatic hydrocarbons, we turn our attention to nomenclature. Notice that in the above examples we have propane, propene, and propyne. The names can essentially be broken down into two parts, the prefix and then the suffix. The prefix ("prop-") tells us that we have three carbons as illustrated in Table 15.2.

The suffix refers to the nature of the bonds, "-ane" corresponds to all single bonds, "-ene" tells us that we have one or more double bonds, and the "-yne" tells us that we have one or more triple bonds (we can refer back to the structures depicted in Table 15.1 to see this). Also note that in Table 15.1 we have both the structural and the condensed skeleton formulas, which were first introduced in Chapter 4 (Table 4.3). We should now take a brief moment to highlight some important points here with respect to both of these types of formulas before going any further. With respect to the structural formulas, it is important to point out that it is really not necessary to memorize how many hydrogen atoms there are in each structure as long as we remember to fill in enough hydrogen atoms such that all carbons have four bonds as described in Chapter 8. With respect to condensed skeleton formulas, the terminal points and vertices are assumed to be carbon (unless otherwise stated) with the correct number of hydrogen atoms, again, such that carbon has four bonds. It is also important to mention here, that we are dealing with a three-carbon structure. Therefore, when we look at propene and propyne, it does not really matter where we put either the double or the triple bond in the structure. That is:

Table 15.2 Table listing the prefixes for base names.

Prefix	Number of Carbons
Meth-	1
Eth-	2
Prop-	3
But-	4
Pent-	5
Hex-	6
Hept-	7
Oct-	8
Non-	9
Dec	10

propene

propyne

If we compare the left and right structures of either propene (top) or propyne (bottom), we notice that they are in fact the same molecule, just rotated by 180°. However, when we are dealing with slightly larger molecules, such as four carbon entities or larger, it becomes important to specify where the double bond is. For example, let us look at butene.

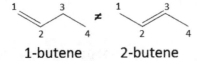

1-butene   **2-butene**

Notice that if we are to compare the left and right structures in this example, they are not the same molecule. In fact, as we will see later in this chapter, these molecules have very different chemical and physical properties. Thus, we must specify the location of the double (or triple) bond. The left structure is therefore referred to as 1-butene, while the right structure is 2-butene. This same logic could be applied for triple bonds if we compared 1-butyne and 2-butyne, which are also very different molecules. That is:

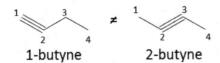

1-butyne   **2-butyne**

Another very important distinction between 1-butene and 2-butene (or 1-butyne and 2-butyne) is how we number the carbons. In order to correctly name 1-butene (or 1-butyne), we count the carbons which form the longest continuous chain of carbon atoms (often called the "main chain") such that we label the position of the double (or triple) bond with the smallest possible number. Thus, we have 1-butene and not 3-butene (or 1-butyne and not 3-butyne), which is what we would get if we numbered the carbons from right to left rather than left to right in this case. However, we notice that it does not matter how we number 2-butene (or 2-butyne), we still arrive at the same number, 2. That is:

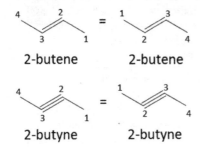

2-butene   **2-butene**

2-butyne   **2-butyne**

Again, we see that the left and right molecules are, in fact, the same structure, just rotated by 180°. However, let's look at another example by considering the following structure:

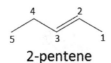

2-pentene

Notice that the correct name for this structure is 2-pentene, not 3-pentene, which is what we would get if we incorrectly numbered this molecule from left to right. Again, in order to correctly name such structures, we count the longest continuous carbon chain such that we arrive at the smallest possible number (in this case 2 not 3). The same logic could also be applied to 2-pentyne (not 3-pentyne):

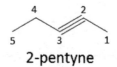

2-pentyne

Let us now work some more examples to get a better feel for this concept.

Example Problem 15.1

What are the names of the following aliphatic compounds? a. b. c. d.	
Solution:	
a.) First, we count the carbons and see that we need an "oct-"prefix for 8 carbons. Also, all single bonds means that it gets an "-ane" suffix.	**octane**
b.) First, we count the carbons and see that we need an "oct-"prefix for 8 carbons. Also, we notice a double bond at the third carbon (counted from left to right) which means that it gets an "-ene" suffix. Make sure that you did not incorrectly count the carbons from right to left and get 5-octene, which is incorrect.	**3-octene**
c.) First, we count the carbons and see that we need a "hept-"prefix for seven carbons. Also, we notice a triple bond at the third carbon (counted right to left) which means that it gets an "-yne" suffix. Make sure that you did not incorrectly count the carbons from left to right and get 4-heptyne, which is incorrect.	**3-heptyne**
d.) First, we count the carbons and see that we need a "hept-"prefix for seven carbons. Also, we notice a double bond at the third carbon (counted left to right) which means that it gets an "-ene" suffix. Make sure that you did not incorrectly count the carbons from right to left and get 4-heptene, which is incorrect.	**3-heptene**

Example Problem 15.2

Draw the structures from the following names. a. ethane. b. nonane. c. 2-hexyne. d. 3-octene.	
Solution:	
a.) First, we recognize that the prefix "eth-" is used for two carbons. The "-ane" suffix tells us that there are all single bonds in the structure.	————

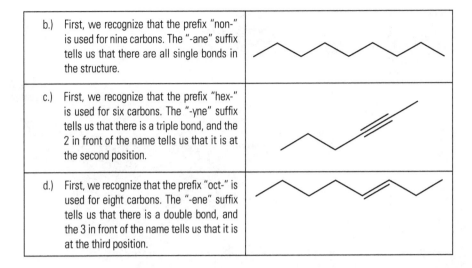

b.)	First, we recognize that the prefix "non-" is used for nine carbons. The "-ane" suffix tells us that there are all single bonds in the structure.	
c.)	First, we recognize that the prefix "hex-" is used for six carbons. The "-yne" suffix tells us that there is a triple bond, and the 2 in front of the name tells us that it is at the second position.	
d.)	First, we recognize that the prefix "oct-" is used for eight carbons. The "-ene" suffix tells us that there is a double bond, and the 3 in front of the name tells us that it is at the third position.	

Now that we have tackled some basic nomenclature of organic molecules involving essentially linear, continuous main chains, how do we handle branching? In other words, recall from the introduction of this chapter that carbon can bond to itself to form long chains in more ways and combinations than any other element on the periodic table. Well this brings up the possibility for branches, which we refer to as **alkyl groups**, coming off the main chain. For example, let us consider the following molecule:

In order to name a molecule that has alkyl groups present, we must be able to first identify the branches versus the main chain. In order to do this, we look for, and identify, the longest continuous chain, the main chain. In this case, we can number this molecule as follows:

In either case, we have correctly identified the longest continuous main chain, with five being the largest number of continuous carbons. We now identify the alkyl groups (the branches) involved. According to Table 15.3, we see that we have two methyl groups present at both the second and the fourth positions regardless of the numbering pattern used. Thus, the name of this molecule (using either numbering system above) is 2,4-dimethylpentane. Notice that in this case, there was more than one way to correctly number the main chain and still arrive at the same correct answer. However, this is not always the case. For example, consider the following molecule:

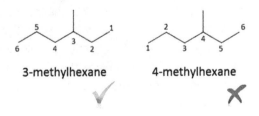

3-methylhexane   **4-methylhexane**

Table 15.3 A list of various common alkyl groups.

Name	Number of Carbons	Condensed Formula	Structural Formula
methyl	1	CH_3-	H_3C—
ethyl	2	CH_3CH_2-	H_3C—$\overset{H_2}{C}$—
propyl	3	$CH_3CH_2CH_2-$	H_3C—$\overset{H_2}{C}$—$\overset{H_2}{C}$—
isopropyl	3	$(CH_3)_2CH-$	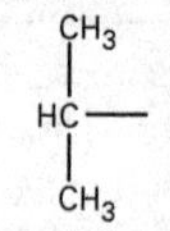 $\underset{CH_3}{\overset{CH_3}{HC}}$—
n-butyl	4	$CH_3CH_2CH_2CH_2-$	H_3C—$\overset{H_2}{C}$—$\overset{H_2}{C}$—$\overset{H_2}{C}$—
sec-butyl	4	$CH_3CH_2(CH_3)CH-$	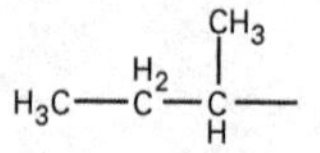 H_3C—$\overset{H_2}{C}$—$\underset{H}{\overset{CH_3}{C}}$—
isobutyl	4	$(CH_3)_2CHCH_2-$	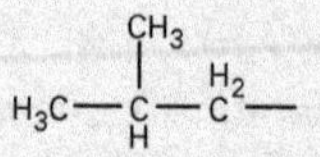 H_3C—$\underset{H}{\overset{CH_3}{C}}$—$\overset{H_2}{C}$—
tert-butyl	4	$(CH_3)_3C-$	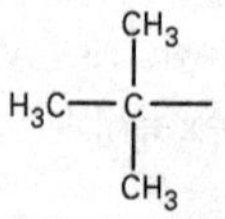 H_3C—$\underset{CH_3}{\overset{CH_3}{C}}$—

In this example, the choice of numbering pattern does, in fact, matter. When faced with such a dilemma, we use the numbering pattern such that we arrive at the lowest possible number for the position of the alkyl group(s). Therefore, in this case, we correctly name the above structure as being 3-methylhexane and not 4-methylhexane. Now the question becomes, how do we name a molecule that has both a double (or triple) bond and an alkyl group? If we have alkyl groups on a molecule and a double or triple bond, it is important to keep a few things in mind. First, the longest continuous chain that we select as our main chain must include the double or triple bond (even if we can identify a longer continuous chain that does not include the double or triple bond). Second, the double or triple gets the priority when numbering the chain such that it gets the lowest possible number rather than the alkyl group. For example, let's consider the following molecule:

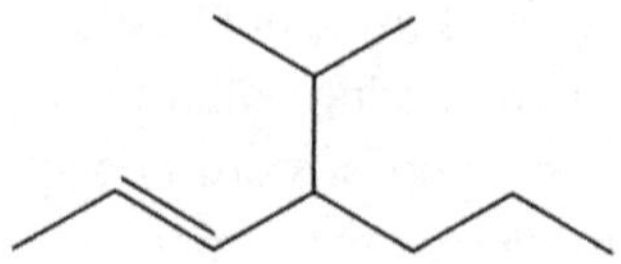

If we follow the rules as outlined thus far, we correctly name this structure as being 4-isopropyl-2-heptene. The longest continuous chain which contains the double bond is seven carbons long (thus, a "hept-" prefix). It gets an "-ene" suffix because of the double bond, which gets the priority when numbering the chain such that it gets the lowest possible number (2 in this case) rather than the alkyl group. This then puts the alkyl group (isopropyl) at the fourth position. Let's look at some more examples.

Example Problem 15.3

Name the following molecules:

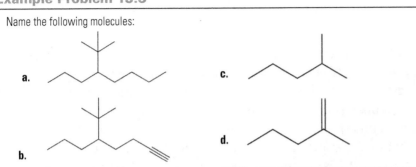

a.

b.

c.

d.

Solution:	
a.) First, we recognize that the longest continuous chain is eight carbons and that it has all single bonds (thus, the "oct-" prefix for the eight carbons and the "-ane" suffix for all single bonds). We also realize that it is numbered left to right such that we get a four for the alkyl group (tert-butyl) position rather than right to left which would put it at the fifth position (lower number preferable for the alkyl group).	**4-tert-butyloctane** 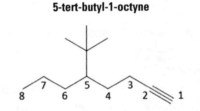
b.) First, we recognize that the longest continuous chain that also contains the triple bond is eight carbons (thus, the "oct-" prefix for the eight carbons and the "-yne" suffix for the triple bond). In this case, the triple bond gets the priority when numbering the chain such that it gets the lowest possible number (one in this case) rather than the alkyl group (tert-butyl). The tert-butyl group is then in the fifth position if we number this right to left.	**5-tert-butyl-1-octyne**
c.) First, we recognize that the longest continuous chain is five carbons and that it has all single bonds (thus, the "pent-" prefix for the five carbons and the "-ane" suffix for all single bonds). We also realize that it is numbered right to left such that we get a two for the alkyl group (methyl) position rather than left to right which would put it at the fourth position (lower number preferable for the alkyl group).	**2-methylpentane**
d.) First, we recognize that the longest continuous chain that also contains the double bond is five carbons (thus, the "pent-" prefix for the five carbons and the "-ene" suffix for the double bond). In this case, the double bond gets the priority when numbering the chain such that it gets the lowest possible number (one in this case) rather than the alkyl group (methyl). The methyl group is then in the second position if we number this beginning with the carbon involved in the double bond.	**2-methyl-1-pentene** 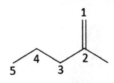

Section 15.3 Functional Groups

Thus far, we have discussed naming hydrocarbons both with and without alkyl groups and/or various types of bonds (i.e. single, double, and triple bonds), but what about hydrocarbons that contain certain functional groups? A **functional group** inserted into a hydrocarbon is an atom, or group of atoms, which is primarily responsible for the chemical and physical properties of that particular molecule (hence the name "functional group," or to give "function to"). It is important to point out here that when naming these types of molecules, the functional group takes preference over alkyl groups as well as double or triple bonds (if present) with respect to choosing a numbering pattern such that we arrive at the lowest possible number for the position of the functional group. Here, we briefly discuss common functional groups to include alcohols, aldehydes, ketones, carboxylic acids, esters, ethers, and amines (Figure 15.1).

Alcohols

Alcohols are defined as organic molecules that contain the $-OH$ (**hydroxyl**) functional group and have many uses. For example, methanol is an alcohol that is commonly used as a laboratory solvent. Ethanol, or ethyl alcohol, is what we commonly find in our alcoholic beverages, and it is this component that determines the strength of the alcoholic drink. For example, beer generally contains approximately 4–5% ethanol, wine usually has 12–15% ethanol, and stronger liquor, such as rum, can have as much as 40–50% ethanol. Ethanol, as well as isopropanol (a.k.a. rubbing alcohol or isopropyl alcohol), is also commonly used in various disinfectants due to its bactericidal characteristics. When naming alcohols, it is important to keep a few things in mind. For example, we must first find the longest continuous chain that contains the $-OH$ functional group for the base name, which is then changed such that it has an "$-ol$" ending. Thus, methane becomes methanol, and ethane becomes ethanol if the functional group is added to these hydrocarbons as follows:

CH_4 $\qquad$ $H_3C\text{---}OH$

methane $\qquad$ methanol

$H_3C\text{---}CH_3$ $\qquad$ ethanol structure

ethane $\qquad$ ethanol

As mentioned earlier, the presence of functional groups can dramatically alter the properties of hydrocarbons such as these. For example, both methane and ethane are gases at room temperature, which is typical of such small hydrocarbons (Table 15.4). If we add the $-OH$ functional group to them to generate methanol and ethanol, respectively, they are now both liquids

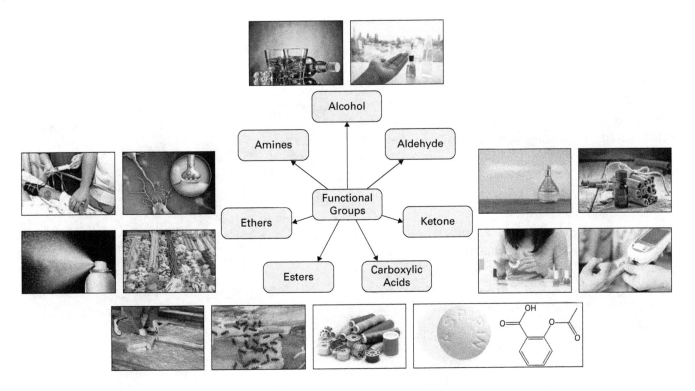

at room temperature due to hydrogen bonding (for a review of hydrogen bonding, see Chapter 9).

Figure 15.1 Common functional groups that can be inserted into hydrocarbons.

Table 15.4 The physical states at room temperature of various alkanes.

State (Room Temperature)	Name	Molecular Formula
Gas	Methane	CH_4
	Ethane	C_2H_6
	Propane	C_3H_8
	Butane	C_4H_{10}
Liquid	Pentane	C_5H_{12}
	Hexane	C_6H_{14}
	Heptane	C_7H_{16}
	Octane	C_8H_{18}
	Nonane	C_9H_{20}
	Decane	$C_{10}H_{22}$

Did you know how chemistry might relate to your job as a non-chemist? As a medical professional, possibly working in the emergency room of a hospital, you will probably see some scary stuff. For example, patients who accidentally (or on purpose in cases involving attempted suicides) ingest the wrong form of alcohol (i.e. isopropanol instead of ethanol) can be in real danger. In fact, human ingestion of isopropanol (IPA) is not as uncommon as one might think. Isopropanol is known to cause rapid intoxication; believe it or not, some people will intentionally drink it for that purpose! IPA is readily available because it is commonly found in hand sanitizers, rubbing alcohol, and various cleaning products. Some common symptoms can be confusion, dizziness, nausea, vomiting, and slow breathing. If too much of it is consumed, it can even lead to a coma or death. Treatment of IPA poisoning in some cases can include dialysis to remove it from the blood, fluid replacement, and oxygen therapy, which can potentially help the lungs get rid of IPA more quickly.

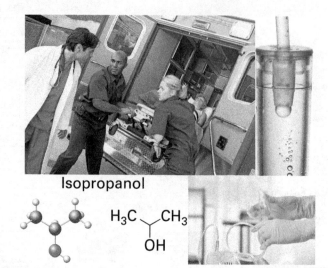

Isopropanol

Patients who ingest the wrong form of alcohol (i.e. isopropanol instead of ethanol) can be in real danger and require prompt medical attention.

Example Problem 15.4

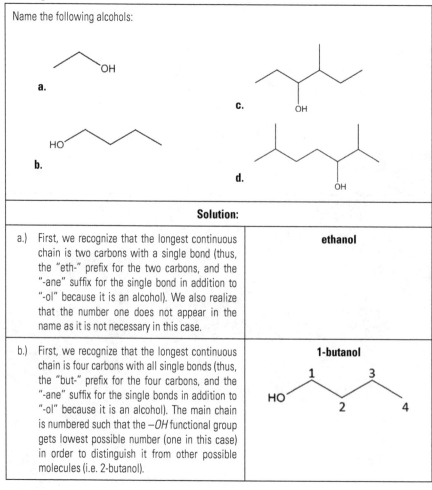

Name the following alcohols:

Name the following alcohols:

a.

b.

c.

d.

Solution:	
a.) First, we recognize that the longest continuous chain is two carbons with a single bond (thus, the "eth-" prefix for the two carbons, and the "-ane" suffix for the single bond in addition to "-ol" because it is an alcohol). We also realize that the number one does not appear in the name as it is not necessary in this case.	**ethanol**
b.) First, we recognize that the longest continuous chain is four carbons with all single bonds (thus, the "but-" prefix for the four carbons, and the "-ane" suffix for the single bonds in addition to "-ol" because it is an alcohol). The main chain is numbered such that the *−OH* functional group gets lowest possible number (one in this case) in order to distinguish it from other possible molecules (i.e. 2-butanol).	**1-butanol** HO 1 2 3 4

c.) First, we recognize that the longest continuous chain that contains the −OH functional group is six carbons and that it has all single bonds (thus, "hex-" prefix for the six carbons and the "-ane" suffix for the single bonds in addition to "-ol" because it is an alcohol). We also realize that it is numbered left to right such that we get a three for −OH group rather than right to left which would put it at the fourth position (lower number preferable for the −OH group rather than the alkyl group). The alkyl group in this case is a methyl group which appears at the fourth position.

4-methyl-3-hexanol

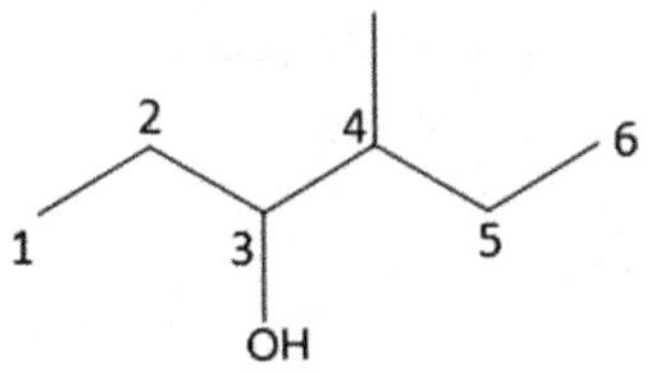

d.) First, we recognize that the longest continuous chain here that contains the −OH functional group is seven carbons and that it has all single bonds (thus, the "hept-" prefix for the seven carbons, and the "-ane" suffix for the single bonds in addition to "-ol" because it is an alcohol). We also realize that it is numbered right to left such that we get a three for −OH group rather than left to right which would put it at the fifth position (lower number preferable for the −OH group rather than the alkyl groups). We use "di" because of the two alkyls groups (methyl groups) that appear at the second and sixth positions. Also, in this case there are technically other ways to correctly number this molecule, but in all cases you will arrive at the same name (2,6-dimethyl-3-heptanol). For example:

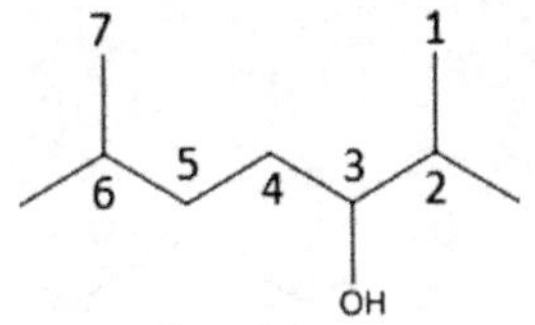

2,6-dimethyl-3-heptanol

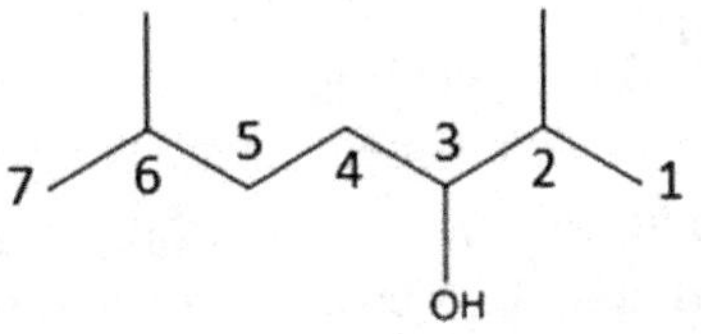

Aldehydes and Ketones

Both formaldehyde and acetone are excellent examples of the next two classes of functional groups that we will now discuss, namely aldehydes and ketones, respectively. Let's look at the chemical structures of these compounds:

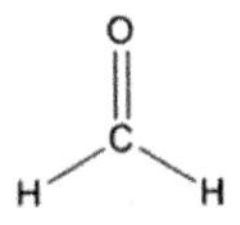

formaldehyde

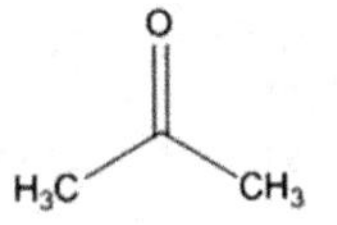

acetone

Formaldehyde, also known as methanal, was first discovered by the Russian chemist Alexander Mikhaylovich Butlerov in 1859. It is a naturally occurring organic compound and is the simplest of the aldehydes. It has a very powerful odor and is commonly used as a preservative. Acetone on the other hand,

Alexander Mikhaylovich Butlerov (1828–1886) was a Russian chemist who is credited with the discovery of formaldehyde in 1859.

also known as propanone, is a commonly used ketone found in nail polish remover. It is the simplest ketone and is a volatile and flammable liquid. Notice that both **aldehydes** and **ketones** have a **carbonyl group** (a C=O double bond), the difference being that aldehydes have one R group and one hydrogen atom, while ketones have two R groups (where R is a hydrocarbon group). That is:

Some aldehydes have very pleasant odors and are used in perfumes such as Chanel No.5 and Estée Lauder Estée. In fact, the use of aldehydes in Chanel No.5 popularized their use in various perfumes. Cinnamaldehyde is an aldehyde responsible for giving cinnamon its aroma and flavor. Some ketones are also associated with pleasant odors, such as 2-heptanone found in cloves. With respect to naming aldehydes and ketones, we simply change the base name to either "-al" if it is an aldehyde or "-one" if it is a ketone. Thus, if we were to add a carbonyl group to methane, we would get methanal (formaldehyde), and if we add a carbonyl group to propane we would get propanone (acetone). Let's see some more examples.

Example Problem 15.5

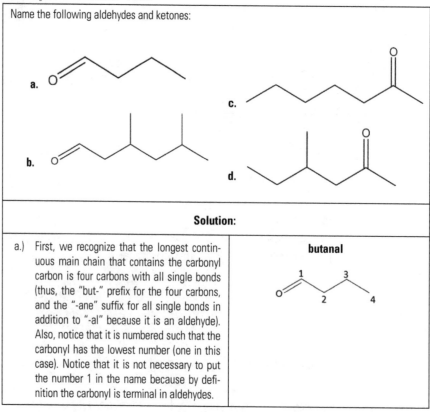

b.)	First, we recognize that the longest continuous main chain is six carbons with all single bonds (thus, the "hex-" prefix for the six carbons, and the "-ane" suffix for the single bonds in addition to "-al" because it is an aldehyde). The main chain is numbered such that the carbonyl functional group gets lowest possible number (one in this case), which puts the methyl alkyl groups at the third and fifth positions (thus, we use "di"). Again, notice that it is not necessary to designate the number 1 for the position of the carbonyl because it is understood in this case to be terminal.	**3,5-dimethylhexanal**
c.)	First, we recognize that the longest continuous main chain is seven carbons, and that it has all single bonds (thus, the "hept-" prefix for the seven carbons, and the "-ane" suffix for the single bonds in addition to "-one" because it is a ketone). We also realize that it is numbered right to left such that we get a two for the carbonyl group rather than left to right which would put it at the sixth position (lower number preferable for the carbonyl group). Here, it is necessary to specify the position of the carbonyl group as other positions are technically possible.	**2-heptanone**
d.)	First, we recognize that the longest continuous main chain is six carbons and that it has all single bonds (thus, the "hex-" prefix for the six carbons, and the "-ane" suffix for the single bonds in addition to "-one" because it is a ketone). We also realize that it is numbered right to left such that we get a two for the carbonyl group rather than left to right which would put it at the fifth position (lower number preferable for the carbonyl group rather than the alkyl group). This then puts the methyl group at the fourth position. Here, it is necessary to specify the position of the carbonyl group as other positions are technically possible.	**4-methyl-2-hexanone**

Carboxylic Acids and Esters

The next two functional groups we will now discuss are carboxylic acids and esters. **Carboxylic acids** contain a terminal carboxyl group (R–COOH), while **esters** are derived from carboxylic acids in which at least one hydroxyl group (–*OH*) is replaced by an –*O*– alkyl group as follows (R–COO–R):

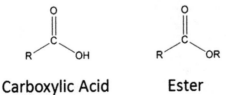

Carboxylic Acid   **Ester**

Formic acid, also known as methanoic acid, is the simplest carboxylic acid and was first distilled by chemists from ants in the seventeenth century. It was the first natural product to be isolated from insects and is present in the venom of carpenter and fire ants. Aspirin is also a carboxylic acid-containing compound and is one of the most commonly used drugs worldwide with about 100 billion tablets being consumed annually! Esters are also a very important diverse class of compounds which are commonly used in everyday items. For example, polyesters can be used to make insulation for homes, plastic bottles, and clothing. Polyesters are good examples of **polymers**, which are molecules composed of repeating units called **monomers**. We will discuss this much further in the next chapter where we will look at carbohydrates, proteins, and DNA. Some esters are particularly known for their sweet smells and taste. For example, methyl butanoate occurs naturally in strawberries and is responsible for their sweet taste. When naming carboxylic acids and esters, we simply change the base name to either "-oic acid" or "-oate," respectively. Let's look at a few examples of these.

Example Problem 15.6

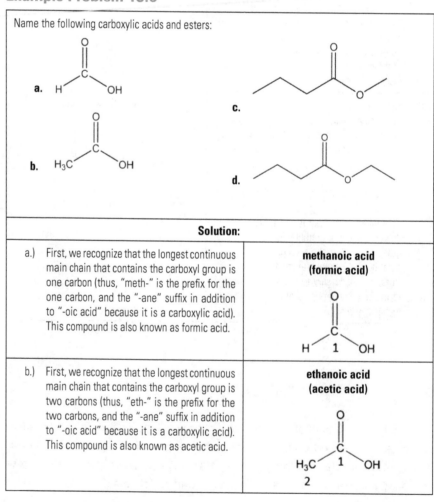

Name the following carboxylic acids and esters:

a.

b.

c.

d.

Solution:	
a.) First, we recognize that the longest continuous main chain that contains the carboxyl group is one carbon (thus, "meth-" is the prefix for the one carbon, and the "-ane" suffix in addition to "-oic acid" because it is a carboxylic acid). This compound is also known as formic acid.	**methanoic acid (formic acid)**
b.) First, we recognize that the longest continuous main chain that contains the carboxyl group is two carbons (thus, "eth-" is the prefix for the two carbons, and the "-ane" suffix in addition to "-oic acid" because it is a carboxylic acid). This compound is also known as acetic acid.	**ethanoic acid (acetic acid)**

c.)	First, we recognize that the longest continuous main chain is four carbons and that it has all single bonds (thus, "but-" is the prefix for the four carbons, and the "-ane" suffix for the single bonds in addition to "-oate" because it is an ester). We also realize that it is numbered right to left such that the carbon containing the ester functional group is at the first position (lower number preferable for the ester group). Also, we recognize that we have a methyl alkyl group.	**methyl butanoate** 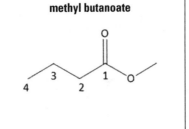
d.)	First, we recognize that the longest continuous main chain is four carbons and that it has all single bonds (thus, "but-" is the prefix for the four carbons, and the "-ane" suffix for the single bonds in addition to "-oate" because it is an ester). We also realize that it is numbered right to left such that the carbon containing the ester functional group is at the first position (lower number preferable for the ester group). Also, we recognize that we have an ethyl alkyl group.	**ethyl butanoate**

Ethers and Amines

The last two functional groups that we will discuss here are ethers and amines. **Ethers** by definition contain an ether group, which is an oxygen atom connected to two alkyl groups (or aryl groups, which are discussed further later), while **amines** are nitrogen-containing compounds derived from ammonia. Dimethyl ether is one of the simplest ethers and is commonly used as an aerosol propellant for a variety of commercially used products and as a low-temperature laboratory solvent. Anisoles are also ethers and a major constituent of anise seed oil, which can be used to flavor candies due to its sweet taste and licorice scent. Methamphetamine and dopamine are both really good examples of compounds containing amine functional groups. With respect to naming both ethers and amines, we simply add the word "ether" or "amine" at the end of the name. For example, let's look at dimethyl ether and ethylamine:

dimethyl ether   **ethylamine**

Now, let's practice with some more examples.

Example Problem 15.7

Name the following ethers and amines:

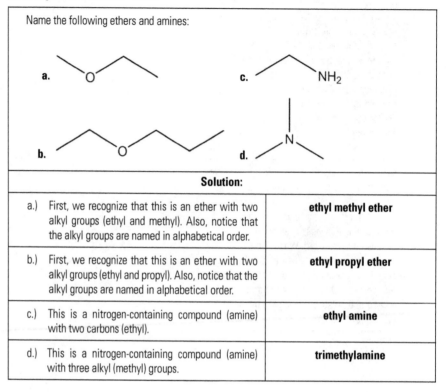

	Solution:	
a.)	First, we recognize that this is an ether with two alkyl groups (ethyl and methyl). Also, notice that the alkyl groups are named in alphabetical order.	**ethyl methyl ether**
b.)	First, we recognize that this is an ether with two alkyl groups (ethyl and propyl). Also, notice that the alkyl groups are named in alphabetical order.	**ethyl propyl ether**
c.)	This is a nitrogen-containing compound (amine) with two carbons (ethyl).	**ethyl amine**
d.)	This is a nitrogen-containing compound (amine) with three alkyl (methyl) groups.	**trimethylamine**

Section 15.4 Hydrocarbons-Isomers

By now, you probably have realized through naming and drawing all of these structures that molecular formulas themselves are somewhat limited in that they can represent more than one chemical structure. For example, other possible arrangements for carbon involve **cyclic aliphatic compounds** (or ring structures). **Homocyclic compounds** contain only one type of element in the ring (i.e. carbon) while **heterocyclic compounds** contain more than one type of element within the ring structure (i.e. carbon and nitrogen). The most common cyclic structures are five- and six-membered rings, with seven-membered rings and greater being less common, while three- and four-membered rings are generally somewhat unstable due to internal strain. For example, let us look at cyclopentane and cyclohexane:

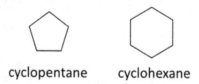

cyclopentane   cyclohexane

If you notice, the molecular formulas for cyclopentane and cyclohexane are C_5H_{10} and C_6H_{12}, respectively, which are the same for various other compounds such as 1-pentene and 1-hexene. The same can be said for butane and isobutane, which also have the same molecular formula (C_4H_{10}) but are very different molecules with different structures. Thus, we see that nomenclature is an important concept, and perhaps now is a good time to further explore the concept of isomers. **Isomers** are molecules that have the same molecular formula but different chemical structures. There are essentially two major types of isomers, structural isomers and stereoisomers (Figure 15.2). **Structural isomers,** or **constitutional isomers**, are molecules that have the same chemical formula but different structures (different connectivity), while **stereoisomers** are molecules in which the atoms have the same connectivity but a different spatial arrangement. Furthermore, stereoisomers can be broken down into two other subcategories, geometric and optical isomers. **Geometric isomers** are two or more compounds which contain the same number and types of atoms and bonds but have different spatial arrangements. It is important to note that with this type of isomerism, the connectivity between atoms is the same. **Optical isomers** can be defined as compounds that also have the same connectivity but are nonsuperimposable images of each other. While all of this may sound confusing at first, the goal here is to clear up some of the confusion by looking at some examples of all of these types of compounds. For example, let us first consider structural isomers by looking at butane and isobutane:

butane   isobutane

Butane and isobutane are different structures with different physical properties even though they have the same molecular formula. For example, the boiling point of butane is −1.0 °C, while isobutane is −11.7 °C. As you can imagine, the number of possible isomers for a hydrocarbon goes up pretty dramatically as you increase in size. For example, while there are only two structural isomers for butane, there are five for hexane and seventy-five structural isomers for decane (Table 15.5)! The five possible isomers for hexane are illustrated below:

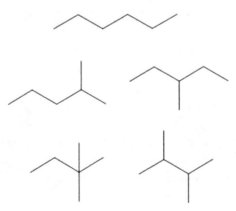

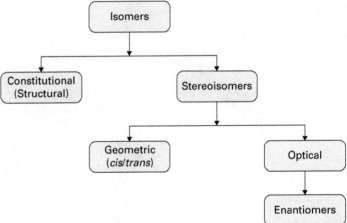

Figure 15.2 The different types of isomers, which are molecules that have the same molecular formula but different chemical structures.

Table 15.5 The number of possible structural isomers for various hydrocarbons.

Name of Hydrocarbon	Number of Carbons	Possible Structural Isomers
Methane	1	1
Ethane	2	1
Propane	3	1
Butane	4	2
Pentane	5	3
Hexane	6	5
Heptane	7	9
Octane	8	18
Nonane	9	35
Decane	10	75

Drawing these structural isomers can be a little tricky and does take some practice. Just remember a very important point when doing this, *rotation is not isomerism!* For example, let's look at the following example problem.

Example Problem 15.8

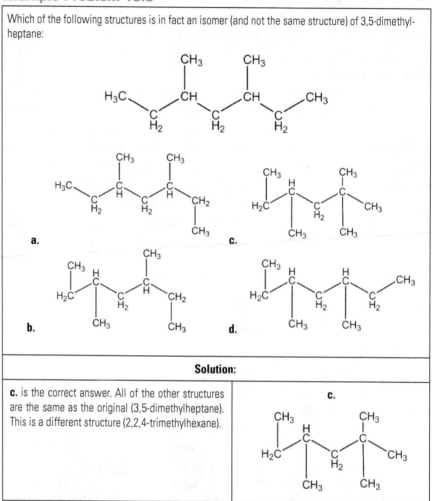

Which of the following structures is in fact an isomer (and not the same structure) of 3,5-dimethylheptane:

a.

b.

c.

d.

Solution:

c. is the correct answer. All of the other structures are the same as the original (3,5-dimethylheptane). This is a different structure (2,2,4-trimethylhexane).

c.

Now that we have a good understanding of constitutional isomers, we now move on to stereoisomers, which have the same connectivity (unlike constitutional isomers) but have a different spatial arrangement. Here, we will discuss two types of stereoisomers, geometric and optical. For example, let us first consider 2-butene. Notice, that we can draw this two different ways:

cis-2-butene   trans-2-butene

We can draw the methyl groups on the same side of the double bond (which we call cis-) or on opposite sides (which we call trans-). This is an example of geometric isomerism (or **cis-trans isomerism**) in which the connectivity is the same, but they have distinctively different spatial arrangements (i.e. they are stereoisomers). As a result, they are different structures with different physical properties. For example, the boiling point of cis-2-butene is 3.7 °C, while the boiling point of trans-2-butene is 0.9 °C. Another type of stereoisomer that we can encounter is optical isomers. To understand this concept, let us look at 3-methylheptane (recall the solid and hashed-wedge notation from Chapter 8):

**Optical isomers of
3-methylheptane**

Notice that these two structures are nonsuperimposable mirror images of each other, which we call optical isomers. In other words, you cannot place the right structure directly on top of the left structure and have everything line up exactly. If we were to do this, we would quickly notice that while it is a close fit, the methyl groups on the third carbon and the hydrogens would not line up. Optical isomers like these are also called **enantiomers**, and any molecule that exhibits optical isomerism is **chiral**. The word chiral comes from the Greek word "cheir," meaning hand. Notice that you cannot put your right hand directly on top of your left hand (palms up) and have everything line up (i.e. your thumbs are on opposite sides). They are, however, mirror

Figure 15.3 Optical isomers are nonsuperimposable mirror images of each other just like your hands.

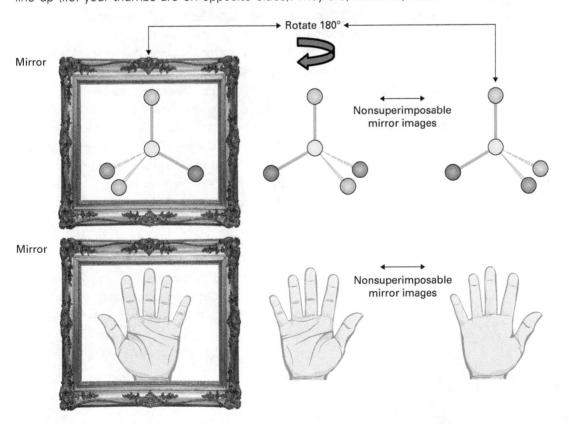

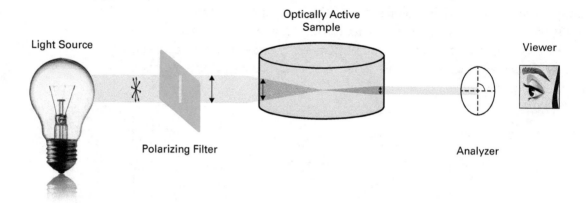

Light Source

Polarizing Filter

Optically Active Sample

Analyzer

Viewer

Figure 15.4 The rotation of plane-polarized light as it passes through an optically active sample.

images of one another (Figure 15.3). For a carbon atom to be chiral, it must be bonded to four different substituents. For example, if we look at the third carbon of 3-methylheptane, we see that it is bonded to ethyl, methyl, and butyl groups, as well as a hydrogen atom.

Again, notice that these structures fit into the definition of stereoisomers as having the same connectivity but different arrangements in space. However, unlike geometric isomers, some of the chemical and physical properties of enantiomers are indistinguishable from each other (i.e. identical densities and boiling/freezing/melting points). How are they different? Well, enantiomers are different in two very important ways. First, they differ in how they rotate plane-polarized light. Second, they exhibit different chemical behaviors in chiral environments. While normal light is made up of electric field waves that oscillate in all directions, plane-polarized light has waves that oscillate in only one plane, which can be obtained when normal light is put through a "polarizer" (Figure 15.4). When this beam of plane-polarized light is directed at a sample that contains two optical isomers, one of the isomers will rotate the light clockwise, which we refer to as the **dextrorotary** isomer (*d* isomer), while the other isomer will rotate plane-polarized light counterclockwise, which we call the **levorotatory** isomer (*l* isomer). A **racemic mixture** is one that contains an equimolar amount of both isomers, which will not rotate plane-polarized light at all (i.e. they cancel each other out).

The differences in the rotation of plane-polarized light by optically active samples brings us to our second important distinction between enantiomers, and that is their behavioral differences in chiral environments. As we will see in Chapter 16, we as humans are in part made up of chiral building blocks (amino acids, discussed further in the next chapter). In fact, all known life forms demonstrate specific chiral properties, and therefore the way in which we handle or tolerate various drugs can, in fact, be enantiomer-specific. For example, the levorotary (*l*-enantiomer) form of methamphetamine (also called levomethamphetamine) is the active ingredient in some over-the-counter nasal decongestant inhalers, while the dextrorotary (*d*-enantiomer) form (also called dextromethamphetamine) is the illegal drug that we commonly associate with euphoria and addiction (Figure 15.5), thus highlighting the importance of this concept.

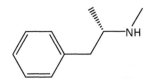

l-methamphetamine
Legal form found in some over-the-counter nasal decongestant inhalers

d-methamphetamine
Illegal and highly addictive form of the drug

Figure 15.5 *l*-methamphetamine is the active ingredient in some over-the-counter nasal decongestant inhalers (left), while *d*-methamphetamine is the illegal drug that we commonly associate with euphoria and addiction (right). They are mirror images of one another.

Example Problem 15.9

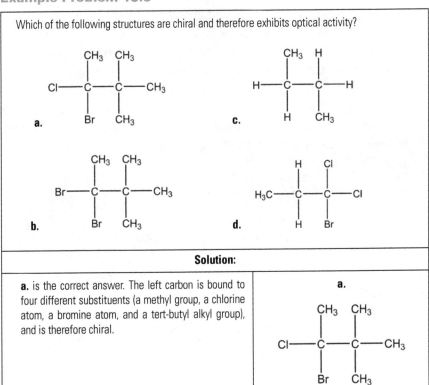

Section 15.5 Aromatic Hydrocarbons

You may have notice the ring structure depicted in Figure 15.5, which contains alternating double and single bonds. This compound is known as a benzene, and while it is sometimes drawn this way with alternating double and single bonds, experimental data show us that all of the carbon-carbon bonds are actually the same length (recall from Chapter 8 that double bonds are shorter than single bonds). This indicates that the following resonance structures are technically a more accurate representation of benzene:

Friedrich August Kekulé (1829–1896) was a German organic chemist who is best known for being the prinicipal founder of the theory of chemical structure (1857–1858). Kekulé's most famous work concerning chemical structure is his determination of the structure of benzene. In 1865 he published a paper suggesting that the structure contained a six-membered ring of carbon atoms with alternating single and double bonds.

The far right structure represents a hybrid of the two resonance structures drawn to the left of it, where the ring represents delocalized π electrons. The history behind determining the structure of the benzene ring is quite interesting. The structure of benzene was determined in 1865 by Friedrich August Kekulé, who was one of the most prominent theoretical chemists in Europe in the mid to late 1800s. Kekulé claimed that he had determined the structure of benzene while day-dreaming of a snake seizing its own tail.

Today, we now know of many compounds that contain benzene rings, many of which have very pleasant aromas (i.e. vanilla, cinnamon, etc.), so these compounds are commonly referred to as **aromatic compounds**, or **aryl compounds**, with aromatic benzene rings. When naming aromatic hydrocarbons, we have two major categories, monosubstituted (one hydrogen is substituted) and disubstituted (two hydrogens are substituted) benzene rings. Generally, we can just name monosubstituted benzenes as derivatives of benzene. For example, consider the following:

chlorobenzene   propylbenzene

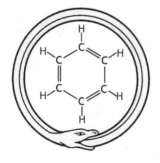

Friedrich August Kekulé claimed that he had determined the structure of benzene while day-dreaming of a snake seizing its own tail.

However, there are some common monosubstituted benzenes that can only be learned through memorization, such as the following:

phenol   toluene

For disubstituted benzenes, they are numbered in order to determine the position of one substitution in relation to the other, and the substituents are listed alphabetically. For example, consider the following names and structures:

1-bromo-3-chlorobenzene   1-ethyl-2-methylbenzene

There is another common technique for naming disubstituted benzenes which eliminates the need for using actual numbers in the name itself. In this method, we use the prefixes ortho (*o*-) for 1,2 disubstituted, meta (*m*-) for 1,3 disubstituted or para (*p*-) for 1,4 disubstituted. Thus, we can consider the following examples which have several correct names:

1,2-dibromobenzene	1,3-dibromobenzene	1,4-dibromobenzene
or	or	or
ortho-dibromobenzene	*meta*-dibromobenzene	*para*-dibromobenzene
or	or	or
o-dibromobenzene	*m*-dibromobenzene	*p*-dibromobenzene

Example Problem 15.10

Name the following monosubstituted and disubstituted benzenes.

Solution:		
a.	Monosubstituted benzene with a fluorine atom; therefore the name is fluorobenzene.	**fluorobenzene**
b.	Monosubstituted benzene with a methyl group; therefore the name is methylbenzene, also better known as toluene.	**toluene (methylbenzene)**
c.	Disubstituted benzene with iodine atoms at the first and second positions; therefore the name is 1,2-diiodobenzene. Also, *ortho*-diiodobenzene or *o*-diiodobenzene would be correct.	**1,2-diiodobenzene** or ***ortho*-diiodobenzene** or **o-diiodobenzene**
d.	Disubstituted benzene with an ethyl group at the first position and the propyl group at the fourth position; therefore the name is 1-ethyl-4-propylbenzene. Also, *para*-ethylpropylbenzene and *p*-ethylpropylbenzene would be correct.	**1-ethyl-4-propylbenzene** or ***para*-ethylpropylbenzene** or **p-ethylpropylbenzene**

Key Terms

1. Alcohols
2. Aldehydes
3. Aliphatic hydrocarbons
4. Alkanes
5. Alkenes
6. Alkynes
7. Amines
8. Aromatic compounds
9. Aryl compounds
10. Carbonyl group
11. Carboxylic acids
12. Catenate
13. Chiral
14. Cis-trans isomerism
15. Constitutional isomers
16. Cyclic aliphatic compounds
17. Dextrorotary
18. Enantiomers
19. Esters
20. Ethers
21. Functional group
22. Geometric isomers
23. Heterocyclic compounds
24. Homocyclic compounds
25. Hydrocarbons
26. Hydroxyl group
27. Isomers
28. Ketones
29. Levorotatory
30. Monomers
31. Optical isomers
32. Organic chemistry
33. Polymers
34. Racemic mixture

35. Stereoisomers

36. Structural isomers

Problems

HYDROCARBONS

1. Define organic chemistry.

2. When we say that carbon has the ability to "catenate," what do we mean by this?

3. What are hydrocarbons?

4. What are some examples of substances that contain hydrocarbons?

5. Define alkanes, alkenes, and alkynes.

6. What is the correct name of the following molecule?

7. What is the correct name of the following molecule?

8. What is the correct name of the following molecule?

9. What is the correct name of the following molecule?

10. What is the correct name of the following molecule?

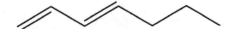

11. Draw the structure of propane.

12. Draw the structure of propene.

13. Draw the structure of 2-hexene.

14. Draw the structure of 2-butyne.

15. Draw the structure of 1,3-octadiene.

16. What are alkyl groups?

17. Fill in the chart below:

Name of Alkyl Group	Number of Carbons	Condensed Formula
	1	CH_3-
ethyl	2	
propyl		$CH_3CH_2CH_2-$
	3	$(CH_3)_2CH-$
n-butyl		$CH_3CH_2CH_2CH_2-$
sec-butyl	4	
isobutyl		$(CH_3)_2CHCH_2-$
tert-butyl	4	

18. What is the correct name of the following molecule?

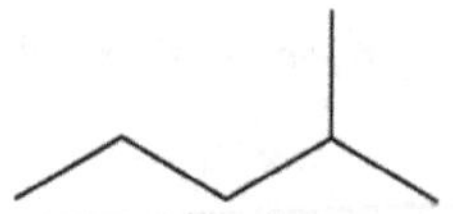

19. What is the correct name of the following molecule?

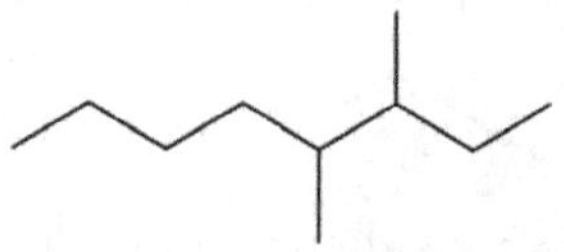

20. What is the correct name of the following molecule?

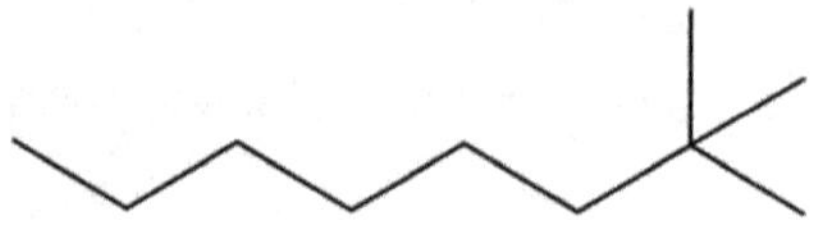

21. What is the correct name of the following molecule?

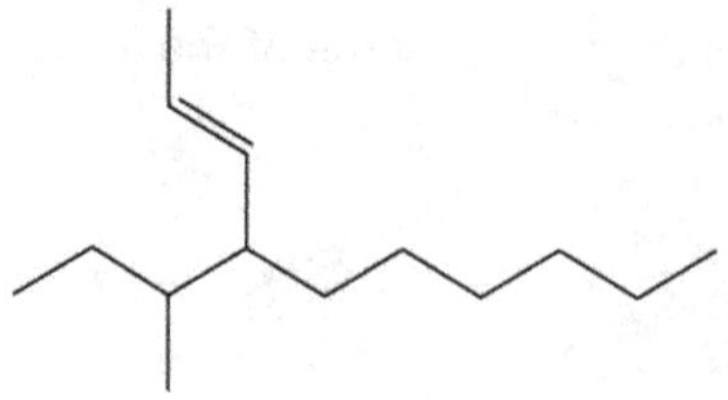

22. What is the correct name of the following molecule?

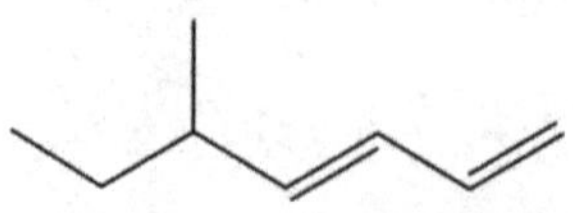

23. Draw the structure of 3-methylheptane.

24. Draw the structure of 5-isobutylnonane.

25. Draw the structure of 2,2,4-trimethylhexane.

26. Draw the structure of 2,3,4-trimethyl-2-pentene.

27. Draw the structure of 5-ethyl-4-methyl-2-heptyne.

28. What is a functional group?

29. List and define the seven major functional groups discussed in this chapter.

30. What is the correct name of the following alcohol?

31. What is the correct name of the following alcohol?

32. Draw the structure of 2-hexanol.

33. Draw the structure of 2-methyl-3-pentanol.

34. What is the correct name of the following aldehyde?

35. What is the correct name of the following aldehyde?

36. Draw the structure of butanal.

37. Draw the structure of 2-methylpropanal.

38. What is the correct name of the following ketone?

39. What is the correct name of the following ketone?

40. Draw the structure of butanone.

41. Draw the structure of 2-pentanone.

42. What is the correct name of the following carboxylic acid?

43. What is the correct name of the following carboxylic acid?

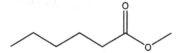

44. Draw the structure of methanoic acid.

45. Draw the structure of ethanoic acid.

46. What is the correct name of the following ester?

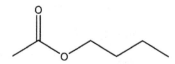

47. What is the correct name of the following ester?

48. Draw the structure of methyl propanoate.

49. Draw the structure of ethyl propanoate.

50. What is the correct name of the following ether?

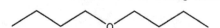

51. What is the correct name of the following ether?

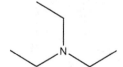

52. Draw the structure of ethyl methyl ether.

53. Draw the structure of ethyl propyl ether.

54. What is the correct name of the following amine?

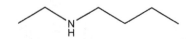

55. What is the correct name of the following amine?

56. Draw the structure of dimethylamine.

57. Draw the structure of diethylamine.

58. What are isomers?

59. What are the different types of isomers discussed in this chapter, and how are they different from one another?

60. Which of the following structures is in fact an isomer (and not the same structure) of 3,5-dimethylheptane:

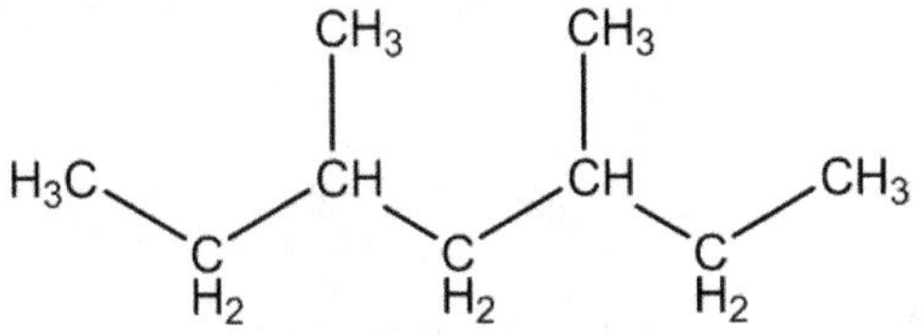

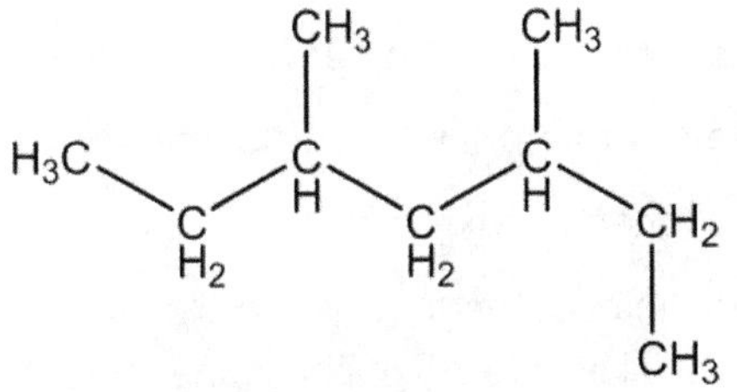

a.

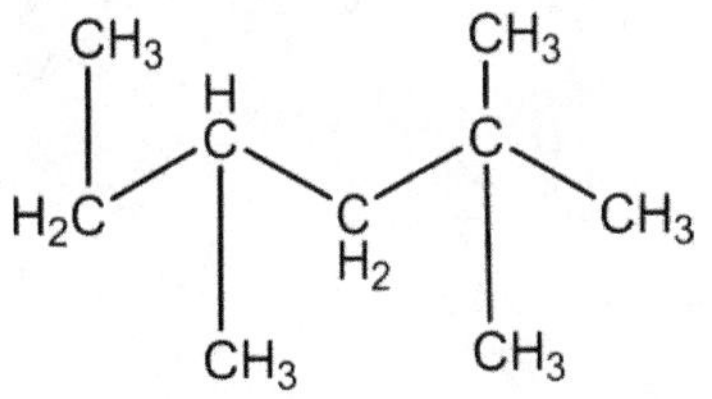

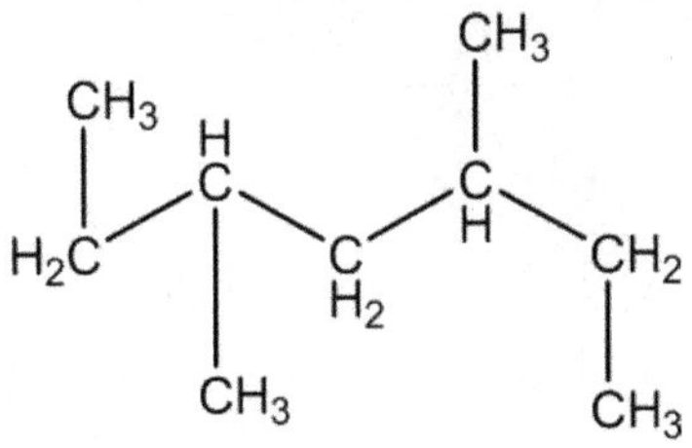

b.

c.

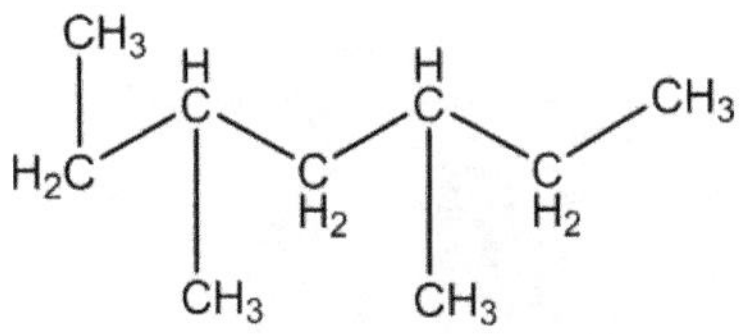

d.

61. Fill in the chart below:

Name of Hydrocarbon	Number of Carbons	Possible Structural Isomers
	1	1
Ethane	2	
	3	1
Butane		2
Pentane	5	
Hexane	6	
	7	9
Octane	8	
Nonane		35
Decane	10	

62. Draw all the possible structural isomers for hexane.

63. Which of the following molecules is *cis*-1,2-dichloroethene and which is *trans*-1,2-dichloroethene? How can you tell?

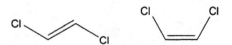

64. What is a chiral molecule? How can you tell if a given carbon atom is chiral?

65. What is a dextrorotary isomer (*d* isomer)?

66. What is a levorotatory isomer (*l* isomer)?

67. What is a racemic mixture?

68. Would you expect the following molecule to be chiral and exhibit optical activity? Explain your answer.

$$H_3C - \underset{\underset{Cl}{|}}{\overset{\overset{CH_3}{|}}{C}} - \underset{\underset{H}{|}}{\overset{\overset{H}{|}}{C}} - CH_3$$

69. Would you expect the following molecule to be chiral and exhibit optical activity? Explain your answer.

$$H_3C - \underset{\underset{Cl}{|}}{\overset{\overset{Br}{|}}{C}} - \underset{\underset{H}{|}}{\overset{\overset{H}{|}}{C}} - CH_3$$

70. What is an aromatic compound?

71. Who is Friedrich August Kekulé and what is he most famous for?

72. What is the correct name of the following molecule?

73. What is the correct name of the following molecule?

74. What is the correct name of the following molecule?

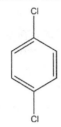

75. Draw the structure of 1-ethyl-3-propylbenzene.

76. Draw the structure of *m*-bromochlorobenzene.

77. Draw the structure of *ortho*-dibromobenzene.

Image Credits

- Fig. 15.Aa: Copyright © Depositphotos/fiftycents.
- Fig. 15.Ab: Copyright © Depositphotos/Mawer79.
- Fig. 15.Ac: Copyright © Depositphotos/johnkwan.
- Fig. 15.Ad: Copyright © Depositphotos/andrewgenn.
- Fig. 15.B: Source: https://commons.wikimedia.org/wiki/File:William_Henry_Perkin.jpg.
- Fig. 15.C: Copyright © Depositphotos/serrnovik.
- Fig. 15.1a: Copyright © Depositphotos/Alex_L.
- Fig. 15.1b: Copyright © Depositphotos/Jummie.
- Fig. 15.1c: Copyright © Depositphotos/tomert.
- Fig. 15.1d: Copyright © Depositphotos/5PH.
- Fig. 15.1e: Copyright © Depositphotos/prudkov.
- Fig. 15.1f: Copyright © Depositphotos/Kzenon.
- Fig. 15.1g: Copyright © Depositphotos/shutswis.
- Fig. 5.1h: Copyright © Depositphotos/Raimund14.
- Fig. 15.1i: Copyright © Depositphotos/Meisterphotos.
- Fig. 15.1j: Copyright © Depositphotos/miltonia.
- Fig. 15.1k: Copyright © Depositphotos/Ale-ks.
- Fig. 15.1l: Copyright © Depositphotos/Dixo.
- Fig. 15.1m: Copyright © Depositphotos/PicsFive.
- Fig. 15.1n: Copyright © Depositphotos/Andreus.
- Fig. 15.1o: Copyright © Depositphotos/lucidwaters.
- Fig. 15.Da: Copyright © Depositphotos/monkeybusiness.
- Fig. 15.Db: Copyright © Depositphotos/ChicagoStock.
- Fig. 15.Dc: Copyright © Depositphotos/logos2012.
- Fig. 15.Dd: Copyright © Depositphotos/belchonock.
- Fig. 15.E: Source: https://commons.wikimedia.org/wiki/File:Butlerov,_A._M._1828-1886.jpg.

Introduction to Biochemistry

CHAPTER 16

LEARNING OBJECTIVES AND OUTCOMES

After reading this chapter, you should be able to do the following:

- Define basic concepts associated with Biochemistry.

- Explain the structure and functions of amino acids, peptides, and proteins.

- Identify essential and nonessential amino acids.

- Explain the structure and functions of carbohydrates.

- Identify key structural differences between cellulose, amylose, amylopectin, and glycogen.

- Explain the structure and functions of the various types of lipids discussed in the chapter (i.e. triglycerides and phospholipids).

- Be able to name various fatty acids.

- Explain the structure and various functions of nucleic acids.

- Define each of the Key Terms listed at the end of the chapter dealing with these concepts.

Section 16.1 Introduction

Biochemistry is the study of the chemical processes that take place within living organisms. When we think of living organisms, thoughts of animals such as elephants, lions, giraffes, or birds might come to mind, but in biology living organisms not only includes animals, but also things like plants, fungi, or microorganisms. In fact, as you may have already guessed, the term "biochemistry" is derived from a combination of biology and chemistry. The exact date associated with the birth of biochemistry is somewhat difficult to pinpoint due to the complexity of the subject matter, and how you choose to view various aspects of this particular scientific discipline. For example, some claim that its birth is associated with the first biochemical demonstration of alcoholic fermentation in 1897 by Eduard Buchner. Buchner was a German chemist born in 1860 in Munich, Germany, who was ultimately awarded the Nobel Prize in Chemistry in 1907 for his work on fermentation. For others, the birth of biochemistry may have happened a bit earlier in history with the discovery of the first enzyme amylase by Anselme Payen in 1833. Payen was

Biochemistry is the study of the chemical processes that take place within living organisms.

Eduard Buchner (1860–1917) was a German chemist who was awarded the Nobel Prize in Chemistry in 1907 for his work on fermentation.

Anselme Payen (1795–1871) was a French chemist credited with the discovery of the first enzyme amylase in 1833.

a French chemist born in 1795, who made significant contributions to this field of study. Yet for others, the study of biochemistry as a unique discipline may, in fact, extend deep into antiquity. While the exact event that sparked the birth of biochemistry as a specific scientific discipline can be debated, there is no doubt that since that time it has become an enormous field of study with great significance to our current way of life. We will soon see that a fundamental understanding of biochemistry allows us to better understand concepts that affect mankind such as diseases and illnesses, as well as drugs used to cure or better treat them. For example, we know what causes things like sickle-cell anemia, cystic fibrosis, Tay-Sachs, and Alzheimer's disease, just to name a few, or vitamin-deficient diseases such as scurvy and pellagra. We can gain a better understanding of diseases such as cancer and the various strategies currently being employed to more effectively treat various types of cancers with improved chemotherapeutics through a better understanding of biochemistry. Besides diseases, illnesses, and cures, biochemistry also allows us to better understand ourselves as human beings in general and the origins of mankind. Therefore, the study of this particular scientific discipline is of extreme importance. In this chapter, we provide a brief overview of this important discipline to include an understanding of the four major classes of macromolecules. Namely, we will discuss proteins, carbohydrates, lipids, and nucleic acids.

Section 16.2 Proteins and Amino Acids

The importance of proteins to living organisms cannot be overstated as they are involved in almost all functions of cell structure. Proteins are present in muscle and skin, and also function to catalyze metabolic reactions in the form of enzymes. They are involved in DNA replication, and the transportation of various molecules throughout living organisms. **Proteins** themselves are large biomolecules composed of individual building blocks called **amino acids**, which are defined as organic compounds that contain amine and carboxyl functional groups, as well as a side-chain which we call the "*R* group." The side-chain is specific to each amino acid, and essentially gives each individual amino acid its unique characteristics. Thus, we can depict a generic amino acid as it exists at physiological *pH* (~7.2–7.4) as follows:

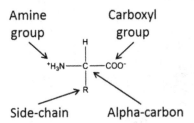

Notice that both the amino group and the carboxyl group are completely ionized at physiological *pH*. Therefore, they are **amphoteric** substances, meaning that they can act as an acid as well as a base. Amino acids are also referred to as **zwitterions,** which are molecules that contain charged groups of opposite polarity. There are 20 standard amino acids in which the identity of the "*R*" groups varies, which can be categorized according to polarity as well as acidity and basicity (Figure 16.1). For convenience, the amino acids also have one-letter and three-letter designations (Table 16.1). Additionally, amino acids can also be classified according to whether they are essential or nonessential amino acids. **Essential amino acids** must be obtained through our diet as we do not have the capabilities to make them ourselves, while we do have the ability to synthesize **nonessential amino acids**. According to this definition, there are nine essential standard amino acids and 11 nonessential standard amino acids. The essential amino acids are valine, leucine, isoleucine, tryptophan, phenylalanine, methionine, threonine, lysine, and histidine. The nonessential amino acids are glycine, alanine, proline, serine, cysteine, tyrosine, asparagine, glutamine, aspartic acid, glutamic acid, and arginine. It is important to note that various vitamin-deficient disorders can result if the appropriate amounts of essential amino acids are not obtained by one's diet. Also, if you recall the definition of a chiral molecule from Chapter 15, which is any molecule that exhibits optical isomerism (i.e. a carbon atom bonded to four different substituents), you will quickly notice that all of the amino acids with the exception of glycine are in fact chiral. Therefore, for reasons beyond the scope of the current discussion, amino acids are designated with either a D- (*dextro-*, for right) or L- (*levo-*, for left). However, this designation should not be confused with the rotation of plane-polarized light (i.e. the use of the *d* and *l* notation for isomers) as described in Chapter 15; rather, they refer to the absolute configuration when compared to D- and L-glyceraldehyde. In fact, while the amino acids found in the human body are of the L- designation (again except glycine, which is not chiral), about half of them rotate plane-polarized light right, while the other half rotate plane-polarized light left.

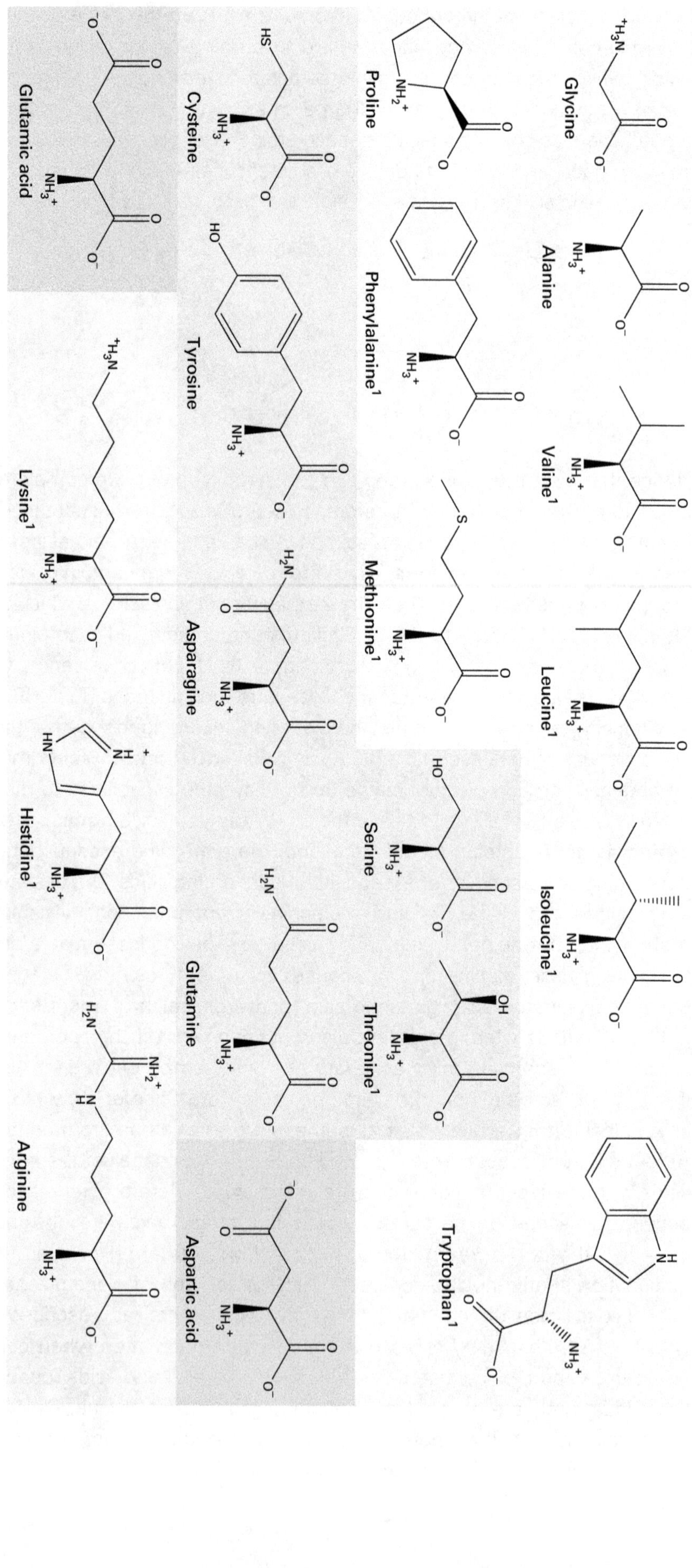

Figure 16.1 Structures of the twenty standard essential[1] and nonessential (not marked) amino acids depicted at physiological *pH*. Nonpolar amino acids in yellow, polar amino acids in purple, acidic amino acids in pink, and basic amino acids in blue. Histidine is essential for children.

Table 16.1 The 20 standard amino acids along with their one-letter and three-letter abbreviations.

Amino Acid	One-letter Abbreviation	Three-letter Abbreviation	Amino Acid	One-letter Abbreviation	Three-letter Abbreviation
Glycine	G	Gly	Tyrosine	Y	Tyr
Alanine	A	Ala	Asparagine	N	Asn
Valine	V	Val	Serine	S	Ser
Leucine	L	Leu	Threonine	T	Thr
Isoleucine	I	Ile	Glutamine	Q	Gln
Proline	P	Pro	Aspartic acid	D	Asp
Phenylalanine	F	Phe	Glutamic acid	E	Glu
Methionine	M	Met	Lysine	K	Lys
Tryptophan	W	Trp	Histidine	H	His
Cysteine	C	Cys	Arginine	R	Arg

Peptides

Now that we have established that the building blocks of proteins are amino acids, we now turn our attention to peptides. In the same way that we have defined proteins as being large biomolecules composed of long chains of amino acids, **peptides** are defined as being short chains of amino acids. The exact size (i.e. how many amino acids in a given chain) that distinguishes a peptide from a protein is somewhat ambiguous but is somewhere around 50–60 amino acids or so. The type of bond that holds amino acids together is called a **peptide bond** and is formed via a **condensation reaction** in which two amino acids combine to form a larger molecule with the loss of water. For example, below we see this type of reaction between valine and alanine amino acids to form a dipeptide:

valine   alanine   dipeptide

The opposite of this process is **hydrolysis**, or the splitting of a chemical bond such that water is added to the resulting products. Notice that a **dipeptide** consists of two amino acids, while a **tripeptide** would contain three amino acids and so on. The **peptide backbone** is defined as the non-*R* groups of the polypeptide or main chain as highlighted below:

dipeptide

Also, notice that by convention we draw peptides such that the amino acid with the free amine group on the main chain is on the left (**amine terminus**), while the amino acid with the free carboxyl group on the main chain is on the right (**carboxylic acid terminus**). As we will soon see when we get to larger peptides, and then ultimately proteins, we should note that the amino acid order is of utmost importance. Thus, when we write the amino acid sequence left to right, it is traditionally written from the amine terminus to the carboxylic acid terminus, respectively. Therefore, the amino acid sequence of the above dipeptide can be written as Val-Ala.

Example Problem 16.1

Draw the structure of the tetrapeptide Tyr-Gly-Ser-Trp.
Solution:
First, we recognize that this sequence is tyrosine, glycine, serine, and then tryptophan from the three-letter designation going from left to right (amine terminus to the carboxylic acid terminus respectively). Then we can draw the structure of this tetrapeptide. Just remember, when combining amino acids, this is a condensation reaction so they combine to form a larger molecule with the loss of water.

Proteins

We now look at both the structure and the function of proteins, which are very much related. In other words, the structure of a protein is critical to its

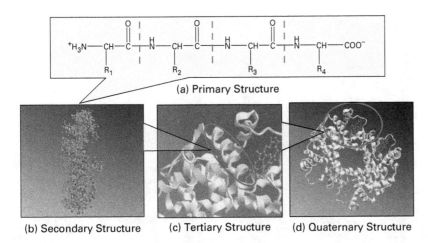

(b) Secondary Structure   (c) Tertiary Structure   (d) Quaternary Structure

Figure 16.2 The four levels of protein structure are the primary structure or the amino acid sequence (a.), the secondary structure (α helix depicted here) (b.), the tertiary structure (c.), and the quaternary structure (d.).

function. For example, in some cases it may be necessary for some structural proteins to impart flexibility and elasticity (i.e. for skin) or strength (i.e. bones and tendons) depending on its intended function. Similarly, proteins intended to catalyze various biochemical reactions (i.e. enzymes) need to be constructed in such a way that they can carry out their intended function. To that end, these large biomolecules must therefore assume very specific three-dimensional structures. Thus, when referring to protein constructs, we can better understand them by taking a look at their primary, secondary, tertiary, and quaternary structures (Figure 16.2). The **primary (1°) structure** of a protein is the amino acid sequence itself. The importance of a particular proteins' primary structure cannot be overstated. For example, sickle-cell anemia is typically an inherited disorder in which the oxygen-carrying protein hemoglobin present in red blood cells is abnormally shaped resulting in a "sickle-like" shape (a sickle is an agriculture tool with a curved blade) (Figure 16.3). It can be caused as a result of a hydrophilic glutamic acid residue being incorrectly substituted for a hydrophobic valine residue in the protein's primary sequence. This negatively affects the optimal functionality of hemoglobin to do its job in part due to the decreased solubility of the protein associated with such a substitution as well as the propensity of "sickle-shaped" cells to stick to each other and form stiff aggregate fibers. Patients who have this disorder will typically develop symptoms early on in life, generally before reaching the age of one.

A proteins' **secondary (2°) structure** is the next level of its structure which results from regular polypeptide folding arrangements attributed to local interactions between individual amino acids, resulting in various geometric patterns. Two common arrangements are the α-helix and β-pleated sheets. The α-**helix** is a coiled or spiraled conformation that can be formed due to hydrogen-bond interactions between the backbone amine groups and carboxyl groups of amino acids approximately three to five residues apart along the main chain (Figure 16.4, left). The result of such interactions orients the "R" groups outwardly. A good example of mostly α-helical-containing proteins is the keratins, which are proteins commonly found in our hair. The keratins are also commonly referred to as **fibrous proteins**, which tend to be relatively simple linear insoluble structures. β-**pleated sheets** on the other hand have a slightly different arrangement in that they are assemblies of multiple polypeptide chains aligned side-by-side which are held together

Figure 16.3 Sickle-cell anemia can result when the normally shaped oxygen-carrying protein hemoglobin present in red blood cells (left) is abnormally shaped, resulting in a "sickle-like" shape (right).

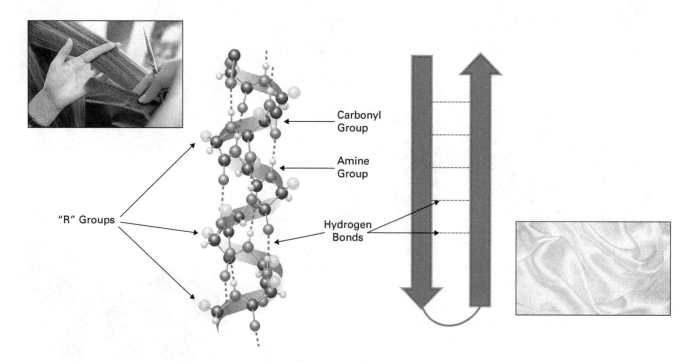

Figure 16.4 The two common secondary structures, the alpha-helix (left) and beta-pleated sheets (right).

Heating an egg irreversibly denatures the protein albumin.

primarily by hydrogen bonds between neighboring chains (Figure 16.4, right). The strands of silk are good examples of proteins that form β-pleated sheets. It is important to point out that while α-helices and β-pleated sheets have regular definable features, they should not be confused with a **random coil**, which is irregularly structured. Often if a protein is heated (or there is a change in *pH*), a protein can be **denatured** in which it loses its secondary structure and can become random coils. For example, heating an egg irreversibly denatures the protein albumin.

Larger protein structures are possible beyond 1° and 2° structures and can therefore have **tertiary (3°)** and/or **quaternary (4°) structures** associated with them. These larger structures can form as a result of a protein folding back on itself and being held together by various intermolecular forces between "*R*" groups, some of which is described in Chapter 9. This can include hydrophobic interactions between nonpolar amino acid side-chains, salt bridges between acidic and basic amino acids as well hydrogen bonding. Furthermore, covalent bonds may in fact be involved in these types of structures. For example, two cysteine residues can form a **disulfide bond** (sometimes referred to as a disulfide bridge) as follows:

In fact, we have already mentioned that keratins are the primary protein found in hair. The presence of many disulfide bonds can result in curly hair versus fewer disulfide bonds found in straight hair. When someone gets a perm, various chemicals can be used (i.e. ammonium thioglycolate) to break disulfide bonds; the hair is then curled usually with hot curling rods, and finally chemicals added to reform the disulfide bonds (i.e. hydrogen peroxide), thereby locking the curls in place. In any event, let's continue our discussion involving the formation of 3° structures in which biological proteins tend to fold in such a way that hydrophobic amino acids are buried in the interior of the protein, while hydrophilic residues are generally oriented outwardly as living systems exist in aqueous environments. Notice from Figure 16.2 (d.), hemoglobin exhibits a higher order of structure, which is a combination of four protein strand subunits that contribute to the overall 4° structure. Also, notice that unlike fibrous proteins (which generally only form 1° and 2° structures), hemoglobin is a **globular protein**, which are generally spherical in shape and tend to be more complex structures. For example, enzymes are, in fact, mainly globular proteins. If you recall from Chapter 14, **enzymes** are biological catalysts that increase the rates of biochemical reactions.

Section 16.3 **Carbohydrates**

The term **carbohydrates** (also called sugars) literally means carbon and water, and, therefore, they often have the general formula $(CH_2O)_n$. They are **polyhydroxy molecules**, meaning that they are molecules containing more than one hydroxyl group, derived from either aldehydes or ketones. For example, glucose is a polyhydroxy aldehyde, while fructose is a polyhydroxy ketone as follows:

glucose   fructose

These are both **monosaccharides,** which are defined as the smallest carbohydrates. Monosaccharides derived from aldehydes are called **aldoses**, while those derived from ketones are called **ketoses**. Notice the use of "-ose" as a suffix here, which is commonly used for sugars. Therefore, a **triose** is a sugar with three carbons, a **tetrose** is a sugar with four carbons, a **pentose** is a sugar with five carbons, and a **hexose** is a sugar with six carbons, and so on. Two monosaccharides can be joined together to form structures called **disaccharides**, or several can be joined together to form more complex structures called **polysaccharides**. In either case, monosaccharides are linked together via glycosidic bonds. A **glycosidic bond** is technically defined as a covalent bond that links a carbohydrate to another entity which may or may not also be a carbohydrate. You might also notice that these structures have multiple chiral carbons. As with our discussion involving amino acids, we will not go into detail here regarding how these designations are determined, but suffice to say for now that most physiologically relevant sugars are of the D- designation; however, there are some that have the L- designation. Again, just remember that this designation should not be confused with the rotation of plane-polarized light. In any event, notice that glucose and fructose are drawn linearly here; however, it is important to recognize that in actuality an equilibrium exists between the linear form and cyclic form as follows:

α-Glucose   Glucose (Linear Form)   β-Glucose

α-Fructose   Fructose (Linear Form)   β-Fructose

Notice that when cyclic glucose forms, the alcohol group on the fifth carbon reacts with the first carbon containing the aldehyde group. Similarly, when cyclic fructose forms, the alcohol group on the fifth carbon reacts with the second carbon containing the ketone group. When this happens, the hydroxyl group on either the first carbon for glucose or the second carbon for fructose will be on the opposite side of the CH_2OH group present at the sixth position (designated as being the α-configuration) or on the same side as the CH_2OH group at the sixth position (designated as being the β-configuration). While this may seem to be somewhat insignificant for monosaccharides as both the linear and cyclic forms exist in equilibrium, this does in fact become of great importance when more complex structures form such as disaccharides and polysaccharides. For example, let's look at sucrose, which is what most of us know as simply "table sugar" found in our homes. It is a very common saccharide that can be refined from sugarcane and is composed of the monosaccharides α-glucose and β-fructose as follows:

α-Glucose

β-Fructose

α-1, β-2-glycosidic bond

Sucrose

Sucrose is a common saccharide that can be refined from sugarcane.

Notice that the glycosidic linkage is designated as being an α, β-1,2-glycosidic linkage. That is because it is formed between the first carbon of α-glucose and the secon carbon of β-fructose. As we saw with the joining of two amino acids to form a peptide bond, linking sugars together to form a glycosidic linkage is also a condensation reaction, and the opposite of this process (i.e. during digestion) is hydrolysis. In fact, we can keep adding sugars to build even bigger polysaccharides, also called **complex carbohydrates**. For example, **cellulose** (Figure 16.5) is the most abundant organic substance on earth and is a linear chain of several hundred and possibly thousands of glucose residues linked by β-glycosidic linkages. It has very rigid properties attributed primarily to the extensive hydrogen bonding that can take place between neighboring cellulose molecules and is an important structural component of cell walls found in plants. Humans lack the enzyme needed to break the β-glycosidic linkages between residues, and are therefore unable to digest cellulose. **Starch** (Figure 16.5), which is a mixture of both amylose and amylopectin, is another example of a complex carbohydrate primarily used for the main energy storage source for plants. **Amylose** is also a linear chain of many glucose residues similar to cellulose; however, the glucose residues here are connected by α-glycosidic

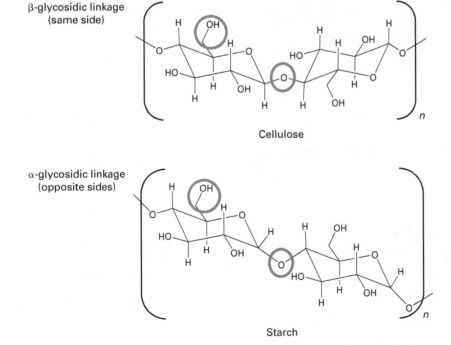

β-glycosidic linkage (same side)

Cellulose

α-glycosidic linkage (opposite sides)

Starch

Figure 16.5 The structural differences between cellulose (top) and starch (bottom), where n is an unspecified number of repeating units.

linkages. **Amylopectin** is structurally similar to amylose but contains branching in the chains. In fact, glycogen is yet another example of a complex carbohydrate that is structurally similar to amylopectin but is even more highly branched. **Glycogen** serves as a form of energy storage for animals. Thus, while humans lack the enzyme to break the β-glycosidic linkages found in cellulose between glucose residues, we do have the ability to break α-glycosidic linkages between glucose residues, and therefore we can digest glycogen.

Example Problem 16.2

Label each of the following as an aldose or ketose, and identify each as a triose, tetrose, pentose, hexose, etc. How many chiral carbons are present on each molecule?

Solution:

a.) This saccharide is a polyhydroxy aldehyde; therefore, it is an aldose. Also, it has three carbons and is a triose. This is *D*-Glyceraldehyde.	This is an **aldose** and a **triose** with only **one chiral carbon** (in red).
b.) This saccharide is a polyhydroxy ketone (the C–O double bond was not on a terminal carbon prior to ring formation), therefore, it is a ketose. Also, it has six carbons and is a hexose. This is α-*D*-Fructose.	This is a **ketose** and a **hexose** with **four chiral carbons** (in red).
c.) This saccharide is a polyhydroxy aldehyde; therefore, it is an aldose. Also, it has five carbons and is a pentose. This is *D*-Xylose.	This is an **aldose** and a **pentose** with **three chiral carbons** (in red).

d.) This saccharide is a polyhydroxy alde-hyde; therefore, it is an aldose. Also, it has four carbons and is a tetrose. This is *D*-Threose.	This is an **aldose** and a **tetrose** with **two chiral carbons** (in red)

Example Problem 16.3

Which of the following complex carbohydrates has an α-linkage? Which one has a β-linkage?

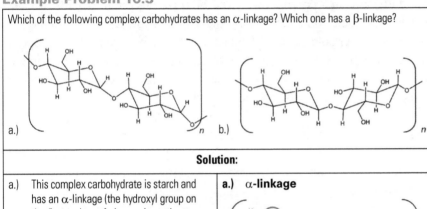

a.)   b.)

	Solution:
a.) This complex carbohydrate is starch and has an α-linkage (the hydroxyl group on the first carbon of glucose is on the opposite side of the CH_2OH group present at the sixth position).	**a.)** α-**linkage**
b.) This complex carbohydrate is cellulose and has a β-linkage (the hydroxyl group on the first carbon of glucose is on the same side of the CH_2OH group present at the sixth position).	**b.)** β-**linkage**

Section 16.4 **Lipids**

The term "lipid" is derived from the Greek word "lipos", meaning fat. They are nonpolar, and, therefore, are not water soluble, but they are very soluble in nonpolar solvents such as chloroform and ether. Lipids are a diverse family of molecules that have various biological functions that include energy storage and insulation, structural components of cell membranes and cell-signaling functions to name a few. One of the simplest types of lipids are **fatty acids**, which are carboxylic acids that contain either saturated or unsaturated long aliphatic hydrocarbon tails. Therefore, they have the following general structure:

$$\underset{\text{HO}}{}\overset{\displaystyle \overset{O}{\parallel}}{\text{HO}-\text{C}-\text{R}}$$

where *R* is a hydrocarbon of various lengths and possible points of unsaturation (Table 16.2). Table 16.2 lists some common fatty acids. For example, lauric acid is found in human breast milk, myristic acid is a component of coconut oil and butter fat, and both palmitic and stearic acid are found in soaps and cosmetics. Common unsaturated fatty acids are also listed in the table to include oleic acid, which is found in olive oil (hence, the name). It should be noted that the presence of the double bond in the tail changes the physical properties quite dramatically. For example, while both fatty acids have a chain containing 18 carbons (often referred to as a "C18" chain), the melting point of stearic acid is 70°C, while that of oleic acid is only 4°C. This is due to the fact that the double bond puts a "kink" in the tail, which prevents the entire chain from interacting with neighboring molecules via hydrophobic interactions (Figure 16.6). As we will soon see with phospholipids, this also allows for increased membrane fluidity.

The term "oleic" is derived from olive oil which contains oleic acid.

Table 16.2 Common saturated (top) and unsaturated (bottom) fatty acids.

Saturated Fatty Acids

Name	Total Number of Carbons: Number of Double Bonds	Chemical Structure
Lauric acid	12:0	$CH_3(CH_2)_{10}COOH$
Myristic acid	14:0	$CH_3(CH_2)_{12}COOH$
Palmitic acid	16:0	$CH_3(CH_2)_{14}COOH$
Stearic acid	18:0	$CH_3(CH_2)_{16}COOH$
Arachidic acid	20:0	$CH_3(CH_2)_{18}COOH$

Unsaturated Fatty Acids

Name	Total Number of Carbons: Number of Double Bonds	Chemical Structure
Palmitoleic acid	16:1	$CH_3(CH_2)_5CH=CH(CH_2)_7COOH$
Oleic acid	18:1	$CH_3(CH_2)_7CH=CH(CH_2)_7COOH$
Linoleic acid	18:2	$CH_3(CH_2)_4(CH=CHCH_2)_2(CH_2)_6COOH$

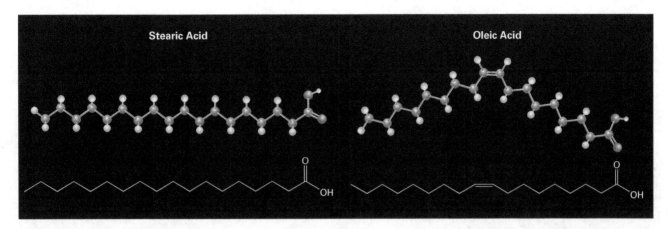

Figure 16.6 The structural differences between stearic acid (left) and oleic acid (right). The double bond puts a "kink" in the tail, which prevents the entire chain from interacting with neighboring molecules via hydrophobic interactions.

Example Problem 16.4

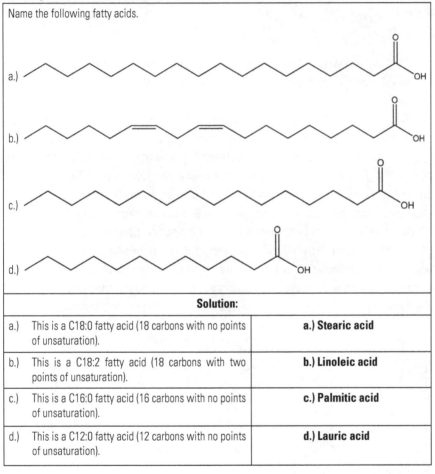

Name the following fatty acids.

a.)

b.)

c.)

d.)

Solution:	
a.) This is a C18:0 fatty acid (18 carbons with no points of unsaturation).	**a.) Stearic acid**
b.) This is a C18:2 fatty acid (18 carbons with two points of unsaturation).	**b.) Linoleic acid**
c.) This is a C16:0 fatty acid (16 carbons with no points of unsaturation).	**c.) Palmitic acid**
d.) This is a C12:0 fatty acid (12 carbons with no points of unsaturation).	**d.) Lauric acid**

It should be noted that fatty acids are chemically reactive and are therefore commonly found as components of other larger types of lipids. For example, **triglycerides** are composed of a glycerol backbone to which three fatty acids are "esterified." They are found in the body fat of humans and animals and are excellent sources of energy. This is due to the fact that both the glycerol backbone and the fatty acids themselves can be broken down to yield a significant amount of energy. In fact, this is in part why seals, which have a high fat content, are a favorite meal source for polar bears. By consuming and storing high levels of triglycerides, polar bears can use them as an energy source during hibernation without having to get rid of excessive amounts of nitrogen through

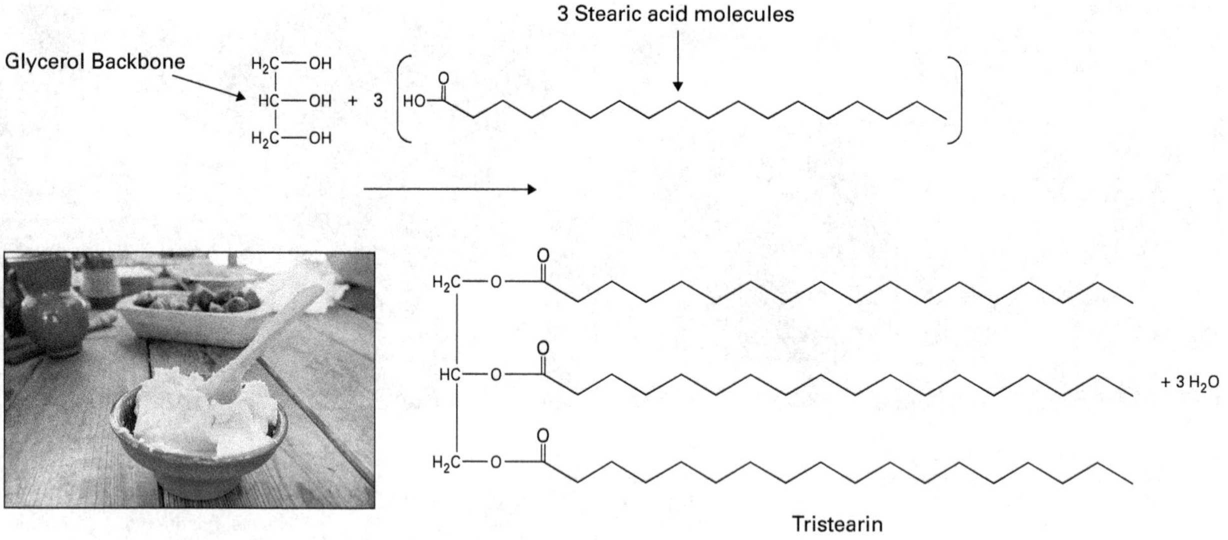

Glycerol Backbone

3 Stearic acid molecules

Tristearin

Figure 16.7 Tristearin, which is a triglyceride composed of a glycerol backbone and 3 stearic acid molecules commonly found in lard.

Polar bears prefer a diet rich in triglycerides.

urination, which would otherwise be necessary with a high protein diet. As a structural example of a triglyceride, let us look at tristearin (Figure 16.7), which is composed of a glycerol backbone and three stearic acid molecules.

Tristearin is an example of a saturated fat and can be found in various food items such as lard. If you recall, oleic acid is an unsaturated fatty acid found in olive oil and can exist in the triglyceride form as triolein (a triglyceride composed of a glycerol backbone and three oleic acid molecules). **Phospholipids** are yet another type of lipid which functions as a major component of cell membranes rather than an energy source but is similar in structure to that of triglycerides in that both the first and the second positions of the glycerol backbone contain fatty acids; however, the third position on the glycerol backbone is replaced by a phosphate group to which various head groups can be linked. In fact, they are named in part according to these head groups. For example, let's look at the structure of two different phospholipids that

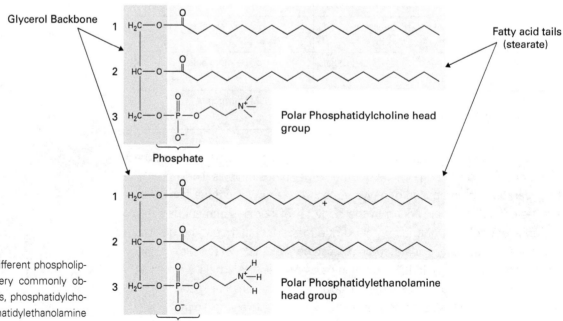

Glycerol Backbone

Fatty acid tails (stearate)

Polar Phosphatidylcholine head group

Phosphate

Polar Phosphatidylethanolamine head group

Phosphate

Figure 16.8 Two different phospholipids that contain very commonly observed head groups, phosphatidylcholine (top) and phosphatidylethanolamine (bottom).

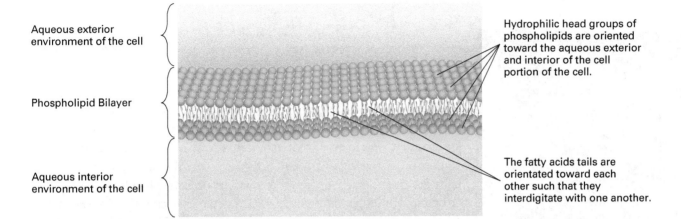

Aqueous exterior environment of the cell

Phospholipid Bilayer

Aqueous interior environment of the cell

Hydrophilic head groups of phospholipids are oriented toward the aqueous exterior and interior of the cell portion of the cell.

The fatty acids tails are orientated toward each other such that they interdigitate with one another.

contain very commonly observed head groups, phosphatidylcholine and phosphatidylethanolamine (Figure 16.8).

Figure 16.9 The lipid bilayer formed by phospholipids in the cell membrane.

Notice that unlike nonpolar fatty acids, phospholipids have a polar portion (i.e. the phosphate head group) and nonpolar portion (i.e. the fatty acid tails). Therefore, phospholipids are **amphiphiles**, which are molecules that possess both hydrophilic and hydrophobic properties. They form the phospholipid bilayer of cell membranes in which the hydrophilic portion of the molecule is oriented toward the aqueous exterior and interior portions of the cell, while the fatty acids tails are orientated toward each other such that they interdigitate with one another (Figure 16.9).

While there are many more different types of lipids that we could examine here, a thorough discussion of this topic is beyond the scope of this introductory chapter in biochemistry. However, we will discuss one more major type of lipid, namely steroids. All steroids have the following characteristic four-ring structure:

Cholesterol is an example of a steroid that is also found in cell membranes along with phospholipids, and it is essential in order to maintain cell membrane structural integrity. In addition, cholesterol is the precursor to all other steroid hormones such as testosterone and β-Estradiol, or the male and female sex hormones, respectively.

HO

cholesterol

Section 16.5 Nucleic Acids

Johannes Friedrich Miescher (1844–1895) was a Swiss physician and biologist who is most famously known for his discovery of nucleic acids in 1869.

Johannes Friedrich Miescher was a Swiss physician and biologist who is most famously known for his discovery of nucleic acids in 1869. **Nucleic acids** are the means by which organisms can transfer genetic information between generations and are necessary for all forms of known life. They are similar to proteins in that they are also macromolecular biopolymers composed of monomeric units, but in this case the individual monomeric units are called nucleotides rather than amino acids. **Nucleotides** by definition have three parts to their overall structure, which include a five-carbon sugar, a nitrogenous base, and a phosphate group. The phosphate group is bound to the 5' carbon on the five-carbon sugar, which is then bound to the nitrogenous base through its 1' carbon (this resulting glycosidic bond is in the β-configuration if you recall our discussion regarding carbohydrates in Section 16.3). The prime system is used when describing the various positions on the sugar to distinguish it from the numbering pattern used on the nitrogenous base. **Ribonucleic acid (RNA)** is necessary for protein synthesis while **deoxyribonucleic acid (DNA)** is the known genetic carrier of information. The nucleotide building blocks of these structures are called **ribonucleotides** and **deoxyribonucleotides**, respectively, which have the following generic chemical structures:

Ribonucleotide

Deoxyribonucleotide

Notice that the five-carbon sugar in the above structures is either ribose in ribonucleotides or deoxyribose (ribose sugar with the hydroxyl group on the 2' carbon replaced by hydrogen) in deoxyribonucleotides. If the phosphate group is missing on a given nucleotide, then the structure becomes a **nucleoside**. With respect to the nitrogenous bases, they are planar aromatic structures that are generally derived from either a **purine** or a **pyrimidine** structure (Figure 16.10).

RNA contains **adenine, cytosine, guanine,** and **uracil** while DNA contains adenine, cytosine, guanine, and **thymine**. Therefore, in addition to having different sugars, RNA and DNA also differ with respect to one of the bases (i.e. RNA has uracil instead of thymine which is present in DNA). While the various reasons for this are really beyond the scope of our discussion here, suffice to say for now, in this way the body can differentiate between the two. In any event, thanks to two Cambridge University scientists, namely James Watson and Francis Crick, we now know that DNA is a double-stranded helix held together by hydrogen bonding between base pairs (Figure 16.11). Notice that the phosphate groups are linked to the 3' carbon of the sugar that precedes each of the individual monomeric units in the polymeric strand and

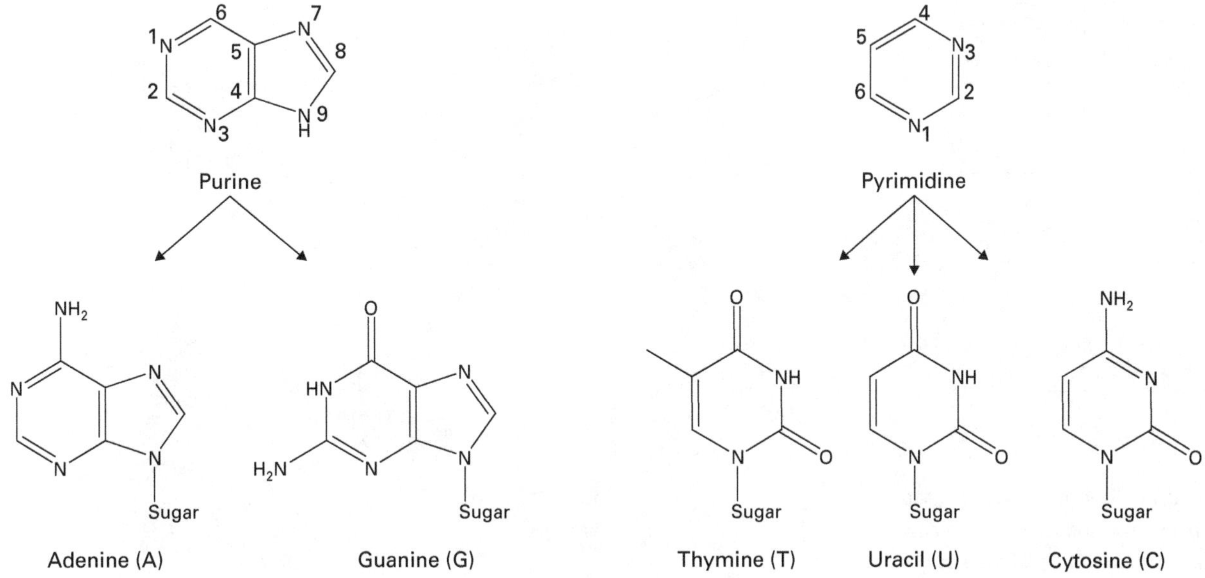

Figure 16.10 Nitrogenous bases generally found in RNA and DNA are planar aromatic structures derived from either a purine or a pyrimidine structure.

the 5' carbon of the sugar following each unit, thereby forming the negatively charged phosphate backbone. Also, we can see that each strand is held together by base pairing between a purine and pyrimidine. Specifically, adenine base pairs with thymine forming two hydrogen bonds, while cytosine base pairs with guanine forming three hydrogen bonds in DNA (in RNA, adenine would base pair with uracil instead of thymine). Also, notice that polynucleotide strands do, in fact, exhibit directionality within the nucleic acid structure. That is to say they have a 5' end (the end where the 5' carbon does not have a neighboring nucleotide) and a 3' end (the end where the 3' carbon does not have a neighboring nucleotide). The two strands run *antiparallel*, such that the 5' end of one strand is aligned alongside the 3' strand of the other in such a way that they ultimately form the double-stranded helix as depicted in Figure 16.11. During cell division, complete copies of the DNA can be made during replication where the two strands can be separated, allowing enzymes such as DNA polymerase to come in and facilitate the replication

Figure 16.11 Figure depicting (a.) a short single strand of DNA (b.) two strands being held together via hydrogen bonding between base pairs and (c.) DNA as a double helix.

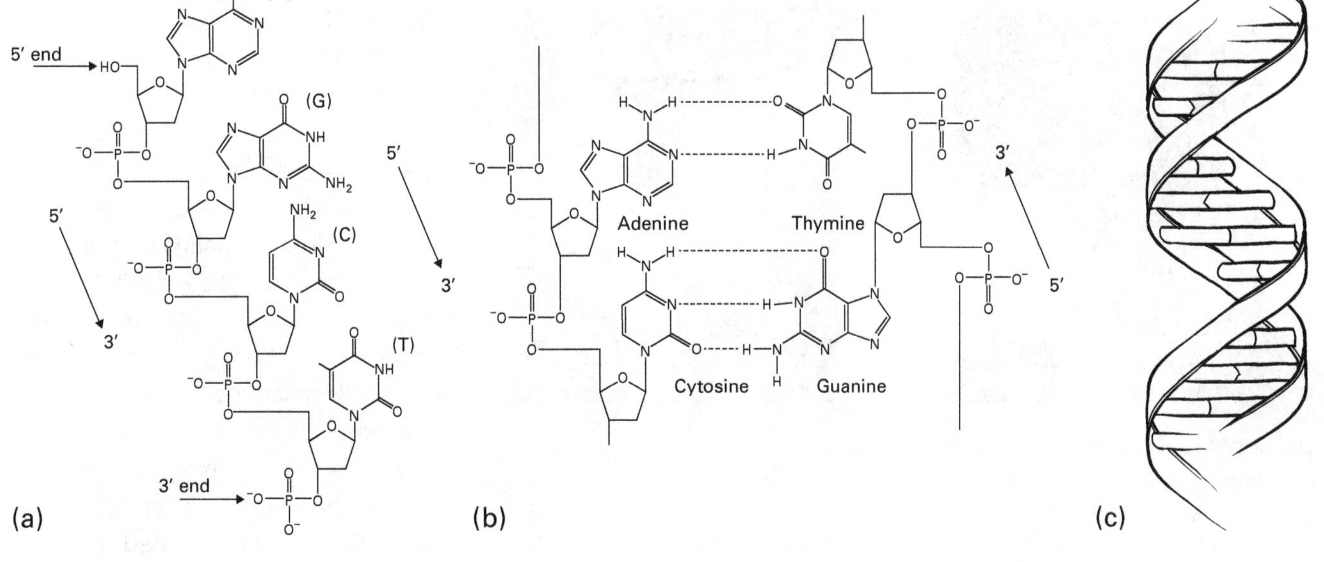

(a)

(b)

(c)

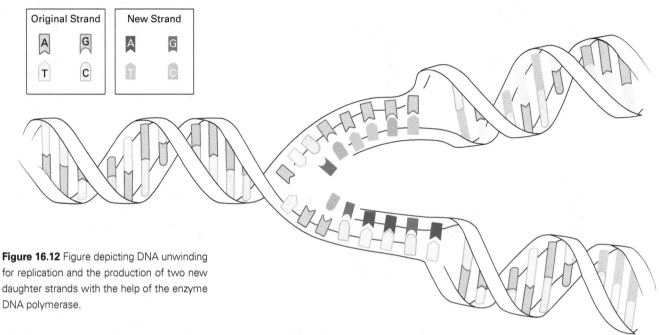

Figure 16.12 Figure depicting DNA unwinding for replication and the production of two new daughter strands with the help of the enzyme DNA polymerase.

Ribosome

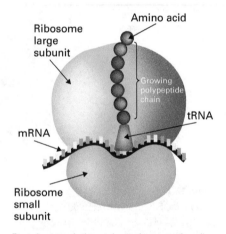

Protein translation takes place at the ribosomes with the help of tRNA.

process, thereby producing two new daughter strands (Figure 16.12). The ultimate result of this process is daughter cells that have the exact DNA copies as the original cell. This is very important because the order in which the bases are arranged in the sequence dictates the order of the amino acids in a particular protein. If the order is incorrect, the protein may not be formed correctly or may not be able to carry out its intended function. It takes a sequence of three bases to code for one amino acid, which we call a **codon**. A **gene** is defined as a sequence of codons present within a DNA molecule that encodes for a single protein, and they are contained within structures called **chromosomes**. Most human cells have 23 pairs of chromosomes, for a total of 46 chromosomes. The genetic code is nearly universal, meaning that the same amino acids are specified by the same codons in almost all organisms. Thus, we know that the DNA sequence AAT codes for a leucine residue, TAG codes for an isoleucine residue, while AGG codes for a serine residue, etc. In order to generate a protein, the DNA sequence is transcribed in a process called **transcription** into **messenger RNA (mRNA)** while in the nucleus. The mRNA then travels to **ribosomes** present in the cytoplasm to ultimately make the protein in a process called **translation** with the help of **transfer RNA (tRNA)**. The tRNA helps to decode the mRNA and ensures that the appropriate amino acid is added in the correct order to the growing end of the amino-acid chain. As you can imagine, there are numerous things that can go wrong with such a complicated process

James Watson, born in 1928, is an American geneticist who jointly received the Nobel Prize with Francis Crick for his co-discovery of the structure of DNA in 1953.

Francis Crick (1916–2004) was a British molecular biologist and physicist who was jointly awarded the Nobel Prize in 1962 for his co-discovery of the structure of DNA in 1953.

which can result in various genetically related diseases. For example, cystic fibrosis is caused by genetic mutations which affects a certain protein (i.e. the cystic fibrosis transmembrane conductance regulator protein) leading to complications which can negatively affect mostly the lungs along with other organs. Tay-Sachs is a genetic disorder that can lead to progressive deterioration of nerve cells. Even Alzheimer's disease is believed to be genetic involving many different types of genes.

Did you know how chemistry might relate to your job as a non-chemist? If you recall, most normal human cells have 23 pairs of chromosomes for a total of 46 chromosomes. As a medical professional or geneticist, you might be interested in chromosome abnormalities observed in humans. In fact, Down syndrome is one of the most common chromosome irregularities, with as many as 1 in 1,000 occurrences being reported in human babies each year. Symptoms of the disorder can include characteristic facial features and overall delayed physical growth, as well as slight to possibly more severe intellectual disability, with grown adults having the mental capabilities of a relatively young child. The disorder was named after the British doctor John Langdon Down who originally classified it in 1862, but the more detailed cause of this genetic disorder was later described in 1957 as being the presence of a third copy of either all or a portion of chromosome 21 (therefore, this disorder is also sometimes referred to as trisomy 21). It is thought that this extra chromosomal copy occurs by chance as parents of these babies are generally genetically normal, but it usually can be detected during pregnancy. One way in which this can be done is through amniocentesis, which is a prenatal test involving the removal of some amniotic fluid from the mother for testing. As such, many potential parents may choose to terminate the pregnancy, and medical professionals (as is always the case in this field) have to be sensitive to such situations and be able to provide a nurturing and comforting environment. This is an innate quality individuals working in such a setting must have in order to have a successful career in this occupation. However, while there is currently no known cure for the disorder, the average life expectancy is approximately 55–60 years old, and proper care including regular screening for health problems by trained medical professionals and ongoing education has been shown to improve overall quality of life. As a geneticist, on the other hand, you are a scientist who specializes in genetics, and disorders such as this one may also be of particular interest to you. You may someday be the scientist working long hours in the lab analyzing amniotic fluid removed from prospective mothers and sent to you for testing in order to possibly detect disorders such as this one!

Common symptoms of Down syndrome can include characteristic facial features and overall delayed physical growth.

John Langdon Down (1828–1896) was a British doctor who originally classified Down syndrome in 1862, and for whom the disorder is named.

Key Terms

1. Adenine
2. Aldoses
3. Amine terminus
4. Amino acids
5. Amphiphiles
6. Amphoteric substances
7. Amylopectin
8. Amylose
9. Biochemistry
10. Carboxylic acid terminus
11. Cellulose
12. Chromosomes
13. Codon
14. Complex carbohydrates
15. Condensation reaction
16. Cytosine
17. Denatured protein
18. Deoxyribonucleic acids (DNA)
19. Deoxyribonucleotides
20. Dipeptide
21. Disaccharides
22. Disulfide bond
23. DNA polymerase
24. Enzymes
25. Essential amino acids
26. Fatty acids
27. Fibrous proteins
28. Gene
29. Globular proteins
30. Glycogen
31. Glycosidic bond
32. Guanine
33. Hexose
34. Hydrolysis

35. Ketoses
36. Messenger RNA (mRNA)
37. Monosaccharides
38. Nonessential amino acids
39. Nucleic acids
40. Nucleoside
41. Nucleotides
42. Pentose
43. Peptide backbone
44. Peptides
45. Phospholipids
46. Polyhydroxy molecules
47. Polysaccharides
48. Primary protein structure (1°)
49. Proteins
50. Purine
51. Pyrimidine
52. Quaternary protein structure (4°)
53. Random coil
54. Ribonucleic acids (RNA)
55. Ribonucleotides
56. Ribosomes
57. Secondary protein structure (2°)
58. Starch
59. Tertiary protein structure (3°)
60. Tetrose
61. Thymine
62. Transcription
63. Transfer RNA (tRNA)
64. Translation
65. Triglycerides
66. Triose
67. Tripeptide
68. Uracil
69. Zwitterions
70. α-helix
71. β-pleated sheets

Problems

PROTEINS AND AMINO ACIDS

1. Define biochemistry.

2. What are proteins and amino acids?

3. What are amphoteric substances?

4. What does it mean to be an essential or a nonessential amino acid? What are they?

5. Are all of the 20 standard amino acids chiral? What designation (the D-*dextro-* or L-*levo*-designation) do we give the standard amino acids commonly found in the human body, and does that mean that they all rotate plane-polarized light in the same direction?

6. Draw all 20 standard amino acids as they appear at physiological *pH* (~7.2–7.4). Which ones are polar, nonpolar, acidic, or basic? What are their one-letter and three-letter designations?

7. Which of the following structures is an amino acid?

a.)

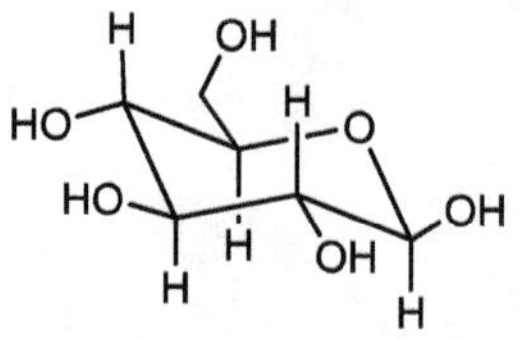

b.)

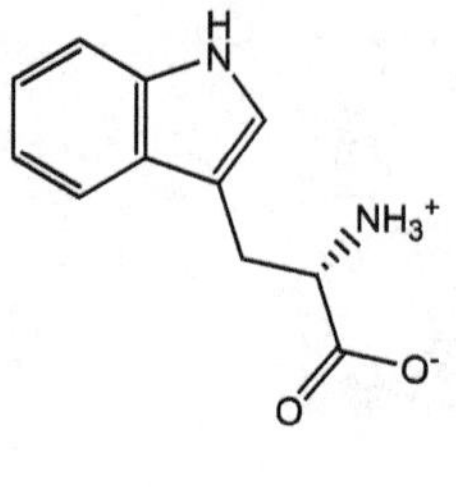

c.)

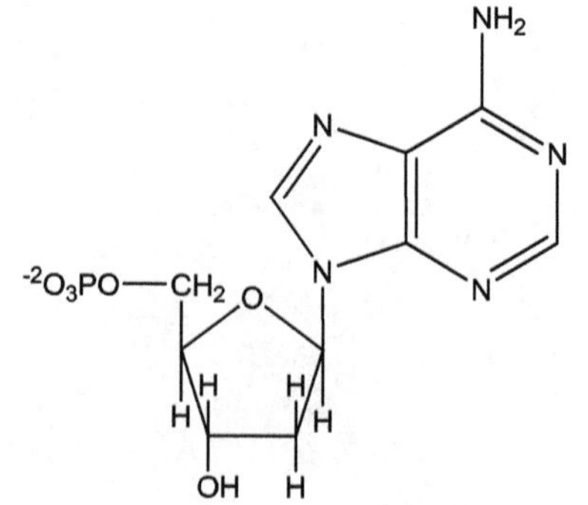

d.)

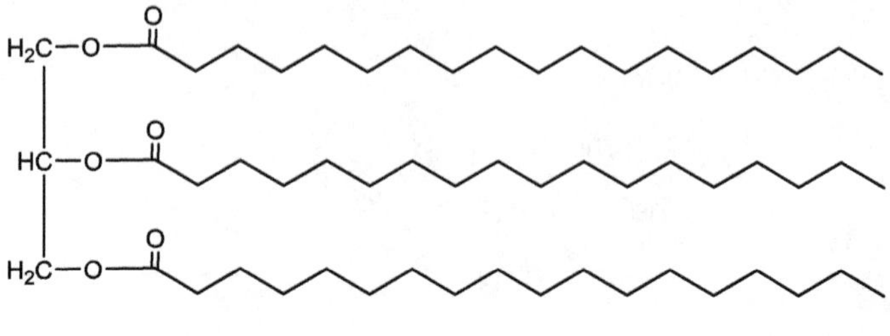

8. Determine the identities of each amino acid listed below based on its one-letter designation.

    a. G

    b. W

    c. N

    d. S

9. Determine the identities of each amino acid listed below based on its one-letter designation.

    a. L

    b. Y

    c. F

    d. R

10. The type of bond that holds amino acids together is called a _____bond, and is formed via a _____reaction in which two amino acids combine to form a larger molecule with the loss of water.

11. A _____consists of two amino acids, while a _____would contain three amino acids.

12. By convention, peptides are written from left to right with the _____terminus on the left and the _____terminus on the right.

13. Draw the structure of the dipeptide Leu-Ser at physiological *pH* (~7.2–7.4).

14. Draw the structure of the tripeptide Arg-Tyr-Ala at physiological *pH* (~7.2–7.4).

15. Describe what is meant by a particular protein's primary, secondary, tertiary, and quaternary structures.

16. Explain the difference between fibrous and globular proteins. Give an example of each.

CARBOHYDRATES

17. What are carbohydrates?

18. Define monosaccharides, disaccharides, and polysaccharides.

19. What is a glycosidic bond?

20. What designation (the D-*dextro-* or L-*levo*-designation) do we give *most* (not all) physiologically relevant sugars?

21. What is an aldose? What is a ketose?

22. Explain how we designate sugars as being either α- or β-during cyclization.

23. What are complex carbohydrates?

24. What is cellulose? Discuss its structure.

25. What is starch? How are amylose and amylopectin different structurally?

26. What is glycogen? How is it different structurally from amylopectin?

27. Which of the following structures is a carbohydrate?

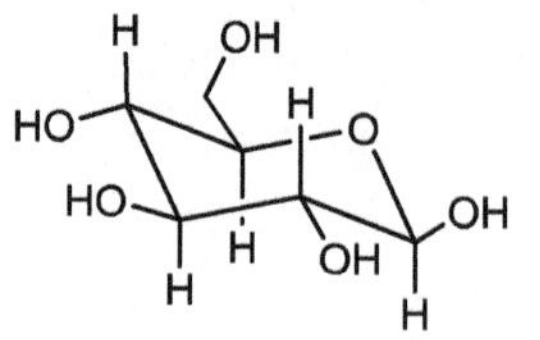

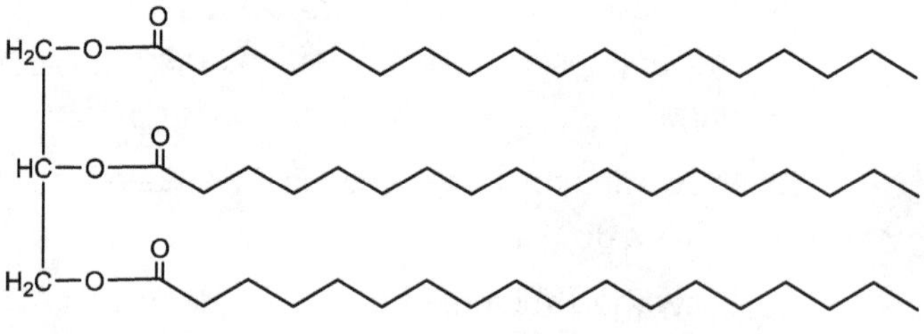

28. Which of the following complex carbohydrates has an α-linkage? Which one has a β-linkage?

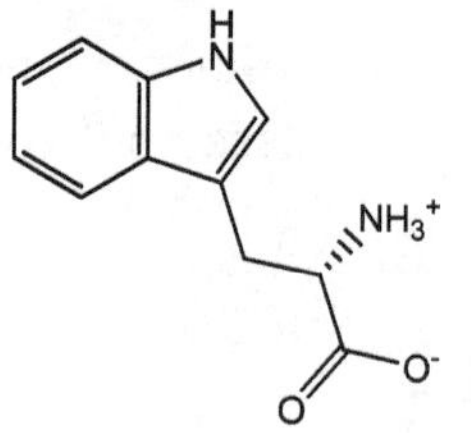

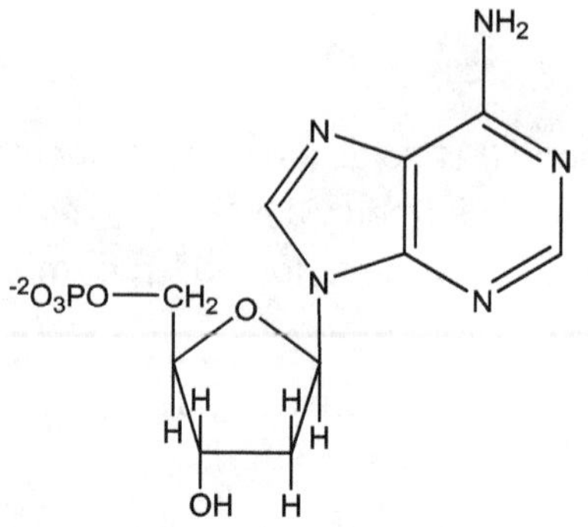

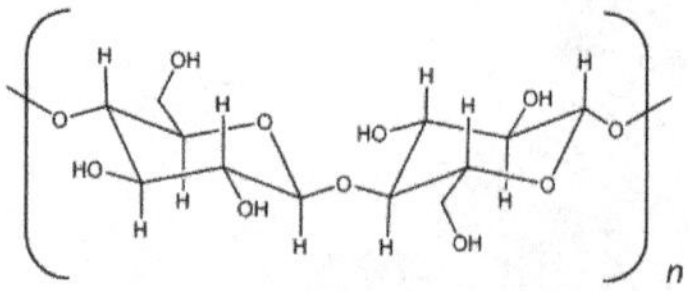

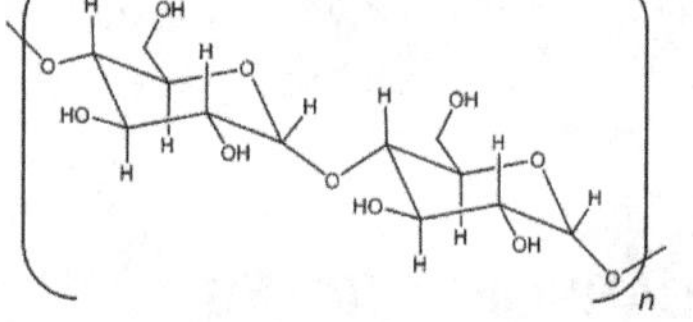

LIPIDS

29. What are lipids?

30. Define fatty acids.

31. What is a saturated fatty acid? What is an unsaturated fatty acid? How does the presence of a double bond in unsaturated fatty acids affect the physical properties when compared to saturated fatty acids of comparable length?

32. What is the name of the following fatty acid?

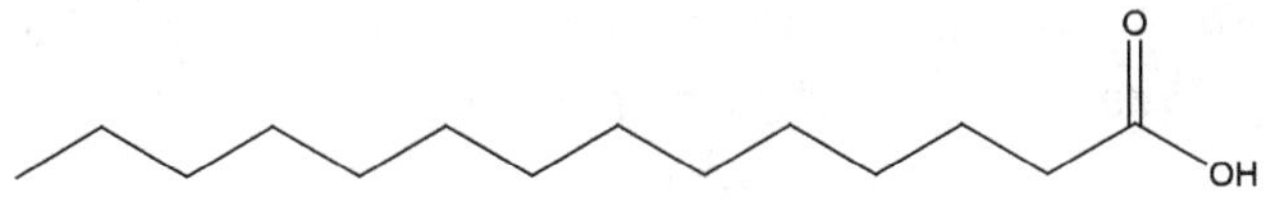

33. What is the name of the following fatty acid?

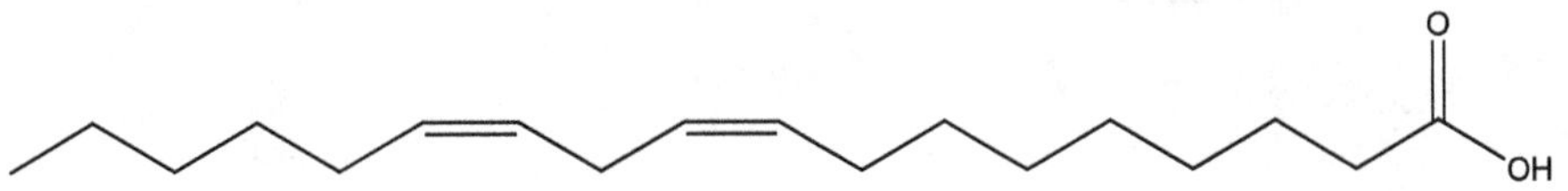

34. What is the name of the following fatty acid?

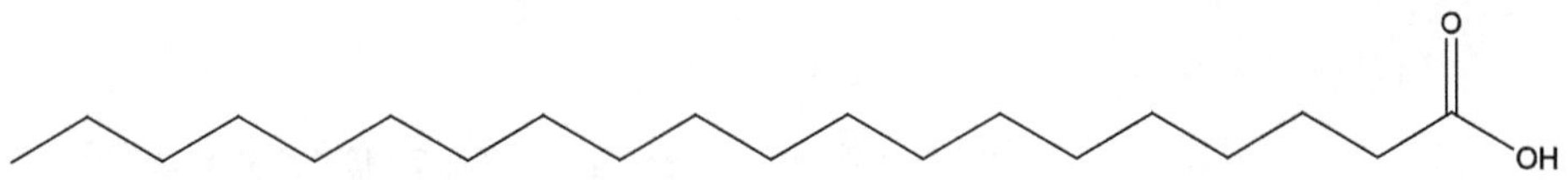

35. Draw the structure of lauric acid.

36. Draw the structure of palmitoleic acid.

37. Draw the structure of oleic acid.

38. What are triglycerides?

39. Which of the following structures is a triglyceride?

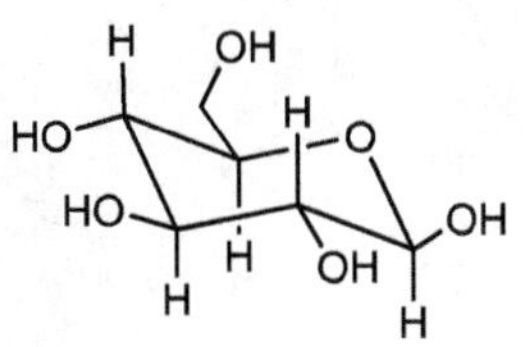

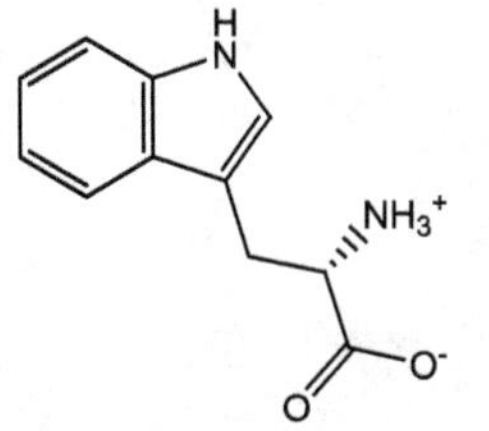

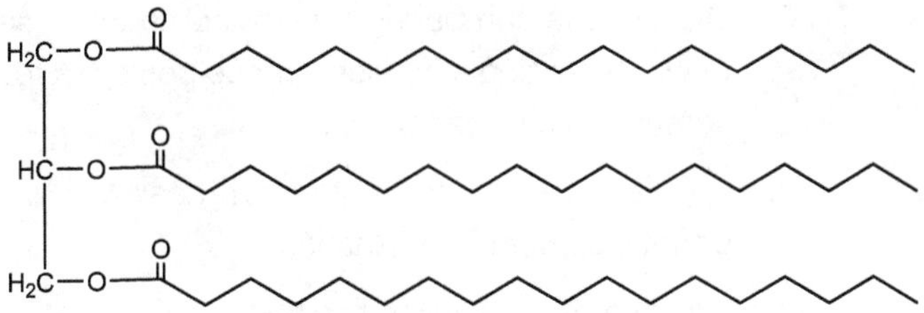

40. Draw the structure of tristearin.

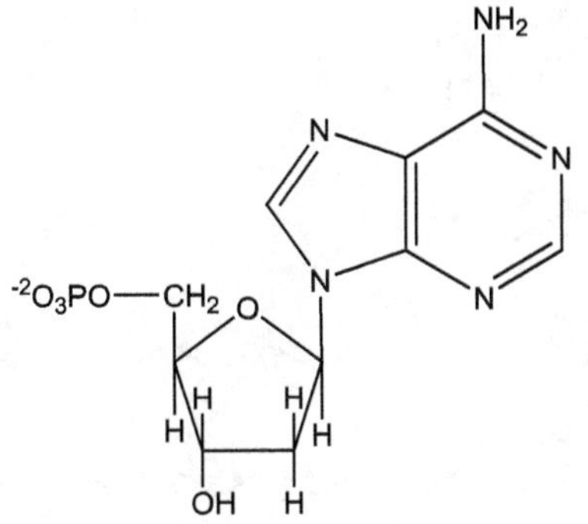

41. Explain why seals are a favorite meal source for polar bears.

42. What are phospholipids and what are they primarily used for? Describe their general structure.

43. What are amphiphilic molecules?

44. Draw the characteristic four-ring structure found in steroids.

45. Cholesterol is the precursor to all other steroid hormones such as _____, which is the male sex hormone and _____, which is the female sex hormone.

NUCLEIC ACIDS

46. What are nucleic acids?

47. _____ was a Swiss physician and biologist who is most famously known for his discovery of nucleic acids in 1869.

48. What are nucleotides?

49. Which of the following structures is a nucleotide?

a.)

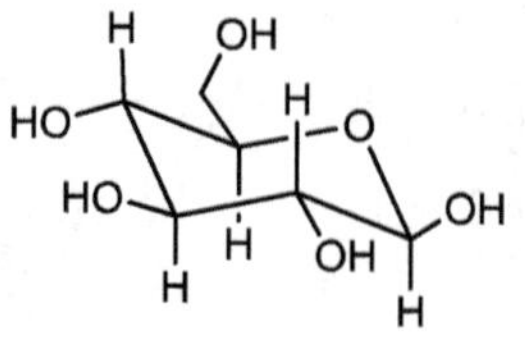

b.)

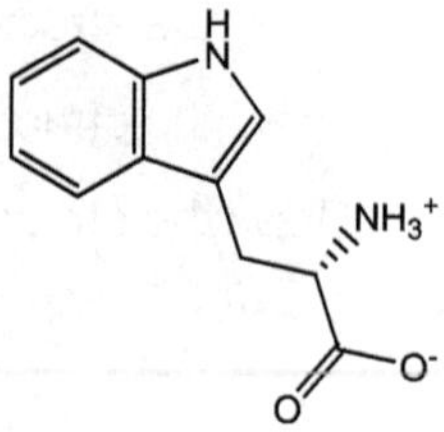

c.)

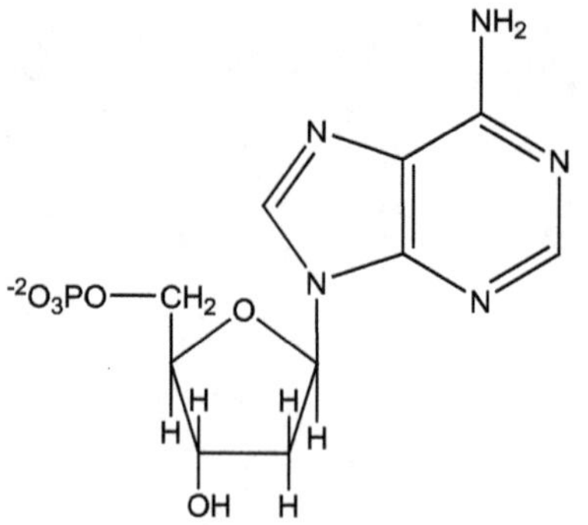

d.)

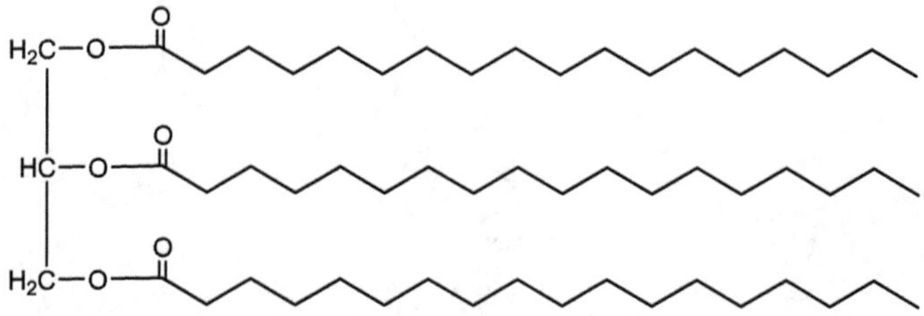

50. Discuss the numbering system commonly used with nucleotides to distinguish various positions found on the sugar versus the nitrogenous base.

51. ____ is necessary for protein synthesis while ___ is the known genetic carrier of information.

52. Which of the following is a ribonucleotide and which is a deoxyribonucleotide? How can you tell?

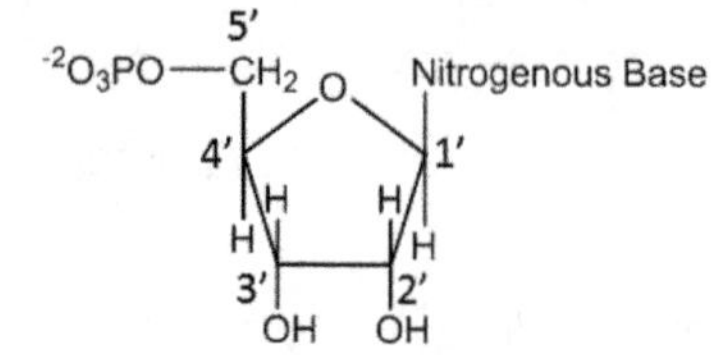

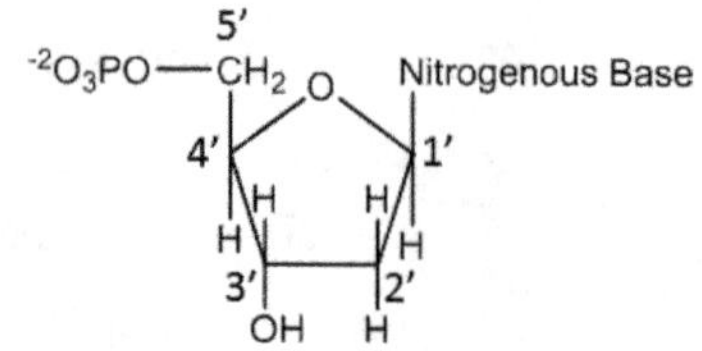

53. What is a nucleoside?

54. Draw the general structures of a purine and pyrimidine.

55. Which nitrogenous bases commonly found in DNA and RNA are derived from the purines?

56. Which nitrogenous bases commonly found in DNA and/or RNA are derived from the pyrimidines? Which ones are found in DNA? RNA?

57. We now know that DNA is a double-stranded helix held together by hydrogen bonding between base pairs thanks to work done by _____ and _____ in 1953.

58. In DNA, each adenine residue base pairs with _____ forming two hydrogen bonds, while each guanine residue base pairs with _____ forming three hydrogen bonds.

59. In RNA, each adenine residue base pairs with _____ forming two hydrogen bonds, while each guanine residue base pairs with _____ forming three hydrogen bonds.

60. In two polynucleotide strands that run antiparallel to each other in DNA held together by hydrogen bonding between base pairs, what is meant by the 5' and 3' ends of the molecule? Label each end of the following molecule:

61. What is a codon?

62. What is a gene?

63. Genes are contained on structures called _____.

64. Most human cells have __ pairs of chromosomes for a total of __ chromosomes.

65. _____ is one of the most common chromosome irregularities and is caused by the presence of a third copy of either all or a portion of chromosome 21 (also called trisomy 21).

Image Credits

Special Topics

Chapter 6: Gases

Kinetic-Molecular Theory of Gases

We have seen how the ideal gas law essentially deals with macroscopic properties of gases such as pressure, volume, and temperature. We can now think of the kinetic molecular theory as dealing with individual gas particles, or microscopic components (i.e. an individual gas molecule).

KINETIC ENERGY, MOLECULAR VELOCITY, AND TEMPERATURE

We can all probably remember talking about kinetic and potential energy at some point in our science classes. Recall the equation for kinetic energy:

$$KE = \frac{1}{2}mv^2$$

KE is kinetic energy, *m* is mass, and *v* is velocity. If we then wanted to study the kinetic energy of an individual gas molecule, we could use the same equation using the speed of that individual gas molecule (*u*):

$$KE = \frac{1}{2}mu^2$$

The challenge for us is that while this can be used for an individual gas molecule with a given speed, it does not represent a collection of gas molecules all moving at different speeds. For example, consider the Maxwell-Boltzmann Distribution curves for oxygen below. Notice that there is a distribution of speeds among gas molecules (i.e. not all of the molecules are moving at the same speed). Most of the oxygen molecules at 20°C are moving between 200 and 800 *m/s*. The other thing that we notice from the graph is that as the temperature is increased, so is the overall speed of the gas molecules. In fact, experimental data tell us that the average kinetic energy of a gas sample is dependent on the temperature (measured in Kelvin). Therefore,

$$\overline{KE} \propto T$$

where $\overline{KE}$ is the average kinetic energy of the molecules or particles comprising a gas sample. Incidentally, we can also mathematically express the average kinetic energy of the gas sample as follows:

$$\overline{KE} = \frac{1}{2}m\bar{u}^2$$

where $\bar{u}^2$ is the average of the squares of the speeds of all of the gas molecules in the gas sample. Thus:

$$\frac{1}{2}\,m\bar{u}^2 \propto T$$

In fact, Maxwell's equation (named after James Clerk Maxwell) relates all of this in the following equation:

$$\sqrt{\bar{u}^2} = \sqrt{\frac{3RT}{MM}}$$

where $\sqrt{\bar{u}^2}$ is the square root of the mean square speed (called the **root mean square velocity** or **rms velocity**), R is the gas constant and is a different value than we have seen before ($8.314\ \frac{J}{mol\cdot K}$) due to different units, T is temperature in Kelvin, and MM is molar mass ($\frac{kg}{mol}$) of the gas. While the root mean square velocity (u_{rms}) is not the same thing as the average velocity, these two numbers are very close in value and can therefore be thought of as conceptually similar.

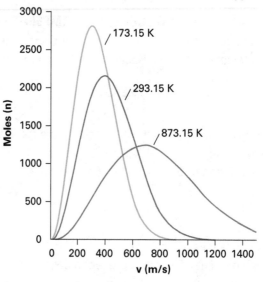

Maxwell-Boltzmann Distribution for Oxygen

Example Problem

Special Topics 6.1

What is the root mean square velocity of oxygen molecules at 20°C?	
Solution:	
Once we have all of the correct units (remember that temperature has to be in Kelvin and that molar mass has to be in *kg/mol* not *g/mol*), we can then substitute all of our values into Maxwell's equation.	$T = 20\ ^\circ C + 273.15 = 293.15\ K$ $MM = 32.00\ \dfrac{g}{mol} = 32.00 \times 10^{-3}\ \dfrac{kg}{mol}$ $\sqrt{\bar{u}^2} = u_{rms} = \sqrt{\dfrac{3RT}{MM}}$ $= \sqrt{\dfrac{3\left(8.314\,\dfrac{J}{mol\cdot K}\right)(293)}{32.00 \times 10^{-3}\,\dfrac{kg\ O_2}{mol\ O_2}}}$ $= \boldsymbol{478\ m/s}$

Gas Diffusion and Effusion

We have now seen that gas molecules travel very fast (u_{rms} at room temperature of hundreds of meters/second). If this is the case, then why does it take so long for us to detect a gas (or odor) in the air? For example, if someone you know is cooking a meal in the kitchen, and you are in the very next room, why does it take a while before you smell the food being cooked? At these speeds, one would think you would instantly pick up the smell with no delay. Well, even though gases move at tremendous speeds, they travel in an unorganized random manner. This is because they do not travel very long before they collide with another molecule, which will randomly change its trajectory. In fact, a gas molecule in the air (room temperature and 1 *atm* atmospheric pressure) can collide several billion times per second. The **mean free path** of a gas molecule is defined as the average distance it travels between collisions. **Diffusion** of a gas is defined as the process by which gas molecules spread out in response to a concentration gradient. As expected, molecular size affects the rate of diffusion, with lighter gas molecules diffusing faster than heavier ones. This is also observed in **effusion rates,** which is defined as the process by which a gas escapes a container through a hole with a diameter significantly smaller than the mean free path of the gas molecules. The rate of effusion is inversely proportional to the square root of the molar mass of the gas. Thus,

$$rate \propto \frac{1}{\sqrt{MM}}$$

If we have two different gases (call them A and B), then we can calculate rate using Graham's Law of Effusion:

$$\frac{rate_A}{rate_B} = \sqrt{\frac{MM_B}{MM_A}}$$

Example Problem
Special Topics 6.2

What is the molar mass (*g/mol*) of an unknown gas that effuses at a rate that is 0.8950 times that of oxygen at the same temperature?
Solution:
Since this is an effusion problem involving two gases, we use Graham's Law of Effusion to solve. Our unknown will be gas "A," and O_2 will be gas "B." $\quad \dfrac{rate_A}{rate_B} = \sqrt{\dfrac{MM_B}{MM_A}}$ $\dfrac{rate_{unknown}}{rate_{O_2}} = \sqrt{\dfrac{MM_{O_2}}{MM_{unknown}}}$ $MM_{unknown} = \dfrac{MM_{O_2}}{\left(\dfrac{rate_{unknown}}{rate_{O_2}}\right)^2}$ $MM_{unknown} = \dfrac{32.00 \frac{g}{mol}}{\left(0.8950\right)^2}$ = **39.95 g/mol**   **The unknown gas is probably argon.**

Chapter 7: Nuclear Chemistry-Special Topics

Types of Radioactivity

At the end of Chapter 7, we mentioned that in order to cover the topic of atomic structure much more comprehensively, it is appropriate that we should also consider the nuclear structure which we present here. **Nuclear chemistry** is the chemistry that deals primarily with radioactivity and nuclear processes. **Radioactivity** is defined as the phenomenon exhibited by certain elements in which they spontaneously emit radiation (in the form of both particles and electromagnetic waves) resulting from changes in the nuclei of atoms. If you recall from Chapter 2 (specifically sections 2.5 and 2.6), we briefly discussed Marie Curie and her work involving the discovery of various kinds of radioactive elements as well as proper isotopic notation, which you may want to review before going any further into this topic. When dealing with nuclear chemistry, it is often common to refer to a particular isotope of a given element as a **nuclide**, which can possibly undergo various types of nuclear "decay" processes, emitting radiation. Specifically, here we discuss **alpha (α) decay, beta (β) decay, gamma (γ) ray emission** as well as **positron emission**. The result of **alpha (α) decay** is the ejection of a helium nucleus (i.e. two protons and two neutrons) at relatively low speeds (can be stopped by a single sheet of paper). Thus, if we look at the notation for the alpha decay of uranium-238, we get the following:

$$^{238}_{92}U \rightarrow {}^{234}_{90}Th + {}^{4}_{2}He$$

or

$$^{238}_{92}U \rightarrow {}^{234}_{90}Th + {}^{4}_{2}\alpha$$

As with all types of radiation discussed here, notice that the law of conservation of mass is in fact observed. In other words, the total atomic weight before the decay is equal to the total atomic weight after the decay. The result of **beta decay** is the ejection of a high speed electron (can't be stopped by a single sheet of paper, but rather something a little more durable, such as aluminum foil). Thus, we can write the beta decay of lead-214 as follows:

$$^{214}_{82}Pb \rightarrow {}^{214}_{83}Bi + {}^{0}_{-1}e$$

or

$$^{214}_{82}Pb \rightarrow {}^{214}_{83}Bi + {}^{0}_{-1}\beta$$

Gamma ray emission is very different from both alpha and beta decay in that gamma radiation is electromagnetic radiation. In other words, here we are dealing with the emission of electromagnetic waves rather than particles, and this is the strongest form of radiation (can be stopped, but only by substantial objects such as concrete blocks or lead etc). For example, if we again look at the alpha decay of uranium-238, we also see that there is the accompanying gamma ray emission as follows:

$$^{238}_{92}U \rightarrow \ ^{234}_{90}Th + \ ^{4}_{2}\alpha + \ ^{0}_{0}\gamma$$

Finally, **positron emission** results when a nucleus emits a positron, which is the antiparticle of the electron (same mass, but opposite charge). Let's take a look at what this notation would be using nitrogen-13 as an example:

$$^{13}_{7}N \rightarrow \ ^{13}_{6}C + \ ^{0}_{+1}e$$

Example Problem

Special Topics 7.1

Write the nuclear equation for the following:
a.) Write the nuclear equation for the alpha decay of polonium-210.
b.) Write the nuclear equation for the beta decay of actinium-227.
c.) Write the nuclear equation for the alpha decay of americium-241.
d.) Write the nuclear equation for the positron emission of oxygen-15.

Solution:	
a.) The result of alpha decay of polonium-210 is the ejection of a helium nucleus, or two protons and two neutrons. Thus, we have the following: $$^{210}_{84}Po \rightarrow \ ^{206}_{82}? + \ ^{4}_{2}He$$ From the periodic table, we see that the daughter nuclide is lead-206.	$$^{210}_{84}Po \rightarrow \ ^{206}_{82}Pb + \ ^{4}_{2}He$$ or $$^{210}_{84}Po \rightarrow \ ^{206}_{82}Pb + \ ^{4}_{2}\alpha$$
b.) The result of the beta decay of actinium-227 is the ejection of a high speed electron. Thus, we have the following: $$^{227}_{89}Ac \rightarrow \ ^{227}_{90}? + \ ^{0}_{-1}e$$ From the periodic table, we see that the daughter nuclide is thorium-227.	$$^{227}_{89}Ac \rightarrow \ ^{227}_{90}Th + \ ^{0}_{-1}e$$ or $$^{227}_{89}Ac \rightarrow \ ^{227}_{90}Th + \ ^{0}_{-1}\beta$$
c.) The result of alpha decay of americium-241 is the ejection of a helium nucleus, or two protons and two neutrons. Thus, we have the following: $$^{241}_{95}Am \rightarrow \ ^{237}_{93}? + \ ^{4}_{2}He$$ From the periodic table, we see that the daughter nuclide is neptunium-237.	$$^{241}_{95}Am \rightarrow \ ^{237}_{93}Np + \ ^{4}_{2}He$$ or $$^{241}_{95}Am \rightarrow \ ^{237}_{93}Np + \ ^{4}_{2}\alpha$$
d.) The result of the positron emission of oxygen-15 is the emission of a positron (the antiparticle of the electron). Thus, we have the following: $$^{15}_{8}O \rightarrow \ ^{15}_{7}? + \ ^{0}_{+1}e$$ From the periodic table, we see that the daughter nuclide is nitrogen-15.	$$^{15}_{8}O \rightarrow \ ^{15}_{7}N + \ ^{0}_{+1}e$$

Example Problem

Special Topics 7.2

Write the nuclear equation for the following:
a.) Write the nuclear equation for the positron emission of bromine-75.
b.) Write the nuclear equation for the alpha decay of neptunium -237.
c.) Write the nuclear equation for the beta decay of protactinium-233.
d.) Write the nuclear equation for the beta decay of plutonium-241.

Solution:	
a.) The result of the positron emission of bromine-75 is the emission of a positron (the antiparticle of the electron). Thus, we have the following: $$^{75}_{35}Br \rightarrow \, ^{75}_{34}? + \, ^{0}_{+1}e$$ From the periodic table, we see that the daughter nuclide is selenium-75.	$$^{75}_{35}Br \rightarrow \, ^{75}_{34}Se + \, ^{0}_{+1}e$$
b.) The result of alpha decay of neptunium-237 is the ejection of a helium nucleus, or two protons and two neutrons. Thus, we have the following: $$^{237}_{93}Np \rightarrow \, ^{233}_{91}? + \, ^{4}_{2}He$$ From the periodic table, we see that the daughter nuclide is protactinium-233.	$$^{237}_{93}Np \rightarrow \, ^{233}_{91}Pa + \, ^{4}_{2}He$$ or $$^{237}_{93}Np \rightarrow \, ^{233}_{91}Pa + \, ^{4}_{2}\alpha$$
c.) The result of the beta decay of protactinium-233 is the ejection of a high speed electron. Thus, we have the following: $$^{233}_{91}Pa \rightarrow \, ^{233}_{92}? + \, ^{0}_{-1}e$$ From the periodic table, we see that the daughter nuclide is uranium-233.	$$^{233}_{91}Pa \rightarrow \, ^{233}_{92}U + \, ^{0}_{-1}e$$ or $$^{233}_{91}Pa \rightarrow \, ^{233}_{92}U + \, ^{0}_{-1}\beta$$
d.) The result of the beta decay of plutonium-241 is the ejection of a high speed electron. Thus, we have the following: $$^{241}_{94}Pu \rightarrow \, ^{241}_{95}? + \, ^{0}_{-1}e$$ From the periodic table, we see that the daughter nuclide is americium-241.	$$^{241}_{94}Pu \rightarrow \, ^{241}_{95}Am + \, ^{0}_{-1}e$$ or $$^{241}_{94}Pu \rightarrow \, ^{241}_{95}Am + \, ^{0}_{-1}\beta$$

It is also important to point out that we do in fact have tools that allow us to detect radiation. For example, both a **Geiger counter** and a **scintillation counter** are both commonly used for this purpose. Both of these devices ultimately generate an electrical signal in response to the presence of radioactive material. However, now that we have looked at various types of radioactive decay, we now ask ourselves a very important question. That is, can we predict whether a particular element is in fact radioactive? In other words, how do we know if we are dealing with a stable nucleus or not? Furthermore, if we determine that something is in fact radioactive, can we then predict when a particular nuclide will undergo beta decay versus positron emission, etc. Well, the answers to these questions are somewhat more complicated than we describe here, but we can get an idea of how this works by looking at the neutron to proton ratio ($\frac{N}{Z}$). Generally speaking, for lighter elements with up to about 20 protons or so, a 1:1 $\frac{N}{Z}$ ratio results in a stable nucleus. Thus, carbon-12 is stable (six protons and six neutrons). As elements get heavier, however (i.e. more protons), this ratio increases slightly. For example, this $\frac{N}{Z}$ ratio is closer to 1.5 for elements with 70-80 protons, and beyond 83 protons stable nuclei do not exist. Thus, bismuth is the heaviest element with nonradioactive isotopes. When a particular element's neutron-to-proton ratio is much higher than the ideal $\frac{N}{Z}$ ratio for stable nuclei mentioned here, then it is not only conceivably radioactive, but beta decay is also very likely. A radioactive nuclide can also have a $\frac{N}{Z}$ ratio that is lower than the ideal neutron-to-proton ratio for stable nuclei; however, in this case positron emission is more than likely. This makes sense as the effect of beta decay would lower the $\frac{N}{Z}$ ratio if it were too high, while positron emission would have the effect of increasing it if it were too low. Thus, we might expect magnesium-28 to undergo beta decay (16 neutrons and 12 protons, thus $\frac{N}{Z}$ = 1.33), while magnesium-21 would more than likely undergo positron emission (9 neutrons and 12 protons, thus $\frac{N}{Z}$ = 0.75). The three stable and naturally occurring isotopes of magnesium are ^{24}Mg, ^{25}Mg and ^{26}Mg.

Half-life and Exponential Decay

If you recall from Chapter 14 during our discussion involving Chemical Kinetics, you will remember that the **half-life** of a reaction refers to the time in which the concentration of a reactant decreases by half. Here see that the relationship between a particular nuclide and its rate constant is the same as the one we derived for a first-order reaction in Chapter 14. That is as follows:

$$t_{1/2} = \frac{0.693}{k} = \frac{1}{k}(0.693)$$

This makes sense because we can see from this expression that nuclides with long half-lives have smaller rate constants, while nuclides with short half-lives have larger rates constants. In any event, regardless of whether a nuclide has a long or short half-life, we also know that by definition after one half-life, the amount of original material decreases by a half. After two half-lives, the amount of original material decreases by a factor of 4, and after three half-lives the amount of original material decreases by a factor of 8, etc. Thus, we can write the following expression:

$$N_t = N_0 \left(\frac{1}{2}\right)^{\# \ of \ half-lives}$$

N_t is the amount of remaining material, and N_0 is the amount of the original material (i.e. at $t = 0$). The resulting **exponential decay** can be seen in the following graph of a hypothetical nuclide with a half-life of 15 minutes:

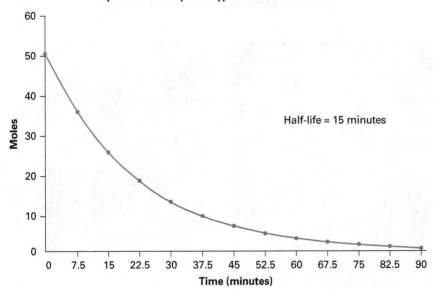

Exponential Decay of a Hypothetical Nuclide

Half-life = 15 minutes

The fact that a particular substance decays at predictable time intervals is of tremendous importance. For example, in **radiocarbon dating** scientists can predict the age of biological samples based on the amount of carbon-14 found in the sample. Carbon-14 is radioactive and undergoes beta decay (eight neutrons and six protons, thus $\frac{N}{Z} = 1.33$) to nitrogen with a half-life of 5,730 years. The nitrogen formed from this process is then converted back to carbon-14 in the upper atmosphere (i.e. by cosmic rays, etc.) in an almost constant equilibrium, thereby allowing for continuous formation of carbon-14 a rate comparable to its decay. Thus, constant atmospheric levels of carbon-14 are maintained, which are then ultimately incorporated into living organisms. This is because carbon-14 is oxidized to carbon dioxide, which is then incorporated into plants via photosynthesis and ultimately finds its way into the food chain of living organisms. Thus, living biological entities contain the same relatively constant levels of carbon-14 as our atmosphere, which allows for the radiocarbon dating of biological samples following death based on the predicted time it takes for the decay of carbon-14. This technique is, of course, limited to dating living organisms, but there are other techniques that can be employed to date objects that were never living based on a similar concept (i.e. measurements involving the predictable rate of decay of uranium-238).

Nuclear Fission and Fusion

In **nuclear fission**, the nucleus of an atom splits into smaller parts containing lighter nuclei. Our understanding of this process goes back to 1934 when Enrico Fermi and his colleagues had bombarded uranium with neutrons and speculated that they had created new heavier elements. However, it was later demonstrated by three scientists (Otto Hahn, Lise Meitner, and Fritz Strassmann) that the bombardment of uranium with neutrons results in several lighter elements, which we now know as nuclear fission. This process results in a **chain reaction** in which the fission of uranium by the **incident neutron** results in even more neutrons, which ultimately go on to split other

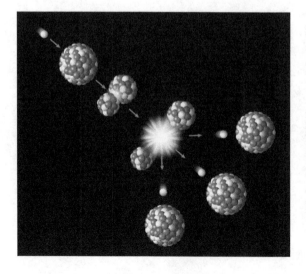

uranium nuclei. The tremendous amount of energy that can be released from this process was put on full display in 1945 with the nuclear fission bomb being released over Nagasaki resulting in the following characteristic mushroom cloud.

Nuclear fusion is very different from nuclear fission in that here we have two lighter nuclei that are combined to form a heavier one. The energy source for our sun is in fact attributed to nuclear fusion in which hydrogen atoms are fused together to form helium atoms. This is also the energy source for modern-day hydrogen bombs, which can be several orders of magnitude stronger than the fission atomic bomb mentioned earlier. Let's take a look at the fusion reaction involving deuterium, which is an isotope of hydrogen with one neutron, reacting with tritium, which is an isotope of hydrogen with two neutrons to form helium-4:

$$\,_1^2H + \,_1^3H \rightarrow \,_2^4He + \,_0^1n$$

The release of large amounts of energy in the above reaction can be attributed to the differences in masses between products and reactants called the **mass defect**, which has an energy associated with it (recall $E = mc^2$ from Chapter 7) called **nuclear binding energy**, or the amount of energy needed to break apart the nucleus. In fact, it would be nice if we could generate usable electricity through nuclear fusion; however, thus far we have been unsuccessful in doing so. One of the major challenges is the high temperatures required for nuclear fusion to take place.

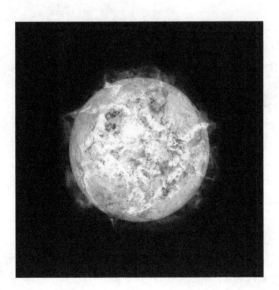

Standard Thermodynamic Quantities for Selected Substances (25°C)

Substance or Ion	$S°$ (J/mol · K)	$\Delta H_f°$ (kJ/mol)	$\Delta G_f°$ (kJ/mol)
Aluminum			
Al(s)	28.3	0	0
Al(g)	164.6	330.0	289.4
$AlCl_3$(s)	110.7	−704.2	−628.9
AlF (g)	215.0	−258.2	−283.7
AlF_3 (s)	66.5	−1510.4	−1431.1
Al_2Cl_6 (g)	490.0	−1290.8	−1220.4
Al_2O_3(s)	50.9	−1675.7	−1582.3
Al^{3+}(aq)	−321.7	−538.4	−481.2
Barium			
Ba(s)	62.5	0	0
Ba(g)	170.2	180.0	146.0
$BaCl_2$(s)	123.7	−858.6	−810.4
$BaCO_3$(s)	112.1	−1213.0	−1134.4
BaF_2 (s)	96.4	−1207.1	−1156.8
$Ba(NO_3)_2$ (s)	213.8	−992.1	−796.6
BaO(s)	70.4	−553.5	−525.1
BaS (s)	78.2	−460.0	−456.0
$BaSO_4$(s)	132.2	−1473.2	−1362.2
Ba^{2+}(aq)	9.6	−537.6	−560.7
Ba^{2+}(g)	—	1649.9	—
Beryllium			
Be(s)	9.5	0	0
$BeCl_2$ (s)	82.7	−490.4	−445.6
BeF_2 (s)	53.4	−1026.8	−979.4
BeI_2 (s)	—	−192.5	—
BeO (s)	13.8	−609.4	−580.1
$Be(OH)_2$(s)	—	—	−907.1
Bismuth			
Bi(s)	56.7	0	0
Bi_2(g)	—	219.7	—

Substance or Ion	$S°$ ($J/mol \cdot K$)	$\Delta H_f°$ (kJ/mol)	$\Delta G_f°$ (kJ/mol)
$BiCl_3(s)$	177.0	−379.1	−315.0
BiI_3 (s)	—	—	−175.3
$Bi_2O_3(s)$	151.5	−573.9	−493.7
Bi_2S_3 (s)	200.4	−143.1	−140.6
$Bi_2(SO_4)_3$ (s)	—	−2544.3	—
Boron			
$B(s)$	5.9	0	0
$B(g)$	153.4	565.0	521.0
BBr (g)	225.0	238.1	195.4
$BBr_3(l)$	229.7	−239.7	−238.5
$BBr_3(g)$	324.2	−205.6	−232.5
$BCl_3(g)$	290.1	−403.8	−388.7
$BF(g)$	200.5	−122.2	−149.8
$BF_3(g)$	254.4	−1136.0	−1119.4
$B_2H_6(g)$	232.1	36.4	87.6
$B_2O_3(s)$	54.0	−1273.5	−1194.3
$B_2S_3(s)$	—	−240.6	—
Bromine			
$Br(g)$	175.0	111.9	82.4
$Br_2(g)$	245.5	30.9	3.1
$Br_2(l)$	152.2	0	0
$BrCl(g)$	240.1	14.6	−1.0
$BrF(g)$	229.0	−93.8	−109.2
$BrF_3(l)$	178.2	−300.8	−240.5
$BrF_3(g)$	292.5	−255.6	−229.4
$HBr(g)$	198.7	−36.3	−53.4
$Br^-(g)$	—	−218.9	—
$Br^-(aq)$	80.71	−120.9	−102.82
Cadmium			
$Cd(s)$	51.8	0	0
$Cd(g)$	167.7	118.8	77.3
$CdCl_2(s)$	115.3	−391.5	−343.9
$CdF_2(s)$	77.4	−700.4	−647.7
$CdO(s)$	54.8	−258.4	−228.7
$CdS(s)$	64.9	−161.9	−156.5
$CdSO_4(s)$	123.0	−933.3	−822.7
$CdTe(s)$	100.0	−92.5	−92.0
$Cd^{2+}(aq)$	−73.2	−75.9	−77.6
Calcium			
$Ca(s)$	41.6	0	0
$Ca(g)$	154.9	177.8	144.0
$CaC_2(s)$	70.0	−59.8	−64.9
$CaCO_3(s)$	91.7	−1207.6	−1129.1
$CaCl_2(s)$	108.4	−795.4	−748.8
$CaF_2(s)$	68.5	−1228.0	−1129.1

Substance or Ion	$S°(J/mol \cdot K)$	$\Delta H_f°(kJ/mol)$	$\Delta G_f°(kJ/mol)$
$CaH_2(s)$	41.4	−181.5	−142.5
$CaH_2O_2(s)$	83.4	−985.2	−897.5
$CaI(s)$	142.0	−533.5	−528.9
$Ca(NO_3)_2(s)$	193.2	−938.2	−742.8
$CaO(s)$	38.1	−634.9	−603.3
$Ca(OH)_2(s)$	83.4	−985.2	−897.5
$Ca(OH)_2(aq)$	76.2	−1002.8	−867.6
$CaS(s)$	56.5	−482.4	−477.4
$CaSO_4(s)$	106.5	−1434.5	−1322.0
$Ca^{2+}(aq)$	−53.1	−542.8	−553.6
Carbon			
$C(s, diamond)$	2.4	1.9	2.9
$C(s, graphite)$	5.7	0	0
$C(g)$	158.1	716.7	671.3
$CBr_4(s)$	212.5	18.8	47.7
$CCl_4(l)$	—	−128.2	—
$CCl_4(g)$	—	−95.8	—
$CHBr_3(l, tribromomethane)$	220.9	−28.5	−5.0
$CHCl_3(l, trichloromethane)$	201.7	−134.5	−73.7
$CHF_3(g, trifluoromethane)$	259.7	−695.4	—
$CHI_3(s, triiodomethane)$	—	141.0	—
$CH_2(g, methylene)$	194.9	390.4	372.9
$CH_2Br_2(g, dibromomethane)$	293.2	—	—
$CH_2Cl_2(l, dichloromethane)$	177.8	−124.1	—
$CH_2F_2(g, difluoromethane)$	246.7	−452.2	—
$CH_2I_2(l, diiodomethane)$	174.1	66.9	90.4
$CH_2O_2(l, formic acid)$	129.0	−427.4	−361.4
$CH_3(g, methyl)$	194.2	145.7	147.9
$CH_3Br(g, bromomethane)$	264.4	−35.5	−26.3
$CH_3Cl(g, chloromethane)$	234.6	−81.9	—
$CH_3F(g, fluoromethane)$	222.9	—	—
$CH_3I(l, iodomethane)$	163.2	−12.3	—
$CH_3NH_2(g, methylamine)$	242.9	−22.5	32.7
$CH_3NO_2(l, nitromethane)$	171.8	−113.1	−14.4
$CH_3OH(l, methanol)$	126.8	−239.1	−166.6
$CH_4(g, methane)$	186.3	−74.4	−50.3
$C_2(g, carbon)$	199.4	831.9	775.9
$C_2H_2(g, acetylene)$	200.9	228.2	210.7
$C_2H_3Cl(g, vinyl chloride)$	264.0	37.3	53.6
$C_2H_4(g, ethylene)$	219.6	52.5	68.4
$C_2H_4O_2(g, acetaldehyde)$	263.7	−166.2	−132.8
$C_2H_4O_2(l, acetic acid)$	159.8	−484.5	−389.9
$C_2H_5OH(l, ethanol)$	160.7	−277.7	−174.8
$C_2H_5OH(g, ethanol)$	282.7	−235.1	−168.5
$C_2H_6(g, ethane)$	229.6	−83.8	−31.9

Substance or Ion	$S°(J/mol \cdot K)$	$\Delta H_f°(kJ/mol)$	$\Delta G_f°(kJ/mol)$
C_3H_6O (l, acetone)	199.8	−248.1	—
C_3H_7OH (l, isopropanol)	181.1	−318.1	—
C_3H_8(g, propane)	—	−104.7	—
C_4H_{10}(l, butane)	—	−146.6	—
C_4H_{10}(g, butane)	—	−125.6	—
C_5H_{12}(l, butane)	—	−173.5	—
C_5H_{12}(g, butane)	—	−146.9	—
C_6H_5OH (s, phenol)	144.0	−165.1	—
C_6H_6(l, benzene)	—	49.0	—
$C_6H_{12}O_6$ (s, glucose)	212.1	−1273.3	−910.4
C_8H_{18}(l, octane)	—	−250.1	—
CO(g)	197.7	−110.5	−137.2
CO_2(g)	213.8	−393.5	−394.4
CO_2(aq)	117.6	−413.8	−368.0
CS_2 (l)	151.3	89.0	64.6
CS_2 (g)	237.8	116.6	67.1
Cesium			
Cs(s)	85.2	0	0
Cs(g)	175.6	76.5	49.6
$CsBr$(s)	117.0	−400.0	−387.0
$CsCl$(s)	101.2	−438.0	−414.0
CsF(s)	92.8	−553.5	−525.5
CsI(s)	127.0	−342.0	−337.0
CsO (s)	146.9	−345.8	−301.8
Cs_2S (s)	—	−359.8	—
Cs^+(aq)	132.1	−258.0	−292.0
Cs^+(g)	169.7	458.5	427.1
Chlorine			
Cl(g)	165.2	121.3	105.3
Cl_2(g)	223.1	0	0
HCl(g)	186.9	−92.3	−95.3
HCl(aq)	56.5	−167.2	−131.2
ClO_2(g)	256.8	102.5	120.5
Cl_2O(g)	266.2	97.9	80.3
Cl^-(g)	153.25	−234.0	−240.0
Cl^-(aq)	56.6	−167.1	−131.2
Chromium			
Cr(s)	23.8	0	0
Cr(g)	174.5	396.6	351.8
Cr^{3+}(aq)	—	−1971.0	—
CrO_4^{2-}(aq)	44.0	−872.2	−717.1
$Cr_2O_7^{2-}$(aq)	238.0	−1476	−1279
Copper			
Cu(s)	33.2	0	0
Cu(g)	166.4	337.4	297.7

Substance or Ion	$S°$ ($J/mol \cdot K$)	$\Delta H_f°$ (kJ/mol)	$\Delta G_f°$ (kJ/mol)
CuO(s)	42.6	−157.3	−129.7
Cu_2O(s)	93.1	−168.6	−146.0
CuS(s)	66.5	−53.1	−53.6
Cu_2S(s)	120.9	−79.5	−86.2
Cu^+(aq)	−26.0	51.9	50.2
Cu^{2+}(aq)	−98.7	64.4	65.5
Fluorine			
F(g)	158.8	78.9	61.8
F_2(g)	202.7	0	0
HF(g)	173.8	−273.3	−275.4
F^-(aq)	−13.8	−335.4	−278.8
F^-(g)	145.5	−255.6	−262.5
Hydrogen			
H(g)	114.6	218.0	203.3
H_2(g)	130.7	0	0
H^+(g)	108.8	1536.3	1517.1
H^+(aq)	0	0	0
Iodine			
I(g)	180.7	106.8	70.2
I_2(g)	260.6	62.4	19.3
I_2(s)	116.1	0	0
HI(g)	206.3	25.9	1.7
I^-(g)	—	−194.7	—
I^-(aq)	109.4	−56.8	−51.6
Iron			
Fe(s)	27.3	0	0
Fe(g)	180.5	416.3	370.7
$FeCl_2$(s)	117.9	−341.8	−302.3
$FeCl_3$(s)	142.3	−399.5	−334.1
FeO(s)	60.8	−272.0	−255.2
Fe_2O_3(s)	87.4	−824.2	−742.2
Fe^{2+}(aq)	113.4	−87.9	−84.9
Fe^{3+}(aq)	−293.0	−47.7	−10.5
Lead			
Pb(s)	64.8	0	0
Pb(g)	175.4	195.2	162.2
$PbCl_2$(s)	136.0	−359.4	−314.1
$Pb(NO_3)_2$(s)	—	−451.9	—
PbO(s)	68.7	−217.3	−187.9
PbO_2(s)	76.6	−276.6	−219.0
Pb^{2+}(aq)	18.5	1.6	−24.4
Lithium			
Li(s)	29.10	0	0
Li(g)	138.7	159.3	126.6
LiBr(s)	74.3	−351.2	−342.0

Substance or Ion	$S°$ ($J/mol \cdot K$)	$\Delta H_f°$ (kJ/mol)	$\Delta G_f°$ (kJ/mol)
LiCl(s)	59.3	−408.6	−384.4
LiF(s)	35.7	−616.0	−587.7
LiI(s)	86.8	−270.4	−270.3
LiNO$_3$(s)	90.0	−483.1	−381.1
Li$^+$(g)	132.9	687.1	650.0
Li$^+$(aq)	12.24	−278.5	−293.3
Magnesium			
Mg (s)	32.7	0	0
Mg (g)	148.6	147.1	112.5
MgCl$_2$ (s)	89.5	−641.8	−591.8
Mg$_3$N$_2$ (s)	91.6	−461.0	−401.0
MgO (s)	27.0	−601.6	−569.3
Mg(OH)$_2$ (s)	63.2	−924.5	−833.5
MgS(s)	50.3	−346.0	−341.8
Mg^{2+} (aq)	−137.0	−467.0	−455.4
Manganese			
Mn (s)	32.0	0	0
MnO$_2$ (s)	53.1	−520.0	−465.1
MnS(s)	78.2	−214.2	−218.4
Mn^{2+} (aq)	−78.8	−219.4	−225.6
MnO$_4^-$ (aq)	190.6	−529.9	−436.2
Mercury			
Hg (l)	75.9	0	0
Hg (g)	175.0	61.4	31.8
Hg$_2$Cl$_2$ (s)	191.6	−265.4	−210.7
HgO (s)	70.3	−90.8	−58.5
HgS(s)	82.4	−58.2	−50.6
Hg^{2+} (aq)	−36.2	170.2	164.4
Hg$_2^{2+}$ (aq)	65.7	166.9	153.5
Nitrogen			
N(g)	153.3	472.7	455.5
N$_2$(g)	191.6	0	0
NH$_3$(g)	192.8	−45.9	16.4
NH$_3$(aq)	111.3	−80.3	−26.5
NH$_4$NO$_3$(s)	151.1	−365.6	−184.0
NH$_4$NO$_3$(aq)	259.8	−339.9	−190.6
NO(g)	210.8	91.3	87.6
NO$_2$(g)	239.9	33.2	51.3
N$_2$O$_3$(l)	—	50.3	—
N$_2$O$_3$(g)	312.3	83.7	139.5
HNO$_3$(aq)	146.0	−206.6	−110.5
HNO$_3$(g)	266.2	−135.1	−74.77
NH$_4^+$(aq)	111.2	−133.3	−79.3
NO$_3^-$(aq)	146.7	−206.9	−110.2

Substance or Ion	$S°(J/mol \cdot K)$	$\Delta H_f°(kJ/mol)$	$\Delta G_f°(kJ/mol)$
Oxygen			
O(g)	161.1	249.2	231.7
O_2(g)	205.2	0	0
O_3(g)	238.9	142.7	163.2
H_2O(g)	188.8	−241.8	−228.6
H_2O(l)	69.9	−285.8	−237.2
H_2O_2(l)	109.6	−187.8	−120.4
H_2O_2(g)	232.7	−136.3	−105.6
OH^-(aq)	−10.5	−229.9	−157.3
Phosphorus			
P(s, white)	41.1	0.0	—
P(s, red)	22.8	−17.6	—
P(s, black)	−39.3	—	—
P(g)	163.2	316.5	280.1
PCl_3(g)	217.1	−319.7	−272.3
PCl_5(g)	364.6	−374.9	−305.0
H_3PO_4(aq)	158.2	−1288.3	−1142.6
H_3PO_4(s)	110.5	−1284.4	−1124.3
$H_2PO_4^-$(aq)	90.4	−1296.3	−1130.2
HPO_4^{2-}(aq)	−33.5	−1292.1	−1089.2
Potassium			
K(s)	64.7	0	0
KBr(s)	95.9	−394.0	−380.7
KCl(s)	82.6	−436.7	−408.5
$KClO_3$(s)	143.1	−397.7	−296.3
KF(s)	66.6	−568.6	−537.8
KI(s)	106.4	−328.0	−324.9
KOH(s)	81.2	−424.8	−379.4
KOH(aq)	91.6	−482.4	−440.5
$KMnO_4$(s)	171.7	−837.2	−737.6
K^+(g)	154.5	89.0	60.5
K^+(aq)	103.0	−252.1	−283.3
Rubidium			
Rb(s)	76.8	0	0
Rb(g)	170.0	80.9	53.1
RbBr(s)	108.3	−394.6	−381.8
RbCl(s)	95.9	−435.4	−407.8
$RbClO_3$(s)	152.0	−392.4	−407.8
RbF(s)	—	−557.7	—
Rb_2SO_4(s)	197.4	−1435.6	−1316.9
Rb^+(aq)	124.0	−251.1	−283.1
Silicon			
Si(s)	18.8	0	0
Si(g)	168.0	450.0	405.5
SiF_4(g)	282.8	−1615.0	−1572.8
SiO_2(s)	41.5	−910.7	−856.3

Substance or Ion	$S°\,(J/mol \cdot K)$	$\Delta H_f°\,(kJ/mol)$	$\Delta G_f°\,(kJ/mol)$
Silver			
Ag(s)	42.6	0	0
Ag(g)	173.0	284.9	246.0
AgBr(s)	107.1	−100.4	−96.9
AgBrO$_3$(s)	151.9	−10.5	71.3
AgCl(s)	96.3	−127.0	−109.8
AgClO$_3$(s)	142.0	−30.3	64.5
AgClO$_4$(s)	—	−31.1	—
AgF(s)	84.0	−204.6	−185.0
AgI(s)	115.5	−61.8	−66.2
AgNO$_3$(s)	140.9	−124.4	−33.4
Ag$_2$O(s)	121.3	−31.1	−11.2
Ag$_2$SO$_4$(s)	200.4	−715.9	−618.4
Ag$^+$(aq)	72.7	105.8	77.1
Sodium			
Na(s)	51.4	0	0
NaCl(s)	72.1	−411.1	−384.0
NaCl(aq)	115.5	−407.2	−393.1
Na$_2$CO$_3$(s)	139.0	−1130.8	−1048.1
NaF(s)	51.2	−575.4	−545.1
NaI(s)	98.5	−287.8	−286.1
NaNO$_3$(s)	116.5	−467.9	−367.0
NaNO$_3$(aq)	205.4	−447.5	−373.2
Na$_2$O(s)	75.1	−414.2	−375.5
NaOH(s)	64.5	−425.6	−379.5
NaOH(aq)	48.2	−470.1	−419.2
Na$_2$SO$_4$(s)	149.6	−1387.1	−1270.2
Na$^+$(aq)	60.2	−239.7	−261.9
Strontium			
Sr(s)	52.3	0	0
Sr(g)	164.6	164.4	130.9
SrCl$_2$(s)	114.9	−828.9	−781.1
Sr(NO$_2$)$_2$(s)	—	−762.3	—
SrO(s)	54.4	−592.0	−561.9
SrS(s)	68.2	−472.4	−467.8
SrSe	—	−385.8	—
SrSO$_4$(s)	117.0	−1453.1	−1340.9
Sr^{2+}(aq)	−39.0	−545.5	−557.3
Sulfur			
S(s, monoclinic)	32.6	0.3	0.1
S(s, rhombic)	31.9	0	0
S(g)	167.8	277.2	236.7
S$_2$(g)	228.1	129.0	80.1
S$_8$(g)	430.9	102.3	49.7
H$_2$S(aq)	122.0	−39.4	−27.7

Substance or Ion	$S°$ (J/mol · K)	$\Delta H_f°$ (kJ/mol)	$\Delta G_f°$ (kJ/mol)
$H_2S(g)$	205.8	−20.6	−33.4
$SO_2(l)$	—	−320.5	—
$SO_2(g)$	248.2	−296.8	−300.1
$SO_3(g)$	256.7	−396.0	−371.0
$H_2SO_4(l)$	156.9	−814.0	−690.0
$H_2SO_4(aq)$	18.5	−909.3	−744.6
$SO_4^{2-}(aq)$	18.5	−909.3	−744.6
$S^{2-}(aq)$	22.0	41.8	83.7
Tin			
Sn(s, white)	51.2	0	—
Sn(s, gray)	44.1	−2.1	0.1
$SnCl_2(s)$	—	−350.0	—
$SnCl_4(l)$	259.0	−511.3	−440.1
$SnCl_4(g)$	365.8	−471.5	−432.2
SnO(s, , tetragonal)	57.2	−280.7	−251.9
SnO_2(s, tetragonal)	49.0	−577.6	−515.8
Titanium			
Ti(s)	30.7	0	0
Ti(g)	180.3	473.0	428.4
$TiCl_3(s)$	139.7	−720.9	−653.5
$TiCl_4(l)$	252.3	−804.2	−737.2
$TiCl_4(g)$	353.2	−763.2	−726.3
TiO(s)	50.0	−519.7	−495.0
TiO_2(s, rutile)	50.6	−944.0	−888.8
Zinc			
Zn(s)	41.6	0	0
Zn(g)	161.1	130.4	94.8
$ZnCl_2(s)$	111.5	−415.1	−369.4
ZnO(s)	43.7	−350.5	−320.5
ZnS(s, sphalerite–zinc blende)	57.7	−206.0	−201.3
$ZnSO_4(s)$	110.5	−982.8	−871.5
$Zn^{2+}(aq)$	−106.5	−152.4	−147.2

CRC Handbook of Chemistry and Physics, 73rd ed., edited by D. R. Lide (Boca Raton, FL: CRC Press, 1993), pp. 8–17.

Aqueous Equilibrium Constant

Ionization Constant for Acids at 25°C

Formula	Compound	K_{a_1}	K_{a_2}
$HC_2H_3O_2$	Acetic	1.8×10^{-5}	—
$HC_9H_7O_4$	Acetylsalicylic	3.3×10^{-4}	—
H_3AsO_4	Arsenic	5.5×10^{-3}	1.7×10^{-7}
$H_2C_6H_6O_6$	Ascorbic	8.0×10^{-5}	1.6×10^{-12}
$HC_7H_5O_2$	Benzoic	6.5×10^{-5}	—
H_3BO_3	Boric	5.4×10^{-10}	—
$HC_4H_7O_2$	Butanoic	1.5×10^{-5}	—
H_2CO_3	Carbonic	4.3×10^{-7}	5.6×10^{-11}
$HC_2H_2O_2Cl$	Chloroacetic	1.4×10^{-3}	—
$HClO_2$	Chlorous	1.1×10^{-2}	—
$H_3C_6H_5O_7$	Citric	7.4×10^{-4}	1.7×10^{-5}
$HCNO$	Cyanic	2.0×10^{-4}	—
$HCHO_2$	Formic	1.8×10^{-4}	—
HCN	Hydrocyanic	4.9×10^{-10}	—
HF	Hydrofluoric	3.5×10^{-4}	—
H_2O_2	Hydrogen peroxide	2.4×10^{-12}	—
H_2S	Hydrosulfuric	8.9×10^{-8}	—
$HBrO$	Hypobromous	2.8×10^{-9}	—
$HClO$	Hypochlorous	2.9×10^{-8}	—
HIO_3	Iodic	1.7×10^{-1}	—
$HC_3H_5O_3$	Lactic	1.4×10^{-4}	—
$H_2C_4H_2O_4$	Maleic	1.2×10^{-2}	5.9×10^{-7}
$H_2C_3H_2O_4$	Malonic	1.5×10^{-3}	2.0×10^{-6}
HNO_3	Nitric	2.4×10^{1}	—
HNO_2	Nitrous	4.6×10^{-4}	—
$H_2C_2O_4$	Oxalic	6.0×10^{-2}	6.1×10^{-5}
HC_6H_5O	Phenol	1.3×10^{-10}	—
H_3PO_4	Phosphoric	7.5×10^{-3}	$6.2 \times 10^{-8} (K_{a3} = 4.2 \times 10^{-13})$
$HC_3H_5O_2$	Propanoic	1.3×10^{-5}	—
$HC_3H_3O_3$	Pyruvic	4.1×10^{-3}	—
H_2SeO_3	Selenous	2.4×10^{-3}	4.8×10^{-9}
$H_2C_4H_4O_4$	Succinic	6.2×10^{-5}	2.3×10^{-6}
H_2SO_4	Sulfuric	1.0×10^{3}	—
H_2SO_3	Sulfurous	1.6×10^{-2}	6.4×10^{-8}
$HC_2Cl_3O_2$	Trichloroacetic	2.2×10^{-1}	—
$HC_2F_3O_2$	Trifluoroacetic	3.0×10^{-1}	—

Ionization Constant for Bases at 25°C

Formula	Compound	K_b
NH_3	Ammonia	1.8×10^{-5}
$C_6H_5NH_2$	Aniline	3.9×10^{-10}
HCO_3^-	Hydrogen Carbonate	2.3×10^{-8}
CO_3^{2-}	Carbonate	1.8×10^{-4}
$(C_2H_5)_2NH$	Diethylamine	6.9×10^{-4}
$(CH_3)_2NH$	Dimethylamine	5.4×10^{-4}
$C_2H_5NH_2$	Ethylamine	5.6×10^{-4}
$C_2H_8NH_2$	Ethylenediamine	8.3×10^{-5}
H_2NNH_2	Hydrazine	1.3×10^{-6}
$HONH_2$	Hydroxylamine	1.1×10^{-8}
CH_3NH_2	Methylamine	4.4×10^{-4}
$C_{17}H_{19}NO_3$	Morphine	1.6×10^{-6}
$C_{10}H_{14}N_2$	Nicotine	1.0×10^{-6}
$C_3H_7NH_2$	Propylamine	3.5×10^{-4}
C_5H_5N	Pyridine	1.7×10^{-9}
$(C_2H_5)_3N$	Triethylamine	5.6×10^{-4}
$(CH_3)_3N$	Trimethylamine	6.4×10^{-5}

Solubility Product Constants at 25°C

Formula	Compound	K_{sp}
Aluminum		
$Al(OH)_3$	Aluminum hydroxide	1.3×10^{-33}
$AlPO_4$	Aluminum phosphate	9.8×10^{-21}
Barium		
$BaCO_3$	Barium carbonate	2.6×10^{-9}
$BaCrO_4$	Barium chromate	1.2×10^{-10}
BaF_2	Barium fluoride	2.5×10^{-5}
BaC_2O_4	Barium oxalate	1.6×10^{-6}
$BaSO_4$	Barium sulfate	1.1×10^{-10}
Cadmium		
$CdCO_3$	Cadmium carbonate	1.0×10^{-12}
$Cd(OH)_2$	Cadmium hydroxide	7.2×10^{-15}
Calcium		
$CaCO_3$	Calcium carbonate	5.0×10^{-9}
$CaCrO_4$	Calcium chromate	7.1×10^{-4}
CaF_2	Calcium fluoride	1.5×10^{-10}
$Ca(OH)_2$	Calcium hydroxide	4.7×10^{-6}
CaC_2O_4	Calcium oxalate	2.3×10^{-9}
$Ca_3(PO_4)_2$	Calcium phosphate	2.1×10^{-33}
$CaSO_4$	Calcium sulfate	7.1×10^{-5}

Formula	Compound	K_{sp}
Cobalt		
$CoCO_3$	Cobalt(II) carbonate	1.0×10^{-10}
$Co(OH)_2$	Cobalt(II) hydroxide	5.9×10^{-15}
Copper		
$CuBr$	Copper(I) bromide	6.3×10^{-9}
$CuCl$	Copper(I) chloride	1.7×10^{-7}
Iron		
$Fe(OH)_3$	Iron(III) hydroxide	2.8×10^{-39}
Lead		
$PbCO_3$	Lead(II) carbonate	7.4×10^{-14}
$PbCl_2$	Lead(II) chloride	1.2×10^{-5}
$PbCrO_4$	Lead(II) chromate	2.8×10^{-13}
PbF_2	Lead(II) fluoride	3.3×10^{-8}
PbI_2	Lead(II) iodide	9.8×10^{-9}
$PbSO_4$	Lead(II) sulfate	1.8×10^{-8}
Magnesium		
$MgCO_3$	Magnesium carbonate	6.8×10^{-6}
MgF_2	Magnesium fluoride	5.2×10^{-11}
$Mg(OH)_2$	Magnesium hydroxide	2.1×10^{-13}
MgC_2O_4	Magnesium oxalate	4.8×10^{-6}
Manganese		
$Mn(OH)_2$	Manganese(II) hydroxide	1.6×10^{-13}
Mercury		
Hg_2CO_3	Mercury(I) carbonate	3.6×10^{-17}
$Hg_2(CN)_2$	Mercury(I) cyanide	5.0×10^{-40}
Nickel		
$Ni(OH)_2$	Nickel(II) hydroxide	5.5×10^{-16}
Silver		
$AgBr$	Silver bromide	5.4×10^{-13}
$AgCl$	Silver chloride	1.8×10^{-10}
Ag_2CrO_4	Silver chromate	1.1×10^{-12}
$AgCN$	Silver cyanide	6.0×10^{-17}
Strontium		
$SrSO_4$	Strontium sulfate	3.4×10^{-7}
Zinc		
$ZnCO_3$	Zinc carbonate	1.5×10^{-10}
$Zn(OH)_2$	Zinc hydroxide	3.0×10^{-17}

APPENDIX IV

Standard Electrode Potentials at 25°C

Reduction Half-Reaction	$E°(V)$
$F_2(g) + 2\ e^- \rightarrow 2\ F^-(aq)$	2.87
$Cu^{3+}(aq) + e^- \rightarrow Cu^{2+}(aq)$	2.4
$Co^{3+}(aq) + e^- \rightarrow Co^{2+}(aq)$	1.92
$H_2O_2(l) + 2\ H^+(aq) + 2\ e^- \rightarrow 2\ H_2O(l)$	1.76
$Au^+(aq) + e^- \rightarrow Au(s)$	1.70
$PbO_2(s) + SO_4^{2-}(aq) + 4\ H^+(aq) + 2\ e^- \rightarrow PbSO_4 + 2\ H_2O(l)$	1.69
$NiO_2(s) + 4\ H^+(aq) + 2\ e^- \rightarrow Ni^{2+}(aq) + 2\ H_2O(l)$	1.68
$MnO_4^-(aq) + 4\ H^+(aq) + 3\ e^- \rightarrow MnO_2(s) + 2\ H_2O(l)$	1.67
$HClO(aq) + H^+(aq) + e^- \rightarrow \frac{1}{2}Cl_2(g) + H_2O(l)$	1.61
$Au^{3+}(aq) + 3e^- \rightarrow Au(aq)$	1.52
$MnO_4^-(aq) + 8\ H^+(aq) + 5\ e^- \rightarrow Mn^{2+}(aq) + 4\ H_2O(l)$	1.51
$BrO_3^-(aq) + 6\ H^+(aq) + 5\ e^- \rightarrow \frac{1}{2}Br_2(l) + 3\ H_2O(l)$	1.48
$ClO_3^-(aq) + 6\ H^+(aq) + 5\ e^- \rightarrow \frac{1}{2}Cl_2(g) + 3\ H_2O(l)$	1.47
$PbO_2(s) + 4\ H^+(aq) + 2\ e^- \rightarrow Pb^{2+}(aq) + 2\ H_2O(l)$	1.46
$Au^{3+}(aq) + e^- \rightarrow Au^{2+}(aq)$	1.40
$Cl_2(g) + 2\ e^- \rightarrow 2\ Cl^-(aq)$	1.36
$Cr_2O_7^{2-}(aq) + 14\ H^+(aq) + 6\ e^- \rightarrow 2\ Cr^{3+}(aq) + 7\ H_2O(l)$	1.23
$O_2(g) + 4\ H^+(aq) + 4\ e^- \rightarrow 2\ H_2O(l)$	1.23
$MnO_2(s) + 4H^+(aq) + 2\ e^- \rightarrow Mn^{2+}(aq) + 2\ H_2O(l)$	1.22
$IO_3^-(aq) + 6\ H^+(aq) + 5\ e^- \rightarrow \frac{1}{2}I_2(s) + 3\ H_2O(l)$	1.20
$ClO_4^-(aq) + 2\ H^+(aq) + 2\ e^- \rightarrow ClO_3^-(aq) + H_2O(l)$	1.19
$IO_3^-(aq) + 6\ H^+(aq) + 6\ e^- \rightarrow I^-(aq) + 3\ H_2O(l)$	1.09
$Br_2(aq) + 2\ e^- \rightarrow 2\ Br^-(aq)$	1.09
$VO_2^+(aq) + 2\ H^+(aq) + e^- \rightarrow VO^{2+}(aq) + H_2O(l)$	0.99
$HNO_2(aq) + H^+(aq) + e^- \rightarrow NO(g) + H_2O(l)$	0.98
$NO_3^-(aq) + 4\ H^+(aq) + 3\ e^- \rightarrow NO(g) + 2\ H_2O(l)$	0.96
$2\ Hg^{2+}(aq) + 2\ e^- \rightarrow Hg_2^{2+}(aq)$	0.92
$Hg^{2+}(aq) + 2\ e^- \rightarrow Hg(l)$	0.85

Reduction Half-Reaction	$E°(V)$
$ClO^-(aq)+H_2O\,(l)+2\,e^- \rightarrow Cl^-(aq)+2\,OH^-(aq)$	0.81
$Ag^+(aq)+e^- \rightarrow Ag\,(s)$	0.80
$Hg_2^{2+}(aq)+2\,e^- \rightarrow 2\,Hg(l)$	0.80
$Fe^{3+}(aq)+e^- \rightarrow Fe^{2+}(aq)$	0.77
$O_2\,(g)+2\,H^+(aq)+2\,e^- \rightarrow H_2O_2(aq)$	0.70
$MnO_4^-(aq)+2\,H_2O\,(l)+3\,e^- \rightarrow MnO_2(s)+4\,OH^-(aq)$	0.60
$MnO_4^-(aq)+e^- \rightarrow MnO_4^{2-}(aq)$	0.56
$I_2\,(s)+2\,e^- \rightarrow 2\,I^-\,(aq)$	0.54
$Cu^+(aq)+e^- \rightarrow Cu\,(s)$	0.52
$O_2\,(g)+2\,H_2O\,(l)+4\,e^- \rightarrow 4\,OH^-\,(aq)$	0.40
$Cu^{2+}(aq)+2\,e^- \rightarrow Cu\,(s)$	0.34
$AgCl\,(s)+e^- \rightarrow Ag\,(s)+Cl^-(aq)$	0.22
$SO_4^-(aq)+4\,H^+(aq)+2\,e^- \rightarrow H_2SO_3(l)+H_2O\,(l)$	0.17
$Cu^{2+}(aq)+e^- \rightarrow Cu^+(aq)$	0.15
$Sn^{4+}(aq)+2\,e^- \rightarrow Sn^{2+}(aq)$	0.15
$AgBr\,(s)+e^- \rightarrow Ag\,(s)+Br^-\,(aq)$	0.07
$2\,H^+(aq)+2\,e^- \rightarrow H_2\,(g)$	0.00
$Fe^{3+}(aq)+3\,e^- \rightarrow Fe\,(s)$	−0.036
$Pb^{2+}(aq)+2\,e^- \rightarrow Pb\,(s)$	−0.13
$Sn^{2+}(aq)+2\,e^- \rightarrow Sn\,(s)$	−0.14
$AgI\,(s)+e^- \rightarrow Ag\,(s)+I^-\,(aq)$	−0.15
$N_2(g)+5\,H^+(aq)+4\,e^- \rightarrow N_2H_5^+(aq)$	−0.23
$Ni^{2+}(aq)+2\,e^- \rightarrow Ni(s)$	−0.26
$Co^{2+}(aq)+2\,e^- \rightarrow Co\,(s)$	−0.28
$Tl^+(aq)+e^- \rightarrow Tl\,(s)$	−0.34
$PbSO_4\,(s)+2\,e^- \rightarrow Pb\,(s)+SO_4^{2-}(aq)$	−0.36
$Cd^{2+}(aq)+2\,e^- \rightarrow Cd\,(s)$	−0.40
$Cr^{3+}(aq)+e^- \rightarrow Cr^{2+}(aq)$	−0.41
$Fe^{2+}\,(aq)+2\,e^- \rightarrow Fe\,(s)$	−0.45
$2\,CO_2\,(aq)+2\,H^+\,(aq)+2\,e^- \rightarrow H_2C_2O_4\,(aq)$	−0.48
$Ga^{3+}\,(aq)+3\,e^- \rightarrow Ga\,(s)$	−0.55
$Fe(OH)_3\,(s)+e^- \rightarrow Fe(OH)_2\,(s)+OH^-\,(aq)$	−0.56
$Cr^{3+}(aq)+3\,e^- \rightarrow Cr\,(s)$	−0.74
$Zn^{2+}(aq)+2\,e^- \rightarrow Zn\,(s)$	−0.76
$2\,H_2O\,(l)+2\,e^- \rightarrow H_2\,(g)+2\,OH^-\,(aq)$	−0.83
$Cr^{2+}(aq)+2\,e^- \rightarrow Cr\,(s)$	−0.91

Reduction Half-Reaction	$E°(V)$
$SnO_2 + 2\,H_2O\,(aq) + 4\,e^- \rightarrow Sn\,(s) + 4\,OH^-\,(aq)$	−0.95
$Zn(NH_3)_4^{2+}(aq) + 2\,e^- \rightarrow Zn\,(s) + 4\,NH_3\,(aq)$	−1.04
$V^{2+}\,(aq) + 2\,e^- \rightarrow V\,(s)$	−1.18
$Mn^{2+}\,(aq) + 2\,e^- \rightarrow Mn\,(s)$	−1.19
$Zn(OH)_4^{2-}(aq) + 2\,e^- \rightarrow Zn\,(s) + 4\,OH^-\,(aq)$	−1.20
$SiF_6^{2-}(aq) + 4\,e^- \rightarrow Si\,(s) + 6\,F^-\,(aq)$	−1.24
$Zn(OH)_2(s) + 2\,e^- \rightarrow Zn\,(s) + 2\,OH^-\,(aq)$	−1.25
$Zr^{4+}(aq) + 4\,e^- \rightarrow Zr\,(s)$	−1.45
$Hf^{4+}(aq) + 4\,e^- \rightarrow Hf\,(s)$	−1.55
$Ti^{2+}(aq) + 2\,e^- \rightarrow Ti\,(s)$	−1.63
$Al^{3+}(aq) + 3\,e^- \rightarrow Al\,(s)$	−1.66
$SiO_3^{\,2-}(aq) + 3\,H_2O\,(l) + 4\,e^- \rightarrow Si\,(s) + 6\,OH^-\,(aq)$	−1.70
$U^{3+}(aq) + 3\,e^- \rightarrow U\,(s)$	−1.80
$Be^{2+}(aq) + 2\,e^- \rightarrow Be\,(s)$	−1.85
$Np^{3+}(aq) + 3\,e^- \rightarrow Np\,(s)$	−1.86
$Th^{4+}\,(aq) + 4\,e^- \rightarrow Th\,(s)$	−1.90
$AlF_6^{3-}(aq) + 3\,e^- \rightarrow Al(s) + 6\,F^-(aq)$	−2.07
$H_2\,(g) + 2\,e^- \rightarrow 2\,H^-$	−2.23
$Mg^{2+}\,(aq) + 2\,e^- \rightarrow Mg\,(s)$	−2.37
$Na^+(aq) + e^- \rightarrow Na\,(s)$	−2.71
$Ca^{2+}(aq) + 2\,e^- \rightarrow Ca\,(s)$	−2.87
$Sr^{2+}\,(aq) + 2\,e^- \rightarrow Sr\,(s)$	−2.90
$Ba^{2+}(aq) + 2\,e^- \rightarrow Ba\,(s)$	−2.91
$K^+(aq) + e^- \rightarrow K(s)$	−2.93
$Rb^+\,(aq) + e^- \rightarrow Rb\,(s)$	−2.98
$Li^+\,(aq) + e^- \rightarrow Li\,(s)$	−3.04

CRC *Handbook of Chemistry and Physics*, 73rd ed., edited by R. R. Lide (Boca Raton, FL: CRC Press, 1993), pp. 8–17.

Lange's Handbook of Chemistry, 16th ed., edited by J. G. Speight (New York: McGraw-Hill, 2005), p. 1380.

Vapor Pressure of Water at Various Temperatures

Temperature (°C)	Vapor Pressure (*torr*)	Temperature (°C)	Vapor Pressure (*torr*)	Temperature (°C)	Vapor Pressure (*torr*)
−10	2.1	30	31.8	70	233.7
−8	2.5	32	35.7	72	254.6
−6	2.9	34	39.9	74	277.2
−4	3.4	36	44.6	76	301.4
−2	4.0	38	49.7	78	327.3
0	4.6	40	55.3	80	355.1
2	5.3	42	61.5	82	384.9
4	6.1	44	68.3	84	416.8
6	7.0	46	75.7	86	450.9
8	8.0	48	83.7	88	487.1
10	9.2	50	92.5	90	525.8
12	10.5	52	102.1	92	567.0
14	12.0	54	112.5	94	610.9
16	13.6	56	123.8	96	657.6
18	15.5	58	136.1	98	707.3
20	17.5	60	149.4	100	760.0
22	19.8	62	163.8	102	815.9
24	22.4	64	179.3	104	875.1
26	25.2	66	196.1	106	937.9
28	28.3	68	214.2	108	1004.4

Chapter 1

INTRODUCTION AND SCIENTIFIC METHOD

1.1 Chemistry is the study of matter, its structure, properties, and the processes it undergoes.

1.3 A Hypothesis is a tentative or speculative explanation for observations.

1.5 A Scientific Law is a summary statement (or mathematical equation) which describes a set of observations and can be used to make predictions about the outcome of future events or experiments.

1.7 A Scientific Theory is a model which describes the underlying explanations of all observations. Theories are at the height of scientific knowledge. They are models of how the world works, which are supported by large bodies of experimental data and can be used to predict entirely new observations across a wide range of phenomena.

1.9 a. Observation

b. Observation

c. Law

d. Theory

SCIENTIFIC NOTATION

1.11 a. 1.101×10^3

b. 3.1×10^{-2}

c. 4.56×10^2

d. 3.3456×10^{-6}

e. 2.3901×10^7

1.13   a. 1.198×10^6

b. 1.963×10^{10}

c. 5.8897×10^{-6}

d. 8.536×10^{-4}

e. 7.8991×10^{-2}

1.15   a. 23,100

b. 0.000231

c. 30,317,000,000

d. 0.00000000030317

e. 0.000000913

1.17   a. 0.0000698

b. 0.000000000698

c. 698,000

d. 711

e. 0.0711

1.19   a. 6.626×10^{-34}

b. 6.626×10^{18}

c. 6.626×10^{-2}

d. 4.133×10^{10}

e. 1.21×10^3

1.21   a. 1.2001×10^4

b. 0.000000452

c. 2.31×10^{-4}

d. 0.00000000000933

e. 1×10^2

UNITS OF MEASUREMENT AND DENSITY

1.23   A Unit is a generally accepted quantity which is used to accurately and reproducibly report experimental measurements.

1.25   These are units which result from multiplication or division of simpler base units. Two such examples are volume (m^3) or density (g/ml).

1.27 $10^9 \ nm = 1 \ m$, $1 \ nm = 10^{-9} \ m$

1.29 $10 \ dL = 1 \ L$, $1 \ dL = 0.1 \ L$

1.31   a. $1.20 \ Tm$

b. $1.20 \ pg$

c. $3.2 \times 10^3 \ ml$

d. $0.80 \ cg$

1.33   a. 2.135×10^3 *ml*

       b. 2.135×10^{-6} *ML*

       c. 2.135×10^{-3} *kL*

       d. 2.135×10^9 *nL*

       e. 2.135×10^{12} *pL*

1.35 7.1×10^5 *cm^3*, 7.1×10^{-1} *m^3*, 7.1×10^2 *L*

1.37   a. 1×10^6 *ms^2*

       b. 5.6×10^2 *mm^2*

       c. 4.8×10^{-6} *m^2*

       d. 7.82×10^{-5} *nm^2*

       e. 2.178×10^{-17} *Tm^2*

1.39   a. 4.91×10^4 *L*

       b. 4.53×10^3 *mm^3*

       c. 1.99 *mL*

       d. 7.39×10^{18} *m^3*

       e. 4.333×10^{-9} *mm^3*

1.41 0.7639 *g/ml*

1.43 1.09 *g/ml*

1.45 8.96 *g/ml*, Copper

1.47 1.07 *g/ml*

1.49 4.58 *g/ml*

1.51 11.3 *g/ml*

1.53 10.5 *g/ml*, Silver

1.55   a. 255 *K*

       b. 273 *K*

       c. 318.2 *K*

       d. 373 *K*

       d. 523 *K*

UNCERTAINTY IN MEASUREMENTS AND SIGNIFICANT FIGURES

1.57   a. 4

       b. 1

       c. 4

       d. 5

       e. 5

1.59   a. 4

        b. 5

        c. 4

        d. 4

        e. 4

1.61   b, c, and d

1.63   1,280,000

1.65 2.0×10^3

1.67   7.7

1.69   36.7

1.71   a. 52.2

        b. 28.45

        c. 10.333

        d. 156.0

1.73   a. 5000

        b. 30.

        c. 1,400

        d. 10,000

1.75   Calculations should be carried out in the following order of mathematical operations:

    1. Parentheses—all operations in parentheses should be carried out first and the resulting number of significant figures determined for the resulting values.

    2. Exponents—all exponential notations should be executed.

    3. Multiplication/Division—All multiplication and division should be carried out from left to right following any operations in parentheses or exponential terms.

    4. Addition/Subtraction—All addition and subtraction should be carried out from left to right following any operations in parentheses, exponential terms, and/or multiplication and division.

   At each step, the last significant figure should be determined in the resulting terms. This allows appropriate application of the rules regarding significant figures to be applied at each step of the process.

1.77   a. 17.8

        b. 31

        c. 0.34

        d. 8.4

DIMENSIONAL ANALYSIS—CREATING AND USING CONVERSION FACTORS

1.79   2.14 *kg*

1.81   3.0 *g*

1.83   17,000 *gallons*

1.85   30.5 *cm*

Chapter 2

EXTENSIVE AND INTENSIVE PROPERTIES

2.1   Extensive properties are dependent upon the amount of the substance present such as mass and volume.

2.3   a. Volume

2.5   c. Melting Point

2.7   Extensive

2.9   Intensive

2.11   Intensive

2.13   a. Extensive

b. Extensive

c. Intensive

d. Intensive

2.15   a. Extensive

b. Extensive

c. Intensive

d. Extensive

MATTER, PHYSICAL AND CHEMICAL PROPERTIES AND CHANGES

2.17   Matter is defined as anything that has mass and occupies space.

2.19   Solids have a definite shape, definite volume, and are not fluid or compressible.

2.21   Gases have an indefinite shape, indefinite volume, and are fluid and compressible.

2.23   A chemical property refers to the ability of a substance to form new substances. Examples of chemical properties can include flammability and *pH*.

2.25 a. Density

2.27 a. Corrosiveness

2.29 A chemical change occurs when a reaction results in the formation of a new substance.

2.31 a. Physical Change

b. Physical Change

c. Chemical Change

d. Chemical Change

2.33 b. Copper metal turns green with prolonged exposure to air

2.35 a. Shaping clay into a ball

2.37 Physical

2.39 Chemical

2.41 Chemical

CLASSIFICATION OF MATTER BASED ON COMPOSITION

2.43 A compound is a substance composed of two or more elements that are joined together in fixed, definite proportions. Table salt (or *NaCl*) is a good example of a compound.

2.45 A homogeneous mixture is the same or uniform throughout. A heterogeneous mixture is not uniform throughout, and it varies in its composition when comparing one region to the next.

2.47 Homogeneous

2.49 Heterogeneous

2.51 Homogeneous

2.53 Distillation can involve the separation of two or more liquids that have different boiling points. This technique can also be used to separate a liquid from a solid.

2.55 Filtration is a separation technique in which a solid can be separated from a liquid by simply pouring a solid/liquid mixture through filter paper which captures a solid while the liquid flows through the paper.

2.57 a. Mixture, homogeneous

b. Mixture, homogeneous

c. Pure Substance, Element

FOUNDATIONAL CHEMICAL LAWS AND ATOMIC THEORY

2.59 3.33 *g* Chlorine

2.61 The law of definite composition states that all samples of a particular compound are composed of the same elements of the same proportions of constituent elements, no matter what their source or how they were prepared.

2.63 $M_{Cu} = 0.732$ g; $M_{Cl} = 0.818$ g

2.65   The law of multiple proportions states that if two elements, we will call them element 1 and element 2 for the purposes of the definition, react to form two different compounds, then the different masses of 2 that combine with a fixed amount of element 1 can be expressed as a ratio of small whole numbers.

ATOMIC STRUCTURE

2.67   Radioactivity

2.69   The electric charge of an electron is -1.602×101^{-19} Coulombs and that of a proton is $+1.602 \times 10^{-19}$ Coulombs. Because these two electric charges are precisely equal in magnitude but opposite in sign, they balance with each other within the atomic structure at a ratio of precisely 1 to 1. That is to say, one electron exactly balances with one proton, and there are no other charged particles in an atom. Owing to this, we simply refer to the charge as either a positive or a negative whole-number multiple of the quantity 1.602×10^{-19} Coulombs. So if there is a charge of a +3 on an Aluminum ion, this is implicitly understood to mean $(+3) \times (1.602 \times 10^{-19}$ $C)$.

2.71   a. 82 Protons, 125 Neutrons, 82 Electrons

         b. 8 Protons, 8 Neutrons, 8 Electrons

         c. 4 Protons, 5 Neutrons, 4 Electrons

         d. 35 Protons, 45 Neutrons, 35 Electrons

2.73   73 Protons, 108 Neutrons, 73 Electrons

2.75   28 Protons, 30 Neutrons, 28 Electrons

2.77   31 Protons, 40 Neutrons, 31 Electrons

2.79   49 Protons, 66 Neutrons, 49 Electrons

2.81   21 Protons, 24 Neutrons

2.83   5 Protons, 6 Neutrons

2.85   Atomic number: 29, Mass number: 65, Number of electrons:29

2.87   John Dalton (Developed the Atomic Theory), Marie Curie (Coined the term "radioactivity"), J.J. Thomson (Discovered the Electron), Ernest Rutherford (Gold Foil Experiment), Eugen Goldstein (Discovered the Proton), James Chadwick (Discovered the Neutron)

2.89   b

2.91   39.09 *amu*

2.93   78.920 *amu*

2.95   29.90 *amu*

2.97 ^{63}Cu

2.99 c. potassium

2.101 d. chlorine

2.103 c. aluminum

2.105 d. arsenic

2.107 c. europium

2.109 c. 7A

2.111 d. 8A

2.113 Potassium (Alkali Metals), Strontium (Alkaline Earth Metal), Tungsten (Transition Metals), Arsenic (Metalloid), Bromine (Halogens), Argon (Noble Gases).

2.115 Aluminum (*Al*), Argon (*Ar*), Arsenic (*As*), Beryllium (*Be*), Calcium (*Ca*), Chlorine (*Cl*), Copper (*Cu*), Chromium (*Cr*), Gold (*Au*), Hydrogen (*H*).

2.117 Chemical bonds are the forces which hold atoms together in a compound.

2.119 Covalent bonds arise when elements share electrons. These typically occur between nonmetals.

2.121 c. $BaCl_2$

2.123 d. PCl_3

2.125 The bond is covalent as it is being formed between two nonmetals.

2.127 a. Pb^{2+} & Cl^-

b. Cu^+ & O^{2-}

c. Fe^{2+} & O^{2-}

d. Fe^{3+} & O^{2-}

Chapter 3

INTRODUCTION AND IONS, IONIC BONDS, AND IONIC COMPOUNDS

3.1 An ion is a charged particle. It can consist of one or more atoms wherein there exists an imbalance in the numbers of electrons and protons. Ions form when either an atom or a molecule loses or gains electrons.

3.3 An anion is a negatively charged ion. Anions are characterized as having more electrons than protons in the nuclei of the atoms which comprise the ion.

3.5 A polyatomic ion is composed of more than one atom.

3.7 When metals react with nonmetals, there is an innate tendency for the metal to lose one or more electrons. When this happens, the nonmetal has a tendency to gain one or more electrons and will do so. This exchange of electrons from the metal to the nonmetal results in the formation of two ions, a cation and an anion. The electrostatic attraction between ions of opposite charge is the basis for the chemical bond formed in this fashion.

3.9 +1

3.11 −2

3.13   a. 13 protons, 10 electrons

     b. 35 protons, 36 electrons

     c. 16 protons, 18 electrons

     d. 26 protons, 23 electrons

3.15   a. 11 protons, 10 electrons

     b. 34 protons, 36 electrons

     c. 38 protons, 36 electrons

     d. 82 protons, 78 electrons

3.17   a. Hydrogen, H^+

     b. Lithium, Li^+

     c. Oxide, O^{2-}

     d. Fluoride, F^-

3.19   a. Chloride, Cl^-

     b. Sulfide, S^{2-}

     c. Phosphide, P^{3-}

     d. Bromide, Br^-

3.21   a. Magnesium, Mg^{2+}

     b. Sodium, Na^+

     c. Calcium, Ca^{2+}

     d. Aluminum, Al^{3+}

FORMULAS AND NAMES OF BINARY IONIC COMPOUNDS

3.23   a. Aluminum Sulfide

     b. Magnesium Selenide

     c. Aluminum Oxide

     d. Sodium Nitride

3.25   a. Rubidium Oxide

     b. Calcium Bromide

    c. Aluminum Nitride

    d. Sodium Iodide

3.27 a. $AlCl_3$

    b. CaSe

    c. $AlBr_3$

    d. Ag_3N

3.29 a. Ag_2O

    b. CaS

    c. ZnS

    d. Sc_2O_3

3.31 a. Chromium(III) Sulfide

    b. Copper(II) Chloride

    c. Chromium(II) Nitride

    d. Nickel(II) Fluoride

3.33 a. Iron(II) Phosphide

    b. Lead(IV) Sulfide

    c. Lead(II) Chloride

    d. Cobalt(II) Iodide

3.35 a. Na_2S

    b. Ba_3N_2

    c. Cs_2O

    d. AlF_3

3.37 a. AlI_3

    b. Co_2Se_3

    c. ZnO

    d. $ScCl_3$

FORMULAS AND NAMES OF POLYATOMIC IONS AND THEIR COMPOUNDS

3.39 a. Chromium(III) Sulfate

    b. Aluminum Nitrate

    c. Barium Hydroxide

    d. Sodium Peroxide

3.41 a. Scandium Sulfate

    b. Sodium Hydroxide

    c. Potassium Phosphate

    d. Copper(I) Sulfite

3.43 a. Aluminum Chromate

b. Iron(II) Phosphate

c. Iron(II) Nitrate

d. Chromium(II) Acetate

3.45 a. $CuMnO_4$

b. $CsClO_3$

c. $RbNO_2$

d. $NaHSO_3$

3.47 a. $CuCN$

b. $Sr(ClO_2)_2$

c. $PbCO_3$

d. SnF_2

3.49 a. $Ca_3(PO_4)_2$

b. $Ca(CN)_2$

c. CaO_2

d. $CaCr_2O_7$

3.51 a. $KMnO_4$

b. $KC_2H_3O_2$

c. $K_2Cr_2O_7$

d. K_2CO_3

FORMULAS AND NAMES OF INORGANIC HYDRATES

3.53 $CuSO_4 \cdot 5H_2O$

3.55 Magnesium Sulfate Heptahydrate

FORMULAS AND NAMES OF BINARY MOLECULAR (COVALENT) COMPOUNDS

3.57 a. Carbon Dioxide

b. Nitrogen Trifluoride

c. Phosphorus Trichloride

d. Dinitrogen Tetroxide

3.59 a. Xenon Tetrafluoride

b. Boron Tribromide

c. Carbon Tetrabromide

d. Diphosphorus Pentasulfide

3.61 a. P_4S_{10}

b. N_2O_3

    c. N_2O_5

    d. SO_2

3.63 No, CaF_2 is an ionic compound.

Chapter 4

MOLAR MASS

4.1 The molar mass is the mass of one mole of that species expressed in grams, which can be either an element (either monoatomic or molecular) or a compound.

4.3 a. 79.90 *g/mol*

    b. 19.00 *g/mol*

    c. 55.85 *g/mol*

    d. 137.33 *g/mol*

4.5 1 aluminum, 3 oxygen, 3 hydrogen

4.7 a. 18.02 *g/mol*

    b. 44.01 *g/mol*

    c. 142.05 *g/mol*

    d. 78.01 *g/mol*

4.9 $\# \text{ of mols} = \text{mass (grams)} \times \frac{1 \text{ mol}}{\# \text{ of grams}}$

4.11 $\# \text{ of entities} = \# \text{ of mols} \times \frac{6.022 \times 10^{23} \text{ entities}}{1 \text{ mol}}$

4.13 0.1399 *mols*

4.15 0.0701 *mols*

4.17 149.1 *g/mol*

4.19 8.13×10^{23} molecules

4.21 2.586×10^{24} molecules

4.23 132 *mols*

4.25 6.704×10^{25} molecules

PERCENT COMPOSITION

4.27 Percent composition takes into account how much of each element is present in a given molecule as a percentage. Percentages are calculated based on mass percent, so the total mass of a given element (in the numerator) as compared to the molecular mass as a whole (in the denominator).

4.29 69.57%

4.31   56.11%

4.33   49.47% carbon, 5.20% hydrogen, 28.85% nitrogen, 16.48% oxygen.

4.35   6.65 g

DETERMINING EMPIRICAL AND MOLECULAR FORMULAS

4.37   The empirical formula is the simplest possible whole number ratio of atoms in a given molecule.

4.39

Empirical Formula	Molecular Formula	Molar Mass (g/mol)
C_4H_9	C_8H_{18}	114.26
C_3H_8	C_3H_8	44.11
CH_3	C_2H_6	30.08
C_5H_{11}	$C_{10}H_{22}$	142.32

4.41 $C_4H_6O_4$

4.43   Empirical formula, $C_4H_6O_5$
       Molecular formula, $C_4H_6O_5$

4.45   Empirical formula, $C_{19}H_{16}O_4$
       Molecular formula, $C_{19}H_{16}O_4$

BALANCING CHEMICAL EQUATIONS

4.47   A balanced chemical equation is important because it provides not only the molecular formulas of both the reactants and the products as well as their respective physical states, but it also allows for quantitative studies of chemical reactions.

4.49   Dissolved in water

4.51   Gas

4.53 $AlCl_3\,(s) + 3H_2O\,(l) \rightarrow Al(OH)_3(s) + 3HCl\,(aq)$

4.55 $NiCO_3\,(s) + 2HNO_3\,(aq) \rightarrow Ni(NO_3)_2(aq) + CO_2\,(g) + H_2O\,(l)$

USING BALANCING CHEMICAL EQUATIONS TO CALCULATE QUANTITIES OF REACTANTS AND PRODUCTS

4.57   1 *mol* N_2/3 *mol* H_2

4.59   3 *mol* H_2/2 *mol* NH_3

4.61   a. 1.47 *mols*

       b. 1.41 *mols*

       c. 1.64 *grams*

       d. 3.31 *grams*

LIMITING REACTANT AND PERCENT YIELD

4.63   The excess reactant is left over following the depletion of the limiting reactant. The reaction stops following depletion of the limiting reactant because while the excess reactant remains, it has nothing to react with in order to generate more of the products for that given chemical reaction.

4.65   a. 0.100 *mols*; Limiting Reagent = Fe_2O_3

      b. 0.109 *mols*; Limiting Reagent = HCl

      c. 0.100 *mols*; Limiting Reagent = $NaOH$

      d. 0.150 *mols*; Limiting Reagent = O_2

4.67   a. 5.59 *grams*

      b. 7.80 *grams*

      c. 10.6 *grams*

      d. 6.60 *grams*

4.69   82.7%; Limiting Reagent = Na; Excess Reagent = F_2

4.71   77.3%; Limiting Reagent = CO; Excess Reagent = Fe_2O_3

4.73   2.70 *grams*

4.75   8.40 *grams*

Chapter 5

AQUEOUS SOLUTIONS OF IONIC COMPOUNDS AND PREDICTING SOLUBILITY

5.1   An electrolyte is a compound that when dissolved in water dissociates into freely solvated ions. Such ions can act as mobile charge carriers allowing for the conduction of electric current. Soluble ionic compounds and acids are electrolytes.

5.3   When an ionic compound dissolves, the electrostatic interaction between the water molecules and the ions comprising the ionic solid are collectively more favorable than those between the anions and cations in the ionic compound itself. This results in "dissociation" of the ions from one another, each moving into solution surrounded by a "solvation sphere" of water molecules.

5.5   a. Soluble

      b. Soluble

      c. Soluble

      d. Insoluble

5.7   a. Insoluble

b. Soluble

c. Soluble

d. Soluble

5.9   a. Nonelectrolyte

b. Electrolyte

c. Electrolyte

d. Electrolyte

5.11   a. $K_2CO_3(s) \xrightarrow{H_2O} 2\,K^+(aq) + CO_3^{2-}(aq)$

b. $Ca(NO_3)_2(s) \xrightarrow{H_2O} Ca^{2+}(aq) + 2\,NO_3^-(aq)$

c. $Ba(C_2H_3O_2)_2(s) \xrightarrow{H_2O} Ba^{2+}(aq) + 2\,C_2H_3O_2^-(aq)$

d. $Li_2SO_4(s) \xrightarrow{H_2O} 2\,Li^+(aq) + SO_4^{2-}(aq)$

5.13   a. $KOH(s) \xrightarrow{H_2O} K^+(aq) + OH^-(aq)$

b. $(NH_4)_2CO_3(s) \xrightarrow{H_2O} 2\,NH_4^+(aq) + CO_3^{2-}(aq)$

c. $Na_2SO_4(s) \xrightarrow{H_2O} 2\,Na^+(aq) + SO_4^{2-}(aq)$

d. $K_3PO_4(s) \xrightarrow{H_2O} 3\,K^+(aq) + PO_4^{3-}(aq)$

5.15   a. 0.2738 *mols*

b. 0.400 *mols*

c. 0.3422 *mols*

d. 0.500 *mols*

5.17   a. 5.347×10^{23} *ions*

b. 6.540×10^{22} *ions*

c. 6.200×10^{22} *ions*

d. 1.400×10^{23} *ions*

WRITING CHEMICAL EQUATIONS OF REACTIONS IN AQUEOUS SOLUTION—PRECIPITATION REACTIONS

5.19   a. Molecular Equation:

$$Pb(NO_3)_2(aq) + 2\,KI(aq) \rightarrow PbI_2(s) + 2\,KNO_3(aq)$$

Complete Ionic Equation:

$$Pb^{2+}(aq) + 2\,NO_3^-(aq) + 2\,K^+(aq) + 2\,I^-(aq) \rightarrow PbI_2(s)$$
$$+ 2\,K^+(aq) + 2\,NO_3^-(aq)$$

Net Ionic Equation:

$$Pb^{2+}(aq) + 2\,I^-(aq) \rightarrow PbI_2(s)$$

b. Molecular Equation:

$$2\,NaOH(aq) + Mg(C_2H_3O_2)_2(aq) \rightarrow 2\,NaC_2H_3O_2(aq)$$
$$+ Mg(OH)_2(s)$$

Complete Ionic Equation:

$$2\,Na^+(aq) + 2\,OH^-(aq) + Mg^{2+}(aq) + 2\,C_2H_3O_2^-(aq)$$
$$\rightarrow Mg(OH)_2(s) + 2\,Na^+(aq) + 2\,C_2H_3O_2^-(aq)$$

Net Ionic Equation:

$$2\,OH^-(aq) + Mg^{2+}(aq) \rightarrow Mg(OH)_2(s)$$

5.21 Complete Ionic Equation:

$$2\,Na^+(aq) + SO_4^{2-}(aq) + Ba^{2+}(aq) + 2\,Cl^-(aq) \rightarrow BaSO_4(s)$$
$$+ 2\,Na^+(aq) + 2\,Cl^-(aq)$$

Net Ionic Equation:

$$SO_4^{2-}(aq) + Ba^{2+}(aq) \rightarrow BaSO_4(s)$$

5.23 No Reaction.

WRITING CHEMICAL EQUATIONS OF REACTIONS IN AQUEOUS SOLLUTION—ACID/BASE NEUTRALIZATIONS AND GAS EVOLVING REACTIONS

5.25 A strong acid is a compound that when dissolved in water will completely dissociate to form H^+ ions. Strong bases will dissociate completely to produce OH^- ions.

5.27 a. Molecular:

$$HCl(aq) + NaOH(aq) \rightarrow NaCl(aq) + H_2O(l)$$

Complete Ionic:

$$H^+(aq) + Cl^-(aq) + Na^+(aq) + OH^-(aq) \rightarrow Na^+(aq)$$
$$+ Cl^-(aq) + H_2O(l)$$

Net Ionic:

$$H^+(aq) + OH^-(aq) \rightarrow H_2O(l)$$

b. Molecular:

$$H_2SO_4(aq) + Ba(OH)_2(aq) \rightarrow BaSO_4(s) + 2\,H_2O(l)$$

Complete Ionic:

$$2\,H^+(aq) + SO_4^{2-}(aq) + Ba^{2+}(aq) + 2\,OH^-(aq)$$
$$\rightarrow BaSO_4(s) + 2\,H_2O(l)$$

Net Ionic:

$$2\,H^+(aq) + SO_4^{2-}(aq) + Ba^{2+}(aq) + 2\,OH^-(aq)$$
$$\rightarrow BaSO_4(s) + 2\,H_2O(l)$$

c. Molecular:

$$2HCl(aq) + Ca(OH)_2(aq) \rightarrow CaCl_2(aq) + 2\ H_2O(l)$$

Complete Ionic:

$$2\ H^+(aq) + 2\ Cl^-(aq) + Ca^{2+}(aq) + 2\ OH^-(aq)$$
$$\rightarrow Ca^{2+}(aq) + 2\ Cl^-(aq) + 2\ H_2O(l)$$

Net Ionic:

$$2\ H^+(aq) + 2\ OH^-(aq) \rightarrow 2\ H_2O(l)$$

5.29 a. Molecular:

$$2\ HCl(aq) + Na_2S(aq) \rightarrow 2\ NaCl(aq) + H_2S(g)$$

Complete Ionic:

$$2\ H^+(aq) + 2\ Cl^-(aq) + 2\ Na^+(aq) + S^{2-}(aq)$$
$$\rightarrow 2\ Na^+(aq) + 2\ Cl^-(aq) + H_2S(g)$$

Net Ionic:

$$2\ H^+(aq) + S^{2-}(aq) \rightarrow H_2S(g)$$

b. Molecular:

$$2\ HClO_4(aq) + K_2CO_3(aq) \rightarrow 2\ KClO_4(aq) + [H_2CO_3]$$

Complete Ionic:

$$2\ H^+(aq) + 2\ ClO_4^-(aq) + 2\ K^+(aq) + CO_3^{2-}(aq)$$
$$\rightarrow 2\ K^+(aq) + 2\ ClO_4^-(aq) + H_2O(l) + CO_2(g)$$

Net Ionic:

$$2\ H^+(aq) + CO_3^{2-}(aq) \rightarrow H_2O(l) + CO_2(g)$$

c. Molecular:

$$H_2SO_4(aq) + K_2SO_3(aq) \rightarrow K_2SO_4(aq) + [H_2SO_3]$$
$$H_2SO_4(aq) + K_2SO_3(aq) \rightarrow K_2SO_4(aq) + H_2O(l) + SO_2(g)$$

Complete Ionic:

$$2\ H^+(aq) + SO_4^{2-}(aq) + 2\ K^+(aq) + SO_3^{2-}(aq) \rightarrow 2\ K^+(aq)$$
$$+ SO_4^{2-}(aq) + H_2O(l) + SO_2(g)$$

Net Ionic:

$$2\ H^+(aq) + SO_3^{2-}(aq) \rightarrow H_2O(l) + SO_2(g)$$

SOLUTION CONCENTRATION—MOLARITY AND DILUTION

5.31   a.   1.67 *M*

      b.   0.0647 *M*

      c.   0.230 *M*

5.33   106.5 *g*

5.35   100. *ml*

5.37   5.18 *g*

5.39   a.   0.125 *M*

      b.   0.250 *M*

      c.   0.375 *M*

5.41   a.   0.00533 *mols*

      b.   0.0591 *mols*

      c.   0.00161 *mols*

5.43   20.0 *ml*

5.45   0.0208 *M*

5.47   8.81 *M*

5.49   103 *ml*

SOLUTION CONCENTRATION—MOLALITY, MOLE FRACTION, AND MASS PERCENT

5.51   a.   0.683 *m*

      b.   0.524 *m*

      c.   0.746 *m*

5.53   a.   0.0122

      b.   0.00935

      c.   0.0133

5.55   a.   3.05%

      b.   5.00%

      c.   13.7%

5.57   molality: 4.58 *m*

      mole fraction: 0.0762

5.59   mass percent: 8.99%

      mole fraction: 0.0101

STOICHIOMETRY OF REACTIONS IN SOLUTION

5.61   1.88 *mL*

5.63   a.   *NaCl*

      b.   0.408 *g*

      c.   86.1%

COLLIGATIVE PROPERTIES—RAOUOLT'S LAW

5.65 40. *torr*

5.67 water: 0.9621

Glycerin: 0.0379

5.69 water mole fraction: 0.9800

unknown molar mass: 84.15 *g/mol*

COLLIGATIVE PROPERTIES—BOILING POINT ELEVATION AND FREEZING POINT DEPRESSION

5.71 a

5.73 101.03°C

5.75 100.101°C

5.77 62.4°C

5.79 b.

5.81 −1.65°

5.83 1.8°C

5.85 $C_{22}H_{44}O_2$

COLLIGATIVE PROPERTIES—OSMOSIS

5.87 Solutions with identical osmotic pressures are referred to as isotonic.

5.89 2.92 *atm*

Chapter 6

PHYSICAL PROPERTIES REALATED TO GAS LAWS

6.1 Pressure is defined as the force applied to the surface of an object (such as the container within which the gas is contained) per unit area over which that force is distributed.

6.3 a. 1.08×10^3 *torr*

b. 1.44×10^5 *Pa*

c. 1.08×10^3 *mmHg*

d. 20.9 *psi*

6.5 Volume is defined as the space occupied by a particular substance.

6.7   a. 305.2 K

      b. 318 K

      c. 374 K

      d. 331.2 K

SIMPLE GAS LAWS (BOYLE'S, CHARLES'S, AND AVOGADRO'S LAWS)

6.9   Boyle's law states that the pressure and volume of a gas are inversely related given a constant temperature in a closed system.

6.11   1.93 *atm*

6.13   Charles's law states that if a given quantity of gas is maintained at constant pressure, then the volume of the gas is directly proportional to the Kelvin temperature.

6.15 3.34×10^{-2} L

6.17 $\dfrac{P_1 V_1}{T_1} = \dfrac{P_2 V_2}{T_2}$

6.19   5.73 L

6.21   Avogadro's law states that the volume of a gas is directly related to the amount of mols (n) of the gas at a given temperature and pressure.

6.23   0.32 *mols of additional gas added*

THE IDEAL GAS LAW

6.25   The ideal gas law is an equation that can be obtained by combining Boyle's, Charles's, and Avogadro's laws. It essentially describes a hypothetical ideal gas, and as such has limitations when it comes to describing the behavior of "real" gases.

6.27   4.61 L

6.29   5.45 L

6.31   0.962 *mols*

6.33   297 K

6.35   1.56 *mols*

6.37   10 °C

6.39   1.27 *mols*

APPLICATIONS INVOLVING THE IDEAL GAS LAW

6.41 $Density = \dfrac{m}{V} = \dfrac{P \cdot MM}{R \cdot T}$

6.43   The standard molar volume is the volume of 1 *mol* of an ideal gas at STP.

6.45 $1.250 \dfrac{g}{L}$

6.47 $1.964 \frac{g}{L}$

6.49 $44.2 \frac{g}{mol}$

6.51 $44.2 \frac{g}{mol}$

6.53 $4\,Al\,(s) + 3O_2\,(g) \rightarrow 2\,Al_2\,O_3$

6.55 $104\ L\ of\ hydrogen$

MIXTURES OF GASES AND PARTIAL PRESSURES

6.57 Dalton's law of partial pressures states that the total pressure exerted in a mixture of gases is equal to the sum of the individual partial pressures of the gases involved in the mixture.

6.59 $P_{H_2} = 0.91\ atm$

$P_{Ne} = 0.40\ atm$

6.61 $0.688\ atm$

6.63 $X_{O_2} = 5.8 \times 10^{-2}$

$P_{O_2} = 0.11\ atm$

6.65 $X_{He} = 0.758$

$X_{CO_2} = 0.242$

$P_{He} = 1.60\ atm$

$P_{CO_2} = 0.511\ atm$

REAL GASES: DEVIATIONS FROM IDEAL BEHAVIOR

6.67 The theory relies on the fact that most of the space in a gas is "empty space," and therefore the individual size of the gas molecules is somewhat insignificant. However, at high pressures, we squeeze out all that empty space and now the size of the individual gas molecules becomes significant and can affect the overall volume.

6.69 $\left(P + a\left[\frac{n}{v}\right]^2\right) \times (V - bn) = nRT$

Chapter 7

THE WAVE NATURE OF LIGHT — ELECTROMAGNETIC RADIATION

7.1 Light is the common word for electromagnetic radiation, a form of radiant energy which consists of oscillating, mutually perpendicular electric and magnetic fields.

7.3 The wavelength (λ) is defined as the distance along the x-coordinate between adjacent peaks (maxima—highest points) or adjacent troughs (minima—lowest points) on a wave.

7.5 Frequency (ν) is defined as the number of cycles (wavelengths) which pass an arbitrary point in space in one second. As such, the frequency is a function of both the velocity of the wave and its wavelength and is typically expressed in units of cycles per second, or simply, "per second" ($1/s$ or s^{-1}), also known as Hertz (*Hz*).

7.7 a. Radio waves

b. Infrared radiation

7.9 a. 10 *nm*

7.11 $9.99 \times 10^{14}\, s^{-1}$

7.13 $4.08 \times 10^{21}\, s^{-1}$

7.15 $9.34 \times 10^{-13}\, m$

7.17 47.4 *m*

THE PARTICLE NATURE OF LIGHT

7.19 a. Gamma rays

7.21 Energy of one photon: $4.01 \times 10^{-19}\, J$

Energy of one mole of photons: 242 *kJ/mol*

7.23 $\lambda = 416\ nm$

$\nu = 7.21 \times 10^{14}\, s^{-1}$

7.25 $\lambda = 6.92 \times 10^{-3}\, m$

$E = 2.87 \times 10^{-23}\, J$

Energy of one mole of photons $= 17.3$ *J/mol*

7.27 $\nu = 5.49 \times 10^{14}\, s^{-1}$

Energy of one photon $= 3.64 \times 10^{-19}\, J$

Energy of one mole of photons $= 219$ *kJ/mol*

7.29 $\nu = 4.47 \times 10^{14}\, s^{-1}$

Energy of one photon $= 2.96 \times 10^{-19}\, J$

Energy of one mole of photons $= 178$ *kJ/mol*

7.31 353 *kJ/mol*

7.33 No

ATOMIC SPECTRA AND THE BOHR MODEL OF THE HYDROGEN ATOM

7.35 $E_n = -R_H Z^2 \left(\frac{1}{n^2} \right)$

7.37 When an electron in an excited state of the hydrogen atom relaxes to a lower energy state, the excess energy lost due to this transition is released as a photon of light the frequency of which must correspond precisely to the difference in energy between the two energy states involved in the transition.

7.39 -4.45×10^{-20} J

7.41 -1.96×10^{-17} J

7.43 c. $n = 7 \rightarrow n = 6$

7.45 a. $\lambda = 9.49 \times 10^{-8}$ m

$\nu = 3.16 \times 10^{15}$ s^{-1}

b. $\lambda = 9.72 \times 10^{-8}$ m

$\nu = 3.08 \times 10^{15}$ s^{-1}

c. $\lambda = 1.03 \times 10^{-7}$ m

$\nu = 2.91 \times 10^{15}$ s^{-1}

d. $\lambda = 1.21 \times 10^{-7}$ m

$\nu = 2.48 \times 10^{15}$ s^{-1}

7.47 $n_i = 6$

$n_f = 4$

7.49 $\lambda = 121$ nm. The nuclear charge (Z) for the He^+ cation is 2, as opposed to 1 for H, which results in lower energies for the electron in its allowed orbits.

DE BROGLIE AND THE WAVE PROPERTY OF THE ELECTRON

7.51 Velocity

7.53 1.19×10^5 m/s

7.55 3.41×10^{-9} m

HEISENBERG'S UNCERTAINTY PRINCIPLE AND SCHRÖDINGER'S EQUATION

7.57 Max Born was stating that the amplitude of the electron-wave at any point was not "how much" of the electron is located there but rather the probability of finding the electron at that point.

7.59 The orbital is simply the region of space around the nucleus of an atom where it is most likely the electron will be found.

7.61 n, the Principal Quantum Number specifies the relative size and energy of an orbital.

l, the Angular Momentum Quantum Number specifies the shape of the orbital.

m_l, the Magnetic Quantum Number specifies the spatial orientation of the orbital.

7.63 $l = 0, 1, 2$

7.65 $m_l = -2, -1, 0, 1, 2$

7.67 $n = 2$

      $l = 1$

      $m_l = -1, 0, 1$

7.69 $n = 5$

      $l = 3$

      $m_l = -3, -2, -1, 0, 1, 2, 3$

7.71 $l = 0 \rightarrow s$

      $l = 1 \rightarrow p$

      $l = 2 \rightarrow d$

      $l = 3 \rightarrow f$

7.73   a.   Allowed, $5s$

      b.   Allowed, $4p$

      c.   Erroneous, n cannot equal l.

      d.   Allowed, $3d$

7.75 $n = 4, l = 2, m_l = 2$

      $n = 4, l = 2, m_l = 1$

      $n = 4, l = 2, m_l = 0$

      $n = 4, l = 2, m_l = -1$

      $n = 4, l = 2, m_l = -2$

7.77   a, b, d

7.79   4

ELECTRON SPIN AND GROUND STATE ELECTRON CONFIGURATIONS

7.81   When filling degenerate orbitals, the orbitals are filled singly first with parallel spins.

7.83   Core electrons are those which occupy the inner shells of an atoms. In other words, they are not in the valence shell.

7.85   +2

7.87   The s-block consists of the groups 1A and 2A elements. The valence electron configuration of group 1A elements is ns^1, and for group 2A it is ns^2. For this reason it is referred to as the s-block.

7.89 $1s^2 2s^2 2p^6 3s^2 3p^4 = [Ne]3s^2 3p^4$ [↑↓] [↑↓][↑] [↑]

                                       $3s$ $3p$

7.91 $1s^2 2s^2 2p^6 3s^2 3p^6 4s^2 3d^{10} 4p^6 5s^2 = [Kr]5s^2$ [↑↓]

                                                     $5s$

7.93 $1s^2 2s^2 2p^2$ [↑↓] [↑] [↑] [↑]

                  $2s$ $2p$

7.95   a. $[Ar]4s^2 3d^6$

b. $[Kr]5s^2$

c. $[Xe]6s^2 4f^{14} 5d^{10} 6p^2$

d. $[Ar]4s^2 3d^2$

IONIC ELECTRON CONFIGURATIONS

7.97   a. $[Ar]3d^9$ paramagnetic

b. $[Kr]4d^{10}$ diamagnetic

c. $[Ar]4s^2 3d^{10} 4p^6$ diamagnetic

d. $[Ar]4s^2 3d^{10} 4p^6$ diamagnetic

7.99   a. $[Ne]3s^2 3p^6$ diamagnetic

b. $1s^2 2s^2 2p^6$ diamagnetic

c. $[Ne]3s^2 3p^6$ diamagnetic

d. $[Ar]3d^5$ paramagnetic

PERIODIC TRENDS

7.101   *Li, Ca, Sr, Ba*

7.103   *Li, K, Cs, Fr*

7.105   a. F^-

b. *Mg*

c. *Al*

d. *Al*

7.107   *Ba, Sr, Ca, Li*

7.109   *Fr, Cs, K, Li*

7.111   Aluminum

Chapter 8

CHEMICAL BONDS AND ELECTRONEGATIVITY

8.1   Bonding occurs between elements because it has the effect of lowering the energy of the elements involved in chemical bonding.

8.3   Ionic bonding is characterized by the complete transfer of one or more electrons from a metal to a nonmetal. As such, we understand ionic bonding to occur between non metals and metals.

8.5   *Covalent bonding occurs between nonmetals and other non-metals.* When two nonmetals come together to form a bond they will do so by "sharing" electrons. Each nucleus in such a bond will exert an attractive force for the valence electrons of a neighboring atom. This has the effect of keeping the two atoms bound close together. Additionally, we say that the atoms in a covalent bond share a "pair" of valence electrons, each atom donating 1 electron to the bonding interaction (see Figure 8.1).

8.7   *Metallic bonding occurs when metals bond to metals and is characterized by pooling of valence electrons over a large number of atoms.* Metals are relatively large compared to nonmetals (recall trends in atomic radii from Chapter 7) and, in addition, their outer valence electrons are not held very strongly (metals tend to have lower ionization energies) and, as such, they tend to share their valence electrons with other metal atoms. Unlike covalent bonding, this arrangement is not localized to a pair of atoms but rather delocalized over an entire sample of metal. Therefore, it is appropriate to consider atoms which make up a metal sample as "cationic cores" (the nuclei plus the core electrons) surrounded by a "sea" of valence electrons which are delocalized over the entire sample (See Figure 8.1).

8.9   Oxygen is a nonmetal and therefore will have a greater electronegativity than magnesium.

LEWIS THEORY—LEWIS SYMBOLS AND STRUCTURES

8.11   a. ·Mg·

b. ·P̈·

c. ·Äs·

d. ·B·

8.13   a. ·N̈·

b. :F̈:

c. :B̈r:

d. ·Ba·

8.15   a. Ca^{2+}

b. Rb^+

c. $\left[:\ddot{S}:\right]^{2-}$

d. $\left[:\ddot{N}:\right]^{3-}$

8.17   a. $\left[:\ddot{B}r:\right]^{-}$ Ba^{2+} $\left[:\ddot{B}r:\right]^{-}$

b. K^+ $\left[:\ddot{C}l:\right]^{-}$

c. $\left[:\ddot{O}:\right]^{2-}$ Al^{3+} $\left[:\ddot{O}:\right]^{2-}$ Al^{3+} $\left[:\ddot{O}:\right]^{2-}$

8.19 Because elements share electrons in covalent bonding, this allows the atoms in a covalent compound to realize an octet, even though they have fewer than eight valence electrons.

8.21 *H* – Because hydrogen forms a duet, it will only ever form one bond and, as such, cannot be the central atom in a covalent molecule.

F – Because fluorine is the most electronegative element, it will never be the least electronegative element in a compound. Since this is the criterion for determining the central atom, fluorine will never be the central atom.

8.23 a.

b.

c.

8.25 a.

b.

c.

8.27

8.29

Resonance Hybrid:

8.31 a.

b.

8.33 a.

b.

c.

8.35 a.

b.

c.

8.37 a.

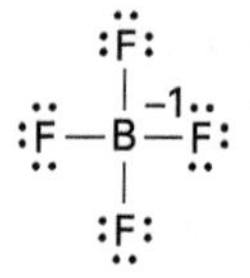

b.

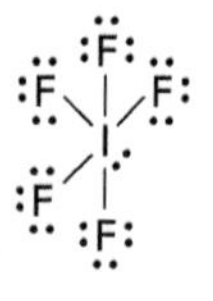

c.

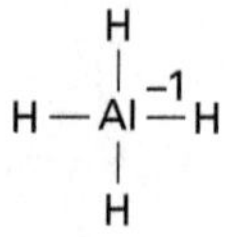

8.39 a.

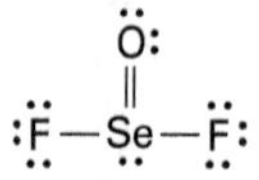

b.

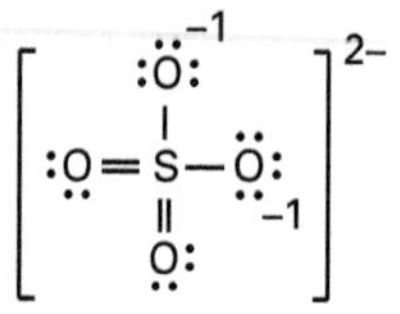

c.

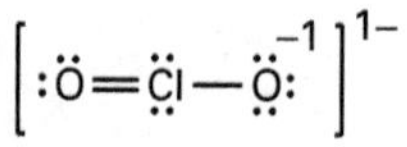

8.41

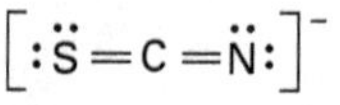

8.43

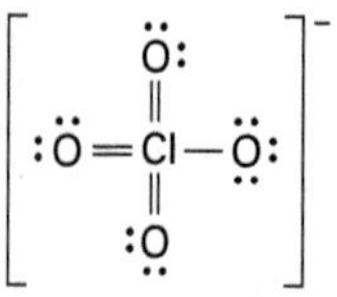

VALENCE SHELL ELECTRON PAIR REPULSION THEORY (VSEPR)

8.45 Electronic Geometry refers to the three-dimensional arrangement of all of the electrons on the central atom. This is the direct result of the application of the VSEPR model. Molecular Geometry refers to the three-dimensional arrangement of the terminal atoms around the central atom. This is a derivative of the electronic geometry. These are the same as long as all electron groups on the central atom are bonding groups. When there is an admixture of bonding groups and lone pairs on the central atom, the molecular geometry will then be different from the electron geometry.

8.47 There are four bonding electron groups and one lone pair on a molecule with see-saw molecular geometry.

8.49 There are four bonding electron groups and two lone pairs on a molecule with square planar molecular geometry.

8.51 There are three bonding electron groups and one lone pair on a molecule with pyramidal molecular geometry.

8.53 There are two bonding electron groups and two lone pairs on a molecule with tetrahedral bent molecular geometry.

8.55 a. $EG = 4$

Electronic geometry = Tetrahedral

Molecular Geometry = Tetrahedral

Bond Angle ~ 109.5°

b. $EG = 3$

Electronic geometry = Trigonal

Molecular Geometry = Trigonal

Bond Angle ~ 120°

c. $EG = 4$

Electronic Geometry = Tetrahedral

Molecular Geometry = Tetrahedral Bent

Bond Angle < 109.5°

8.57 a. $EG = 6$

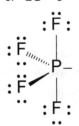

b. $EG = 5$

c. $EG = 5$

8.59 $SO_3^{2-} < SO_4^{2-} < SO_2 < SO_3$

BOND AND MOLECULAR POLARITY

8.61 Separation of electric charge over a given distance is called an **electric dipole**. Covalent bonds which exhibit a measurable electric dipole (due to uneven sharing of bonding electron pairs) are referred as **polar covalent bonds**.

8.63 $\Delta EN = EN_N - EN_H = 3.0 - 2.1 = 0.9$

We expect this bond to be **polar covalent**. Because $0.4 < (\Delta EN = 0.9) < 2.0$ we expect there to be sufficient charge separation over the bond to result in a strong dipole.

8.65 Bond polarity and ΔEN increase in the order b, a, d, c

8.67 a. polar

b. polar

c. nonpolar

d. polar

8.69 a. nonpolar

b. nonpolar

c. polar

d. nonpolar

VALENCE BOND THEORY

8.71 a. 180°

b. 120°

c. 109.5°

d. 120° (equatorial) and 90° (axial)

e. 90°

8.73 a. sp^3d^2

b. sp^3

c. sp^2

d. sp^2

8.75

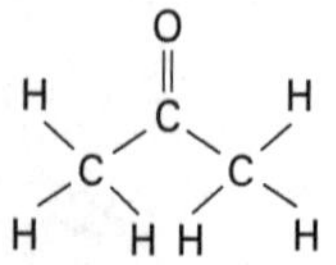

The two outside carbons have four σ-bonds (four electron groups) and therefore these are sp^3. However, the middle carbon has three σ-bonds (three electron groups) and it is therefore sp^2. There is one π-bond between the middle carbon and oxygen.

8.77 a. All the carbon atoms are sp^3 and the oxygen atom is also sp^3.

  b. All the carbon atoms are sp^2

  c. The nitrogen is sp^3, the left-most carbon is sp^3, the right-most carbon is sp^2, the oxygen on the far right is sp^3 and the oxygen with the double bond is sp^2.

MOLECULAR ORBITAL THEORY

8.79 Again, when waves interact, they can do so constructively or destructively. When they are in phase, they interact constructively, building up electron density in the region between the two atomic nuclei. This is referred to as a **bonding molecular orbital** or simply a **bonding orbital**, in MO theory. Likewise, when the wave functions are out of phase they interact destructively, reducing the probability of finding an electron in the region between the nuclei. This is referred to as an **antibonding orbital** and is characterized by a nodal plane perpendicular to the inter-nuclear axis. Note: the number of orbitals is always conserved.

8.81 a. $BO = 1$, exists.

  b. $BO = 0.5$, exists.

  c. $BO = 0.5$ exists.

  d. $BO = 0.5$, exists.

  e. $BO = 0$, nonexistant.

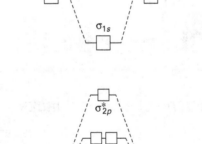

8.83 a. $(\sigma_{2s})^2 (\sigma_{2s}^*)^2 (\pi_{2p})^2$

  b. $(\sigma_{2s})^2 (\sigma_{2s}^*)^2 (\pi_{2p})^1$

  c. $(\sigma_{2s})^2 (\sigma_{2s}^*)^2 (\pi_{2p})^3$

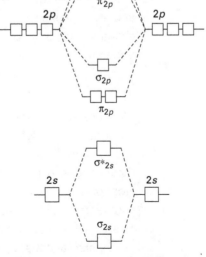

8.85 a. $(\sigma_{2s})^2 (\sigma_{2s}^*)^2 (\sigma_{2p})^2 (\pi_{2p})^4 (\pi_{2p}^*)^4$

     b. $(\sigma_{2s})^2 (\sigma_{2s}^*)^2 (\sigma_{2p})^2 (\pi_{2p})^4 (\pi_{2p}^*)^3$

     c. $(\sigma_{2s})^2 (\sigma_{2s}^*)^2 (\sigma_{2p})^2 (\pi_{2p})^4 (\pi_{2p}^*)^4 (\sigma_{2p}^*)^1$

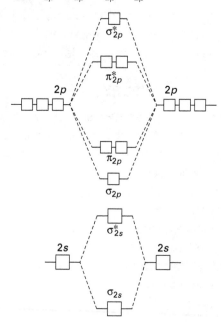

8.87 $B_2^+ < B_2 < B_2^-$

8.89 $F_2^- < F_2 < F_2^+$

Chapter 9

INTERMOLECULAR FORCES

9.1 Intermolecular forces are essentially responsible for holding condensed matter together and occur between atoms and molecules based on differences in charges, temporary charges, and partial charges. It is very important for us to understand why these forces exist as all living organisms are dependent on them. For example, intermolecular forces are responsible for holding the two strands of DNA together.

9.3 All atoms and molecules experience dispersion forces, which occur based on slight fluctuations in electron distribution within them. Based on probability given any point in time, the electrons will be unevenly distributed throughout the atom or molecule resulting in an electron rich region, leaving another region of the atom or molecule electron deficient. This unsymmetrical distribution of electrons can then result in an instantaneous temporary dipole in neighboring atoms or molecules. Hydrocarbons such as ethane, propane, and butane are all good examples of molecules that experience this type of intermolecular force.

9.5 $CH_4 < CH_3CH_3 < CH_3CH_2CH_3 < CH_3CH_2CH_2CH_3$

9.7   Dipole-dipole forces exist in all polar molecules, which have a dipole, in which the molecule contains permanent electron-rich and electron-deficient regions. This gives rise to partially negative and partially positive "poles" of the molecule. Acetone and formaldehyde are both good examples of molecules that experience this type of intermolecular force (in addition to dispersion forces).

9.9   Miscible substances are two substances that mix with one another without separating into two states of liquids. They form a homogenous mixture. Water (H_2O) and ethanol (CH_3CH_2OH) are miscible substances. Both substances are polar.

9.11   Amphiphilic molecules are molecules that possess both nonpolar and polar properties. The molecules present in soap are amphiphilic molecules.

9.13   Pentanol (right molecule) has a higher boiling point than pentane (left molecule). While both molecules have dispersion forces, pentanol also experiences dipole-dipole interactions as well as hydrogen bonding. This dramatically increases the boiling point (compare 36 °C for pentane and greater than 130 °C for pentanol).

9.15   Dispersion forces.

9.17   Dispersion forces.

9.19   Dispersion forces, dipole-dipole forces, and hydrogen bonding.

9.21   Dispersion forces and dipole-dipole forces.

9.23   Dispersion forces.

9.25   Water has a bent geometry, and the highly polar $O–H$ bonds gives water a significant dipole moment. The two $O–H$ bonds present in water allow for one water molecule to hydrogen bond with four other water molecules resulting in a somewhat uniquely intricate network. This extensive hydrogen bonding pattern allows water to be a liquid at room temperature, which is obviously very important in order to sustain life as it is the main solvent in living organisms allowing for nutrients to readily travel throughout the body. Water is also a very unique substance in that it is less dense in the solid phase than in the liquid phase, which is not the case with most substances. This is because this unique hydrogen bonding pattern allows water molecules to be regularly arranged resembling an "open-cage" structure containing lots of empty space making it less dense in the solid state versus the liquid. Thus, ice floats on top of the liquid water on a frozen lake, which is also an important fact as it relates to sustaining life because if solid ice sank to the bottom of a lake every time it froze, it would essentially eliminate all aquatic life in the lake.

PROPERTIES OF LIQUIDS ATTRIBUTED TO INTERMOLECULAR FORCES

9.27 Condensation is a process which involves a substance changing from the gas state to a liquid state. This is an exothermic process.

9.29 The heat of vaporization is the amount of heat energy required to vaporize one mole of a liquid to the gas state under standard conditions (units are generally given in *kJ/mol*).

9.31 Vapor pressure is defined as the pressure of the vapor in dynamic equilibrium with its liquid and is dependent on the intermolecular forces of the liquid at a given temperature. Essentially, vapor pressure is a measure of how easily molecules can escape the liquid state and go into the gas state.

9.33 The boiling point is defined as the temperature at which a liquid's vapor pressure is equal to the external pressure, whereas the normal boiling point is the temperature at which a liquid's vapor pressure is 1 *atm* (atmospheric pressure at sea level). In the definition of normal boiling point, the external pressure is specified and therefore does not change with geographical location (which is not the case for boiling point).

9.35 Surface tension is the energy required to break the attractive interaction of molecules on the surface of the liquid. These attractive interactions at the surface exist due to the fact that surface molecules have fewer neighbors to interact with when compared to those present in the interior of the liquid. The effect of this on molecules present on the surface is an inward force of attraction between surface molecules that can act like an elastic skin layer giving rise to surface tension.

9.37 The attraction between the molecules of a liquid and its container are known as adhesive forces, whereas the attractions between the molecules within the liquid are known as cohesive forces.

9.39 The viscosity of a liquid is the resistance of the liquid to flow. The more viscous a liquid, the less readily it will flow.

9.41 Water (left).

9.43 Acetone (right).

9.45 Isopropanol (right) has stronger intermolecular forces. It has dispersion forces, dipole-dipole interactions, and hydrogen bonding. Diethyl ether (left) has dispersion forces and dipole-dipole interactions.

9.47 Diethyl ether is more volatile (weaker intermolecular forces when compared to isopropanol).

9.49 Yes, the vapor pressure of a liquid and the temperature are in fact related. As the temperature increases, the vapor pressure also increases exponentially (not linearly). As the temperature decreases, the vapor pressure also decreases exponentially.

9.51 The acetone will evaporate faster than the water because of the weaker intermolecular forces associated with the acetone. Water can form hydrogen bonds, while acetone cannot. Acetone will have a higher vapor pressure when compared to the water at the same temperature.

9.53 Shelby's clean graduated cylinder allows for strong adhesive forces between the water molecules and the cylinder resulting in a nice concave meniscus. Rusty's dirty cylinder containing the oily residue, however, interferes with these adhesive forces as water and oil do not mix (water is polar and oil is nonpolar). The result is essentially a flat meniscus as the water is unable to rise along the tube's interior (cohesive forces among the water molecules are stronger).

9.55 No, carbon tetrachloride is nonpolar and water is polar. Therefore, they do not form a homogenous mixture and are immiscible substances.

PHASE DIAGRAMS

9.57 A phase diagram summarizes the various states of matter (solid, liquid, gas) using the relationship between temperature (*x*-axis) and pressure (*y*-axis). The lines on the phase diagram represent the temperature and pressure conditions in which two phases exist at equilibrium.

9.59 C

9.61 D

9.63 A

Chapter 10

EQUILIBRIUM CONSTANT

10.1 We define the term dynamic equilibrium in a chemical reaction as that state in which the rate of the forward reaction is equal to the rate of the reverse reaction. In other words, reactions are continuously proceeding in both the forward and reverse directions such that a dynamic steady state is established respecting product and reactant concentrations.

10.3 $\quad K_c = \dfrac{[CF_4][HF]^4}{[CH_4][F_2]^4}$

$\quad K_p = \dfrac{P_{CF_4} \cdot P_{HF}{}^4}{P_{CH_4} \cdot P_{F_2}{}^4}$

10.5 $\quad K_c = \dfrac{[N_2]^2[H_2O]^6}{[NH_3]^4[O_2]^3}$

$\quad K_p = \dfrac{P_{N_2}{}^2 \cdot P_{H_2O}{}^6}{P_{NH_3}{}^4 \cdot P_{O_2}{}^3}$

10.7 $\quad K_c = \dfrac{[H_2SO_4]}{[SO_3]}$

10.9 $\quad$ a. $\quad K_c \ll 1$; Reactant-favored

$\qquad$ b. $\quad K_c \gg 1$; Product-favored

10.11 $\quad K_c = 4.11 \times 10^{-26}$

10.13 $\quad K_c = 2.74 \times 10^{-84}$

10.15 $\quad K_c = 3.04 \times 10^{35}$

EQUILIBRIUM CONSTANT IN TERMS OF PARTIAL PRESSURE

10.17 $\quad K_c = 4.77 \times 10^{13}$

10.19 $\quad K_c = 2.09 \times 10^{29}$

10.21 $\quad K_p = 7.54 \times 10^{6}$

10.23 $\quad$ a, b

HETEROGENEOUS EQUILIBRIA—SOLIDS AND LIQUIDS

10.25 $\quad K_c = \dfrac{1}{[O_2]^5}$

$\quad K_p = \dfrac{1}{P_{O_2}{}^5}$

10.27 $\quad K_c = [CO_2]$

$\qquad K_p = P_{CO_2}$

DETERMINING THE EQUILIBRIUM CONSTANT

10.29 $\quad K_c = 0.838$

10.31 $\quad K_p = 9.14 \times 10^{-6}$

10.33 $\quad K_c = 30.2$

THE REACTION QUOTIENT

10.35 $\quad Q = 4.51 \times 10^{-2}$; $Q_c > K_c$. Therefore, the reaction will proceed to the left (toward reactants) as it establishes equilibrium.

10.37 The reaction is not at equilibrium since $Q_p \neq K_p$ ($Q_p = 104$). Further, since $Q_p > K_p$, the reaction must proceed to the left (toward reactants) as it establishes equilibrium.

DETERMINING EQUILIBRIUM CONCENTRATIONS

10.39 $[C] = 0.0141\ M$

10.41 $[CO] = [Cl_2] = 0.265\ M$; $[COCl_2] = 1.135\ M$

10.43 $[CO_2] = [H_2] = 0.137\ M$

$[CO] = 0.363\ M$

$[H_2O] = 0.113\ M$

10.45 $P_{COCl_2} = 0.05\ atm$

$P_{Cl_2} = 0.45\ atm$

LE CHÂTELIER'S PRINCIPLE

10.47 a. left

b. left

c. right

d. right

10.49 a. right

b. left

c. right

d. no shift

SOLUBILITY PRODUCT - K$_{SP}$

10.51 a. $K_{sp} = [Al^{3+}][OH^-]^3$

b. $K_{sp} = [Ca^{2+}][F^-]^2$

c. $K_{sp} = [Pb^{2+}][Cl^-]^2$

d. $K_{sp} = [Co^{2+}][CO_3^{2-}]$

10.53 a. 2.6×10^{-9} moles/liter

b. 3.35×10^{-4} moles/liter

c. 1.4×10^{-2} moles/liter

d. 7.1×10^{-5} moles/liter

10.55 a. 8.4×10^{-3} moles/liter

b. 7.1×10^{-4} moles/liter

c. 3.6×10^{-4} moles/liter

Chapter 11

ACIDS AND BASES DEFINITIONS

11.1 An Arrhenius acid produces H^+ ions in aqueous solution while an Arrhenius base produces OH^- ions in aqueous solution.

11.3 A Brønsted-Lowry acid is a proton donor, while a Brønsted-Lowry base is a proton acceptor.

11.5 An amphoteric substance is defined as any substance that can act like either an acid or a base. Water is a good example.

11.7 a. $HClO_4$

b. H_2CO_3

c. NH_4^+

d. H_2O

ACIDS AND BASES NOMENCLATURE

11.9 A binary acid contains hydrogen and a nonmetal.

11.11 a. Hypochlorous acid

b. Hydrochloric acid

c. Sulfurous acid

d. Hydrobromic acid

11.13 a. H_3PO_4

b. HI

c. $HClO_3$

d. $HC_2H_3O_2$

11.15 a. $Mg(OH)_2$

b. $LiOH$

c. NH_3

d. $Ca(OH)_2$

AUTOIONIZATION OF WATER AND SCALES USED TO QUANTIFY ACIDITY AND BASICITY

11.17 $K_w = 1.0 \times 10^{-14}$

11.19 a. $[H^+] < [OH^-]$

11.21 a. 1.0×10^{-7}, neutral

b. 1.6×10^{-7}, slightly acidic

c. 2.4×10^{-13}, very basic

d. 4.3×10^{-5}, acidic

11.23 The pH is the negative log of the hydronium ion concentration and the *pOH* is the negative log of the hydroxide ion concentration as follows:

$$pH = -\log[H_3O^+]$$

$$pOH = -\log[OH^-]$$

11.25 a. $pH = 3.47$

$pOH = 10.53$

b. $pH = 10.07$

$pOH = 3.93$

c. $pH = 2.28$

$pOH = 11.72$

d. $pH = 4.01$

$pOH = 9.99$

ACID AND BASE TITRATIONS: A COMMON LABORATORY TECHNIQUE

11.27 A burette is a device used in chemistry to dispense precise amounts of chemical solutions (see Figure 11.5).

11.29 $HCl(aq) + NaOH(aq) \rightarrow H_2O(l) + NaCl(aq)$

11.31 $H_3PO_4(aq) + 3NaOH(aq) \rightarrow 3H_2O(l) + Na_3PO_4(aq)$

11.33 0.127 M HCl

11.35 0.204 M H_2SO_4

11.37 0.187 M H_3PO_4

11.39 0.311 M $HClO_4$

11.41 The titration curve on the left is of a strong acid, while the one on the right is of a weak acid. Strong acids tend to have a low starting pH value (< 2.00) as we would expect, while weaker acids have higher pH values prior to the titration (> 2.00). Also, strong acids being titrated with a strong base have an equivalence point of approximately 7.00 and a relatively steeper curve, while weaker acids being titrated with a strong base have a slightly basic equivalence point (~8.00) and a more gradual curve.

ACID STRENGTH

11.43 $pH = 0.60$

11.45 $pH = 1.70$

11.47 2.6×10^{-3} M

11.49 1.41 g

11.51 $K_a = \dfrac{[H^+][A^-]}{[HA]}$

11.53 We can simplify our calculations when the change (or percent ionization) is less than 5% of the initial acid concentration. If the percent ionization is greater than 5%, then we would use the quadratic equation as follows:

$$x = \frac{-b \pm \sqrt{b^2 - 4ac}}{2a}$$

11.55 $pH = 2.00$

11.57 $pH = 1.96$

11.59 $pH = 1.89$

11.61 $pH = 2.40$

11.63 0.42%

11.65 1.3%

11.67 We can generally focus on Ka_1 only as Ka_2 (and Ka_3 if it applies) generally tend to be negligible (not always the case, such as dilute solutions of certain acids). This is in part due to the fact that polyprotic acids ionize in successive steps, and the formation of hydronium ions in the first step inhibits their formation in the second (and third step if it applies) as Le Châtelier's principle would predict. Therefore, we can determine the pH of most solutions of polyprotic acids by just using the K_{a1} value.

11.69 $pH = 3.54$

11.71 HCl is a stronger acid due to the presence of the electronegative chlorine atom, which results in a very polarized bond.

11.73 HI is a much stronger acid (acidic strength increases as you go down column 7A) because hydrogen is released easier with larger atoms.

BASE STRENGTH

11.75 Strong bases completely dissociate into ions when dissolved in water, while weak bases only partially ionize when dissolved in water.

11.77 $pH = 13.18$

11.79 $1.8 \times 10^{-3} M$

11.81 $1.8 \times 10^{-2} M$

11.83 $pH = 13.85$

11.85 The base ionization constant (K_b) is the equilibrium constant for the ionization reaction of bases, which is very useful for calculations involving weak bases.

11.87 $pH = 11.48$

11.89 $pH = 12.04$

11.91 $pH = 12.38$

11.93 $pH = 10.15$

11.95 $pH = 11.90$

11.97 $pH = 10.96$

11.99 0.35%

BUFFERS

11.101 Buffers are solutions that resist drastic changes in pH by neutralizing added acid or base, thereby allowing them to maintain a relatively small specific pH range. Human blood is a good example of a buffer.

11.103 Acidic buffers are composed of a weak acid and its conjugate base, while a basic buffer contains a weak base and its conjugate acid.

11.105 Strong acids and bases are not used for a buffer system because they ionize completely. A buffer needs to contain both the weak acid and its conjugate base (or weak base and conjugate acid) for it to be effective at resisting dramatic pH changes. This can only occur with partial (not complete) ionization of either acid or base. Thus, weak acids and bases are used in buffer systems.

11.107 Added base would react with the acid (HA) to make more conjugate base (A^-). The pH may go up, but only slightly as the added base would be effectively neutralized by the presence of the acid.

11.109 $pH = 4.92$

11.111 $pH = 3.74$

11.113 $pH = 10.91$

11.115 $pH = 9.26$

11.117 d. $[A^-] = [HA]$

11.119 $pH = 4.92$

11.121 $pH = 3.74$

11.123 $pH = 9.10$

11.125 $pH = 10.63$

11.127 $pH = 3.72$

11.129 0.32:1

11.131 0.32:1

11.133 $pH = 4.56$

11.135 $pH = 2.00$

11.137 $pH = 10.71$

11.139 The two major factors that influence buffer effectiveness include the relative concentrations of the weak acid and conjugate base (or weak base and conjugate acid), as well as the absolute concentrations of both components. Buffers tend to be more effective when the relative concentrations of weak acid and conjugate base (or weak base and conjugate acid) are equal, or in a 1:1 ratio, and with higher concentrations of both.

11.141 Hypochlorous acid would be a better choice for a buffer solution with a *pH* of 7.20 because its *pK$_a$* value is much closer to this *pH* (7.54).

Chapter 12

THE FIRST LAW OF THERMODYNAMICS AND THE NATURE OF ENERGY

12.1 Thermodynamics is defined as the scientific discipline that is concerned with the transfer of energy from one system to another, and its transformation from one form to another. Thermochemistry is the field of thermodynamics which deals with the energy changes associated with chemical change.

12.3 Potential energy is the energy associated with, or due to, composition or position (i.e. stored energy). Kinetic energy is the energy associated with, or due to, motion. The kinetic energy of an object with a mass, *m*, is given as:

$$KE = \frac{1}{2}mv^2$$

where *v* is the velocity of the mass (or object) in question.

12.5 27.9 *J*

12.7 The internal energy of a system is defined as the sum of all of the potential and kinetic energies of all the particles which constitute the system.

12.9 loss

12.11 **Heat (q)** is the transfer of thermal energy (measured in joules) between the system and surroundings. Not to be confused with *temperature*, which is a measure of the average kinetic energy of the particles which make up the system.

12.13 $q_{sys} < 0$

12.15 A state function is a property that depends only on the current state of the system in question.

12.17 less than/releases energy

12.19 −295.5 *KJ*

12.21 −14.5 *KJ*

QUANTIFYING HEAT

12.23 The heat capacity of a substance represents the amount of energy required to raise the temperature of the substance by 1°C. Therefore, the higher the heat capacity the more energy required to increase the temperature of the system.

12.25 $-143\ J$

12.27 $0.385\ \frac{J}{g\cdot°C}$, copper

12.29 $20.0\ ml$

12.31 $69.9\ g$

12.33 $53.78°C$

12.35 $19.6\ g$

12.37 a. the aluminum.

b. the water.

c. $0.897\ \frac{J}{g\cdot°C}$

QUANTIFYING WORK

12.39 When work is done on the surroundings by the system, $\Delta V > 0$ and $w < 0$.

12.41 $-58.5\ J$

12.43 $495\ J$

ENTHALPY

12.45 Enthalpy is an extensive property.

12.47 Reactions which absorb heat $(\Delta H_{rxn} > 0)$ are referred to as endothermic reactions.

12.49 Endothermic

12.51 a. Exothermic

b. Exothermic

c. Endothermic

12.53 $-5\ kJ$

12.55 a. $-936\ kJ$

b. $-233\ kJ$

12.57 a. $237\ kJ$

b. $238\ kJ$

12.59 HCl is not the limiting reagent.

CALORIMETRY

12.61 A calorimeter is an apparatus which is used to perform chemical reactions under controlled conditions such that temperature changes can be carefully measured.

12.63 $-5.17 \times 10^3\ kJ\cdot mol^{-1}$

HESS'S LAW

12.65 Hess's Law states that the enthalpy change of an overall chemical process is equal to the sum of the enthalpy changes for individual steps in that process.

12.67 When a particular reaction is divided by a certain factor, then ΔH is divided by the same factor (enthalpy is an extensive property).

12.69 $+142.7 \ kJ$

12.71 $\Delta H = 66.4 \ kJ$

12.73 $\Delta H = -198.4 \ kJ$

12.75 $\Delta H = -812.9 \ kJ$

STANDARD CONDITIONS AND ENTHALPIES OF FORMATION

12.77 The standard enthalpy of formation is defined as the enthalpy change associated with the standard formation reaction of a substance.

12.79 $131.3 \ \frac{kJ}{mol}$

12.81 $179.2 \ \frac{kJ}{mol}$

THE ENTHALPY OF BONDING

12.83 $\Delta H_{rxn} = -136 \ kJ \ / \ mol$

12.85 $CsBr < RbBr < CaO < MgO$

12.87 $Lattice \ Energy = 717 \ kJ$

SPONTANEITY, ENTROPY, AND THE SECOND LAW OF THERMODYNAMICS

12.89 a. $\Delta S < 0$

   b. $\Delta S > 0$

12.91 a. $556 \ \frac{J}{mol \cdot k}$

   b. $47.75 \ \frac{J}{mol \cdot k}$

   c. $-556 \ \frac{J}{mol \cdot k}$

   d. $-47.75 \ \frac{J}{mol \cdot k}$

12.93 a. nonspontaneous

   b. spontaneous

   c. spontaneous

   d. nonspontaneous

12.95 $24.8 \ \frac{J}{mol \cdot k}$

12.97 $-391.0 \ \frac{J}{mol \cdot k}$

THE GIBBS FREE ENERGY

12.99 A negative ΔH and a positive ΔS would indicate in an exothermic system which would be spontaneous at any temperature.

12.101 A positive ΔH and a positive ΔS would mean that the system would be spontaneous only at higher temperatures.

12.103 $\Delta G^{\circ}_{rxn} = -193 \ kJ$ This reaction is spontaneous at any temperature.

12.105 $\Delta G^{\circ}_{rxn} = +23 \ kJ$ This reaction becomes spontaneous at a temperature at or above of 378 K.

12.107 $\Delta G^{\circ}_{rxn} = +175.2 \ kJ$

12.109 $\Delta G^{\circ}_{rxn} = -1007.5 \ kJ$

GIBBS FREE ENERGY AND NONSTANDARD CONDITIONS

12.111 a. $K = e^{-36.89} = 9.53 \times 10^{-17}$

   b. $88.0 \ kJ \cdot mol^{-1}$; Not spontaneous

12.113 $K_2 = 388$

Chapter 13

OXIDATION-REDUCTION (REDOX) REACTIONS

13.1 The gain of electrons is referred to as reduction.

13.3 We define oxidation numbers as imaginary charges which are assigned based on a set of rules. These are determined by assigning shared (bonding) electrons in covalent species to the atoms with greatest electronegativity.

13.5 The reactant which contains the element which is oxidized is referred to as the reducing agent (electron donor).

13.7 a. $Cs = +1$

   $Br = -1$

   b. $H = +1$

   $O = -2$

   $C = +4$

   c. $Na = +1$

   $O = -1$

13.9 a. $Cl = 0$

   b. $Mg^{2+} = +2$

   c. $N = +4$

   $O = -2$

13.11 $Na(s) = Reducing\ Agent$

$Cl_2(g) = Oxidizing\ Agent$

13.13   Not a redox reaction.

BALANCING REDOX REACTIONS

13.15   A redox reaction can be divided into two chemical reactions, one representing oxidation and the other reduction. These are referred to as half-reactions.

13.17   a. $IO_3^-(aq) + 6\,H^+(aq) + 6\,e^- \rightarrow I^-(aq) + 3\,H_2O\,(l)$

b. $ClO^-(aq) + H_2O(l) + 2\,e^- \rightarrow Cl^-(aq) + 2\,OH^-(aq)$

13.19   a. $Cr(s) \rightarrow Cr^{3+}(aq) + 3e^-$

b. $MnO_4^-(aq) + 2\,H_2O(l) + 3\,e^- \rightarrow MnO_2(s) + 4\,OH^-(aq)$

13.21   a. $H_2O_2(aq) + Zn(s) + 2\,H^+(aq) \rightarrow 2\,H_2O(l) + Zn^{2+}(aq)$

b. $2\,BrO_3^-(aq) + 5\,Fe(s) + 12\,H^+(aq) \rightarrow Br_2(l) + 5\,Fe^{2+}(aq)$
      $+\,6\,H_2O(l)$

c. $2\,Cu^{2+}(aq) + N_2H_5^+(aq) \rightarrow N_2(g) + 2\,Cu(s) + 5\,H^+(aq)$

13.23   a. $2\,MnO_2(s) + 3\,Cl_2(g) + 8\,OH^-(aq) \rightarrow 2\,MnO_4^-(aq)$
      $+\,6\,Cl^-(aq) + 4\,H_2O(l)$

b. $3\,ClO^-(aq) + 3\,H_2O(l) + 2\,Fe(s) \rightarrow 3\,Cl^-(aq) + 2\,Fe^{3+}(aq)$
      $+\,6\,OH^-(aq)$

13.25   a. $2\,Cr(OH)_4^-(aq) + 3\,ClO^-(aq) + 2\,OH^-(aq) \rightarrow 2\,CrO_4^{2-}(aq)$
      $+\,3\,Cl^-(aq) + 5\,H_2O(l)$

b. $6\,Br_2(l) + 12\,OH^-(aq) \rightarrow 2\,BrO_3^-(aq) + 10\,Br^-(aq) + 6\,H_2O(l)$

GALVANIC (VOLTAIC) CELLS

13.27   The anode is the electrode where oxidation occurs in all electrochemical cells.

The cathode is the electrode where reduction occurs in all electrochemical cells.

13.29   Galvanic cells (also referred to as voltaic cells) are devices which use spontaneous redox reactions to generate an electric current which is then used to do work. Electrolytic cells are devices which use an external electric current to drive redox reactions which are not spontaneous.

13.31 $\Delta G° = -nFE°_{cell}$

13.33 $Mg(s)\,|\,Mg^{2+}(aq)\,\|\,Zn^{2+}(aq)\,|\,Zn(s)$

13.35 $Li^+ < Ti^{2+} < Cr^{2+} < Sn^{2+}$

13.37 $E°_{cell} = 0.76\ V$

13.39 $E°_{cell} = 0.93\ V$

13.41 a. $E^\circ_{cell} = 0.45\ V$

   b. $E^\circ_{cell} = 0.62\ V$

   c. $E^\circ_{cell} = 1.21\ V$

13.43 a. Spontaneous

   b. Spontaneous

   c. Non-spontaneous

13.45 $E^\circ_{cell} = 2.12\ V$

GIBBS FREE ENERGY, EQUILIBRIUM, AND CELL POTENTIAL

13.47 a. $\Delta G^\circ = -8.10 \times 10^5\ J$

   b. $\Delta G^\circ = -5.29 \times 10^5\ J$

13.49 a. $\Delta G^\circ = -2.08 \times 10^5\ J$

   b. $\Delta G^\circ = -2.70 \times 10^4\ J$

13.51 a. $K = 7.80 \times 10^{141}$

   b. $K = 3.69 \times 10^{92}$

13.53 a. $K = 3.07 \times 10^{36}$

   b. $K = 5.37 \times 10^4$

13.55 a. $E^\circ_{cell} = 0.724\ V$

   b. $E_{cell} = 0.65\ V$

   c. $E_{cell} = 0.80\ V$

13.57 $E_{cell} = 0.95\ V$

ELECTROLYSIS

13.59 a. $Mg^{2+}(aq) + 2e^- \rightarrow Mg(s)$ $E^\circ = -2.37\ V$

   b. $Fe(s) \rightarrow Fe^{2+}(aq) + 2e^-$ $E^\circ = -0.45\ V$

   c.

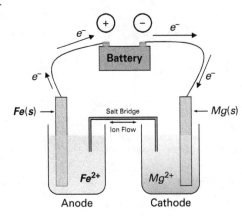

13.61 Cathode (reduction): $K^+ + e^- \rightarrow K$

   Anode (oxidation): $2\,Cl^- \rightarrow Cl_2 + 2e^-$

13.63 Hydrogen gas. Water has a more positive reduction potential
   than that of magnesium (at neutral pH), and overvoltage does

not change this. As such, water is preferentially reduced at the cathode, resulting in a hydrogen gas as the product.

13.65 Cathode: $Cu^{2+}(aq) + 2\,e^- \rightarrow Cu(s)$

Anode: $2\,Br^-(aq) \rightarrow Br_2(g) + 2\,e^-$

13.67 Cathode: $2\,H_2O(l) + 2\,e^- \rightarrow H_2(g) + 2\,OH^-$

Anode: $2\,Cl^-(aq) \rightarrow Cl_2(g) + 2\,e^-$

13.69 1.24 g Zn

13.71 5.83 hrs

Chapter 14

OVERVIEW OF CHEMICAL REACTION RATES

14.1 Reaction rates involve the change in either reactant or product concentrations as a function of time.

14.3 The rates of reactions are defined as the negative of the change of reactant concentrations with respect to time because the reactants are decreasing as the reaction proceeds making the change a negative number. The negative sign in front of this change makes the overall rate of reaction positive (as it should be). The rates of reactions can also be defined as the positive of the change of product concentrations with respect to time because products increase as the reaction proceeds, making the change positive as well as the rate of reaction (again, as it should be).

14.5 Rate of reaction $= -\dfrac{\Delta[A]}{\Delta t} = -\dfrac{1}{3}\dfrac{\Delta[B]}{\Delta t} = \dfrac{1}{2}\dfrac{\Delta[C]}{\Delta t} = \dfrac{1}{2}\dfrac{\Delta[D]}{\Delta t}$

14.7 a. Rate of reaction $= -\dfrac{1}{4}\dfrac{\Delta[NH_3]}{\Delta t}$

b. Rate of reaction $= -\dfrac{1}{6}\dfrac{\Delta[NaOH]}{\Delta t}$

c. Rate of reaction $= \dfrac{1}{2}\dfrac{\Delta[Fe(OH)_2]}{\Delta t}$

d. Rate of reaction $= \dfrac{1}{18}\dfrac{\Delta[H_2O]}{\Delta t}$

14.9 Rate of reaction $= 2.0 \times 10^{-2}\,M/s$

14.11 Rate of depletion of $O_2 = -6.0 \times 10^{-3}\,\dfrac{M}{s}$

14.13 Rate of depletion of $N_2O = -2.9 \times 10^{-2}\,\dfrac{M}{s}$

14.15 Rate of production of $C_2H_4 = 2.8 \times 10^{-2}\,\dfrac{M}{s}$

14.17 Rate of production of $C_2H_4 = 1.1 \times 10^{-2}\,\dfrac{M}{s}$

CONCENTRATION EFFECTS ON CHEMICAL REACTION RATES

14.19 The reaction order tells us how the reaction rate depends on the reactant concentrations.

14.21 The rate constant (k) is the proportionality constant, which is related to the slope of the line in a graph of concentration versus time.

14.23 $Rate = k$

14.25 $Rate = k[A]^2$

14.27 s^{-1}

14.29 a. Zero-order

14.31 c. Second-order

14.33 First-order

14.35 $k = 2.5 \ M^{-1} \cdot s^{-1}$

14.37 Second-order

14.39 Third-order

14.41 $Rate = 9.0 \times 10^{-5} \ M^{-2} \cdot s^{-1} [NO]^2 [O_2]$

14.43 $[A]_t = -kt + [A]_0$

14.45 $\frac{1}{[A]_t} = kt + \frac{1}{[A]_0}$

14.47 c.

14.49 Reaction half-lives refer to the time in which the concentration of a reactant decreases by half.

14.51 $t_{1/2} = \frac{0.693}{k} = \frac{1}{k} (0.693)$

14.53 Zero-order

14.55 $Rate = 4.0 \times 10^{-3} \ \frac{M}{s}$

14.57 First-order

14.59 $Rate = 8.0 \times 10^{-3} \ s^{-1} [A]$

14.61 According to the collision theory of kinetics, reactant molecules must collide with sufficient energy and proper orientation for the reaction to take place (i.e. effective collisions).

14.63 The activation energy (E_a) is defined as the energy barrier which must be overcome in order to temporarily form the activated complex as reactants are used to produce products.

14.65 A is the pre-exponential factor (or frequency factor) which represents the number of times that reactants approach the activation barrier.

14.67 Catalysts increase reaction rates by lowering the activation energy of a particular reaction. They can do this without being consumed in the reaction.

14.69 A homogenous catalyst would be one in which the catalyst is in the same phase as the reactants.

14.71 A reaction mechanism is the series of individual reactions that contribute to the overall chemical reaction.

14.73 The rate-limiting step is a much slower reaction than the others in a particular mechanism and is often a point of regulatory control of the whole reaction mechanism.

Chapter 15

HYDROCARBONS

15.1 Organic chemistry is the study of carbon-containing compounds, which may also contain various other elements such as hydrogen, nitrogen, and oxygen to name a few.

15.3 Hydrocarbons are organic compounds that contain only carbon and hydrogen.

15.5 Alkanes are hydrocarbons that contain all single bonds, while alkenes and alkynes have either a double or a triple bond, respectively.

15.7 butane

15.9 2-pentyne

15.11

15.13

15.15

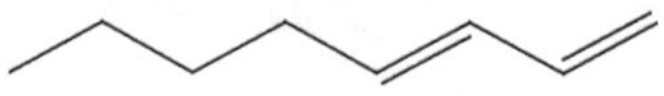

15.17

Name of Alkyl Group	Number of Carbons	Condensed Formula
methyl	1	CH_3-
ethyl	2	CH_3CH_2-
propyl	3	$CH_3CH_2CH_2-$
isopropyl	3	$(CH_3)_2CH-$
n-butyl	4	$CH_3CH_2CH_2CH_2-$
sec-butyl	4	$CH_3CH_2(CH_3)CH-$
isobutyl	4	$(CH_3)_2CHCH_2-$
tert-butyl	4	$(CH_3)_3C-$

15.19 3,4-dimethyloctane

15.21 4-sec-butyl–2-decene

15.23

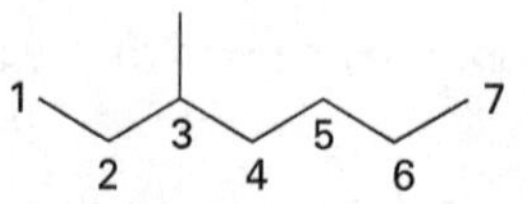

15.25

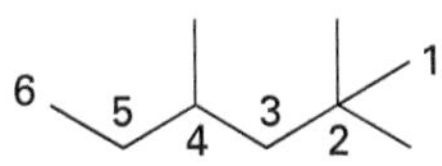

15.27

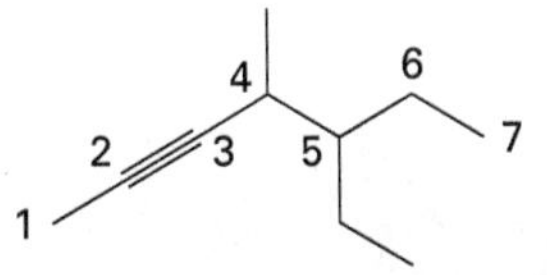

15.29 The seven major functional groups discussed in this chapter include alcohols (*R-OH*), aldehydes (contains a terminal carbonyl
group), ketones (contains a carbonyl group in the middle of
the structure or between two other carbon atoms), carboxylic
acids (contains carboxyl group), esters (derived from carboxylic
acids in which at least one hydroxyl group is replaced by an
—*O*–alkyl group), ethers (an oxygen atom connected to two
alkyl groups) as well as amines (nitrogen-containing compounds derived from ammonia).

15.31 3-methyl–3-hexanol

15.33

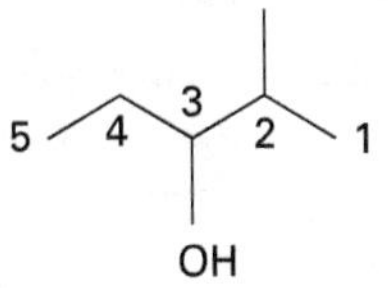

15.35 2-methylheptanal

15.37

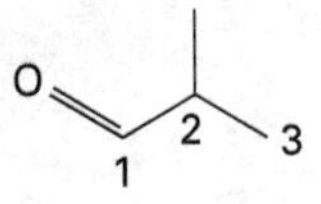

15.39 4-methyl–2-hexanone

15.41

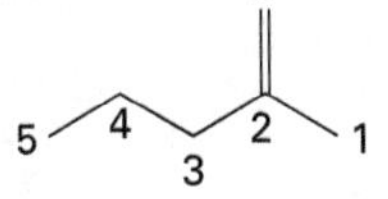

15.43 3-methylpentanoic acid

15.45

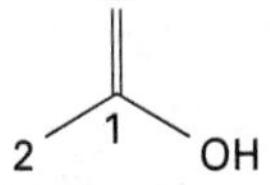

15.47 butyl ethanoate

15.49

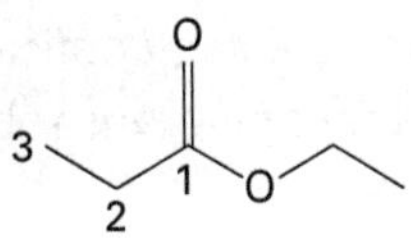

15.51 dibutyl ether

15.53

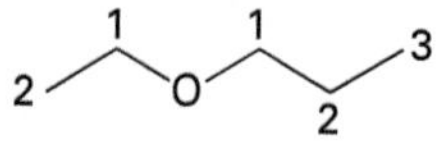

15.55 butylethylamine

15.57

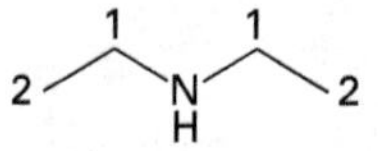

15.59 Structural isomers (or constitutional isomers) are molecules that have the same chemical formula but different connectivity, while stereoisomers are molecules in which the atoms have the same connectivity but a different spatial arrangement. Stereoisomers can be further broken down into two other subcategories, geometric and optical isomers. Geometric isomers are two or more compounds which contain the same number and types of atoms and bonds but have different spatial arrangements. It is important to note that with this type of isomerism, the connectivity between atoms is the same. Optical isomers can be defined as compounds that also have the same connectivity, but are nonsuperimposable images of each other.

15.61

Name of Hydrocarbon	Number of Carbons	Possible Structural Isomers
Methane	1	1
Ethane	2	1
Propane	3	1
Butane	4	2
Pentane	5	3
Hexane	6	5
Heptane	7	9
Octane	8	18
Nonane	9	35
Decane	10	75

15.63 Left, *trans*–1,2-dichloroethene and right, *cis*–1,2-dichloroethene. The chlorine atoms are on the same side of the double bond (which we call *cis*-) or on opposite sides (which we call *trans*-).

15.65 The dextrorotary isomer (*d* isomer) rotates plane-polarized light clockwise.

15.67 A racemic mixture is one that contains an equimolar amount of both isomers, which will not rotate plane-polarized light at all (i.e. they cancel each other out).

15.69 Yes, this molecule is chiral and would exhibit optical activity because the left carbon atom has four different substituents bonded to it.

15.71 The structure of benzene was determined in 1865 by Friedrich August Kekulé, who was one of the most prominent theoretical chemists in Europe in the mid to late 1800s. He claimed that he had determined the structure of benzene while day-dreaming of a snake seizing its own tail.

15.73 toluene or methyl benzene

15.75

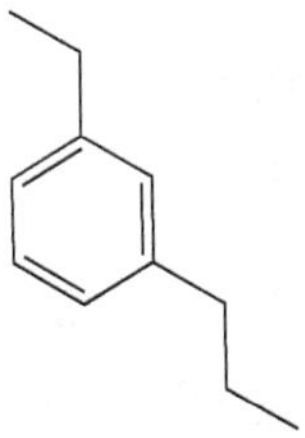

15.77

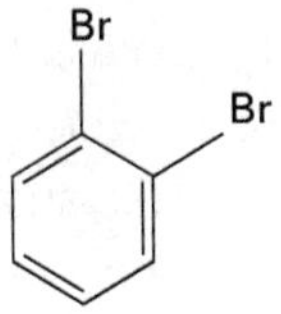

Chapter 16

PROTEINS AND AMINO ACIDS

16.1 Biochemistry is the study of the chemical processes that take place within living organisms.

16.3 Amphoteric substances can act as both an acid as well as a base. Amino acids are good examples of amphoteric substances.

16.5 All of the 20 standard amino acids commonly found in the human body with the exception of Glycine are chiral. These chiral amino acids are all of the L-designation, except Glycine, which is not chiral. However, about half of the chiral amino acids rotate plane-polarized light right, while the other half rotate plane-polarized light left. Thus, we can conclude that the D-dextro- or L-levo-designation used for the amino acids (and carbohydrates for that matter) has nothing to do with the rotation of plane-polarized light.

16.7 b.

16.9 a. Leucine

b. Tyrosine

c. Phenylalanine

d. Arginine

16.11 Dipeptide, Tripeptide

16.13

16.15 A protein's primary structure (1°) is the amino acid sequence itself; the secondary structure (2°) results from regular poly-peptide folding arrangements attributed to local interactions between individual amino acids, resulting in various geometric patterns such as α-helices and β-pleated sheets. A protein's tertiary structure (3°) and quaternary (4°) structures result from larger-scale interactions of the protein which can be held together by various intermolecular forces to include hydropho-bic interactions between nonpolar amino acid side-chains, salt bridges between acidic and basic amino acids, and hydrogen bonding. Furthermore, covalent bonds may be involved in these types of structures such as disulfide bonds. Quaternary (4°) structures are generally thought of as the arrangements of various subunits being held together in the larger protein structure.

CARBOHYDRATES

16.17 Carbohydrates are also called sugars and literally means carbon and water. Therefore, they often have the general formula $(CH_2O)_n$. They are polyhydroxy molecules, meaning that they are molecules containing more than one hydroxyl group, derived from either aldehydes or ketones.

16.19 A glycosidic bond is defined as a covalent bond that links a carbohydrate to another entity which may or may not also be a carbohydrate.

16.21 Aldoses are sugars derived from aldehydes, while those derived from ketones are called ketoses.

16.23 Complex carbohydrates are polysaccharides made up of long and "complex" chains of sugar molecules.

16.25 Starch is a complex carbohydrate primarily used for the main energy storage source for plants and is a mixture of both amylose and amylopectin. Amylose is a linear chain of many glucose residues similar to cellulose; however, the glucose resi-dues here are connected by α-glycosidic linkages. Amylopectin is structurally similar to amylose but contains branching in the chains.

16.27 a.

LIPIDS

16.29 The name lipids is derived from the Greek word "lipos" meaning fat and are therefore nonpolar molecules. They are a diverse family of molecules that have various biological functions to include energy storage and insulation, structural components of cell membranes, and cell signaling functions.

16.31 A saturated fatty acid has no points of unsaturation along its aliphatic hydrocarbon tail, while unsaturated fatty acids have at least one point of unsaturation (i.e. double bond) in the tail group. The presence of the double bond in the tail changes the physical properties quite dramatically, as the double bond puts a "kink" in the tail, which prevents the entire chain from interacting with neighboring molecules via hydrophobic interactions. This can also influence membrane fluidity when unsaturated fatty acids are present in the phospholipid bilayers of cell membranes.

16.33 Linoleic acid (C18:2)

16.35

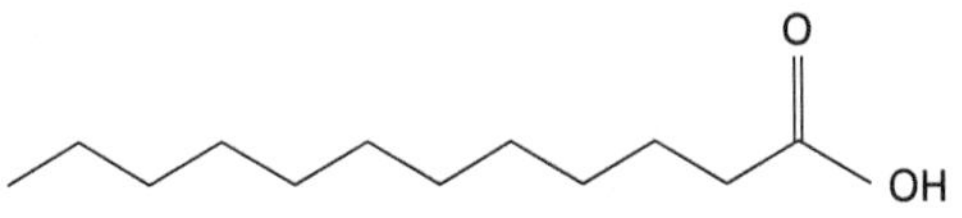

16.37

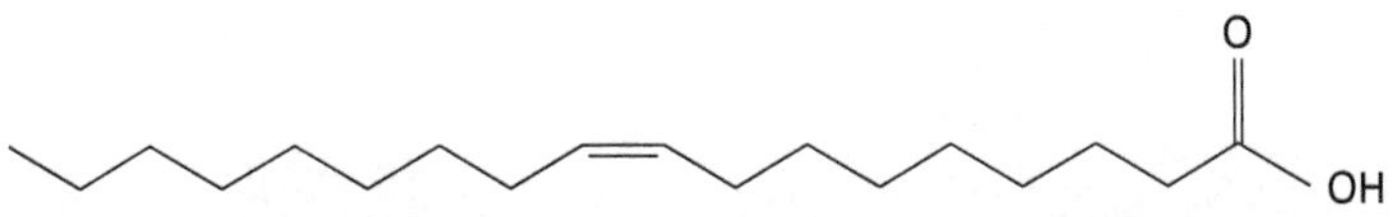

16.39 d.

16.41 By consuming the fat found in seals and storing high levels of triglycerides, polar bears can use them as an energy source during hibernation without having to get rid of excessive amounts of nitrogen through urination, which would otherwise be necessary with a high protein diet.

16.43 Amphiphilic molecules possess both hydrophilic and hydrophobic properties (i.e. phospholipids are amphiphilic molecules).

16.45 Testosterone, β-Estradiol

NUCLEIC ACIDS

16.47 Johannes Friedrich Miescher

16.49 c.

16.51 RNA, DNA

16.53 A nucleoside is basically a nucleotide minus a phosphate group.

16.55 Adenine and guanine are purines and found in both DNA and RNA.

16.57 James Watson, Francis Crick

16.59 Uracil, cytosine

16.61 Three bases to code for one amino acid, which we call a codon.

16.63 Chromosomes

16.65 Down syndrome

Image Credits

- Fig. A7.2a: Copyright © Depositphotos/Furian.
- Fig. A7.2b: Source: https://commons.wikimedia.org/wiki/File:Atomic_Cloud_Rises_Over_Nagasaki,_Japan_-_NARA_-_535795.tif.
- Fig. A7.3: Copyright © Depositphotos/magann.

INDEX

CONVERSION FACTORS AND RELATIONSHIPS

Temperature
- SI Unit : kelvin (K)
- $0\ K = -273.15\ °C = -495.67\ °F$
- $K = °C + 273.15$
- $°C = \frac{5}{9}(°F - 32)$
- $°F = \left(\frac{9}{5}°C\right) + 32$

Energy (Derived)
- SI Unit : joule (J)
- $1\ J = 1\ kg \cdot m^2 / s^2 = 0.2390\ cal$
- $1\ cal = 4.184\ J$
- $1\ eV = 1.6022 \times 10^{-19}\ J$
- $1\ J = 9.4781 \times 10^{-4}\ Btu$
- $1\ C \cdot V = 1\ J$

Mass
- SI Unit : kilogram (kg)
- $1\ kg = 2.2046\ lb$
- $1\ lb = 453.59\ g = 16\ oz$
- $1\ amu = 1.66053873 \times 10^{-27}\ kg$
- $1\ ton = 2000\ lb = 907.185\ kg$
- $1\ metric\ ton = 1000\ kg$

Length
- SI Unit : meter (m)
- $1\ m = 1.0936\ yd$
- $1\ cm = 0.39370\ in$
- $1\ in = 2.54\ cm$
- $1\ km = 0.62137\ mi$
- $1\ mi = 5280\ ft = 1.6093\ km$
- $1\ Å = 10^{-10}\ m$

Pressure (Derived)
- SI Unit : pascal (Pa)
- $1\ Pa = 1\ kg/(m \cdot s^2)$
- $1\ Pa = 1\ N/m^2$
- $1\ atm = 101325\ Pa$
  - $= 101.325\ kPa$
  - $= 760\ mmHg$
  - $= 29.92\ in\ Hg$
  - $= 760\ torr$
  - $= 1.01325\ bar$
  - $= 1013.25\ mbar$
  - $= 14.7\ psi$
- $1\ bar = 10^5\ Pa$
- $1\ torr = 1\ mmHg$

Volume (Derived)
- SI Unit : cubic meter (m^3)
- $1\ L = 10^{-3}\ m^3$
  - $= 1\ dm^3$
  - $= 10^3\ cm^3$
  - $= 1.0567\ qt$
- $1\ gal = 4\ qt = 3.7854\ L$
- $1\ cm^3 = 1\ mL$
- $1\ in^3 = 16.39\ cm^3$
- $1\ qt = 32\ fluid\ oz$
- $1\ m^3 = 35.3\ ft^3$

Unit Abbreviations
- A : ampere
- Å : angstrom
- atm : atmosphere
- C : coulomb
- cal : calorie
- Da : dalton
- g : gram
- J : Joule
- L : Liter
- mmHg: millimeters of mercury
- M : molar
- min : minute
- mol : mole
- Pa : pascal
- s : second
- V : volt

SI Unit Prefixes		
Giga	G	10^9
Mega	M	10^6
Kilo	k	10^3
Deci	d	10^{-1}
Centi	c	10^{-2}
Milli	m	10^{-3}
Micro	µ	10^{-6}
Nano	n	10^{-9}
Pico	p	10^{-12}

GEOMETRIC RELATIONSHIPS AND EQUATIONS

- $\pi = 3.14159.....$
- Area of a Circle $= \pi r^2$
- Circumference of a circle $= 2\pi r$
- Volume of a cylinder $= \pi r^2 h$
- Volume of a sphere $= \frac{4}{3}\pi r^3$
- Surface Area of a Sphere =

FUNDAMENTAL CONSTANTS

Atomic mass unit	$1\ amu = 1.66 \times 10^{-27}\ kg$ $1\ g = 6.022 \times 10^{23}\ amu$	Mass of an electron	$m_e = 5.49 \times 10^{-4}\ amu$ $= 9.112 \times 10^{-31}\ kg$
Avogadro's number	$N_A = 6.022 \times 10^{23}/mol$	Mass of a neutron	$m_n = 1.01\ amu$
Bohr radius	$\alpha_0 = 5.29 \times 10^{-11}\ m$		$= 1.67 \times 10^{-27}\ kg$
Boltzmann's constant	$k = 1.38 \times 10^{-23}\ J/K$	Mass of a proton	$m_p = 1.01\ amu$
Electron Charge	$e = 1.602 \times 10^{-19}\ C$		$= 1.67 \times 10^{-27}\ kg$
Electron Volt	$eV = 1.602 \times 10^{-19}\ J$	Planck's constant	$h = 6.626 \times 10^{-34}\ J \cdot s$
Faraday's constant	$F = 9.6485 \times 10^4\ C/mol$	Speed of light (in a vacuum)	$c = 2.9979 \times 10^8\ m/s$
Gas constant	$R = 8.314\ J/(mol \cdot K)$		

Relative Atomic Size of the Main Group Elements Based on Empirical Radii

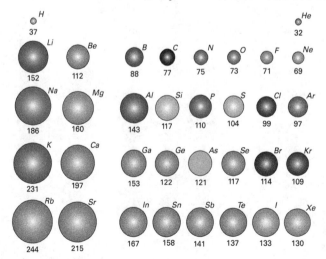

*All values reported here are in picometers

CPSIA information can be obtained
at www.ICGtesting.com
Printed in the USA
LVHW022138201119
638043LV00014B/24/P